R. Gupta's®

Guide Book of LIFE SCIENCES

For CSIR-NET, DBT-JRF, GATE-BT and GATE-LS Exams

3300+ SOLVED MCQs

Dr. Praveen Gupta	Dr. Pranav Prasoon	Dr. Kumar Abhiram Jha
M.Sc. (Jamia Millia Islamia, New Delhi), Ph.D. (Saurashtra University, Rajkot), CSIR-NET, GATE, ICAR-NET, GSET) Assistant Professor, Department of Biotechnology Atmiya University, Rajkot, Gujarat	M.Sc. (Cochin University), Ph.D. (AIIMS, New Delhi), CSIR-UGC-NET, DBT-JRF, ICMR-JRF, GATE PDF (University of Pittsburgh, Pennsylvania, USA)	M.Sc. (Cochin University), Ph.D. (AIIMS, New Delhi), PDF (Hemilton Eye Institute, UTHSC, Memphis, USA) CSIR-UGC-NET, GATE

2026 EDITION

KEY FEATURES

- Single Solution of All **Life Sciences** Exams
- Year and Exam-wise Division of Questions that Help in Study Mapping
- Topic-wise Divison of Chapters

RAMESH PUBLISHING HOUSE, NEW DELHI

Published by
O.P. Gupta *for* Ramesh Publishing House

Admin. Office
12-H, New Daryaganj Road, Opp. Officers' Mess,
New Delhi-110002 ✆ 23275224, 23245124

E-mail: info@rameshpublishinghouse.com
For Online Shopping: www.rameshpublishinghouse.com

Showroom
• Balaji Market, Nai Sarak, Delhi-6 ✆ 23253720, 23282525
• 4457, Nai Sarak, Delhi-6, ✆ 23918938

Book Code: R-2523

ISBN: 978-93-5477-576-5

Price: ₹ 540

Printed at: Deepak Offset, Delhi

Preface

The domain of Life Science stands as a beacon, illuminating our exploration of the living world. As scientific information proliferates and recent developments unfold, it's paramount to cultivate a skilled workforce in the field of Life Science. It's an opportune time to probe into the unexplored facets of Science, particularly as India emerges as a powerful force within the Life Science sector, wielding the potential to become a premier player.

To realize sustainable development and foster improvements in academics and research, students must develop a deep understanding of life processes, a robust knowledge base in Life Science, and a clear inclination towards its concepts. As times change, students must also adapt their strategies for succeeding in various competitive examinations.

This book embodies an earnest effort to compile a comprehensive practice guide that not only aligns with the respective syllabi but also maintains the standards expected in the previous papers of different national exams in Life Science and its related branches. The examinations primarily focused on in this book include the CSIR-NET (Life Science), DBT-JRF (BET), GATE (Biotechnology) and GATE (Life Science).

A distinctive feature of this book is the inclusion of over 3300+ multiple-choice questions (MCQs) derived from the past six years' papers. This is reflective of a pattern of minor trend shifts that occur at approximately five-year intervals. This book, painstakingly prepared after a meticulous analysis of unit or topic-wise questions (with corresponding subtopics in Biology), deliberately excludes aptitude-based questions. It serves to enable students to review and understand the pattern of questions, analyze the content for preparation, and understand the changing trends.

This book is our humble attempt to cater to all the needs of the students within one comprehensive guide. We believe and hope that it will be instrumental in your future endeavours.

—Authors

☆☆☆☆☆☆

Contents

☆☆☆☆☆☆

CHAPTER

1

BIOCHEMISTRY

CSIR-NET, JUNE, 2017

Water, PH, Thermodynamics, Bond

1. Protein stability is represented as

$$\text{Folded} \underset{}{\overset{K_{eq}}{\rightleftharpoons}} \text{Unfolded}$$

Prior to development of sensitive calorimeters, thermodynamic parameters of processes were determined by following equation

$$\ln K_{eq} = \frac{-\Delta H^\circ}{R}\left(\frac{1}{T}\right) + \frac{\Delta S^\circ}{R}$$

ΔH° and ΔS° are standard changes of enthalpy and entropy, respectively.

Which one of the following statements is correct for estimating ΔG, ΔH and ΔS?

A. Determining the ratio of folded and unfolded protein at 37°C
B. Plotting K_{eq} as a function of ΔH
C. Plotting K_{eq} against ΔS
D. Plotting K_{eq} against temperature

2. Which one of the following is the most powerful buffer system of blood?

A. Bicarbonate
B. Phosphate
C. Proteins
D. Haemoglobin

3. Three electron acceptors 'X', 'Y' and 'Z' have redox potential (E_o') of +0.15V, +0.05V and −0.1V, respectively. For a reaction

$$B + 2H + 2e^- \text{——} BH_2 \quad E_o' = +\,0.05V$$

Which of these three electron acceptors are appropriate? [useful equation: $\Delta G_0' = -nE_0'$, $\Delta G_0'$ = free energy change; n = number of electrons F = Faraday constant]

A. X and Y
B. Only X
C. Y and Z
D. Only Z

Vitamin-structure & Biochemical Function

4. Which one of the following vitamins is NOT absorbed in the small intestine by Na^+ – co-transporters?

A. Thiamine
B. Riboflavin
C. Folic acid
D. Ascorbic acid.

Protein-structure & Function

5. From the following statements:

(*a*) In proteins the amino acids that can undergo oxidation are Cys and Met.

(*b*) A tetrasaccharide composed of alternate L and D isomers will not be optically active.

(*c*) The ΔG(Kcal/mol) values for K_{eq} of 0.1, 0.01 and 0.001 are 1.36, 2.72 and 4.09, respectively. It can be concluded that the relationship between ΔG and K_{eq} is parabolic.

(*d*) The oxidation states of Fe in haemoglobin is +2. In cytochrome C, the oxidation states of Fe can be +2 or +3. E. In DNA, the sugar and bases are planar.

(*e*) High-energy bonds hydrolyze with large negative ΔG.

Choose the combination with only one wrong statement.

A. (*a*), (*e*), (*f*) B. (*b*), (*c*), (*d*)
C. (*c*), (*d*), (*e*) D. (*a*), (*b*), (*c*)

6. Given below are statements related to protein structures:

(*a*) The dihedral angles of an amino acid X in Acetyl-X-N-Methyl amide in the Ramachandran plot, occur in very small but equal areas in the left and right quadrants. It can be concluded that X is not one of the 20-coded amino acids.

(*b*) The dihedral angles of a 20-residue peptide are represented in the Ramachandran plot. It is possible to conclude that the peptide does not have a proline.

(*c*) Two proteins can have a similar fold even if they do not share significant similarity in their primary structure.

(*d*) On denaturation of a protein by urea, the interactions that would be disrupted are ionic bonds and van der Waal's interaction but not disulfide bonds.

Choose the combination with all correct answers:

A. (*a*), (*b*), (*c*) B. (*a*), (*c*), (*d*)
C. (*b*), (*c*), (*d*) D. (*a*), (*b*), (*d*)

7. A serine protease was tested for its activity on the following peptide substrates of different lengths and sequences. The obtained kinetic parameters of the protease are shown along with the peptide.

Peptide substrate	Kcat(S^{-1})	Km (Mm)
Ac-X-Ala-CO ↓ – NH_2	0.01	100
Ac-Y-X-Ala-CO ↓ – NH_2	0.10	4.0
Ac-Z-Y-X-Ala-CO ↓ – NH_2	8.0	4.0
Ac-Y-X-Val-CO ↓ – NH_2	6.0	35.0

Arrow denotes site of cleavage.

Based on the above data, the following statements are made:

(*a*) Catalytic efficiency (Kcat/Km) increases with the size of the peptide.

(*b*) Amino acid at the hydrolytic cleavage position of the peptide is critical for binding of the peptide with the protease

(*c*) Catalytic efficiency decreases from three amino acid peptide to four amino acid peptide.

Which of the following combinations of the above statements is correct?

A. (*a*) and (*b*) B. (*a*) and (*c*)
C. (*b*) and (*c*) D. (*a*), (*b*) and (*c*)

8. The P50 value of haemoglobin for oxygen is increased during exercise. The mechanism of this change is described in the following proposed statements.

A. Increased CO_2 production by muscles elevated pCO_2 of blood which affects P50 value

B. The affinity of haemoglobin for oxygen increases as 2,3-bisphosphoglycerate (2,3-BPG) level is elevated

C. Increased body temperature shifts the oxyhaemoglobin dissociation curve of the left

D. The decreased pH of blood reduces the affinity of haemoglobin for oxygen.

Which of the above statement(s) is (are) incorrect?

A. Only (*a*) B. (*b*) and (*c*)
C. Only (*c*) D. (*a*) and (*d*)

Carbohydrate Metabolism & Regulation

9. The energy-rich fuel molecules produced in the TCA cycle are

A. 2 GTP, 2 NADH and 1 F ADH2
B. 1 GTP, 2 NADH and 2 FADH2
C. GTP, 3NADH and 1 FADH2
D. 2 GTP and 3 NADH

10. Given below are statements that may or may not be correct.

(*a*) Fructose 2, 6- biphosphate is an allosteric inhibitor of phosphofructokinase-I.

(*b*) The TCA cycle intermediates, succinate and oxaloacetate can both be derived from amino acids.

(*c*) A diet rich in cysteine can compensate for a methionine deficient diet in humans.

(*d*) TTP for DNA synthesis can be obtained from UTP.

(*e*) In the fatty acid biosynthetic pathway, the carbon atom from HCO_3^- in the synthesis of malonyl CoA is not incorporated into palmitic acid.

Choose the option that represents the combination of all the CORRECT statements

A. (*a*), (*b*), (*c*) and (*e*) B. (*b*), (*d*) and (*e*)
C. (*a*), (*d*) and (*e*) D. Only (*b*) and (*c*)

Fat-structure & Function

11. Glycerol is added to protein solutions to stabilize the preparations by

A. increasing the viscosity of solution
B. stabilizing the pH
C. preferential hydration of proteins
D. interacting and neutralising the surface charges on the proteins

Fatty Acid Metabolism & Regulation

12. Which one of the following statements is NOT true?

A. Beta-oxidation of long chain fatty acids occurs in mitochondria
B. Fatty acid biosynthesis occurs in peroxisomes
C. Peroxisomes utilize H_2O_2 to oxidize a variety of substrates
D. Peroxisomes import their repertoire of proteins using sorting signals

13. In Tay-Sachs disease, accumulation of glycolipids occurs especially in nerve cells. These cells are greatly enlarged with swollen lipid-filled endosomes and the children with this disease die at a very early stage.

Such condition occurs due to a specific defect in:

A. Specific lysosomal enzyme that catalyzes a step in the breakdown of gangliosides
B. Sorting of an enzyme that adds a phosphate group at 6th position of mannose in all acid hydrolases
C. One of the Rab proteins involved in recycling of vesicles
D. *v*-SNARE molecules which cause abnormal vesicle tethering and docking and affect vesicle fusion with lysosomes

ETC

14. Rotenone is an inhibitor of the electron transport chain. The addition of rotenone to cells results in which of the following?

A. Generation of mitochondrial reactive oxygen species and block in ATP generation.
B. Block in ATP generation but no generation of reactive oxygen species.
C. Generation of reactive oxygen species but no block in ATP generation.
D. Permeabilization of the inner membrane to compounds which are usually not able to traverse the membrane.

15. A researcher wanted to study light reaction during photosynthesis by blocking photosynthetic electron flow using the herbicide, di chloro phenyl dimethyl urea (DCMU) and paraquat.

The researcher listed the following observations:

(*a*) Both DCMU and paraquat block the electron flow in Photosystem II
(*b*) Both DCMU and paraquat block the electron flow in Photosystem I
(*c*) DCMU blocks electron flow in Photosystem I while paraquat blocks in Photosystem II
(*d*) DCMU blocks electron flow in Photosystem II while paraquat blocks in Photosystem I

Which of the following combinations of the above statements is INCORRECT?

A. (*a*), (*b*) and (*c*) B. (*a*), (*b*) and (*d*)
C. (*a*), (*c*) and (*d*) D. (*b*), (*c*) and (*d*)

CSIR-NET, DECEMBER-2017

Enzyme-Action, Kinetics & Inhibition

16. Indicate the INCORRECT statement from the following:

A. Allosteric enzymes function through reversible noncovalent binding of allosteric modulators or effectors.
B. Monoclonal antibodies that catalyze hydrolysis of esters or carbonates can be produced.
C. Enzymes are not inhibited irreversibly by heavy metals such as Hg^{2+}, Ag^{+}.
D. Acid phosphatases hydrolyze biological phosphate esters at ~ pH 5.0.

17. From the following statements

(*a*) Enzymes enhance reaction rates by a factor of 2 to 10.
(*b*) The activation energy for a reaction is lowered by enzymes.
(*c*) The interactions between enzymes and substrates are hydrogen bonding, hydrophobic and ionic.
(*d*) Substrate concentration does not affect the rate of enzyme catalyzed reactions.

Pick the combination with all INCORRECT statements.

A. (*a*), (*b*) B. (*b*), (*c*)
C. (*a*), (*c*) D. (*a*), (*d*)

Vitamin-structure & Biochemical Function

18. Match the coenzymes in column I serving as transient carriers of specific atoms or functional groups in column II

Column I	Column II
(*a*) Coenzyme A	(*i*) Aldehyde groups
(*b*) Flavin adenine dinucleotide	(*ii*) Amino groups
(*c*) Pyridoxal phosphate	(*iii*) Hydrogen atoms
(*d*) Thiamine pyrophosphate	(*iv*) Acyl group

Select correct combinations from the options given below:

	(*a*)	(*b*)	(*c*)	(*d*)
A.	(*iv*)	(*iii*)	(*ii*)	(*i*)
B.	(*iii*)	(*iv*)	(*i*)	(*ii*)
C.	(*i*)	(*ii*)	(*iii*)	(*iv*)
D.	(*ii*)	(*i*)	(*iv*)	(*iii*)

Protein-structure & Function

19. Choose the correct statement from the following:

A. Disulfide bonds in a 20-residue peptide can be formed only if the cysteines are adjacent to each other.
B. The amino acid isoleucine has only one chiral centre.

C. Both bases and sugar contribute to chirality of nucleic acids.
D. The pI of aspartic acid is less than that of glutamic acid

20. The ϕ and ψ values of a β-strand composed of all D-amino acids will mainly occupy which quadrant in the Ramachandran plot?
A. upper left
B. upper right
C. lower left
D. lower right

21. Out of the statements mentioned below
(*a*) L-threonine and L-allo-threonine interact identically with plane polarized light.
(*b*) van der Waals' interactions are always attractive.
(*c*) Poly (pro) II-helix is not stabilized by intermolecular hydrogen bonds.
(*d*) The folding of a protein is associated with an overall positive change in free energy and negative change in entropy.
(*e*) Lysine acetylation on histone is associated with loosening of the histone complex from DNA.

Which of the following combinations is INCORRECT?
A. (*a*) and (*c*)
B. (*b*) and (*d*)
C. (*c*) and (*e*)
D. (*d*) and (*e*)

Carbohydrate-structure & Function

22. The following statements are made:
(*a*) α and β anomers of glucose are inter convertible and the ratio of their abundance is 1:2, respectively.
(*b*) Single chain lipids ($\geq$C14) form micelles and double chain lipids form bilayers in water.
(*c*) Proline is energetically favoured at the Ctermini of an α-helix than at the N-termini.
(*d*) Major groove of DNA readily accommodates several common structural motifs in protein than the minor groove.
(*e*) Replacement of a canonical Watson-Crick pairing by Wobble base pairs does not change the surface properties in t-RNA.

Which one of the following combinations is INCORRECT?
A. (*a*) and (*d*)
B. (*b*) and (*e*)
C. (*c*) and (*e*)
D. (*b*) and (*c*)

Carbohydrate Metabolism & Regulation

23. What is the effect of sudden increase in the levels of ATP and citrate on an erythrocyte undergoing glycolysis?
A. It inhibits glycolysis.
B. It stimulates glycolysis.
C. The rate of glycolysis remains unaltered.
D. The rate of glycolysis increases gradually

ETC

24. Match the chemical agents that interfere in oxidative phosphorylation process with their respective mode of action.

Column I	Column II
(*a*) Antimycin A	(*i*) Inhibits Fo component of ATP synthase
(*b*) Oligomycin	(*ii*) Disrupts inner mitochondrial membrane potential
(*c*) Valinomycin	(*iii*) Prevent electron transport from Fe/Scluster to ubiquinone
(*d*) Rotenone	(*iv*) Blocks electron transfer from cytochrome b to cytochrome c1
	(*v*) Inhibits adenine nucleotide translocase

Choose the correct combination from below:

	(*a*)	(*b*)	(*c*)	(*d*)
A.	(*ii*)	(*iv*)	(*v*)	(*iii*)
B.	(*iv*)	(*i*)	(*ii*)	(*iii*)
C.	(*i*)	(*iii*)	(*ii*)	(*v*)
D.	(*v*)	(*ii*)	(*i*)	(*ii*)

DBT-JRF—2017

Biomolecular Structure and Function

25. What will be the required volumes of 1N HCl and 4N NaOH to prepare one-liter solution of pH 7?
A. 500 ml; 500 ml
B. 800 ml; 200 ml
C. 600 ml; 400 ml
D. 200 ml; 800 ml

26. Calculate the ionic strength (M) of 50 ml of 0.75% (w/v) NaCl solution?
A. 0.128
B. 0.256
C. 7.8
D. 0.064

27. The strength of the hydrogen bond represented by D-H...A (where D is the donor atom, H is the hydrogen atom and A is the acceptor atom) depends on
A. the D-H bond length and the nature of the D and A atoms.
B. the nature of the D and A atoms and the D...A distance.
C. the D...A distance and linearity of the angle DHA
D. the H...A distance, linearity of the angle DHA and the nature of the atoms D & A

28. According to the Induced-fit theory, an agonist is defined as:
A. A compound which produces an exothermic effect
B. A compound which occupies the receptor for a longer period
C. A compound that induces a specific conformational change in the macromolecule
D. A compound which hits the receptor center more often.

29. What is referred by the term k in the following energy expression $E = \frac{1}{2} k (b-b_0)^2$ where b and b_o refer to the bond length and reference bond length respectively?
A. van der Waals radius
B. stretching constant for bond length variation
C. torsional potential
D. kinetic energy of an atom.

30. Which one of the statements given below is NOT true? Equilibrium constant (K) of a chemical reaction at a specific temperature can be determined if the:
A. $\Delta G°$ of the reaction is known
B. Equilibrium concentrations of reactants and products are known
C. ΔH and ΔS of the reaction are known
D. ΔH and initial concentrations of the reactants and products are known

31. The van der Waals energy of a single water molecule is:

A. 0	B. -0.2Kcal/mol
C. -0.5 Kcal/mol	D. 0.2. Kcal/mol

32. For a single substrate reaction, doubling the substrate concentration increases the rate by 10 fold. The order of the reaction is

A. 2	B. 3
C. 4	D. Between 3 and 4

33. An enzyme reaction follows Michaelis Menten kinetics. What will be the reaction velocity at a substrate concentration = $K_m/3$?

A. V_{max}	B. $V_{max}/3$
C. $V_{max}/2$	D. $V_{max}/4$

34. The activity of Enzyme X (total volume 5.3 ml) is 2.34 micromoles of product formed per min. The total protein content of this solution is 0.8 mg. What is the specific activity?

A. 2.93	B. 1.87
C. 18.2	D. 15.5

35. Match the enzyme in Group I with the application/ function in Group II

Group I	**Group II**
(*a*) Pectinase	(*i*) Lactose free milk products
(*b*) Papain	(*ii*) High Fructose Corn Syrup
(*c*) Glucose isomerase	(*iii*) Juice Clarification
(*d*) β- Galactosidase	(*iv*) Meat tenderisation

	(*a*)	(*b*)	(*c*)	(*d*)
A.	(*iv*)	(*iii*)	(*ii*)	(*i*)
B.	(*iii*)	(*iv*)	(*ii*)	(*i*)
C.	(*i*)	(*ii*)	(*iv*)	(*iii*)
D.	(*ii*)	(*i*)	(*iii*)	(*iv*)

36. Enzyme inactivation by suicide inhibitors should be:
A. allosteric-site directed
B. active-site directed
C. regulatory-site directed
D. both allosteric and regulatory-site directed.

37. Stoichiometric matrices in metabolic pathways are used in:
A. Gene regulatory network analysis
B. Measuring robustness of a system
C. Flux Balance Analysis
D. Analysis of phenotypic characters from genome

38. What would be the number of protein molecules present in 1.0 mg of protein having a molecular weight of 25 kDa?

A. 2.4×10^{15}	B. 2.4×10^{16}
C. 2.4×10^{17}	D. 2.4×10^{18}.

39. Protein kinases phosphorylate proteins at hydroxyl groups on amino acid side chains. Which one of the following groups of amino acids contain side chain hydroxyl groups?
A. Aspartate, glutamate and serine
B. Serine, threonine and tyrosine
C. Lysine, arginine and proline
D. Threonine, phenylalanine and arginine

40. The α-helix in a protein is primarily due to:
A. Intramolecular hydrogen bond
B. Intermolecular hydrogen bond
C. van der Waals interaction between amino acids
D. covalent interactions

41. In an experiment, 4 different N-terminal blocked purified proteins were treated with glutaraldehyde, individually. One of the proteins did not get modified. What may be the reason?
A. The protein lacks histidine
B. The protein lacks phenylalanine
C. The protein lacks lysine
D. The protein lacks arginine

42. Which of the following signatures (the stretch of amino acids) in a protein will target it to the nucleus?
A. Arg-Glu-Glu-Trp-Glu-Cys
B. Arg-Lys-Lys-Lys-Arg-Lys
C. Trp-Phe-Phe-Phe-Phe-Gly
D. Phe-Pro-Pro-Arg-Tyr-Tyr

43. The main difference between domain and motif in protein structure is:

A. Domain can remain stable, independent of the rest of the protein while motif cannot.
B. Domain cannot remain stable, independent of the rest of the protein while motif can.
C. Domain can be predicted but motif cannot be predicted.
D. Both are synonyms and there is no difference

44. The jelly roll in protein structure is:
A. made of eight alpha helices
B. made of. four alpha/beta motifs
C. made of seven hydrophobic strands and an amphipathic helix
D. formed from eight beta strands

45. The length of Beta Hairpin motif is usually:
A. 2 to 7 residues B. 12 to15 residues
C. 22 to 25 residues D. 6 to 10 residues

46. Amino acids with asymmetric Cβ atoms are:
A. Pro, Met B. Lys, Ile, Val
C. Thr, Ile D. Cys, Ser, Met

GATE (BIOTECHNOLOGY) – 2017

Enzyme-Action, Kinetics & Inhibition

47. An enzyme catalyzes a reaction by
A. Decreasing the energy of the substrate
B. Decreasing the activation energy of the reaction
C. Decreasing product stability
D. Increasing the activation barrier of the reaction

Protein-structure & Function

48. If a protein contains four cysteine residues, the number of different ways they can simultaneously form two intra-molecular disulphide bonds is
A. 1 B. 2
C. 3 D. 4

Enzyme-Action, Kinetics & Inhibition

49. An enzyme reaction exhibits Michaelis – Menten Kinetics. For this reaction, on doubling the concentration of enzyme while maintaining [S] >> $[E_0]$.
A. both Km and Vmax will remain the same.
B. Km will remain the same but Vmax will increase.
C. Km will increase but Vmax will remain the same.
D. both Km and Vmax will increase.

Amino acid Metabolism & regulation

50. Which one of the following amino acids has three ionizable groups?
A. Glycine
B. Leucine
C. Valine
D. Lysine

Nucleotide metabolism & regulation

51. Which one of the following graphs represents the kinetics of protein precipitation by addition of ammonium sulphate? On the Y-axis, [Protein] represents the concentration of free protein in solution.

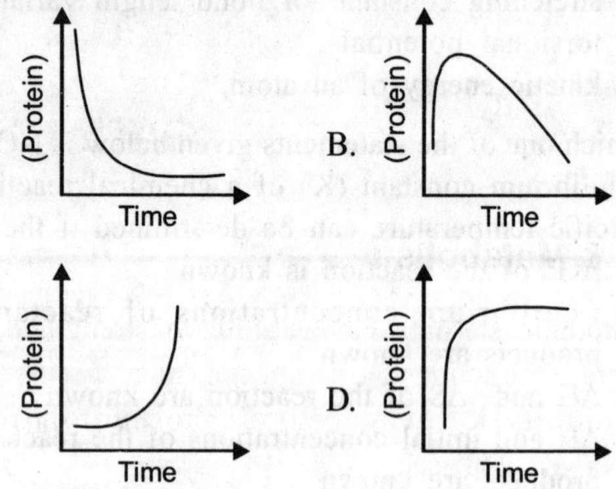

52. The circular dichroism spectra of three proteins P, Q and R are given below:

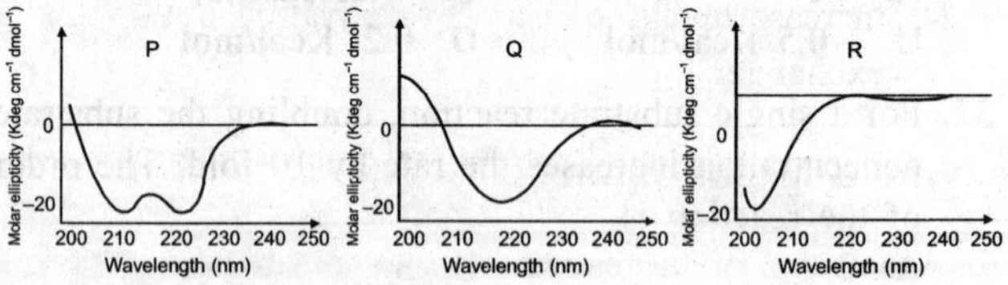

A. P: α-helix, Q: β-sheet and R: Random coil
B. P: β-sheet, Q: α-helix and R: Random coil
C. P: α-helix, Q: Random coil and R: β-sheet
D. P: Random coil, Q: α-helix and R: β-sheet

53. The interaction energy E between two spherical particles is plotted as a function of the distance (*r*) between them. When *r* < *a*, where a is a constant, the net force between the spherical particles is repulsive. When *r* ≥ *a*, they attract via van der Waals attraction. Which one of the following plots correctly represents the interaction energy between the above two particles?

A.
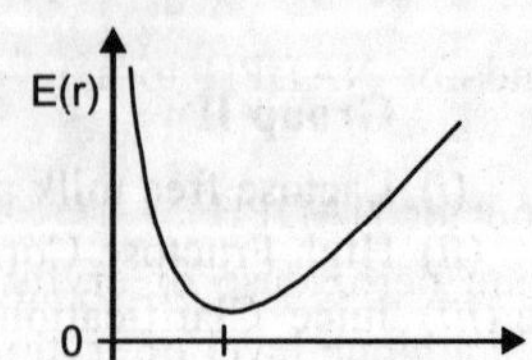

B. 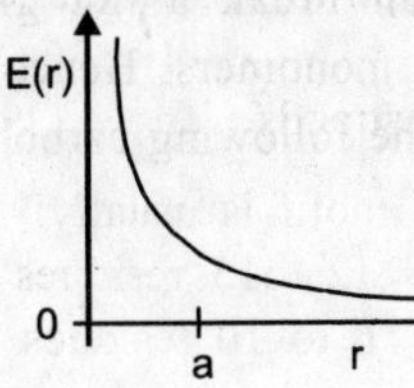

C. 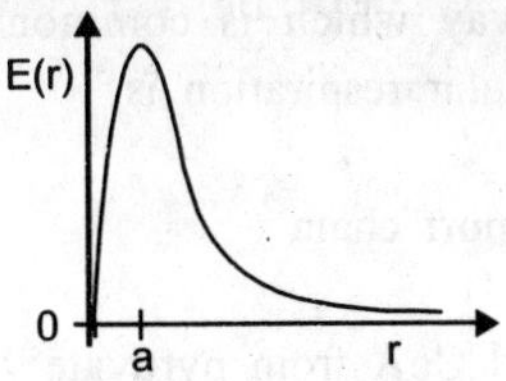

D. 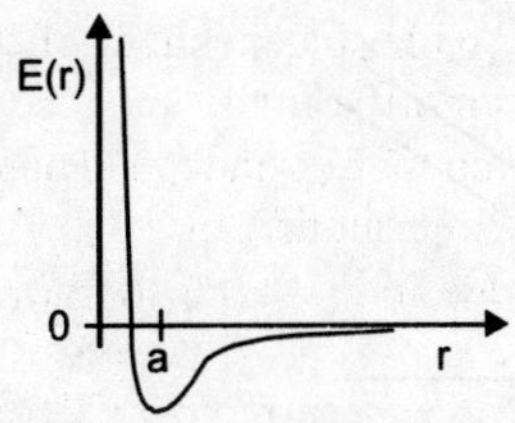

54. Natural proteins are composed primarily of 20 alpha amino acids. Which one of the following statements is true for any of these amino acids in a solution of pH 1.5?

A. Only the amino group is ionized.
B. Only the Carboxyl group is ionized.
C. Both amino and carboxylic acid groups are ionized.
D. Both amino and carboxylic acid groups are ionized.

GATE (LIFE SCIENCE)–2017

Enzyme & Metabolism

55. Cardiotonic steroids have ability to strengthen heart muscle contraction due to the fact that these steroids

A. Inhibits K^+-dependent dephosphorylation of Na^+-K^+ ATPase
B. activate Na^+-K^+ ATPase
C. increase uptake of Na^+ by activation of Na^+-Ca^+ exchanger
D. increase uptake of Ca^{2+} by activation of Na^+-Ca^+ exchanger

Enzyme & Metabolism

56. Which one of the enzymes is responsible for arsenic toxicity?

A. Pyruvate kinase
B. Aldolase
C. Phosphofructokinase
D. Pyruvate dehydrogenase

57. Which one is TRUE for Calvin cycle?

A. Glycerol 3-phosphate is generated in this cycle
B. CO2 is not consumed in this cycle
C. This is a reductive pentose phosphate cycle
D. Ribose 5-phosphate is a carboxylation substrate in this cycle

58. Administration of primaquine causes severe hemolytic anemia because it

A. increases the demand for NADPH to a level that cells can't meet
B. decreases the demand for NADPH
C. inactivates glutathione peroxidase of erythrocytes
D. increases reduced glutathione level of erythrocytes

59. Match the following enzymes in Column I with their cofactors in Column II

Column I	Column II
(*a*) Pyruvate decarboxylase	(*i*) Biocytin
(*b*) Glyceraldehyde 3-phosphate dehydrogenase	(*ii*) $NADP^+$
(*c*) Pyruvate carboxylase	(*iii*) NAD^+
(*d*) Glucose-6-phosphate dehydrogenase	(*iv*) Thiamine pyrophosphate

	(*a*)	(*b*)	(*c*)	(*d*)
A.	(*ii*)	(*i*)	(*iv*)	(*iii*)
B.	(*iv*)	(*iii*)	(*i*)	(*ii*)
C.	(*i*)	(*ii*)	(*iii*)	(*iv*)
D.	(*iii*)	(*i*)	(*iv*)	(*ii*)

60. In an in vitro dehydrogenation reaction of succinate catalyzed by succinate dehydrogenase, malonate is added. Which one of the following curves represents the effect of malonate on the catalysis of succinate dehydrogenase?

A. 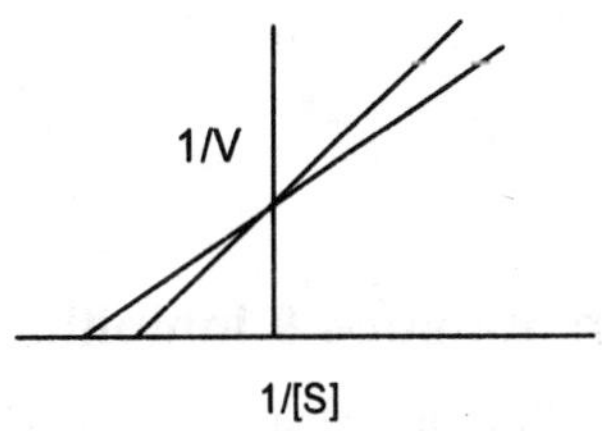

B. 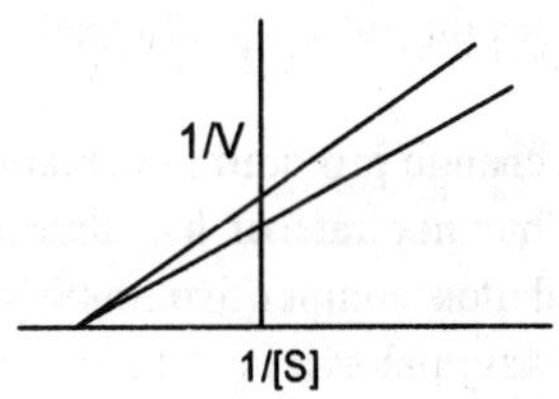

C. 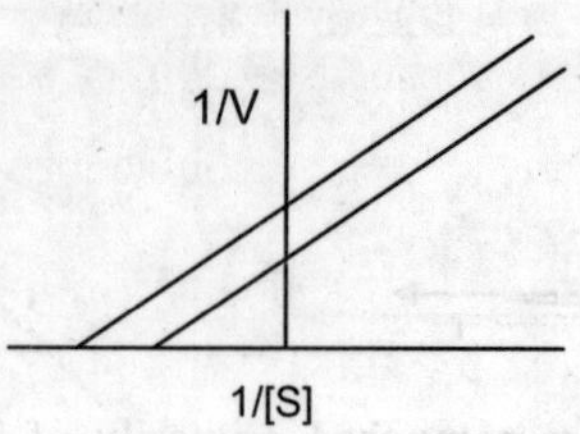

D. 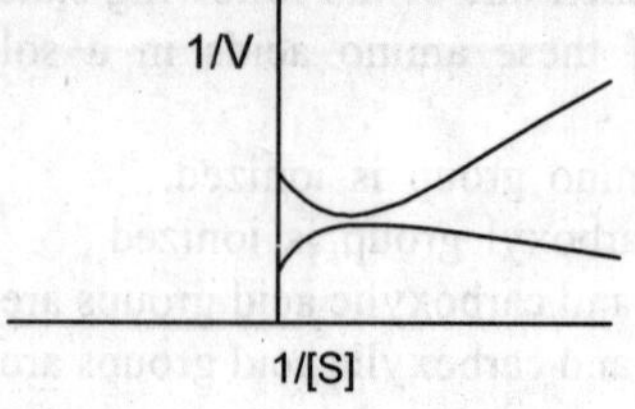

61. The enzyme amylase can break alpha glycosidic linkages between glucose monomers. Hence amylase can digest which one of the following carbohydrates?
A. Cellulose
B. Starch
C. Chitin
D. Xylans

62. The metabolic pathway which is common to both fermentation and cellular respiration is
A. the TCA cycle
B. the electron transport chain
C. glycolysis
D. synthesis of acetyl CoA from pyruvate

CSIR-NET, JUNE–2018

Water, PH, Thermodynamics, Bond

63. The (OH^-) of 0.1 N HCI solution is :
A. 10^{-14} M
B. 10^{-13} M
C. 10^{-12} M
D. 10^{-7} M

64. From the following statements:
(*a*) Biosynthesis of proteins and nucleic acids from precursors results in production of chemical energy in the form of ATP, NADH, NADPH and $FADH_2$,
(*b*) The spontaneity of a reaction in cells does not depend whether $\Delta G°$ for the reaction is positive or negative.
(*c*) Both oxidative phosphorylation and photo-phosphorylation involve oxidation of H_2O to O_2.
(*d*) Only chemical potential energy contributes to proton motive force in mitochondria.
Which one of the following combinations represents all INCORRECT statements?
A. (*a*), (*b*), (*c*)
B. (*b*), (*c*), (*d*)
C. (*a*), (*b*), (*d*)
D. (*a*), (*c*), (*d*)

Enzyme-Action, Kinetics & Inhibition

65. Which one of the following statements is NOT correct?
A. Allosteric enzymes do not obey Michaelis-Menten kinetics.
B. The free-energy change provides information about the spontaneity but not rate of a reaction.
C. Competitive and non-competitive inhibitions are kinetically indistinguishable.
D. A Kcat/Km (M^{-1} S^{-1}) of ~2*x* 10^8 for an enzyme indicates that the value is close to diffusion-controlled rate of encounter.

66. The Vmax and Km from a Lineweaver-Burk plot of an enzyme reaction where = 40 M^{-1} min at = 0 and = -1.5×10^2 mM^{-1} at = 0 are:
A. 0.025 μM min^{-1} and 0.67×10^{-2} mM
B. 0.025 $μM^{-1}$ min and 0.67×10^{-2} mM
C. 0.025 μM min^{-1} and 1.5×10^2 mM^{-1}
D. 0.038 μM min^{-1} and 0.67×10^{-2} mM

Protein-structure & Function

67. Which one of the following peptides can coexist in both cis- and trans conformation?
A. Ala-Ala-$CONH_2$ B. Pro-Gly-$CONH_2$
C. Asn-Gly-$CONH_2$ D. Val-Pro-$CONH_2$

68. Which one of the following pair of amino acids are glucogenic and ketogenic in nature?
A. Alanine and Lysine
B. Lysine and Leucine
C. Isoleucine and Phenylalanine
D. Aspartate and Lysine

69. Following statements are made related to protein structure
(*a*) The hydrogen bonding patterns between the CO and NH groups are $n \rightarrow n + 3$ in α-helix; $n \rightarrow n + 4$ in 310 helix and $n \rightarrow n + 5$ in π helix.
(*b*) In a β turn, there are 10 atoms between the hydrogen bond donor and acceptor.
(*c*) In a tum, there are 6 atoms between the hydrogen bond donor and acceptor.
(*d*) Parallel sheets have evenly spaced hydrogen bonds, which bridge the strands at an angle.

Which one of the following combinations of above statements is correct?
A. (*a*) and (*c*) B. (*a*) and (*b*)
C. (*c*) and (*d*) D. (*b*) and (*d*)

Carbohydrate-structure & Function

70. Following are structures of stereoisomers of aldohexoses which differ in the stereochemistry based on above structures, following information was given below:

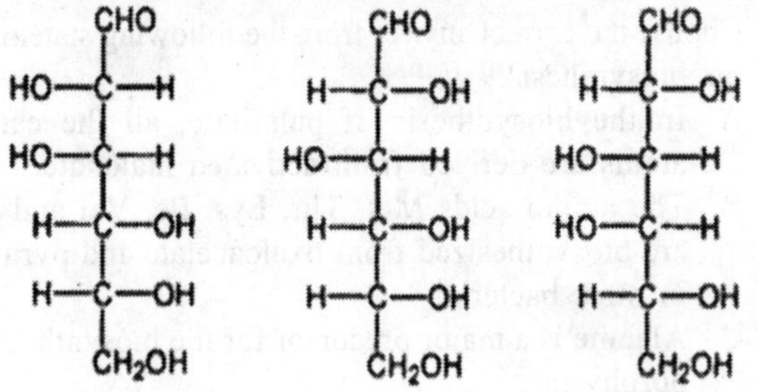

D-Mannose **D-Glucose** **D-Galactose**

(*a*) D-glucose and D-mannose are epimers because they differ in the stereochemistry at C-2 position.
(*b*) D-glucose and D-galactose are epimers because they differ in the stereochemistry at C-4 position.
(*c*) D-mannose and D-glucose are epimers because they differ in the stereochemistry at C-3 position.
(*d*) D-galactose and D-glucose are epimers because they differ in the stereochemistry at C-5 position.

Choose one of the correct combinations of above statements:
A. (*a*) and (*b*) B. (*c*) and (*d*)
C. (*b*), (*c*) and (*d*) D. (*a*) and (*d*)

Fat-structure & Function

71. Two liposome preparations ("X" and "Y") are made using basic lipid composition as phosphatidylcholine (PC) and cholesterol (Chol). In "Y" a ganglioside (asialo-GM1) is incorporated during the preparation besides PC and Chol. In an attempt to find out the localization of asialo-GM1, in the membrane bilayer of "Y" (taking "X" as a negative control) and considering liposome as a true depiction of lipid bilayer structure of cellular membrane, following reagents are provided as probes:
(*a*) Phospholipase A
(*b*) Galactose binding lectin
(*c*) Exoglycosidase
(*d*) Cyclodextrin

Choose the most appropriate reagent(s) from the above list to ascertain the localization of asialo-GM1:
A. Only (*a*) B. Both (*c*) and (*d*)
C. Both (*b*) and (*c*) D. Both (*a*) and (*d*)

CSIR-NET, DECEMBER–2018

72. Which one of the following statements is true?
A. The specific rotation of enantiomers will be identical
B. The rate constant of a first order reaction has only time but no concentration units.
C. The value of pH + pOH depends on temperature.
D. The bond disassociation energy (kJ/mol) of –C–C– will be greater than –C = C–.

73. Match the following bonds with their approximate energies:

(*a*) Hydrogen bond		(*i*) 0.5 Kcal
(*b*) Van der walls forces		(*ii*) 40 Kcal
(*c*) Covalent bond		(*iii*) 80 Kcal
(*d*) Ionic bond		(*iv*) 3 Kcal

	(*a*)	(*b*)	(*c*)	(*d*)
A.	(*iv*)	(*iii*)	(*ii*)	(*i*)
B.	(*ii*)	(*i*)	(*iii*)	(*iv*)
C.	(*i*)	(*iv*)	(*ii*)	(*iii*)
D.	(*iv*)	(*i*)	(*iii*)	(*ii*)

Enzyme-Action, Kinetics & Inhibition

74. For a reversible non-competitive inhibition of an enzyme, choose the plot that you would use to determine K_m:

———— No Inhibitor
— — — + Inhibitor

A.

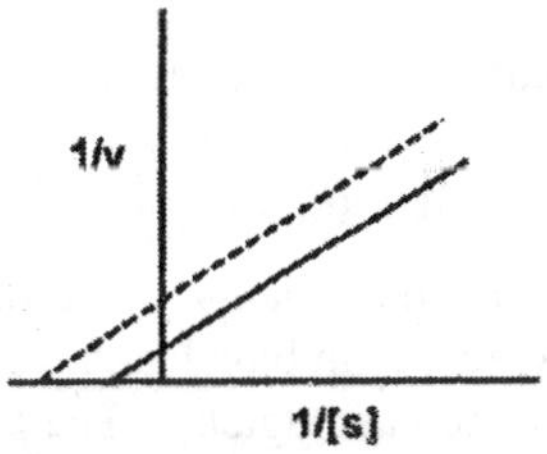

B.

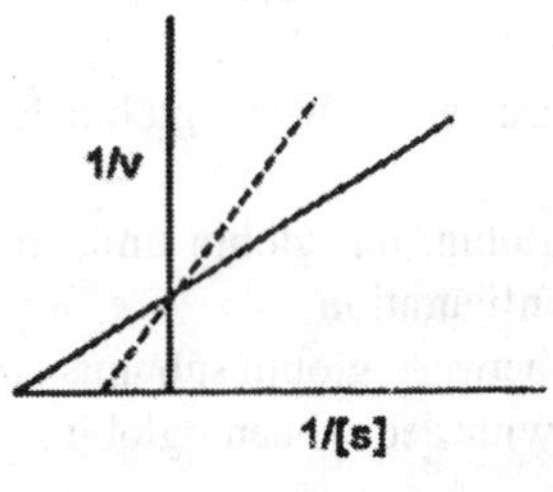

C.

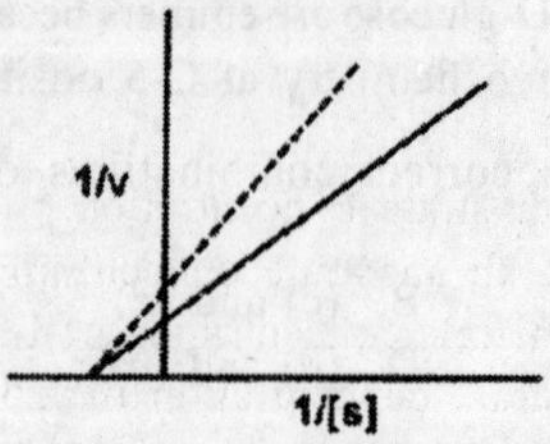

D.

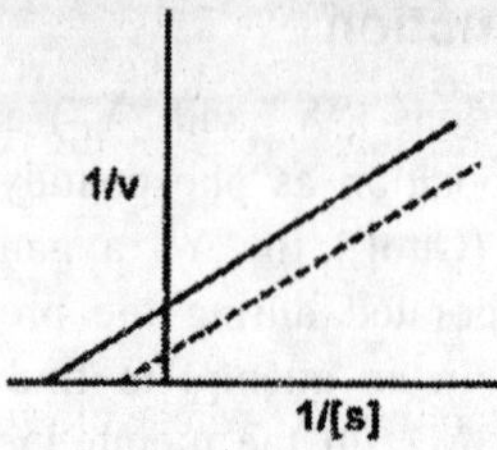

Vitamin-structure & Biochemical Function

75. The maturation of red blood cells does not depend on

A. folic acid B. vitamin B_{12}
C. pyridoxine D. tocopherol

Protein-structure & Function

76. Which one of the following statements on 'protein conformation is NOT true?

A. Dihedral angles of side-chains in amino acids are depicted in the Ramachandran plot.
B. Infrared spectroscopy can be used to deduce hydrogen bonding in peptides.
C. Three dimensional structures of protein composed of 100 amino acids can be obtained by nuclear magnetic resonance spectroscopy
D. Globular proteins have α-helical and β-sheet components

77. Following are statements on β-turns:

(*a*) All the 20 coded amino acids have equal propensity to form β-turns.
(*b*) Pro cannot occur in β-turns.
(*c*) Pro- Gly sequence strongly favours β-turns.
(*d*) In Asn-Gly β-turns, Asn can have positive φ, ψ values.

Choose the combination with all correct statements

A. (*b*), (*d*) B. (*a*), (*c*)
C. (*a*), (*d*) D. (*c*), (*d*)

78. The oxygen-haemoglobin dissociation curve illustrates the relationship between pO_2 in blood and the number of O_2 molecules bound to haemoglobin. The 'S' shape of the curve has been explained in the following proposed statements:

(*a*) The quaternary structure of haemoglobin determines its affinity to O_2.
(*b*) In deoxyhaemoglobin, the globin units are tightly bound in a T-configuration.
(*c*) The interactions between globin subunits are altered when O_2 binds with deoxyhaemoglobin.
(*d*) The affinity to O_2 in T-configuration of haemoglobin is increased.
(*e*) In the relaxed configuration of haemoglobin, the affinity to O_2 is reduced.

Choose one of the following combinations with both INCORRECT statements.

A. (*a*) and (*b*) B. (*b*) and (*c*)
C. (*c*) and (*d*) D. (*d*) and (*e*)

Amino Acid Metabolism & Regulation

79. Choose the correct answer from the following statements on biosynthesis.

A. In the biosynthesis of palmitate, all the carbon atoms are derived from activated malonate.
B. The amino acids Met, Thr, Lys, Ile, Val and Leu are biosynthesized from oxaloacetate and pyruvate in most bacteria.
C. Alanine is a major precursor for the biosynthesis of porphyrin.
D. Tryptophan is converted to L-DOPA in the biosynthesis of epinephrine.

80. Detergents at low concentration generally do not denature proteins and are thus used for extracting proteins in their folded and active form. For isolation of Porins, an E. coli membrane protein, which one of the following purification approaches will be most appropriate?

A. Use of low concentration of non-ionic detergent without salt.
B. Use of low concentration of ionic detergent.
C. Use of salt solution containing non-ionic detergent.
D. Use of salt solution containing ionic detergent.

Carbohydrate Metabolism & Regulation

81. The following are some statements regarding glycolysis:

(*a*) Glycolysis is not regulated by pyruvate kinase.
(*b*) Lactate can be an end product of glycolysis.
(*c*) Glycolysis cannot function anaerobically.
(*d*) In erythrocytes, the second site in glycolysis for ATP generation can be bypassed.

From the above, choose the combination with both INCORRECT statements:

A. (*a*) and (*b*) B. (*b*) and (*d*)
C. (*c*) and (*d*) D. (*a*) and (*c*)

Fat-structure & Function

82. If one of the two fatty acyl chains is removed from- the phosphoglyceride by hydrolysis in solution, such phospholipids will form:

A. liposomes
B. micelles
C. phospholipid bilayer
D. symmetric phospholipid bilayer

DBT-JRF–2018

Biomolecular Structure and Function

83. The driving force for mass transfer by molecular diffusion is the difference in
A. Potential energy
B. Vapour pressure
C. Gibbs free energy
D. Chemical potential

84. Arrange the following compounds based on increasing order of acid strength

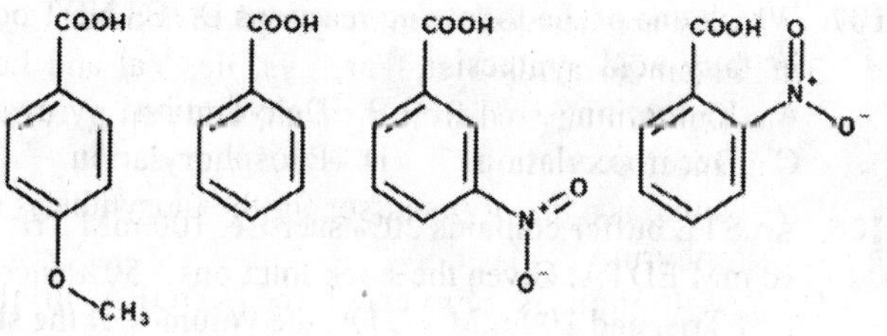

(i) (ii) (iii) (iv)

A. (i) < (ii) < (iii) < (iv)
B. (i) < (ii) < (iv) < (iii)
C. (ii) < (i) < (iv) < (iii)
D. (iv) < (iii) < (ii) < (i)

85. Two experiments were conducted with an enzyme following Michaelis Menten kinetics at substrate concentrations of 0.5 g/l and 1 g/l. If the enzymatic reaction velocity increases approximately 2-fold at the higher substrate concentration, the K_m for the enzyme would be around:
A. 0.001 g/l B. 0.01 g/l
C. 0.1 g/l D. 1 g/l.

86. An enzyme is reported to have a Km of 10 mM and Vmax of 30 mM/s. Assuming Michaelis Menten kinetics, the reaction velocity at a substrate concentration of 20 mM will be:
A. 10 mM/s B. 15 mM/s
C. 20 mM/s D. 30 mM/s

87. Which of the following amino acid changes in the active site of an enzyme is most likely to change its activity?
A. Lys → Arg B. Leu → Ile
C. Glu → Asp D. Lys → Pro

88. How does the rate of a typical chemical reaction vary as a function of temperature?
A. $k = (A)e^{-\Delta E/RT}$ B. $k = \ln(\Delta E/RT)$
C. $k = (A)e^{-RT/\Delta E}$ D. $k = (\Delta E/RT)$

89. An enzyme follows Michaelis-Menten kinetics with the following parameters: V_{max} = 5 mM/s and K_m = 2.5 mM. The reaction velocity would be:
A. 2.5 mM/s at all substrate concentration
B. equal to Vmax at all substrate concentration
C. 1.67 mM/s at a substrate concentration of 1.25 mM
D. 5 mM/s at a substrate concentration of 2.5 mM

90. In a CSTR, first order reaction takes place converting A to B If at a dilution rate (D) = 0.5 h^{-1}, 50% of A gets converted to B, then the rate constant 'k' of the reaction is:
A. 0.5 h^{-1} B. 1.0 h^{-1}
C. 0.25 h^{-1} D. 2.0 h^{-1}

91. We wish to produce a metabolite 'X' whose biosynthetic pathway is feedback inhibited in the wild type strain. A mutation, which leads to overproduction of X, is discovered in the gene coding for a homodimeric enzyme which catalyses the first step in the biosynthetic pathway of 'X'. This mutation is most likely to occur at:
A. Answers: the catalytic active site
B. the regulatory site
C. the point of contact between the two monomers
D. in the random coil structure of the protein

92. Internal coordinates for representation of the three-dimensional structure of a protein consists of:
A. bond lengths, bond angles and dihedral angles
B. Cartesian coordinates X, Y and Z for all the atoms
C. spherical polar coordinates R, θ, Φ for all atoms
D. all possible inter atomic distances

93. Cis-peptide unit corresponds to the O-C-N-H dihedral angle (degrees) of:
A. 0 B. –60
C. 120 D. 180

94. Which of the following corresponds to the amino acid pair having maximum and minimum number of allowed conformations in the Ramachandran plot?
A. Max: Gly, Min: Pro
B. Max: Pro, Min: Gly
C. Max: Ala, Min: Lys
D. Max: Lys, Min: Ala

95. If the energy of a protein structure is calculated using mechanics forcefield, which of the following energy component CANNOT have a negative value?
A. Bond energy
B. Dihedral energy
C. van der Waals energy
D. Electrostatic energy

96. X, Y and Z correspond to three different conformers of an 18-residue peptide, where X: α helix, Y: β strand and Z: 3_{10} helix. Which of the following correspond to the conformers in the decreasing order of end to end distance?

A. Y, Z, X B. X, Y, Z
C. Z, X, Y D. Y, X, Z

97. Which one of the following protein structure prediction methods is based on the principle of locating lowest energy minimum in the conformation space of a protein?
A. Ab initio structure prediction
B. Threading
C. Fold prediction
D. Homology modeling

98. Which one of the following can be used to measure the extent of similarity between the predicted structure of a protein and its experimentally determined structure?
A. Root mean square deviation (RMSD)
B. Radius of gyration
C. Solvent accessibility of amino acids
D. Tanimoto coefficient

99. The amino acid that can act both as an acid and a base in an enzyme catalyzed reaction is:
A. Tryptophan B. Lysine
C. Histidine D. Aspartic acid.

100. Which one of the following amino acid biosynthesis pathways is affected in folic acid deficiency?
A. Aspartate from oxaloacetate & glutamate
B. Glycine from glucose and alanine
C. Glutamate from glucose and ammonia
D. Serine from glucose and alanine

101. Phosphorylation of proteins is a typical post-translational modification that modulates their activities. Which one of the following amino acid residues can be phosphorylated?
A. Glutamic acid B. Lysine
C. Asparagine D. Aspartic acid

102. The number of 1° hydroxyl groups present in fructose and glucose are:
A. 2 and 1 B. 2 and 2
C. 1 and 2 D. 1 and 1.

103. During glycolysis, fructose-1,6-diphosphate undergoes .... to produce two C3 - fragments.
A. Retroaldol reaction
B. Oxidation
C. Isomerization
D. Hydrolysis

104. Which of the following compound(s) on oxidation gets converted into optically active tartaric acid:

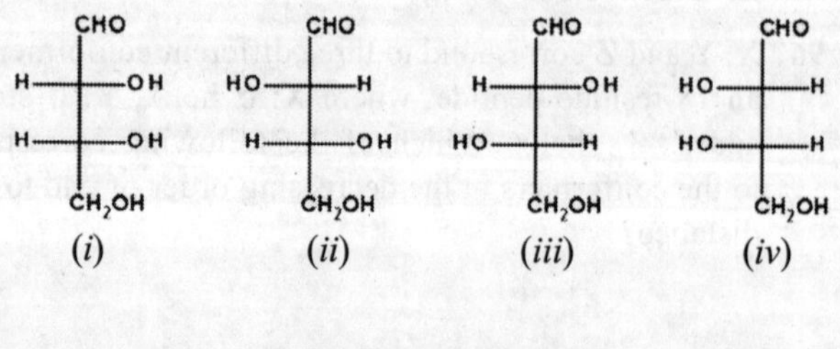

(*i*) (*ii*) (*iii*) (*iv*)

A. (*ii*) and (*iii*) B. (*i*) and (*iv*)
C. (*i*), (*ii*) and (*iv*) D. (*i*), (*ii*) and (*iii*)

105. The Carbon (C1) of glucose is labelled with ^{14}C (specific activity of 10 mCi/mmole). After one round of glycolysis, the specific activity of radiolabeled pyruvate is:
A. 0 B. 10
C. 5 D. 20

106. Vitamin D3 formed in the skin is converted to 1, 25-dihydroxycholecalciferol in the:
A. Muscle and liver B. Liver and kidney
C. Spleen and kidney D. Bone and pancreas

107. Which one of the following reactions DOES NOT occur in fatty acid synthesis?
A. Reduction B. Dehydration
C. Decarboxylation D. Phosphorylation

108. An STE buffer contains 20% sucrose, 100 mM Tris and 10 mM EDTA. Given the stock solutions – 50% sucrose, 1 M Tris, and 200 mM EDTA, the volumes of the stock solutions required to make 1 liter of the buffer solution are, respectively:
A. 400 ml, 100 ml, 100 ml
B. 200 ml, 50 ml, 100 ml
C. 400 ml, 100 ml, 50 ml
D. 200 ml, 100 ml, 50 ml

109. In a continuous crystallizer, 100 g of a saturated solution of sugar at 85% (w/w) enters the crystallizer and leaves the crystallizer at 70% (w/w). The weight of input solids converted to crystals in the crystallizer is
A. 30 B. 50
C. 70 D. 85

110. A liquid stream is cooled from 80°C to 30°C in a double pipe heat exchanger as illustrated below:

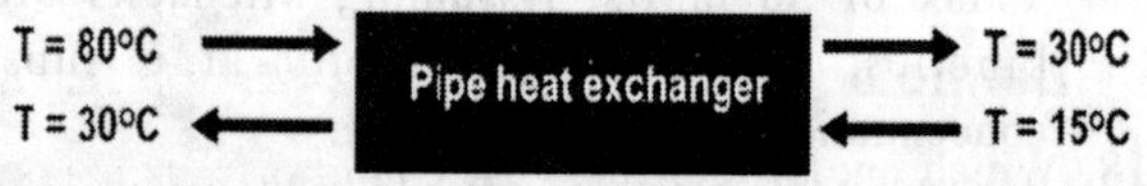

Fluid flowing counter currently with this stream is heated from 15°C to 30°C. Calculate the log mean temperature difference
A. 18.1°C B. 29.1°C
C. 19.6°C D. 32.5°C

111. A hypothetical polypeptide hormone binds to its receptor with an association rate constant (k_a) of 3.0 × 10^4 M^{-1} sec^{-1} and a dissociation rate constant (k_d) of 6.9 × 10^{-6} sec^{-1}. What is the equilibrium dissociation constant?
A. 4.7 × 10^9 M^{-1} B. 2.3 × 10^{-10} M
C. 2.3 × 10^{10} M^{-1} D. 3.3 × 10^{-6} M

112. A food package label displays composition of the food product in g/100g as: protein = 8g, fat = 20g,

carbohydrate = 60g (of which sugar is 20g). The calorific value of this product before and after complete replacement of sugar (w/w) by a non-calorific sweetener would be:
A. 352 Cal/100g, 272 Cal/100g
B. 452 Cal/100g, 212 Cal/100g
C. 432 Cal/100g, 352 Cal/100g
D. 452 Cal/100g, 372 Cal/100g

113. Two sucrose solutions 'A' = 30g/100g and 'B'= 60 g/100 g have to be mixed to prepare 1 kg of 50g/100g sugar syrup. The amounts of 'A' and 'B' solutions to be mixed would be:
A. 333 g A + 667 g B
B. 667 g·A + 333 g B
C. 500 g A + 500 g B
D. 400 g A + 600 g B

GATE (BIOTECHNOLOGY)—2018

114. Which of the following components constitute a molecular mechanics force field?
P. Bond stretching
Q. Bond angle bending
R. Torsional bond rotation
S. Non-bonded interactions
A. P and Q only
B. P, Q and R only
C. P, Q and S only
D. P, Q, R and S

115. Which one of the following is INCORRECT about protein structures?
A. A protein fold is stabilized by favourable non-covalent interactions.
B. All parts of a fold can be classified as helices, strands or turns.
C. Two non-covalent atoms cannot be closer than the sum of their van der Waals radii.
D. The peptide bond is nearly planar.

116. Determine the correctness or otherwise of the following Assertion [a] and the Reason [r]

Assertion [a]: The association constant in water for the G-C base pair is three times lower than that for the A-T base pair.

Reason [r]: There are three hydrogen bonds in the G-C base pair and two in the A-T base pair.
A. Both [a] and [r] are true and [r] is the correct reason for [a]
B. [a] is false but [r] is true
C. Both [a] and [r] are false
D. Both [a] and [r] are true and [r] is not the correct reason for [a]

117. Which one of the following metabolic processes in mammalian cells does NOT occur in the mitochondria?
A. Citric acid cycle
B. Oxidative phosphorylation
C. Fatty acid β-oxidation
D. Glycolysis

GATE (LIFE SCIENCE) – 2018

Biomolecules

118. Which one of the following conformations of glucose is most stable?
A. Boat B. Half Chair
C. Chair D. Planar

119. Which one of the following amino acids is responsible for the intrinsic fluorescence of proteins?
A. Pro B. Met
C. His D. Trp

120. Which one of the following is NOT a neurotransmitter?
A. Adrenaline B. Glutamate
C. Histamine D. Histidine

Enzyme & Metabolism

121. To which one of the following classes of enzymes does chymotrypsin belong?
A. Oxidoreductase B. Hydrolase
C. Transferase D. Isomerase

122. The substrate saturation profile of an enzyme that follows Michaelis-Menten kinetics is depicted in the figure. What is the order of the reaction in the concentration range between 0.8 to 1.4 M?

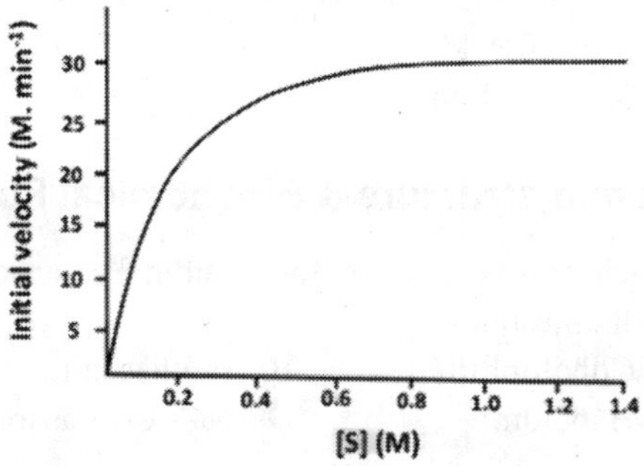

A. Zero B. Fraction
C. First D. Second

123. Which one of the following profiles represent the phenomenon of cooperativity?

A. 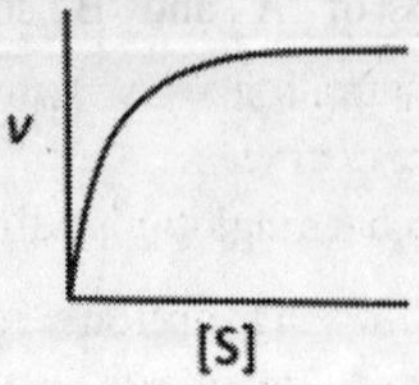

B. 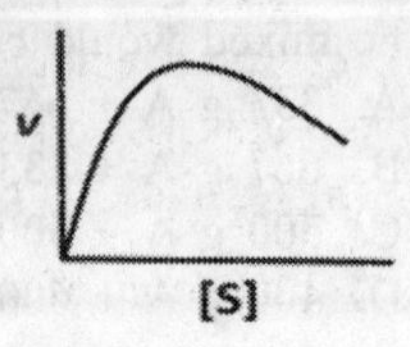

C. 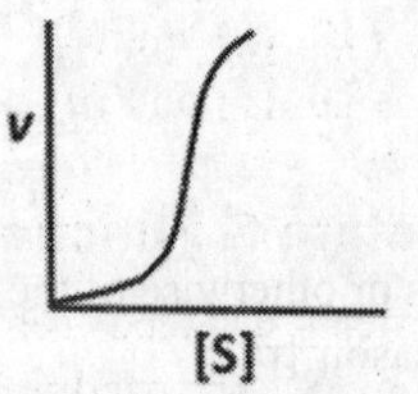

D. 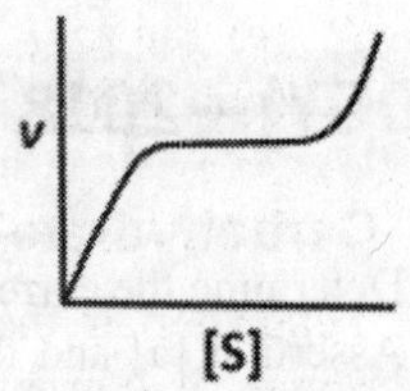

124. Which one the following reaction mechanisms drives the conversion of low energy 3- phosphoglyceraldehyde to high energy 1,3-bisphosphoglycerate?

A. Oxidation without anhydride bond formation
B. Oxidation coupled with anhydride bond formation
C. Substrate level phosphorylation
D. Formation of carboxylate

125. In a chemical reaction where the substrate and product are in equilibrium in solution, what will occur if an enzyme is added?

A. The equilibrium of the reaction will not change.
B. There will be a decrease in product formed.
C. Additional substrate will be formed.
D. The free energy of the system will change.

126. Glucose monomers are joined together by glycosidic linkages to form a cellulose polymer. During this process, changes in the free energy, total energy, and entropy respectively are represented correctly by which ONE of the following options?

A. $+\Delta G, +\Delta H, +\Delta S$. B. $+\Delta G, -\Delta H, -\Delta S$.
C. $-\Delta G, +\Delta H, +\Delta S$. D. $+\Delta G, +\Delta H, -\Delta S$.

CSIR-NET, JUNE–2019

Water, PH, Thermodynamics, Bond

127. Equal volumes of pH 4.0 and pH 10.0 solutions are mixed. What will be the approximate pH of the final solution?

A. 7.0 B. 5.0
C. 6.0 D. 4.0

Enzyme-Action, Kinetics & Inhibition

128. Choose the INCORRECT statement from the following statements made for an enzyme-catalyzed reaction

A. The kinetic properties of allosteric enzyme do not diverge from Michaelis-Menten behaviour.
B. In feedback inhibition, the product of a pathway inhibits an enzyme of the pathway
C. An antibody that binds tightly to the analog of the transition state intermediate of the reaction S→P, would promote formation of P when the analog is added to the reaction.
D. An enzyme with $K_{cat} = 1.4 \times 10^4\ s^{-1}$ and $K_m = 9 \times 10^{-5}$ M has activity close to the diffusion controlled limit.

Vitamin-structure & Biochemical Function

129. Which one is required for vitamin B_{12} absorption in small intestine?

A. Cobalophilin B. Hephaestin
C. Hepcidin D. Na^+–Co-transporter

130. Some coenzymes that serve as transient carriers of specific chemical groups are shown below:

Coenzymes Group	*Chemical transfer*
(*a*) Coenzyme A	(*i*) Electrons
(*b*) Flavin adenine Dinucleotide	(*ii*) Acyl groups
(*c*) Pyridoxal phosphate	(*iii*) Hydride ions
(*d*) Nicotinamide adenine dinucleotide	(*iv*) Amino groups

Choose the combination with all correct matches :

	(*a*)	(*b*)	(*c*)	(*d*)
A.	(*i*)	(*ii*)	(*iii*)	(*iv*)
B.	(*ii*)	(*i*)	(*iv*)	(*iii*)
C.	(*iii*)	(*iv*)	(*ii*)	(*i*)
D.	(*iv*)	(*iii*)	(*i*)	(*ii*)

Protein-structure & Function

131. Which one of the statements on protein conformation, detailed below is INCORRECT?

A. L-amino acids can occur in Type I' β-turns where φ, ψ are positive
B. A peptide rich in proline is unlikely to adopt α-helical structure
C. Proline residues have high propensity to occur in β-turns
D. The dihedral angles φ, ψ of amino acids in unfolded proteins are exclusively positive

132. The emission maximum of tryptophan fluorescence in a protein is ~ 335 nm. This suggests that tryptophan

A. is in a hydrophobic environment.
B. occurs in a helical segment

C. has proximal cysteine residues
D. is oxydized.

Amino Acid Metabolism & Regulation

133. The inborn error of amino acid metabolism, alkaptonuria is due to the lack of one of the following enzymes:
A. Fumaryl acetoacetate hydrolase
B. α-keto acid decarboxylase
C. Homogentisate oxidase
D. *p*-hydroxyphenylpyruvate dehydroxylase

134. The CO_2 dissociation curves of oxygenated and deoxygenated blood are given along with dissolved CO_2: below

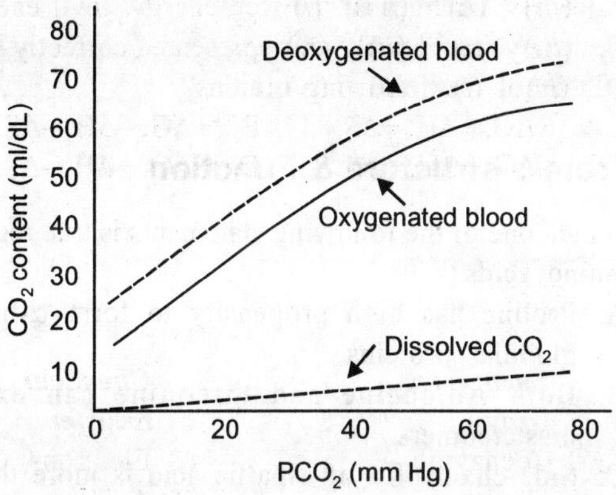

Following are the statements deduced from the curves above and or based on the knowledge about CO_2 transport, which may or may not be correct
(*a*) The deoxygenated haemoglobin has greater affinity for CO, than oxygenated haemoglobin
(*b*) The deoxygenated haemoglobin does not bind with free H^+ ions released during the formation of HCO_3^- from CO_2 .
(*c*) The haemoglobin saturation with O_2 has no effect on CO_2, dissociation curve.
(*d*) O_2 and CO_2 bind to haemoglobin at different sites.

Which one of the following options represents a combination of all correct statements?
A. (*a*) and (*b*)
B. (*b*) and (*c*)
C. (*c*) and (*d*)
D. (*a*) and (*d*)

Carbohydrate-structure & Function

135. Following are the statements deduced from the curves above and or based on the knowledge about CO_2 transport, which may or may not be correct

The first step in glycogen breakdown releases glucose units as
A. glucose 6-phosphate
B. glucose 1-phosphate
C. glucose
D. glucose and glucose 6- phosphate

Fat-structure & Function

136. Which one of the following agents cause relaxation of mesangial cells?
A. Histamine
B. Thromboxane A2
C. Norepinephrine
D. Dopamine

CSIR-NET, 15 DECEMBER–2019

Water, PH, Thermodynamics, Bond

137. Which one of the following graphs best describes the dependence of free energy change (ΔG) of ATP hydrolysis on Mg^{2+} concentration?

A.
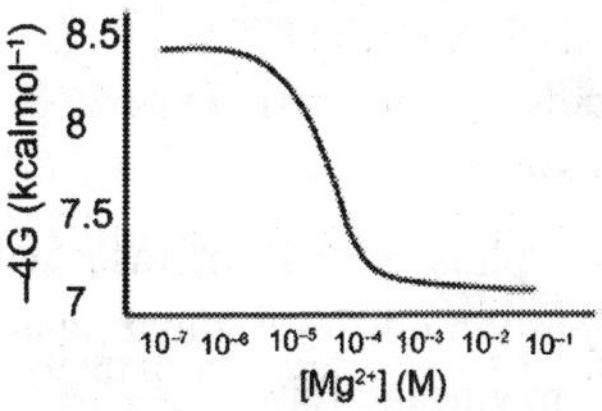

B.
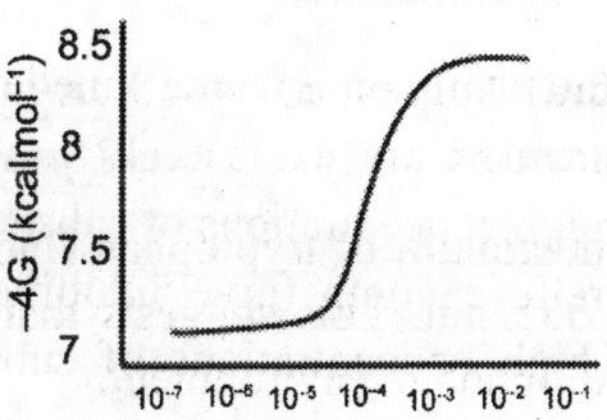

C.
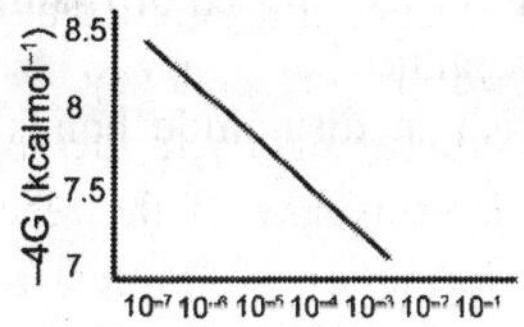

D.
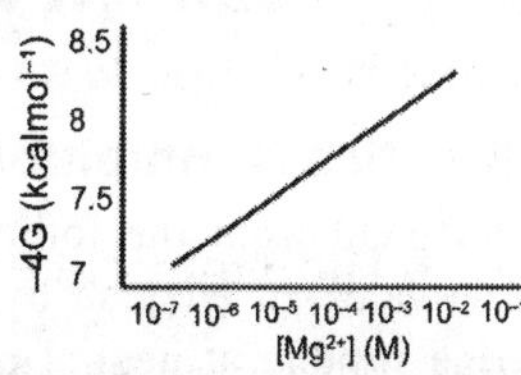

138. The interaction energy between two opposite charges separated by 3Å in vacuum is –500 $kJmol^{-1}$. The interaction energy between these two charges in water will be closest to
A. –1500 $kJmol^{-1}$
B. –166 $kJmol^{-1}$
C. –55 $kJmol^{-1}$
D. –6 $kJmol^{-1}$

Enzyme-Action, Kinetics & Inhibition

139. Given below is the [P] vs time plot of an enzymatic reaction carried out by the enzyme X

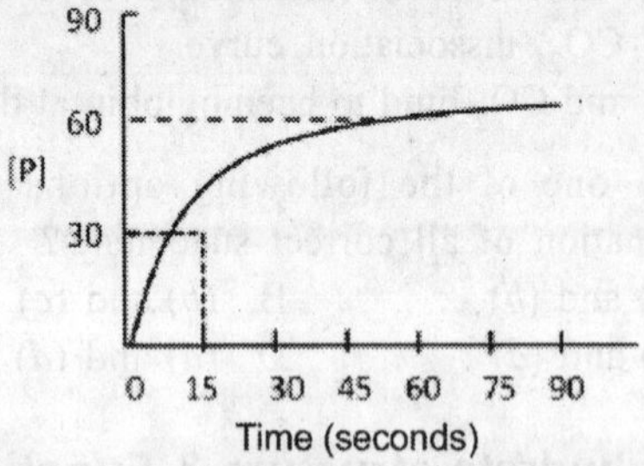

Which one of the following statements is the correct interpretation of the data?

A. The K_m and V_{max} of the enzyme X are 15 and 60 units, respectively.

B. The V_{max} is 60 but the Km cannot be determined

C. The K_m 15 but the V_{max} cannot be determined

D. neither the K_m nor the V_{max} of the enzyme X can be determined from these data

Protein-structure & Function

140. The following observations are made on a 30-residue polypeptide

(*a*) Unordered structure is observed in water but a helical conformation is observed in medium of low dielectric constant.

(*b*) The peptide is resistant to degradation by proteases.

(*c*) Red blood cells are lysed by the peptide.

(*d*) β-mercaptoethanol has no effect on peptide structure.

Which of the following statements can be correctly attributed to the above observations?

A. The peptide is entirely composed of D-amino acids and is amphipathic.

B. The peptide is entirely composed of L-amino acids and is not amphipathic.

C. The peptide is rich in disulphide bonds between D-cysteines.

D. The peptide is entirely composed of L-aromatic amino acids.

Vitamin-structure & Biochemical Function

141. Match the following vitamins with the corresponding pathological conditions arising from their deficiencies.

Vitamin	Disease
(*a*) A	(*i*) Pernicious anaemia
(*b*) B_{12}	(*ii*) Subdermal haemorrhaging
(*c*) D	(*iii*) Night blindness
(*d*) K	(*iv*) Rickets

	(*a*)	(*b*)	(*c*)	(*d*)
A.	(*iii*)	(*i*)	(*iv*)	(*ii*)
B.	(*iii*)	(*ii*)	(*iv*)	(*i*)
C.	(*iii*)	(*i*)	(*ii*)	(*iv*)
D.	(*iv*)	(*i*)	(*ii*)	(*iv*)

Protein-structure & Function

142. Which one of the following statements is true regarding amino acids?

A. Proline has high propensity to form α-helix in globular proteins

B. Both isoleucine and threonine can exist as diastereomers

C. Side chain pKa of aspartic acid is more than the side chain pKa of glutamic acid

D. The ψ dihedral angle of proline is more restricted than the ϕ dihedral angle

Carbohydrate Metabolism & Regulation

143. Phosphoenol pyruvate : sugar phosphotransferase system (PTS) transports a variety of sugars into bacteria. In *E. coli*, PTS consists of EI, EII (EIIA, EIB, and EIIC), and Hpr. During this process the sugar molecule is phosphorylated by direct transfer of phosphate group from :

A. EI-P B. EIIA-P
C. EIIB-P D. Hpr-P

CSIR-NET, 27 DECEMBER–2019

Enzyme-Action, Kinetics & Inhibition

144. Choose the correct statement from the following:

A. Iodoacetamide inactivates an enzyme by reaction with a critical serine residue at neutral pH.

B. Proline racemase causes isomerisation of L-proline to D-proline. Ribose will be anappropriate transition state analog.

C. Tosyl-1-phenylalanine chloromethyl ketone binds at the active site of chymotrypsinand modifies an essential arginine residue.

D. binds to triose phosphate isomerase at the active siteand covalently modifies a glutamic acid residue required for enzyme activity.

145. Following are statements on enzyme kinetics. Choose the correct statement.

A. Sufficiently high concentrations of substrate cannot completely relieve competitive inhibition.

B. Sufficiently high concentrations of substrate can relieve non-competitive inhibition.

C. Allosteric nature of an enzyme cannot be inferred from a plot of reaction velocity and substrate concentration.
D. For an enzyme following Michaelis-Menten kinetics, the initial velocity is determined at the beginning when enzyme-substrate dissociation is insignificant.

146. An allosteric enzyme has two heterotropic effectors, X and Y. The allosteric constant, L for the enzyme in the absence of effector molecules is 180. For the X-saturated form, the value of L increases from 180 to 1200, while for Y-saturated form it decreases to 60. What kind of effector molecules are X and Y?
A. X and Y both are positive regulators.
B. X is a negative regulator while Y is a positive regulator.
C. X is a positive regulator while Y is a negative regulator.
D. X and Y are not allosteric regulators.

147. An enzyme follows Michaelis-Menten kinetics. The activity of the enzyme was measured in the presence or absence of a molecule, "X". Given below are the double reciprocal equations for the enzyme activity with or without 'X'

(*i*) Without molecule 'X' $\frac{1}{v_0} = \frac{K_m}{V_{max}}\left(\frac{1}{[S]}\right) + \frac{1}{V_{max}}$

(*ii*) Without molecule 'X'

$$\frac{1}{v_0} = \frac{K_m}{V_{max}}\left(\frac{1}{[S]}\right) + \frac{1}{V_{max}}\left(1 + \frac{[X]}{K_x}\right)$$

What kind of molecule is 'X'? Select from the options given below.
A. Temperature independent competitive inhibitor
B. Temperature dependent competitive inhibitor
C. Non-competitive inhibitor
D. Uncompetitive inhibitor

Protein-structure & Function

148. Which one of the statements given below is correct?
A. The Ramachandran plots of Acetyl-L-Ala-CONHMe and Acetyl-D-Ala-CONHMe will be identical.
B. Fe is a transition metal but Ca is not.
C. Side chain pKa of L-Glu and D-Glu will not be identical.
D. Hydrogen bonds are fundamentally van der Waals interaction.

149. Which one of the following amino acids is induced drastically in dark adapted plants?
A. Glutamine B. Glycine
C. Asparagine D. Serine

150. Given below are some statements made on the buffering capacity of hemoglobin (Hb) in contributing to acid-base balance in the body.
(*a*) Hb buffering capacity is due to large number of histidine residues
(*b*) Imidazole groups of Hb dissociate less than those of oxyhemoglobin (HbO_2)
(*c*) Hb buffering capacity is due to large number of threonine residues
(*d*) Hb is a strong acid

Which one of the following options represents a combination of correct statements?
A. (*a*) and (*b*) B. (*b*) and (*c*)
C. (*c*) and (*d*) D. (*a*) and (*d*)

Carbohydrate-structure & Function

151. Which one of the following glycosaminoglycans is generally NOT covalently attached to protein as proteoglycans?
A. Chondroitin sulphate
B. Dermatan sulphate
C. Heparan sulphate
D. Hyaluronan

152. The following statements are made regarding a plant cell:
(*a*) Polysaccharides of various sugars with methyl esters of galacturonic acid aregenerically referred as chitin.
(*b*) Suberin and cutin are polymers and are mixtures of polyesters of hydroxy fatty acids and glycerol
(*c*) Cellulose is a polymer of glucose and fructose which can be stained by light green and haematoxylin
(*d*) Plasmodesmata maintain continuity between the cytoplasm of adjacent cells and allow large molecules to pass between them without crossing membrane.

Which one of the following options represents a combination of correct statements?
A. (*a*) and (*c*) B. (*b*) and (*c*)
C. (*b*) and (*d*) D. (*a*) and (*b*)

Carbohydrate Metabolism & Regulation

153. The molecule citrate, isocitrate, malate and succinate take part in the citric acid cycle. Identify the structure with correct name:

A. $^{-}OOC-CH_2-C(COO^-)(OH)-CH_2-COO^- \rightarrow$ Isocitrate

B. 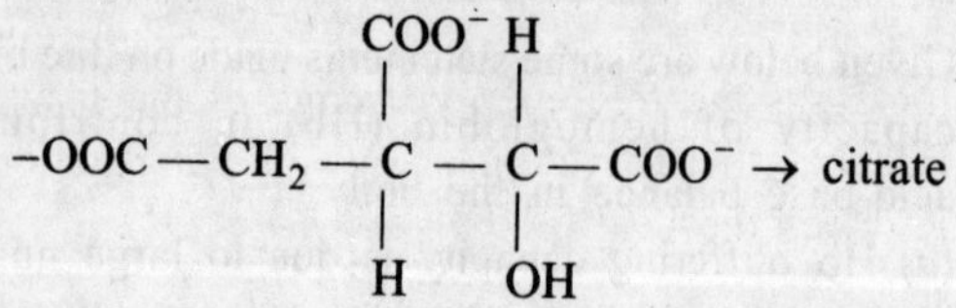

C. 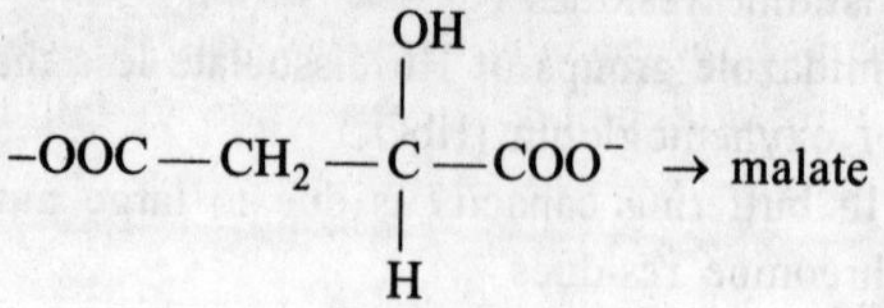

D. 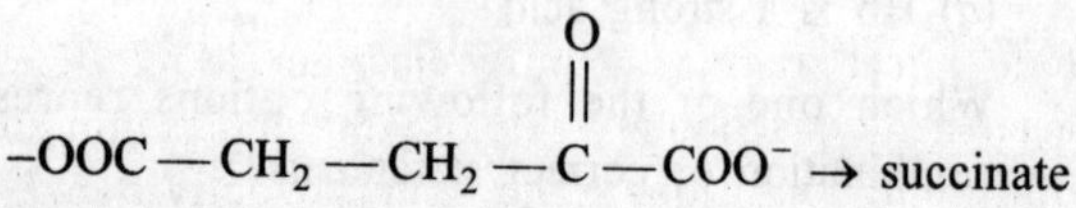

154. In the following transformations,

Succinate + X $\rightleftharpoons$ fumarate

Malate + Y $\rightleftharpoons$ oxaloacetate

Pyruvate + Z $\rightleftharpoons$ oxaloacetate

Which is the correct combination of X, Y, Z is:

A. X = FAD, Y = NAD, Z = ATP

B. X = ATP, Y = FAD, Z = NAD

C. X = NAD, Y = FAD, Z = ATP

D. X = NAD, Y = ATP, Z = FAD

155. First committed precursor in the biosynthesis of chlorophyll is:

A. δ-aminolevulinic acid

B. Porphobilinogen

C. Protoporphyrin IX

D. Coproporphyrinogen III

DBT-JRF–2019

Biomolecular Structure and Function

156. A TE buffer contains 200 mM Tris and 50 mM EDTA. Given the stock solutions – 0.5 M Tris and 0.5 M EDTA, volumes of stock solutions required to make 1 liter of buffer solution are respectively:

A. 400 ml, 100 ml   B. 200 ml, 50 ml

C. 500 ml, 125 ml   D. 100 ml, 25 ml

157. The pH of a 0.001 molar HCl solution in H_2O is:

A. 1   B. 2

C. 3   D. 4

158. To make 2 liters of 0.4 M HCl, how many ml of 28% w/w HCl (specific gravity = 1.15) is required?

A. 80.7   B. 90.7

C. 100.7   D. 110.7

159. While making 100 ml of 2M NaCl solution, a student left the solution on a heating platform reducing the volume by 50 ml. This solution was diluted 1:100 for use. What is the final concentration of NaCl in this solution?

A. 20 mM   B. 80 mM

C. 40 mM   D. 400 mM

160. The pKa of acetic acid is 4.76. At what pH would the concentration of acetic acid and acetate ion be the same?

A. pH = 7   B. pH = 6.7

C. pH = 9.8   D. pH = 4.76

161. ^{14}C has a half-life of 5760 years; 100 mg of a sample of ^{14}C will completely disintegrate in:

A. 23,040 years   B. 1440 years

C. 11,520 years   D. infinite time

162. Competitive inhibition of an enzyme can be reduced by:

A. Reducing the amount of the substrate

B. Increasing the amount of the substrate

C. Decreasing the amount of the enzyme

D. Diluting the reaction mixture

163. Which one of the following enzymes can hydrolyze both ester and amide bonds?

A. Methionine racemase

B. Thrombin

C. Chymotrypsin

D. Peroxidase

164. With reference to protein precipitation by organic solvents, which one of the following statements is correct?

A. It is not influenced by pH.

B. It is dependent on the change in dielectric constant.

C. It is unaffected by ionic strength.

D. It is independent of the molecular size of the protein.

165. A young scientist was interested in creating a dipeptide using L-alanine and L-glycine. How many different dipeptides can be generated?

A. One   B. Two

C. Three   D. Four

166. The measured values of main chain torsion angles of a residue in a polypeptide has values (Φ = +50, Ψ = +60). What type of secondary structure is it most likely to be present in?

A. Left-handed α-helix   B. Right-handed α-helix

C. Type II β-turn   D. Parallel β-sheet

167. Which of the following is NOT true of protein folds?

A. Proteins assume a limited number of folds

B. Proteins with the same fold may perform different functions

C. Proteins with different folds can carry out the same function
D. A stable fold is a prerequisite for the function of all proteins

168. In the citric acid cycle operating under aerobic conditions, which one of the following is not directly involved?
A. NAD+ B. FAD
C. Molecular oxygen D. Succinate

169. Statins inhibit the biosynthesis of:
A. Prostaglandins
B. Leukotrienes
C. Serotonin
D. Cholesterol

170. Thallium-208 has a half-life of 3.053 min. How long will a sample containing 120.0 μCi of Thallium-208 take to decay to 7.50 μCi?
A. 6.11 min
B. 9.36 min
C. 12.21 min
D. 18.46 min

171. Proteins can act as excellent buffers because of:
A. The wide range of pKa values of side chains found within the proteins.
B. The ability of the terminal regions of the protein to accept or donate H^+ ions.
C. Their hydrogen-bonding capabilities in forming secondary & tertiary structures.
D. The ease with which H^+ & OH^- ions can be absorbed once the protein is hydrolyzed.

172. Glycerol is a:
A. Newtonian fluid
B. Pseudoplastic fluid
C. Thixotropic fluid
D. Dilatant fluid

173. A catalyst:
A. Reduces the free energy change of the reaction
B. Increases the free energy change of the reaction
C. Reduces the activation energy of the reaction
D. Reduces the heat of the reaction

174. A substrate is consumed in a zero order reaction such that the concentration falls from 40 g/l to 20 g/l in 4 h. How long will it take the substrate to fall from 20 g/l to 2 g/l:
A. 2.5 h B. 1.8 h
C. 3.6 h D. 4.8 h

175. One microgram of a pure enzyme (MW: 92,000) catalyzed a reaction at a rate of 0.50 μmoles/min under optimum conditions. The specific activity of the enzyme [(μmoles/min)/mg protein] is:
A. 0.5 B. 5.0
C. 500 D. 5000

176. Two charged molecules are at a distance '*r*' from each other. Which one of the following is correct regarding the electrostatic interactions between them?
A. The interaction energy is proportional to r^{-1} and the force is proportional to r^{-2}
B. The interaction energy is proportional to r, and the force is proportional to r^2
C. The interaction energy is proportional to r^2, and the force is proportional to r^{-3}
D. The interaction energy is proportional to r^{-3}, and the force is proportional to r^{-2}

177. The structure of two molecules P and Q with three atoms (*u*, *v*, *w*) each, are defined by coordinates given below.

	U	V	W
P	1,4,1	4,1,1	4,4,1
Q	0,0,1	2,0,1	3,2,1

The root mean square deviation between the two structures is:
A. √3 B. 3
C. 9 D. 27

GATE (BIOTECHNOLOGY) – 2019

Biochemistry

178. Which one of the following statements is CORRECT for enzyme catalyzed reactions? (ΔG is Gibbs free energy change, *Keq* is equilibrium constant)
A. Enzymes affect ΔG, but not *Keq*
B. Enzymes affect *Keq*, but not ΔG
C. Enzymes affect both ΔG and *Keq*
D. Enzymes do not affect ΔG or *Keq*

179. In general, which one of the following statements is NOT CORRECT?
A. Hydrogen bonds result from electrostatic interactions
B. Hydrogen bonds contribute to the folding energy of proteins
C. Hydrogen bonds are weaker than van der Waals interactions
D. Hydrogen bonds are directional

GATE (LIFE SCIENCE) – 2019

Biomolecule

180. The dipeptide with least rotational barrier in the peptide bond is

A. 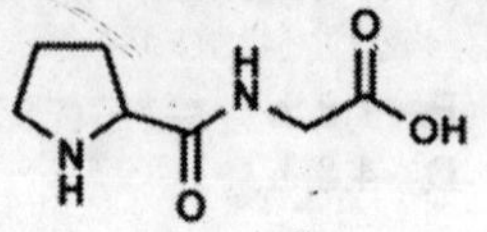

B. 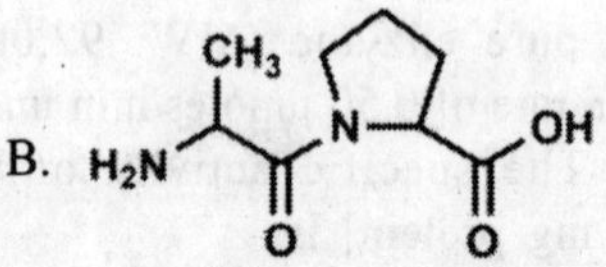

C. 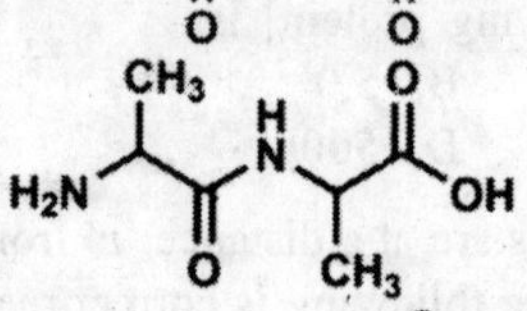

D. 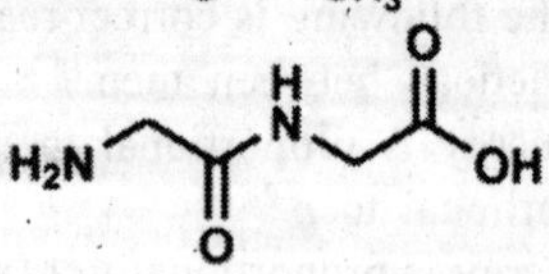

181. The light-harvesting pigment NOT used by Cyanobacteria for photosynthesis is

A. Rhodopsin B. Phycobilin
C. Phycoerythrobilin D. Phycocyanobilin

182. The ascending order of half-life for the radioactive isotopes, ^{125}I, ^{3}H, ^{14}C and ^{32}P, is

A. $^{14}C < ^{125}I < ^{3}H < ^{32}P$
B. $^{32}P < ^{3}H < ^{125}I < ^{14}C$
C. $^{14}C < ^{3}H < ^{32}P < ^{125}I$
D. $^{32}P < ^{125}I < ^{3}H < ^{14}C$

183. Which one of the following is an incorrect biomolecule-modification pair?

A. Lipid-Palmitoylation
B. DNA and Protein-Methylation
C. Protein-Glycosylation
D. RNA-Polyadenylation

184. The enzyme NOT involved in oxidation of the molecule shown below is

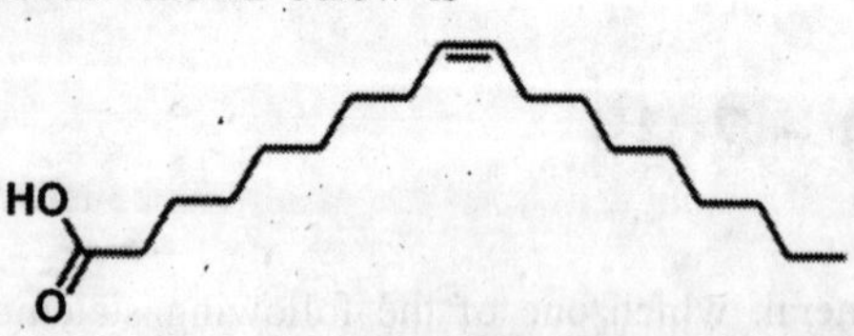

A. Δ3, Δ2 - Enoyl –CoA isomerase
B. Propionyl-CoA caboxylase
C. Acyl CoA dehydrogenase
D. Enoyl CoA hydratase

185. The crystal structure of a peptide has an ordered structural repeat of amino acids with a distance of ~ 6.5 Å between the alternate C α atoms. Which one of the following pair of dihedral angles (Φ and ψ) accurately represents the peptide structure?

A. $\Phi \approx -60°$, $\Psi \approx -50°$
B. $\Phi \approx -120°$, $\Psi \approx -50°$
C. $\Phi \approx -60°$, $\Psi \approx +120°$
D. $\Phi \approx -120°$, $\Psi \approx +120°$

Enzyme & Metabolism

186. The example of substrate level phosphorylation in glycolysis is

A. Conversion of Glucose to Glucose-6-phosphate
B. Conversion of Glyceraldehyde-3-phosphate to 1,3-Bisphosphoglycerate
C. Conversion of 1,3-Bisphosphoglycerate to 3-Phosphoglycerate
D. Conversion of Dihydroxyacetone phosphate to Glyceraldehyde-3-phosphate

187. Slow intravenous infusion of ethanol is a therapy to treat methanol poisoning. The underlying chemical reaction is an example of

A. Competitive inhibition
B. Non-competitive inhibition
C. Mixed inhibition
D. Enzyme activation

188. Match the given vitamins in Column I with the related proteins in Column II

Column I	Column II
(*a*) Vitamin C	(*i*) Thrombin
(*b*) Vitamin K	(*ii*) Rhodopsin
(*c*) Vitamin A	(*iii*) Pyruvate dehydrogenase
(*d*) Vitamin B1	(*iv*) Prolyl hydroxylase

	(*a*)	(*b*)	(*c*)	(*d*)
A.	(*iv*)	(*i*)	(*ii*)	(*iii*)
B.	(*iv*)	(*i*)	(*iii*)	(*ii*)
C.	(*ii*)	(*i*)	(*iv*)	(*iii*)
D.	(*iii*)	(*iv*)	(*ii*)	(*i*)

CSIR-NET, NOVEMBER (MORNING)–2020

Enzyme-Action, Kinetics & Inhibition

189. The rate constant for conversion of a substrate into the product is $10^{-4}s^{-1}$ while the reverse rate constant is $10^{-6}s^{-1}$. An enzyme enhance the rate of this reaction by 100-fold. The equilibrium constant for this enzyme-catalyzed reaction is

A. 100 B. 10000
C. 10 D. 1000

190. The following statements were made of suggest the existence of an enzyme-substrate complex.

(*a*) at constant concentration of enzyme, the reaction rate increase with increasing substrate concentration

(*b*) An enzyme-catalyzed reaction has a maximal velocity

(*c*) At constant concentration of the enzyme and substrate, an increase in the reaction rate is observed.

(*d*) An enzyme catalyzed reaction is not influenced by high substrate concentration.

Which of the above statements suggest the existence of an enzyme-substrate complex?

A. (*a*) and (*b*) B. (*b*) and (*c*)
C. (*a*) and (*c*) D. (*d*) only

191. An enzyme catalyzed reaction comparing proton and deuteron transfer reactions yielded the following kinetic date

K_{cat} [H], s^{-1}	70.7
K_M [H], mM	1.03
K_{cat}[H], s^{-1}	10.3
K_M [H], mM	1.06

Which of the following represents the turn over number (M^{-1} — s^{-1}) for proton transfer, deuteron transfer and the kinetic isotope effect, respectively?

A. 68640, 9717,14
B. 6864, 972, 7
C. 728210, 1091, 14
D. 68640, 9717, 7

192. The first step in the biosynthesis of valine begines with enzyme catalyzed condensation of two molecules of pyruvic acid. If an equimolar mixture of $^{13}CH_3COCOOH$ and $^{12}CH_3COCOOH$ are used as substrates for the reaction, which one of the following would represent the correct isotope incorporation pattern of the pro-R and pro-S diastereotopic methly group in valine?

A. 50% $^{13}CH_3$ (pro-R), $^{12}CH_3$ (pro-S)
50% $^{12}CH_3$ (pro-R), $^{13}CH_3$ (pro-S)

B. 75% $^{13}CH_3$ (pro-R), $^{12}CH_3$ (pro-S)
25% $^{12}CH_3$ (pro-R), $^{13}CH_3$ (pro-S)

C. 25% $^{13}CH_3$ (pro-R), $^{12}CH_3$ (pro-S)
25% $^{12}CH_3$ (pro-R), $^{13}CH_3$ (pro-S)
25% $^{13}CH_3$ (pro-R), $^{13}CH_3$ (pro-S)
25% $^{12}CH_3$ (pro-R), $^{12}CH_3$ (pro-S)

D. 75% $^{12}CH_3$ (pro-R), $^{13}CH_3$ (pro-S)
25% $^{13}CH_3$ (pro-R), $^{13}CH_3$ (pro-S)

Vitamin-structure & Biochemical Function

193. Which one of the following options represent a series of the amino acids with the decreasing pk_a values of their side chain?

A. Arg Lys Cys His
B. Lys Arg Cys His
C. Lys Arg His Cys
D. Arg Cys Lys His

194. The following disulfide bond containing peptide was digested using trypsin. How many peptide fragments will be produced by the digestion?

MTPQKAVILNSCTYRPYPM

NQGCLKVCVNPCGRLTDEH

A. Three B. Four
C. Five D. Six

Carbohydrate-structure & Function

195. A stoichiometric mixture of α and β anomers of D-glucose in water exhibits

A. net optical rotation proportional to the sum of the optical activities of each anomer

B. no optical activity as the sign of optical rotation are opposite and they cancel each other

C. no optical activity as the α and β anomers in the linear forms that are optically inactive

D. no optical activity as they form a racemic mixture

CSIR-NET, NOVEMBER (AFTERNOON)–2020

Water, PH, Thermodynamics, Bond

196. In the enzyme-linked antibody used in ELISA, the interaction between the enzyme and antibody is stabilized by

A. hydrogen bond
B. ionic bond
C. covalent bond
D. van der Waal's interactions

197. The following statements were made to describe the role of Gibbs free energy

(*a*) Reaction can take place spontaneously if ΔG is negative

(*b*) Reaction can take place spontaneously if ΔG is positive

(*c*) ΔG provides no information about the rate of a reaction

(*d*) ΔG estimation provides the rate of a reaction.

Which one of the following represents all correct statements?

A. (*a*) and (*c*) B. (*b*) and (*c*)
C. (*a*) and (*d*) D. (*b*) and (*d*)

Enzyme-Action, Kinetics & Inhibition

198. A plot with which one of the following axes is drawn to exhibit enzyme inhibition kinetics applying Dixon's plot?

A. V_i vs [I]
B. $\frac{1}{V_i}$ vs $\frac{1}{[I]}$
C. $\frac{1}{V_i}$ vs [I]
D. V_i vs $\frac{1}{[I]}$

199. The Hill equation and its plot describe the following enzyme kinetic behaviours
(*a*) Saturation Kinetics
(*b*) Cooperative Kinetics
(*c*) Log $V_i/(V_{max} - V_i)$ versus Log[s]
(*d*) Log Log $(V_{max} - V_i)/V_i$ versus $Log[s]^{-1}$

Which one of the following combination represents correct descriptions?

A. (*a*) and (*c*)
B. (*b*) and (*c*)
C. (*b*) and (*d*)
D. (*a*) and (*d*)

Protein-structure & Function

200. Spermidine represents which of the following group of compounds:

A. jasmonic acid
B. polyamine
C. auxin
D. strigolactone

201. If the pyrollidine ring of proline is reduced to a linear form, the new amino acid will have

A. constrained φ than proline
B. constrained ψ than proline
C. relaxed φ than proline
D. unaffected φ and ψ

202. The following table lists names of scientists and advances made by them:

Column A	Column B
(*a*) Linus Pauling	(*i*) Myoglobin structure
(*b*) Emil fischer	(*ii*) Model of α-helix
(*c*) John Kendrew	(*iii*) Lock and key model
(*d*) Christian Anfinsen	(*iv*) Sequence structure relationship

Which one of the following options correctly matches contents of column A with column B?

	(*a*)	(*b*)	(*c*)	(*d*)
A.	(*iii*)	(*iv*)	(*ii*)	(*i*)
B.	(*ii*)	(*iii*)	(*i*)	(*iv*)
C.	(*ii*)	(*i*)	(*iii*)	(*iv*)
D.	(*i*)	(*iii*)	(*ii*)	(*iv*)

203. In high altitude, a number of compensatory mechanisms operate over a period of time to increase altitude tolerance in humans which is called acclimatization. The following statements propose these compensatory changes:
(*a*) The initial increase of ventilation is relatively small in high altitude but the ventilation steadily increases over next few days.
(*b*) Red blood cell 2, 3-DPG is increased.
(*c*) The blood pH becomes more alkaline.
(*d*) The oxygen dissociation curve is shifted to the left.
(*e*) The pH of cerebrospinal fluid is further increased.

Choose the option with both INCORRECT statements:

A. (*a*) and (*b*)
B. (*b*) and (*c*)
C. (*c*) and (*d*)
D. (*d*) and (*e*)

204. The following statements describe the propensity and role of amino acids in the secondary structure of proteins
(*a*) Alanine has a high frequency of occurrence in α-helices
(*b*) Proline has a high frequency of occurrence in α-helices
(*c*) The X_1 does not affect the helix propensity of serine, threonine and valine
(*d*) Peptide bonds involving 'N' of proline may display cis-trans isomerism

Choose the correct combination.

A. (*a*) and (*d*)
B. (*a*) and (*c*)
C. (*b*) and (*c*)
D. (*c*) and (*d*)

Carbohydrate Metabolism & Regulation

205. Which one of the following enzymes present in erythrocytes helps bypass the first step of ATP formation in glycolysis?

A. Bisphosphoglycerate mutase
B. Phosphoglycerate kinase
C. Glyceraldehyde 3-phosphate dehydrogenase
D. Phosphofructose mutase

Fat-structure & Function

206. Which one of the statements given below is INCORRECT?

A. The three common types of membrane lipids are cholesterol, phospholipids and glycolipids.
B. Phosphoglycerides carry a glycerol backbone, two fatty acid chains, and a phosphorylated alcohol.
C. Most phospholipids and glycolipids form bimolecular sheets rather than micelles in aqueous media.
D. The common alcohol moieties in phosphoglycerides are glycerol, inositol, choline, ethanolamine and tyrosine.

ETC

207. Electron transfer from donors such as NADH and $FADH_2$ to O_2 occurs in

A. membranes of ER, chloroplast and mitochondria
B. chloroplast only
C. mitochondria only
D. organellar membranes which possess ATP synthase

DBT-JRF–2020

Biomolecular Structure and Function

208. A buffer contains 10% glucose, 20 mM Tris, and 50 mM HCI. For making 1 litre of buffer from the following stock solutions – 50% glucose, 1M Tris, and 1 M HCI, the correct combination of volume each of the stock solutions will be:

A. 200 ml, 50 ml, 20 ml
B. 50 ml, 100 ml, 10 ml
C. 50 ml, 50 ml, 50 ml
D. 200 ml, 20 ml, 50 ml

209. Someone tells you that the pH of a solution is minus 2. Which one of the following is false?

A. concentration of is H_3O^+ 100 m
B. such a value of pH is possible in theory
C. such a value of pH is unlikely to occur in practice
D. such a value of pH is impossible even in theory

210. How much sodium hydroxide will you weigh to prepare 0.25 L of 3 M solution?

A. 40 g B. 80 g
C. 40 Kg D. 30 g

211. Two film theory of mass transfer considers

A. variable resistance at the interface
B. maximum resistance at the interface
C. 50 % resistance at the interface
D. negligible resistance at the interface

212. The fluid property, due to which, mercury does not wet the glass is

A. surface tension B. specific gravity
C. polarity D. viscosity

213. Choose the correct order in terms of pka

A. Acetic acid > TFA > HCI < H_2SO_4
B. Acetic acid > TFA < HCI < H_2SO_4
C. Acetic acid < TFA < H_2SO_4 < HCI
D. Acetic acid > TFA > HCI > H_2SO_4

214. What will be the molarity of a 4 mg/ml solution of NaOH?

A. 1M B. 0.1 M
C. 4 M. D. 0.0844 M

215. Which is the correct arrangement of the polarity of solvents?

A. Water > DMSO > DME > THE
B. Water < DMSO > DMF < CH_3CN
C. Water > DMSO < DMF > CH_3CN
D. Water DMSO > DMF > CH_3CN

216. Which of the following is true for acetyl-CoA?

A. it is an acetyl group attached to a type of coenzyme
B. it is another name for oxaloacetate
C. it is a protein
D. it is an acetyl group joined with a form of cobalt

217. In enzyme kinetics, if the enzyme concentration in doubled

A. Km becomes double
B. Km does not change
C. Km becomes half
D. Km increases 4-fold

218. Enzymes bind their substrates via

A. hydrogen bonds
B. hydrophobic interactions
C. shape complementarity
D. all of the given options are correct

219. The artificial sweetener, aspartame, is enzymatically produced using

A. galactosidase B. rennin
C. lipase D. Thermolysin

220. Immobilization of enzymes to water insoluble, anionic porous carriers often results in an apparent shift in the pH optima of the enzyme. The physico-chemical interaction likely to cause such a behavior is

A. enzyme deactivation
B. partitioning effect
C. internal mass transfer limitation
D. external mass transfer limitation

221. The mucopolysaccharide hyaluronic acid is composed of

A. N-acetyl D-glucosamine only
B. D-glucuronic acid only
C. neither N-acetyl D-glucosamine nor D-glucuronic acid
D. both N-acetyl D-glucosamine and D-glucuronic acid

222. Cellulose is a linear polymer of glucose with

A. beta-1,4-glycosidic linkage
B. alpha1,4-glycosidic linkage
C. beta-1,3-glycosidic linkage
D. alpha-1,3-glycosidic linkage

223. The molecular weight of Val and Ser are 117 Dalton and 105 Dalton, respectively. Val and Ser form a dipeptide Val-Ser. The molecular weight (in Daltons) of the dipeptide is

A. 204 B. 222
C. 186 D. 240

224. Which of the following is NOT a rational grouping of amino acids bases on their polarity properties?
A. Val and Leu B. Met and Leu
C. Asn and Gin D. Glu and Ile

225. Histones
A. contains high amount of basic amino acids
B. contain both α – *helix* and β – *pleated* sheet
C. have molecular weights in excess of 100,000 Da
D. is negatively-charged globular proteins

226. Trypsin cleaves a protein at the
A. C – terminus side of Arg/Lys residues
B. N – terminus side of Arg/Lys residues
C. C – terminus side of Val/Ile residues
D. N- terminus side of Val/Ile residue

227. The egg white protein, ovalbumin, is denatured in a hard-boiled egg. Which of the following least affected?
A. quaternary structure of ovalbumin
B. primary structure of ovalbumin
C. secondary structure of ovalbumin
D. tertiary structure of ovalbumin

228. Which of the following represents a quantitative measure of the structural similarity between two proteins?
A. revised mode square deviation
B. root mean square distance
C. standard deviation
D. root mean square deviation

229. The primary structure of a protein is stabilized by
A. the angle formed between plane ABD and plane ACD
B. covalent bond
C. ionic bond
D. hydrogen bonds

230. The amino acid residue with the least preference for any quadrant in the Ramachandran map is
A. Valine B. glycine
C. serine D. alanine

231. Which of the following amino acids is most likely to disrupt an alpha-helix?
A. proline B. valine
C. lysine D. arginine

232. Two amino acids with negatively charged side chains are
A. aspartic acid and glycine
B. aspartic acid and lysine
C. lysine and glutamic acid
D. aspartic acid and glutamic acid

233. Which interactions are generally observed at the core of stable protein-protein complexes?
A. salt bridges B. hydrogen bonds
C. disulfide bonds D. hydrophobic

234. Computational Prediction of protein folding assumes that
A. the folded state is a global free energy minimum
B. folding takes place at the monomeric level
C. all the given options are correct
D. contributions of Potential Energy parameters to fold stability are reliable

235. The comparison of the structures of haemoglobin and myoglobin shows that they have
A. different primary structure but similar tertiary structure
B. similar primary structure but different tertiary structure
C. different primary and tertiary structures
D. similar primary and tertiary structures

236. Which of the following does not have a quaternary structure?
A. collagen B. RNA polymerase
C. haemoglobin D. myoglobin

237. A protein of 100 KDa would have approximately how many amino acids?
A. 100 B. 1000
C. 800 D. 900

238. The enzyme used in glucometers to estimate blood glucose levels is
A. glucose isomerase B. insulin
C. glucose oxidase D. hexokinase

239. Which of the following is a non-reducing sugar?
A. fructose B. galactose
C. ribose D. sucrose

240. Which of following is a trisaccharide?
A. kestose B. cellobiose
C. trehalose D. mannose

241. The genetic disease familial Hypercholesterolemia that leads to an increase in blood cholesterol is caused due to
A. consuming cholesterol rich foods
B. mutation in the low-density lipoprotein (LDL) receptor
C. increased hydrolysis of stored intracellular cholesteryl esters
D. increased de novo cholesterol synthesis

242. A student made 0.15 M solution of copper sulphate. The absorbance of the solution was found to be 0.3 when using a cuvette with a path length of 1 cm. Copper sulphate solution made by a second student gave an absorbance of 0.45 using the same cuvette at the same wavelength. What is the concentration of the copper sulphate solution made by the second student?
A. 0.425 M B. 0.125 M
C. 0.225 M D. 0.325 M

243. Chlorine is assigned and atomic weight of 35.5. This is due to
A. presence of half of proton
B. none of the given options
C. presence of isotopes
D. presence of half a neutron

244. Sam was investigating impact of lactate dehydrogenase knockout on glycolytic pathway. What will be the net NADH production that he would expect in conversion of Glucose to pyruvate in this case?
A. 4 NADH   B. 3 NADH
C. 0 NADH   D. 2 NADH

245. If four atoms A, B, C, and D are connected linearly and there is rotation possible along bond BC, dihedral angel on this bond is described as
A. the angel between AB and CD
B. the angel formed between plane ABD and plane ACD
C. the angel formed between plane ABC and plane BCD
D. the angel between AC and BD

GATE (BIOTECHNOLOGY) – 2020

246. Which of the following types of molecules acts as biological catalysts?
P. Protein
Q. RNA
R. Phospholipid
A. P and Q only   B. P and R only
C. Q and R only   D. P, Q and R

247. A block of ice at O°C is supplied heat at a constant rate to convert ice to superheated steam. Which one of the following trajectories correctly represents the trend of the temperature of the system with time? Assume that specific heat of H_2O is not a function of temperature.

A. 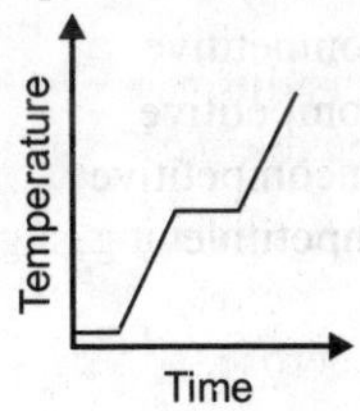

B. 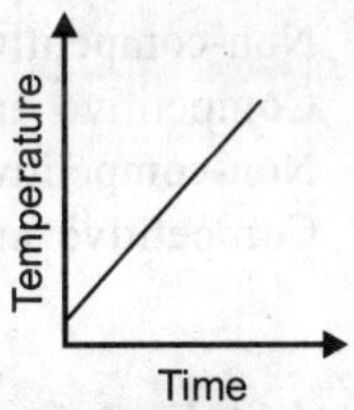

C. 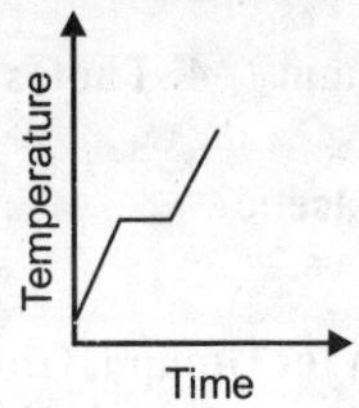

D. 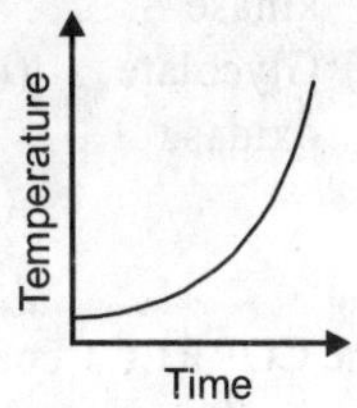

248. Which of the following strategies are used by cells for metabolic regulation?
P. Phosphorylation – dephosphorylation
Q. Allostery
R. Feedback inhibition
A. P and Q only
B. P and R only
C. Q and R only
D. P, Q and R only

GATE (LIFE SCIENCE) – 2020

Biomolecule

249. Choose the correct order of molecules according to their ability to diffuse across a lipid bilayer
A. CO_2 > H_2O > Glucose > RNA
B. CO_2 > Glucose > H_2O > RNA
C. RNA > Glucose > CO_2 > H_2O
D. H_2O > CO_2 > RNA > Glucose

250. One mole of a native protein upon N-terminal analysis yielded one mole each of Asp and Val. Therefore, the protein in its native state exists as a
A. Monomer   B. Homo-dimer
C. Hetero-dimer   D. Tetramer

251. The correct combination of glycosidic linkages present in glycogen is
A. α 1 → 4 and α 1→ 6
B. α 1 → 4 and β 1 → 6
C. α 1 → 6 and β 1 → 4
D. α 1 → 6 and β1 → 6

Enzyme & Metabolism

252. Which one of the following bonds is NOT present in ATP?
A. Phosphoester   B. Phosphoanhydride
C. N-Glycosidic   D. α-Glycosidic

253. The prosthetic groups/cofactors involved in the both $1e^-$ and $2e^-$ transfer in the mitochondrial electron transport chain are
A. NAD and NADP
B. NAD and FAD

C. Heme and FMN
D. Coenzyme Q and FMN

254. The reaction involved in the direct conversion of L-phenylalanine to L-tyrosine is
A. Hydroxylation B. Decarboxylation
C. Transamination D. Reduction

255. Group I, Group II and Group III represent enzyme, product of the enzymatic reaction, and metabolic process, respectively.

Group I	Group II	Group III
(*a*) Hexokinase	(*i*) Malate	1. Glycolysis
(*b*) Fumarase	(*ii*) Glucose-6-p	2. Photorespiration
(*c*) PEP carboxy-kinase	(*iii*) Hydrogen peroxide	3. TCA cycle
(*d*) Glycolate oxidase	(*iv*) Cinnamic acid	4. Photosynthesis
	(*v*) Oxaloacetic acid	

The CORRECT combination for Group I, Group II and Group III is

	(*a*)	(*b*)	(*c*)	(*d*)
A.	(*ii*)-1	(*iv*)-3	(*v*)-2	(*iii*)-4
B.	(*ii*)-1	(*i*)-3	(*v*)-4	(*iii*)-2
C.	(*ii*)-2	(*v*)-3	(*i*)-2	(*iii*)-1
D.	(*iii*)-1	(*i*)-3	(*iv*)-4	(*ii*)-2

256. Match the following in CORRECT combination between Group I and Group II with reference to the agents that interfere with oxidative phosphorylation

Group I	Group II
(*a*) Cyanide	(*i*) Block electron transfer from cyt b to cyt c1
(*b*) Antimycin A	(*ii*) Inhibit F1
(*c*) Aurovertin	(*iii*) Uncoupling of photophosphorylation from electron transfer
(*d*) 2,4-Dinitrophenol	(*iv*) Inhibits cytochrome oxidase
	(*v*) Inhibit K+ inophore

	(*a*)	(*b*)	(*c*)	(*d*)
A.	(*iv*)	(*i*)	(*ii*)	(*iii*)
B.	(*v*)	(*i*)	(*iii*)	(*iv*)
C.	(*iv*)	(*iii*)	(*ii*)	(*v*)
D.	(*v*)	(*ii*)	(*iii*)	(*iv*)

257. The graph below shows the activity of enzyme pepsin in the presence of inhibitors aliphatic alcohols (P) or N-acetyl-1-phenylalanine(Q). Which ONE of the following represents the nature of inhibitions by P and Q, respectively?

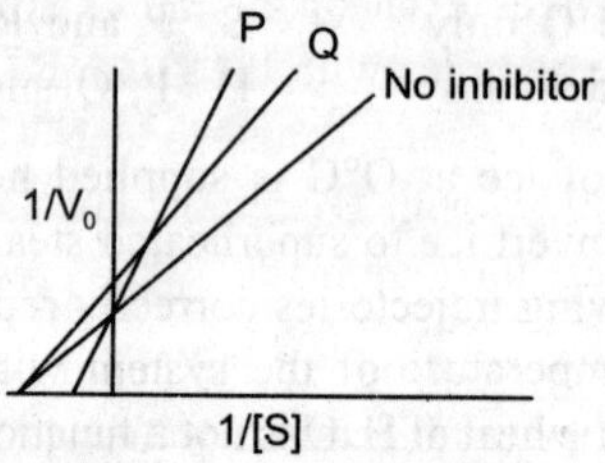

A. Non-competitive and competitive
B. Competitive and non-competitive
C. Non-competitive and uncompetitive
D. Competitive and uncompetitive

CSIR-NET, JUNE (MORNING)–2021

Enzyme-Action, Kinetics & Inhibition

258. The enzyme alkaline phosphatase was tested for its catalytic activity using the substrate para-nitrophenyl-phosphate. The k_m obtained was 10 mM and V_{max} was 100 μmol/min. Which one of the following options represents the initial velocity of the reaction at a substrate concentration of 10 mM?
A. 50 μmol/min
B. 100 μmol/min
C. 500 μmol/min
D. 20 μmol/min

259. Following statements are made about uncompetitive inhibition of an enzyme:
(*a*) Uncompetitive inhabitor binds both two free enzyme as well as an enzyme subtract complex.
(*b*) Addition of Uncompetitive inhibitor lowers the value of the reaction.
(*c*) Apparent K_m of the enzyme is lowered.
(*d*) Apparent K_m of the enzyme remains unchanged.

Which of the following option represent the correct combination of statements?
A. (*b*) and (*c*) B. (*a*) and (*c*)
C. (*a*) and (*b*) D. (*a*) and (*d*)

260. The following statements are being made to the define the Michelis constant (K_m) it is:
(*a*) Independent of enzyme conc. [E] and substrate conc. [S]
(*b*) Equal to the dissociation constant when the [ES] complex dissociated more rapidly than [ES] product formation
(*c*) Equal to the dissociation constant when product formation is more rapid than [ES] compiex is dissociated.
(*d*) An intrinsic property of the enzyme and does not depand on ph, temperature and ionic strength.

Which one of the following statement is correct?
A. (*a*) & (*b*) only
B. (*a*), (*b*) & (*d*) only
C. (*c*) & (*d*) only
D. (*a*) & (*d*) only

Protein-structure & Function

261. How many hydrogen bonds involving the backbone CO and NH can be observed in an α-helix consisting of 15 amino acid residues?
A. 10 B. 11
C. 12 D. 13

262. Some cells possess peptides which contain D-form of amino acids. How do they arise?
A. These peptides are produced by ribosomes by incorporating D-amino acids at specific positions.
B. Ribosome makes peptides with L-amino acids only. However, some of the amino acids in the peptide are replaced by D-amino acids by a pathway that involves excision of the L-amino acids.
C. The peptides with the D-amino acids are produced in a ribosome- independent manner.
D. Peptides with D-amino acids exist only in archeae where they are made by the presence of racemases.

263. A protein solution of unknown concentration was dilute with 0.8 ml of water to 0.5 ml this diluted solution 4.5 ml of biured reagent was added and the color allowed to develop at 540 nm was observed to be 0.20. 0.5 ml of BSA solution plus 4.5 pml of burnt gave an absorbance in the undiluted unknown solution?
A. 20 B. 40
C. 50 D. 80

264. Following are the pka's of the ionizable groups in lysine
Pka1 = 2.16 (α-carboxylic acid)
Pka2 = 9.06 (α-amino group)
Pka3 = 10.54 (ε-amino group)

Which one of the following options represents the pI of lysine?
A. 7.25 B. 5.61
C. 6.35 D. 9.8

265. The pI of four proteins (A, B, C, D) are shown in the table below:

Protein	pI
A	4
B	5.5
C	7
D	9

To purify "D" from a maximum of these four protein in a single step using ion exchange chromatography of the buffer pH send icon exchange resion would you select?
A. PH 11, cation exchanger resion phl
B. PH 2, anion exchanger resion ph2
C. PH 6, anion exchanger resion ph6
D. PH 8, cation exchanger resion ph 8

266. The curve B in the figure below shows the oxygen dissociation profile at physiological concentration of CO_2 and pH 7.

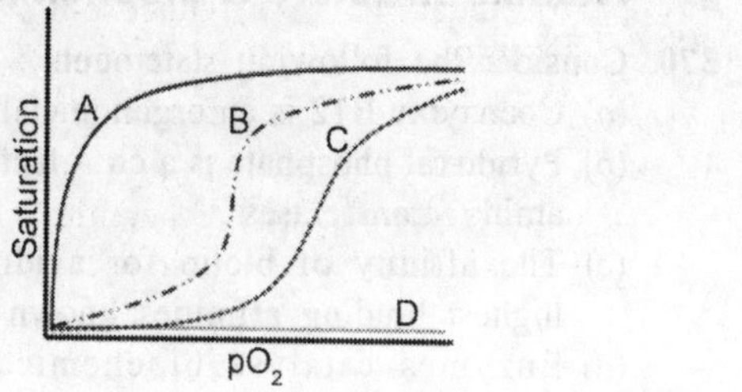

An increase in pH would lead to oxygen dissociation profile indicated by:
A. curve B (no change in the dissociation profile)
B. curve A
C. curve C
D. curve D

267. Hemoglobin (Hb) transport co2 in venous blood as carbamates. The following refers to formation of these carbamates:
(*a*) CO_2 interacts with amino terminal nitrogens of Hb polypeptide chains.
(*b*) CO_2 interacts with carboxyl terminal carbons of Hb polypeptide chains.
(*c*) Carbamates helps formation of salt bridges between alpha and beta chains of Hb.
(*d*) Carbamates helps formation of disulfide bridges between alpha and beta chains of Hb.

Which of the following option is a combination of correct statement?
A. (*a*) and (*c*)
B. (*b*) and (*c*)
C. (*b*) and (*d*)
D. (*a*) and (*d*)

ETC

268. Iron Sulphur cluster are the [Fe-S] are the key prostatic groups that carry electrons in all of the below EXCEPT
A. NADH-CoQ reductase NADH-CoQ B.
B. succinate-CoQ reductase
C. cytochrome C oxidase
D. CoQH2-cytochrome C reductase CoQH2

CSIR-NET, JUNE (AFTERNOON)–2021

Enzyme-Action, Kinetics & Inhibition

269. What is the fold difference between v at [S] = K_m and v at [S] = 1000 Km, where v is the initial velocity of an enzyme catalyzed reaction, [S] is substrate concentration and Km is the Michaelis constant?

A. 1.998 B. 1000
C. 2.998 D. 3.998

Vitamin-structure & Biochemical Function

270. Consider the following statements :

(*a*) Coenzyme B12 is an organometallic compound D.
(*b*) Pyridoxal phosphate is a co – factor used by many amino- transferases .
(*c*) The affinity of biotin for avidin is one of the highest binding affinities known in biochemistry
(*d*) Enzymes catalyse biochemical reactions by lowering the energy of the transition state

Which one of the following options represents all correct statements?

A. (*a*), (*b*), (*c*) and (*d*)
B. (*b*), (*c*) and (*d*) only
C. (*c*) and (*d*) only
D. (*d*) only

Protein-structure & Function

271. Protein X is an all helical protein with 100 amino acids including 2 cysteines and a pI of 7.0. Which one of the following graphs best describes the solubility of this protein under different ammonium sulphate (salt) concentrations?

A.
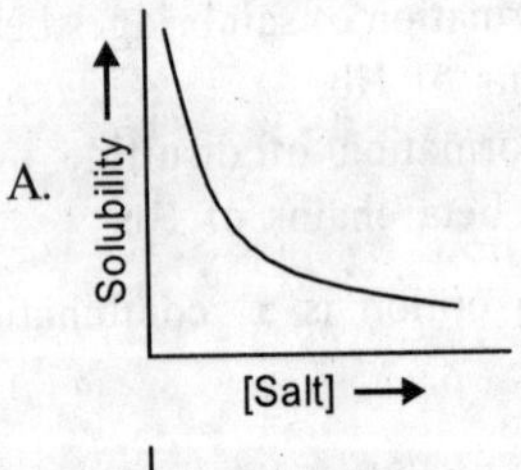

B.
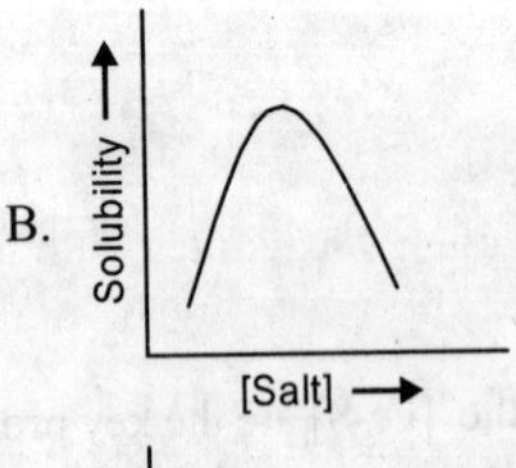

C.
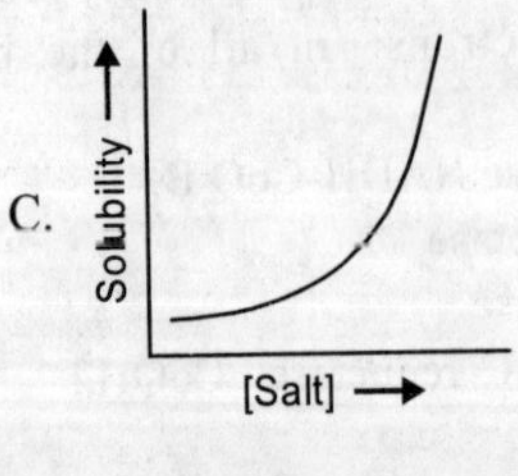

D.
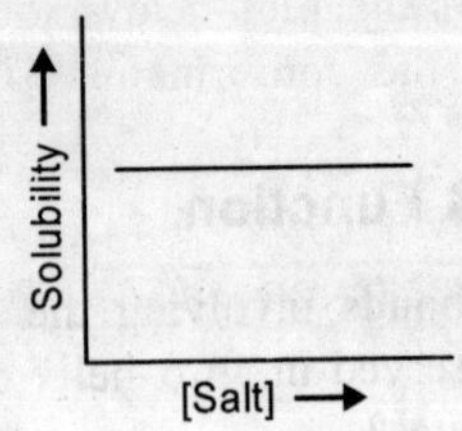

272. What is the net charge of the peptide Tyr-Val-Arg at pH 5.0? The pKa of alpha amino and carboxyl groups are 9.6 and 2.3, respectively. The pKa of Tyr and Arg side chains are 10.46 and 12.48, respectively

A. 1.0 B. 5
C. 2.5 D. 11

273. The amount of haemoglobin in blood is one of the important health markers. Following statements are made regarding haemoglobin degradation when older red blood cells(RBCs) are destroyed by the tissue macrophages.

(*a*) The globin protein of the haemoglobin is split off and heme is converted first to bilirubin by the action of heme oxygenase.
(*b*) The globin protein of the haemoglobin is split off and heme is converted first to biliverdin by the action of heme oxygenase.
(*c*) Carbon monoxide (CO) is formed in the process
(*d*) Nitric oxide (NO) is formed in the process

Which one of the following represents correct combination of statements?

A. (*a*) and (*c*) B. (*b*) and (*c*)
C. (*a*) and (*d*) D. (*b*) and (*d*)

274. The pKa of the Ionizable groups in the tripeptide shown below are indicated in the structure.

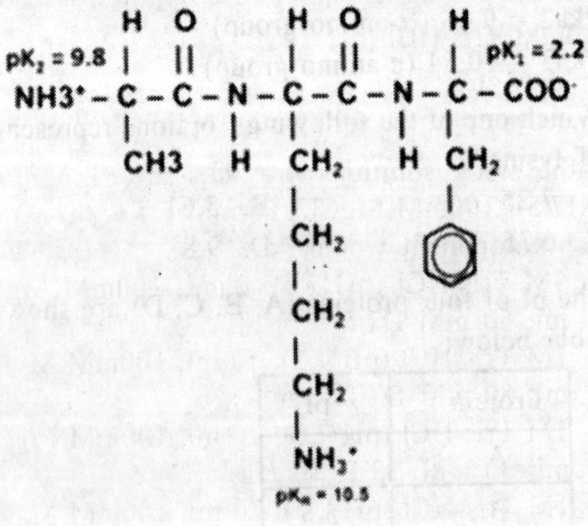

The isoelectric point (pI) of this peptide is

A. 10.15 B. 6
C. 6.35 D. 7.5

275. The Ramachandran plot graphically shows which combination of torsional angle phi (ϕ) and psi (ψ) of amino acids residues contained in a peptide are possible. Examination of the plot below shows that only certain regions of the conformation space are permissible.

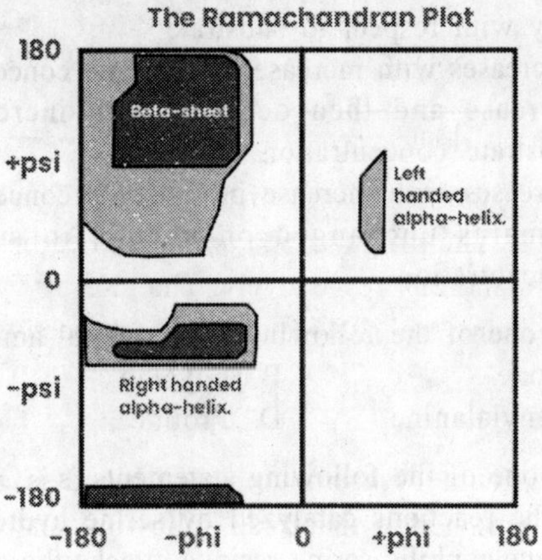

Why are all the theoretical combination of ϕ and Ψ not possible?

A. Two atoms cannot occupy the same space.
B. The geometry of the peptide bond that links two amino acid residues restricts φ and Ψ angles.
C. Beta sheets and alpha helices determine the allowed regions of conformational space.
D. The tertiary fold of polypeptide restricts conformational space.

Carbohydrate Metabolism & Regulation

276. Phosphofructokinase catalyses one of the regulatory steps in glycolysis. Which one of the following metabolic changes leads to the activation of phosphofructokinase?

A. Increased ATP concentration ATP,
B. Decreased AMP concentration AMP,
C. High citrate levels
D. Increased fructose 2, 6, bisphosphate concentration

277. Which one of the following correctly states the action of sucrose phosphate synthase enzyme?

A. UDP-glucose and fructose-6-phosphate are used as substrates.
B. UDP-glucose and fructose-6-phosphate are the products
C. Sucrose is formed as product.
D. Sucrose-6-phosphate and UDP-glucose are the products are the products

ETC

278. Cyanide, a chemical warfare agent, is toxic because it:

(*a*) Bind to the heme a3 in mitochondrial cytochrome c oxidase
(*b*) Inhibits electron transport and thus oxidative phosphorylation
(*c*) Directly blocks mitochondrial DNA replication
(*d*) Blocks the protein trafficking inside the mitochondria by affecting TIM and TOM channels

Choose the combination with all correct statements.

A. (*a*) and (*c*)
B. (*a*) and (*b*)
C. (*b*) and (*c*)
D. (*a*), (*b*), (*d*)

DBT-JRF–2021

Biomolecular Structure and Function

279. You are preparing 100ml of a solution containing 100mM Tris-HCl (pH 7.5);
5mM $MgCl_2$
1 mM DTT.

If the stock solutions provided are: 1 M Tris-HCl (pH7.5); 100mM $MgCl_2$; 50 mM DTT, the amount of each component would be

A. 1M Tris-HCl (pH 7.5): 05ml; 100mM $MgCl_2$: 10 ml; 50 mM DTT: 2.5 ml
B. 1M Tris-HCl (pH 7.5): 10 ml; 100mM $MgCl_2$: 5.0 ml; 50 mM DTT: 2 ml
C. 1M Tris-HCl (pH 7.5): 10 ml; 100mM $MgCl_2$: 7.5 ml; 50 mM DTT: 10 ml
D. 1M Tris-HCl (pH 7.5): 20 ml; 100mM $MgCl_2$: 2.5 ml; 50 mM DTT: 5 ml

280. Treatment of glyceraldehyde with $HIPO_4$ produces one among the following:

A. One molecules of formic acid and one molecules of formaldehyde
B. One molecules of formic acid and two molecules of formaldehyde
C. One molecules of formic acid, one molecules of CO_2 and one molecules of formaldehyde
D. Two molecules of formic acid and one molecules of formaldehyde

281. 100 mL of 0.1 N HCl solution was diluted with 50mL of 0.05 N HCl solution. The normality of the final solution is:

A. 0.067 B. 0.083
C. 0.125 D. 0.25

282. What is the pH of a mixture of 0.042 M NaH_2PO_4 and 0.42 M NaH_2PO_4 (pKa = 6.86)?

A. 4.86 B. 5.86
C. 6.86 D. 7.86

283. In an enzymatic reaction following Michaelis-Menten Kinetics, doubling the substrate concentration from S_o to $2S_o$ resulted in an increase in the rate of reaction by 2 percent which of the following statement is True?

A. $K_m > 2S_o$
B. $S_o < K_m > 2S_o$
C. $S_o/2 < K_m > 2S_o$
D. $K_m << S_o/2$

284. Match the components of List I with those in List II

List I	List II
(*a*) Isomerization	(*i*) Transfer of a functional group from one molecule to another
(*b*) Redox reaction	(*ii*) Electron transfer from one species to another
(*c*) Group transfer	(*iii*) Cleavage of bonds by addition of water
(*d*) Hydrolysis	(*iv*) Rearrangement of atom to form isomers

	(*a*)	(*b*)	(*c*)	(*d*)
A.	(*i*)	(*ii*)	(*iii*)	(*iv*)
B.	(*iv*)	(*ii*)	(*i*)	(*iii*)
C.	(*ii*)	(*i*)	(*iii*)	(*iv*)
D.	(*ii*)	(*i*)	(*iv*)	(*iii*)

285. Baeyer-Villiger monooxygenases (BVMOs) are flavin dependent enzymes that catalyse oxidations. Which one of the following oxidation is NOT carried out by BVMOs?

A. Aldehydes to carboxylic acids
B. Ketones and cyclic ketones to esters and lactones
C. Noxidations (amines to Noxides)
D. Sulfoxidations (conversion of sulphides to sulphoxides)

286. For reactions catalysed by an enzyme following Michaelis Menten Kinetics, the elasticity of the reaction velocity with respect to substrate:

A. Decreases with increase in substrate concentration
B. Increases and then declines with increase in substrate concentration
C. Increases with increase in substrate concentration
D. Remains unchanged on change in substrate concentration

287. Match the components of List I with List II

List I	List II
(*a*) Rhodopsin	(*i*) Vitamin-C
(*b*) Tocopherol	(*ii*) Vitamin-A
(*c*) Isoflavonoids	(*iii*) Vitamin-E
(*d*) Ascorbic acid	(*iv*) Soybean

Choose the correct answer from the options given below:

	(*a*)	(*b*)	(*c*)	(*d*)
A.	(*i*)	(*ii*)	(*iv*)	(*iii*)
B.	(*ii*)	(*i*)	(*iv*)	(*iii*)
C.	(*ii*)	(*iii*)	(*iv*)	(*i*)
D.	(*iv*)	(*iii*)	(*ii*)	(*i*)

288. Cellulose is a polymer of glucose which is made by— glycosidic bond:

A. β-(1-2) linkage
B. β-(1-4) linkage
C. β-(1-6) linkage
D. α-(1-4) linkage

289. For reactions catalyzed by an enzyme following Michaelis Menten Kinetics, the elasticity of the reaction velocity with respect to substrate

A. Decreases with increase in substrate concentration
B. Increase and then declines with increases in substrate concentration
C. increases with increase in substrate concentration
D. Remains unchanged on change in substrate concentration

290. Which one of the following is an achiral amino acid

A. Alaine
B. Glycine
C. Phenylalanine
D. Proline

291. Which one of the following statements is CORRECT about the reactions catalyzed by serine hydrolases?

A. A nucleophilic serine residue attacks the carboxyl carbon of aspartic acid
B. An aspartate residue abstracts a proton from a serine
C. An aspartate residue abstracts a proton from a histidine
D. An aspartate residue attacks the carboxyl carbon of the ester to be hydrolysed

292. Which one of the following amino acids has a strong tendency to disrupt α-helices and β-strands?

A. Alanine
B. Glutamate
C. Proline
D. Tyrosine

293. Which one of the following is NOT a characteristic of a collagen fiber?

A. Each of the strand is independently stable due to the presence hydrogen bonds
B. It is a fibrous protein with alpha-helical coiled-coil structure
C. It is the main component of skin, bones, tendons and teeth
D. The core of the triple-stranded helix is populated with glycine residues

294. Match the components of List I with those in List II.

List I	List II
(*a*) Methylation of lys	(*i*) Collagen structure
(*b*) Hydroxylation of proline	(*ii*) Activates gene by modify histones in chromatin
(*c*) Phosphorylation of Tyr	(*iii*) Targets a protein degradation
(*d*) Poly-ubiquitination of Lys	(*iv*) Cell signaling

	(*a*)	(*b*)	(*c*)	(*d*)
A.	(*i*)	(*ii*)	(*iii*)	(*iv*)
B.	(*i*)	(*iii*)	(*iv*)	(*ii*)
C.	(*ii*)	(*i*)	(*iii*)	(*iv*)
D.	(*ii*)	(*i*)	(*iv*)	(*iii*)

295. Match the components of List I with those in List II under physiological conditions

List I	List II
(a) Leucine	(i) Negatively charged
(b) Lysine	(ii) Non polar
(c) Glutamic acid	(iii) Uncharged polar
(d) Glutamine	(iv) Positively charged

	(a)	(b)	(c)	(d)
A.	(i)	(ii)	(iii)	(iv)
B.	(ii)	(iv)	(i)	(iii)
C.	(ii)	(i)	(iii)	(iv)
D.	(ii)	(i)	(iv)	(iii)

296. A protein X is active when phosphorylated on Thr residue. You wish to mimics this phosphorylation by mutating Thr to another residue. Which one of these residues will mutate Thr into?

A. Glu B. Gly
C. His D. Tyr

297. Which one of the following is a malnutrition disease?

A. Ketosis B. Arthritis
C. Hepatitis D. Marasmus

298. Which one of the following defines the ψ angle in the protein backbone?

A. N-C_α-C-N B. C_α-C-N-C
C. C-N-C_α-C D. N-C_α-C-O

299. Which one of the following is used to validate the secondary structure of Proteins?

A. Dot plot
B. Neutral network
C. Ramachandran plot
D. Sigma plot

300. Trp florescence can be used to study protein folding and unfolding. Which properties of Trp are critical in ensuring that this can be used for studying the process?

A. Trp in the only amino acid present in most of the proteins.
B. Trp is a better hydrogen bond acceptor than most other amino acids
C. Trp is positively charged amino acid
D. Trp is an environment sensitive fluorophore which is typically buried in a folded protein

301. Given below are two statements:

Statement I: The peptides bond is a planar bond

Statement II: The Ramachandran Plot describes Omega Torsion Angles in Proteins In light of the above statements, choose the most appropriate answer from the options given below-

A. Both Statement I and Statement II are correct
B. Both Statement I and Statement II are incorrect
C. Statement I is correct and Statement II are incorrect
D. Statement II is correct and Statement I are incorrect

302. Given below are two statements:

Statement I: Serine is part of a catalytic triad in proteases that also includes histidine and aspartic acid.

Statement II: Catalytic triads are responsible for peptide hydrolysis

In light of the above statements, choose the most appropriate answer from the options given below

A. Both Statement I and Statement II are correct
B. Both Statement I and Statement II are incorrect
C. Statement I is correct and Statement II are incorrect
D. Statement II is correct and Statement I are incorrect

303. Which one of the statements relating to properties and structures of two proteins is most appropriate?

A. Two proteins with very similar secondary structures will have similar stability
B. Two proteins with very similar secondary structures will have similar tertiary structures
C. Two proteins with very similar tertiary structures will be localized to similar compartments inside the cell
D. Two proteins with very simple tertiary structures will have very similar secondary structures

304. Protein folding is highly cooperative. Which one of the following statements define this cooperativity?

A. If one protein unfolds, it forces a nearby protein to unfold too
B. If one proteins chain fold, it facilitates the folding of a nearby chain
C. Many molecules of polypeptides come together to fold at the same time
D. The protein chain completely unfolds if key interactions are broken in an "all or none" manner

305. If two sequences are 1 PAM apart, then they will be:

A. 1% identical amino acid residues
B. 1% similar nucleotide bases
C. 99% identical amino acid residues
D. 99% similar nucleotide bases

306. Conversion of L-pyruvate to L-lactate is an example of:

A. Isomerization B. Oxidation
C. Reduction D. Transesterification

307. Conversion of UDP-Galactose to UDP-Glucose occurs by:

A. Dehydration and hydration
B. Oxidation and reduction
C. Oxidative addition
D. Reductive elimination

308. The enzyme that plays a key role in glucose homeostasis is:

A. Fructokinase B. Galactokinase
C. Glucokinase D. Hexokinase

309. Pyruvate decarboxylase catalyses the decarboxylation of pyruvic acid to acetaldehyde and carbon dioxide. Its action depends on cofactors thiamine pyrophosphate (TPP) and magnesium. In this process, the role of TPP in the initial step is to act as a:

A. electron donor B. Carbanion
C. Carbocation D. Thiolate anion

310. The enzyme that plays a key role in glucose homeostasis is:

A. Fructokinase B. Galactokinase
C. Glucokinase D. Hexokinase

311. Given below are two statements: one is labelled as Assertion A and another one is labelled as Reason R

Assertion A: Within a few hours after an animal is killed, rigor mortis sets in with a contraction of muscle fibers and an increasing toughness of the meat.

Reason R: The loss of glycogen and disappearance of ATP from the muscles are observed in freshly killed animals.

In light of the above statements, choose the correct answer from the options below:

A. A is false but R is true
B. A is true but R is false
C. Both A and R is true and R is NOT the correct explanation of A
D. Both A and R is true and R is the correct explanation of A

312. Which one of the following statements is NOT common between oxidative phosphorylation and photophosphorylation?

A. Generation of ATP
B. Involvement of a kinase
C. Involvement of electron transport
D. Involvement of Oxygen

313. Though DNA and RNA are nucleic acids, isolating RNA in the laboratory requires extreme precautions and pre-preparations than isolating DNA This could be because:

A. RNA is more prone to hydrolysis than DNA
B. RNA is smaller in size than DNA
C. RNA molecules tend to form RNA-RNA hybrids
D. There is lesser RNA content per cell than DNA

314. The hypochromic effect is used to estimate the melting temperature for double stranded DNA. It arises because:

A. Double stranded DNA absorbs more UV light than single stranded DNA
B. Double stranded DNA is less colorful than single stranded DNA
C. Double stranded DNA is more colorful than single stranded DNA
D. Stacked bases in double stranded DNA absorb less UV light than unstacked base in single stranded DNA

GATE (BIOTECHNOLOGY) –2021

315. Under standard temperature (T) and pressure (P) conditions, 128g of an ideal gas molecule A occupies a volume of 1L. The gas molecule A obeys the relationship RT PV = 0.25. R and V are universal gas constant and ideal gas volume, respectively. The molecule A is

A. CO_2 B. H_2
C. N_2 D. O_2

316. A protein without its prosthetic group is known as

A. Apoprotein B. Hemoprotein
C. Holoprotein D. Lipoprotein

317. Which of the following chemical messenger(s) is/are derivative(s) of tryptophan?

A. γ-amino butyric acid B. Indole acetic acid
C. Melatonin D. Serotonin

GATE (LIFE SCIENCE) –2021

Biomolecule

318. Which one of the following molecules (~ 1mg/mL) do NOT absorb at 280 nm in an aqueous solution of pH 7.00 at room temperature?

A. Poly Deoxy-Guanylate (poly dG)
B. Adenosine triphosphate
C. Phenylalanine
D. Tyrosine

319. A molecule that forms a donor-acceptor energy transfer pair with the dansyl group is ____

A. Aspartate B. Histidine
C. Lysine D. Tryptophan

320. pKa value of the guanidinium group of Arginine is ____

A. 4.30 B. 7.40
C. 9.20 D. 12.50

321. The non-coenzyme vitamin is ______

A. Ascorbic acid B. Folic acid
C. Nicotinic acid D. Thiamine

322. Which of the following lipids is non-ionic?

A. Sphingomyelin
B. Galactocerebroside
C. Lecithin
D. Phosphatidyl inositol

323. Considering the open chain forms, which of the following pair(s) represent/s an epimer?

A. D-mannose and D-fructose
B. D-glucose and D-mannose
C. D-glucose and D-fructose
D. D-galactose and D-glucose

324. In the plot given below, the solid line represents oxygen binding to haemoglobin under physiological conditions. The broken line represents the condition(s) of

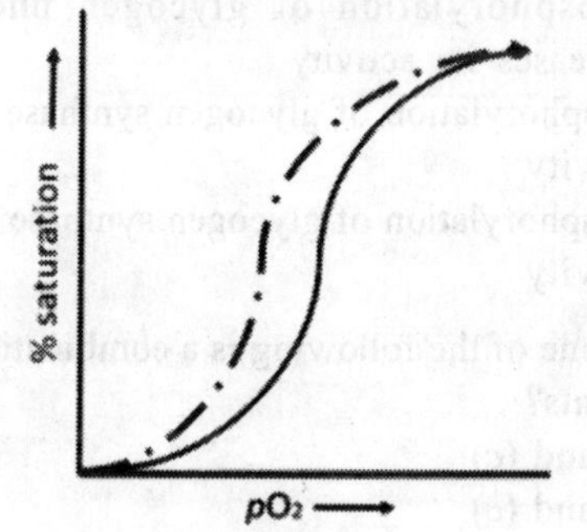

A. High CO_2 concentration
B. Increase in 2,3-Bisphosphoglycerate concentration
C. High pH
D. Loss of cooperativity

Enzyme & Metabolism

325. The high energy compound(s) is/are:

A. Phosphoenol pyruvate
B. Adenosine monophosphate
C. 1,3-Bisphosphoglycerate
D. Vitamin K

326. Given below are four plots obtained from separate experiments on enzyme inhibition kinetics. The velocity (v) of the reaction is plotted at varying concentrations of substrate (s) and inhibitor (I). The plot(s) corresponding to competitive inhibition is/are

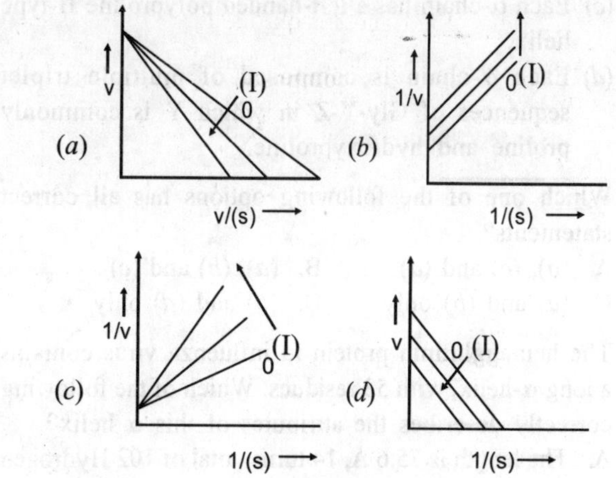

A. (*a*) B. (*b*)
C. (*c*) D. (*d*)

327. Which of the following amino acids contain more than one chiral center?

A. Leucine B. Isoleucine
C. Serine D. Threonine

CSIR-NET, SEPTEMBER (MORNING)–2022

Enzyme-Action, Kinetics & Inhibition

328. A student was asked to plot a graph representing enzyme kinetic data for initial velocity, v_o, and substrate concentration, [S] using any of the equations given below. The student used an equation for which neither X-axis nor Y-axis had independent variables. Which one of the following equations might the student have used?

A. $1/v_o = (K_m/V_{max})1/[S] + 1/V_{max}$
B. $[S]/v_o = [S]/V_{max} + (K_m/V_{max})$
C. $v_o/[S] = (V_{max} / K_m) - v_o/K_m$
D. $v_o = V_{max} [S] / K_m + [S]$

329. Dixon plot is used to study the enzyme inhibition by plotting various expressions of velocity (v) and inhibitor concentration (I) on the X-axis (column A) and Y-axis (column B) as given below:

Column A (X-axis)	Column B (Y-axis)
(*i*) v	(*i*) 1/v
(*ii*) 1/v	(*ii*) (I)
(*iii*) 1/(I)	(*iii*) 1/(I)
(*iv*) (I)	(*iv*) v

Which one of the following options is the correct combination from columns (*a*) and (*b*) to dra

A. Column A–(*iv*), Column B–(*i*)
B. Column A–(*i*), Column B–(*ii*)
C. Column A–(*ii*), Column B–(*iii*)
D. Column A–(*iii*), Column B–(*iv*)

Protein-structure & Function

330. Which one of the following correctly describes the spectroscopic experiment that would help distinguish a 3_{10} helix and a π helix?

A. Near UV absorption spectrum between 250-300 nm

B. Fluorescence emission spectra between 350-400 nm
C. 1H NMR spectroscopy involving Hydrogen/Deuterium exchange
D. Near UV Circular Dichroism spectrum between 250-300nm

331. The following statements were made to describe a typical collagen structure.
(*a*) Collagen has a triple-helical domain structure which consists of three distinct α-chains.
(*b*) The collagen triple helix is stabilized by isoprenyl bonds.
(*c*) Each α-chain has a left-handed polyproline II-type helix.
(*d*) Each α-chain is composed of multiple triplet sequences of Gly-Y-Z in which Y is commonly proline and hydroxyproline.

Which one of the following options has all correct statements?
A. (*a*), (*c*) and (*d*)
B. (*a*), (*b*) and (*c*)
C. (*a*) and (*b*) only
D. (*b*) and (*d*) only

332. The hemagglutinin protein in influenza virus contains a long α-helix, with 53 residues. Which of the following correctly describes the attributes of this α helix?
A. The length is 75.6 Å, 14 turns, total of 102 Hydrogen bonds
B. The length is 106 Å, 14 turns, total of 106 Hydrogen bonds
C. The length is 75.6 Å, 14 turns, total of 104 Hydrogen bonds
D. The length is 75.6 Å, 10 turns, total of 102 Hydrogen bonds

Amino acid Metabolism & Regulation

333. Which one of the following small molecule neurotransmitters is NOT synthesized from tyrosine?
A. Epinephrine
B. Dopamine
C. Serotonin
D. Norepinephrine

334. A number of statements have been made regarding heme, a component of hemoglobin, as given below:
(*a*) It is synthesized in mature erythrocytes
(*b*) It is synthesized by the condensation of succinyl-CoA and glycine
(*c*) It is synthesized by the condensation of acetyl-CoA and glycine
(*d*) Its synthesis is catalyzed by δ amino levulinate synthase

Which one of the following combinations has both INCORRECT statements?
A. (*a*) and (*d*)
B. (*a*) and (*c*)
C. (*b*) and (*c*)
D. (*b*) and (*d*)

Carbohydrate Metabolism & Regulation

335. Which one of the following correctly describes the effect of a mutation in phosphofructokinase (PFK), the loss of allosteric regulation by ATP?
A. Decrease in the activity of PFK
B. Increase in the activity of PFK
C. Decrease in the amount of ADP generated by PFK
D. Increase in the amount of ATP generated by PFK

336. Absorbed monosaccharides in intestinal epithelial cells exit via which one of the following transporters?
A. GLUT2
B. GLUT3
C. GLUT4
D. GLUT5

337. Following statements are made regarding glycogen phosphorylase and glycogen synthase activities in relation to their phosphorylation status:
(*a*) Phosphorylation of glycogen phosphorylase increases its activity
(*b*) Phosphorylation of glycogen phosphorylase decreases its activity
(*c*) Phosphorylation of glycogen synthase increases its activity
(*d*) Phosphorylation of glycogen synthase decreases its activity

Which one of the following is a combination of correct statements?
A. (*a*) and (*c*)
B. (*b*) and (*c*)
C. (*b*) and (*d*)
D. (*a*) and (*d*)

338. Glycolysis and citric acid cycle contribute precursors to many biosynthetic pathways in plants. Column X lists names and column Y lists the product synthesized

Column X	Column Y
(*a*) Hexose phosphate	(*i*) Aspartate
(*b*) Pyruvate	(*ii*) Alanine
(*c*) Pentose phosphate	(*iii*) Cellulose
(*d*) Oxaloacetate	(*iv*) Nucleotides

Which one of the following options represents the correct match between column X and Y?

	(*a*)	(*b*)	(*c*)	(*d*)
A.	(*ii*)	(*iii*)	(*i*)	(*iv*)
B.	(*iii*)	(*ii*)	(*iv*)	(*i*)
C.	(*iv*)	(*i*)	(*iii*)	(*ii*)
D.	(*i*)	(*ii*)	(*iii*)	(*iv*)

Nucleotide Metabolism & Regulation

339. The pathway for de novo biosynthesis of purine nucleotides involves the production of inosine monophosphate (IMP) serves as a precursor for AMP and GMP synthesis. IMP has the base hypoxanthine whose structure is given below

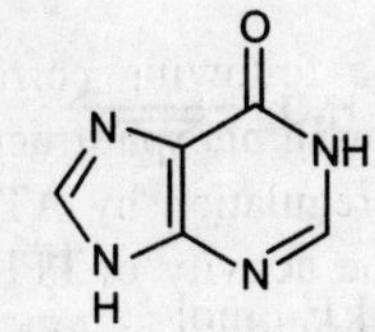

If hypoxanthine were incorporated into double stranded DNA, which of the following options correctly re of its pairing preference?

A. adenine > thymine > guanine > cytosine
B. cytosine > adenine > thymine > guanine
C. guanine > adenine > thymine > cytosine
D. cytosine > thymine > adenine > guanine

ETC

340. At which one of the following electron transport chain complexes does Antimycin A typically inhibit the respiratory chain?

A. Complex I
B. Complex II
C. Complex III
D. Complex IV

CSIR-NET, SEPTEMBER (EVENING)–2022

Water, PH, Thermodynamics, Bond

341. Which of the following represents the most oxidized form of carbon?

A. HCOOH
B. HCHO
C. CH_3OH
C. CO_2

Enzyme-Action, Kinetics & Inhibition

342. Given below are plots of the linear derivation of Michaelis-Menten kinetic equation and statements related to the variable (Initial velocity-V_0 and substrate concentration-[S] used.

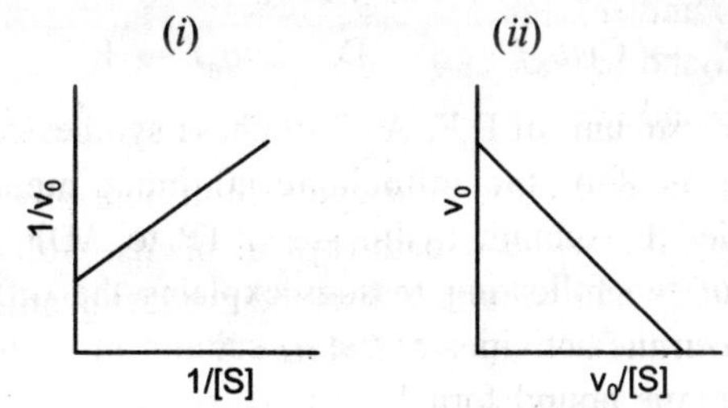

In plot (*i*), both *x* and *y*-axes have dependent variables.

In plot (*ii*), neither *x* nor *y*-axes have independent variables.

In plot (*i*), only *y*-axes has a dependent variable.

In both the plots, *x*-axes has an independent variable.

Select the option that has all the correct statements

A. A, (*b*) and (*d*) only
B. (*a*) and (*c*) only
C. (*b*) and (*c*) only
D. (*b*) and (*d*) only

343. An enzyme has a K_m of 5×10^{-5} M and a V_{max} of 100 µmoles.lit^{-1}.min^{-1} (K_m is the Michaelis constant and V_{max} is the maximal velocity).

What is the velocity in the presence of 1×10^{-4} M substrate and 2×10^{-4} M competitive inhibitor, given that the K_i for the inhibitor is 2×10^{-4} M?

A. 0.005 µmoles. lit^{-1}. min^{-1}
B. 50 µmoles. lit^{-1}. min^{-1}
C. 5 µmoles. lit^{-1}. min^{-1}
D. 500 µmoles. lit^{-1}. min^{-1}

Protein-structure & Function

344. Hemoglobin A1c (HbA1c) from diabetic mellitus individuals has a glucose molecule attached to which one of the terminal amino acid residues of globin chain?

A. Lysine of each α chain
B. Lysine of each β chain
C. Valine of each α chain
D. Valine of each β chain

345. Which one of the following is NOT CORRECT in the context of protein structure and folding?

A. β-sheets are more common in the interiors of proteins than surfaces
B. β-sheets are less likely to form than α-helices in the earliest stages of protein folding
C. Proline residues can occupy the N-terminal turn of an α-helix
D. α-helices are less likely to form than β-sheets in the earliest stages of protein folding

346. The regions of phi, psi space occupied by well characterized protein secondary structures are marked on a Ramachandran plot as shown above. Which of the following statements is correct:

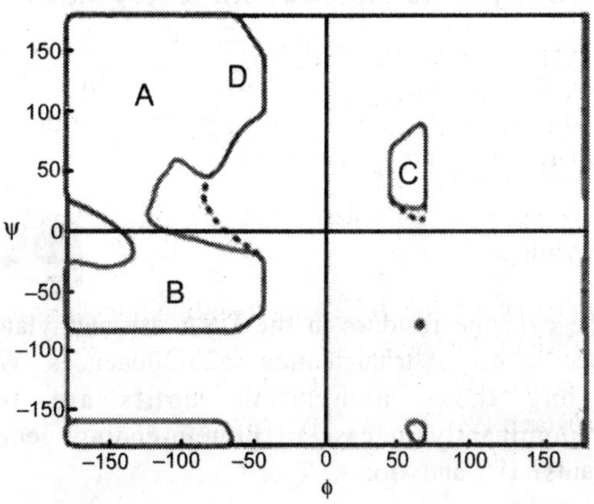

A. A-right handed α helix, B-β strand, C-left handed α helix, D-collagen A
B. A-β strand, B-right handed α helix, C-left handed α helix, D-collagen
C. A-collagen, B-right handed α helix, C-left handed α helix, D-β strand
D. A-left handed α helix, B-β strand, C-collagen, D-right handed α helix

347. Which of the four molecules shown below are optically active?

(a) 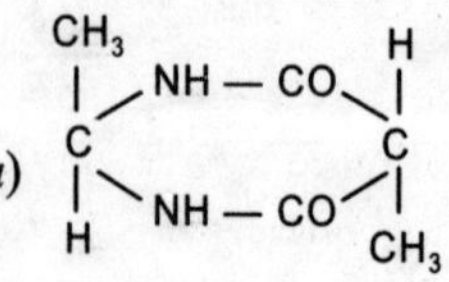 (b) 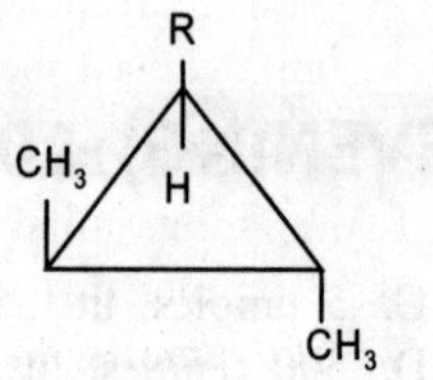

(c) 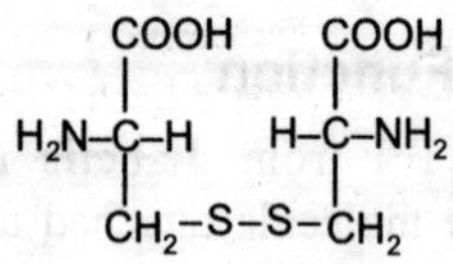 (d) 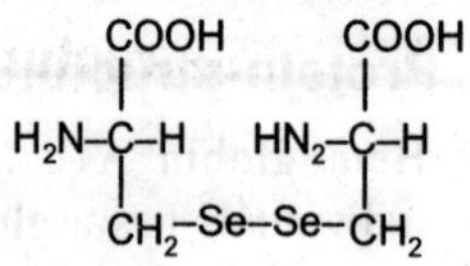

A. (a), (b), (c) and (d) B. (b) and (d) only
C. (a) and (c) only D. (b) only

Amino acid Metabolism & Regulation

348. The first common enzyme in the biosynthesis of the branched-chain amino acids (Leu, Ile and Val) is acetohydroxyacid synthase (AHAS). Following statements are made about the enzyme:
(a) AHAS requires thiamine diphosphate as cofactor.
(b) The plant AHAS comprises a large catalytic subunit and a smaller regulatory subunit.
(c) The large subunit alone is sensitive to inhibition by Leu, Ile and Val in plants.
(d) Most of the bacterial and fungal AHAS enzymes are sensitive to inhibition by Val only.

Select the option with all correct statements.
A. (a), (b) and (c) B. (a), (c) and (d)
C. (b), (c) and (d) D. (a), (b) and (d)

Carbohydrate Metabolism & Regulation

349. Pyruvate kinase, the enzyme that catalyzes the conversion of pyruvate transfer the Pi from PEP to ADP to generate ATP, The standard free energies of the half-reactions are given below.

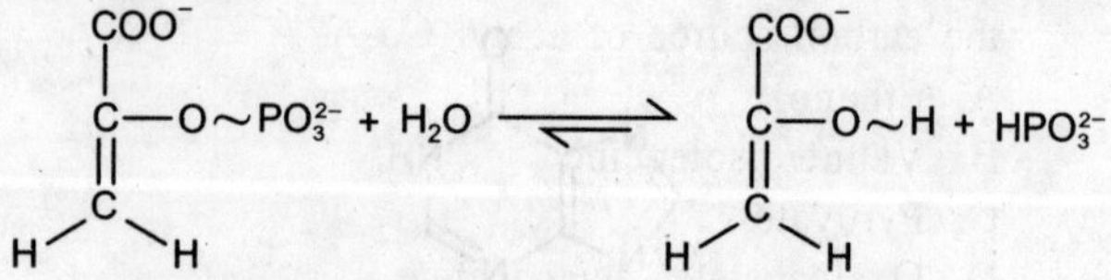

$\Delta G° = -16 \text{ kJ} - \text{mol}^{-1}$

ADP + Pi = ATP $\Delta G° = +30.5 \text{kJ mol}^{-1}$

How is the energy for generation of ATP from ADP in the reaction catalyzed by pyruvate kinase?
A. through coupling with keto-enol tautomerism where the enol form of pyruvate is converted to the keto form
B. through condensation of Pi with ADP ADP
C. through linking to proton motive force
D. through coupling with hydrolysis of PPi

Nucleotide Metabolism & Regulation

350. Catabolic end product of purines is
A. Xyloric acid B. Allantoin
C. Urea D. Uric acid

ETC

351. Identify the correct site of action of DBMIB (2, 5-dibromo-3-methyl-6-isopropyl-*p*-benzoquinone), an inhibitor of the chloroplast electron transport chain.
A. $Q_A \rightarrow Q_B$ B. $Q_B \rightarrow P_Q$
C. $P_Q \rightarrow Cytb_6f$ D. $Cytb_6f \rightarrow$ PC

352. The F_1 subunit of F_0F_1 ATP synthase synthesizes ATP from ADP in the mitochondrial inner membrane. Purified F_1 subunit hydrolyses ATP to ADP. Which one of the following reasons explains the difference between the activities of the F_1 subunit in soluble and membrane bound form?
A. A conformational change in the F_1 subunit between the two environments.
B. The lipid bilayer environment facilitates the synthesis of ATP by enhancing the rate of the dehydration reaction.
C. The ATP synthesis reaction is driven by coupling to an electrochemical potential across the inner mitochondrial membrane ATP.
D. In the soluble form, the electrochemical potential drives the F_1 subunit to hydrolyze ATP

DBT-JRF–2022

353. The cytosine residues in the DNA are methylated at specific di- or trinucleotide se27-200uences. Which among these methylation motifs are found predominantly in case of protein-coding genes in plants? H stands for A, T or C.
A. CpG and CpHpG
B. CpHpG and CpHpH
C. CpGpG and CpHpH
D. CpG and CpHpH

354. Which one of the following compound(s) is/are NOT the carbon source of acetyl Co-A?
A. Ethanol
B. Valine/ isoleucine
C. Pyruvate
D. Oxaloacetate/ acetoacetate

355. What is the concentration of D20 in heavy water (density 1.11 g/ml)?
A. 0.5 M B. 5.0 M
C. 50.0 M D. 55.5 M

356. Which one of the following statements is true with respect to optical activity?
A. A relationship exists between the (R) and (S) configurations of enantiomers and the direction [(+) or (–)] in which they rotate plane-polarized light
B. E27-200uimolar mixture of D and L isomers of the same compound will be optically active
C. Meso compounds that are optically inactive may contain stereogenic centers or chiral centers
D. Optical activity is independent of temperature

357. What will be the length of a DNA molecule containing 10 million bp?
A. 340 mm B. 34 mm
C. 3.4 mm D. 0.34 mm

358. The enzyme that links carbon and nitrogen metabolism is:
A. Glutamine synthetase
B. Transketolase
C. Glutamate dehydrogenase
D. Enolase

359. The melting temperature (tm) of DNA is higher when the content of:
A. A:T base pairs is higher
B. G:C base pairs is higher
C. A:T base pairs is same as G:C base pairs
D. G:C base pairs is lower

360. An enzyme is governed by Michaelis-Menten Kinetics. The apparent K_m increases four fold due to the addition of inhibitor but the reaction rate declines by 50%. The substrate concentration in the reaction is:
A. $S = K_m$ B. $S = 2\ K_m$
C. $S = 3\ K_m$ D. $S = 4\ K_m$

361. You are given a 5 mM solution of sucrose. If you hydrolyse it by adding e27-200ual volume of 10 mM HCl, what would be the final concentration of glucose and fructose in the hydrolysate?
A. 5 mM glucose and 5 mM fructose
B. 2.5 mM glucose and 2.5 mM fructose
C. 1.25 mM glucose and 1.25 mM fructose
D. 1.25 mM glucose and 2.5 mM fructose

362. The introduction of the nonpolar molecule (toluene) into water results in:
A. a decrease in the entropy of water
B. an increase in the entropy of water
C. no change in entropy of water
D. modest exothermic dissolution

363. Identify the INCORRECT statement for a competitive reaction.
A. The Vmax is unchanged
B. The dissociation constant (K_d) is increased
C. Km will increase
D. The intercept on the x-axis will shift towards the left in the Lineweaver–Burk plot

364. A protein se27-200uence has twenty consecutive hydrophobic amino acids followed by a few hydrophilic residues and this pattern repeats itself five to seven times. Which kind of a protein is described here?
A. A secretory protein
B. A transmembrane protein
C. A cytoplasmic soluble enzyme
D. A ribosomal protein

365. In an enzyme catalyzed reaction following Michaelis-Menten kinetics, both the enzyme amount and substrate (S) are doubled and we observe that the reaction rate is also doubled. From this, we can conclude that:
A. Enzyme amount has no effect on enzyme kinetics
B. The substrate is toxic to enzyme
C. Initial substrate (S) concentration << Km
D. Initial substrate (S) concentration >> Km

366. If an enzyme is NOT damaged during the process of entrapment in a bead, then internal pore diffusion will:
A. Change the observed V_{max} only
B. Change the observed K_m only
C. Change both the V_{max} and K_m
D. Both the observed V_m and K_m will remain unchanged

367. 15 to 30% of collagen residues are 4-hydroxyproline residues (Hyp). When rats are fed with14C labeled Hyp, the collagen produced by them is not radioactive, but when they are fed with 14C labeled Proline, the collagen produced is radioactive. What is the most plausible reason?
A. Hyp is an essential amino acid in rats
B. Free Hyp is dehydroxylated to form Proline in the rats
C. Proline residues are hydroxylated once they are incorporated into collagen in rats
D. Free 14C labelled Hyp is degraded in rats

368. Ground shark cartilage ointment is popular for its role in fast wound recovery. The active ingredient primarily responsible for this function is:
A. N-acetylglucosamine

B. Hydroxyproline
C. Dihydroxyproline
D. 3,4-dihydroxyphenylalanine (DOPA)

369. For determining Vm and Km of an enzyme catalyzed reaction, we often use a double reciprocal plot of 1/v versus 1/s. This is NOT the best method because:
A. Errors in measurement are not normally distributed
B. A straight line fit does not minimize the error
C. Errors increase for larger values of v & s
D. Errors increase for smaller values of v & s

370. Which one of these is a metal containing Vitamin?
A. Vitamin C
B. Vitamin B_1
C. Vitamin B_{12}
D. Vitamin A

371. What will be the molecular weight of the tri-peptide Trp-Gly-His?

Molecular weights of Trp, Gly, and His are 204.2, 75.07, and 155.2 respectively.
A. 434.47
B. 300.00
C. 398.47
D. 502.25

372. Where is the greatest likelihood of the occurrence of a Cysteine residue in a protein structure?
A. In the active site pocket
B. In the beta sheets
C. In the turns and loops
D. In the alpha helices

373. Arrange the following chemical bonds/interactions in the order of their strengths in vacuum - Hydrogen bond, Covalent bond, van der Waals attraction and Ionic bond:
A. Covalent bond > Ionic bond> hydrogen bond > van der Waals attraction
B. Ionic bond > Covalent bond > hydrogen bond > van der Waals attraction
C. Covalent bond > Ionic bond > van der Waals attraction > hydrogen bond
D. Ionic bond > Covalent bond > van der Waals attraction > hydrogen bond

374. The entropy of a growing cell does NOT keep increasing continuously because:
A. The cell is a highly structured system
B. The information content in the DNA is very high
C. Various regulatory loops provide feedback to the system
D. The cell is an open system allowing both matter and energy to be exchanged with surroundings

375. When ice absorbs latent heat at a constant pressure to melt from solid to li27-200uid state at constant temperature, which of the following changes are happening?
(*a*) Entropy of the system is increasing.
(*b*) Cp (heat capacity at constant pressure) of the system is infinite or undefined.
(*c*) Enthalpy of the system is increasing.
(*d*) Cp of the system is zero.

Choose the correct answer:
A. (*a*), (*b*), (*c*)
B. (*a*), (*c*), (*d*)
C. (*a*), (*b*)
D. (*c*), (*d*)

376. Proteins usually have hydrophobic interiors or cores and hydrophilic exteriors. If a protein comprises hydrophobic patches on its outer surface, what can it mean?
A. The protein is unstable
B. Structure prediction was done wrongly
C. It could be part of a multimeric protein complex
D. It is a DNA-binding protein

377. Which one of the following will NOT change upon adding an enzyme to a chemical reaction or changing the concentration of reactants or products?
(*a*) $\Delta G°$
(*b*) Ke27-200
(*c*) ΔG
A. (*a*), (*b*)
B. (*b*), (*c*)
C. (*a*), (*b*), (*c*)
D. Only (*a*)

378. The CO-NH moiety between two C-alpha atoms constitutes the Peptide bond. The measured bond lengths (Angstroms) are : C(alpha)-CO (1.51); C=O (1.24); C-N(1.33); N-C(alpha)1.46. In which of these, there is a decrease from the expected bond length due to partial double bond character of the peptide bond?
A. C(alpha)-CO
B. C = O
C. C – N
D. N – C(alpha)

379. Where is the greatest likelihood of the occurrence of a proline residue in a protein structure?
A. In the active site pocket
B. In the beta sheets
C. In the turns and loops
D. In the alpha helices

380. Which of the following are the sulfur containing amino acids?
(*a*) Methionine
(*b*) Histidine

(*c*) Leucine
(*d*) Cysteine

A. (*b*) and (*a*) B. (*a*) and (*d*)
C. (*d*) and (*b*) D. (*c*) and (*b*)

381. Match the items in List I with the items in List II

List I	List II
(*a*) Sucrose	(*i*) β-glycosidic link (D-glucose)
(*b*) Lactose	(*ii*) α-glycosidic link (D-glucose)
(*c*) Maltose	(*iii*) β-glycosidic link (D-glucose)
(*d*) Cellobiose	(*iv*) α-1,β-2-glycosidic link (D-glucose and D-fructose)

	(*a*)	(*b*)	(*c*)	(*d*)
A.	(*ii*)	(*iv*)	(*i*)	(*iii*)
B.	(*i*)	(*iii*)	(*iv*)	(*ii*)
C.	(*iii*)	(*ii*)	(*i*)	(*iv*)
D.	(*iv*)	(*iii*)	(*ii*)	(*i*)

382. Amide bonds between two amino acids (as shown below) are generally in trans-conformation. The atoms are labeled as A1 through A6. The angle measured for defining the trans conformation of the amide bond is the angle between:

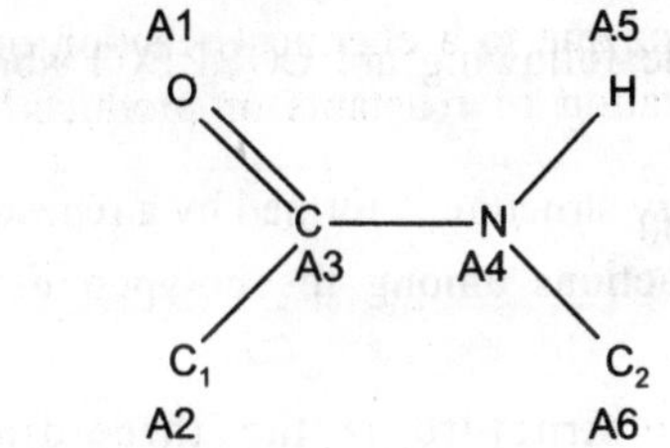

A. the atoms A2, A3 and A4
B. the planes formed by A1,A3,A4 and A3,A4,A6
C. the planes formed by A2,A3,A4 and A6,A4,A5
D. the planes formed by A2,A3,A4 and A3,A4,A6

383. The energy landscape or the energy of a reaction:

A ↔ B

Along its reaction coordinate follows the following pattern:

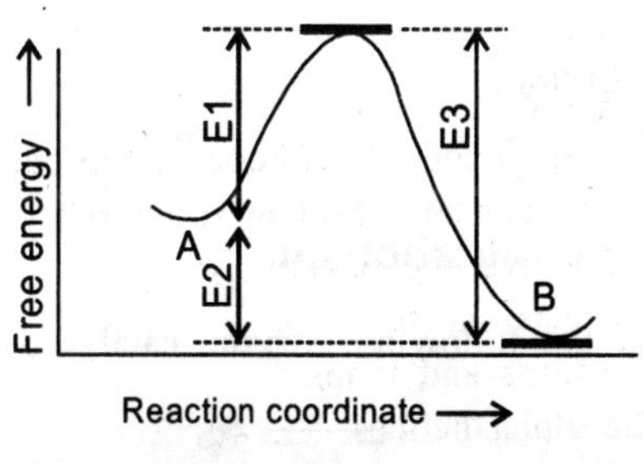

Which one of the following statements are true?
A. The rate at which A changes to B is independent of E1
B. The rate at which B converts to A is determined by E3
C. The rate at which A converts to B is determined by E2
D. The rate at which B converts to A is independent of E3

384. Match the items in left column with those in the right column:

Conjugated protein	Prosthetic group
(*a*) Casein	(*i*) Calcium
(*b*) Hemoglobin	(*ii*) Iron
(*c*) Calmodulin	(*iii*) Flavin nucleotides
(*d*) Succinate dehydrogenase	(*iv*) Heme
(*e*) Ferritin	(*v*) Phosphate group

Choose the correct answer from the options given below:

	(*a*)	(*b*)	(*c*)	(*d*)	(*e*)
A.	(*v*)	(*iv*)	(*i*)	(*iii*)	(*ii*)
B.	(*iii*)	(*iv*)	(*i*)	(*v*)	(*ii*)
C.	(*v*)	(*iv*)	(*ii*)	(*iii*)	(*i*)
D.	(*iii*)	(*iv*)	(*ii*)	(*v*)	(*i*)

385. Given the molecular structure of glucose, the molecular formula and molecular weight of maltose will be:

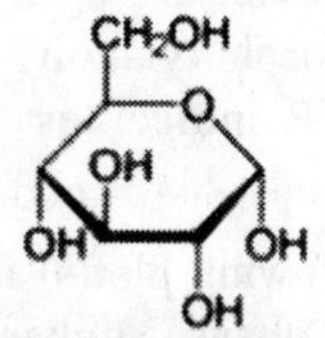

A. $C_{12}H_{24}O_{12}$, 360 Daltons
B. $C_{12}H_{24}O_{12}$, 460 Daltons
C. $C_{12}H_{22}O_{11}$, 342 Daltons
D. $C_{12}H_{22}O_{11}$, 490 Daltons

386. A protein completely unfolds in 8 M Urea. The stability of the folded state in water is calculated to be 8 kCal/mole at 25°C. What is the likely ΔG of the following reaction in 8 M Urea?

A(native) → A(unfolded)

Choose the correct answer:
A. Zero
B. Less than zero
C. 8^2 kcal/mole
D. 8 kcal/mole

387. Which one of the following properties of naturally occurring D-amino acids is INCORRECT:
A. Peptides arising from them are more susceptible to attack by peptidases
B. They are components of bacterial cell wall
C. Peptides arising from them are not synthesized by ribosomal machinery
D. They are components of many bacterially produced peptide antibiotics

GATE (BIOTECHNOLOGY) – 2022

388. The binding free energy of a ligand to its receptor protein is –11.5 kJ mol^{-1} at 300 K. What is the value of the equilibrium binding constant?
Use R = 8.314 J mol^{-1} K^{-1}.
A. 0.01 B. 1.0
C. 4.6 D. 100.5

389. Which of the following statements about reversible enzyme inhibitors are CORRECT?
P. Uncompetitive inhibitors bind only to the enzyme-substrate complex
Q. Non-competitive inhibitors bind only at a different site from the substrate
R. Competitive inhibitors bind to the same site as the substrate
A. P and Q only B. P and R only
C. Q and R only D. P, Q and R

390. Which of the following is(are) COMMON feature(s) for both aerobic and anaerobic bacterial cultures?
A. Glycolysis
B. NAD^+ is the oxidising agent
C. Oxidative phosphorylation
D. Two net ATP molecules formed per glucose molecule

391. Which of the following plot(s) is(are) CORRECT for an enzyme that obeys Michaelis-Menten kinetics, assuming [S] << K_m?
[S] is the concentration of the substrate, K_m is the Michaelis constant, and v_0 is the initial reaction velocity.

A.
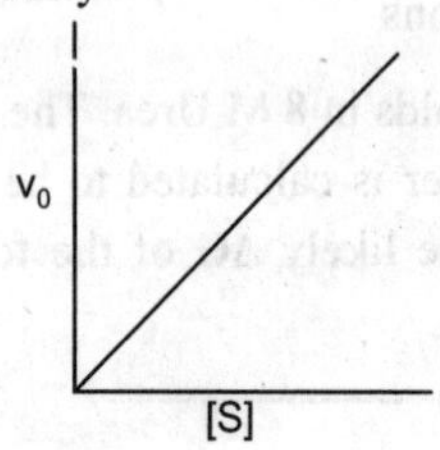

B.
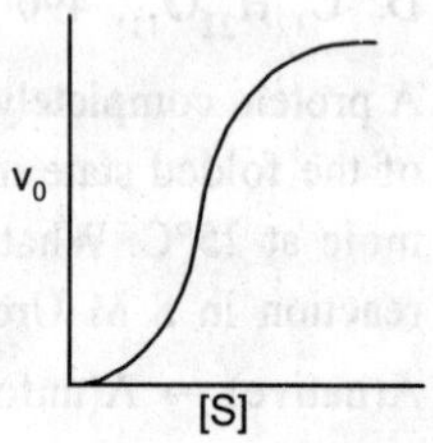

C.
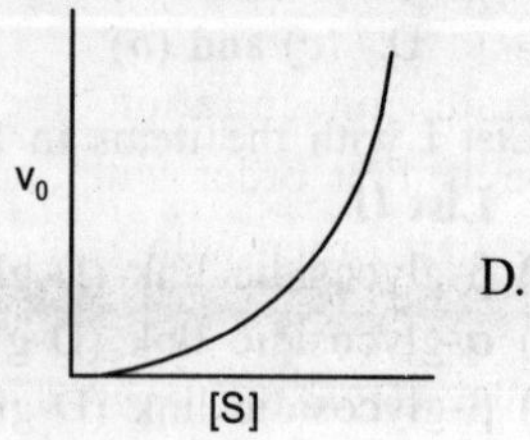

D.
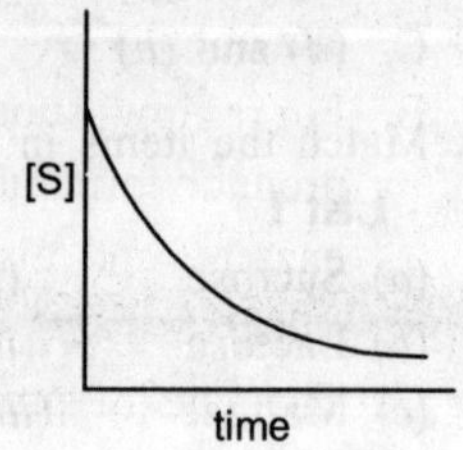

392. Which of the following statements are CORRECT for an enzyme entrapped in a spherical particle?
A. Effectiveness factor is ratio of the reaction rate with diffusion-limitation to the reaction rate without diffusion-limitation
B. Internal diffusion is rate-limiting at low values of Thiele modulus
C. Effectiveness factor increases with decrease in Thiele modulus
D. Internal diffusion-limitation can be reduced by decreasing the size of the particle

393. Which of the following are CORRECT about protein structure?
P. Secondary structure is formed by a repeating pattern of interactions among the polypeptide backbone atoms
Q. Tertiary structure is the three-dimensional arrangement of the polypeptide backbone atoms only
R. Quaternary structure refers to an assembly of multiple polypeptide subunits
A. P and Q only
B. P and R only
C. Q and R only
D. P, Q and R

GATE LIFE SCIENCE – 2022

Biomolecule

394. Which of the following is the CORRECT statement about hexoses?
A. D-mannose is C-4 epimer of D-glucose
B. D-galactose is C-2 epimer of D-glucose
C. D-glucose and L-glucose are diastereomers
D. D-glucose and D-galactose are diastereomers

Enzyme & Metabolism

395. Consider the following enzyme catalyzed reaction:

$$E + S \underset{k_{-1}}{\overset{k_1}{\rightleftharpoons}} ES$$

$$ES \xrightarrow{k_2} P + E$$

where E is enzyme, S is substrate, ES is enzyme-substrate complex and P is product.

The correct statement(s) for the above reaction is/are

A. Maximum possible rate of product formation is dependent on k_2 and initial concentration of enzyme.

B. For a low substrate concentration, the rate of product formation is first order with respect to enzyme and also first order with respect to the substrate.

C. The rate of product formation is independent of the concentration of enzyme-substrate complex.

D. For a very high substrate concentration, initial rate of product formation is zero order with respect to the substrate.

396. Which one of the following enzymes is located in the outer mitochondrial membrane?

A. Citrate synthase
B. Fumarase
C. Monoamine oxidase
D. Succinate dehydrogenase

397. Which one of the following enzymes converts testosterone to estradiol?

A. Aromatase
B. 3β-hydroxysteroid dehydrogenase
C. 5α-reductase
D. 17β-hydroxysteroid dehydrogenase

398. Which of the following carbohydrates has/have a β1 → 4 glycosidic linkage?

A. Cellulose
B. Chitin
C. Lactose
D. Maltose

399. Match Group-I (enzyme), Group-II (reaction catalyzed by the enzyme), and Group-III (subcellular localization of the enzyme and the associated metabolic process) in CORRECT combination.

Group-I	Group-II		Group-III
P. PEP Carboxylase	I.	2 Glycolate + 2 O_2 = 2 Glyoxylate + 2 H_2O_2	a. Cytosol – C_4 cycle
Q. Rubisco	II.	Pyruvate + NAD^+ + CoA = Acetyl-CoA + CO_2 + NADH	b. Peroxisome – C_2 cycle
R. Glycolate oxidase	III.	Phosphoenolpyruvate + HCO_3^- = Oxaloacetate + Pi	c. Mitochondria – aerobic respiration
S. Pyruvate dehydrogenase	IV.	3 (Ribulose 1,5-bisphosphate) + 3 CO_2 + 3 H_2O = 6 (3-phosphoglycerate) + 6 H^+	d. Chloroplast – C_3 cycle

A. P-III-a, Q-IV-d, R-I-b, S-II-c
B. P-II-a, Q-III-d, R-I-b, S-IV-c
C. P-IV-a, Q-II-b, R-I-d, S-III-c
D. P-IV-a, Q-II-d, R-I-b, S-III-c

400. The action of which class of enzyme inhibitors can be reversed by adding an excess of substrate?

A. Uncompetitive inhibitors
B. Competitive inhibitors
C. Non-specific inhibitors
D. Allosteric inhibitors

401. Which of the following is/are responsible for reversible receptor-ligand interaction?

A. Ionic interactions
B. Hydrogen bonding
C. Peptide bonding
D. Hydrophobic interactions

402. 2-Deoxyglucose (2-DG) inhibits the proliferation of cells and hence finds use as an anti-cancer agent. It is also used in COVID therapy, where it blocks hyperproliferation of virus-infected cells. Mechanistically, 2-DG blocks glycolysis by inhibiting the activities of which of the following enzyme/s?

A. Hexokinase
B. Glucose 6-phosphate isomerase
C. Glucose-6 phosphate dehydrogenase
D. Phosphofructokinase

ANSWERS

1	2	3	4	5	6	7	8	9	10
D	A	B	C	A	B	A	B	C	B
11	12	13	14	15	16	17	18	19	20
C	B	A	A	A	C	D	A	D	D
21	22	23	24	25	26	27	28	29	30
C	C	A	B	B	A	B	C	B	D
31	32	33	34	35	36	37	38	39	40
A	D	D	A	B	B	C	B	B	A
41	42	43	44	45	46	47	48	49	50
B	B	A	D	A	C	B	D	B	D
51	52	53	54	55	56	57	58	59	60
A	A	D	A	A	D	C	A	B	A

61	**62**	**63**	**64**	**65**	**66**	**67**	**68**	**69**	**70**
B	C	B	D	C	A	D	C	D	A
71	**72**	**73**	**74**	**75**	**76**	**77**	**78**	**79**	**80**
C	C	D	C	D	A	D	D	B	C
81	**82**	**83**	**84**	**85**	**86**	**87**	**88**	**89**	**90**
C	B	D	A	D	C	D	A	C	A
91	**92**	**93**	**94**	**95**	**96**	**97**	**98**	**99**	**100**
B	A	A	A	A	A	A	B	C	B
101	**102**	**103**	**104**	**105**	**106**	**107**	**108**	**109**	**110**
D	A	A	A	C	B	D	C	B	B
111	**112**	**113**	**114**	**115**	**116**	**117**	**118**	**119**	**120**
B	D	A	D	B	B	D	C	D	D
121	**122**	**123**	**124**	**125**	**126**	**127**	**128**	**129**	**130**
B	A	C	B	A	D	D	A	A	B
131	**132**	**133**	**134**	**135**	**136**	**137**	**138**	**139**	**140**
D	A	C	D	B	D	A	D	D	A
141	**142**	**143**	**144**	**145**	**146**	**147**	**148**	**149**	**150**
A	B	C	D	D	B	D	B	C	A
151	**152**	**153**	**154**	**155**	**156**	**157**	**158**	**159**	**160**
D	C	C	A	A	A	C	B	C	D
161	**162**	**163**	**164**	**165**	**166**	**167**	**168**	**169**	**170**
D	B	C	A	D	A	D	C	D	C
171	**172**	**173**	**174**	**175**	**176**	**177**	**178**	**179**	**180**
A	A	C	C	C	A	B	D	C	B
181	**182**	**183**	**184**	**185**	**186**	**187**	**188**	**189**	**190**
A	D	A	D	D	C	A	A	A	A
191	**192**	**193**	**194**	**195**	**196**	**197**	**198**	**199**	**200**
D	C	A	A	A	C	A	C	B	B
201	**202**	**203**	**204**	**205**	**206**	**207**	**208**	**209**	**210**
C	B	D	A	A	D	C	D	D	D
211	**212**	**213**	**214**	**215**	**216**	**217**	**218**	**219**	**220**
D	A	B	B	A	A	B	D	D	B
221	**222**	**223**	**224**	**225**	**226**	**227**	**228**	**229**	**230**
D	A	A	B	A	A	B	D	B	B
231	**232**	**233**	**234**	**235**	**236**	**237**	**238**	**239**	**240**
A	D	D	C	A	D	D	C	D	A
241	**242**	**243**	**244**	**245**	**246**	**247**	**248**	**249**	**250**
B	C	C	D	B	A	A	D	A	C
251	**252**	**253**	**254**	**255**	**256**	**257**	**258**	**259**	**260**
A	D	D	A	B	A	B	A	A	A
261	**262**	**263**	**264**	**265**	**266**	**267**	**268**	**269**	**270**
B	C	A	D	D	B	A	C	A	A
271	**272**	**273**	**274**	**275**	**276**	**277**	**278**	**279**	**280**
B	A	B	A	A	D	A	B	B	D
281	**282**	**283**	**284**	**285**	**286**	**287**	**288**	**289**	**290**
B	D	D	B	A	A	C	B	A	B
291	**292**	**293**	**294**	**295**	**296**	**297**	**298**	**299**	**300**
C	C	A	D	B	A	D	A	C	D
301	**302**	**303**	**304**	**305**	**306**	**307**	**308**	**309**	**310**
C	A	D	D	C	C	B	C	B	C

311	312	313	314	315	316	317	318	319	320
D	B	A	D	D	A	B,C,D	C	D	D
321	**322**	**323**	**324**	**325**	**326**	**327**	**328**	**329**	**330**
A	B	B,D	C	A,C	A,C	B,D	C	A	A
331	**332**	**333**	**334**	**335**	**336**	**337**	**338**	**339**	**340**
A	A	C	B	B	A	D	B	B	C
341	**342**	**343**	**344**	**345**	**346**	**347**	**348**	**349**	**350**
D	C	B	D	D	B	B	D	A	D
351	**352**	**353**	**354**	**355**	**356**	**357**	**358**	**359**	**360**
C	C	B	A	D	C	C	A	B	B
361	**362**	**363**	**364**	**365**	**366**	**367**	**368**	**369**	**370**
B	A	D	B	D	A	C	A	D	C
371	**372**	**373**	**374**	**375**	**376**	**377**	**378**	**379**	**380**
C	A	A	D	C	C	A	C	C	B
281	**282**	**283**	**284**	**285**	**286**	**287**	**288**	**289**	**290**
D	D	B	A	C	B	A	D	D	A,B
291	**292**	**293**	**294**	**295**	**296**	**297**	**298**	**299**	**400**
A,D	A,C,D	B	D	A,B,D	C	A	A,B,C	A	B
401	**402**								
A,B,D	A,B								

CHAPTER

2

CELL BIOLOGY

CSIR-NET, JUNE, 2017

Membrane Structure and Function

1. A membrane associated protein is composed of seven "α-helices", with each helix containing 19 hydrophobic residues. While treating the membrane with all kinds of proteases, a major portion of this protein remains intact. Treatment with high salt (till 1.5M NaCl) and buffer with pH 5.0 failed to dissociate this protein from the membrane. Predict the most appropriate nature and orientation of this protein in the membrane.
   A. Peripheral glycoprotein
   B. Integral protein with seven membrane spanning regions
   C. Peripheral protein with both N and C-terminals remain exposed to outer surface of the cell membrane
   D. Peripheral protein with both N and C-terminal remain exposed to cytosolic surface of the cell membrane

Structural organization and function of intracellular organelles

2. Metachromatic leukodystrophy (MLD) is caused by a deficiency of arylsulfatase A and affects the CNS. MLD is
   A. a lysosomal storage disorder
   B. a disease due to dysfunctional mitochondria
   C. caused by loss of the myelin sheath
   D. caused by a defect in proteins of the nuclear envelope

3. Which one of the following statements regarding 'Endosymbiotic hypothesis of origin of eukaryotes' is INCORRECT?
   A. Mitochondria arose from an α-proteobacterium and plastids arose from cyanobacteria.
   B. The event of engulfinent of a photosynthetic cyariobacterium by a host cell was primitive to engulfinent of an á- proteobacterium during the eukaryotic origin.
   C. Protists chlorarachniophytes, likely evolved when a heterotrophic eukaryote engulfed green alga, exemplifying secondary cndmymbiosis.
   D. One of the membranes of the engulfed double-membraned cyanobacteria was lost in some of the hosts that eventually led to red and green algae descendants.

Cell division and Cell Cycle

4. In *Schizosaccharomyces pombe*, the recessive ($cdc2^r$) and dominant ($cdc2^D$) mutants have opposing phenotypes. While $cdc2^D$ produces abnormally small cells, $cdc2^r$ produces abnormally long cells.

   Some possible explanations are given below.
   (*a*) $cdc2^D$ may lack interaction with WEE1
   (*b*) $cdc2^r$ may not interact with CDC13 kinase

(*c*) $cdc2^D$ may not interact with CDC25 phosphatase
(*d*) $cdc2^r$ cells may be deficient in interaction with either CDC25 or WEE1

Which combination of the above statements is correct?
A. (*a*) and (*b*) only B. (*a*), (*c*) and (*d*) only
C. (*b*) and (*c*) only D. (*a*), (*b*) and (*c*) only

Cytoskeleton

5. Preventing the blocking action of Patched protein leads to activation of Cos-2, which dissociates itself from microtubules, activates Ci/Gli which binds to CBP (CREB-binding protein) and promotes transcription of target genes. Which one of the following treatment of cells will mostly prevent Ci/Gli activated transcription in the cells?
A. Small molecules which target Frizzled.
B. Azepine, an inhibitor of γ-secretase.
C. Cyclopamine, which binds to heptahelical bundle of Smoothened.
D. Cdk blockers, which negatively regulate TGFβ-induced growth.

Signal Molecule & Cell signalling

6. The second messenger, which opens calcium ion pores in endoplasmic reticulum and plasma membrane is
A. Diacylglycerol
B. cAMP
C. Phosphatidyl inositol biphosphate
D. Inositol triphosphate

7. When the cholera toxin (protein of Mr 90,000 Da) gains access to the human intestinal tract, it binds tightly to specific receptors in the plasma membrane of the epithelial cells lining the small intestine, causing membrane bound adenylyl cyclase to undergo prolonged activation resulting in extensive loss of H_2O and Na^+. Pretreatment of the epithelial cells with various phospholipases and proteases failed to inhibit the binding of cholera toxin to its receptor and the fluid loss but treatment with exoglycosidase, prior to binding, significantly reduces these effects. Which of the following molecule could be the receptor for this toxin?
A. Phosphatidyl choline
B. Sodium potassium ATPase
C. Ganglioside
D. Chloride-bicarbonate exchanger

8. The second messenger cAMP, synthesised by adenylyl cyclase transduces a wide variety of physiological signals in various cell types in mammalian cells. Most of the diverse effects of cAMP are mediated through activation of protein kinase A (PKA), also called cAMP dependent protein kinase. Which of the following statements regarding PKA is NOT correct?
A. Inactive PKA is a tetramer consisting of two regulatory (R) subunits and two catalytic (C) subunits.
B. Each R subunit binds the active site in a catalytic domain and inhibits the activity of the catalytic subunits.
C. Each R subunit has two distinct cAMP binding sites and binding of cAMP occurs in a cooperative fashion.
D. Binding of cAMP to R subunit causes a conformational change resulting in binding to site other than catalytic site causing strengthening of binding to C subunit activating its kinase activity.

9. Following are some statements about the mechanism of stimulation of receptors for touch, pain, vision and warmth that may or may not be correct.
(*a*) The touch receptor does not require any voltage gated cation channel for its activation.
(*b*) Light causes closing of Na^+ channels in the outer segments of rods and cones
(*c*) Pain sensation is caused by opening of Na^+ or Na^+/Ca^{++} channels in free sensory nerve endings.
(*d*) The warmth receptor is activated by non- selective anion channels.

Choose the option with both statements as correct.
A. (*a*) and (*c*) B. (*b*) and (*c*)
C. (*c*) and (*d*) D. (*a*) and (*d*)

Cellular Communication

10. Given below are a list of some extracellular matrix (ECM) proteins in column A and their characteristics in column B, but not in correct order:

A		B
(*a*) Fibronectin	(*i*)	Trimeric protein made from three polypeptides which can twist together into a special triple helix
(*b*) Laminin	(*ii*)	Heterotrimeric protein comprising α, β and γ chains and many of them are large, cross shaped protein
(*c*) Nidogen	(*iii*)	Dimers of two similar polypeptides linked at their C-termini by two disulphide bonds and contain RGD sequence for binding of certain integrins
(*d*) Collagen	(*iv*)	A rod-like molecule also called enactin that cross-links with many ECM proteins and also stabilize basal laminae

Which one of the following is the most appropriate match?

	(*a*)	(*b*)	(*c*)	(*d*)
A.	(*i*)	(*ii*)	(*iii*)	(*iv*)
B.	(*ii*)	(*iii*)	(*iv*)	(*i*)
C.	(*iii*)	(*ii*)	(*iv*)	(*i*)
D.	(*iv*)	(*i*)	(*ii*)	(*iii*)

CSIR-NET, DECEMBER, 2017

Membrane Structure and Function

11. Sphingolipids (S) and cholesterol (C) molecules of the lipid bilayer aggregate into multiple tiny rafts instead of a single large one. Considering that size of a lipid raft depends on the affinity of S and C for one another and other lipids in the membra choose the option that best describes this property.

A. S and C bind to one another tightly and independent of any other lipid molecules.
B. S and C bind to one another with same affinity as they bind to other lipid species of the membrane.
C. S and C bind to one another with high affinity under the influence of some cytoskeletal elements.
D. S and C have slightly higher affinity than other lipid molecules of the membrane and are in dynamic equilibrium with their free forms.

12. Several types of molecules including the transmembrane glycoproteins can function as matrix receptors and co-receptors. However, the principal receptors on animal cells for binding most extracellular matrix proteins are the integrins. Which of the following statements is NOT true for integrins?

A. Integrins are transmembrane linker proteins that link to the cytoskeleton.
B. An integrin molelcule is composed of two non-covalently associated glycoprotein subunits α and β. Both subunits span the cell membrane, with short intracellular C-terminal tails and large N-terminal extracellular domains.
C. The extracellular portion of the integrin dimer binds to specific carbohydrate residues in extracellular matrix proteins or to ligands on the surface of other cells.
D. The intracellular portion binds to a complex of proteins that form a linkage to the cytoskeleton

Structural Organization and Function of Intracellular Organelles

13. Select a cellular body which is NOT a part of the nuclear bodies:

A. P-bodies
B. Nucleolus
C. Cajal bodies
D. Interchromatin granule clusters

14. Given below are organelles (column A) and properties associated with the organelles (column B).

Column A	Column B
(*a*) Lysosomes	(*i*) Anterograde transport from ER to Golgi
(*b*) *cis*–Golgi	(*ii*) Clathrin – coated vesicles
(*c*) *trans* –Golgi	(*iii*) Cop I vesicle budding
(*d*) Cop II vesicles	(*iv*) Mannose-6-phosphate receptor
(*e*) Endocytic vesicles	(*v*) Protein aggregate for secretion

Choose the option that matches the organelles with the most appropriate property.

	(*a*)	(*b*)	(*c*)	(*d*)	(*e*)
A.	(*iv*)	(*iii*)	(*v*)	(*i*)	(*ii*)
B.	(*v*)	(*iv*)	(*i*)	(*v*)	(*ii*)
C.	(*iii*)	(*v*)	(*i*)	(*iv*)	(*ii*)
D.	(*iv*)	(*v*)	(*ii*)	(*i*)	(*iii*)

Cell Division and Cell Cycle

15. During eukaryotic cell division, metaphase to anaphase transition is regulated by degradation of

A. Cyclin B1
B. CDK1
C. Aurora A kinase
D. Polo-like kinase

16. Cell cycle checkpoints are surveillance mechanisms that ensure order and fidelity of events of the cell cycle. Given below are some of the checkpoint proteins and their functions

(*a*) Mad2	(*i*) Prevention of Cdc14 activation
(*b*) Tem1	(*ii*) Prevention of Cdc20 activation
(*c*) ATM	(*iii*) Inhibition of $p21^{CIP}$
(*d*) ATR	(*iv*) Inhibition of separase action

Match the checkpoint protein with its function.

	(*a*)	(*b*)	(*c*)	(*d*)
A.	(*iv*)	(*i*)	(*ii*)	(*iii*)
B.	(*ii*)	(*iv*)	(*i*)	(*iii*)
C.	(*ii*)	(*i*)	(*iii*)	(*iv*)
D.	(*ii*)	(*iv*)	(*iii*)	(*i*)

17. To assess the impact of a newly identified drug when added to a culture of subconfluent HeLa cells, a researcher analyzes the fluorescence activated cell sorting (FACS) profile of untreated (– Drug) versus treated (+ Drug) cells.

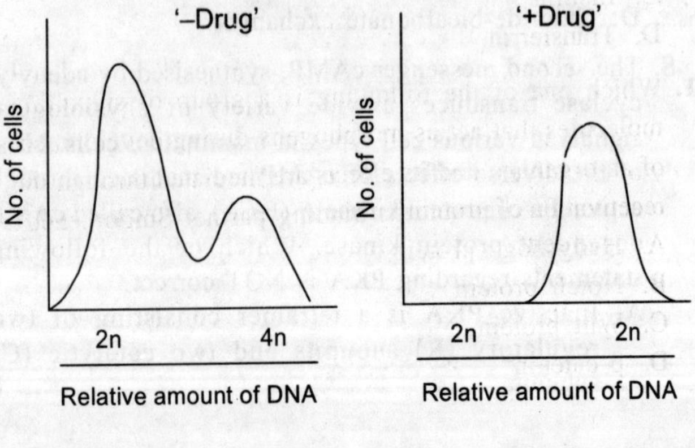

Based on the FACS profile shown above, this drug inhibits
A. G1 phase of the cell cycle
B. S phase of the cell cycle
C. G2 /M phase of the cell cycle
D. G0 phase of cell cycle

Cytoskeleton

18. To understand the microtubule-dependent motor activity of a freshly purified motor protein from budding yeast, a researcher set up microtubule based gliding assay. In such an assay where microtubules are fluorescently tagged at its (+) end, the researcher observed that this motor protein moves the microtubule in the direction of its (+) end as shown below:

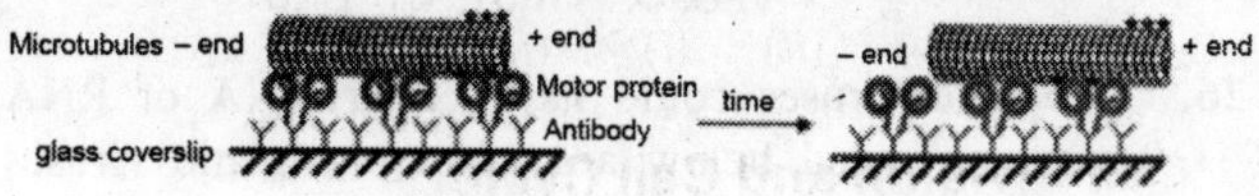

The newly identified motor protein is
A. Dynein
B. Myosin
C. Kinesin 1
D. Either Dynein or Kinesin

Signal Molecule & Cell Signaling

19. In a signalling event, binding of an extracellular ligand activates G-protein coupled receptor (GPCR) that eventually activates phospholipase C-β. Which one of the following statements truly reflects the function of phospholipase C-β?
A. Phospholipase C-β converts PI (3, 4, 5)P3 to PI (4, 5)P2
B. Phospholipase C-β converts PI (4)P to PI (4, 5)P2
C. Phospholipase C-β converts PI (4, 5)P2 to diacylglycerol and IP3
D. Phospholipase C-β converts PI (5)P to PI (4, 5)P2

20. Proteins with cytoplasmic domains having tyrosine kinase activity do NOT act as receptors for
A. Epidermal growth factor (EGF)
B. Platelet-derived growth factor (PDGF)
C. Insulin
D. Transferrin

21. Which one of the following is a group of signalling molecules that act as morphogens during development of an organism and its effects are mediated through the receptor Patched and its binding partner Smoothened?
A. Hedgehog protein
B. Notch protein
C. Wnt protein
D. β-catenin

22. In a type of signal transduction pathway, ligand binding to a receptor triggers activation of a receptor-associated kinase.This kinase may be an intrinsic part of the receptor protein or tightly bound to the receptor. Receptors in which the tyrosine kinase is an intrinsic part of it's polypeptide chain are called the receptor tyrosine kinase (RTK). Which one of the following statements regarding RTK is INCORRECT?
A. All RTKs have three essential components:an extracellular domain containing ligand binding site, a transmembrane domain and a cytoplasmic segment that includes a domain with protein tyrosine kinase activity.
B. Most RTKs are monomeric and ligand binding to the extracellular domain induces formation of receptor dimers.
C. All cytokine receptors belong to RTKs and cytokine binding activates tyrosine kinase and receptor dimerization.
D. Ligand binding to RTK leads to autophosphorylation of the protein tyrosine kinase in the cytoplasmic domain. The activated kinase then phosphorylates several tyrosine residues in the receptor's cytoplasmic domain.

Cellular Communication

23. Junctions which tether cytoskeletal filaments inside the cell are known as
A. Anchoring junctions
B. Occluding junctions
C. Channel – forming junctions
D. Signal – relaying junctions

Cancer

24. Two classes of genes - proto-oncogene and tumor suppressor gene usually contribute to the development of cancer. Following are some of the statements regarding both the genes.
(*a*) Proto-oncogenes result in the development of cancer by gain-offunction mutation whereas tumor suppressor gene leads to cancer development by loss of function mutation.
(*b*) Proto-oncogenes result in development of cancer by loss-of-function mutation whereas tumor suppressor gene leads to cancer development by gain-of-function mutation.
(*c*) Mutation in both the alleles of a proto-oncogene is required for induction of cancer whereas mutation in one of the two alleles in tumor suppressor gene is sufficient for promoting tumorigenesis.
(*d*) Mutation in one of the two alleles in proto-oncogene is sufficient for induction of cancer whereas mutation in both the alleles of a tumor suppressor gene is required for promoting tumorigenesis.

Which combinations of the above statements are true for both the genes?
A. (*a*) and (*b*)
B. (*a*) and (*c*)
C. (*a*) and (*d*)
D. (*b*) and (*c*)

25. Two important features which aid the development of a tumor and its metastasis are epithelial-to-mesenchymal transition and angiogenesis. A student tested four cell lines to determine their invasiveness and proliferation capability by checking the expression of VEGF-A, TWIST and Cyclin D1. Which one of the following figures is most likely to exhibit the characteristics of a highly metastatic cancer cell?

A.
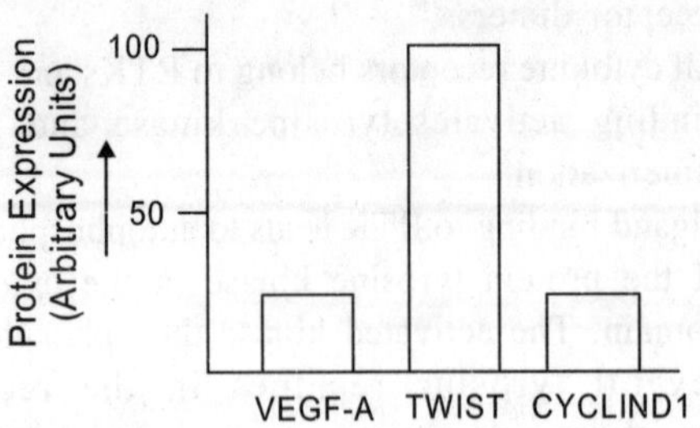

B.
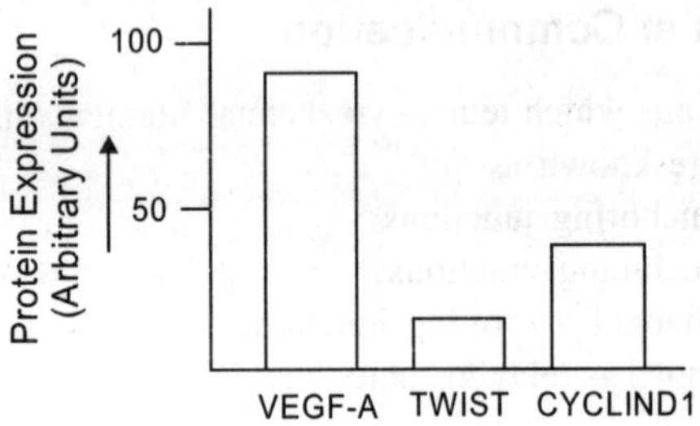

C.
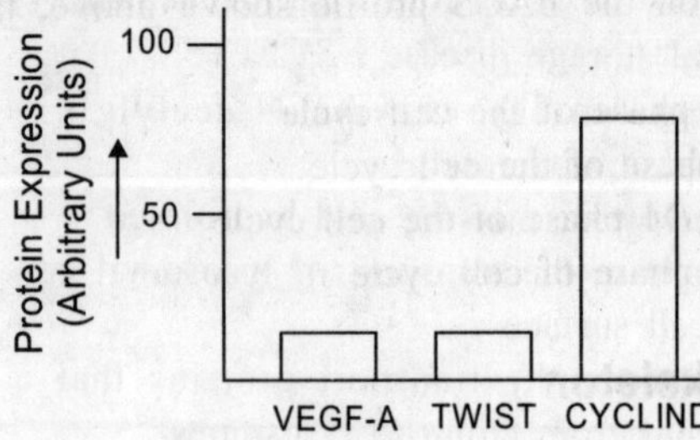

D.
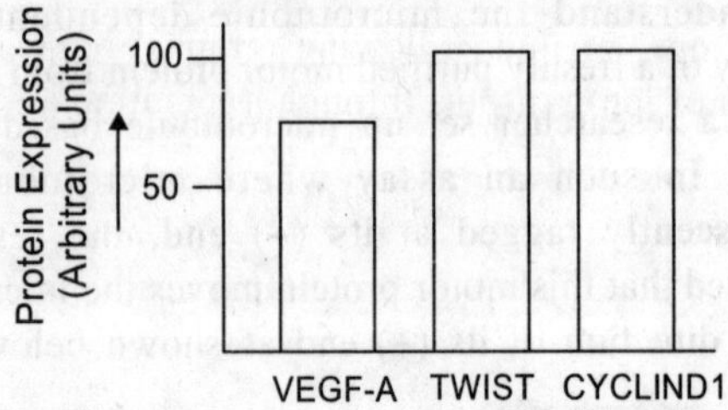

26. Oncogenic viruses could have either DNA or RNA genomes. Listed below are some oncogenic viruses (Column A), their genome types (Column B) and the cancers caused by these viruses (Column C).

A	B	C
(*a*) Hepatitis B	(*i*) DNA	(*x*) Burkitt's lymphoma
(*b*) Epstein Barr Virus	(*ii*) RNA	(*y*) T-cell leukaemia
(*c*) HTLV		(*z*) Hepatocellular carcinoma

Find out the correct combination.
A. (*a*) (*i*) (*x*), (*b*) (*ii*) (*y*), (*c*) (*ii*) (*z*)
B. (*a*) (*ii*) (*y*), (*b*) (*i*) (*z*), (*c*) (*ii*) (*x*)
C. (*a*) (*ii*) (*y*), (*b*) (*ii*) (*z*), (*c*) (*i*) (*y*)
D. (*a*) (*i*) (*z*), (*b*) (*i*) (*x*), (*c*) (*ii*) (*y*)

DBT-JRF, 2017

Organization of Structure and Functions of Prokaryotic and Eukaryotic Cell

27. Most organisms can regulate membrane fluidity by changing the lipid composition. If cells are transferred from a warm environment to a cold one, it can be expected that:
A. There will be a decrease in the proportion of 16-carbon fatty acids compared to 18-carbon fatty acids
B. There will be an increase in the proportion of 16-carbon fatty acids compared to 18-carbon fatty acids
C. There will be an increase in the proportion of saturated fatty acids
D. Phospholipids will not be incorporated into the membrane

28. Glycosylation of membrane proteins and lipids is carried out by enzymes present in the lumen of endoplasmic reticulum and Golgi. The glycosylated part of membrane proteins and lipids in the plasma membrane is likely to be
A. Oriented towards the cytosol
B. Exposed to the extracellular environment
C. The glycosylated parts of the proteins are towards the cytoplasm but glycosylated lipid are exposed to extracellular environment
D. The glycosylated parts of the lipids are towards the cytoplasm but glycosylated proteins are exposed to the extracellular environment

29. Lysosomal storage diseases are a group of inherited diseases that are characterized by the accumulation of specific substances or class of substances within the lysosomes. All of the following mechanisms can cause lysosomal storage disease EXCEPT:

A. Defects in the enzyme N-acetylglucosamine phosphotransferase
B. Defective or missing acid hydrolases
C. Defects in the transport of lysosomal enzymes to the cell surface
D. Defects in the transport proteins that transport proteins from Golgi to lysosomes.

30. Which one of the following graphs represent the kinetics of ion transport through a membrane channel?

A. 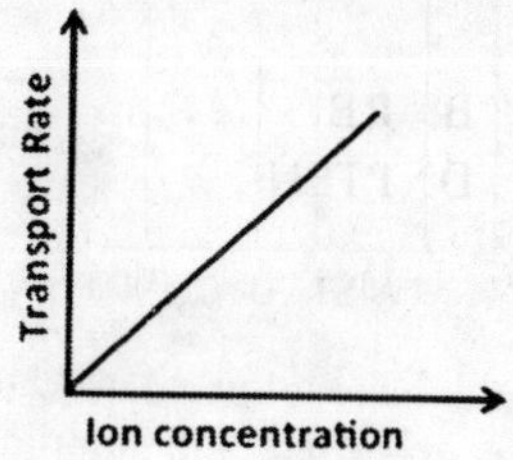

B. 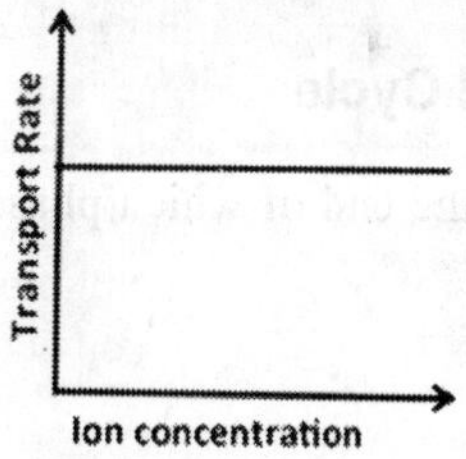

C. 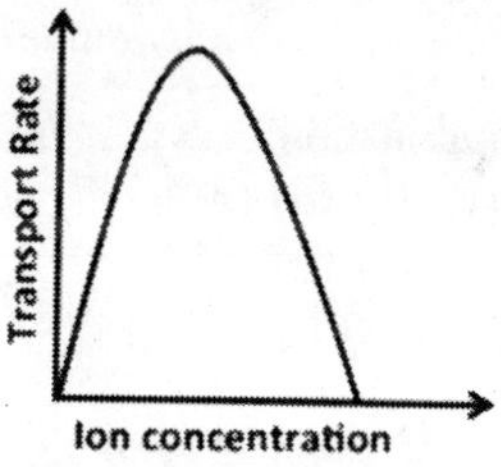

D. 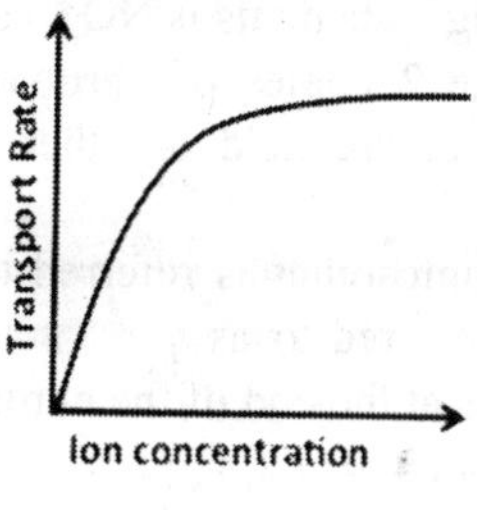

31. The function performed in the smooth ER is:

A. Biosynthesis of secretory proteins
B. Folding of membrane proteins
C. Addition of N-linked sugars
D. Detoxification of drugs

32. Match the proteins in Group I with members in Group II

Group I	**Group II**
(*a*) Alkaline phosphatase	P. Extracellular
(*b*) F_0 component of ATP synthase	Q. Cytoplasm
(*c*) Alcohol dehydrogenase	R. Inner membrane
(*d*) Pectinase	S. Periplasm

	(*a*)	(*b*)	(*c*)	(*d*)
A.	S	R	Q	P
B.	P	R	Q	S
C.	R	S	P	Q
D.	Q	P	S	R

33. Four yeast mutants block membrane and secretory proteins in following compartments:

Mutant A: Golgi
Mutant B: ER Mutant C: Cytosol
Mutant D: Secretory vesicles

If two new mutants are made that have combined defects of A+C and B+D, proteins of the new mutants will accumulate in:

A. Golgi and ER, respectively
B. Golgi and secretory vesicle, respectively
C. Cytosol and ER, respectively
D. Cytosol in both cases

34. Histone code implies which of the following?

A. Combination of different histone proteins to form a nucleosome.
B. Modification of histones.
C. Different histone proteins present in different eukaryotic organisms.
D. Different order of histone proteins in a given nucleosome

35. If the DNA content of a diploid cell in the G1 phase of the cell cycle is X, then the DNA content of the same cell at metaphase of meiosis I would be:

A. 2X
B. 4X
C. 0.5X
D. X

36. Following fertilization, zygote divides rapidly to form a large number of cells within a short time through a process called cleavage. In some organisms like sea urchin the cells of the early embryos skip some stages of cell cycle in order to achieve this. Which of the following steps may be skipped?

A. G_1
B. G_1 and G_2
C. S
D. G_0

37. If the doubling time of a prokaryotic cell becomes progressively shorter, than it can be predicted then it can be predicted that the ribosome concentration will:

A. remains constant
B. decrease
C. increase
D. remains constant but their composition will be different

38. Specificity factor which activates ubiquitin ligase activity of APC/C during separation of sister chromatids is:

A. CDC10
B. CDC20
C. CDH1
D. CDC45A

39. Cell cycle regulatory genes (CDC) were originally discovered by Paul Nurse in yeasts using genetic approach involving temperature sensitive mutant screening. Which of the following was used to identify CDC?

A. Genome sequencing
B. cDNA complementation assay
C. RNAi method
D. Homologous recombination

40. In human carcinomas, many proteins including most cytoskeletal proteins undergo modifications, thereby making it difficult for a clinician to identify the origin of the cancer cells. In this context, which one of the following can be relied upon for identification of the origin of cancer cells?

A. microtubules
B. F-actin
C. G-actin
D. Intermediate filament

41. Which of the following mechanisms converts c-erbB (EGFR) to an oncogene?

A. Point mutation
B. Truncation
C. Recombination
D. Gene amplification

42. The anticancer drug, Halichondrin – D is isolated from:

A. Corals
B. Gorgonians
C. Sponges
D. Sea anemone

43. In Li-Fraumeni syndrome most frequent mutation occurs in:

A. p53
B. RB
C. BRCA1
D. PTEN

GATE (BIOTECHNOLOGY), 2017

Structural Organization and Function of Intracellular Organelles

44. Secretory proteins synthesized by ER- associated ribosomes traverse through

A. mitochondria
B. peroxisomes
C. the Golgi apparatus
D. the nucleus

Cell Division and Cell Cycle

45. The genome is diploid at the end of which phases of a human mitotic cell cycle?

A. G2 & S B
B. G1 & M
C. M & S
D. G1 & G2

GATE (LIFE SCIENCE), 2017

Cell Organelle and Signalling

46. Which one of the following will NOT form lipid bilayer?

A. Cholesterol
B. Phosphatidyl ethanolamine
C. Triacylglycerol
D. Phosphatidyl serine

47. Match the molecule in Column I with its function in Column II

Column I	Column II
P. Cholera toxin	(*i*) modifies $G_{\alpha i}$
Q. Pertusis toxin	(*ii*) Inhibits c-AMP phosphodiesterase
R. IP3	(*iii*) $G_{\alpha i}$
S. Caffeine	(*iv*) Increases intracellular Ca^{2+} lrvel

A. P (*iii*); Q (*i*); R (*iv*); S (*ii*)
B. P (*iv*); Q (*i*); R (*iii*); S (*ii*)
C. P (*ii*); Q (*iv*), R (*i*); S (*iii*)
D. P (*iii*); Q (*i*); R (*ii*); S (*iv*)

Cell Biology

48. Which one of the following statements is NOT correct?

A. During metaphase, the 2 copies of chromosomal DNA are held together are held together at the centromere
B. The short arm of chromosomes is referred to as *p* and the long arm is referred to as *q*
C. The terminal structures at the end of the chromatids are referred to as telomeres
D. The terms heterochromatin and euchromatin refer to the active and repressed regions of the chromosome respectively

49. The covalent modification performed by kinases which regulate proteins in signalling pathways is

A. glycosylation
B. methylation
C. ubiquitination
D. phosphorylation

50. Upon activation of phospholipase C by ligands binding to G-protein coupled receptor, the Ca^{+2} concentration in cytosol will

A. decrease due to blockage of $InsP_3$ gated channel on endoplasmic reticulum

B. decrease due to blockage of $InsP_3$ gated channel on plasma membrane
C. increase due to efflux of Ca^{+2} blockage of $InsP_3$ gated channel on mitochondria
D. increase due to efflux of Ca^{+2} blockage of $InsP_3$ gated channel on endoplasmic reticulum as well as influx of Ca^{+2} from $InsP_3$ gated channel on plasma membrane

CSIR-NET, JUNE, 2018

Membrane Structure and Function

51. Ability of a membrane protein to span the lipid bilayer strictly depends on the presence of
A. Zinc finger domain
B. α- helices
C. parallel β sheet
D. antiparallel β sheet

52. Which one of the listed below is a P-type ion transporter?
A. Mg^{+2} and Fe^{+2}
B. Mg^{+2} and Fe^{+3}
C. Mg^{+2} and Cl^-
D. Na^+–K^+, Ca^{+2} and H^+

53. Prestin, a membrane protein, is found in which one of the following cells of the organ of Corti?
A. Inner hair cells
B. Inner phalangeal cells
C. Outer hair cells
D. Outer phalangeal cells

54. An integral membrane protein (P) has been identified as a cell surface protein of hepatocytes and assigned to bind to hepatitis B virus (HBV) and promote its entry into cytosol. Upon binding to HBV particles, the C-terminal of P interacts with F-actin in the cytosol and in turn, helps in the entry of the HBV particles. P was successfully cloned and expressed in animal cells in culture wherein its N-terminal is exposed on the surface while the C-terminal resides in the cytosol. The recombinant protein P so expressed retains its complete structure and function. From the list of experiments given below, which one of the experiments will you perform to show that C- terminal of the protein P via interacting with F-actin helps in IIBV entry?
A. Incubating radiolabelled HBV with hepatocytes in culture and follow up its association with F-actin by immuno-precipitation analysis using anti-F-actin antibody.
B. Incubating radiolabelled HBV with hepatocytes over-expressing the C-terminal mutant of P and repeat the rest of the experiment as in "1"
C. Incubating radiolabelled HBV with hepatocytes over-expressing the N-terminal mutant of P and repeat the rest of the experiment as in "1".
D. Using wild type P as well as C-terminal mutant of P and their individual over-expression in a heterologous cell line (completely devoid of endogenous P protein) and then repeat experiment as in "1".

55. The cell membrane of neuron maintains intracellular conditions that differ from those of the extracellular environment. Such difference in intra- and extracellular conditions are critical to the function of the nerve cell as the nerve cell membrane resembles a charged capacitor. Assuming the electric field (E) across a parallel-plate capacitor is uniform and if membrane thickness is 7 nm and potential difference across the membrane is -60 mV, calculate E of the membrane.
A. 6×10^5 V m^{-1}
B. 7×10^5 V m^{-1}
C. 8.6×10^6 V m^{-1}
D. 6.6×10^6 V m^{-1}

Structural Organization and Function of Intracellular Organelles

56. The cell maintains a high concentration of protons inside the lysosome because of
A. antiporter in the lysosomal membrane
B. ATP-powered proton pump in the lysosomal membrane
C. facilitated diffusion proton channel in the lysosomal membrane
D. facilitated diffusion proton uniporter in the lysosomal membrane

57. A group of scientists performed an experiment where the)' artificially fused mouse cells with monkey cells. The resulting fused cells were labelled with fluorescently tagged antibodies against mouse and monkey surface receptor proteins, X and Y respectively. At the time 0 minute just after fusion events, two receptors were confined to their own half in the heterokaryon. However, such surface receptors (X and Y) intermixed on the cell surface after 60 minutes. Which one of the given statements correctly reflects the outcome of the experiment?
A. The proteins in cytoplasm are in a dynamic state.
B. The proteins on the membrane surface are in a dynamic state.
C. Surface membrane proteins exchange with the cytosolic proteins.
D. Membrane surface proteins are in a static phase.

58. The following intracellular event occurs in a cell that is subjected to conditions of starvation.

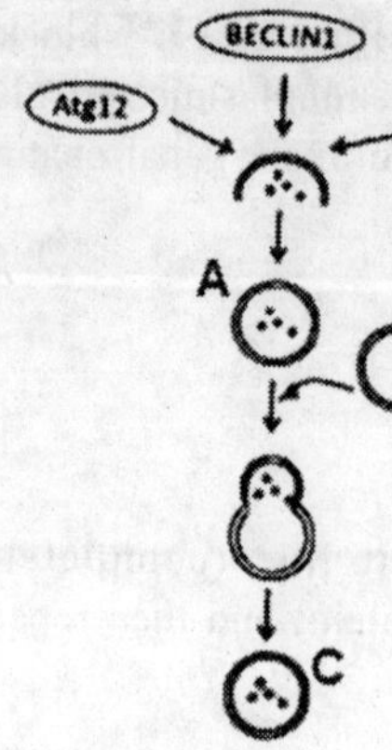

Which one of the following statements correctly represents the event shown above?

A. The cell is undergoing apoptotic cell death with the help of lysosomes (A).
B. The cell is undergoing autophagy by formation of autophagolysosomes (C).
C. The cell is undergoing necroptosis.
D. The cell is undergoing autophagy and fusion occurs between lysosome (B) and autophagolysosome (A).

Organization of Genes and Chromosomes

59. It is known that there is a large difference in the DNA content between two organisms with similar developmental complexity. This is due to large differences in the number of

A. transposable elements, repetitive DNA and coding sequences
B. transposable elements and repetitive DNA
C. introns and coding sequences
D. introns and transposable elements

60. An intron was cloned within a transposable element. Absence of the intron following transposition of the element, will indicate that it

A. follows conservative mode of transposition
B. follows replicative mode of transposition
C. is a retrotransposon
D. is an insertion element

Cell Division and Cell Cycle

61. Cervical cancer-causing papilloma virus produces two oncoproteins E6 and E7 which are responsible for interfering with cell cycle regulation by

A. inactivating pRb and p53, respectively
B. modulating p53 and pRb, respectively
C. binding to cyclin DI and CDK4
D. activating expression of p21

Signal Molecule & Cell Signalling

62. G protein-coupled receptors (GPCRs) are used to detect and respond to many different types of signals, including neurotransmitters, hormones involved in glycogen and fat metabolism and even photons of light.

Which one of the following statements regarding GPCR is INCORRECT?

A. GPCRs are a large family with a common structure of seven membrane spanning α helices.
B. GPCRs are coupled to trimeric G proteins comprising three subunits α, β and γ.
C. The Gα subunit is a GTPase switch protein that alternates between an active ('on') state with bound GTP and an inactive ('off') state with GDP.
D. The 'on' form gets bound to β and subunits and activates a membrane bound effector like adenylyl cyclase, phospholipase C or ion channel.

Cellular Communication

63. Which one of the following permits the rapid diffusion of small, water-soluble molecules between the cytoplasm of adjacent cells?

A. Tight junctions B. Anchoring junctions
C. Adherens junctions D. Gap junctions

64. The extracellular matrix (ECM) is a complex combination of secreted proteins that is involved in holding cells and tissues together. The components of ECM form a network by binding to each other and communicate with cells by binding to adhesion receptors on the cell surface. ECM comprises mainly two classes of macromolecules, proteoglycans and very high molecular weight large proteins. Which one of the following statements regarding ECM constituents is INCORRECT?

A. Proteoglycans are a subset of secreted or cell surface- attached glycoproteins containing covalently linked specialized polysaccharide chains called glycosaminoglycans (GAGs).
B. GAGs are long branched polymers of specific repeating disaccharides of sialic acid and glucose or galactose.
C. Major types of GAGs present in ECM are heparan sulphate, chondroitin sulphate, dermatan sulphate, keratan sulphate and hyaluronan.
D. Major types of large proteins present in ECM are collagen, laminin, elastin and fibronectin.

Cancer

65. Present-day cancer treatment uses many approaches. Beyond surgery and radiation treatment, which are most often employed in cases of larger, more discrete tumors, drug therapies can be used to target residual tumor cells and to attack dispersed cancers. Chemotherapies by anti-cancer drugs are mostly aimed at blocking DNA synthesis and cell division. A list of anti-cancer drugs is given in column A, their chemical nature in column Band their mechanism of action in column C.

A	B	C
(*a*) Methotrexate	(*i*) Podophyllotoxin	I. Inhibits formation of tetrahydrofolate
(*b*) Etoposide	(*ii*) Pirimidine analogue	II. Inhibit thymidylate synthase
(*c*) 5-flurouracil	(*iii*) Alkaloid	III. Interferes with breakdown of microtubules required for cell division
(*d*) Paclitaxel	(*iv*) Folic acid analogue	IV. Forms stable-complex with DNA and topoisomerase II affecting religation of DNA strands

A. (*a*) (*i*) I, (*b*) (*ii*) II, (*c*) (*iii*) III, (*d*) (*iv*) IV
B. (*a*) (*ii*) II, (*b*) (*i*) III, (*c*) (*iv*) I, (*d*) (*iii*) IV
C. (*a*) (*iii*) III, (*b*) (*iv*) IV, (*c*) (*i*) II, (*d*) (*ii*) I
D. (*a*) (*iv*) I, (*b*) (*i*) IV, (*c*) (*ii*) II, (*d*) (*iii*) III

CSIR-NET, DECEMBER, 2018

Structural Organization and Function of Intracellular Organelles

66. Membrane-bound, Golgi-derived structures containing proteolytic enzymes in sperms of sea urchin are called
A. cortical granules B. micromeres
C. acrosomal vesicles D. macromeres

67. Which one of the following proteins is most likely to be found in the intermembrane space of mitochondria?
A. A protein containing an N-terminal matrix targeting sequence followed by hydrophobic stop-transfer anchor sequence
B. an N-terminal matrix targeting sequence followed by a cleavable hydrophobic sequence that blocks complete translocation
C. a protein with multiple internal sequences that are recognized by Tim 22 complex
D. a protein with an outer membrane localization sequence followed by a matrix targeting signal

Organization of Genes and Chromosomes

68. Which one of the following statements is true about human chromosomes?
A. The chromosomes that have highest gene density generally localize towards the centre of the nucleus.
B. The chromosomes that have highest gene density generally localize near the nuclear periphery to facilitate rapid transport of the nascent transcripts.
C. The centromeres of different chromosomes tend to cluster together at the centre of the nucleus.
D. Chromosomal positioning in the nucleus is absolutely random

Cell Division and Cell Cycle

69. In metazoan cell cycle, metaphase to anaphase transition is regulated by the activity of:
A. Cdkl/cyclinB B. APC/C
C. Cdc25 D. Weel

70. Following observation was made when a mammalian cell in one phase of cell cycle was fused with a cell in another phase of cell cycle:
(*a*) Fusion of a cell in G1 phase with S phase caused the G1 nucleus to enter S phase.
(*b*) Upon fusion of a G2 cell with an S phase cell, G2 cell does not enter S phase.
(*c*) Upon fusion of a G1 cell with G2 cell, G1 nucleus enters G2 phase.
(*d*) Fusion of an S phase cell with a M phase causes the S phase cell to immediately enter mitosis.

Choose the combination with all correct statements.
A. (*a*), (*b*), (*c*) B. (*a*), (*c*), (*d*)
C. (*b*), (*c*), (*d*) D. (*a*), (*b*), (*d*)

Cytoskeleton

71. An investigator expresses a GFP-fused protein that localizes to the outer membrane of Golgi apparatus. Upon visualising GFP signal in the fluorescence microscope, it was noted that GFP is pericentrosomal in its localization (Fig A). Treatment of such GFP expressing cells with a newly identified drug disrupted the Golgi into small vesicles (Fig B).

Figure A Figure B

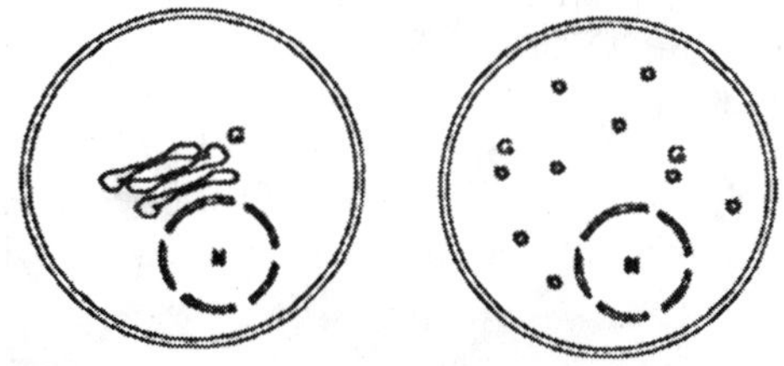

Following is a list of potential targets of the drug:
(*a*) Dynein complex (*b*) Myosin
(*c*) Microtubules (*d*) Dicer

Choose the combination with all correct targets:
A. (*a*), (*b*) and (*d*) only B. (*b*) and (*d*) only
C. (*a*) and (*c*) only D. (*a*) only

72. A single protofilament of microtubule grows at the speed of 2 μm/min. Considering that there is no catastrophe in the microtubule nucleation and the size of the tubulin unit is of the order of *5* nm, how many tubulin units are added to the growing microtubule per minute?

A. 400 B. 1600
C. 3200 D. 5200

Signal Molecule & Cell Signalling

73. Which one of the following is NOT secreted by capillary endothelium?

A. Prostacyclin
B. Guanosine
C. Endothelin
D. Nitric oxide

74. Bacterial chemotaxis response is mediated by histidine-kinase-associated receptors that activate a two-component signalling pathway which enables chemotaxis receptors to control the flagellar motors. When bacteria move towards attractant, they produce smooth swimming by rotating flagella counter-clockwise, whereas when bacteria move away from repellent, they produce increased tumbling by rotating flagella clockwise.

Which of the following characteristics regarding chemotaxis receptor is NOT true?

A. The receptors are dimerictransmembrane proteins that bind specific attractants and repellents on the outside of the plasma membrane.
B. The cytoplasmic tail of the receptor is stably associated with a histidine kinase CheAyia an adapter protein CheW.
C. The receptor and its associated proteins are all clustered at one end of the cell.
D. The binding of an attractant increases the activity of the receptor whereas binding of a repellent decreases the activity.

Cellular Communication

75. Following are a list of extracellular matrix proteins (Column A) along with their functional characteristics (Column B):

Column A	Column B
(*a*) Connexin	(*i*) The chief endothelial cell proteins that are recognized by the white blood cell integrins and member of immunoglobulin (Ig) super family.
(*b*) Plasmo-desmata	(*ii*) Cell surface carbohydrate binding proteins that mediate a variety of transient cell-cell adhesion interactions in the bloodstream.
(*c*) ICAM	(*iii*) Four-pass transmembrane protein which is the major constituent of gap junctions in forming a continuous aqueous channel.
(*d*) Selectin	(*iv*) It is the only class of intercellular junctions in plants that directly connect the cytoplasm of adjacent cells.

Which one of the following is the correct match?

	(*a*)	(*b*)	(*c*)	(*d*)
A.	(*i*)	(*iv*)	(*iii*)	(*ii*)
B.	(*ii*)	(*iii*)	(*iv*)	(*i*)
C.	(*iii*)	(*iv*)	(*i*)	(*ii*)
D.	(*iv*)	(*i*)	(*ii*)	(*iii*)

Cancer

76. Match the following tumor cell origin with their nomenclature.

Tumor cell origin	Nomenclature
(*a*) Muscle cell	(*i*) Carcinoma
(*b*) Germ cell	(*ii*) Sarcoma
(*c*) Epithelial cell	(*iii*) Lukemia
(*d*) White blood cell	(*iv*) Teratocarcinoma

	(*a*)	(*b*)	(*c*)	(*d*)
A.	(*i*)	(*iii*)	(*iv*)	(*ii*)
B.	(*iv*)	(*i*)	(*ii*)	(*iii*)
C.	(*iii*)	(*ii*)	(*iv*)	(*i*)
D.	(*ii*)	(*iv*)	(*i*)	(*iii*)

DBT-JRF, 2018

Organization of Structure and Functions of Prokaryotic and Eukaryotic Cells

77. Which of the following statements about $Na^+ - K^+$ ATPase is correct?

A. It is responsible for generating the resting membrane potential
B. It transports Na^+ and K^+ ions down their respective gradients
C. It is responsible for generating an action potential
D. It indirectly regulates the volume of the cell

78. During subcellular fractionation, a protein is recovered in the membrane fraction. However, upon washing the

membrane fraction with high salt, the protein is obtained in the soluble fraction. The mode of association of the protein with the membrane is via:
A. A transmembrane domain
B. A covalent bond
C. Noncovalent bond
D. A lipid anchors

79. If a fluorescent dye is injected into the lumen of the endoplasmic reticulum (ER), in which of the following compartments can fluorescence signal be observed?
A. ER only
B. Golgi only
C. ER and Golgi
D. ER, Golgi and nuclear envelope

80. Which one of the following organelles disappears during cell division and is regenerated in the daughter cells?
A. Endoplasmic reticulum
B. Golgi
C. Mitochondria
D. Peroxisomes

81. In a migrating cell, the relative position of the _____ and the _______ determines the polarity of the cell.
A. Nucleus, Golgi
B. Golgi, centriole
C. Nucleus, mitochondria
D. Golgi, mitochondria

82. A cargo has to be delivered from the center of the cell to the cell periphery using the microtubule network. To which protein does it need to be associated with?
A. Dynein
B. Kinesin
C. Microtubule associated protein 4
D. Myosin

83. In an organism, the amount of DNA per haploid genome is about 1.6×10^9 nucleotide pairs. Given that the length of DNA helix occupied by one nucleotide pair is 3.4 Å, approximately how long a double helix could be formed from this DNA?

A. 22 cm B. 55 cm
C. 1.1meter D. 2.2-meter

84. In meiosis, an inversion in one member of a pair of homologous chromosomes will most likely lead to which of the following?
A. Non-disjunction of the affected chromosome
B. Chromosome with duplications and deficiencies
C. Increased recombination frequency in the inverted region
D. Mispairing of the affected chromosome with a non-homologous chromosome.

85. Random DNA hexamers containing A, T, G and C are generated by DNA synthesis. The fraction of the hexamers that will have 3 purines followed by 3 pyrimidines is:

A. $9/4^6$ B. $1/2^6$
C. $6/4^6$ D. $^6C3/3^6$

86. Phosphates, carboxylates, sulfonates are esters of phosphoric, carboxylic and sulfonic acids, respectively. Which one of the following statements is NOT true?
A. The nucleophile attack occurs at acyl carbon in carbohydrates.
B. The nucleophile attack occurs at the alkyl carbon in sulfonates.
C. The nucleophile attack occurs at the oxygen or phosphorous in phosphates
D. Sulfonates can be easily hydrolysed.

87. Pyran is a:
A. Six membered oxygen heterocycle
B. Five membered oxygen heterocycle
C. Six membered nitrogen heterocycle
D. Five membered nitrogen heterocycle

88. The core functional unit present in NADH is:
A. Pyridine
B. Dihydro Pyridine
C. Purine
D. Pyramidine.

89. During apoptosis, lipid asymmetry is lost permitting Annexin V to bind to _______ in the outer leaflet of the plasma membrane.
A. phosphatidylserine
B. phosphotidylcholine
C. Phosphotidylinositol
D. Phosphatidylethanolamine

90. The Warburg effect in cancers refers to their ability to:
A. Perform aerobic glycolysis
B. Perform anaerobic glycolysis
C. Promote angiogenesis
D. Promote angiogenesis and metastasis

91. An in vitro translation system containing microsomes was used to an mRNA encoding a secretory protein lacking the stop codon. Which one of the following outcomes can be expected?
A. The protein will not be translated
B. The protein translation will start but stop after some time
C. The protein will be fully synthesized but not incorporated into the microsomal membrane
D. The protein will be synthesized and incorporated into the microsomes but will not be released from the ribosome

GATE (BIOTECHNOLOGY), 2018

92. Which one of the following amino acids is catalysed by activated macrophages to produce reactive nitrogen species?

A. Arginine B. Asparagine
C. Cysteine D. Histidine

GATE (LIFE SCIENCE), 2018

Cell Organelle and Signalling

93. The glycosylation of the proteins occurs in ____.
A. glyoxysomes B. lysosomes
C. Golgi apparatus D. plasma membrane

94. The movement of protons through the F_oF_1 ATPase during mitochondrial respiration is required for ____
A. the increase in pH of mitochondrial matrix.
B. changing the conformation of FoF1-ATPase to expel the ATP.
C. importing Pi from inter membrane space.
D. decreasing the affinity of ADP to FoF1-ATPase

95. Match the proteins / molecules listed in column I with the cellular location mentioned in the column II.

Coulmn I	Column II
(*a*) Galactosyl transferase	(*i*) Vesicles
(*b*) Cytochrome oxidase	(*ii*) Cytosol
(*c*) Clathrin	(*iii*) Golgi complex
(*d*) Tubulin	(*iv*) Mitochondria

	(*a*)	(*b*)	(*c*)	(*d*)
A.	(*ii*)	(*iii*)	(*i*)	(*iv*)
B.	(*iii*)	(*iv*)	(*i*)	(*ii*)
C.	(*iii*)	(*iv*)	(*ii*)	(*i*)
D.	(*iv*)	(*iii*)	(*ii*)	(*i*)

96. Tay-Sachs disease is a human genetic disorder that is associated with defects in which ONE of the following cellular organelles?
A. Endoplasmic reticulum
B. Mitochondria
C. Golgi apparatus
D. Lysosome

97. Which ONE of the following is NOT a characteristic of a cancer cell?
A. Increase in cell motility
B. Loss of contact inhibition
C. Decrease in apoptosis
D. Uncontrolled me

CSIR-NET, JUNE, 2019

Membrane Structure and Function

98. The Na^+/ K^+ ATPase pumps found on the plasma membrane of most animal cells. A mutation in the intrinsic phosphorylation site of the pump is most likely to affect
A. the outward movement of Na^+ only.
B. inward movement of K^+ only
C. both the inward and outward movement of K^+ and Na^+.
D. has no effect on pump activity but affects its stability

99. A patient comes to the hospital complaining of vomiting and diarrhea. The doctor suggested that the patient take glucose and electrolyte solution orally. Which one of following membrane prtoeins is likely to be involved in rehydrating the patient?
A. Cystic fibrosis transmembrane regulator (CFTR)
B. Sodium glucose transporter protein 1(SGLT1)
C. Insulin receptor protein (IRP)
D. Sucrase –isomaltase protein (SIP)

100. Following are the list of some cellular receptors (Column X) and with possible functional characteristics (Column Y):

Column X	Column Y
(*a*) Asialoglycoprotein receptor	(*i*) Intracellular high affinity receptor which upon binding with ligand acts as transcription factor and binds to DNA
(*b*) Transferrin receptor	(*ii*) Extracellular receptor which upon binding with ligand is subjected to endocytosis Receptor-ligand complex accumulates in acidic endosomes/CURL (compartment of uncoupling of receptor and ligand), delivers the cargo, receptor-ligand complex recycles back to cell

		surface and the ligand disassociates.
(*c*) Steroid receptor	(*iii*)	Extracellular receptor which upon binding with ligand is subjected to endocytosis. Receptor-ligand complex accumulates in acidic endosomes / CURL, ligand gets dissociated, transfers to lysosomes and the receptor recycles back to cell surface.

Which one of the following is the correct match?

	(*a*)	(*b*)	(*c*)
A.	(*i*)	(*ii*)	(*iii*)
B.	(*ii*)	(*iii*)	(*i*)
C.	(*iii*)	(*ii*)	(*i*)
D.	(*i*)	(*iii*)	(*ii*)

Structural Organization and Function of Intracellular Organelles

101. The site of the division plane during cytokinesis of animal cells is determined
A. by position of nucleus
B. by the central spindle
C. by the pre-prophase band
D. randomly

102. Table below shows the list of organelles (column A) AND the signals (Column B) that target proteins to the organelle.

A		B
(*a*) Lysosome	(*i*)	Stretch of amino acid sequence rich in Lys and Arg residues
(*b*) Mitochondria	(*ii*)	C-terminal tripeptide
(*c*) Nucleus	(*iii*)	N-terminal amphipathic helix rich in Lys and Arg
(*d*) Peroxisome	(*iv*)	Mannose-6-Phosphate

Choose the option that shows all correct matches

	(*a*)	(*b*)	(*c*)	(*d*)
A.	(*ii*)	(*iii*)	(*iv*)	(*i*)
B.	(*ii*)	(*iv*)	(*iii*)	(*i*)
C.	(*iv*)	(*iii*)	(*i*)	(*ii*)
D.	(*iv*)	(*iii*)	(*ii*)	(*i*)

Organization of Genes and Chromosomes

103. Which one of the following statements is NOT true about nucleosomal organization of core particle?
A. The physical structure of DNA is altered in the middle of the core particle.
B. In the core particle, DNA is organized as flat super helix with 1.65 turns around the histone octamer.
C. While forming 30 nm fibers, generally 6 nucleosomal per turn organize into a two start helix.
D. The N-terminal histone tails in a core particle are strictly ordered and exit from the nucleosomes between turns of the DNA

104. Following observations were made about variations among genomes of eukaryotic organisms:
(*a*) Single nucleotide polymorphisms are the numerically most abundant type of genetic variants
(*b*) Both. interspersed and tandem repeated sequences can show polymorphic variation
(*c*) Mitotic recombination between mispaired repeats causes change in copy number and generates minisatellite diversity in population
(*d*) Smaller variable segments in the genome can be identified by paired end mapping technique

Select the option with all correct statements
A. (*a*), (*b*), (*c*) B. (*a*), (*c*), (*d*)
C. (*b*), (*c*), (*d*) D. (*a*), (*b*), (*d*)

105. Following statements are made about chromatin remodelling in human cells:
(*a*) Local chromatin conformation may play more important role than the local DNA sequence of the promoter.
(*b*) Histones in nucleosome can undergo many different covalent modifications, which in turn, alter the chromatin architecture locally.
(*c*) Chromatin remodelling is a developmentally regulated passive process which does not require ATP.
(*d*) Several histone variants exist, which replace the standard histones in specific types of chromatin.

Select the option that has the combination of all correct answers.
A. (*a*), (*c*), (*d*) B. (*a*), (*b*), (*c*)
C. (*a*), (*b*), (*d*) D. (*b*), (*c*), (*d*)

Cell Division and Cell Cycle

106. In eukaryotic cells, replication initiation from a replication origin occurs only once per cell cycle and S- phase CDKs play a vital role in the regulation of DNA replication. In budding yeast a protein complex known as the origin recognition complex (ORC) is associated with DNA replication origin during G1; however origins fire only once at the beginning of S-phase. DNA replication does not start in G1 because:
(*a*) MCM helicases are inactive in G1.
(*b*) Spindle checkpoint is active in G1.
(*c*) DNA polymerase is not recruited in G1.
(*d*) ORC and initiation factors Cdc6 and Cdt1 do not recruts MCM helicases to the site of replication initiation in G1.

Which of the above statements are correct.

A. (*a*) and (*b*) B. (*a*) and (*c*)
C. (*b*) and (*c*) D. (*b*) and (*d*)

Cytoskeleton

107. Measurements of the rate of actin treadmilling *in vivo* show that it can be several timeshigher than can be achieved with pure actin in vitro. The tread milling in vitro can be enhanced by providing

(*a*) Profilin that binds G-actin on the site opposite the nucleotide binding cleft.
(*b*) co-filin binds specifically to the ADP containing F-actin and destabilizes the actin filament.
(*c*) buffer with ATP and low levels of cations.
(*d*) buffer with ADP and low levels of cations.

Which of the above statements are correct

A. (*a*) and (*d*) B. (*a*) and (*c*)
C. (*c*) and (*d*) D. (*a*) and (*b*)

Signal Molecule & Cell Signalling

108. Which one is the correct sequence of events that takes place during phototransduction when light falls onto the retina?

A. Closure of Na^+ channels - activation of transducing decreased release of glutamate- decrease in intracellular cGMP -structural changes in rhodopsin
B. Decreased release of glutamate-structural changes in rhodopsin-activation of transducin - decrease in intracellular cGMP Closure of Na^+ channels
C. Structural changes in rhodopsin-activation of transducin-decrease in intracellular cGMP -Closure of Na+ channels-Decreased release of glutamate
D. Decrease in intracellular cGMP-activation of transducin - decreased release of glutamate - structural changes in rhodopsin - Closure of Na+ channels

109. During prolonged illumination, rhodopsin is desentitized which leads to the termination of visual response. The associated proteins (Colum A) and their effects (Column B) are given below:

Column-I	Column-II
(*a*) Phosphorylated opsin	(*i*) Phosphorylates opsin
(*b*) Rhodopsin kinase	(*ii*) Binds to phosphorylated opsin
(*c*) Arrestin	(*iii*) Decreases activation of transducing
(*d*) Phosphatse	(*iv*) Reverses the termination process.

Which one of the matched combinations is correct.

	(*a*)	(*b*)	(*c*)	(*d*)
A.	(*iv*)	(*ii*)	(*i*)	(*iii*)
B.	(*ii*)	(*iii*)	(*iv*)	(*i*)
C.	(*iii*)	(*i*)	(*ii*)	(*iv*)
D.	(*ii*)	(*iv*)	(*iii*)	(*i*)

Cellular Communication

110. To prepare individual tissue cells from a primary culture, the cell-cell and cell-matrix interaction must be broken. To achieve this would NOT use:

A. EDTA B. Trypsin
C. Collagenase D. Separase

111. The extracellular matrix contains a number of non-collagen proteins that typically have multiple domains, each with specific binding sites for other matrix molecules and cell surface receptors. These proteins therefore contribute to both organizing the matrix and helping cells attach to it. The most well characterized matrix

A. It is a large glycoprotein found in all vertebrates and important for manycell-matrix interactions.
B. It is composed of three polypeptides that are disulfide bonded into a crosslink structure.
C. In human genome, there is only one fibronectin gene containing about 50 exons, but the transcripts can be spliced in different ways to produce manydifferent fibronectin isoforms.
D. Fibronectin binds to integrin through an RGD motif. Even very short peptide containing RGD sequence can inhibit attachment of cells to fibronectin matrix.

Cancer

112. In an experiment it was observed that a protein was upregulated in cancer tissues (compared to control tissues) that showed correlation with disease progression. Following are a few possibilities, which can explain the above observation.

(*a*) A mutation could be located in the 3'UTR of the corresponding mRNA at a miRNA binding site.
(*b*) A mutation changes the conformation of the protein, resulting in its better stability.
(*c*) A mutation in the corresponding mRNA promotes ribosome read-through of the termination codon resulting in increased synthesis of the protein.
(*d*) A mutation in the corresponding mRNA increased the stability of the RNA due to change in secondary structure.

Which one of the following combinations represents the most likely explanations?

A. (*a*), (*b*) and (*c*) B. (*b*), (*c*) and (*d*)
C. (*c*), (*d*) and (*a*) D. (*a*), (*b*) and (*d*)

113. While testing the effect of several potent anti-cancer compounds on cycling human oral cancer cells, a student observed that a major percentage of cells showed dose-deep cell death after 12 hours of drug treatment. However the remaining cells repopulated the culture dish once the comp ounds were removed and the cells were cultured in complete medium. The student made the following assumptions:

(*a*) Not all cells were equally affected by the compounds as they were not synchronized before treatment.

(*b*) The compound selectively killed cells which were in G_0 phase.

(*c*) The cancer stem cells were impervious to the effects of the compounds and therefore repopulated the culture.

(*d*) The cancer cells differentiated into a mesenchymal phenotype and grew in fresh culture medium containing inhibitors of epithelial-to-mesenchymal transition (EMT).

Which one of the following combination of assumptions would best justify the results?

A. (*b*) and (*c*) B. (*a*) and (*c*)
C. (*b*) and (*d*) D. (*a*) and (*b*)

CSIR-NET, 15 DECEMBER, 2019

Membrane Structure and Function

114. The sodium-independent iodide/chloride transporter is named as

A. megalin B. pendrin
C. transthyretin D. prestin

115. The membrane phospholipid structures in bacteria and archaea differ. Which one of the following correctly states the differences between the two?

A. The bacterial membrane phospholipid consist of D-glycerol linked to hydrophobic chains (tails) with ester bonds whereas those of the archaeal membranes consist of L-glycerol linked to hydrophobic tails through ether bonds.

B. The bacterial membrane phospholipid consist of L-glycerol linked to hydrophobic chains (tails) with ester bonds whereas those of the archaeal membranes consist of D-glycerol linked to hydrophobic tails through ether bonds.

C. The bacterial membrane phospholipid consist of D-glycerol linked to hydrophobic chains (tails) with ether bonds whereas those of the archaeal membranes consist of L-glycerol linked to hydrophobic tails through ester bonds.

D. The bacterial membrane phospholipid consist of L-glycerol linked to hydrophobic chains (tails) with ether bonds whereas those of the archaeal membranes consists of D-glycerol linked to hydrophobic tails through ester bonds.

Structural Organization and Function of Intracellular Organelles

116. Which one of the following synaptic vesicle proteins is involved in tethering of the vesicle to the cytoskeletal system in the nerve terminus?

A. Synaptotagmin B. Synapsin
C. Synaptophysin D. Synaptobrevin

117. Thousands of proteins that are synthesized in the cytoplasm are imported into the nucleus through the nuclear pore complex (NPC) every minute. These proteins contain Nuclear Localization Signal (NLS) that direct their selective transport into the nucleus. This nuclear import requires

(*a*) A small monomeric G-protein Ran.

(*b*) A nuclear transport receptor that interacts with the NLS on a cargo protein.

(*c*) A GTPase activating protein (GAP) bound to the chromatin tethered to the nuclear membrane

(*d*) A Guanine Exchange Factor (GEF) bound to the chromatin inside the nucleus.

Which one of the following options represents all correct statements?

A. (*a*), (*c*), (*d*) B. (*a*), (*b*), (*d*)
C. (*b*), (*c*) only D. (*a*), (*c*) only

Organization of Genes and Chromosomes

118. The nucleosome is the fundamental subunit of chromatin in eukaryotes. Following statements are made about nucleosome:

(*a*) Generally, a typical nucleosome contains ~200bp of DNA and two copies of each histone (H2A, H2B, H3 and H4)

(*b*) 146 bp length of DNA per nucleosome core particle is strictly maintained across the organisms

(*c*) The histone octamers are not conserved during/after replication, however, $H3_2$-$H4_2$ tetramers are.

(*d*) Variants have been identified for all core histones except histone H3

(*e*) While wrapping around the core histones, the structure of DNA is altered at the middle of the nucleosome core particle and exhibits increased number of base pairs per turn

Which one of the following combination of statements is most appropriate?

A. (*a*), (*c*) and (*e*)
B. (*a*), (*b*) and (*d*)
C. (*b*), (*d*) and (*e*)
D. (*a*), (*c*) and (*d*)

Cell Division and Cell Cycle

119. During cell cycle, entry in the S-phase is tightly regulated. This is possible because:

(*a*) APC/C promotes ubiquitination of S-phase cyclins and mitotic cyclins, marking them for proteolyses at the mitotic exit.

(*b*) Cyclin B1 helps in the activation of S-phase CDKs only in late G1.

(*c*) As mitotic CDK activity declines in late mitosis, cdc14 phosphatase activates APC/C by dephosphorylating Cdh1, thus promoting formation of APC/C^{cdh1}.

(*d*) Securin keeps S-phase cyclins in inactive state till late G1.

Which one of the options represents all correct statements?

A. (*a*) and (*b*) B. (*a*) and (*c*)
C. (*b*) and (*c*) D. (*b*) and (*d*)

Cytoskeleton

120. In a neuron, proteins and membranes are primarily synthesized in the cell body. These materials must be transported down the axon to the synaptic region using microtubules in an anterograde fashion. Such axonal transport is directed by

A. Dynein
B. Kinesin I
C. Dynein and Kinesin I
D. Myosin

121. Cells are physically linked to one another and to extracellular matrix through their cytoskeleton and this impart strength and rigidity of tissues and organs. Most of the animal cells have three types of cytoskeletal filaments, which are listed in Column A. The possible functions are listed in Column B.

Column A	Column B
A. Intermediate filaments	(*i*) Determine the shape of cell surface and are necessary for cell locomotion
B. Microtubules	(*ii*) Maintain the position of membrane-enclosed organelles and provide intracellular transport
C. Actin filaments	(*iii*) Provide mechanical strength of a cell

Which one is the correct match?

	(*a*)	(*b*)	(*c*)
A.	(*i*)	(*ii*)	(*iii*)
B.	(*ii*)	(*i*)	(*iii*)
C.	(*i*)	(*ii*)	(*i*)
D.	(*iii*)	(*i*)	(*ii*)

Signal Molecule & Cell Signaling

122. Which one of the following is not a G-protein coupled receptor?

A. Epinephrine receptor
B. Transferrin receptor
C. Glucagon receptor
D. Thyroid stimulating hormone receptor

123. Which one of the following lipid-soluble hormones can interact with a cell surface receptor?

A. Progesterone B. Estradiol
C. Thyroxine D. Prostaglandin

124. In the table below Column A lists ligands and Column B lists classes of receptors

Column A	Column B
(*a*) Serotonin	(*i*) Binding activates a G-protein which activates or inhibits an enzyme that generates a specific second messenger and opens ion channel
(*b*) Interferons	(*ii*) Binding causes receptor monomers to dimerize. Dimeric receptor then interacts with and activates one or more cytosolic-tyrosine protein kinases
(*c*) Glycine	(*iii*) Binding changes the conformation of the receptor so that specifications flow through it
(*d*) Insulin	(*iv*) Binding leads to activation of intrinsic tyrosine kinase activity

Which one is the correct match?

	(*a*)	(*b*)	(*c*)	(*d*)
A.	(*i*)	(*ii*)	(*iii*)	(*iv*)
B.	(*i*)	(*iii*)	(*iv*)	(*i*)
C.	(*iii*)	(*iv*)	(*i*)	(*ii*)
D.	(*iv*)	(*i*)	(*ii*)	(*iii*)

125. Acetylcholine is a potent neurotransmitter, which is released from the neurons. After release theydiffuse across the synaptic cleft and combine with nicotinic acetylcholine receptor molecules in the membrane of the postsynaptic cell. The interaction of acetylcholine with the nicotinic acetylcholine receptor produces large transient increase in the permeability of the membrane to specialized ions resulting in signal transduction for nerve impulse. Acetylcholine receptor is a

A. ligand-gated cation channel
B. ligand-gated anion channel
C. voltage-gated cation channel
D. voltage-gated anion channel

126. Hormone act by producing/activating a variety of effectors intracellularly. Below are given a variety of effectors in column 'X' and hormones in column 'Y

Column X	Column Y
(*a*) Inositol triphosphate (IP3)	(*i*) Leptin
(*b*) cGMP	(*ii*) IGF-1
(*c*) cAMP	(*iii*) Oxytocin
(*d*) Receptor Kinase	(*iv*) Somatostatin
(*e*) Associated Kinase	(*v*) ANF

Which one of the following combinations of effector and the specific hormone is correct?

A. (*a*)-(*i*) and (*b*)-(*ii*) B. (*b*)-(*iv*) and (*a*)-(*iii*)
C. (*c*)-(*iv*) and (*d*)-(*ii*) D. (*e*)-(*ii*) and (*c*)-(*i*)

Cancer

127. In what respect does the genome of slow-acting retroviruses differ from those of transducing viruses?
A. They cannot activate nearby cellular proto-oncogenes after integration into the genome of the host cell
B. They lack an oncogene
C. They exclude mouse mammary tumor viruses
D. They have acquired mutations during acquisition of an oncogene

CSIR-NET, 27 DECEMBER, 2019

Organization of Genes and Chromosomes

128. Following statements were made while describing the characteristics of transposable elements:
(*a*) Most transposons use a common mechanism in which DNA is nicked to generate blunt ends for its subsequent incorporation.
(*b*) Homologous recombination between the repeats of a transposon may result in precise or imprecise excision.
(*c*) P elements are transposons which show differential splicing pattern in germline and somatic cells.
(*d*) In a transposon, cis-acting mutants that may prevent its transposition are generally located near the ends.
(*e*) An insertion sequence (IS) is a transposon, which is always flanked by long (more than 30 bases) direct repeats known as Long Terminal Repeats (LTR).

Which one of the following combinations of statements is correct?

A. (*a*), (*c*), (*e*) B. (*b*), (*c*), (*d*)
C. (*c*), (*d*), (*e*) D. (*a*), (*b*), (*d*)

Cell Division and Cell Cycle

129. Which one of the following statements about M-phase cyclin is correct?
A. Cyclin synthesis and destruction is essential for cell cycle progression
B. Synthesis of new cyclin, but not destruction is essential for cell cycle progression
C. Cyclin and the corresponding kinase(s), both exhibit cyclic expression pattern during cell cycle
D. Cyclic pattern of cyclin protein is regulated by the controlled translation of stored cyclin transcripts, and not dependent on fresh transcription.

130. How many kinetochores are present in a human cell at mitosis?
A. 46 B. 23
C. 92 D. 84

131. A reciprocal translocation heterozygote at the end of meiosis I generate
A. An acentric and a dicentric chromosome
B. Viable gametes with deletions and duplications
C. Viable gametes with only parental type chromosomes
D. All non-viable gametes

132. During mitosis in a eukaryotic cell incorrect kinetochore attachments are corrected by a system of trials and errors. The tension-based mechanism acting at the kinetochore is linked with ensuring that sister chromatid pairs are properly oriented at the spindle. Which one of the following kinases is tethered to the inner kinetochore and phosphorylates the microtubule attachment site, including the Ndc 80 complex to regulate sister chromatids attachments in a bi-orientation manner?
A. Aurora A kinase
B. Aurora B kinase
C. Aurora C kinase
D. C-Jun N-terminal kinase

Cytoskeleton

133. Bacterial actin homologs contribute to the cell shape by serving as a scaffold to direct the synthesis of the peptidoglycan cell wall. Which of the following is/are actin homolog/sin bacteria?
A. MreB and Mbl B. FtsZ
C. DnaK D. DnaJ

134. Given below are cytoskeleton filaments (Column X) and their component/associated proteins (Column Y)

Column X	Column Y
(*a*) Actin	(*i*) Formin
(*b*) Microtubule	(*ii*) Arp 2/3 complex
(*c*) Intemediate filaments	(*iii*) EB 1
	(*iv*) Lamin A
	(*v*) Xmap 215

Choose the option that matches cytoskeleton filament (Column X) with the most appropriate protein (Column Y)

	(a)	(b)	(c)
A.	(i), (ii)	(iii), (v)	(iv)
B.	(iii), (v)	(ii), (i)	(iv)
C.	(iv), (v)	(i), (ii)	(iii)
D.	(ii), (v)	(i), (iv)	(v)

Signal Molecule & Cell Signaling

135. Heat shock protein binding region is located in which one of the following domains of glucocorticoid receptor protein?

A. DNA-binding B. Ligand-binding
C. N-terminal D. Hinge region

Cellular Communication

136. Physical attachment of cells in a tissue or organ is mediated by different types of junctions, one of which is anchoring junctions. This includes both cell-cell adhesions and cell-extracellular matrix adhesions. The central role of anchoring junctions is played by transmembrane adhesion proteins of which the major ones are cadherin and integrin.

Which one of the following statements regarding cadherin and integrin is NOT correct?

A. Generally, cadherin mediates attachment of cell to cell whereas integrin mediates attachment of cells to extracellular matrix
B. Cadherin molecules of a specific subtype on one cell bind to cadherin molecules of the same or closely related subtype on adjacent cells
C. Both cadherin and integrin are composed of two non-covalently attached glycoprotein subunits which span the cell membrane
D. Integrin molecules generally act as extracellular matrix receptor

DBT-JRF, 2019

Organization of Structure and Functions of Prokaryotic and Eukaryotic Cells

137. Which one of the following statements is INCORRECT about facilitated diffusion?

A. Its rate is higher than simple diffusion.
B. The partition coefficient of the solute is irrelevant for it.
C. It can be saturated at high concentration of the solute.
D. It works against the concentration gradient.

138. The type of transport that does NOT reach Vmax is:

A. Simple diffusion across lipid bilayer
B. Facilitated diffusion via uniporters
C. Movement of ions through ion channels
D. Primary active transport via ATP powered pumps

139. The ion transport that will be the most affected following mutation in Cystic fibrosis transmembrane conductance regulator (CFTR) gene is:

A. Sodium B. Potassium
C. Chloride D. Calcium

140. Which one of the following intermediate filament proteins is present in the nucleus?

A. Vinculin B. Lamin
C. Nestin D. Laminin

141. Which one of the following changes occurs in a directionally migrating eukaryotic cell?

A. The ER is fragmented.
B. The mitochondrial membrane potential drops.
C. The nucleus moves towards the back and behind the Golgi.
D. The Golgi is fragmented.

142. Following statements are about chromatin organization in eukaryotes:

(a) The length of DNA per nucleosome varies for individual tissue or species.
(b) Typical nucleosomal packaging pattern is strictly maintained across the genome of an organism.
(c) While wrapping around the histone core particle, uniform structure of DNA is maintained.
(d) Histone tail mediated internucleosomal contact is one of the essential factors to achieve the 30 nm fibre structure.

Select the correct combination of statements.

A. (a) and (c) B. (b) and (c)
C. (a) and (d) D. (c) and (d)

143. If a cell carries 21 pairs of chromosomes just after completion of mitotic telophase, how many chromatids will be there in metaphase?

A. 21 B. 42
C. 84 D. 168

144. All the DNA strands of a cell containing 4 chromosomes are labelled. After one division how many chromosomes in the daughter cell will have labelled DNA?

A. 1 B. 2
C. 4 D. 8

145. Which one of the following results is expected when a mammalian cell in S phase is fused with another in G2?

A. G2 phase nucleus will wait for the S phase nucleus to complete the replication and both the nuclei simultaneously enter into M phase.
B. S phase nucleus would immediately enter into G2 phase without completing the replication phase.

C. Both the nuclei would follow their corresponding cell cycle without influencing each other.
D. Due to influence of S phase promoting factor, G2 phase nucleus will enter into S phase.

146. If nondisjunction of a chromosome occurs in meiosis II, what will be the product at the completion of meiosis?
A. All the gametes will be diploid
B. Two gametes will be $n + 1$, and two will be $n - 1$
C. One gamete will be $n + 1$, one will be $n - 1$, and two will be n
D. Two of the four gametes will be haploid, and two will be diploid

147. Hayflick limit of mammalian cells refers to which one of the following?
A. Cells in primary cell culture undergo senescence after 50-60 passages.
B. Primary cells cultured in vitro do not cross the limit of cell transformation.
C. Cell lines when cultured in vitro have a limit for their surface to volume ratio.
D. Malignant cell lines undergo senescence after 50-60 passages.

148. If the intracellular pH of a cell becomes basic, which one of the following will help reduce the pH?
A. Export of Cl^- and import of HCO_3^-
B. Import of Cl^- and export of HCO_3^-
C. Import of Na^+ and HCO_3^- and export of Cl^-
D. Export of Na^+ and Cl

149. Which one of the following statements about signal recognition particles (SRPs) is INCORRECT?
A. contains RNA and protein.
B. is an integral membrane protein.
C. docks with a receptor on the surface of the ER membrane.
D. binds to localization signal at the N-terminus of the emerging polypeptide chain.

150. Metaplasia represents:
A. Uncontrolled proliferation of cells initiated at the metaphase of the cell cycle
B. Transformation of one differentiated cell type to another
C. Cell proliferation during metamorphosis
D. A measure of metabolic activity in hyperplastic cells

GATE (BIOTECHNOLOGY), 2019

151. DNA synthesis in eukaryotes occurs during which phase of the mitotic cell cycle?
A. M B. Gl
C. S D. G0

152. Match the organelles in Group I with their functions in Group II.

Group I	Group II
P. Lysosome	1. Digestion of foreign substances
Q. Smooth ER	2. Protein targeting
R. Golgi apparatus	3. Lipid synthesis
S. Nucleolus	4. Protein synthesis
	5. rRNA synthesis

A. P-1, Q-3, R-2, S-5
B. P-1, Q-4, R-5, S-3
C. P-2, Q-5, R-3, S-4
D. P-1, Q-3, R-4, S-5

GATE (LIFE SCIENCE), 2019

Cell Organelle and Signalling

153. Nitric oxide synthase is responsible for generation of Nitric oxide, an important signaling molecule. The substrate for this enzyme is:
A. Glycine B. Lysine
C. Histidine D. Arginine

154. Catalase is found exclusively in :
A. Lysosomes B. Golgi apparatus
C. Peroxisomes D. Mitochondria

155. In eukaryotic chromatin organization, which one of the histones seals off the nucleosome at the location at which linker DNA enters and leaves the nucleosome?
A. H1 B. H2A-H2B
C. H3 D. H4

Cell Biology

156. Match the following terms in Column I with the appropriate explanation in Column II

Column I	Column II
(*a*) Spliceosome	(*i*) Cell scavengers
(*b*) Peroxisome	(*ii*) Metabolism of long chain fatty acids
(*c*) Lysosome	(*iii*) Microtubules
(*d*) Centrosome	(*iv*) Post transcriptional modifications

	(*a*)	(*b*)	(*c*)	(*d*)
A.	(*iii*)	(*i*)	(*iv*)	(*ii*)
B.	(*iv*)	(*ii*)	(*i*)	(*iii*)
C.	(*iii*)	(*ii*)	(*i*)	(*iv*)
D.	(*iv*)	(*iii*)	(*i*)	(*ii*)

CSIR-NET, NOVEMBER (MORNING), 2020

Membrane Structure and Function

157. Which one of the following is NOT involved in the formation of lipid rafts?
A. Sphingomyelin B. Cholesterol
C. Glycolipid D. Phosphatidylserine

Structural Organization and Function of Intracellular Organelles

158. Following statements are made about KDEL receptor.
A. KDEL receptor is found in COPI vesicles.
B. KDEL receptor affinity for KDEL sequence is high at higher pH
C. KDEL receptor is synthesized on the ER
D. KDEL receptor is present in the ER and Golgi

Identify the option that contains all correct statements about the KDEL receptor.
A. (*a*) and (*b*) only B. (*a*), (*b*), (*c*)
C. (*a*), (*c*), (*d*) D. (*c*) and (*d*) only

159. Which one of the following is NOT an extracellular matrix protein?
A. Keratin B. Laminin
C. Collagen D. Vitronectin

Organization of Genes and Chromosomes

160. Which one of the following statements about human LINEs (long interspersed nuclear elements) is FALSE?
A. LINEs are located primarily in euchromatic regions.
B. LINEs cannot encode all the product needed for their retrotransposition, and are dependent on SINEs for some somponents
C. Of the three human LINE families, LINE-1 is the only family to have actively transposing members.
D. Active LINE-1 elements possess an internal promoter located within the 5' untranslated region

161. Which of the following statements about R- banding chromosomes is FALSE?
A. The heat treatment preferentially denature the GC rich DNAto produce R-banding pattern.
B. This is essentially the reserve of the G-banding pattern.
C. The R bands are Q(quinacrine) negative
D. The DNA of R bands generally replicate early during the S-phase of cell cycle

162. Which one of the following genomes is most appropriate to determine hybrids in plants and animals?
A. Nuclear
B. Mitochondrial
C. Chloroplast
D. Mitochondria and chloroplast

163. The following statements are made wireference to characteristics of glycosaminoglycans and proteoglycans, which are major constituents of extracellular matrix. Which one of them is INCORRECT?
A. Glycosaminoglycans are very long polysaccharide chains composed of repeating disaccharide units of an amino sugar and a uronic acid.
B. Except for hyaluronic acid, all glycosaminoglycans are covalently attached to protein as proteoglycan.
C. Glycoproteins contain less carbohydrate usually in the form of relatively short, branched oligosaccharide chains whereas proteoglycans contain more carbohydrate in the form of long unbranched glycosaminoglycan chains.
D. Like O-linked and N-linked glycoproteins, in proteoglycan also glycosaminoglycans are linked to serine or threonine and asparagine residues.

Cell Division and Cell Cycle

164. Following statements were made about the characteristics of cyclin proteins:
(*a*) Synthesis of M-cyclin is dependent on the cyclin mRNA that is newly transcribed after every cycle.
(*b*) Destruction of M-cyclin toward the end of mitosis is driven by ubiquitin independent proteolytic system.
(*c*) G1 cyclins can be activated by mitogenic factors.
(*d*) Retinoblastoma (Rb) is a key target of the activated cyclin D-Cdk 4/6 complex.
(*e*) While cyclin A1 expression is ubiquitous, cyclin A2 expression is restricted to the germ cell lineages.

Which one of the following options contains a combination of all correct statements?
A. (*a*), (*b*), (*d*) B. (*b*), (*c*), (*e*)
C. (*b*), (*d*), (*e*) D. (*a*), (*c*), (*d*)

Cytoskeleton

165. Myosin molecules that assemble into bipolar filaments in the muscle are
A. Myosin I B. Myosin II
C. Myosin III D. Myosin IV

Signal Molecule & Cell Signalling

166. Which one of the following signaling molecules is NOT a protein or a peptide?
A. Transforming growth factor a (TGF-a)
B. Erythropoietin
C. Granulocyte colony stimulating factor
D. Epinephrine

167. Receptor tyrosine kinases (RTKS) form a large and important class of cell surface receptors whose ligands are soluble or membrane bound protein or peptide hormones. Which of the following statement is INCORRECT?
A. All RTKs are transmembrane proteins with extracellular ligand-binding site and a cytosolic domain.
B. Binding of ligand causes most RTKs to dimerize
C. Cytosolic tyrosine kinase phosphorylates a distinct set of tyrosine residues in the cytosolic domain of the dimer.
D. Adapter proteins and enzymes involved in signalling pathways bind to different phosphotyrosine residues via a conserved polypeptide domain called SH2 domain.

CSIR-NET, NOVEMBER (AFTERNOON), 2020

Membrane Structure and Function

168. The following statements are made with reference to membrane fusion reactions in vesicle transport catalyzed by transmembrane SNARE proteins.
(*a*) The SNARE transmembrane proteins exist as complementary sets, with *v*-SNARES on vesicle membranes and *t*-SNARES on target membranes
(*b*) A *v*-SNARE is usually composed of 3 proteins and t-SNARE is a single polypeptide chain
(*c*) The *v*-SNARE and *t*-SNARE proteins of a pair interact via helical domains possessed by the two proteins, resulting in formation of a stable two-helix bundle
(*d*) Membrane fusion is catalysed by the energy that is freed when the interacting helices wrap around each other to pull the membrane faces together, concurrently squeezing out water molecules from the interface.
Which one of the following combinations represents all correct statements?
A. (*a*) and (*b*) B. (*b*) and (*c*)
C. (*c*) and (*d*) D. (*a*) and (*d*)

169. The following statements are being made about the archaeal cell wall/membrane:
(*a*) Archaeal cell walls could stain Gram +ve or Gram −ve depending on the genus
(*b*) Archaea are characterized by Gram +ve staining of the cell wall
(*c*) Archaeal cell walls are susceptible to degradation by lysozyme
(*d*) Archaeal cell membranes possess branch chain hydrocarbons linked to glycerol by ether links
Which of the following combinations of statements represents all correct statements?
A. (*a*) and (*d*) B. (*b*) and (*c*)
C. (*c*) and (*d*) D. (*b*) and (*d*)

Structural Organization and Function of Intracellular Organelles

170. The translocation into which one of the organelles listed below DOES NOT depend on an amino acid sequence as a signal for import?
A. Nucleus
B. Endoplasmic reticulum
C. Lysosome
D. Peroxisome

Organization of Genes and Chromosomes

171. Which one of the following plant pathogens has largest genome size?
A. Phytophthora infestans
B. Ustilago maydis
C. Botrytis cinerea
D. Fusarium graminearum

172. A gene was located on 10p11. This means the gene was located on the
A. short arm of chromosome 10 at G-sub band 1 of band 1
B. short arm of chromosome 10 at G-band 11
C. short arm of chromosome 10 much away from the centromere
D. long arm of chromosome 10 at G-sub band 1 of band

173. Genome of an organism was analysed by Cot curve analysis. Highly repeated sequences represented 30% of the total genome fraction. The Cot value of the highly repeated sequence was found to be 0.001 moles nucleotide liter^{-1}. What would be the actual Cot value (in moles nucleotide liter^{-1}) of the highly repeated sequence?
A. 0.003 B. 0.001
C. 0.0003 D. 0.007

174. The mammalian protein HP1 plays a major role in heterochromatinization and silencing. The following mutations are proposed to negatively impact HP1 function.
(*a*) Mutation inactivating the deacetylase that targets H3K14AC
(*b*) Mutation inactivating HP1 bromodomain
(*c*) Mutation inactivating HP1 chromodomain.
(*d*) Mutation inactivating the KMT1A methyltransferase whose target site is H3K9

Which one of the following combinations represents all correct statements?
A. (*a*), (*c*) and (*d*)
B. (*a*), (*b*) and (*d*)
C. (*b*) and (*d*) only
D. (*c*) and (*d*) only

Cell Division and Cell Cycle

175. The table below lists cell cycle regulatory proteins and their known functions

Cell Cycle Regulatory Proteins	Function
(*a*) Cdk – activating kinase (CAK)	(*i*) Suspresses G1/S-Cdk and S-Cdk activation in G1; helps cells withdraw from cell cycle when they terminally differentiate; phosphorylation by Cdk2 triggers its ubiquitylation by SCF.
(*b*) Wee 1 kinase	(*ii*) Suspresses G1/S-Cdk and S-Cdk activities following DNA damage
(*c*) P27 (mammals)	(*iii*) Phosphorylates inhibitory sites in Cdks: primarily involved in suppressing Cdk1 activity before mitosis
(*d*) P21 (mammals)	(*iv*) Phosphorylates an activating site in Cdks

Which one of the following options represents the correct match between cell cycle regulatory proteins with their known functions?

	(*a*)	(*b*)	(*c*)	(*d*)
A.	(*iv*)	(*iii*)	(*i*)	(*ii*)
B.	(*iii*)	(*ii*)	(*iv*)	(*i*)
C.	(*ii*)	(*iv*)	(*i*)	(*iii*)
D.	(*i*)	(*ii*)	(*iii*)	(*iv*)

Signal Molecule & Cell Signalling

176. Receptor for which one of the following proteins spans the plasma membrane of target cells but DOES NOT contain intrinsic protein kinase activity?
A. Epidermal growth factor
B. Insulin
C. Insulin like growth factor
D. Growth hormone

177. cGMP is produced from GTP by the enzyme guanylate cyclase which exists in soluble and membrane-bound forms. Following statements are made related to signaling molecules that are associated with cGMP signaling cascade.
(*a*) Atrial natriuretic factor causes natriuresis and diuresis by interacting with membrane-bound form of guanylate cyclase.
(*b*) Nitroglycerin causes smooth muscle relaxation and vasodilation by interacting with soluble form of guanylate cyclase.
(*c*) Nitroprusside causes smooth muscle relaxation and vasodilation by interacting with membrane-bound form of guanylate cyclase.
(*d*) Atrial natriuretic factor causes natriuresis and diuresis by interacting with soluble form of guanylate cyclase.

Which one of the following combinations is correct?
A. (*a*) and (*b*) B. (*b*) and (*c*)
C. (*c*) and (*d*) D. (*a*) and (*d*)

DBT-JRF, 2020

Organization of Structure and Functions of Prokaryotic and Eukaryotic Cells

178. Synthesis of majority of lipids in a cellular system occurs in the
A. mitochondria
B. lysosomes
C. nucleus
D. endoplasmic reticulum

179. Which of the following is NOT true?
A. prokaryotes are unicellular organisms
B. eukaryotes can be either multicellular or unicellular organisms
C. prokaryotic cells lack nucleus whereas eukaryotic cells have a nucleus
D. eukaryotic cells are evolutionarily more ancient than prokaryotic cells

180. The following cellular process involves formation of double membrane vesicles that engulf and degrade the cellular organelles and macromolecules
A. Necrosis B. Autophagy
C. Macro pinocytosis D. Apoptosis

181. Synthesis of which of the following liquids is completed in the Golgi bodies
A. phosphatidylserine
B. phosphatidylcholine
C. sphingolipids
D. cholesterol

182. A supramolecular complex that serves to degrade damaged or unneeded proteins in the cell is called as

A. lysosome B. flagella
C. proteasome D. ribosome

183. Primary cilia biogenesis typically starts at the

A. S phase of the cell cycle
B. S and G2 phase of the cell cycle
C. G2 phase of the cell cycle
D. G1/G0 phase of the cell cycle

184. What is Endoreduplication?

A. replication of DNA in the nuclei and endocytosis of one copy to another organelle
B. mobilization of DNA into ER and replication of DNA in the ER
C. splitting up of endoplasmic reticulum (ER) to form rough and smooth ERS
D. recurrent DNA replication without subsequent mitosis and cytokinesis

185. Which of the following process does NOT contribute to conversion of a protooncogene to oncogene?

A. deactivating mutation in tumour suppressor
B. activating mutation in proto-oncogene
C. increased expression of protooncogene
D. deactivating mutation in protooncogene

186. Which of the following organelle is NOT a site for Reactive Oxygen Species (ROS) generation?

A. nucleus
B. mitochondria
C. peroxisomes
D. endoplasmic reticulum

187. The Budapest Treaty related to the international patent process concern with

A. non-living materials
B. higher plants
C. human subjects
D. microorganisms

GATE (BIOTECHNOLOGY), 2020

188. Which of the following are energy transducing membrane?

[P] Plasma membrane of bacteria
[Q] Inner membrane of chloroplast
[R] Inner membrane of chloroplast

A. P and Q only B. P and R only
C. Q and R only D. P, Q and R

189. Which of the following statements are CORRECT about eukaryotic cell cycle?

[P] CDKs can phosphorylate proteins in the absence of cyclins.
[Q] CDKs can be inactivated by phosphorylation
[R] Degradation of cyclins is required for cell cycle progression.
[S] CDKs are not involved in chromosome condensation.

A. P and R only B. P and S only
C. P, Q and R only D. Q and R only

190. Match sub-cellular organelles listed in Group I with their features listed in Group II:

Group I	Group II
P. Mitochondrion	1. Single-membrane enclosed
Q. Chloroplast	2. Double-membrane enclosed
R. Nucleus	3. Maternal inheritance
S. Endoplasmic reticulum	4. Endosymbiotic origin

A. P-1, Q-4, R-2, S-3
B. P-2, Q-3, R-4, S-1
C. P-3, Q-4, R-2, S-1
D. P-3, Q-1, R-4, S-2

191. Ras Protein

A. trimeric GTPase involved in relaying signal from cell surface to nucleus.
B. monomeric GTPase involved in relaying signal from cell surface to nucleus.
C. trimeric GTPase involved in regulation of cytoskeleton.
D. monomeric GTPase involved in regulation of cytoskeleton.

192. Which of the following statements are correct?

P. Viruses can play a role in causing human cancer
Q. A tumour suppressor gene can be turned off without any change in its DNA sequence.
R. Alteration in miRNA expression levels contributes to the development of cancer.

A. P and Q only B. Q and R only
C. P and R only D. P, Q and R

193. Determine the correctness or otherwise of the following Assertion [a] and the Reason [r] regarding mammalian cells.

Assertion [a]: Cells use Ca^{2+} and not Na^{+}, for cell -to- signalling

Reason [r]: In the cytosol, concentration of Na^{+} is lower than that of Ca^{2+}.

A. Both [a] and [r] are true and [r] is the correct reason for [a].
B. Both [a] and [r] are true and [r] is the not correct reason for [a].
C. Both [a] and [r] are true.
D. [a] is true but [r] is false.

GATE (LIFE SCIENCE), 2020

Cell Organelle and Signalling

194. Which one of the following hormones initiates a signalling cascade by Directly binding to an intra-cellular receptor?

A. Insulin B. Gonadotropin
C. Progesterone D. Epinephrine

195. Match the following subcellular organelles in Column I with associated functions in Column II

Column I	Column II
(*a*) Nucleolus	(*i*) Glycoprotein biosynthesis
(*b*) Peroxisome	(*ii*) Oxidation of fatty acid and amino acid
(*c*) Endoplasmic reticulum	(*iii*) Protein trafficking
(*d*) Golgi bodies	(*iv*) Ribosome biogenesis

	(*a*)	(*b*)	(*c*)	(*d*)
A.	(*iii*)	(*ii*)	(*i*)	(*iv*)
B.	(*i*)	(*ii*)	(*iii*)	(*iv*)
C.	(*iv*)	(*ii*)	(*i*)	(*iii*)
D.	(*ii*)	(*iii*)	(*i*)	(*iv*)

196. Visual signal transduction cascade is activated by rhodopsin and involves degradation rather than synthesis of which ONE of the following second messenger molecules?

A. cAMP B. IP3
C. cGMP D. DAG

CSIR-NET, JUNE (MORNING), 2021

Membrane Structure and Function

197. In eukaryotic cells, covalently attached lipids help to anchor some water soluble proteins to the plasma membrane. One group of cytosolic proteins are anchored to the cytosolic face of membrane by a fatty acid group (e.g. myristate or palmitate). These groups are generally covalently attached to which amino acids present at the N- terminus of the polypeptide chain?

A. Glycine B. Tyrosine
C. Serine D. Lysine

198. The movement of proteins bigger than 50 kDa across the nuclear envelope requires:

A. sec 61 B. Tom 20
C. Lmportin-β D. tim 44

199. Given below are a few statements about nuclear transport.

(*a*) RanGTP levels are higher in the nucleus than the cytoplasm.
(*b*) Nuclear import receptors can shuttle between the nucleus and cytoplasm.
(*c*) NIF2 transports RanGDP into the cytosol.
(*d*) Export of mRNA is not directly dependent on Ran.
(*e*) tRNA and miRNA export is mediated by exportins.

Which one of the following is correct combination?

A. (*a*), (*b*), (*c*), (*d*) only B. (*b*), (*c*), (*d*) only
C. (*a*), (*b*), (*d*), (*e*) only D. (*a*), (*c*), (*e*) only

Structural Organization and Function of Intracellular Organelles

200. To delineate the steps in endoplasmic reticulum (ER) transport, a PhD student homogenized pancreatic acinar cells to isolate microsomes, which retain most of the biochemical properties of the ER. For this experiment, the student has planned a number of controls as mentioned below.

(*a*) Treat one set of microsomes first with detergent and then with protease.
(*b*) Treat one set of microsomes with protease only
(*c*) Treat one set of microsomes with micrococcal nuclease
(*d*) Treat one set of microsomes with detergent only

Select the options that represents the best combination of control?

A. (*a*), (*b*) and (*d*) only B. (*b*), (*c*) and (*d*) only
C. (*a*) and (*c*) only D. (*b*) and (*d*) only

Organization of Genes and Chromosomes

201. Which one of the following combinations represents the major protein or protein complex involved in chromatin condensation yeast and human, respectively?

A. HP1 and SIR complex
B. SIR complex and HP1
C. HP1 and Su(var)
D. SIR complex and Su(var)

202. A group of transposable elements described as retroelements encompass

A. P element in Drosophila; LINES but not SINES in human.
B. Copia element in Drosophila; SINES but not LINES in human
C. Copia element in Drosophila; LINES as well as in human
D. P element in Drosophila; LINES as well as SHINES in human

Cell Division and Cell Cycle

203. Progression across G1/5 boundary followed by entry into 5- phase is promoted by the activation of which one of the following protein complex?

A. Cdk4/ cyclin D B. Cdk2/ cyclin E
C. Cdk4, 6 /cvclin D. Cdk4, 6/cycin D, E

204. During cytokinesis, a small GTPase, RhoA, localizes to the equatorial membrane above the spindle midzone. The localization/activity of RhoA is potentially modulated by:

(*a*) RhoGEF Ect2
(*b*) Aurora B kinase
(*c*) PLK 1 kinase
(*d*) MKLP1 kinase
(*e*) ATM and ATR

Which one of the following combination contains all correct statements?

A. (*a*), (*b*) and (*d*) B. (*a*), (*b*), (*c*) and (*d*)
C. (*b*), (*c*), (*d*) and (*e*) D. (*a*), (*c*) and (*d*)

205. Following statements were made about chromosome cohesion during mitosis and meiosis.

(*a*) Though cohesin is important for pairwise alignment of the chromosomes on the mitotic spindle, it is not important for the generation of tension across the centromere.
(*b*) Cohesin binds to the chromosome even before the initiation of S-phse.
(*c*) In fission yeast, centromere specific localization of Moa1 and Rec8 regulates the orientation of kinetochores at meiosis 1
(*d*) Cohesin exhibits uniform distribution/localization pattern across the chromosomal length.
(*e*) Polo/Cdc5 is a positive regulator of separase, an endopeptidase that facilitate opening of the cohesin ring.

Which of the following combinations contains all correct statements?

A. (*a*), (*b*) and (*d*) only
B. (*a*), (*c*) and (*e*) only
C. (*b*), (*c*) and (*d*) only
D. (*b*), (*c*) and (*e*) only

Cytoskeleton

206. Cellular actin levals cn be as high as 100 – 400 uM. Of this unpolorised actin concentration can be as much as 50 – 200uM. However the critical for actin for actin polorization in-vitro is about 0.2 uM. Some of the following protein inhibit polymrazation of actin in cell?

(*a*) Thyomysin – B4
(*b*) Capping protein CapZ
(*c*) Tropomodulin
(*d*) XMAP215

Which one of the following is inhibitor?

A. (*a*), (*b*) and (*c*) only
B. (*b*), (*c*) and (*d*) only
C. (*c*), (*d*) and (*a*) only
D. (*d*), (*a*) and (*b*) only

Signal molecule & Cell Signalling

207. Function as tyrosine kinase?

A. Epidermal growth factor
B. Platelet derived growth factor
C. Insulin
D. Asialoglycoprotein

208. Some cellular and extracellular proteins are enlisted in List I and their typical characteristics are enlisted in List II.

List I		List II
(*a*) Nidogen	(*i*)	In human genome, one gene of this protein is present but many different isoforms are there due to alternative splicing
(*b*) Fibronectin	(*ii*)	An intermediate filament protein that is typically expressed in epithelial and mesenchymal cells
(*c*) Integrin	(*iii*)	One of the principal structural proteins of basal laminae
(*d*) Vimentin	(*iv*)	Heterodimer of α and β subunit and binds to extracellular matrix proteins

Which one of the following is the most appropriate match?

	(*a*)	(*b*)	(*c*)	(*d*)
A.	(*i*)	(*ii*)	(*iii*)	(*iv*)
B.	(*ii*)	(*iii*)	(*iv*)	(*i*)
C.	(*iii*)	(*i*)	(*iv*)	(*ii*)
D.	(*ii*)	(*iv*)	(*i*)	(*iii*)

209. Localized increases in the cytosolic level of free Ca+2 are critical to its function as second messenger. Calmodulin, a small cytosolic protein, mediates many cellular effects of Ca+2. Which of the following is NOT CORRECT for Ca+2 -calmodulin interaction?

A. Each calmodulin molecule binds six Ca+2 ions in a cooperative fashion.
B. Binding of Ca+2 causes calmodulin to undergo a conformational change leading to active calmodulin.
C. Since Binding of Ca+2 is cooperative, a small change in the level of cytosolic Ca+2 leads to a large change in the level of active calmodulin.
D. One of the many enzymes activated by Ca+2–calmodulin is cAMP phosphodiesterase, which degrade cAMP and links Ca+2 cAMP signaling.

Cancer

210. Tumors are generally classified by

A. The virus which caused them
B. The person who discovered them
C. Their metastatic ability
D. The tissue or cell of origin

211. Following statements have been proposed for cancer cells and cancer stem cells:

(*a*) Cancer cells mostly have mutations whereas cancer stem cells do not.
(*b*) Cancer cells divide to form two different population of cells whereas cancer stem cells do not divide.
(*c*) Cancer stem cells cam undergo self-renewal whereas cancer cells cannot.
(*d*) Cancer cells are predominantly resistant to chemotherapy and radiation
(*e*) Cancer stem cells are found only in the bone marrow and placenta.

Which of the following combination of statement is correct?

A. (*a*) and (*c*)
B. (*a*) and (*b*)
C. (*c*) and (*e*)
D. (*c*) and (*d*)

212. Consider the four results that were obtained from immunophenotypinh of human breast cancer cells.

(*a*)

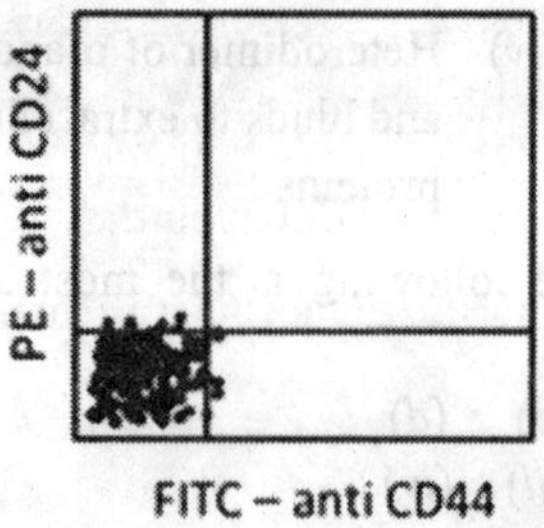

(*b*)

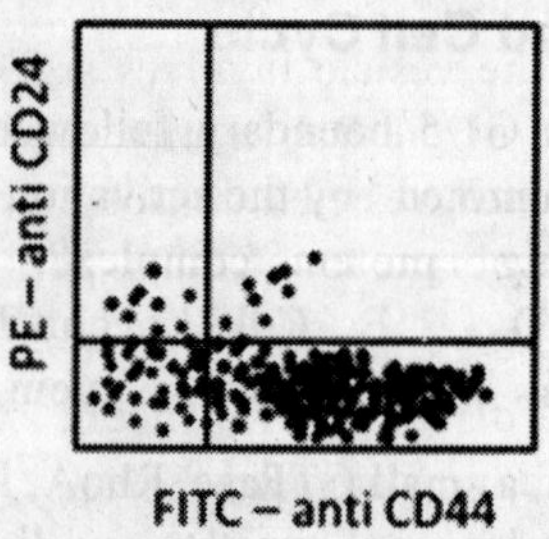

(*c*)

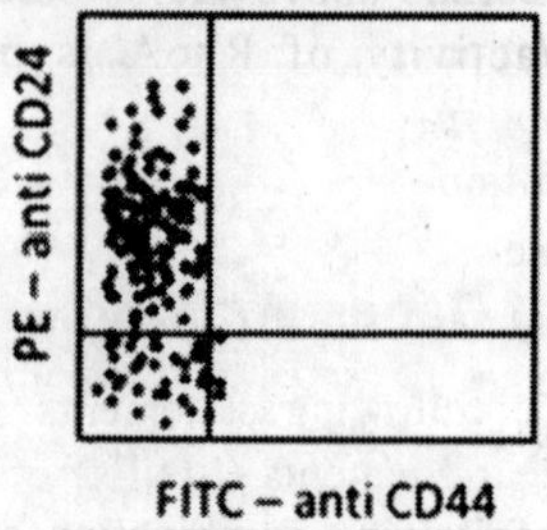

(*d*)

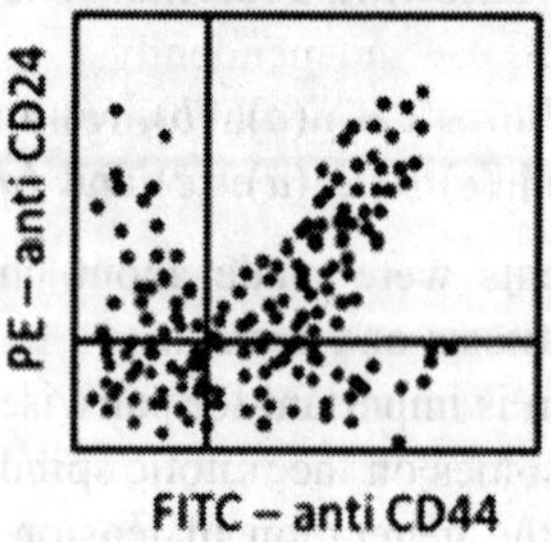

Which one of the following options correctly depicts the above results?

A. '(*b*)' represents a plot that denotes a high percentage of cancer stem cells in the breast cancer cells.
B. '(*d*)' denotes a plot where dual positive cells predominate, representing the dead cells.
C. '(*a*)' denotes a plot only cells stained with CD44 and CD24 are observed.
D. '(*c*)' represents a plot where only fibroblast cells are present.

CSIR-NET, JUNE (AFTERNOON), 2021

Membrane Structure and Function

213. Signal sequences direct proteins to the correct intracellular locations. Which one of the following sequences is typically used to import proteins into the nucleus?

A. -Pro-Pro-Lys-Lys-Lys-Arg-Lys-Val-
B. -Leu-Ala-Leu-Lys-Leu-Ala-Gly-Leu-Asp-Ile-,
C. -Ser-Lys-Leu-COO-,
D. -Lys-Asp-Glu-Leu-COO-

Structural Organization and Function of Intracellular Organelles

214. Membrane-enclosed organelles often have a characteristic position in the cytosol. In animal cells, for example, the Golgi apparatus is located close to the nucleus. Which component is directly involved in ensuring correct Golgi localization in animal cells?

A. Actin cytoskeleton
B. Microtubules
C. Nucleolus
D. Peroxisomes

215. Following statements were made about protein trafficking in cells :

(*a*) Cargo selection occurs when coat proteins bind to the sorting signals either directly or indirectly via adopter complexes.
(*b*) Protein export from the ER is exclusively mediated through the COPII -coated vesicles.
(*c*) Identical coat protein is used in the exocytic pathways or endo cyclic pathways.

(*d*) Tethering of the vesicle involves small guanosine triphosphatase of the Rab family.

(*e*) Clathering coated vesicles transport proteins from the plasma membrane to the trans- golgi network to late endosomes

Which of the following represent the correct combination of above statements?

A. (*a*), (*b*), (*d*) option
B. (*a*), (*b*), (*e*) option
C. (*b*), (*c*), (*d*) option
D. (*c*), (*d*), (*e*) option

Organization of Genes and Chromosomes

216. Which one of the following statements about Short Interspersed Nuclear Elements (SINEs) is TRUE?

A. SINs represent a class of retrotransposons
B. SINs can transpose independently
C. SINs can mobilize the neighboring LINE repeats
D. SINs are normally transcribed by RNA polymerase 1

217. The following statements are made with reference to the structure of the nucleosome :

(*a*) The histone tetramer in the core of the nucleosome comprises H2A, H2B, H3 and H4.

(*b*) The N-terminal tails of the core histones are believed to stabilize the 30 nm fiber of nucleosome DNA by their interactions with adjacent nucleosomes.

(*c*) The post-translation modifications of the N-terminal tails as well as globular domains of the core histones modulate transcriptional events.

(*d*) According to the zigzag model of the 30 nm fiber the linker DNA circles around the central axis of the fiber as the DNA moves from one nucleosome to the next.

Which of the following combinations represents all correct statements?

A. (*b*) and (*c*) only
B. (*a*), (*b*) and (*c*) only
C. (*c*) and (*d*) only
D. (*b*) and (*d*) only

218. Following statements were made about transposons:

(*a*) Transposons have inverted terminal repeats and their integrationg enerates inverted repeats at the flanks of the target site in the host genome.

(*b*) A composite transposon can transpose as a unit.

(*c*) The transposition event may cause deletions or inversions or move a host sequence to a new location.

(*d*) The transposition event may cause deletions or inversions but cannot move a host sequence to a new location.

(*e*) Replicative transposition proceeds through cointegration.

Which one of the following represents the combination of the correct statements?

A. (*a*), (*b*) and (*d*) B. (*b*), (*c*) and (*e*)
C. (*b*) and (*d*) only D. (*c*) and (*e*) only

Cell Division and Cell Cycle

219. Following statements were made about cell cycle regulation :

(*a*) De novo synthesis and destruction of Cyclin B are essential for cell cycle progression in yeast.

(*b*) De novo synthesis and destruction of Cyclin B and the related Cyclin dependent Kinase (CDK) are essential for cell cycle progression.

(*c*) CDK activity is regulated by both activating and inhibitory phosphorylation.

(*d*) Retinoblastoma (Rb) functions as an inhibitor of G2 to M transition.

(*e*) Inactivation of Sic 1 is essential for transition into S phase.

Which one of the following represents the combination of the correct statements?

A. (*a*), (*b*), (*d*) B. (*b*), (*c*), (*d*)
C. (*a*), (*c*), (*e*) D. (*b*), (*c*), (*e*)

Signal Molecule & Cell Signalling

220. The release of which neurotransmitter from the rods of retina is reduced when light strikes its outer segment?

A. Glutamate B. Acetylcholine
C. GABA D. Glycine

221. Nitric oxide (NO) acts as intracellular second messenger by stimulating

A. Phosphodiesterase
B. Nitric oxide synthase
C. Adenylyl cyclase
D. Guanylyl cyclase

222. Although a majority of G protein - coupled receptors (GPCRs) act through adenylyl cyclise, many of them (GPCR) exert their effects by activating the plasma membrane - bound enzyme phospholipase C-B (PLC-B). These receptors activate the so - called inositol phospholipid signaling pathway mainly via a G protein called Gq, which activates PLC - ß in much the same way that Gs activates adenylyl cyclase. Mentioned below are some of the steps with functional characteristics of inositol phospholipid signaling pathway, one of which is not correct. Select the INCORRECT.

A. PLC – B acts on phosphatidyl inositol 4, 5 – biphosphate (PIP_2), which is present in the inner half of the plasma membrane lipid bilayer.

B. Activated PLC – B cleaves the PIP_2 to generate two products : inositol 1, 4, 5 triphosphate (IP3) and diacylglycerol (DAG).

C. IP3 is a small lipid – soluble molecule that binds to IP3 receptor on plasma membrane thereby increasing Ca2 + concentration in the cytosol.

D. DAG gets further cleaved to release arachidonic acid , which is used in the synthesis of eicosanoids including prostaglandins. DAG also activates Ca^{2+} dependent protein kinase C or PKC.

223. With reference to the signaling pathway shown above, which one of the following options correctly identifies the intracellular components

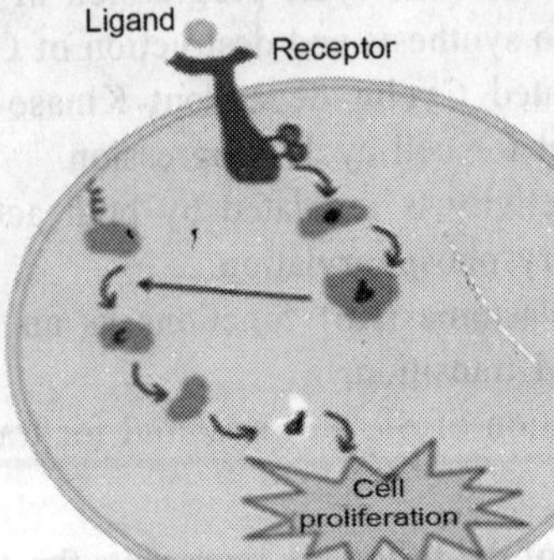

A. A = Grb * 2 b = SOS c = Ras – GTP d = ERK
B. A = Grb * 2 b = Ras – GDP c = MEK d = ERK
C. A = SOS b = Grb * 2 c = Ras – GTP d = MAPK
D. A = RTK b = SoS c = Ras – GDP d = EER

Cancer

224. The gradient of oxygen available to cells at inner regions of a tumour tissue environment is typically low that creates a hypoxic micro - environment. If enough oxygen is supplied to the cancer cells residing in hypoxic micro environment, which one of the following processes may NOT occur?

A. HIF – 1a stable in the cells under hypoxic conditions, may undergo oxygen dependent hydroxylation, targeting it for ubiquitination and proteolysis by tumour suppressor protein VHL.
B. Warburg effect will be reversed and conversion of glucose to lactate will not take place as sufficient oxygen will be available for oxidative phosphorylation.
C. Expression of HIF – 1. dependent genes will be lowered
D. Lactate generation in the tumour microenvironment, which contributed to M2 polarization of tissue – associated macrophages, will continue.

DBT-JRF, 2021

Organization of Structure and Functions of Prokaryotic and Eukaryotic Cells

225. The presence of Cardiolipin is a characteristic of the membrane of:

A. Endoplasmic reticulum
B. Lysosomes
C. Mitochondria
D. Myelin sheets

226. Peroxisomes are different from mitochondria and chloroplast mainly because they are:

A. Not the major sites of oxygen utilization
B. Surrounded by double membrane,
C. Surrounded by single membrane and contain genome
D. Surrounded by single membrane

227. Which one of the following components of an enveloped virus particle is NOT encoded by the viral genome?

A. Capsid proteins
B. Envelope lipids
C. Nonstructural proteins
D. Structural proteins

228. Lysosomal lumen is maintained at an acidic pH by:

A. de novo generation of H^+ ions in the lysosomes
B. H^+ ATPase that pumps H^+ ions into lysosomes
C. H^+ ATPase that pumps H^+ out of lysosomes
D. Specialized luminal proteins that lower the pH

GATE (BIOTECHNOLOGY), 2021

229. Which of the following cell organelle(s) is/are surrounded by a single phospholipid membrane?

A. Golgi apparatus
B. Lysosome
C. Mitochondria
D. Nucleus

230. The process by which intracellular macromolecules are supplied for lysosomal degradation during nutrient starvation is

A. Apoptosis
B. Autophagy
C. Phagocytosis
D. Pinocytosis

GATE (LIFE SCIENCE), 2021

Cell Organelle and Signalling

231. In hepatocytes, the detoxification of drugs occurs in

A. Golgi apparatus
B. Nucleolus
C. Rough endoplasmic reticulum
D. Smooth endoplasmic reticulum

232. Which one of the following antibiotics can form an ion channel in the bacterial membrane?

A. Ampicillin B. Gramicidin A
C. Gentamicin D. Rifampicin

233. Which of the following are energy requiring processes?

A. Facilitated diffusion
B. Active transport
C. Nonmediated transport
D. Na^+ /K^+ transport

234. Which of the following cellular component(s) is/are NOT part(s) of cytoskeleton in Angiosperms?

A. Microtubules
B. Microfilaments
C. Intermediate filaments
D. Centrioles

235. Match the cell organelles in Column I with the appropriate functions in Column II

Column I	Column II
(*a*) Peroxisome	(*i*) Conversion of lipid to carbohydrate
(*b*) Endoplasmic reticulum	(*ii*) Oxidation of fatty acids
(*c*) Glyoxysome	(*iii*) N-linked glycosylation
(*d*) Golgi complex	(*iv*) Microtubule organization center
(*e*) Centrioles	(*v*) O-linked glycosylation

	(*a*)	(*b*)	(*c*)	(*d*)	(*e*)
A.	(*ii*)	(*iii*)	(*v*)	(*i*)	(*iv*)
B.	(*iv*)	(*v*)	(*i*)	(*ii*)	(*iii*)
C.	(*iv*)	(*v*)	(*iii*)	(*i*)	(*ii*)
D.	(*ii*)	(*iii*)	(*i*)	(*v*)	(*iv*)

236. Cohesin and Condensin proteins of eukaryotes belong to which one of the following groups?

A. Structural maintenance of chromosomes (SMC) proteins
B. Histones
C. DNA polymerases
D. Topoisomerases

CSIR-NET, SEPTEMBER (MORNING), 2022

Structural Organization and Function of Intracellular Organelles

237. A few organelles that are present in a eukaryotic cell are mentioned below:

(*a*) Centrosomes (*b*) Peroxisomes
(*c*) Nucleolus (*d*) Endosomes

Which one of the following options represents organelles that are not membrane-bound?

A. (*a*) and (*b*) B. (*b*) and (*c*)
C. (*a*) and (*c*) D. (*a*) and (*d*)

Organization of Genes and Chromosomes

238. Histone variants play important roles in chromatin function in mammalian cells. Which one of the following statements is correct in the context of the histone variants?

A. Histone variants have been reported for H3 and H4 but not for H2A and H2B
B. Histone variants have been reported for H3, H4, H2A but not for H2B
C. Histone variants have been reported for H3, H4, H2B but not for H2A
D. Histone variants have been reported for H3, H4, H2A and H2B

239. Following statements were made about some of the characteristics of the human genome:

(*a*) Evidence derived by chromosome conformation capture (3C) suggests that each chromosome comprises a series of topologically associated domains.
(*b*) Insulators typically mark the boundaries of topologically associated domains, preventing the genes within a domain from being influenced by the regulatory modules of an adjacent domain being influenced by the regulatory modules of an adjacent domain.
(*c*) Presence of insulators does not overcome the positional effect after integration of a transgene into the genome.
(*d*) Insulators can provide barrier against the spread of heterochromatin.
(*e*) Insulator sequences are absent in the Drosophila genome, which suggests their essentiality in achieving highest degree of gene regulation in humans.

Which one of the following represents the correct combination of above statements?

A. (a), (b) and (c) B. (a), (b) and (d)
C. (b), (c) and (d) D. (c), (d) and (e)

Cell Division and Cell Cycle

240. Following statements were made about cell cycle regulation in eukaryotes:

(a) Activity of maturation promoting factor (MPF) rises and falls in synchrony with the concentration of cyclin B

(b) Cdc25 phosphatase mediates removal of phosphate from the inhibitory tyrosine residue (Y15) to yield highly active MPF

(c) MPF specifically phosphorylates and depolymerizes lamin A and C, but not lamin B.

(d) MPF phosphorylates H1 histone.

(e) In Schizosaccharomyces pombe, overproduction of Wee1 protein decreases the length of G2 phase an of M phase by functioning as a mediator of MPF activity.

Which one of the following represents the combination of correct statements?

A. (a), (b) and (c) B. (a), (b) and (d)
C. (b), (c) and (e) D. (c), (d) and (e)

241. There are many superfamilies of adhesion proteins, which play a central role in cell-cell adhesion in animals. Ig superfamily proteins are one such adhesion proteins. Which one of the following statements about Ig superfamily proteins is INCORRECT?

A. The white blood cell proteins recognized by endothelial cell integrins are called ICAM (intercellular cell adhesion molecule) or VCAM (vascular cell adhesion molecules)

B. These are called Ig superfamily because they contain one or more extracellular Ig-like domains that are characteristic of antibody molecules

C. ICAM and VCAM mediate heterotrophic binding to integrin, whereas NCAM (neural cell adhesion molecule) mediates homotrophic binding

D. They contain large quantities of sialic acid which inhibit adhesion by charge-based repulsion contributing to fine tuning of cell-cell adhesion

242. The HIPPO signaling pathway is important for cell proliferation. It is regulated by the protein kinases MST1/2 and LATS1/2, and the transcriptional activators YAP and TAZ. Accordingly, the following events may be observed within a cell

(a) Activation of TEADs by phosphorylated YAP/TAZ

(b) Activation of YAP/TAZ on phosphorylation by MST/LATS

(c) Activation of TEADs by dephosphorylated YAP/TAZ

(d) Inactivation of MST / LATS by repressors

Which one of the following situations can support progression of cancer?

A. (a) and (b) B. (b) and (c)
C. (c) and (d) D. (a) and (d)

243. Column (A) lists enzymes involved in cell cycle and typical function in a particular cell cycle phase is listed in Column (B)

(Column A) Enzyme	(Column B) Cell cycle function
(a) Cdk1	(i) Cytokinesis
(b) APC/C^{cdc20}	(ii) S-phase entry
(c) Cdk2	(iv) Mitotic entry
(d) Aurora B	(v) Anaphase onset

Which one of the following options represents the correct match between column A and column B?

	(a)	(b)	(c)	(d)
A.	(iv)	(iii)	(ii)	(i)
B.	(iii)	(iv)	(ii)	(i)
C.	(i)	(ii)	(iii)	(iv)
D.	(ii)	(i)	(iv)	(iii)

244. Individual chromosomes are clearly seen during which phase of the cell cycle?

A. G0 B. G1
C. S D. M

Cancer

245. The table below lists the characteristics of specific tumor types (Column A) and their names (Column B)

Column A Tumor types	Column B Nomenclature
(a) A tumor that has arisen from endodermal tissue	(i) Neoplasm
(b) Cancer cells arisen from hematopoietic stem cells that do not grow as solid tumor	(ii) Carcinoma
(c) A permanent change in the genome of a cell that results in abnormal growth	(iii) Sarcoma
(d) A tumor that has arisen from mesodermal connective tissue	(iv) Leukemia
	(iv) Lymphoma
	(v) Transformation

Which of the following options represents the correct match between Column A and Column B?

	(a)	(b)	(c)	(d)
A.	(iii)	(iv)	(i)	(ii)
B.	(ii)	(iv)	(vi)	(iii)
C.	(iii)	(v)	(vi)	(i)
D.	(iv)	(v)	(i)	(ii)

246. Following statements are made about some of the abnormally expressing proteins in human cancers:
(*a*) Increased telomerase expression always contributes to increased cell death in cancer cells.
(*b*) Overproduction of anti-apoptotic protein (Bcl2) can lead to inappropriate cell survival and is associate lymphoblastic leukemia (CLL).
(*c*) The E5, E6 and E7 proteins encoded by human papilloma virus (HPV) are tumor suppressors.
(*d*) Overexpression of cyclin D1 or loss of p16 and Rb can cause inappropriate, unregulated passage through the restriction point in late G1.

Which of the following options represents the combination of all correct statements?
A. (*a*) and (*b*) B. (*a*) and (*c*)
C. (*b*) and (*d*) D. (*c*) and (*d*)

Signalling

247. The signal transduction pathway involved in glycogen metabolism triggered in the liver by the hormone epinephrine involves the following steps:
(*a*) Activation of G protein (Gαβγ) by the activated receptor
(*b*) Protein kinase A activation
(*c*) Second messenger generation (3', 5' cyclic AMP)
(*d*) Adenylyl cyclase activation

Which one of the following combinations describes these processes in the right order?
A. (*a*), (*d*), (*c*), (*b*)
B. (*a*), (*c*), (*d*) (*b*)
C. (*d*) (*a*), (*b*), (*c*)
D. (*a*), (*d*) (*b*), (*c*)

CSIR-NET, SEPTEMBER (AFTERNOON), 2022

Membrane Structure and Function

248. Which one of the following is abundant in the plasma membranes of mammalian cells but is absent from most prokaryotic and plant cell
A. Phosphoglycerides B. Ergosterol
C. Cholin D. Cholesterol

Structural Organization and Function of Intracellular Organelles

249. Which one of the following proteins is NOT related to extracellular matrix?
A. Cadherin B. Vitronectin
C. Lamin D. Selectin

250. Given below are a few steps in clathrin-coated vesicle formation in the secretory pathway.
(*a*) Receptor-ligand recognition and binding
(*b*) Recruitment of adapter protein and clathrin
(*c*) Vesicle formation
(*d*) Uncoating of clathrin coats

Choose the option that correctly identifies the sequence of events in making a clathrin-coated vesicle.
A. (*a*), (*b*), (*c*), (*d*) B. (*b*), (*a*), (*c*), (*d*)
C. (*a*), (*b*), (*d*), (*c*) D. (*b*), (*a*), (*d*), (*c*)

251. Physical attachment between cells and extracellular matrix is critical in both animals and plants because it imparts rigidity and strength to tissues and organs. However, junctions between cell-cell or between cell-matrix are diverse in structure and play roles beyond providing physical support. Column "X" lists some of the cell junctions and column "Y" lists their characteristic functions

Column X	Column Y
(*a*) Tight junction	(*i*) Connect intermediate filaments in one cell to those in the next cell
(*b*) Gap junction	(*ii*) Seal gaps between epithelial cells
(*c*) Plasmodesmata	(*iii*) Allow passage of small water soluble molecules from cell to cell in animal tissues
(*d*) Desmosomes	(*iv*) Allows passage of small molecules but not macro-molecules (with some exceptions) in plants

Select the option with all correct matches.

	(*a*)	(*b*)	(*c*)	(*d*)
A.	(*i*)	(*ii*)	(*iv*)	(*iii*)
B.	(*ii*)	(*iii*)	(*iv*)	(*i*)
C.	(*iii*)	(*iv*)	(*i*)	(*ii*)
D.	(*iv*)	(*i*)	(*ii*)	(*iii*)

Organization of Genes and Chromosomes

252. CENP-A containing nucleosomes are found at the centromeric region of the chromosomes. CENP-A is a variant of which one of the following histones?
A. H1 B. H2A
C. H3 D. H4

253. The table lists information about different classes of retroelements:

Column X	Column Y
A. LTR retrotransposons	(*i*) 7-21 bp target sequence
B. Non-LTR retroposons	(*ii*) copia elements
C. SINEs	(*iii*) Alu elements
	(*iv*) L1

Which one of the following options has all correct matches between column X and Y?

	(a)	(b)	(c)
A.	(ii)	(i)	(iii)
B.	(i)	(iii)	(ii)
C.	(iii)	(ii)	(iv)
D.	(iv)	(iii)	(i)

Cell Division and Cell Cycle

254. To study the cell cycle progression for cultured mammalian cells, one would typically NOT utilize?

A. Artificial thymidine analog BrdU
B. Kinase inhibitor, LY294002
C. Flow cytometry analysis
D. Live cell imaging

255. To ensure proper segregation of chromosomes during mitosis, the sister chromatid pairs must be stably bi-oriented on the mitotic spindle. In animal cells, after nuclear envelope breakdown (NEBD), chromosomes glide along the microtubules' length with the help of the motor proteins. When the chromosomes reach the plus-end of microtubules, the kinetochores attach to the microtubules. Which one of the following is the correct option for the kinetochore-microtubules attachment configuration that ensures proper chromosome segregation?

A. Monotelic B. Merotelic
C. Amphitelic D. Syntelic

Cancer

256. Which one of the following statements about cancers is INCORRECT?

A. The c-myc gene is translocated to one of the immunoglobulin loci in a majority of Burkitt's lymphomas.
B. Viral integration into the cellular genome may convert a proto-oncogene into an oncogene.
C. The functions of p53 and Rb are augmented by E6 and E7 proteins of human papillomavirus.
D. Many cases of metastatic breast cancer display increased expression of human epidermal-growth-factor–like receptor 2(HER2).

257. Consider the cancer types in Column P and the cancer related descriptions (Column Q)

Column X	Column Y
(a) Leukemia	(i) A tumor that has arisen from endodermal tissue
(b) Sarcoma	(ii) Hematopoietic cell cancer that does not grow as a solid tumor
(c) Carcinoma	(iii) A tumor that develops from mesodermal connective tissue
(d) Melanoma	(iv) Cancer that develops from the pigment producing cells of skin

Select the option that represent all the correct matches

	(a)	(b)	(c)	(d)
A.	(ii)	(iii)	(i)	(iv)
B.	(iv)	(i)	(iii)	(ii)
C.	(i)	(iii)	(ii)	(iv)
D.	(ii)	(i)	(iii)	(iv)

Cytoskeleton

258. The actin-binding proteins regulate microfilament turnover in a eukaryotic system. Match the actin-binding protein (in column I) with their functions (in column II).

Column I	Column II
(a) Cofilin	(i) Bind ADP-G-actin and catalyzes the exchange of ADP for ATP
(b) Profilin	(ii) Bind preferentially to filament containing ADP-actin
(c) Thymosin	(iii) Assembles unbranched filament
(d) Formin	(iv) Bind to ATP-G-actin and inhibits addition of actin subunit to filament

Choose the CORRECT combination from below:

	(a)	(b)	(c)	(d)
A.	(iii)	(iv)	(ii)	(i)
B.	(ii)	(iii)	(i)	(iv)
C.	(ii)	(i)	(iv)	(iii)
D.	(iii)	(ii)	(iv)	(i)

Signalling

259. Plant nodulation genes encode proteins with receptor-like-features. Following are the list of some nodulation proteins (Column X) and their possible domain characteristics (Column Y):

Column X	Column Y
(a) Entry receptor	(i) Extracellular leucine rich repeat domains in a large N-terminal segment and the cytoplasmic portion having kinase domains
(b) Signaling receptor	(ii) Extracellular LysM domains and the cytoplasmic kinase domain/s
(c) Symbiosis receptor kinase	(iii) Extracellular LysM domains but lacks the kinase features in the cytoplasmic portion

Which of the following is the correct match?

	(a)	(b)	(c)
A.	(i)	(ii)	(iii)
B.	(ii)	(iii)	(i)
C.	(iii)	(ii)	(i)
D.	(i)	(iii)	(ii)

260. Which of the following domains is present in symbiosis receptor-like kinase (SYMRK) proteins?
A. Nucleotide binding repeat
B. Leucine-rich repeat region
C. NAC domain
D. W-box

261. Which one of the following best describes the ability of the cells to respond to a specific inducing signal?
A. Potency
B. Equivalence
C. Competence
D. Specification

DBT-JRF, 2022

Organization of Structure and Functions of Prokaryotic and Eukaryotic Cells

262. The cytosine residues in the DNA are methylated at specific di- or trinucleotide se27-200uences.Which among these methylation motifs is predominantly found in case of protein-coding genes in animals? (H stands for A, T or C)
A. CpG B. CpHpG
C. CpHpH D. CpGpG

263. In eukaryotes, nucleosomes comprise of which one of the following histones?
A. H1, H2A, H2B, and H3
B. H2A, H2B, H3, and H4
C. H1, H2B, H3, and H4
D. H1, H2A, H3, and H4

264. During signal transduction, one molecule of phosphatidylinositol 4,5-bisphosphate (PIP2) is cleaved into one molecule each of inositol triphosphate (IP3) and diacylglycerol (DAG) by the enzyme:
A. Lipolyase C
B. Phosphatase C
C. Phosphodiesterase C
D. Phospholipase C

265. Which one of the following acts as a linker histone?
A. H1 B. H2A
C. H2B D. H3

266. Gap junctions are absent in:
A. Brain cells
B. Cardiac muscle cells
C. Liver cells
D. Erythrocytes

267. Which of the following statements are correct?
(*a*) Lipid bilayer lacking proteins is highly impermeable to all the charged molecules.
(*b*) Channels have specific binding pockets for the solute molecules they allow to pass.
(*c*) Transporters allow solutes to cross a membrane at much slower rates than do channels.
(*d*) The plasma membrane of many animal cells contains open K^+ channels, yet the K^+ concentration in the cytosol is much higher than outside the cell.
(*e*) The membrane potential of an axon temporarily becomes more negative when an action potential excites it.
A. (*a*), (*c*), (*d*) B. (*a*), (*c*), (*e*)
C. (*a*), (*b*), (*e*) D. (*b*), (*d*), (*e*)

268. Which one of the following is NOT a major checkpoint in the cell division cycle of eukaryotic cell?
A. Beginning of S-phase
B. Transition from S to G2 phase
C. Transition from G2 to M phase
D. Transition from Metaphase to Anaphase during Mitosis

269. A specialized histone associated with the centromeric region of the chromosome is:
A. CenH3 B. H2A.Z
C. H3.3 D. H2A.X

270. Given below are two statements: one is labelled as Assertion (A) and the other is labelled as Reason (R).

Assertion (A): Histones bind to DNA with high affinity.

Reason (R): Histones are small proteins rich in valine and isoleucine residues.

In the light of the above statements, choose the correct answer from the options given below:
A. Both (A) and (R) are true and (R) is the correct explanation of (A)
B. Both (A) and (R) are true but (R) is not the correct explanation of (A)
C. (A) is true but (R) is false
D. (A) is false but (R) is true

271. DNA isolated from four unidentified species of bacteria – (*a*), (*b*), (*c*) and (*d*) has been estimated to have 38%, 26%, 24% and 12% thymine, respectively. One of these four species was isolated from a hot spring (64°C). Identify the candidate which is most likely to be a thermophilic bacterium.
A. (*a*) B. (*b*)
C. (*c*) D. (*d*)

272. In animal cloning, donor somatic cells should be in which stage of cell cycle?
A. G1 B. S
C. G2 D. G0

273. Proteins are glycosylated in the endoplasmic reticulum. In the final structures, the glycan moieties are typically present:

A. on the surface of these proteins
B. in the core of these proteins
C. on the surface as well as in the core of these proteins
D. on the membrane inserted segments of these proteins

274. Which one of the following is NOT applicable for a chemical synapse?

A. Usually synaptic cleft is approx. 20 – 40 nm
B. May release excitatory or inhibitory neurotransmitter
C. Cannot modulate signal intensity
D. There is a delay of signal propagation

275. The ligand binding domain of a ligand gated channel (LGC) has a serine residue, phosphorylation of which is essential for ligand binding. By site directed mutagenesis it was replaced by aspartic acid. The likely conse 27-200 uences will be:

A. LGC becomes non-functional
B. LGC becomes constitutively active
C. No change in function
D. It will rapidly shift between active and inactive forms

GATE (BIOTECHNOLOGY), 2022

276. Match the component of eukaryotic cells (Column I) with its respective function (Column II).

Column I	Column II
P. Lysosome	1. Digestion of macromolecules
Q. Peroxisome	2. Detoxification of harmful compounds
R. Glyoxysome	3. Conversion of fatty acids to sugar
S. Cytoskeleton	4. Involvement in cell motility

A. P-1, Q-2, R-3, S-4
B. P-2, Q-1, R-3, S-4
C. P-3, Q-1, R-2, S-4
D. P-4, Q-3, R-1, S-2

277. Which of the following statement(s) regarding trafficking in eukaryotic cells is(are) CORRECT?

A. Dynamin binds GTP and is involved in vesicle budding
B. Dynamin is involved in cytoskeletal remodelling
C. Dynein binds ATP and is involved in movement of organelles along microtubules
D. Dynein binds GTP and is involved in movement of organelles along microtubules

278. The enzymes involved in ubiquitinylation of cell-cycle proteins are

A. E1 and E2 only
B. E1 and E3 only
C. E1 and E4 only
D. E1, E2 and E3

ANSWERS

1	2	3	4	5	6	7	8	9	10
B	A	B	A	C	D	C	D	B	C
11	**12**	**13**	**14**	**15**	**16**	**17**	**18**	**19**	**20**
D	C	A	A	A	B	C	A	C	D
21	**22**	**23**	**24**	**25**	**26**	**27**	**28**	**29**	**30**
A	C	A	C	D	D	B	B	C	D
31	**32**	**33**	**34**	**35**	**36**	**37**	**38**	**39**	**40**
D	A	C	B	A	B	C	B	B	D
41	**42**	**43**	**44**	**45**	**46**	**47**	**48**	**49**	**50**
B	C	A	C	B	C	A	D	D	C
51	**52**	**53**	**54**	**55**	**56**	**57**	**58**	**59**	**60**
B	D	C	D	C	B	B	B	D	C
61	**62**	**63**	**64**	**65**	**66**	**67**	**68**	**69**	**70**
B	D	D	B	D	C	B	A	B	D
71	**72**	**73**	**74**	**75**	**76**	**77**	**78**	**79**	**80**
C	D	B	D	C	D	D	C	D	B

81	**82**	**83**	**84**	**85**	**86**	**87**	**88**	**89**	**90**
A	B	C	B	B	C	A	B	A	A
91	**92**	**93**	**94**	**95**	**96**	**97**	**98**	**99**	**100**
D	A	C	B	B	D	D	C	B	C
101	**102**	**103**	**104**	**105**	**106**	**107**	**108**	**109**	**110**
B	C	D	D	C	B	D	C	C	D
111	**112**	**113**	**114**	**115**	**116**	**117**	**118**	**119**	**120**
B	D	B	B	A	B	B	A	B	B
121	**122**	**123**	**124**	**125**	**126**	**127**	**128**	**129**	**130**
C	B	D	A	A	C	B	B	A	C
131	**132**	**133**	**134**	**135**	**136**	**137**	**138**	**139**	**140**
C	B	A	A	B	C	D	A	C	B
141	**142**	**143**	**144**	**145**	**146**	**147**	**148**	**149**	**150**
C	C	D	C	A	C	A	B	B	B
151	**152**	**153**	**154**	**155**	**156**	**157**	**158**	**159**	**160**
C	A	D	C	A	B	D	C	A	B
161	**162**	**163**	**164**	**165**	**166**	**167**	**168**	**169**	**170**
A	A	D	D	B	D	C	D	A	C
171	**172**	**173**	**174**	**175**	**176**	**177**	**178**	**179**	**180**
A	A	C	A	A	D	A	D	D	B
181	**182**	**183**	**184**	**185**	**186**	**187**	**188**	**189**	**190**
C	C	D	D	D	A	D	B	D	C
191	**192**	**193**	**194**	**195**	**196**	**197**	**198**	**199**	**200**
B	D	A	D	C	C	A	C	C	A
201	**202**	**203**	**204**	**205**	**206**	**207**	**208**	**209**	**210**
B	C	B	B	D	A	D	C	A	D
211	**212**	**213**	**214**	**215**	**216**	**217**	**218**	**219**	**220**
A	A	A	B	A	A	A	B	C	A
221	**222**	**223**	**224**	**225**	**226**	**227**	**228**	**229**	**230**
D	C	A	B	C	D	B	B	A,B	B
231	**232**	**233**	**234**	**235**	**236**	**237**	**238**	**239**	**240**
D	B	B,D	C,D	D	A	C	D	D	B
241	**242**	**243**	**244**	**245**	**246**	**247**	**248**	**249**	**250**
D	C	B	D	B	C	A	D	C	A
251	**252**	**253**	**254**	**255**	**256**	**257**	**258**	**259**	**260**
B	C	A	B	C	C	A	C	B	B
261	**262**	**263**	**264**	**265**	**266**	**267**	**268**	**269**	**270**
C	A	B	D	A	D	A	B	A	C
271	**272**	**273**	**274**	**275**	**276**	**277**	**278**		
D	D	D	C	B	A	A,C	D		

CHAPTER

3

MOLECULAR BIOLOGY

CSIR-NET, JUNE, 2017

Nucleic Acids-forms, Conformation & Stability

1. Various modifications of nucleotides occur in nucleic acids. Which of the following combinations contains at least one modification that does NOT occur in nucleic acids?

A. N,N-dimethylguanosine, pseudouridine. 2'O-methyluridine
B. 2-thiouridine, dihydrouridine, Nisopentenyladenine
C. 5-methyldeoxycytosine, 5-thiouridine, pseudouridine
D. dihydrouridine, 4-thiouridine, 2'O- methyluridine

DNA Replication, Repair and Recombination

2. In eukaryotic replication, priming of DNA synthesis and removal of RNA primer is catalyzed by

A. DNA Pol α and PCNA, respectively.
B. DNA Pol α and FEN1, respectively.
C. DNA Pol δ and FEN1, respectively.
D. DNA Pol ε and PCNA, respectively.

3. Two experiments were performed. In the first one, Okazaki fragments were prepared from a replicating cell of *E. coli* grown in the presence of 32P. In the other, the two strands of *E. coli* chromosome were separated into a H strand and L strand, immobilized onto a nitrocellulose membrane and hybridized with the Okazaki fragments prepared in the first experiment.

Which one of the following options correctly describes the observation?

A. Okazaki fragments will hybridize to only H strand
B. Okazaki fragments will hybridize to only L strand
C. Okazaki fragments will hybridize with both H and L strands
D. Because the H and L strands have been prepared from different cultures of *E. coli*, the Okazaki fragments will hybridize to neither

4. In *E. coli* grown under nutrient rich conditions, replication of entire genome takes about 40 min., yet it can divide every 20 min. This is so because:

A. While *E. coli* divides every 20 min, equal transfer of genetic material occurs only in the alternate rounds of cell divisions.
B. A second round of genome replication begins before the completion of first round of replication, and by the time cell is ready to divide, two copies of the genome are available.
C. Genome replication cell division are not coordinated with each other.
D. During cell division, only one of the strands of the genome whose synthesis can be achieved in 20 min, is transferred to the daughter cell.

5. In the following diagram, segments A and C are copies of 10 base pair repeat DNA sequences, flanking a unique stretch shown as B. A and C are in inverted orientation as indicated by arrows. Intramolecular recombination between A and C leads to which event:

A. The complete region encompassing A to C will be inverted
B. Only A and B will be inverted
C. Only B will be inverted
D. Only regions A and C will be inverted

RNA Synthesis and Processing

6. In eukaryotes, precursors of micro RNAs (miRNAs) and small interfering RNAs (siRNAs) are usually synthesized by
A. RNA Pol I and III, respectively
B. RNA Pol III and I, respectively
C. Only RNA Pol I
D. Only RNA Pol II

7. Scientists usually find difficulty in identifying the exact transcription termination site in eukaryotes because
A. Immediately following termination of transcription, the 3' end is polyadenylated
B. The 3' end is generated by cleavage prior to actual termination of transcription
C. Poly A binding proteins present at 3' end of transcript hides the termination site
D. 3' end of transcript is complexed with 5' end for initiation of translation

8. Eukaryotic mRNAs have an enzymatic appended cap structure consisting of a 7-methylguanosine residue joined to the initial 5' nucleotide of the transcripts. Given below are a few statements regarding capping.

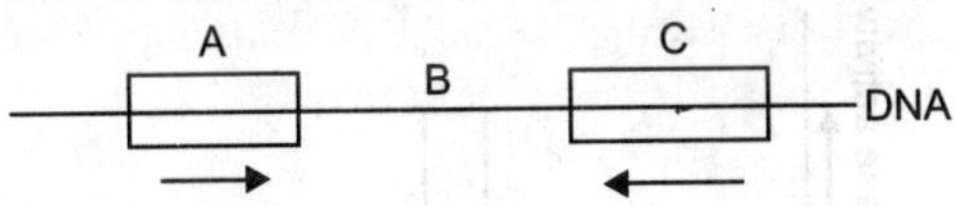

(*a*) Capping protects the mRNA from degradation by 5'-exoribonucleases.
(*b*) During capping, the α-phosphate is released from the 5'-end of the nascent mRNA.
(*c*) Phosphorylation mediated conformational change in carboxyl terminal domain (CTD) of RNA Pol II enables its binding with capping enzymes.
(*d*) During capping, a 5' -5' triphosphate bond is formed between the β-phosphate of the nascent mRNA and α-phosphate of GTP.

Which of the above statement(s) is/are INCORRECT?
A. (*c*) only B. (*b*) only
C. (*a*) and (*b*) D. (*c*) and (*d*)

Protein Synthesis and Processing

9. Aminoacyl tRNAs are escorted to the ribosome by the elongation factor
A. EF-Ts B. EF-G
C. EF-Tu D. eEF-2

10. Which one of the following is NOT formed after post-translational processing of pre-proglucagon?
A. Glicentin
B. β-lipotropin
C. Major proglucagon fragment
D. Oxyntomodulin

11. Which one of following modification of proteins is co-translational?
A. Palmitoylation
B. Myristoylation
C. Famesylation
D. Addition of cholesterol

12. Chloramphenicol is a broad-spectrum antibiotic which inhibits protein synthesis in prokaryotes. Given below are a few statements regarding the mode of action of chloramphenicol.
(*a*) Chloramphenicol inhibits the peptidyl-transferase activity of ribosomes.
(*b*) Chloramphenicol can be used to treat moderate to severe infections, because mitochondrial ribosomes are not sensitive to chloramphenicol.
(*c*) Chloramphenicol binds to one of the domains of 23S rRNA
(*d*) Chloramphenicol competes for binding with the E-site tRNA

Which of the following options describes correctly the mechanism of action of chloramphenicol?
A. (*b*) and (*d*) only B. (*a*) and (*c*) only
C. (*a*), (*c*) and (*d*) D. (*b*), (*c*) and (*d*)

13. A comparsion of Bacteria, Archaea and Eukarya wit' respect to a few characteristics is given below:

Characteristics	Bacteria	Archaea	Eukarya
(*a*) Initiator amino acid for protein synthesis	Formyl Met	Met	Met
(*b*) Histones associated with DNA	Absent	Present in some species	present
(*c*) Response to Streptomycin and chloramphenicol.	Growth not Inhibited	Growth not Inhibited	Growth usually Inhibited
(*d*) RNA Polymerase	Three	Three	Three or more
(*e*) Introns in genes	Very rare	Present in some genes	Present in many genes.

Which of the following combinations present a correct comparison of characteristics in the table above?
A. (*a*), (*b*), (*c*) and (*e*)
B. (*a*), (*c*) and (*d*)
C. (*b*), (*d*) and (*e*)
D. (*a*), (*b*) and (*e*)

Gene Regulation-phage, pro & eukaryotes

14. A lac- culture of E. coli was mutagenised. On what media would one spread the mutagenised cells to select for lac+ cells?

A. Minimal media+ lactose.
B. Rich media + lactose.
C. Minimal media + glycerol + IPTG + X-Gal
D. Rich media + IPTG + X-Gal

15. The lambda (λ) and P22 phages are two related lambdoid bacteriophages. A recombinant lambda phage (λMut) was derived from the wild type lambda phage (λWT) by replacing its CI repressor gene and the CI binding sites with those from the P22 phage. Both the λWT and the λMut were used independently to infect Escherichia coli strain over-producing λWT CI repressor. Following outcomes were surmised
(*a*) Infection with λWT will lyse the E. coli used
(*b*) Infection with λWT will invariably establish lysogeny in the
(*c*) coli used
(*d*) Infection with λMut will lyse the E. coli used
(*e*) Infection with λMut will invariably establish lysogeny in the E. coli used.

Which combination of the above statements is correct?
A. (*a*) and (*b*)
B. (*b*) and (*c*)
C. (*c*) and (*d*)
D. (*d*) and (*a*)

16. A merodiploid strain of *E. coli* with the genotype $F^+O^cZ^-Y^+$ / $O^+Z^+Y^+$ was constructed. The activity of β-galactosidase enzyme was measured in this strain upon following treatments.
(*a*) no induction
(*b*) induction with *n* moles of IPTG
(*c*) induction with *n* moles of lactose
(*d*) induction with *n* moles of lactose in the presence of *n* moles of glucose

Which one of the following graphs depicts the expected trends in β-galactosidase activity under the four different conditions?

A.
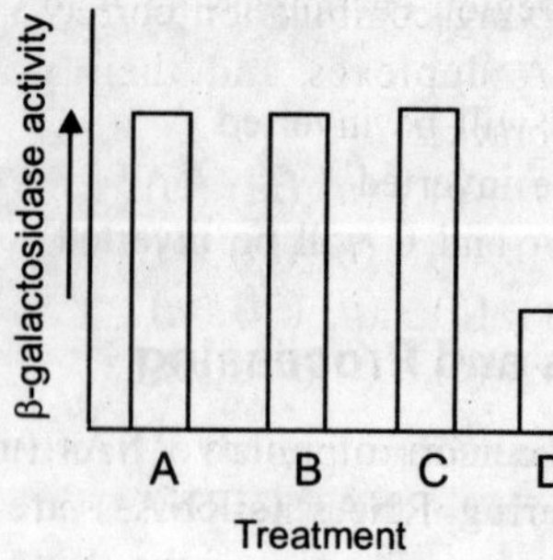

B.
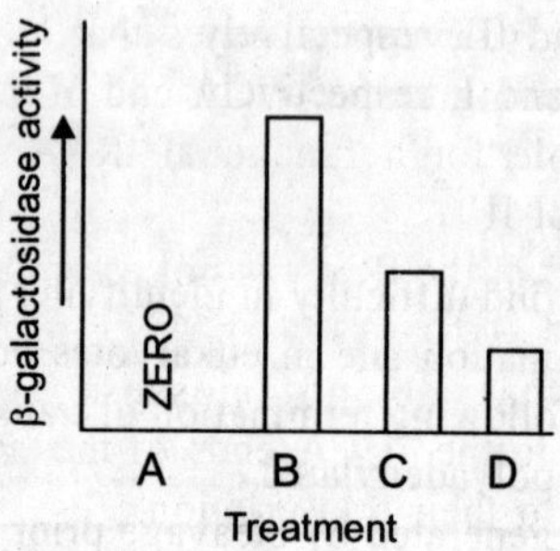

C.
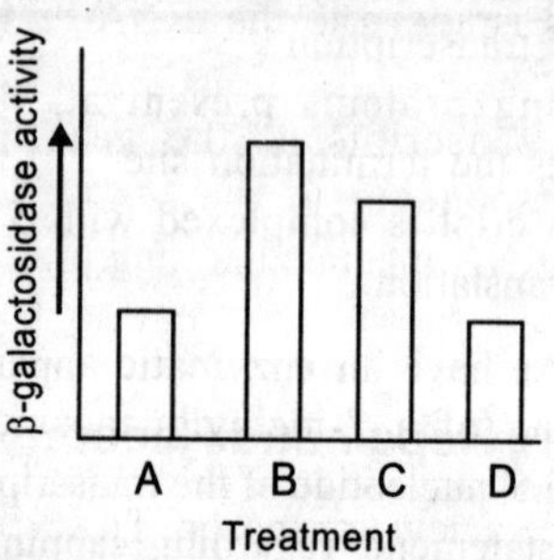

D.
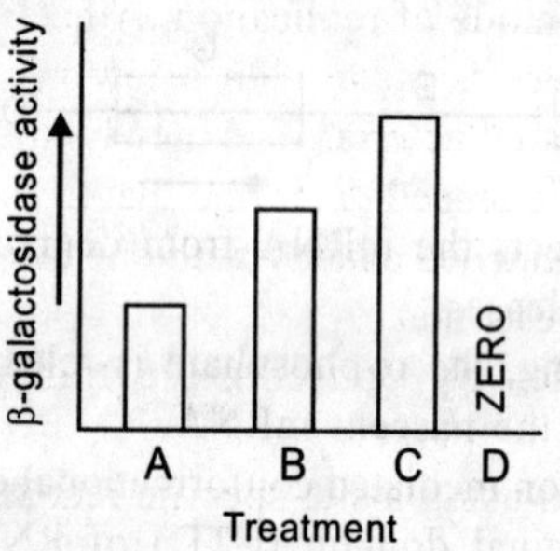

CSIR-NET, DECEMBER, 2017

Nucleic Acids-forms, Conformation & Stability

17. Which one of the following statements about chromatin is NOT true?
A. DNA winds approximately 1.65 times around the nucleosomes
B. H2A-H2B bind to both the entry and exit ends of DNA in nucleosomes
C. Covalent modification of histones influence chromatin compaction
D. Non-histone proteins are part of mitotic chromosomes

18. Following table lists the two major forms of DNA duplexes, conformation of base attached to the sugar and the nature of major and minor grooves.

DNA Duplex	Properties
(*a*) A form	(*i*) Syn conformation of the base to sugar
(*b*) B form	(*ii*) Anti conformation of the base to sugar
	(*iii*) Wide major groove
	(*iv*) Narrow major groove
	(*v*) Wide minor groove
	(*vi*) Narrow minor groove

Which of the following combination correctly depicts the types of DNA duplexes and their properties (numbered within bracket)?

A. (*a*) - (*i*) (*iii*) (*vi*); (*b*) - (*ii*) (*iii*) (*vi*)
B. (*a*) - (*i*) (*iii*) (*vi*); (*b*) - (*ii*) (*iii*) (*v*)
C. (*a*) - (*ii*) (*iv*) (*v*); (*b*) - (*ii*) (*iii*) (*vi*)
D. (*a*) - (*ii*) (*iv*) (*v*); (*b*) - (*i*) (*iii*) (*vi*)

19. t-RNA genes of a Gram positive bacteria were sequenced. While some of the genes possessed sequence corresponding to the –CCA end of the tRNA, others did not. Interestingly, even the genes that lacked the sequence corresponding to the –CCA end of the tRNA were found to code for a functional tRNA. This is because

A. The –CCA end in the tRNA is not essential for its function.
B. The genes that do not possess sequence corresponding to the –CCA ends of the tRNA are repaired prior to their transcription.
C. The –CCA end is added to the tRNA during their maturation.
D. The primary transcripts of the genes lacking sequence corresponding to the – CCA end are subjected to g-RNA mediated editing prior to their maturation.

DNA Replication, Repair and Recombination

20. You have discovered a new transposon, TnX, and would like to identify its mode of replication. A heteroduplex of the TnX sequence is made with a few mismatches and introduced into bacteria. The newly transposed genomic loci are sequenced. You find that the sequence of the transposon matched exactly with one of its parent strands. This suggests that

A. TnX transposes by conservative transposition mechanism.
B. TnX transposes using a site-specific recombination mechanism.
C. Single-strands of the duplex are inserted.
D. TnX transposes by replicative mechanism.

21. In all organisms, it is critical that replication initiation be tightly controlled to ensure that chromosome number and cell number remain appropriately balanced. Given below are several statements regarding regulation of replication in *E. Coli.*

(*a*) Hemimethylation and sequestration of oriC (origin of replication) by a protein called SeqA prevents initiation of replication.
(*b*) Availability of DnaA protein is an important requirement for initiation of replication.
(*c*) The ratio of ADP : ATP is important as high level of ADP is required for initiation of replication.
(*d*) Recruitment of Hda protein by sliding clamp inhibits ATP hydrolysis required for initiation of replication.

Which of the above statements are NOT true?

A. (*a*) and (*b*) B. (*b*) and (*c*)
C. (*c*) and (*d*) D. (*d*) and (*a*)

22. In *E. coli,* though DNA polymerase I (Pol I) plays an essential role in the replication process, it is not the major polymerase. Instead, the enzyme responsible for advancement of replication fork is Pol III. From the four DNA structures (*a*), (*b*), (*c*) and (*d*)) given below, students made several interpretations about the shorter arm being extended by Pol I and/or Pol III

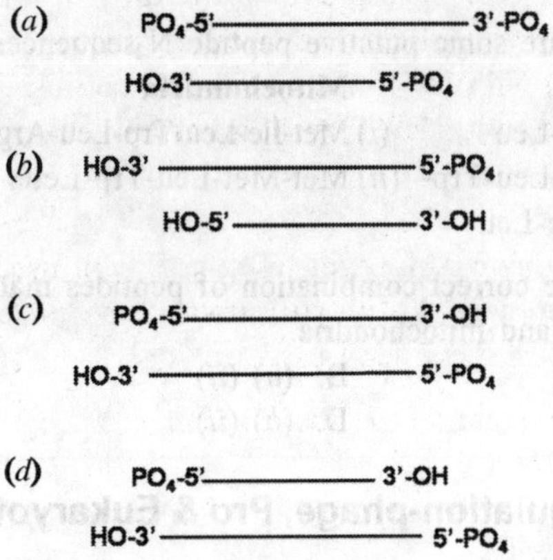

Which one of the interpretation written below is correct?

A. A will be extended by Pol III but not by Pol I.
B. Neither B nor C will be extended by either Pol I or Pol III.
C. C will be extended by both Pol I and Pol III.
D. D will be extended only by Pol I, but not by Pol III.

RNA Synthesis and Processing

23. One of the mechanisms used by bacteria for adaptation to changed environment is altering transcription of their genes. In this regard, which one of the following responses is NOT found in bacteria?

A. A gene with two different promoters for expression in different conditions
B. Use of different sigma factors for transcription of genes
C. Expression of alternate α, β and β′ subunits
D. Expression of anti-sigma factors

24. A highly specific inhibitor that targets the phosphorylation activity of TFIIH is added to an *in vitro* transcription reaction. Which one of the following steps is most likely to be affected?

A. Binding of RNA polymerase to promoter sequence
B. Promoter clearance
C. Recruitment of TFIID
D. Open promoter complex formation

Protein Synthesis and Processing

25. During eukaryotic protein synthesis, stress conditions result in activation of specific kinases leading to phosphorylation of a key translation initiation factor that inhibits protein synthesis from a large number of cellular mRNA. Which one of the following factors is the target of the kinase?

A. eIF4E B. eIF4G
C. eIF2α D. Gcn4

26. Imagine the following RNA sequence is translated in the mammalian cytosol and mitochondria.

RNA sequence:
AUG AUA CUG UGA CUU AGG CUC UAA

Following are some putative peptide N-sequences

Cytosol	Mitochondria
(*a*) Met-Ile-Leu	(*i*) Met-Ile-Leu-Trp-Leu-Arg-Leu
(*b*) Met-Ile-Leu-Trp-Leu-Arg-Leu	(*ii*) Met-Met-Leu-Trp-Leu

Find out the correct combination of peptides made in the cytosol and mitochondria.

A. (*a*) (*i*) B. (*a*) (*ii*)
C. (*b*) (*i*) D. (*b*) (*ii*)

Gene Regulation-phage, Pro & Eukaryotes

27. Which one of the following λ proteins acts both as an activator and repressor of transcription?

A. cI protein B. N protein
C. cII protein D. Q protein

28. A construct (shown below) was generated to access the activity of bidirectional promoter (A and B) which has a common regulatory DNA element (X). The construct was used to transform *E. coli*.

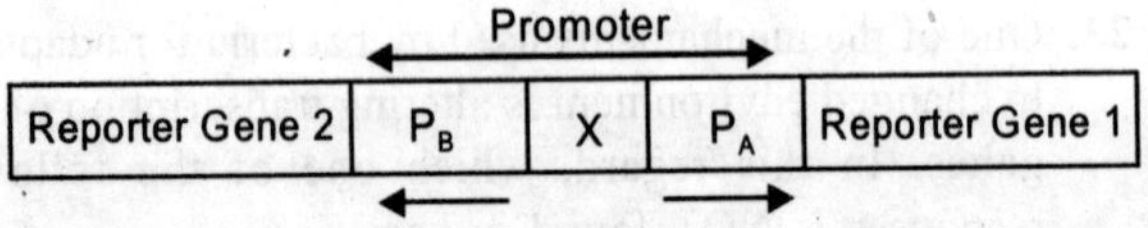

The activity of the promoter (as shown in the graph below) is recorded in the presence of increasing levels of an *E. coli* encoded regulatory protein which binds to DNA element X.

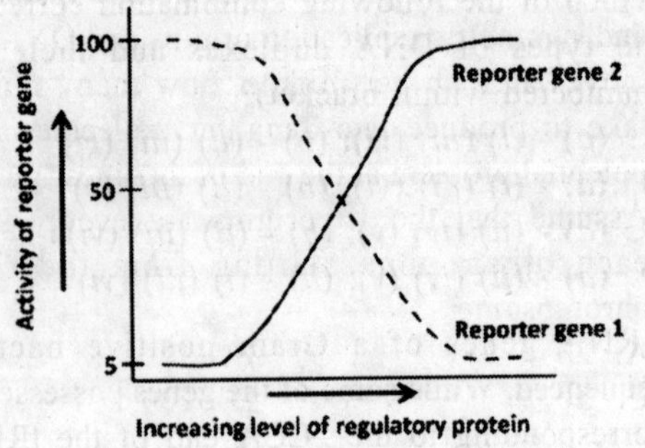

The above experiment is repeated in a mutant *E. coli* with mutation which abolishes binding of the regulatory protein to element X. Which one of the following graphs best depicts the activity of the reporter genes in the mutant strain?

A.
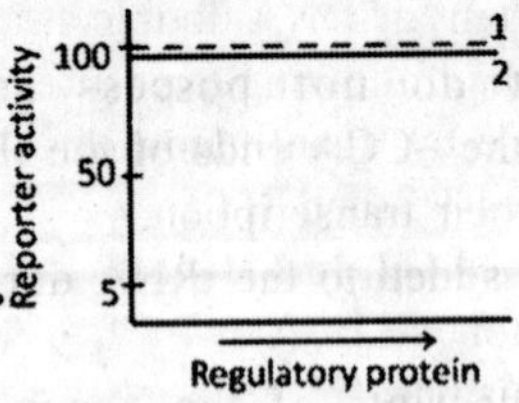

B.
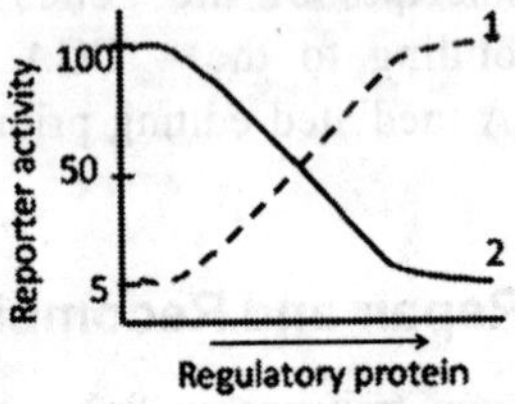

C.
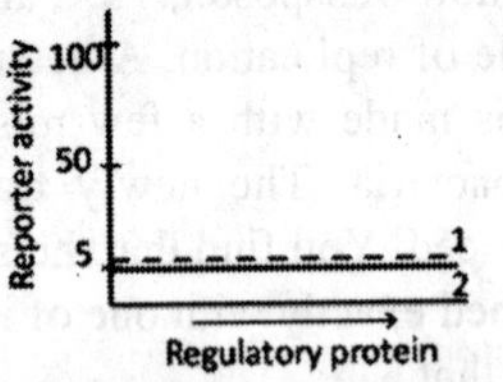

D.
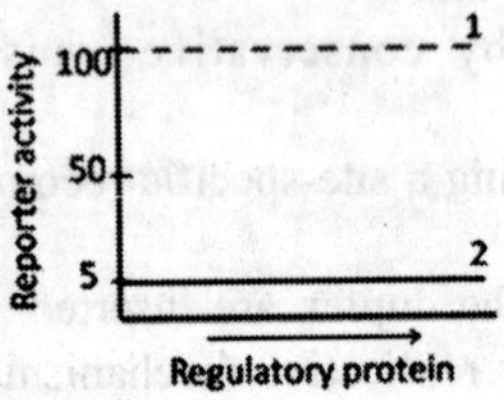

DBT-JRF, 2017

Cellular Processes

29. When DNA is extracted from bacterial cells and analyzed for base composition, it is found that 38% of bases are Cytosine (*C*). What percentage of bases is Adenine (*A*)?

A. 12 B. 24
C. 38 D. 62

30. How many DNA molecules of 6 base pairs length are possible where the first base is a purine and the last base is a pyrimidine?

A. 32 B. 256
C. 4096 D. 1024

31. In a segment of a transcribed gene, the non-template strand of DNA has the following sequence 5 AGCTCACTG..3. What will be the corresponding 5 to 3 sequence in the RNA produced from this segment of the gene?

A. CAGUGAGCU
B. AGCUCACUG
C. CAGTGAGCT
D. UCGAUGAC

32. If a 1000 kb fragment of DNA has 10 evenly spaced and symmetric replication origins and DNA polymerase moves at 1 kb per minute, how many minutes will it take to produce two daughter molecules ignoring the potential problem at the end of the linear piece of DNA? Assume that the 10 origins are evenly spaced from each other, none starting from the ends of the chromosome.

A. 20 B. 30
C. 50 D. 100

33. Transition type of gene mutation is caused when
A. GC is replaced by TA
B. CG is replaced by GC
C. AT is replaced by CG
D. AT is replaced by GC

34. Assessment of the extent of DNA double strand breaks in cultured human cells, following exposure to ionizing radiation, can be done by quantitation of:
A. acetylated histones H3 and H4
B. methylated histones H3 and H4
C. ubiquitylated histone H2A.X
D. phosphorylated histone H2A.X.

35. The melting curve of a DNA solution is represented below. It suggests that:

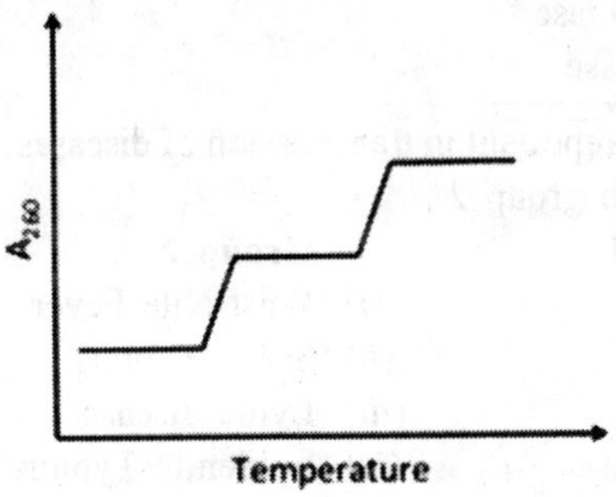

A. The given DNA has one stretch with a biased base composition
B. The given DNA has two stretches with a biased base composition
C. The given DNA has three stretches with a biased base composition
D. The given DNA has an unbiased base composition.

36. From among the options given below, RNA polymerase II transcribes which one of the following?
A. rRNA
B. tRNA
C. MicroRNA
D. None of the given options.

37. E. *coli* RNA polymerase has six subunits two α, one β, one β′, one ω and one σ. Which among these subunits imparts specificity of transcription of a gene and how?
A. ω, by binding to -10 sequence
B. σ, by binding to both -10 and -35 sequences
C. β, by binding to -10 sequence
D. Both σ and ω, by binding to -10 and -35 sequences

38. α-Amanitin is a fungal toxin which inhibits eukaryotic RNA polymerases. The three eukaryotic RNA polymerases show differential sensitivity to this toxin. Which one of the following order (higher to lower) is correct with respect to sensitivity towards α-amanitin?
A. RNA POL III > RNA POL II > RNA POL I
B. RNA POL II > RNA POL III > RNA POL I
C. RNA POL I > RNA POL III > RNA POL II
D. RNA POL II > RNA POL I > RNA POL III

39. Protein synthesis in eukaryotic cells terminates at the stop codon because:
A. mRNA synthesis stops at the stop codon.
B. The tRNA corresponding to the stop codon cannot bind to an amino acidd.
C. There is no naturally occurring tRNA with an anticodon corresponding to the stop codon.
D. The conformation around stop codons prevents binding of aminoacyl tRNA.

40. Which one of the following eIF2α kinases get activated during unfolded protein response (UPR) in mammalian cells?
A. PKR B. GCN_2
C. PERK D. HRI

41. Epidermolysis bullosa simplex (EBS) disease is caused by a mutation in which one of the following genes?
A. β–tubulin B. Keratin
C. Collagen D. Tau

42. The DNA binding domain of a transcription factor that is specifically required for the regulation of gene A is exchanged with the DNA binding domain of another transcription factor that is required specifically for the regulation of gene B. This chimeric transcription factor will regulate:
A. Gene A only
B. Gene B only
C. Both Gene A and B
D. Neither Gene A nor Gene B

43. Which one of the following is NOT important for regulation of the tryptophan operon by attenuation?
A. Presence of two adjacent codons for tryptophan in the leader peptide sequence
B. Coupled transcription-translation
C. Concentration of tRNA charged with tryptophan
D. The operator sequence of tryptophan operon

44. Microscopic evaluation of a post-mortem brain exhibits hyperchromatic areas when stained with glial fibrillary acidic protein (GFAP). This suggests activation of
A. astrocytes B. oligodendrocytes
C. Microglia D. Neurons

45. There are 3 genes A, B and C that are functionally related. There is a point mutation in gene A due to which gene B is not expressed resulting in a non-functional gene C product. What is the possible relationship between these 3 genes?

A. A is an enzyme, B and C are substrates of A
B. A is transcription factor for A and B is needed for C to be functional.
C. B is transcription factor for A and A
D. C is enzyme that requires A and B as its substrate.

46. Which one of the following is NOT enriched in eukaryotic promoters located in active chromatin?
A. Acetylated histones
B. DNase I hypersensitive sites
C. Methylated cytosine
D. Bound TFIID

47. One of the reasons why non-substrate inducers (*e.g.* IPTG) are preferred over substrate inducers (*e.g.* lactose) for induction of an inducible operon is because:
A. They directly interact with the promoter sequences
B. They directly interact with the repressor
C. They directly interact with operator region
D. They interact with the activation sequences and induce enhancers

48. The gene encoding an enzyme A that functions in a metabolic pathway for conversion of metabolite "*x*" to "*y*" was knocked out but it still resulted in the formation of metabolite "*y*". From this it can be concluded that:
A. Enzyme A is necessary but not sufficient for formation of "*y*"
B. Enzyme A is sufficient but not necessary for formation of "*y*"
C. Enzyme A is neither necessary nor sufficient for formation of "*y*"
D. Enzyme A is both necessary and sufficient for formation of "*y*"

49. Introns which are self-splicing and do not require any cofactor for their splicing, are present in the primary transcripts of:
A. miRNA B. Nuclear mRNA
C. tRNA D. Mitochondrial mRNA

50. A recombinant protein is expressed in *E. coli* under T7 promoter at 37°C. However, no biological activity is obtained in the cell lysate. If the same experiment is carried out at 25°C, the cell lysate shows a reasonable biological activity. The most probable explanation for this is:
A. lower temperature increases recombinant protein stability
B. lower temperature increases rate of production of recombinant protein
C. IPTG used for induction does not get degraded
D. recombinant protein is properly folded at low temperature.

51. IPTG is used as an inducer in the T7 expression system for recombinant protein expression in E.coli. This is because of:
A. availability of special *E.coli* cells which have the T7 RNA polymerase gene integrated into their genome under a regulatable promoter
B. T7 promoter is recognized by *E.coli* RNA polymerase
C. High copy number of plasmid allows sequestration of *E.coli* RNA polymerase by T7 promoter
D. IPTG facilitates binding of *E.coli* RNA polymerase to the T7 promoter

52. In humans, the enzyme having reverse transcriptase activity is:
A. Ribonuclease P
B. Ribonuclease D
C. Recombinase
D. Telomerase

53. Vectors are important in transmission of diseases. Match group 1 with group 2

Group 1	Group 2
(*a*) Louse	(*i*) West Nile Fever
(*b*) Tick	(*ii*) Scrub Typhus
(*c*) Mite	(*iii*) Lyme disease
(*d*) Mosquito	(*iv*) Epidemic Typhus

	(*a*)	(*b*)	(*c*)	(*d*)
A.	(*iv*)	(*iii*)	(*ii*)	(*i*)
B.	(*i*)	(*ii*)	(*iii*)	(*iv*)
C.	(*ii*)	(*iii*)	(*iv*)	(*i*)
D.	(*iii*)	(*iv*)	(*i*)	(*ii*)

54. A 20mer DNA contains A, G and C only. In how many ways can this DNA sequence be constructed?
A. 4^{20} B. 20^4
C. 3^{20} D. 20^3

GATE (BIOTECHNOLOGY), 2017

Protein Synthesis and Processing

55. A polymerase chain reaction (PCR) was set up with the following reagents: DNA templates, *Taq polymerase*, buffer, dNTPs, and Mg^{2+} Which one of the following is missing in the reaction mixture?
A. helicase
B. Single- stranded binding protein
C. Primers
D. Reverse Transcriptase

56. In Eukaryotes, cytokinesis is inhibited by
A. cytochalasin D B. vinblastine
C. nocodazole D. colchicine

57. Match the proteins in Group I with cellular processes in Group II

Column I	Column II
P. p53	1. DNA packaging
Q. Lysozyme	2. Apoptosis
R. Tubulins	3. Hydrolysis of polysaccharides
S. Histones	4. Chromosome segregation

A. P-4, Q-2, R-3, S-1
B. P-2, Q-3, R-1, S-4
C. P-4, Q-3, R-1, S-2
D. P-2, Q-3, R-4, S-1

58. A recombinant protein is to be expressed under the control of the lac promoter and operator in a strain of *E.coli* having the genotype $lacI^+$ crp^+. Even in the absence of inducer IPTG, low levels of expression of the recombinant protein are seen (leaky expression). Which one of the following should be done to minimize such leaky expression?

A. Addition of lactose to the medium.
B. Removal of all glucose from the medium.
C. Addition of excess glucose to the medium.
D. Addition of *allo*-lactose to the medium.

GATE (LIFE SCIENCE), 2017

59. Puromycin is a structural analog of

A. alanyl-tRNA B. tyrosyl-tRNA
C. methionyl-tRNA D. glycyl-tRNA

CSIR-NET, JUNE, 2018

Nucleic Acids-forms, Conformation & Stability

60. The following statements are made on nucleic acid structure:

(*a*) In the B-form of DNA, the sugar pucker is C2' endo.
(*b*) In RNA, the sugar pucker is C3' exo.
(*c*) The wobble base pair is formed between G and A in RNA.
(*d*) A change in the sugar pucker from C2' endo in the B form of DNA to C3' endo alters the width and depth of the major groove.

Which one of the following combinations of above statements is correct?

A. (*a*) and (*c*) B. (*b*) and (*d*)
C. (*a*) and (*d*) D. (*b*) and (*c*)

61. A plasmid with a linking number (Lk) of 200, topological winding (Tw) number of 200 and a writhing number (Wr) of 0 was transformed into *E. coli*. The plasmid was re-isolated from the culture of the transformant. The re-isolated plasmid was found to possess the same molecular weight as the original plasmid, but it possessed a writhing number of –5. Following statements are made about this observation.

(*a*) Lk of the re-isolated plasmid would be 195.
(*b*) Lk of the re-isolated plasmid would remain 200.
(*c*) Tw of the re-isolated plasmid would remain 200.
(*d*) Tw of the re-isolated plasmid would be 195.

Which one of the following combinations of the above statements is correct representation of the facts?

A. (*a*) only B. (*a*) and (*c*)
C. (*a*) and (*d*) D. (*d*) only

62. Following statements are being made about the orientation of the N-glycosidic bond between the base and the sugar in the following DNA duplexes.

(*a*) 'anti' for B form DNA duplexes
(*b*) 'syn' for B form DNA duplexes
(*c*) 'anti' for A form DNA duplexes
(*d*) 'syn' for A form DNA duplexes

Which one of the following combinations of the above statements is correct?

A. (*a*) and (*c*) B. (*b*) and (*c*)
C. (*a*) and (*d*) D. (*b*) and (*d*)

DNA Replication, Repair and Recombination

63. *E. coli* takes 40 min. to duplicate its genome using a bi- directional mode of replication. If *E. coli* were to use uni- directional mode of replication to synthesize a full copy of DNA complementary to just one of the strands of the genome, it would take

A. 40 min B. 80 min
C. 20 min D. 60 min

64. *E. coli* DNA ligase catalyses formation of a phosphodiester pond between the adjoining 3' hydroxyl, and the 5' phosphoryl ends in DNA duplexes. The energetic need for this reaction is met by the hydrolysis of NAD+ to NMN+ and AMP in a three- step reaction. Following statements are being made about the mechanism of this reaction.

(*a*) AMP is linked to the 5' phosphoryl end of the nicked DNA.
(*b*) Adenylyl group of NAD+ is transferred to the -amino group of Lys in DNA ligase to form a phosphoamide adduct.

(*c*) DNA ligase catalyses the formation of a phosphodiester bond by the nucleophilic attack of the 3' hydroxyl group onto the phosphate and releases AMP.

Based on the statements made above, identify the correct sequence of the reaction steps.

A. (*a*), (*b*), (*c*)
B. (*a*), (*c*), (*b*)
C. (*b*), (*a*), (*c*)
D. (*c*), (*a*), (*b*)

RNA Synthesis and Processing

65. During maturation process of some RNA molecules, formation of a 2'- 5' phospho-diester bond takes place. Following statements are made about this phenomenon.

(*a*) Spliceosome mediated removal of intronic sequences occurs through the formation of a 2'- 5' phosphodiester bond.

(*b*) Removal of group II introns occurs through the formation of 2'- 5' phospho-diester bond.

(*c*) Enzymatic removal of introns from the yeast tRNA precursors involves 2' - 5' phosphodiester bond formation.

(*d*) RNaseP mediated 5'-end maturation of tRNA precursors involves formation of a 2' - 5' phosphodiester bond.

Which one of the following combinations of the statements is a true representation?

A. (*a*) only
B. (*a*) and (*d*)
C. (*a*) and (*b*)
D. (*c*) and (*d*)

66. A 1257 bp genomic DNA sequence of a prokaryotic gene was cloned under a strong constitutive promoter along with a suitable polyA signal and used for development of transgenic tobacco plants. Molecular analysis revealed the presence of three types/lengths of transgene derived mRNAs: 555 bp, 981 bp and 1257 bp - in the leaves of transgenic plants. The following statements were proposed to explain the above results

(*a*) The three mRNAs represent alternatively spliced transcripts due to the presence of putative intronic sequence in the gene.

(*b*) The gene sequence was characterized by the presence of potential polyadenylation signals that resulted in premature termination of transcription.

(*c*) Expression of full-length transcripts (1257 bases) was lethal to the transformed cells.

(*d*) The transgenic plants were chimeric in nature and comprised of a mix of transformed and untransformed cells.

Which of the following combinations of the above statements would correctly explain the obtained results?

A. (*a*) and (*c*)
B. (*b*) and (*d*)
C. (*a*) and (*b*)
D. (*c*) and (*d*)

Protein Synthesis and Processing

67. Phosphorylation of eIF2 α subunits (at Ser 51) leads to

A. inactivation of Met-tRNA*i*, binding activity of eIF2B.
B. sequestration of eIF2B because of tight binding between eIF2 and eIF2B.
C. degradation of eIF2B.
D. enhanced guanine exchange activity of eIF2B.

68. During translation in prokaryotes, when ribosomes reach the termination codon, the termination codon is recognized by the class I release factors (RF1 or RF2) leading to the release of the polypeptide. A second class II release factor (RF3) facilitates the termination process. Which of the following statements regarding the mechanism of action of the release factors is INCORRECT?

A. Class I release factors decode the stop codons while the RF3 is a GTPase that stimulates recycling of the class I release factors.
B. Free RF3 has a higher affinity for GTP than GDP
C. RF1 and RF2 share a conserved segment of 'GGQ' sequence which is essential for the polypeptide release.
D. RF1and RF2, individually possess another stretch of tripeptide sequences which are involved in the recognition of the termination codons.

Gene Regulation-phage, Pro & Eukaryotes

69. Transcriptional regulation of *trp* operon by tryptophan involves binding of tryptophan to

A. the repressor protein and inhibition of transcription by its interaction with the operator region.
B. RNA polymerase and inhibition of transcription.
C. the repressor protein leading to structural changes and its degradation by proteases.
D. the repressor protein leading to its interaction with the sigma subunit and inhibition of transcription

70. Genes translocated to the heterochromatic regions of chromosomes are silenced. In *S. pombe*, a translocation event was detected wherein a gene of interest was translocated to the centromere region and is silenced. Mutagenesis leading to loss of function of the following target genes was done to allow expression of the gene of interest from its new locus.

(*a*) Mutation in histone deacetylase (Clr3).

(*b*) Mutation in histone acetyltransferase (HAT-8).

(*c*) Mutation in histone H3 lysine 9 methyl transferase (Clr4).

(*d*) Loss of Dicer, an RNA processing enzyme.

Which of the above events could allow the expression of this gene from the centromeric region?

A. (*a*), (*b*) and (*c*)
B. (*a*), (*c*) and (*d*)
C. (*b*) and (*c*) only
D. (*a*) and (*c*) only

CSIR-NET, DECEMBER, 2018

Nucleic Acids-forms, Conformation & Stability

71. Which one of the following statements on nucleic acids is NOT true?
    A. The conformation of ribose in DNA is α- 2'-deoxy-D- ribofuranose.
    B. Hydrolysis of RNA takes place under alkaline conditions unlike DNA, as the 2'-hydroxyl in RNA acts as a nucleophile in an intramolecular displacement
    C. DNA can occur in different three- dimensional forms.
    D. In DNA, deamination of cytosine to uracil can occur in a non-enzymatic manner.

72. Which one of the following statements is NOT correct?
    A. Together with proteins, rRNA provides a site for polypeptide synthesis.
    B. All DNA molecules are unbranched polymers of nucleotides.
    C. DNA is synthesized in a 5'- 3' direction while RNA synthesis occurs in a 3'- 5' direction.
    D. A tRNA anticodon may pair with more than one codon.

73. Deamination of bases is a common chemical event that produces spontaneous mutation. Which one of the following bases will be formed by deamination of 5-methylcytosine?
    A. Uracil   B. Thymine
    C. Cytosine   D. Guanine

74. DNA melting temperature (Tm) was found to be 47°C and enthalpy measured at Tm was 0.032 kJ. The entropy change would be:
    A. 1×10^{-3} kJ   B. 1×10^{-4} kJ
    C. 3×10^{-2} kJ   D. 6×10^{-2} kJ

DNA Replication, Repair and Recombination

75. Following statements have been made about recombination in a diploid organism:
    (*a*) Recombination could be identified by genotyping parents and offsprings for a pair of loci.
    (*b*) Recombination frequency does not exceed 0.5, and therefore, 50cM would be the maximum distance between two loci.
    (*c*) Recombination is a reciprocal process. However, a non-reciprocal exchange may cause gene conversion.
    (*d*) Occasionally non-homologous recombination happens and this functions as a source of chromosomal rearrangement.

    Select the combination with all correct statements.
    A. (*a*), (*b*), (*c*)   B. (*a*), (*b*), (*d*)
    C. (*b*), (*c*), (*d*)   D. (*a*), (*c*), (*d*)

RNA Synthesis and Processing

76. Which one of the following statements is generally true about RNA polymerase II?
    A. It is dedicated to transcribing RNA from a single transcription unit, generally a large transcript which is then processed to yield three types of ribosomal RNA.
    B. It transcribes varieties of small non- coding RNAs which are expressed in all cell types.
    C. It generally synthesizes various types of mRNAs and small non-coding RNAs.
    D. It is exclusively involved in synthesis of rRNA and tRNA.

77. An intron in a yeast reporter gene carries a mutation in the splice site branch point (UACUAAC to UACA*AAC). To suppress the mutation, a library of point mutants of snRNAs was introduced into the mutant strain. The suppressor is most likely to have a point mutation in:
    A. U1 snRNA   B. U2 snRNA
    C. RNaseP   D. U6 snRNA

Protein Synthesis and Processing

78. Which one of the following activities is NOT involved in protein folding in the endoplasmic reticulum?
    A. Peptidylprolylisomerase
    B. Protein disulphide isomerase
    C. Protein glycosylation
    D. Protein ubiquitination

79. What would be the tripeptide produced by translation of the transcript produced by the following DNA sequence?
    3'-AAGTA CTCT-5'
    A. Arg-Phe-Trp   B. Arg - Leu - Gly
    C. Thr- Lys –Ser   D. Phe - Met – Arg

80. Which one of the following inactivates the serine/threonine protein kinase, mTOR, related to cell growth in mammalian system?
    A. Rifamycin   B. Rapamycin
    C. Erythromycin   D. Chloramphenicol

81. Presence of selenocysteine in proteins in *E. coli* is a consequence of:
    A. post-translational modification of cysteine present in special structural regions of the proteins by SelB and SelC.

B. post-translational modification of serine present in special structural regions of the proteins by SelB and SelC.
C. aminoacylation of a special tRNA (tRNASeCys) by serine tRNA synthetase with serine followed by further modification of the attached serine to selenocysteine followed by its transport to the ribosome by SelB.
D. aminoacylation of a special tRNA (tRNASeCyt) by serine tRNAsynthetase with selenocysteine followed by its transport to ribosome by SelB.

Gene Regulation-phage, Pro & Eukaryotes

82. mRNA of a gene was depleted in human cells using siRNA that arrest cells in the G2 phase of the cell cycle. In order to test whether the G2 arrest is due to an off-target or all on-target effect of siRNA mediated mRNA depletion, an investigator can:
(*a*) re-introduce an ectopic copy of the gene coding for the wild-type mRNA and protein
(*b*) re-introduce an ectopic copy of the gene that is different in its mRNA sequence at the siRNA target site but encodes for the same protein
(*c*) re-introduce an ectopic copy of the gene that codes for-different mRNA and protein
(*d*) utilize few more siRNAs targeting different regions of the mRNA in question

Choose the combination with correct statements:
A. (*a*), (*b*), (*c*) only B. (*c*) and (*d*) only
C. (*b*) and (*d*) only D. (*b*), (*c*), (*d*) only

83. A DNA segment was cloned into the active site region of *lacZ*gene and the recombinant plasmid introduced into lac Z- strain of *E. coli* and plated on a medium containing X-gal. The colonies showed blue color. Which one of the following statements is correct?
A. The nature of the cloned DNA segment need not be special as cloning of any DNA in *lacZ*will result in disruption of its reading frame and production of blue colour on X-gal plates.
B. The cloned DNA segment could be a Group I intron whose removal from the precursor *lac Z* transcript in *E. coli* results in production of mature *lac Z* mRNA which can then produce active Lac Z protein.
C. The cloned sequence is likely to be *lac* sequence which is naturally a part of *lac* operon in *E. coli.*
D. The cloned sequence is likely to be an anti-terminator sequence which allows full length transcription of *lacZ.*

84. A researcher wanted to identify the enhancer sequences of a newly discovered gene. Shown below are the relevant regions of some of the reporter constructs the researcher designed to identify the enhancer.

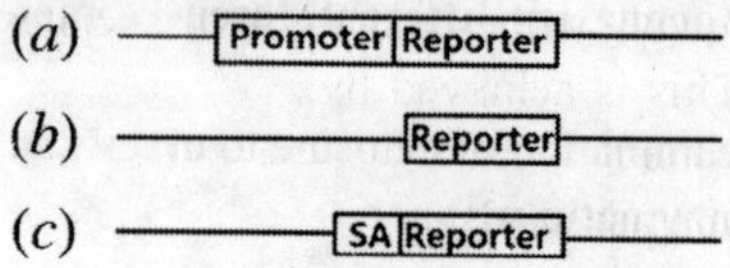

SA = Splice site Acceptor

Which of the above constructs can be used to identify the enhancer?
A. (*a*) only
B. (*b*) only
C. Both (*a*) and (*c*)
D. (*c*) only

85. Construction of knockout mice may be performed using the Cre-LoxP system. Eventually, the Cre recombinase of the bacteriophage P1 mediates site- specific recombination at a 34 bp sequence, lox P. From the following statements, choose the INCORRECT event:
A. The alteration of the chromosomal copy of the target gene requires a guide RNA.
B. The *lox*P containing mice should not express *Cre* recombinase prior to mating.
C. The *Cre* recombinase can be expressed by an inducible promoter.
D. Induction of the promoter results in the expression of *Cre*, recombination at lox P sites and excision of the sequence in between.

DBT-JRF, 2018

Cellular Processes

86. If a completely radioactive double stranded DNA molecule undergoes two rounds of replication in a non-radioactive medium, what will be the radioactivity status of the four resulting molecules?
A. Half the number of molecules contains no radioactivity
B. All four molecules contain radioactivity
C. Three out of four molecules contain radioactivity
D. Radioactivity is lost from all four molecules

87. Asymmetry of the DNA denaturation-renaturation curve
A. is directly proportional to the genomic complexity
B. is inversely proportional to the genomic complexity
C. is directly proportional to the AT content
D. has no correlation with genomic complexity.

88. In E. coli, mismatch during replication is corrected by the mismatch repair (MMR) pathway. For this, the MMR proteins differentiate between the parent and daughter strand by:
A. Identifying the methylation on the daughter strand

B. Identifying the methylation on the parent strand
C. Identifying methylation on both strands
D. Identifying lack of methylation on both strands

89. The deletion of gene X in mice did not result in any abnormality. Further, to investigate the function of the gene, at least five null mice of the same sex are needed. What is the minimum number of pups from heterozygous parents to be screened to obtain the required number?

A. 10 B. 20
C. 40 D. 80

90. During DNA replication the newly generated strand remains attached the template. However, during transcription newly synthesized RNA dissociates from the template. This is achieved by:

A. RNase H
B. RNA polymerase itself
C. DNA Polymerase
D. Spontaneous dissociation

91. Deamination of which of the following bases will NOT be recognized by the DNA damage repair machinery?

A. Cytosine B. 5-Methyl cytosine
C. Adenine D. Guanine

92. In an eukaryotic pre-mRNA the number of positions where polyadenylate modifications occur is:

A. 5 B. 2
C. 3 D. 4

93. The DNA sequence in the box undergoes an inversion. What is the final DNA sequence after inversion?

5'-TAGCC|GGTATC|CCGAT-3'
3'-ATCGG|CCATAG|GGCTA-5'

A. TAGCC|GATACC|CCGAT
ATCGG|CTATGG|GGCTA

B. TAGCC|CCATAG|CCGAT
ATCGG|GGTATC|GGCTA

C. TAGCC|CTATGG|CCGAT
ATCGG|GATACC|GGCTA

D. CCGAT|GATACC|TAGCC
GGCTA|CTATGG|ATCGG

94. The natural primer for reverse transcriptase in RNA tumor viruses is:

A. Oligo-dT B. rRNA
C. 5S RNA D. tRNA

95. Taq DNA polymerase differs from the Klenow fragment in having:

A. 5'-3' polymerase activity
B. 5'-3' exonuclease activity
C. 3'-5' exonuclease activity
D. Endonuclease activity

96. The common feature of Rho-independent and Rho-dependent termination of transcription is:

A. the active signal lies in the direct repeats in nascent RNA
B. the active signal lies in double stranded DNA template
C. the active signal lies in nascent RNA
D. both require ATP

97. Protein glycosylation can take place only on the following amino acid(s):

A. Asparagine
B. Serine and Threonine
C. Asparagine, serine and threonine
D. Asparagine, serine, threonine and arginine

98. Gamma phosphate labelled ATP molecule was used to labela DNA fragment using the nick translation protocol. This would result in:

A. Labelling at 5' end
B. Labelling at 3' end
C. Labelling at both 3' and 5' ends
D. No labelling of DNA

99. Primer extension is a technique employed for mapping the:

A. Translational start site
B. Transcription factor binding site
C. Transcription initiation site
D. Ribosome binding site

100. UGA is NOT a stop codon in:

A. Plant nuclear encoded proteins
B. Plant mitochondria
C. Yeast nuclear encoded proteins
D. Yeast mitochondria

101. Among the merodiploid of the lac operon in E. coli, which one is NOT inducible by lactose?

A. $i^- p\ o\ z / i\ p\ o\ z$
B. $i^- p\ o\ z / i\ p^- o\ z$
C. $i^- p\ o^- z / i\ p\ o^- z$
D. $i\ p\ o\ z / i\ p\ o\ z^-$

102. A sample genetic code is given below:

Amino Acid	Pro	Val	Gly	His	Asp	Tyr	Thr	Lys
Codon	CCN	GUN	GGN	CAY	GAY	UAY	CAN	AAR

If an amino acid substitution matrix based on genetic code is derived for sequence alignment and analysis from evolutionary studies, which one of the following is true?

A. Pro is most similar to His
B. Pro is most similar to Thr
D. Gly is most similar to Lys
C. Asp is most similar to Thr.

103. 'P' is a cis-acting element, while 'Q' is a trans-acting element. Possible examples of 'P' and 'Q' are:

A. Enhancer and transcription factor
B. Transcription factor and operator
C. Promoter and operator
D. Transcription factor and promoter

104. Promoter: transcription:
A. Shine-Dalgarno: translation
B. DNA polymerase:replication
C. Ribosome:translation
D. DnaA:replication

105. A linear double stranded DNA is self-circularized by ligation with T4 DNA ligase. At which concentration (μg/ml) of DN would the self-circularization yield be maximum?
A. 30 B. 10
C. 5 D. 0.5

106. In a cell, a repressor binds to its cognate operator with a KD = 10^{-9}M. The cellular concentration of the repressor is 10^{-8}M. The extent of repressor bound to the operator is:
A. 100% B. 50%
C. 37% D. 0%

107. Termination of mRNA transcription in Saccharomyces cerevisiae is mediated by:
A. Rho-dependent termination
B. Rho-independent termination
C. Polyadenylation signal
D. Sigma factor directed termination

108. A Bacillus culture growing in a rich medium was shifted to a sporulation medium. Which of the following is expected to occur?
A. Genome and transcriptome will change
B. Genome will not change, but transcriptome will change
C. Transcriptome will not change, but proteome will change
D. Genome, transcriptome and proteome will not change

109. Which of the following statements is NOT correct about enhancers?
A. They can function in either orientation
B. They decrease the binding of activators near the promoter
C. They increase the binding of activators near the promoter
D. They can function upstream or downstream of the gene

110. Positive and negative selection markers are utilized to screen for recombinants from wild type populations. Which one of the following can be used for negative selection in bacteria?
A. Lac Z
B. β-lactamase
C. Sac B
D. Neomycin amino phosphotransferase

111. A mammalian cell culture is treated with cycloheximide. Protein synthesis of cells after treatment was recorded through incorporation of labelled amino acids. In which of the following organelles will fresh protein synthesis be detected?
A. Nucleus B. ER
C. Mitochondria D. Golgi

GATE (BIOTECHNOLOGY), 2018

112. If a segment of a sense strand of DNA is 5'-ATGGACCAGA-3', then the resulting RNA sequence after transcription is
A. 5'-AGACCAGGTA-3'
B. 5'-UCUGGUCCAU-3'
C. 5'-UACCUGGUCU-3'
D. 5'-AUGGACCAGA-3'

113. Match the classes of RNA molecules in Group I with their functions in Group II.

Group I	Group II
P. snoRNA	1. Protects germline from transposable elements
Q. piRNA	2. Blocks translation of selected mRNA
R. miRNA	3. Template for telomere elongation
S. snRNA	4. Modification and processing of rRNA
	5. Splicing of RNA transcripts

A. P-3, Q-5, R-2, S-4 B. P-1, Q-3, R-2, S-5
C. P-1, Q-4, R-5, S-2 D. P-4, Q-1, R-2, S-5

114. The repeat sequence of telomere in humans is
A. 5'-TATAAT-3' B. 5'-TTAGGG-3'
C. 5'-GGGCCC-3' D. 5'-AAAAAA-3'

CSIR-NET, JUNE, 2019

Nucleic Acids-forms, Conformation & Stability

115. On sequence analysis of a double stranded DNA, the results showed the content of cytosine, C was 20%. What is the amount of A and T put together?
A. 20% B. 30%
C. 50% D. 60%

116. Sugar puckering in double stranded nucleic acids is exclusively
A. C-2' endo in double stranded DNA

B. C-3' endo in double stranded DNA
C. C-2' endo in double stranded RNA
D. C-3' endo in hybrid duplex with one strand as DNA and other as RNA

117. The different arms in the tRNA structure are shown in Column A. The specific signatures associated with the different arms are shown in Column B.

Column A	Column B
(*a*) Acceptor arm	(*i*) Dihydrouridine
(*b*) Anticodon Arm	(*ii*) 8 bp stem and CCA sequence
(*c*) TψC arm	(*iii*) 5 bp stem
(*d*) D-arm	(*iv*) Pseudo-uridine

Choose the correct matches from the following:

	(*a*)	(*b*)	(*c*)	(*d*)
A.	(*ii*)	(*iv*)	(*i*)	(*iii*)
B.	(*i*)	(*iii*)	(*iv*)	(*ii*)
C.	(*iv*)	(*i*)	(*ii*)	(*iii*)
D.	(*ii*)	(*iii*)	(*iv*)	(*i*)

DNA Replication, Repair and Recombination

118. During replication, RNaseH removes all of the RNA primer except the ribonucleotide directly linked to the DNA end. This is because
A. it can degrade RNA and DNA end. From their 5' end.
B. it can only cleave bonds between two ribonucleotides.
C. it can degrade RNA and DNA from their 3' end.
D. activity of RNaseH is inhibited by the presence of duplex containing both strands as DNA.

119. In a human cell line, a large fraction of double-strand DNA breaks are repaired by non-homologous end joining (NHEJ). An inhibitor of FLAP endonuclease will affect
A. recruitment of DNA–dependent kinase
B. gap trimming
C. DNA unwinding
D. pairing of micro-homology regions.

120. Following statements have been made about removal of supercoiling produced by DNA unwinding at the replication fork:
(*a*) Accumulation of supercoils is the result of DNA helicase activity during unwinding of DNA
(*b*) Problem of DNA supercoiling is valid only for circular chromosomes of bacteriaand not for the linear chromosomes
(*c*) Supercoiling of DNA is removed by topoisomerases by breaking either one or both strands of DNA on the unreplicated DNA in front of replication fork.
(*d*) Both topoisomerase I and topoisomerase can remove positive super-coiling during replication

Which one of the following options has all correct statements?
A. (*a*), (*b*) and (*c*)
B. (*a*), (*b*) and (*d*)
C. (*a*), (*c*) and (*d*)
D. (*b*), (*c*) and (*d*)

121. For Escherichia coli chromosomal DNA replication, which one of the following statements is true?
A. DNA polymerase I is the main polymerase required for DNA replication
B. DNA polymerase I though identified originally by Kornberg as the one responsible for replication, is not important for the DNA replication process
C. Requirement of DNA polymerase I is in the context of removal of RNA primer needed for DNA synthesis, and then fill in the same with DNA equivalent
D. DNA polymerase I is the primary enzyme for error prone DNA synthesis in response to SOS.

RNA Synthesis and Processing

122. Eukaryotic mRNA are modified to possess a 5' cap structure. Which one of the following is an INCORRECT statement about the function of the 5' cap structure?
A. It protects the mRNA from 5'→3' exo-ribonuclease attack.
B. It facilitates splicing of the nascent transcripts
C. It protects the transcripts from degradation by RNAse III family enzymes.
D. It facilitates attachments to 40S subunit of ribosome

123. In an experiment, the student has infected mammalian host cell with cytoplasmic RNA virus. The virus growth was monitored by measuring the intracellular viral RNA at different time intervals. It was observed that viral RNA titre progressively went down with time, particularly 12 hours post infection.

Following are few possibilities which can explain this observation.
(*a*) The virus infection triggered upregulation of miRNAs that might have down-regulated the host factor critical for viral RNA replication.
(*b*) The virus might encode miRNAs that regulate (inhibits) its own replication.
(*c*) One of the viral proteins inhibits replication of the viral RNA to restrict rapid proliferation.
(*d*) Viral RNA goes to nucleus with time and thus not detectable in the cytoplasm 12 hour post infection.

Which one of the following options has all correct statements?
A. (*a*), (*b*) and (*c*)
B. (*a*), (*c*) and (*d*)
C. (*a*), (*b*) and (*d*)
D. (*b*), (*c*) and (*d*)

Protein Synthesis and Processing

124. Thermodynamics of protein folding is depicted as a free energy funnel below.

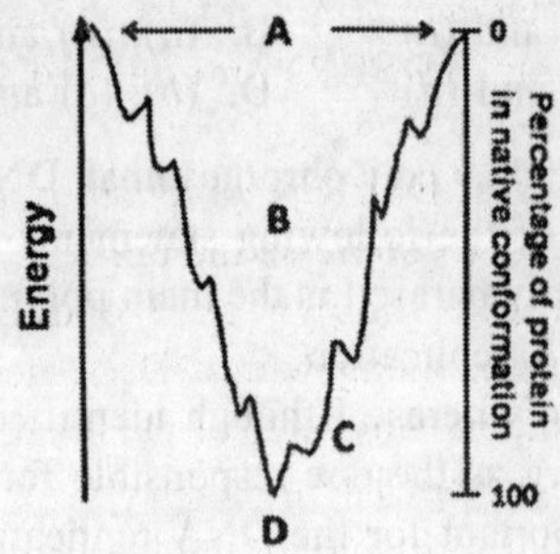

Gives below are regions in the diagram (Column X) and their representation (Column) Y

X	Y
(*a*)	(*i*) Native structure
(*b*)	(*ii*) Structure with highest entropy
(*c*)	(*iii*) Molten Globule
(*d*)	(*iv*) Discrete folding intermediates

A. A – (*ii*); B – (*iii*); C – (*iv*); D – (*i*)
B. A – (*i*); B – (*ii*); C – (*iii*); D – (*iv*)
C. A – (*iii*); B – (*iv*); C – (*ii*); D – (*i*)
D. A – (*iv*); B – (*i*); C – (*ii*); D – (*iii*)

125. Phosphorylation of the α-subunit of eIF2 at Ser 51 position in *Saccharomyces cerevisiae* leads to sequestration of eIF2B, guanosine exchange factor. This phenomenon is
A. known to activate translation of the capped mRNAs in the cytosol
B. known to activate translation of many key mRNAs possessing short ORFs (uORFs) in the mRNA sequence that proceed the main ORF.
C. an essential requirement for translation of IRES containing mRNAs.
D. an essential requirement for the transport of mature mRNAs out of the nucleus.

Gene Regulation-phage, Pro & Eukaryotes

126. In a strain of *E. coli*, a fusion between the *lac* and *trp* operon took place and the new locus structure is shown below. The strain lacks the wild-type *trp* operon.

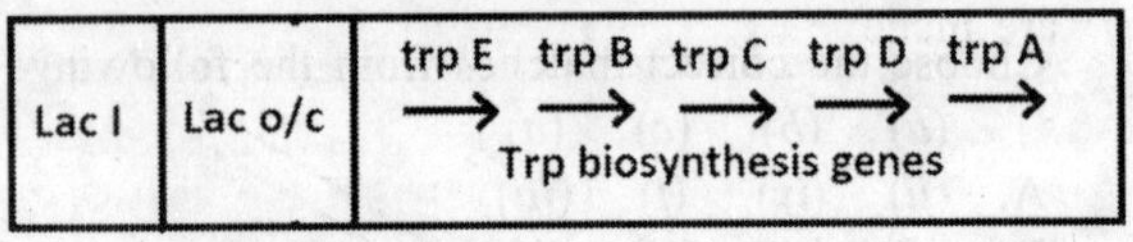

Given below are some of the potential scenarios:
(*a*) Tryptophan will be synthesized in a medium containing lactose and tryptophan.
(*b*) Tryptophan synthesis will be repressed in a medium containing glucose.
(*c*) Tryptophan synthesis will take place only in the absence of sufficient tryptophan in the medium.

Choose the option that correctly describes the behaviours of the fusion operon.
A. (*a*) and (*b*)
B. (*a*) and (*c*)
C. (*c*) only
D. (*b*) and (*c*)

CSIR-NET, 15 DECEMBER, 2019

Nucleic Acids-forms, Conformation & Stability

127. In context of DNA methylation, which one of the following statements is FALSE?
A. Generally, methylation occurs at the 3rd carbon position of cytosine and converts it to 3-methyl cytosine
B. Maintenance methyl transferase acts constitutively on hemi-methylated sites and converts them to fully methylated sites
C. During mammalian gametogenesis, the genomic methylation patterns are erased in primordial germ cells
D. Replication converts a fully methylated site to hemi-methylated site

128. A form and Z form of double stranded DNA differ in the handedness of their helices, nucleotide sequences, and configuration of base to sugar. Based on these properties, which one of the following statements defines a correct combination for A and Z forms of DNA?
A. Right handed double helix and anti-configuration for the base to sugar arrangement inA DNA; and left handed double helix with alternating Sequence of G and C(as a general pattern), and alternating syn and anti- configurations for the base to sugar arrangement in the Z DNA.
B. Right handed double helix and syn-configuration for the base to sugar arrangement in A DNA; and left handed double helix with alternating A and G sequence (as a general pattern), and anti-configurations for base to sugar arrangement in the Z DNA.
C. Left handed double helix and anti-configuration for base to sugar arrangement in the A for DNA and right handed double helix and syn-configuration for base to sugar arrangement in the Z form DNA.
D. Left handed double helix and syn-configuration for base to sugar arrangement in the A form DNA and right handed double helix and anti-configuration for the base to sugar arrangement for the Z form DNA.

129. The following statements are made
(*a*) B form of DNA has –10 base pairs/turn and A form of DNA has -2.3Å helix rise per base pair
(*b*) Both the A and B form of DNA have wider major groove and narrow minor groove

(*c*) The crystalline nature of cellulose is brought about by α(1-4) linkage between the glucose subunits.
(*d*) The double bonds in natural lipids are always cis, which provides fluidity to the plasma membrane.

Which of the following combinations represent the correct statements?

A. (*a*) and (*c*) B. (*b*) and (*c*)
C. (*a*) and (*d*) D. (*c*) and (*d*)

DNA Replication, Repair and Recombination

130. The figure below shows the structure of a replication fork. Based on this information following statements are made:

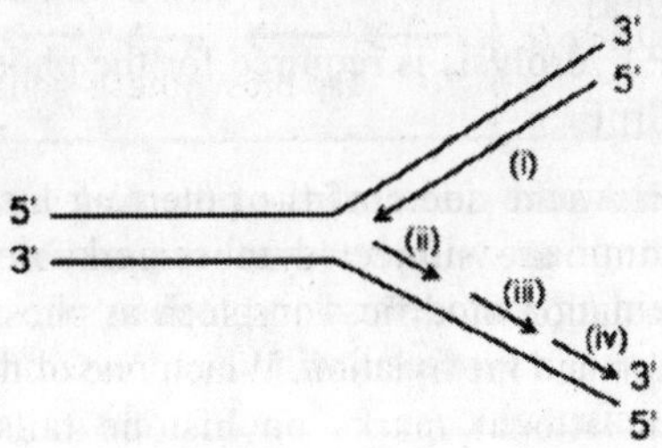

(*a*) (*i*) represents the leading strand while (*ii*), (*ii*) and (*iv*) represent the Okazaki fragments.
(*b*) Among the Okazaki fragments, synthesis of (*iv*) occurs prior to the synthesis of (*iii*) and (*i*)
(*c*) Among the Okazaki fragments, synthesis of (*ii*) occurs prior to the synthesis of (*iii*) and (*iv*).

Which one of the following options represents the correct statement(s)?

A. (*a*) only B. (*b*) only
C. (*a*) and (*b*) D. (*a*) and (*c*)

131. In the diagram below, the dotted line marks the point of initiation of bidirectional replication

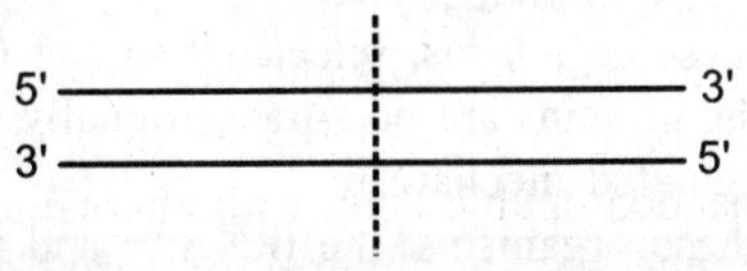

(*a*) On the right side of the dotted line, leading strand synthesis occurs using the upper strand as the template.
(*b*) On the right side of the dotted line, leading strand synthesis occurs using the lower strand as the template.
(*c*) A ligase deficient (*lig*⁻) mutant would affect replication of the upper strand on the left side of the dotted line.
(*d*) A ligase deficient (*lig*⁻) mutant would affect replication of the lower strand on the left side of the dotted line.

Which one of the following options represents the combinations of the correct statements?

A. (*a*) and (*d*) B. (*b*) and (*c*)
C. (*b*) and (*d*) D. (*a*) and (*c*)

132. Following statements are made about double-strand break repair (DSBR) model of homologous recombination:

(*a*) A Process of DSBR recombination is triggered by introducing a double-strand break in a DNA duplex
(*b*) In a process known as 3-end resection, the exonucleases along with a DNA helicase degrade one strand on either side of the break and generates 3'-single stranded termini
(*c*) One strand of the donor duplex is displaced due to formation of heteroduplex DNA and generates a displacement loop (D-Loop)
(*d*) Branch migration allows the point of crossover to move in 5'3' direction of recipient strand
(*e*) Completion of DSBR recombination may generate either crossover recombinant or non-recombinant product

Which one of the following combination of statements is correct?

A. (*a*), (*b*) and (*d*) B. (*a*), (*c*) and (*e*)
C. (*a*), (*c*) and (*d*) D. (*a*), (*b*) and (*e*)

RNA Synthesis and Processing

133. Which one of the following statements related to transcription and processing of mRNA is INCORRECT?

A. During prokaryotic transcription, DNA binding properties of RNA polymerase are altered by sigma factor
B. In eukaryotic transcription, synthesis of rRNA, mRNA and some small RNAs occurs by RNA polymerases I, II and III, respectively
C. Splicing observed in tRNA involves successive/sequential cleavage and ligation reactions while pre-mRNA splicing proceeds through lariat formation.
D. mRNA with premature stop codons are degraded by Nonsense-Mediated Decay (NMD) and mRNAs without an in-frame stop codon get accumulated and translated in the cytoplasm

134. Deletion analysis of a promoter region of a gene was carried out to identify the regulatory elements in it. In the figure below, the filled boxes denote the areas of deletion and the observed activities (in arbitrary units) of the promoter are as shown.

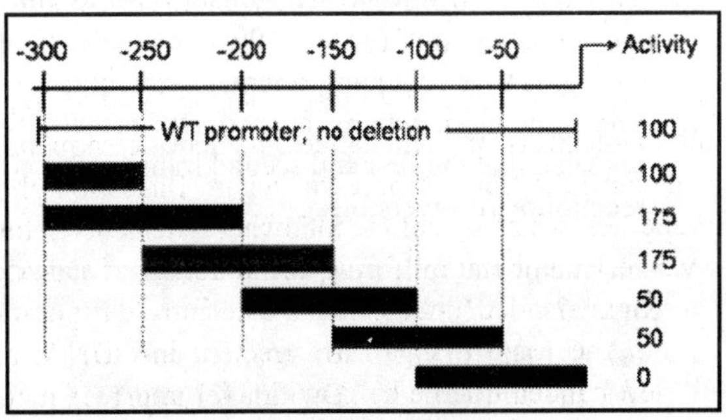

Based on the observations, following statements were made:

(*a*) The region between-100 and -50 houses a positive regulatory element.

(*b*) The region between -200 and -250 houses a negative regulatory element

(*c*) The region between -150 and -200 houses a positive regulatory element.

Which one of the following options represents the correct interpretation of the data?

A. Both (*a*) and (*b*) B. (*a*) only
C. (*b*) only D. Both (*b*) and (*c*)

135. Following statements were made with respect to transcription in eukaryotes:

(*a*) A RNA polymerase III synthesizes mRNAs in the nucleoplasm

(*b*) The target promoter for RNA polymerase III is usually represented by a bipartite sequence downstream of the transcription start site.

(*c*) The assembly factors TFIIIA and TFIIIC assist the binding of the positioning factor TFIIIB at the precise location.

(*d*) TFIIIB is the last factor that joins the initiation complex.

(*e*) Phosphorylated Ser residues in the C-terminal domain (CTD) of RNA polymerase II serve as binding sites for mRNA processing enzymes.

Which one of the following options represents the correct combination of the statements?

A. (*a*), (*b*) and (*c*) B. (*b*), (*c*) and (e)
C. (*b*), (*d*) and (e) D. (*a*), (*c*) and (e)

136. Following statements were made about the post-transcriptional processing of RNA in eukaryotes.

(*a*) Soon after transcription initiation, RNA polymerase II pauses -30 nucleotides downstream from the site of initiation until the Cap structure is added to the 5' end of the nascent pre- mRNA

(*b*) The 5' splice sites are functionally divergent whereas the 3 sites are functionally equivalent.

(*c*) In addition to helping in recognition of the splice sites, the exon definition also functions as a splicing regulator by allowing pairing and linking of adjacent 5 and 3' splice sites.

(*d*) The intron definition mechanism applies only to the larger introns (above 500 nucleotides length) and assists in achieving alternate splicing.

(*e*) The splicing reactions carried out in vitro have revealed that the first and second trans-esterification reactions are reversible.

Which one of the following combination of statements is correct?

A. (*a*), (*b*) and (*d*) B. (*b*), (*c*) and (*d*)
C. (*b*), (*d*) and (*e*) D. (*a*), (*c*) and (*e*)

Protein Synthesis and Processing

137. In a form of stress response, bacteria synthesize a group of proteins called stress proteins (or heat shock proteins) such as DnaK, DnaJ, GroEL, GroES, and GrpE. DnaK is an ATP binding protein, which attaches to the newly synthesized polypeptide in conjunction with DnaJ. Which one of the following statements correctly states a step in the subsequent process of protein folding?

A. The affinity of DnaK to the polypeptide increases upon hydrolysis of the ATP to ADP.
B. DnaJ is an exchange factor that replaces ADP with ATP in DnaK
C. ATP hydrolysis is required for the phosphorylation of DnaJ
D. ATP hydrolysis is required for the phosphorylation of GrpE

138. The amino acid side chains of the four histones in the nucleosome are subjected to remarkable variety of post-translation modifications such as phosphorylation, acetylation and methylation. Which one of the following post-translational marks on histone tails is usually associated with transcriptional repression?

A. Acetylation of H3K9
B. Methylation of H3K9
C. Acetylation of H4K5
D. Phosphorylation of H3S10

139. Many organisms encode only 18 aminoacyl-tRNA synthetases (aaRS). These organisms lack aaRS that use Asn or Gln (as one of the substrates) for direct aminoacylation of the $tRNA^{Asn}$and $tRNA^{Gln}$, respectively. Which one of the following statements represents the correct option?

A. The organisms lacking AsnRS and InRs lack Asn and Gln in their proteins.
B. In these organisms, selected Asp and Glu residues in the proteins are post-translationally modified by a regulated mechanism.
C. In these organisms, the $tRNA^{Asn}$ and $tRNA^{Gln}$ are first aminoacylated by AspRS and GluRS, respectively, and then the Asp and Glu attached to the tRNAs are modified to Asnand Gln, respectively.
D. In these organisms, the precursors of mRNAs that encode AspRS and GluRS are alternatively spliced to generate AsnRs and GinRs.

140. Ribosomes prepared from a bacterium were fractionated by sucrose density gradient centrifugation (panel i) to separate the 30S, 50S and 70S populations. When the ribosome preparation was incubated individually with either elongation factor-G (EF-G), or a newly identified protein X, Or GTP, the profile remained unchanged. Likewise, no changes were seen in the profile when the ribosomal preparation was incubated with EF-G + GTP or protein X + GTP. However, when the ribosomal preparation was incubated with protein X, EF-G and

GTP together, it resulted in a change of profile which showed a decrease of the 70S peak area and increase in the peak areas for 30S and 50S (panel *ii*).

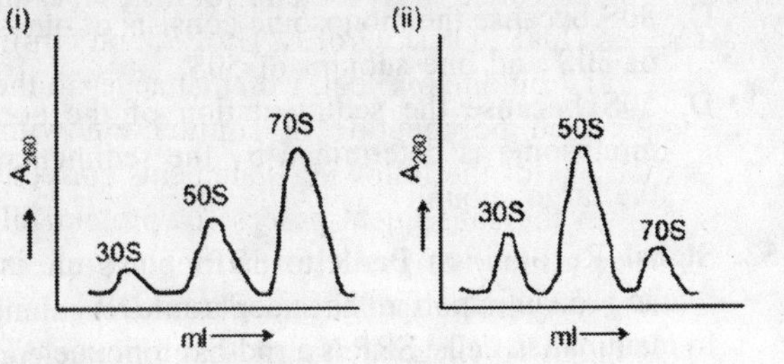

Choose the option that defines a correct conclusion from the observations.

A. Protein X is an anti-association factor which functions in the presence of EF-G and GTP
B. Protein X is a dissociation factor which functions in the presence of EF-G and GTP
C. Protein X binds GTP
D. EF-G is known to bind GTP, hence it can be concluded that the effect of GTP is through EF-G and protein X does not bind GTP.

Gene Regulation-phage, Pro & Eukaryotes

141. Which one of the following regulatory proteins can act as a positive and negative regulator on binding to the same DNA elements?

A. Lac repressor (LacI)
B. Lambda (CI) repressor
C. Ara C protein (AraC)
D. Tip repressor (TrpR)

142. Readers of histone modifications include:

A. SUN domain proteins
B. BAG domain proteins
C. PAS domain proteins
D. TUDOR domain proteins

CSIR-NET, 27 DECEMBER, 2019

Nucleic Acids-forms, Conformation & Stability

143. Following statements were made about the presence of various hydrogen bond acceptor/donor groups in the major groove of B form DNA.

(*a*) 4 and 6 amino groups, of cytosine and adenine, respectively.
(*b*) 4 and 6 keto groups of thymine and guanine, respectively.
(*c*) 2 and 6 amino groups of guanine and adenine, respectively.
(*d*) 2 keto and 4 amino groups of thymine and cytosine, respectively.

Which one of the following options consists of all correct statements?

A. (*a*) and (*b*) B. (*b*) and (*c*)
C. (*c*) and (*d*) D. (*a*) and (*d*)

144. Following observations were made about tRNA.

(*a*) tRNA encoding genes cluster at specific regions of the human genome
(*b*) 5' end of the mature tRNA is generated by RNAse P mediated cleavage
(*c*) Modified bases may confer increased stability to tRNA
(*d*) Modified bases of tRNA do not affect the pattern of wobble pairing
(*e*) Suppressor tRNAs compete with the release factors to read the termination codons

Which one of the following combinations of statements represents correct observations?

A. (*a*), (*c*), (*e*) B. (*b*), (*e*), (*d*)
C. (*b*), (*c*), (*e*) D. (*a*), (*b*), (*d*)

DNA Replication, Repair and Recombination

145. Which one of the following proteins catalyzes branch migration activity in Holliday junction?

A. Spo11 B. RuvB
C. Zip1 D. RuvC

146. A guanine (G) base in DNA is susceptible to modification to 8-oxo-G because of oxidative damage. If the modified G residues are not removed by a DNA glycosylase (*Mut M* or Fpg) prior to replication, an adenine (*A*) may be incorporated against 8-oxo-G. To avoid mutations, the cells have another DNA glycosylase called *Mut Y*. However, when the gene coding for *Mut Y* is deleted in *Escherichia coli*, the strain survives. This observation suggests that in E. coli

A. MutY is not responsible for the excision of 'A' incorporated against 8-oxo-G
B. Alternate DNA repair pathways may substitute for the repair of A incorporated against 8-oxo-G
C. Incorporation of 'A' against 8-oxo-G does not cause mutation in E. coli
D. The 8-oxo-G:A base pair in DNA distorts its structure in such way that, during the next round of replication a 'G' is incorporated against A in the 8-oxo-G:A mispair.

147. Which one of the following statements about DNA replication is INCORRECT?

A. During DNA replication, when adjacent bidirectional forks converge, the lagging strand will meet the leading strand of the same template strand
B. Mispaired nucleotide at the 3'-OH end of the primer strand triggers the 3-5' exonucleolytic proof reading activity

C. In a replication bubble moving bidirectionally, the same parental DNA strand cannot serve as a template for both the lagging and leading strand synthesis
D. DNA replication involves a RNA-DNA chimeric molecule

RNA Synthesis and Processing

148. Presence of sigma factor (σ70) in *Escherichia coli* facilitates
A. Sequence specific localization of RNA polymerase on the promoter regions of genes
B. Phosphorylation of C-terminal tail of RNA Polymerase
C. Interaction of β-subunit of RNA polymerase with α-subunit
D. Interaction of ω-subunit with β β'α2, complex of RNA polymerase

149. Which one of the following statements about mRNA export from the nucleus is INCORRECT?
A. Cellular pre-mRNAs with introns are generally not exported out of nucleus
B. Dbp5 is an RNA helicase that releases mRNA from the transport complex
C. ATP hydrolysis is required for mRNA transport across the nuclear pore complex
D. Phe-Gly proteins of the nuclear pore complex are not involved in mRNA export

150. Following observations were made about mRNA degradation pathway in the eukaryotic organism:
(*a*) A sequence independent endonuclease attack initiates degradation pathway for all mRNAs
(*b*) Degradation of the majority of mRNAs is deadenylation dependent
(*c*) Initially, the poly(*A*) tail is shortened by the PAN2/3 complex, followed by a rapid digestion by CCR4-NOT complex
(*d*) mRNA decay occurs only by 3 to 5' exonuclease activity
(*e*) The 3' to 5' mRNA degradation step is catalyzed by the exosome complex

Which one of the following options represents the combination of correct statements?
A. (*b*), (*c*), (*e*) B. (*b*), (*d*), (*e*)
C. (*a*), (*b*), (*d*) D. (*a*), (*c*), (*e*)

Protein Synthesis and Processing

151. Bacterial ribosomes consist of 30S and 50S ribosomal subunits. The translating monosome has a sedimentation value of
A. 70S because a fixed set of the ribosomal proteins (totalling to a value of ~10S) are removed when 30S and 50S subunits interact with each other
B. 70S because the interaction between the two subunits (30S and 50S) excludes some surface area decreasing the overall resistance of movement through the medium
C. 80S because the monosome consists of one subunit of 30S and one subunit of 50S
D. 50S because the sedimentation of the combined monosome is determined by the sedimentation of the large subunit

152. Signal Recognition Particle (SRP) plays an essential role in protein import in the endoplasmic reticulum (ER). In mammalian cells, SRP is a rod-like ribonucleoprotein complex containing six protein subunits and one RNA molecule. SRP stalls protein translation by blocking:
(*a*) elongation of the polypeptide chain
(*b*) mRNA loading onto the ribosomes.
(*c*) assembly of 60S and 40S ribosome particles.
(*d*) binding of the initiation factors.

Which one of the following represents the correct statement/s?
A. (*a*) only B. (*a*) and (*b*)
C. (*b*) and (*c*) D. (*a*) and (*d*)

Gene Regulation-phage, Pro & Eukaryotes

153. Which one of the following statements is correct?
A. Epigenetic memory depends on DNA acetylation by trithorax group of proteins
B. An epigenetic change could be inherited from a cell to a daughter cell
C. Parental origin does not influence the expression level of imprinted loci
D. Epigenetic changes do not alter the chromatin landscape

154. In human cells, centrioles assemble centrosomes, and centrosomes are essential for microtubular nucleation. Centriole duplication is tightly coupled to the cell cycle progression. To discover which genes are crucial for centriole duplication, an investigator will conduct:
(*a*) RNAi-based functional genomics screen in human cells to uncover novel genes involved in centriole duplication.
(*b*) experiments to generate constitutive knockout human cell lines.
(*c*) chemical based screen in human cell lines.
(*d*) RNA sequencing followed by generating constitutive knockout human cell lines.

Choose the combination with correct statements:
A. (*a*) and (*b*) B. (*a*) and (*c*)
C. (*b*) and (*c*) D. (*b*) and (*d*)

155. Chromatin remodelling leading to histone modifications is invariably required for regulation of transcriptional activity of eukaryotic genes. The residues in histone tails may be methylated or acetylated. The nature of these modifications

A. is identical on all the nucleosomes of a gene
B. varies between the nucleosomes present in the transcription initiation and elongation regions
C. is always fixed for the nucleosomes in the promoter regions of the genes that are transcriptionally active
D. in the transcription initiation regions is identical for the genes that are sensitive to nuclease activity

156. A mutant Trp repressor (TrpRm) that cannot bind tryptophan is isolated. In this mutant
(*a*) Trp operon is constitutively expressed.
(*b*) Trp operon is super-repressed.
(*c*) Trp repressor does not bind to the operator.
(*d*) only Trp leader sequence is transcribed.

Which one of the following options represents all correct statements?
A. A and (*c*) only
B. (*b*) and (*c*) only
C. (*a*) and (*d*) only
D. A only

157. Duschene muscular dystrophy (DMD) is caused by a defective dystrophin gene and can be cured by removing a specific faulty exon. If a CRISPR/Cas9 based genome editing approach is to be designed to remove the faulty exon, some of the following conditions have to be met.
(*a*) Two guide RNA molecules to match the flanking regions of the faulty exon
(*b*) An efficient non-homologous end joining system in the host
(*c*) Two separate, specific Cas9 endonucleases to target both ends of the exon
(*d*) A single guide RNA that targets the intron preceding the exo

Choose the option that includes all the correct conditions.
A. (*a*), (*b*) and (*c*) only
B. (*a*) and (*b*) only
C. (*c*) and (*d*) only
D. (*a*) and (*c*) only

DBT-JRF, 2019

Cellular Processes

158. Of the dsDNA sequences given below, the sequence that is expected to have a higher melting temperature is:
A. ATGACATTATTACATTAGTG
B. GCGCGTGCATGCCCGATGCC
C. ATTATTATACGTATTTATAT
D. CGCGATCGGGGATTACGAGC

159. The sequence of first strand of DNA obtained after reverse transcription of a bacterial mRNA is the same as:
A. Anti-sense DNA strand
B. Sense DNA strand
C. mRNA
D. Anti-sense RNA

160. In the DNA methylation reaction mediated by S-adenosylmethionine (SAM) methyltransferase, the nucleophilic species involved is:
A. an alcohol
B. an amine
C. a thiol
D. a carboxylate

161. Which one of the following statements regarding base excision DNA repair system is FALSE?
A. It can be triggered by damaged DNA
B. The pol-β pathway facilitates replacement of a long polynucleotide stretch of DNA
C. The enzymes that remove bases from DNA are glycosylases and lyases.
D. Damaged DNA that has not been repaired causes stalling of DNA polymerase III.

162. In genomic DNA denaturation and renaturation experiments, which one of the following regions would renature the earliest?
A. Single-copy gene
B. Satellite DNA
C. Pseudogenes
D. Multi copy gene families

163. Which one of the following represents an autonomous retrotransposon?
A. SINEs
B. LINEs
C. P-element
D. Tn-10

164. Underwinding or overwinding of circular dsDNA generates supercoils only when it does NOT have any of the following:
A. Nicks
B. repeat sequences
C. G:C rich regions
D. A:T rich regions

165. In a class, students were divided into 3 different groups and each group was given different DNA sample to find the melting temperature (Tm). All the groups observed same Tm for their samples. This is because:
A. They got different DNA samples from the same organism with different lengths and same GC content.
B. They got different DNA samples with same lengths and different GC contents.
C. They got different DNA samples with same length and same GC content.
D. They got different DNA samples from different organisms with different length and same GC content.

166. Which one of the following statements is TRUE for long non-coding RNAs?
A. They are less than 22 base pair
B. They are processed in the nucleus by RISC complex
C. They have > 300 amino acid open reading frame
D. They may have a poly-A tail

167. Which kind of post-translationally modified protein targets are recognized by Bromodomain containing proteins?
A. Acetylated protein
B. Glycosylated protein
C. Ubiqutinylated protein
D. Sumoylated protein

168. A tRNA containing an anticodon for leucine was charged with leucine. Subsequently, the attached leucine was chemically modified to arginine. This tRNA will incorporate:
A. Arginine against codon of arginine in mRNA
B. Leucine against codon of arginine in mRNA
C. Arginine against codon of leucine in mRNA
D. Leucine against codon of leucine in mRNA

169. Which one of the following graphs correctly represents unfolding of a protein in presence of increasing concentration of urea?

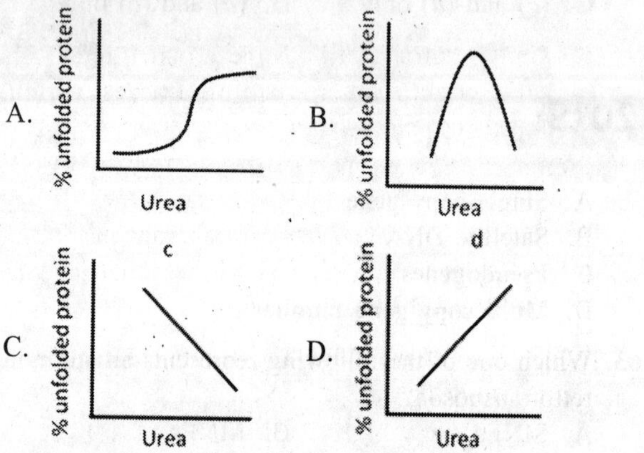

170. What is the minimum number of tRNAs required to recognize all six codons of serine (UCU, UCA, UCG, UCC, AGU and AGC)?
A. 2 B. 3
C. 4 D. 6

171. For efficient translation of certain eukaryotic mRNAs under many physiological and pathological stress conditions, the small subunit of ribosome binds to the mRNA at the:
A. 5′ Cap.
B. Internal ribosome entry sites.
C. Secondary structure at 3′ UTR.
D. Initiation codon.

172. A mutation in the coding region of a mammalian gene leads to the loss of a single amino acid at the N-terminus of the nascent polypeptide. This is possible when:
A. The mutation occurs at 3'-end of coding strand.
B. The mutation leads to shift of ribosome binding site.
C. the first two codons code for methionine.
D. the mutation leads to the introduction of premature stop codon.

173. Which one of the following statements is NOT TRUE for an enhancer element?
A. it can be downstream of the gene it regulates
B. it can only regulate a nearby gene
C. it can be upstream of the gene it regulates
D. it can be within the intron of the gene

174. A peptide of sequence -SHELR- is isolated from bacteria. Which one of the following options lists the possible phosphorylation site in this peptide?
A. H B. L
C. R D. E

175. Labeled circular single stranded DNA and linear short DNA (oligo) were annealed to form a product shown in figure I. Helicase assay was performed using the annealed product and three proteins A, B, C. Below is the gel profile of the results (figure II).

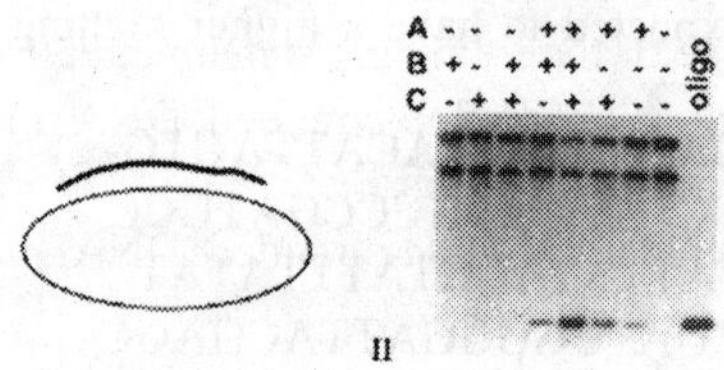

I II

Based on the results identify the protein with helicase activity?
A. protein A
B. protein B
C. Protein C
D. Both Protein A and C

176. Glycosylation of a monoclonal antibody DOES NOT affect
A. *in vivo* stability of antibody
B. mediation of phagocytosis and cytotoxicity of antibody
C. efficacy of monoclonal antibody
D. fluorescence spectrum of antibody

GATE (BIOTECHNOLOGY), 2019

177. Tetracycline inhibits the
A. interaction between tRNA and mRNA
B. translocation of mRNA through ribosome
C. peptidyl transferase activity
D. binding of amino-acyl tRNA to ribosome

178. Which of the following factors affect the fidelity of DNA polymerase in polymerase chain reaction?
P. Mg2+ concentration
Q. pH
R. Annealing temperature
A. P and Q only
B. P and R only
C. Q and R only
D. P, Q and R

GATE (LIFE SCIENCE), 2019

Fundamental Process & Molecular Techniques

179. DpnI is used to digest the PCR product during site directed mutagenesis because

A. DpnI digests irrespective of methylation status of DNA

B. DpnI digests only unmethylated DNA

C. DpnI digests only methylated DNA

D. DpnI digests GC-rich sequences

180. Absence of detectable protein expression upon blunt-ended mutation-free cloning of an E. coli gene with its own promoter in E. coli cells can be due to

A. Cloning occurred in reverse orientation

B. Cloning occurred out of frame

C. Codon bias

D. Rapid degradation of expressed protein

CSIR-NET, NOVEMBER (MORNING), 2020

Nucleic Acids-forms, Conformation & Stability

181. The 15 base-paired nucleic acid molecule shown below is disolved in an aqueous buffer of pH 7.3

5'-AGUUCGGAUAUCGU G-3'

3'-UCAUGCCUAUAGCA C-5'

Which one of the following statement is INCORRECT?

A. It can be a double-stranded DNA molecule in a B-form helix

B. It can be a double-stranded DNA molecule in a A-form helix

C. It can be a double-stranded RNA molecule in a A-form helix

D. It can be a double-stranded RNA molecule in a B-form helix

DNA Replication, Repair and Recombination

182. UV-induced DNA damage causes advancing replication forks to stall. To avoid a collapse of these stalled replication forks the cell uses:

A. non-homologous end joining

B. lesion bypass

C. mismatch repair

D. base excision repair

RNA Synthesis and Processing

183. Which one of the snRNAs given below base pairs with 5 splice site of pre mRNA?

A. U_1 B. U_2

C. U_4 D. U_5

184. Following statements were made about catalytic introns:

(*a*) Group I introns may undergo self-splicing by transesterification.

(*b*) Group II introns do not require any factor/protein for autosplicing either in vivo or in vitro

(*c*) Certain introns of both the group I and II classes may contain open reading frames which are translated into protein.

(*d*) Generally, group I introns migrate by DNA-mediated mechanisms, whereas group II introns migrate by RNA-mediated mechanisms.

(*e*) Ribonuclease P (RNase P) is essential for bacteria and archaea but not eukaryotes.

Which one of the following combinations represents statements which are all correct?

A. (*a*), (*b*), (*d*) B. (*b*), (*d*), (*e*)

C. (*a*), (*c*), (*d*) D. (*c*), (*d*), (*e*)

185. Which one of the following statements about eukaryotic RNA processing is INCORRECT?

A. Termination of transcription occurs co-transcriptionally at the polyadenylation site.

B. Phosphorylation of the Ser 2 of the RNA polymerase II CTD is required for the recruitment of polyadenylation factors.

C. Polyadenylation requires both cleavage at the polyadeny-lation site and addition of poly A.

D. Xrn 2 is the nuclease that degrades the cleaved RNA to release RNA polymerase II from the template.

186. The following statements are made with reference to the fact that tRNAs are known to possess T in their sequence.

(*a*) RNA polymerase III utilizes TTP as one of the substrates.

(*b*) Like any other RNA polymerase, RNA polymerase III also utilizes UTP but when the RNA pol III reaches a looped structure it binds to S-adenosylmethionine to methylate C-5 position of the incorporated U to result in a thymine in a co-transcriptional manner.

(*c*) During transcription of tRNA genes at the designated positions, DNA polymerase replaces

RNA polymerase III to incorporate T in the tRNA transcript

(*d*) A specific methyltransferase utilizes a methyl group donor to post-transcriptionally modify the specific U residues into T residues.

(*e*) Uracil to thymine conversion occurs in a large number of tRNAs in the TVC loop.

The option with all the correct statements is

A. (*a*) and (*b*) only B. (*b*) and (*c*) only

C. (*c*) and (*e*) only D. (*d*) and (*e*) only

Protein Synthesis and Processing

187. Which one of the following RNAs possesses the peptidyl transferase activity?

A. tRNA B. 5S rRNA

C. 16S rRNA D. 23S rRNA

188. Insulin is a heterodimer made up of A and B peptide chains joined by the intra and interchain disulfide bridges formed between amino acid of respective chains as suggested below:

(*a*) A_6 A_{11} (*b*) A_7 B_7

(*c*) A_{20} B_{19} (*d*) A_5 B_{15}

Which one of the following represents the correct disulfide bridges joining A and B chains of insulin hormone?

A. (*a*), (*b*) and (*d*) B. (*a*), (*c*) and (*d*)

C. (*a*), (*b*) and (*c*) D. (*b*), (*c*) and (*d*)

Gene Regulation-phage, Pro & Eukaryotes

189. Which one of the following statements about GAL gene expression is FALSE?

A. GAL4 is a positive regulator of GAL genes

B. The UAS region that regulates the GAL gene expression harborsshort, phased AT repeats every 10 base pairs

C. GAL80 is a positive regulator of GAL4

D. GAL80 is negatively regulated by GAL3

190. The following figure represent the growth curve of wild type E. Coli grown in a medium containing both glucose and lactose.

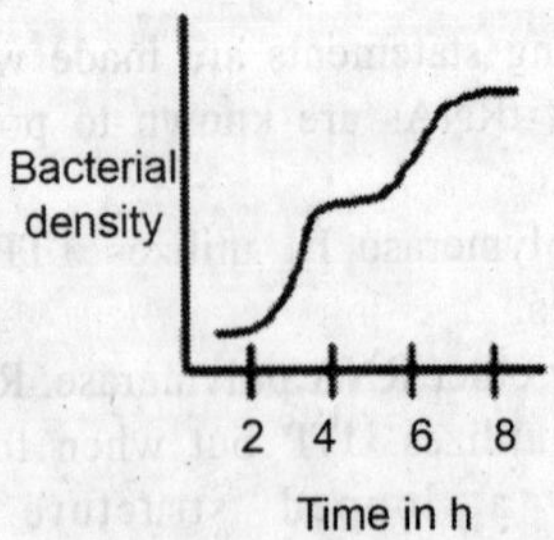

In E. Coli, the catabolite repression of lactose operon by glucose ha been explained by the different levels of cAMP in presence and absence of glucose. This model was challenged and experiments showed that catabolite repression occured because the activity of lactose permease was inhibited in the presence of glucose. Considering the scond model, which one of the following plots correctly represents the growth pattern of a mutant E. Coli witha loss of function mutation in the lad gene growing in a medium containing glucoxse and lactose?

A.

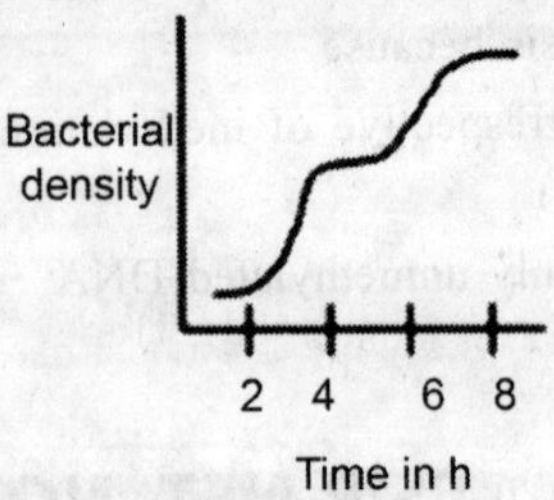

B.

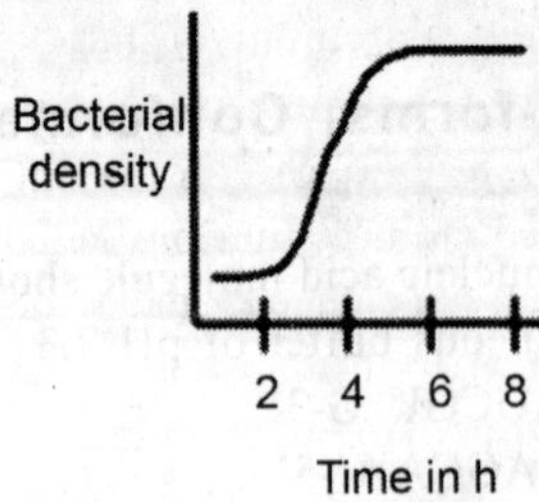

C.

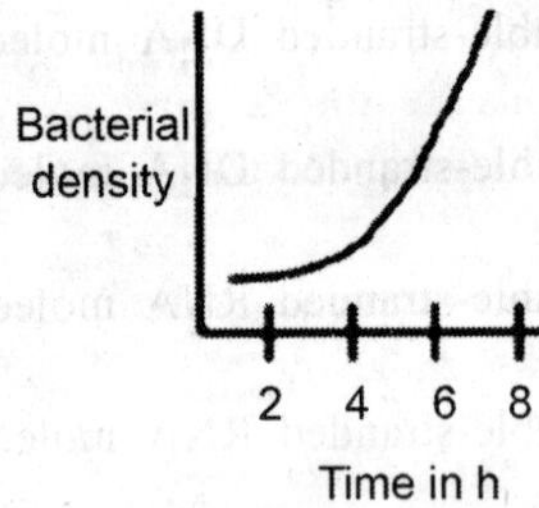

D.

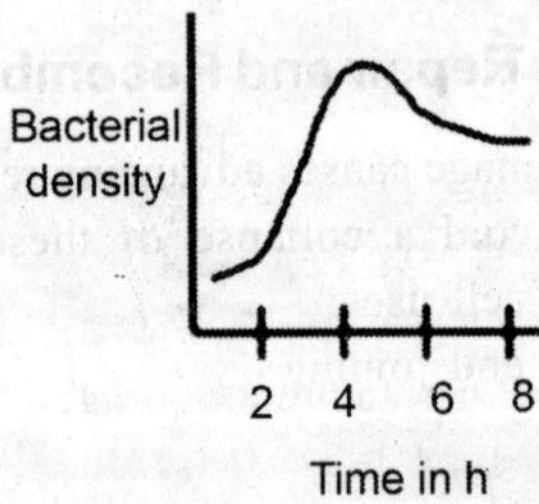

191. Following statements were made about regulation of eukaryotic gene expression.

(*a*) It is usually regulated at the level of initiation of transcription by altering the chromatin architecture.

(*b*) The eukaryotic genome is divided into domains by insulator elements.

(*c*) A chromatin remodeling complex binds to the promoter of a gene in sequence specific manner.

(*d*) Architectural proteins regulate gene expression by promoting DNA bending.

(*e*) The chromatin remodeling complex can alter nudeosomal architecture, but cannot displace them.

The option with all the correct statements is

A. (*a*), (*b*), (*d*) B. (*a*), (*c*), (*e*)
C. (*b*), (*d*), (*e*) D. (*b*), (*c*), (*d*)

192. Contents in Column I and II are with respect to bacterial transcriptional regulation.

Column I	Column II
(*a*) Positive regulation by cAMP	(*i*) Ara operon
(*b*) Short abortive transcripts	(*ii*) Lac operon
(*c*) DNA looping	(*iii*) Riboswitch
(*d*) FMN synthesis	(*iv*) Transcription initiation

Which one of the options below correctly matches contents in column I and Column II?

	(*a*)	(*b*)	(*c*)	(*d*)
A.	(*ii*)	(*iv*)	(*i*)	(*iii*)
B.	(*iii*)	(*ii*)	(*i*)	(*iv*)
C.	(*ii*)	(*i*)	(*iv*)	(*iii*)
D.	(*iv*)	(*iii*)	(*ii*)	(*i*)

CSIR-NET, NOVEMBER (AFTERNOON), 2020

DNA Replication, Repair and Recombination

193. Given below are few statements related to DNA replication:

(*a*) Replication in eukaryotic chromosomes from the origin(s) is initiated multiple times in each cell cycle while it is initiated only once in each cell cycle at the origin in bacterial chromosomes
(*b*) Improper reinitiation of replication in a eubacterial chromosome is prevented by hemimethylation status of the bacterial origin
(*c*) DNA polymerase III is the major replication polymerase responsible for de novo synthesis of both leading and lagging strands of DNA in E. coli
(*d*) Rolling circle mode of replication produces multiple units of the original molecule

Which one of the following options represents INCORRECT statement(s)?

A. A only B. Both (*b*) and (*c*)
C. Both (*a*) and (*d*) D. (*b*) only

194. The following statements are made with reference to the replication of DNA.

(*a*) The eukaryotic counterpart of the bacterial β-clamp protein is proliferating cell nuclear antigen (PCNA)
(*b*) Mutation inactivating one of the subunits of the Mem 2-7 complex negatively affects the initiation of DNA replication in eukaryotes, but has no effect on elongation of the replication fork
(*c*) All DNA polymerases responsible for replicating the eukaryotic genome catalyze DNA chain extension in a DNA template- dependent manner.
(*d*) The FENI protein plays a role in the synthesis of the lagging strand during DNA replication as well as in base excision repair

Which one of the following options represents Incorrect statement(s)?

A. (*b*) only B. (*b*) and (*c*) only
C. (*b*) and (*d*) only D. A, (*b*) and (*c*)

RNA Synthesis and Processing

195. In Trypanosoma, some of the introns generate Y shaped structure in place of a lariat. Such structure is generated during

A. cis-splicing B. trans-splicing
C. alternate splicing D. RNA editing

196. Which one of the following ensures stable binding of RNA polymerase at the promoter site?

A. DNA photolyase B. Sigma factor
C. DNA glycosylase D. Rec A

197. Given below are four sentences with blanks (labelled X, Y, Z and L).

(*a*) RNA Pol I transcribes X
(*b*) miRNA genes are transcribed by Y
(*c*) The RIMA polymerase found only in plants is Z
(*d*) tasiRNAs are synthesized by L

Which one of the fcllowing options would present the combination of all terms (in the order X, Y, Z and L) to complete the above sentences correctly

A. X-mRNAs; Y-RNA Pol II; Z-RNA pol IV; L-RNA Pol III
B. X-tRNAs; Y-RNA Pol III; Z-RNA pol V; L-RNA Pol I
C. X-45S rRNA; Y-RNA Pol II; Z-RNA pol V; L-RNA Pol II
D. X-18S rRNA; Y-RNA Pol V; Z-RNA pol IV; L-RNA Poll

198. The following statements are related to transcription in bacterial eukaryotes.

(*a*) During concurrent promoter sequence recognition and melting, melting commences with base flipping where two bases are flipped out into pockets of the primary sigma factor
(*b*) Binding of α-amanitin to RNA polymerase II permits entry of nucleotides into RNA pol II active site and synthesis of RNA, but prevents translocation
(*c*) RNA polymerase I can use upstream promoters with 3 consensus sequences, as well as internal promoters having a bipartite structure

(*d*) FACT is associated with RNA polymerase during transcriptional elongation and helps displace histone octomers during transcription

Which of the following combinations of statements represents all correct statements?

A. (*a*), (*b*) and (*c*)   B. (*a*), (*b*) and (*d*)
C. (*b*), (*c*) and (*d*)   D. (*b*) and (*d*) only

Protein Synthesis and Processing

199. Erythromycin is an inhibitor of protein synthesis. It acts by:

A. binding to 305 subunit of bacterial ribosome, thus inhibiting binding of aminoacyl - tRNAs.
B. binding to 50S subunit of bacterial ribosome, thus inhibiting translocation.
C. inhibits peptidyl transferase activity of eukaryotic 60S ribosomal subunit.
D. causes premature chain termination by acting as an analog of aminoacyl-tRNA in both prokaryotes and eukaryotes.

200. In regulating the quantity of enzyme, its degradation plays a pivotal role. Following statements are made to represent the degradation of enzymes in the 26S proteasome.

(*a*) The active sites of proteolytic subunits face exterior of the proteasome cylinder
(*b*) The active sites of proteolytic subunits face interior of the proteasome cylinder
(*c*) Degrading enzymes are targeted to exterior of proteasome by covalent attachment of one or more molecules of ubiquitin
(*d*) Degrading enzymes are targeted to interior of proteasome by covalent attachment of one or more molecules of ubiquitin

Which one of the following combinations of statements represent correct mode of enzyme degradation?

A. (*a*) and (*b*)   B. (*b*) and (*c*)
C. (*b*) and (*d*)   D. (*a*) and (*c*)

201. In classical Anfinsen's protein folding experiment the enzymatically active ribonuclease is treated with β-mercaptoethanol and 8 M urea. Following which, the preparation was

(*a*) dialyzed to remove the β-mercaptoethanol and 8 M urea
(*b*) the sample was completely oxidized in 8M urea after dialysis
(*c*) trace amounts of β-mercaptoethanol was added to the dialysed sample
(*d*) 8M urea was added to the dialyzed sample

Which one of the following steps will lead to regaining of the full enzymatic activity of ribonuclease?

A. A followed by (*c*)
B. A followed by (*b*)
C. A followed by (*d*)
D. A alone

202. Given below is a partial coding sequence of a gene:

5'-AATGGACGCATGTGTCGATGG-3

Which one of the following polypeptides CANNOT be produced by transcription and translation of the above DNA sequence in any of the three possible reading frames?

A. Asn - Gly - Arg - Met - Cys - Arg - Trp
B. Asn - Ala - Cys - Phe - Ser - His
C. Met - Asp - Ala - Cys - Val - Asp
D. Trp - Thr - His - Val - Ser – Met

203. The following statements were made regarding the role of protein modifications

(*a*) Attachment of acetyl groups to the amino termini of proteins makes it more resistant to degradation.
(*b*) Attachment of hydroxyl groups to proline residues stabilizes fibres of newly synthesized collagen
(*c*) Addition of sugars (glycosylation) makes protein more hydrophilic enabling protein- protein interactions
(*d*) Addition of sugars (glycosylation) makes protein more hydrophobic enabling protein folding

Which one of the following combinations represents all correct statements?

A. (*a*), (*b*) and (*c*)
B. (*a*), (*b*) and (*d*)
C. Band (*c*) only
D. (*a*) and (*d*) only

Gene Regulation-phage, Pro & Eukaryotes

204. Which one of the following conditions will switch on Lac operon in E. coli?

A. + Glucose, + Lactose
B. + Glucose, – Lactose
C. - Glucose, – Lactose
D. - Glucose, + Lactose

205. The statements given below refer to the lambda phage.

(*a*) Clear plaques are formed in Q mutants
(*b*) No plaques are formed in nut mutants
(*c*) Clear plaques are formed in ell mutants
(*d*) Turbid plaques are formed in integrase mutants
(*e*) Clear plaques are formed in P mutants
(*f*) No plaques are formed in cl mutants

Which of the following combination of statements is correct?

A. (*a*), (*b*) and (*f*) only
B. (*d*) and (*e*) only
C. (*b*) and (*c*) only
D. (*d*) and (*f*) only

DBT-JRF, 2020

Cellular Processes

206. Nucleic acid structures are stabilized by
A. hydrophilic interactions
B. covalent interactions
C. covalent and hydrophilic interactions
D. hydrophobic interactions and hydrogen bonding

207. In the DNA helix, the GC and AT base pairs
A. stack on top of each other, parallel to the helix axis
B. stack on top of each other, perpendicular to the helix axis
C. stack sideways, perpendicular to the helix axis
D. stack sideways, parallel to the helix axis

208. Which histone is NOT a part of the nucleosomes?
A. H2B B. H2A
C. H3 D. H1

209. For a tetranucleotide sequence, the number of possible combinations using A, T and G are
A. 512 B. 81
C. 27 D. 256

210. In a DNA molecule, two antiparallel strands that are complementary in their nucleotide sequence are paired to form a
A. none of the given options
B. right-handed double helix with 8 nucleotide pairs per helical turn
C. right-handed double helix with 10 nucleotide pairs per helical turn
D. left-handed double helix with 10 nucleotide pairs per helical turn

211. Met-Ile-Val-His-Tyr was the sequence of a hypothetical peptide. Assuming that there are two possible codons each for His, val and Try, one possible codon for Met, and four possible codons for Ile, the number of possible nucleotide sequences coding for this peptide would be
A. 11 B. 32
C. 13 D. 66

212. Sequence-specific recognition of DNA by proteins occurs primarily through the
A. major groove
B. minor groove
C. Histones
D. polyphosphate backbone

213. The technique used to locate specific genes in chromosomes
A. colony hybridization
B. dot blot technique
C. in-situ hybridization
D. western blotting

214. The role of DNA ligase in DNA replication is
A. addition of new nucleotides to the leading strand
B. addition of new nucleotides to the lagging strand
C. formation of a phosphodiester bond between the 3'-OH of one Okazaki fragment and the 5'-phosphate of the next on the lagging strand
D. base pairing of the template and the newly formed DNA strand

215. What is the frequency with which a 4bp cutter will cut the DNA, assuming random distribution of base in the genome?
A. 1/254 B. 1/64
C. 1/256 D. 1/4096

216. Which of the following is/are critical for genome replication?
A. all of the given options are correct
B. polymerase
C. ligase
D. helicase

217. Denaturation of DNA is a
A. temperature-independent process
B. linear process
C. cooperative phenomenon
D. neither linear nor a cooperative process

218. Which one of the following can be extended by Klenow enzyme upon addition of dNTPs and Mg2+?
A. restriction fragment with a 5' overhang
B. restriction fragment with a 3' overhang
C. single-stranded DNA
D. restriction fragment with blunt ends

219. A covalently closed circular DNA was in a relaxed state in water at 30°C. What will happen if the water temperature increases to 60°C or decreases to 10°C?
A. DNA will undergo positive supercoiling at 60°C and negative supercoiling at 10°C
B. DNA will be relaxed at 60°C and positively supercoiled at 10°C
C. DNA will be negatively supercoiled at both 60°C and 10°C
D. DNA will undergo negative supercoiling at 60°C and positive supercoiling at 10°C

220. Which of the following is NOT a feature of bacterial DNA replication?
A. semi-conservative
B. semi-discontinuous
C. chain growth in the 5' → 3' direction
D. Unidirectional

221. DNA glycosylases are DNA repair enzymes involved in:
A. base excision repair
B. negative supercoiling of DNA
C. SOS response
D. DNA replication

222. Identify the incorrect pair
A. DNase I: Cleaves only double stranded DNA
B. Alkaline Phosphatase : Removes 5' phosphate from the DNA
C. RNA polymerase: Transcription
D. DNA Polymerase 1: Nick Translation

223. Which of the following are NOT transcribed by RNA polymerase II ?
A. miRNA and some snRNA
B. mRNA and snoRNA
C. miRNA and snoRNA
D. tRNA and 5S rRNA

224. Which one of the following involves RNA Editing?
A. deletion, insertion or chemical modification of nucleotides that are present in the mRNA
B. joining of exons from one pre-mRNA molecule to form mRNA
C. deletion, insertion or chemical modification of nucleotides in the gene encoding the mRNA
D. joining of exons from two different pre-mRNA molecules to form mRNA

225. Small/short interfering RNA (siRNA) is a commonly used RNA tool that causes
A. duplication of protein encoding genes
B. deletion of protein encoding genes
C. permanent silencing of protein coding genes
D. short-term silencing of protein coding genes

226. Ligands 'A' and 'B' bind to protein 'P' with dissociation constants of 1 nM and 100 nM, respectively. Which of the following true?
A. 'A' binds 'P' with more affinity
B. Dissociation constant is not related to affinity
C. 'B' binds 'P' with more affinity
D. Both 'A' and 'B' bind 'P' with equal affinity

227. Which post-translational modification is observed most commonly in signal transduction?
A. Nitrosylation B. phosphorylation
C. carbonylation D. acetylation

228. In the cloverleaf structure of tRNA, the cognate amino acid is attached at
A. acceptor stem B. T loop
C. anticodon arm D. D loop

229. ATP with y^{-32} p can be used for which of the following type of reaction?
A. all of the given options are correct
B. reverse transcription
C. end-labelling
D. nick translation

230. What are the cellular sites for protein glycosylation?
A. endoplasmic reticulum and golgi body
B. endoplasmic reticulum and lysosomes
C. mitochondria and lysosomes
D. endoplasmic reticulum and mitochondria

231. Bacteria protect themselves from phages by producing the following enzymes which fragment the phage genome
A. endonucleases B. methylases
C. topoisomerases D. exonucleases

232. If a nonsense mutation is present in the Lacz gene of the lac operon, the mRNA of β-galactosidase would
A. be expressed in response to binding of the lac repressor to the CAP protein
B. be expressed in response to the presence of lactose
C. not be expressed at all
D. always be expressed

233. If neurons that produce the neurotransmitter dopamine could be generated from stem cells grown in culture, it might be possible to treat patient suffering with
A. Cystic fibriosis
B. Parkinson's Disease
C. Diabetes
D. Amytrophic lateral sclerosis

234. Which type of post-translational modification does not occur in plastids?
A. s-nitrosylation
B. glycosylation
C. acetylation
D. phosphorylation

GATE (BIOTECHNOLOGY), 2020

235. Protein P becomes functional upon phosphorylation of a serine residue, replacing this serine with...will result in a phosphomimic mutant of P
A. alanine B. aspartic acid
C. phenylalanine D. lysine

236. DNA synthesized from an RNA template is called
A. recombinant DNA
B. transcript
C. T- DNA
D. complementary DNA

237. Determine the correctness or otherwise of the following Assertion (A) and the Reason (R)

Assertion (A): Dam methylase protects *E.coli* 1DNA from phage endonucleases.

Reason (R): E.coli Dam methylase methylates the adenosine residue in the sequence "GATC".

A. Both (A) and (R) are true and (R) is the correct reason for (A).
B. Both (A) and (R) are true and (R) is the not correct reason for (A).
C. Both (A) and (R) are false
D. (A) is false but (R) is true.

GATE (LIFE SCIENCE), 2020

Fundamental Process

238. Polypeptides are either biosynthesized on the ribosomes using an mRNA template or chemically synthesized by the Merrifield's solid phase method. The correct directions of peptide synthesis are

A. C→N direction on the ribosome and N→C direction on the solid phase.
B. N→C direction on the ribosome and C→N direction on the solid phase
C. N→C direction in the both cases
D. C→N direction in the both cases

239. Har Gobind Khorana and Marshall Nirenberg elucidated the genetic code by using a cell-free protein synthesizing system. It was found that poly(U) and poly(C) result in the synthesis of poly(L-Phe) and poly(L-Pro), respectively. Based on these observations, which one of the following conclusions is correct?

A. Codon GGG specifies L-Phe codon AAA specifies L-Pro
B. Codon CCC specifies L-Phe codon UUU specifies L-Pro
C. Codon AAA specifies L-Phe codon GGG specifies L-Pro
D. Codon UUU specifies L-Phe codon CCC specifies L-Pro

CSIR-NET, JUNE (MORNING), 2021

DNA Replication, Repair and Recombination

240. The basic differences between direct repair and base excision repair is

A. Direct repair restores original structures of altered nucleotide without replacement, while in base excision repair the section of DNA containing the distortion is removed, the correct base is added and resealed.
B. In direct repair, homologous recombination repair the broken region while base excision repair restores original structures of altered nucleotide by modification.
C. Direct repair restores original structure by non-homologous end joining without using homologous template while in base excision repair the section of DNA containing the distortion is repaired by using homologous recombination.
D. In direct repair, an exonuclease, a DNA polymerase and a ligase are used, while in base excision repair a translation polymerase that by passes the bulky lesions is used by the cell.

241. Reproduction of $\phi \times 174$, a single stranded DNA phage involves several steps. A few statements are given below to explain the mechanism.

(*a*) The single stranded $\phi \times 174$ DNA is converted into double stranded replicative form (RF)
(*b*) Replication of double stranded replicative form results in the production of single stranded phages, about 50% of which are +ve sense phages and the remaining are –ve sense phages.
(*c*) Replication of the double stranded replicative form results in the production of only –ve sense phages
(*d*) Replication of the double stranded replicative form results in the production of only +ve sense phages

Choose the option that correctly describes the process

A. (*a*) only
B. (*a*) and (*b*) only
C. (*a*) and (*c*) only
D. (*a*) and (*d*) only

242. The following statements are made with reference to DNA replication :

(*a*) Campotothecin causes intra-strand and inter-strand crosslinks in DNA, leading to staling of replication forks.
(*b*) Prevention of reinitiation of DNA replication during the same cell cycle is mediated by regulating the loading of the initiator complex ORC
(*c*) A glu→ala mutation in the nucleotide building pocket of DNA polymerase III could lead to the incorporation of ribonucleotides in the extending DNA chain.
(*d*) A mutation in the gene encoding Topoisomerase II could lead to entanglement of DNA daughter strands during replication.

Which one of the following options represents all correct statements?

A. (*a*) and (*b*)   B. (*b*) and (*c*)
C. (*c*) and (*d*)   D. (*b*), (*c*) and (*d*)

243. DNA replication occurs in s phase. The entry of cells into s phase is regulated by the tumor suppressor protein Rb. The statements below are made with reference to the role of Rb.

(*a*) Rb binds to E2F in the cytosol and prevents E2F entry into the nucleus.
(*b*) Rb is phosphorylated by cyclin A / cdk 4.
(*c*) Phospho Rb activates E2F.
(*d*) E2F activates cyclin E production which promotes the G1/S transition.

Which one of the following options represents all correct statements?

A. (*a*), (*b*) and (*c*) only
B. (*b*), (*c*) and (*d*) only
C. (*a*), (*c*) and (*d*) only
D. (*c*) and (*d*) only

RNA Synthesis and Processing

244. Which one of the following regions of the target gene is NOT used for making an RNAI construct to knock down its expression?

A. 5' UTR of the mature transcript
B. 3' UTR of the mature transcrirpt
C. Exonic region
D. Intronic region

245. Which one of the following schematic depicts the potential relationship among the subunits IIo, IIa and IIb of RNA polymerase II?

A. 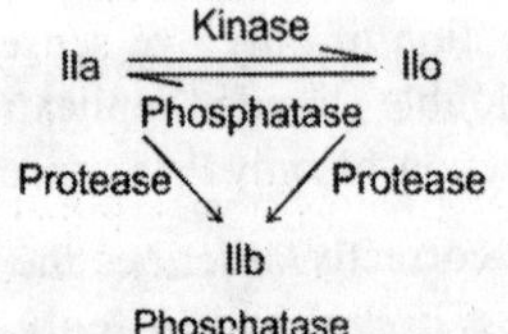

B. 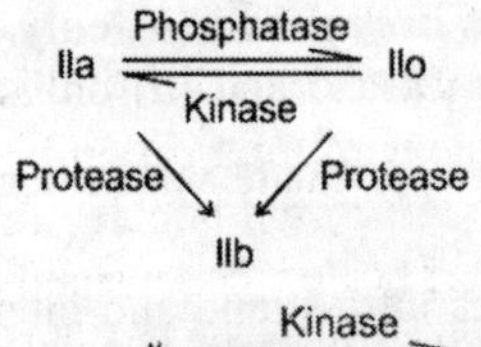

C. 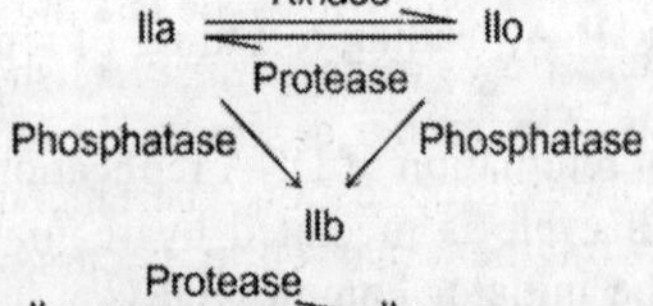

D. 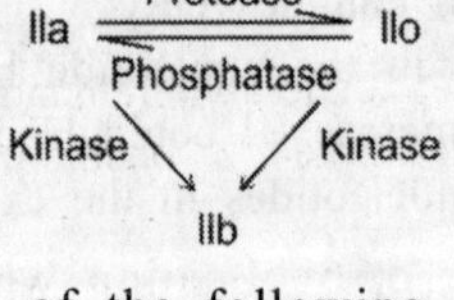

246. All of the following statements about bacterial transcription termination are true EXCEPT

A. Some terminator sequences require Rho protein for termination.
B. Inverted repeat and 'T' rich non-template strand define intrinsic terminators.
C. Rho-dependent terminators may possess inverted repeat elements.
D. Nus A is necessary for intrinsic transcription termination.

Protein Synthesis and Processing

247. In bacteria many of the tRNA genes do not contain the CCA sequence found at the 3' end of tRNA in this context which one of the following statements represents the correct explanation?

A. In these Trans amino actuation occurs at the 3 end of the tRNA irrespective of the present of the CCA sequence
B. CCA sequence is added to these tRNA transcripts In a DNA template independent manner.
C. These tRNAs exploit the process of trans-splicing to include a CCA sequence at their 2 end
D. The absence of CCA sequence occurred only in the last common ancestors during the course of evolution and the current da tRNA genes always posses a sequence to encode tha CCA end of the tRNA.

248. Mitochondrial protein synthesis is of prokaryotic origin. Following statements are being made about the ribosomes from bacteria and Mitochondria:

(*a*) The bacterial ribosomes consists of small and large subunits of 30S and 50S respectively, whereas in mitochondria of mammals these subunits are of 28S and 39S.
(*b*) In the bacterial ribosomes the RNA: protein ratio is about 2:1 whereas in mitochondria ribosomes this ratio is usually 1:2.
(*c*) Both the bacterial and Mitochondrial ribosomes consists of 30S and 50S subunits.
(*d*) Both the bacterial and Mitochondrial ribosomes consists of RNA and protein in the ratio of 1:1.

Choose the option that represents all correct statements.

A. (*a*) and (*b*) only   B. (*b*) and (*c*) only
C. (*c*) and (*d*) only   D. (*a*) and (*d*) only

Gene Regulation-phage, Pro & Eukaryotes

249. Given below are a few statements about the *gama* infection cycle

(*a*) Competition between *cI* and *cII* gene products determines the establishment of lysogeny versus lysis.
(*b*) cI binds Or1 first while cro binds to Or3 first
(*c*) Cro binding to Or represses cI transcription
(*d*) Rich medium favours lytic because cII is protected from cellular protease

Which one of the following options represents all correct statements?

A. (*b*) and (*c*)   B. (*a*) and (*b*)
C. (*c*) and (*d*)   D. (*a*) and (*c*)

CSIR-NET, JUNE (AFTERNOON), 2021

Nucleic Acids-forms, Conformation & Stability

250. Arrange the DNA fragments (A to D) in the order of decreasing melting temperature.

A.
5'- AGTAGTATCAACTATCATGA-3'
3'- TCATCATAGTTGATAGTACT-5'
B.
5'- GACGTGCCAGGTGCGAGGTC-3'
3'- CTGCACGGTCCACGCTCCAG-5'
C.
5'- TACGATGCACATGCTTGGAC-3'
3'- ATGCTACGTGTACGAACCTG-5'
D.
5'- GAACGCTACGTTGCGATCCG-3'
3'- CTTGCGATGCAACGCTAGGC-5'

A. B > D > C > A B. C > A > B > D
C. D > C > A = B D. A = B > C > D

251. Heating of some nucleic acids shows an increase in the absorbence at 260nm(A260) typified by the plot shown above. The sharp transition midpoint is defined as melting temperature(Tm). Which one of the following nucleic acid samples is NOT expected to generate such a typical profile upon heating of its solutions
A. Double stranded DNA
B. Double stranded RNA
C. DNA-RNA hybrid
D. Single stranded DNA having imperfect secondary structure

DNA Replication, Repair and Recombination

252. Given below are a set of enzymes in Column A and enzyme activities in Column B.

Column A		Column B
(*a*) DNA topoisomerase I	(*i*)	Synthesis of okazaki fragment
(*b*) DNA topoisomerase II	(*ii*)	Leading strand synthesis
(*c*) Polymerase-ε	(*iii*)	Double strand break and ligation
(*d*) Polymerase-δ	(*iv*)	Single strand nicking

Choose the option that matches the content of column A with that of A.

	(*a*)	(*b*)	(*c*)	(*d*)
A.	(*iv*)	(*iii*)	(*ii*)	(*i*)
B.	(*iii*)	(*iv*)	(*ii*)	(*i*)
C.	(*iv*)	(*iii*)	(*i*)	(*ii*)
D.	(*iii*)	(*iii*)	(*ii*)	(*i*)

253. Which one of the following statements about Cre-mediated site-specific recombination at loxP sites is INCORRECT?
A. When loxP sites flanking a test sequence are oriented in same directiom, Cre mediates the excision of the intervening sequence
B. LoxP sites in inverted orientation around an intervening sequence lead to inversion upon action by Cre recombinase
C. LoxP sites recognized by the Cre recombinase are palindromic around a spacer sequence
D. LoxP-Cre system cannot be used to generate translocation between chromosomes

254. Which one of the following statements is NOT a correct feature of Escherichia coli RNA polymerase?
A. Presence of the σ subunit along with α2ββ'ω core RNA polymerase is required for the its promoter-specific binding.
B. Presence of the σ subunit along with α2ββ'ω core RNA polymerase is not necessary for the core RNA polymerase (α2ββ'ω) to bind to the DNA template.
C. Mutation in β subunit in its rifampicin resistance defining region (RRDR) confers rifampicin resistance phenotype.
D. Mutations in α subunit in its rifampicin resistance defining region (RRDR) confer rifampicin resistance phenotype.

255. In the figure below, replication of DNA beginning from the origin ofreplication of the chromosome of a newly identified bacterium having a double stranded circular DNA genome is shown.

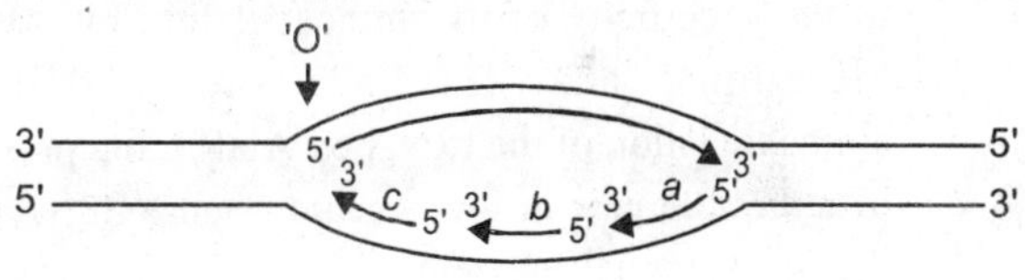

Characterization of DNA polymerase responsible for genome replication showed that DNA synthesis occurred in 5 ' to 3 ' direction and it depends on the presence of a primer (as is the case in Escherichia coli). Polarities of DNA (5' or 3') are as shown . Replication begins at a point marked 'o' on the left of the bubble, and both the parent strands were replicated concurrently. The longer arrow inside the bubble shows the leading strand, whereas the shorter arrows (marked *a*, *b*, *c*) show the Okazaki fragments. The model depicts a :
A. bidirectional mode of replication wherein synthesis of the Okazaki fragment marked '*c*' occurs prior to those marked '*a*' and '*b*'
B. bidirectional mode of replication wherein synthesis of the Okazaki fragment marked '*a*' occurs prior to those marked '*b*' and '*c*'
C. unidirectional mode of replication wherein synthesis of the Okazaki fragment marked '*c*' occurs prior to those marked '*a*' and '*b*'

D. unidirectional mode of replication wherein synthesis of the Okazaki fragment marked '*a*' occurs prior to those marked '*b*' and '*c*'.

256. Which one of the following protein is essential for both the initiation of DNA replication as well the continued advance of the replication fork?

A. ORC B. Geminin

C. Cdc45 D. Cdc6

RNA Synthesis and Processing

257. A mutation in which one of the following sigma factors may be a possible cause for E. coli failing to adapt in response to thermal stress?

A. Sigma ^ 70

B. Sigma ^ 32

C. Sigma ^ 54

D. Sigma ^ 45

Protein Synthesis and Processing

258. Precise recognition of tRNAs by their cognate aminoacyl-tRNA synthetases is crucial for the fidelity of protein synthesis. In the context of the aminoacylation of tRNA^Ala with its cognate aminoacyl-tRNA synthetase (AlaRS) and based on the studies on the molecules of *Escherichia coli* origin, following statements are made. Which one of the statements is INCORRECT?

A. Anticodon of tRNA makes important contribution to the specificity of its aminoacylation by AlaRS

B. Mutational analyses have shown that for aminoacylation of the tRNA by AlaRS, the presense of a wobble pair in the acceptor stem (G3:U70) is the most crucial element

C. Aminoacylation of tRNA by AlaRS occurs even if the anticodon of tRNA is mutated

D. A microhelix lacking a clover leaf structure and harboring only the acceptor stem sequence of the tRNA is specifically aminoacylated by AlaRS

Gene Regulation-phage, Pro & Eukaryotes

259. A heterozygote of E. Coli was produced with the following combination of mutations:

$trpR^{+}trpO^{-}trpE^{+}$ / $trpR^{+}trpO^{+}trpE^{+}$

Where R is the repressor, O is the operator and trpE encodes the first enzyme in the biosynthetic cascade for tryptophan. Assume all other enzymes required are wild type. Which one of the following is the most likely phenotype of this E. coli ?

A. Synthesizes tryptophan irrespective of tryptophan status in the medium.

B. Synthesizes tryptophan only when tryptophan is absent.

C. Synthesizes tryptophan only when tryptophan is present.

D. Cannot synthesizes tryptophan under any condition

260. The following observations are being made in the context of the regulation of iron homeostasis in mammalian cells.

(*a*) The levels of transferrin receptor mRNA increase 30 - fold in the absence of iron

(*b*) Certain mutations in the 3'UTR of transferrin receptor mRNA fail to support increase in mRNA levels under low iron concentrations

(*c*) The level of transferrin receptor mRNA continues to be high in low iron concentration even when the cells are treated with a - amanitin

(*d*) The transferrin receptor mRNA levels decrease rapidly when iron is added to the cells.

Based on these observations, which one of the following statements represents the most likely scenario?

A. Transferrin receptor is only transcriptionally regulated, and the 3' end of the gene is the regulatory site

B. Transferrin receptor is post – transcriptionally regulated, and 3'UTR is the regulatory site

C. Iron induces expression of transferrin receptor, and the transferrin receptor protein is degrades in the presence of iron

D. Regulation of transferrin receptor is not sensitive to iron

DBT-JRF, 2021

Cellular Processes

261. Though DNA and RNA are nucleic acids, isolating RNA in the laboratory requires extreme precautions and pre-preparations than isolating DNA. This could be because:

A. RNA is more prone to hydrolysis than DNA.

B. RNA is smaller in size than DNA

C. RNA molecules tend to form RNA-RNA hybrids

D. There is lesser RNA content per cell than DNA

262. During replication, DNA polymerase-

A. Can initiate DNA synthesis de novo

B. Cannot initiate DNA synthesis de novo

C. Synthesizes DNA in 3' to 5' direction

D. Unwinds DNA in a 5' to 3' direction

263. If a single-stranded DNA sequence of 250 nucleotides consists of 30% thymine, the number of Adenine, Guanine and Cytosine nucleotides present in it is

A. 50, 50, 75,75

B. 75, 50, 75, 50
C. 75, 75, 50, 50
D. Cannot be calculated

264. DNA replication requires DNA Topoisomerase to remove the supercoiling of DNA that accumulates at the end of a growing replication fork. You wish to perform a PCR amplification of a gene that has been provided to you in a 6 kb plasmid vector. Why will you NOT use topoisomerase in your PCR reaction mix?
A. Denaturation step in the PCR protocol precludes formation of supercoils
B. Reaction buffer has a pH that denatures DNA and avoids supercoiling
C. Taq polymerase has innate topoisomerase activity
D. The 5′ 3′ exonuclease activity of Taq polymerase does not allow supercoiling

265. Following is a table in which the List I contain names of various steps of gene expression and in List II are the enzymes associated with those. Match the components of List I with those in List II

List I	List II
(*a*) Epigenetic regulation	(*i*) Endonuclease
(*b*) DNA repair	(*ii*) Histone methyltransferase
(*c*) Transcription	(*iii*) eIF2 Kinase
(*d*) Translation	(*iv*) RNA polymerase

Choose the correct answer from the option given below:

	(*a*)	(*b*)	(*c*)	(*d*)
A.	(*ii*)	(*i*)	(*iv*)	(*iii*)
B.	(*ii*)	(*iv*)	(*i*)	(*iii*)
C.	(*iii*)	(*ii*)	(*iv*)	(*i*)
D.	(*iv*)	(*iii*)	(*ii*)	(*i*)

266. The consequences of a DNA base change in a mutation are maximum, if the base change is located in the:
A. First or second position of a codon
B. Middle of an intron
C. Repetitive DNA elements
D. Third position of a codon

267. The Telomerase enzyme is a:
A. DNA–dependent DNA Polymerase
B. DNA dependent RNA Polymerase
C. Reverse Transcriptase
D. RNA–dependent RNA Polymerase

268. Given below are two statements: one is labelled as Assertion (A) and the other is labelled as Reason (R).

Assertion (A): Ionizing radiation can cause damage to the DNA

Reason (R): Ionizing radiation generates free radicals

In light of the above statements, choose the most appropriate answer from the options given below:
A. (A) is false but (R) is true
B. (A) is true but (R) is false
C. Both (A) and (R) are true and (R) is the correct explanation of (A)
D. Both (A) and (R) are true but (R) is NOT the correct explanation of (A)

269. Which one among the following is a nuclease?
A. DNase I
B. Helicase
C. Ligase
D. Polymerase

270. Which one of the following statements is NOT common between oxidative phosphorylation and photophosphorylation?
A. Generation of ATP
B. Involvement of a kinase
C. Involvement of electron transport
D. Involvement of oxygen

271. If the codons for translation of mRNAs to protein were 4 letters long instead of 3, what would be maximum number of hypothetical amino acids that could uniquely be recognized by tRNAs, assuming only one codon as stop codon?
A. 1295
B. 255
C. 63
D. 728

272. During translation, which one of following aminoacyl-tRNA binds first to the P site of bacterial ribosomes
A. fMet-tRNA^{fMet}
B. fMet-tRNA^{Met}
C. Met-tRNA^{fMet}
D. Met-tRNA^{Met}

273. A protein cargo X is destined for lysosomal degradation in cells under specific conditions. This can be tracked by red fluorescence emitted by the tag when it reaches lysosomes. What will happen when you treat the cells with NH_4Cl:
A. No red fluorescence will be emitted
B. Red fluorescence will be emitted in dotted structures in the cytoplasm
C. Red fluorescence will be emitted only at the periphery of the cell.
D. Red fluorescence will be emitted throughout the cell

274. Which one of the following is the most effective reducing agent of disulfide bonds in proteins?
A. 2-mercaptoethanol
B. Dithiothreitol
C. Ethanethiol
D. Ethanol

275. In the following table, List I have different nucleic acids and List has certain base modification. Match the components from List I with those in the List II

List I	List II
(*a*) DNA	(*i*) 7-methyl guanosine
(*b*) t-RNA	(*ii*) 5-methylcytosine
(*c*) m-RNA	(*iii*) pseudouridine

	(*a*)	(*b*)	(*c*)
A.	(*i*)	(*ii*)	(*iii*)
B.	(*ii*)	(*i*)	(*iii*)
C.	(*ii*)	(*iii*)	(*i*)
D.	(*iii*)	(*ii*)	(*i*)

276. During eukaryotic replication, ________ degrades the RNA primer by 5' – 3' exonuclease activity.
A. DNA polymerase V
B. FEN-1
C. RNAseH1
D. Topoisomerase IIB

277. Prokaryotic ribosomes bind to which one of the following:
A. Kozak sequence
B. Ori sequence
C. Promoter sequence
D. Shine-Dalgarno sequence

278. Which one of the following molecules causes catabolite repression of lac operon?
A. Arabinose B. Galactose
C. Glucose D. Lactose

279. Which one among the following is NOT a characteristic of an "Enhancer"?
A. It is conserved in evolution
B. It is transcribed to form enhancer RNA
C. Its function is independent of its location in the genome
D. Its function is independent of its orientation in genome

GATE (BIOTECHNOLOGY), 2021

280. The enzyme that transcribes the eukaryotic genes encoding precursor ribosomal RNAs (pre-rRNAs) of 28S, 18S and 5.8S rRNAs is
A. RNA polymerase I
B. RNA polymerase II
C. RNA polymerase III
D. RNA polymerase IV

GATE (LIFE SCIENCE), 2021

Fundamental Process & Molecular Techniques

281. According to the "wobble hypothesis" inosine at the third position of the anticodon cannot form hydrogen bonds with ________
A. Adenine B. Cytidine
C. Guanine D. Uracil

282. Telomerase has a function similar to ________
A. DNA dependent DNA polymerase
B. RNA polymerase
C. DNA gyrase
D. Reverse transcriptase

283. Which of the following are correctly paired?
A. Replication: DnaA
B. Recombination: RecA
C. DNA repair: Rho factor
D. Transcription: Sigma factor

284. Assume that the anticodon for an unknown amino acid is 3′ AUG 5′. The corresponding code on DNA sequence would be
A. 3′ TAC 5′ B. 5′ TAG 3′
C. 3′ ATG 5′ D. 5′ ATG 3′

CSIR-NET, SEPTEMBER (MORNING), 2022

Nucleic Acids-forms, Conformation & Stability

285. Identify the ribose conformation in the nucleotide shown below

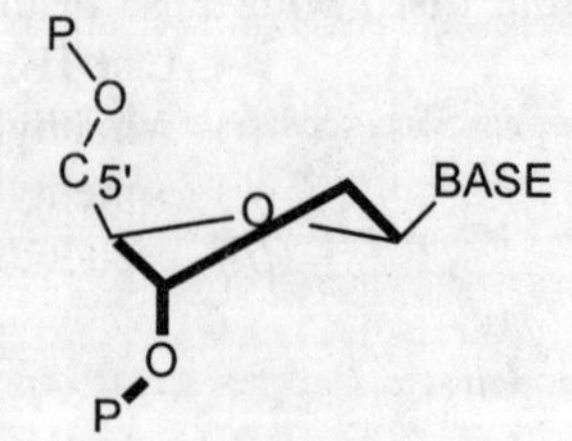

A. C2'-endo B. C2'-exo
C. C3'-endo D. C5'-exo

286. The diffraction patterns of two forms of DNA (A and B) and statements related to these patterns are given below.

Form 1 Form 2

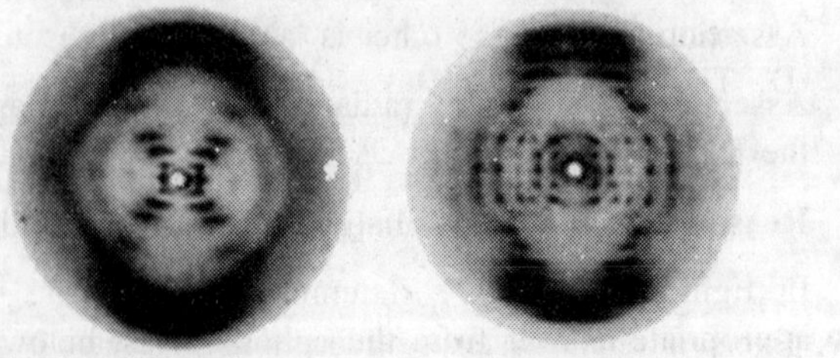

(*a*) The diffraction pattern corresponding to A-DNA is shown by form 1 with 11.6 base pairs per turn.

(*b*) The diffraction pattern of B-DNA is shown by form 2 with 11.6 base pairs per turn.
(*c*) The diffraction pattern of A-DNA is shown by form 2 with 11.6 base pairs per turn.
(*d*) The diffraction pattern of B-DNA is shown by form 1 with 10 base pairs per turn.

Which one of the following options have all correct statements?

A. (*c*) and (*d*)　　B. (*a*) and (*b*)
C. (*b*) only　　D. (*d*) only

287. The figure below represents the denaturation-renaturation profile of a double stranded DNA in citrate buffer

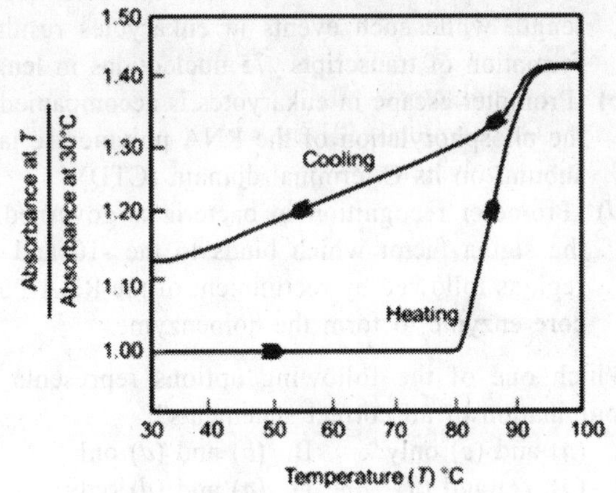

The percent of DNA that remains denatured at 30°C after cooling from 100°C is :

A. < 25%　　B. 30 – 35%
C. > 75%　　D. 65 – 70%

DNA Replication, Repair and Recombination

288. Which one of the following statements made about the bacterial replisome is INCORRECT?

A. The rate of forward movement of DnaB helicase along the template DNA increases 10-fold when DnaB and DNA Pol III interact, thus ensuring that the helicase does not move ahead rapidly without the polymerase
B. The transient interaction of the primase with the helicase allows activation of primase activity by 1000-fold, promoting RNA primer synthesis
C. The length of the Okazaki fragments is typically restricted to 1000-2000 nucleotides
D. The E. coli oriC carries repeats of two sequence motifs: repeats of a 9-mer that collectively form the site at which the origin first becomes single-stranded, and repeats of a 13-mer to which the DnaA initiator protein binds

289. Excision repair systems replace a short stretch of DNA around the site of damage. The following statements are made about nucleotide excision repair in E. coli:

(*a*) UvrB homodimer creates the nicks on one strand on both side of the lesion.
(*b*) The 50-60 residue-long stretch of DNA between the two nicks is removed by the action of UvrD.
(*c*) The gap generated is filled in typically by DNA polymerase I.
(*d*) The distortion caused by the lesion is recognized and bound by UvrA-UvrB complex.

Which one of the following options represents the combination of all correct statements?

A. (*a*) and (*b*) only
B. (*a*), (*b*) and (*d*)
C. (*c*) and (*d*) only
D. (*b*), (*c*) and (*d*)

290. In eukaryotes, DNA replication must occur with extreme accuracy and only once to prevent the damaging amplification. The following statements were made regarding possible mechanisms involved in achieving DNA replication:

(*a*) High APC/C activity in mitosis and early G1 phase of the cell cycle that triggers the destruction of Cdt1 thus allowing Cdt1 to be active in early G1 to load helicases.
(*b*) Activation of S-Cdks that regulate the phosphorylation of specific initiator proteins in the S-phase.
(*c*) MCM helicase loads at the S-phase of the cell cycle, so that replication begins only at S-phase.
(*d*) Cdc6 and Cdt1 bind to the origin recognition complex (ORC) and help in pre-replicative complex assembly only after mitosis.

Which one of the options has all correct statements?

A. (*a*), (*b*), and (*c*) only
B. (*b*), (*c*), and (*d*) only
C. (*a*), (*b*), and (*d*) only
D. (*a*), (*b*), (*c*), and (*d*)

291. An individual is heterozygous for a reciprocal translocation as shown below in the given diagram:

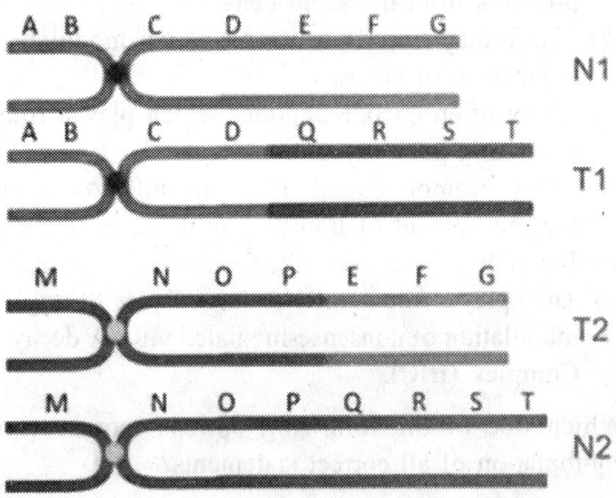

The following statements are made about segregation of such chromosomes during meiosis and gamete

(*a*) The complexly paired 4 chromosomes fail to segregate, pass into one cell at anaphase I and the cell eventually dies.

(*b*) Chromosomes pair between regions of maximum homology keeping the translocated part unpaired an occurs.

(*c*) One of the ways the chromosomes segregate is by alternate segregation (N1, N2 moving to one pole to the other pole).

(*d*) Alternate segregation produces non-viable gametes.

(*e*) Reciprocal translocations are considered as crossover suppressors as no gametes with crossover prod

Select the option from the following that describes the meiotic consequences of such translocation corre

A. (*a*) only B. (*c*) only
C. (*b*) and (*d*) D. (*a*) and (*e*)

RNA Synthesis and Processing

292. Which one of the following statements about the recognition of tRNAs by their cognate aminoacyl-tRNA synthetases is correct?

A. Aminoacyl-tRNA synthetases recognize their cognate tRNAs by the exclusive recognition of their anticodons
B. Aminoacyl-tRNA synthetases recognize their cognate tRNAs by recognition of their anticodons in some tRNAs only
C. Aminoacyl-tRNA synthetases cannot aminoacylate a tRNA that lacks the conserved modifications in the TeC loop
D. Aminoacyl-tRNA synthetases cannot aminoacylate a tRNA that lacks the conserved modifications in the DHU loop

293. Although introns are not a part of the processed transcript that gets translated, they are important for s following statements are made with reference to the possible ways in which introns are crucial to cell su

(*a*) They permit the generation of different protein products from the same gene.

(*b*) They may encode miRNAs which modulate the expression of genes.

(*c*) They often encode peptides which play a role in regulating gene expression.

(*d*) They promote export of certain mRNAs through the recruitment of transport proteins by the Exon Jun (EJC).

(*e*) They play a role in mRNA surveillance through the modulation of nonsense-mediated mRNA decay via Complex (EJC).

Which one of the following options represents the combination of all correct statements?

A. (*a*), (*b*) and (*e*) only
B. (*a*), (*c*) and (*d*) only
C. (*a*), (*b*), (*d*) and (*e*)
D. (*b*), (*c*) and (*d*) only

294. The initiation of transcription is a complex process involving promoter recognition, conversion of the initiation complex from closed to open form, abortive initiation events, and finally promoter escape. The following statements are made regarding these steps in transcription initiation:

(*a*) Promoter escape in bacteria is usually accompanied by the release of the sigma factor from the RNA polymerase holoenzyme complex.

(*b*) Abortive initiation events in prokaryotes result in the formation of short transcripts ~10 nucleotides in length while such events in eukaryotes result in formation of transcripts ~75 nucleotides in length.

(*c*) Promoter escape in eukaryotes is accompanied by the phosphorylation of the RNA polymerase large subunit on its C-terminal domain (CTD).

(*d*) Promoter recognition in bacteria is governed by the sigma factor which binds to the -10 and -35 regions followed by recruitment of the RNA Pol II core enzyme to form the holoenzyme.

Which one of the following options represents the combination of all correct statements?

A. (*a*) and (*c*) only B. (*b*) and (*d*) only
C. (*a*), (*c*) and (*d*) D. (*a*) and (*d*) only

Protein Synthesis and Processing

295. Regulation of mRNA translation is a major mechanism that maintains stoichiometric availability of ribosomal proteins (r-proteins) to rRNA molecules they bind to. Translational regulation is facilitated by general occurrence of the r-protein genes in several operons containing multiple genes. Which one of the following represents an established mechanism to ensure optimal production of the r-proteins in E. coli, when the r-proteins accumulate in free form (molar excess over rRNA)

A. The free r-protein(s) often bind to corresponding DNA sequence and activate transcription of rRNA genes to increase rRNA availability.
B. The free *r*-protein(s) bind to RNA polymerase and represses transcription of the *r*-protein genes to decrease the availability of their mRNAs.
C. The free *r*-protein(s) bind to the mRNA(s) and downregulate their translation.
D. The free r-protein(s) bind free NTPs which then activates their cryptic ribonuclease activity leading to the degradation of their mRNAs

296. Fidelity of protein synthesis depends to a large extent on the accuracy of aminoacylation of tRNAs with correct amino acids. However, given that the side chains of many amino acids are not sufficiently different, aminoacyl-tRNA synthetases (aaRS) are often prone to misacylate the tRNAs. One such example of misacylation is of $tRNA^{Thr}$ by ThrRS. In this context, following statements are being made about E. coli ThrRS.

(*a*) It misacylates $tRNA^{Thr}$ equally with Ser and Cys

(*b*) It possesses a distinct editing site that preferentially deacylates the misacylated $tRNA^{Thr}$

(*c*) The editing of the misacylated $tRNA^{Thr}$ occurs frequently in cis before the release of the misacylated $tRNA^{Thr}$

(*d*) It possesses a distinct editing site that does not discriminate between the misacylated $tRNA^{Thr}$ and $Thr\text{-}tRNA^{Thr}$

(*e*) The aminoacylation and the editing sites of ThrRS are the same.

Choose the option that represents all correct statements.

A. (*a*) and (*b*) B. (*b*) and (*c*)
C. (*c*) and (*d*) D. (*d*) and (*e*)

297. A 'nonsense' mutation in the protein coding region of an upstream gene of a group of genes in an operon often leads to depletion of the downstream gene products. This is a classic example of the phenomenon of "polar effect" of the mutation. Following statements are being made about this phenomenon.

(*a*) It occurs primarily because the termination codon generated in the upstream open reading frame (OR termination of protein synthesis depleting the ribosomes for translation of the downstream ORFs but it does not affect the process of transcription.

(*b*) The phenomenon of polar effects of mutation occurs only in the operons where the point mutation lea 'nonsense' mutation also leads to formation of a stem-loop structure resulting in Rho-independent termination.

(*c*) While the presence of termination codon in the upstream ORF may deplete the ribosomes that travel downstream ORF, the depletion of ribosomes downstream of the 'nonsense' mutation allows loading of t then results in premature transcription termination.

(*d*) Presence of the suppressor tRNA reading the 'nonsense' codon generated by the mutation, is essential effect of the mutation.

(*e*) Presence of the suppressor tRNA reading the 'nonsense' codon generated by the mutation diminishes of the polar effects.

Choose the option that represents all correct statements

A. (*a*) and (*c*) B. (*b*) and (*d*)
C. (*c*) and (*e*) D. (*a*) and (*d*)

Gene Regulation-phage, Pro & Eukaryotes

298. Following statements were made about chromatin remodeling in eukaryotes:

(*a*) Chromatin remodeling completely alters and/or slides the nucleosome, but cannot displace it.

(*b*) Chromatin remodeling is an energy driven, developmentally regulated active process.

(*c*) Histone acetylation is a reversible process, in which each direction of the reaction is catalyzed by different enzymes.

(*d*) In general, acetylation of core histones reduces their affinity for DNA and destabilizes the chromatin transcriptional repression.

(*e*) Phosphorylation of Ser1 of histone H2A has been associated with transcription repression.

Which one of the following represents the combination of correct statements?

A. (*a*), (*b*) and (*c*) B. (*a*), (*c*) and (*d*)
C. (*b*), (*c*) and (*e*) D. (*c*), (*d*) and (*e*)

299. Which of the options correctly matches the proteins involved in transcription (Column A) with the DNA binding domains they carry (Column B)?

Column A	Column B
(*a*) TFIIIA	(*i*) Helix-turn-helix
(*b*) MyoD	(*ii*) Zinc finger
(*c*) Jun	(*iii*) Helix-loop-helix
(*d*) Cro	(*iv*) Leucine zipper

	(*a*)	(*b*)	(*c*)	(*d*)
A.	(*iv*)	(*iii*)	(*i*)	(*ii*)
B.	(*ii*)	(*i*)	(*iv*)	(*iii*)
C.	(*iii*)	(*i*)	(*ii*)	(*iv*)
D.	(*ii*)	(*iii*)	(*iv*)	(*i*)

CSIR-NET, SEPTEMBER (AFTERNOON), 2022

Nucleic Acids-forms, Conformation & Stability

300. The B-form double stranded DNA was invaded by a complementary RNA sequence to form an R-loop structure. During this process,

A. sugar puckering on the DNA strand that pairs with RNA will remain unchanged.

B. sugar puckering on the DNA strand that pairs with RNA will change.

C. sugar puckering on the DNA strand that pairs with RNA will remain unchanged but the number of base pairs per turn in the RNA-DNA hybrid will increase.

D. sugar puckering on the DNA strand that pairs with RNA will change but the number of base pairs per turn in the RNA-DNA hybrid with remain unchanged.

DNA Replication, Repair and Recombination

301. In Saccharomyces cerevisiae, DNA replication is tightly controlled, and DNA should replicate once per cell cycle. Choose the INCORRECT statement regarding why the cells do not re-replicate their DNA in the S-phase.

A. Pre-replicative complex (Pre-RC) remains bound to the DNA in the S-phase and does not allow the re-replication
B. Assembly of Pre-RC is inhibited by Cdk activity
C. Assembly of Pre-RC is initiated at the end of mitosis, at the early G1 phase of the cell cycle (when the APC activity is high)
D. Cdt1 that helps in the recruitment of MCM proteins in the G1phase is inactivated by geminin in the S-phase of the cell cycle

302. Which one of the following statements about DNA replication is INCORRECT?

A. Once DNA replication commences, it always continues uninterrupted until the entire process is complete
B. Eukaryotic genomes replicate from multiple origins of replication.
C. A consensus sequence for the origins of DNA replication has been identified in Saccharomyces cerevisiae
D. Both, fully methylated as well as non-methylated oriC can initiate DNA replication, while hemi-methylated oriC does not.

303. The long DNA strand depicted below is serving as a template for lagging strand DNA synthesis . The short lines represent the newly synthesized Okazaki fragments.

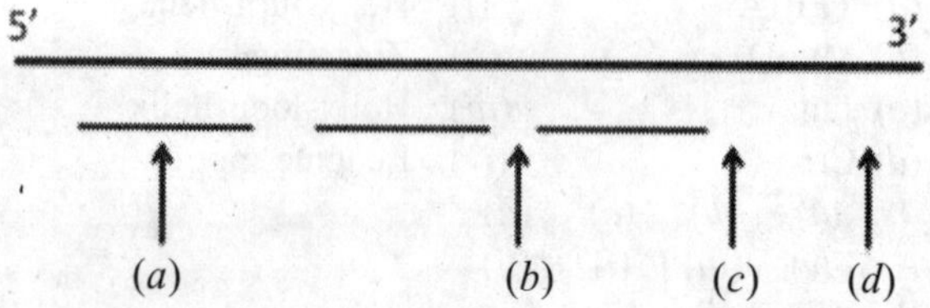

At which positions among (*a*), (*b*), (*c*) and (*d*) would DNA primase act next?

A. (*a*) B. (*b*)
C. (*c*) D. (*d*)

304. The following statements refer to E. coli replicative DNA polymerase:

(*a*) DNA Pol I displays very limited processivity and possesses 3'-5' exonuclease activity allowing fidelity of DNA replication.
(*b*) DNA Pol III is suitable for leading strand DNA synthesis due to its high processivity and 5'-3' exonuclease activity that removes incorrect nucleotides incorporated during DNA synthesis.
(*c*) DNA Pol I possesses 3'-5' exonuclease activity which allows removal of the RNA primer while its 5'-3' polymerase activity allows it to fill the gap created by removal of RNA primer.
(*d*) DNA Pol III is suitable for lagging strand DNA synthesis due to its high processivity and 5'-3' exonuclease activity.

Which one of the options below represents the combination of all correct statements?

A. (*d*) only B. (*b*) and (*c*)
C. (*a*) and (*b*) D. (*a*) and (*c*)

305. Some of the steps in the process of eukaryotic DNA replication mentioned below require hydrolysis of ATP.

(*a*) Phosphodiester bond formation
(*b*) DNA strand separation by helicase
(*c*) Clamp-loader association with clamp and DNA
(*d*) Joining of Okazaki fragments

Choose the following option that correctly identifies all the steps utilizing ATP hydrolysis

A. (*a*), (*b*) and (*d*) only
B. (*b*), (*c*) and (*d*) only
C. (*b*) and (*c*) only
D. (*b*) and (*d*) only

Protein Synthesis and Processing

396. The post-translational modifications in one or more core histones that are known to be associated with DNA repair pathways are:

A. Phosphorylation at specific tyrosine residues
B. Ubiquitination at specific lysine residues
C. Acetylation at specific serine residues
D. Methylation at specific serine residues

307. The amino acid arginine is encoded by six codons: CGU, CGC, CGA, CGG, AGA and AGG. Assuming inosine is not an option in the tRNA anticodon, what is the minimum number of tRNAs (from the options given below) that would be sufficient to read these codons?

A. Six B. Four
C. Three D. Five

308. Following statements were made about mitochondria:

(*a*) The D loop of the mitochondrial genome is required for replication, but not for the regulation of transcription.
(*b*) The L strand of mitochondrial genome possesses more cytosine.
(*c*) In plants, most mitochondrial tRNAs are encoded by the nuclear genome and then imported into the mitochondrion.
(*d*) Cycloheximide inhibits protein synthesis by mitochondrial ribosomes, but does not affect eukaryotic cytosolic ribosomes.
(*e*) Some organisms have been found to carry linear mitochondrial DNA.

Which one of the following options represents a combination of the correct statements?

A. (*a*), (*b*), (*c*)
B. (*b*), (*d*), (*e*)
C. (*a*), (*c*), (*d*)
D. (*b*), (*c*), (*e*)

309. The sequence below represents part of the coding strand of the bacterial gene Z. The arrow indicates the transcription start site

5' TATAATCGCACTCAAAGCCTAAGGAGGATCCGAATGCACGCGGAATCTTTCCGAC
+1 +10 +20

CACTACTGCATAGCGCCCAGAGCTCGCTAAATCGAGCGTGACATAATCAC..........3'

The following statements were made with reference to transcription & translation of the strand:

(*a*) Insertion of an 'A' nucleotide after position +8 increases the length of the transcript by 1 nucleotide and changes the amino acid sequence of the protein being translated.
(*b*) Substitution of the 'T' at position 22 changes the primary structure of the protein without altering transcript length.
(*c*) Insertion of 'A' after position 26 changes the primary structure of the protein and results in synthesis of truncated protein
(*d*) Deletion of 'A' at position 9 creates the STOP codon that prevents translation of the protein

Which one of the action below represents the combination of all correct statements?

A. (*c*) only B. (*a*) and (*d*)
C. (*b*) and (*c*) D. (*a*) and (*b*)

Gene Regulation-phage, Pro & Eukaryotes

310. The 5' UTR of ferritin mRNA forms a stem-loop structure called the iron regulatory element [IRE]. The Iron Regulatory Binding Protein [IRBP] binds this IRE. The following statements were made with reference to IRBP- IRE interaction:

(*a*) IRBP-IRE interaction prevents eIF4A from resolving the stem-loop structure, thus preventing initiation of translation of ferritin genes.
(*b*) IRBP-IRE interaction recruits eIF4A to the 5' UTR, thus promoting translation initiation.
(*c*) In presence of ferrous ions IRBP is unable to bind the IRE.
(*d*) eIF4A binds directly at the 5' UTR and disrupts the stem-loop structure, thus promoting translation initiation.

Which one of the options below represents the combination of all correct statements?

A. (*b*) only B. (*a*) and (*d*)
C. (*a*) and (*c*) D. (*b*) and (*c*)

311. Which of these describes a similarity between the lac and ara operons?

A. Expression of structural genes does not occur at high glucose concentrations.
B. lacI and araI both encode trans acting factors.
C. Binding of a regulatory protein is prevented in the presence of an inducer.
D. All of these are similarities.

312. Which one of the following statements relating to the mechanism of color development in response to LacZ expression in *Escherichia coli* is INCORRECT?

A. *E. coli* growth on LB agar with X-gal results in blue colored colonies because LacZ produced in the cell hydrolyses X-gal present in the medium into a blue colored product.
B. When the membranes of the cells harboring LacZ are permeabilized and cells incubated in a buffer with ONPG, the solution turns yellow because LacZ encoded protein hydrolyzes ONPG.
C. E. coli growth on MacConkey agar results in pink colored colonies because LacZ encoded protein produced in the cell hydrolyzes the neutral red dye present in the medium into a pink colored product.
D. E. coli growth on MacConkey agar results in pink colored colonies due to shift in pH of the medium.

DBT-JRF, 2022

313. For transcribing protein coding genes, the RNA Polymerase forms the preinitiation complex (PIC) in association with:

A. TFIIA, TFIID, TFIIG
B. TFIIA, TFIIG, TFIIH
C. TFIIH, TFIIF, TFIID
D. TFIIC, TFIID, TFIIF

314. The motifs commonly found in the core promoter of eukaryotic protein coding genes are:

A. TATA and Pribnow box
B. Motif ten element and TATA
C. BRE and Kozak consensus se27-200uence
D. TRE and TATA

315. Eukaryotic RNA Polymerase II transcribes:

A. rRNA and tRNA genes
B. mRNA and tRNA genes
C. mRNA and 5S rRNA genes
D. mRNA, miRNA and snRNA genes

316. Given below are two statements:

Statement I: Large subunit of rubisco is encoded by chloroplast genome while small subunit of Rubisco is encoded by nuclear genome

Statement II: Small subunit of rubisco has a transit peptide, which is cleaved off at the time of its translocation into plastids.

Choose the correct answer from the options given below:

A. Both Statement I and Statement II are true
B. Both Statement I and Statement II are false
C. Statement I is true but Statement II is false
D. Statement I is false but Statement II is true

317. miRNAs are major regulators of gene expression. In an experiment, it was observed that gene 'X' is a direct target of miRNA 'A'. Upon overexpression of miRNA 'A' in Arabidopsis thaliana:

A. only transcript abundance of X will be affected
B. the resultant protein X will be of smaller size
C. only specific activity of protein X will get reduced
D. both transcript and protein abundance of X may get reduced

318. TATA box involved in the initiation of transcription is located in the:

A. Promoter region
B. Enhancer region
C. Exon region
D. Intron region

319. Which one of the following enzymes help the DNA to overcome the tension generated by the unwinding during replication?

A. Nickase   B. Helicase
C. Topoisomerase   D. DNA ligase

320. Given below are two statements:

Statement I: Polycistronic mRNAs are found in archaea and bacteria.

Statement II: Plastid genes in eukaryotes have only monocistronic mRNA.

In the light of the above statements, choose the most appropriate answer from the options given below:

A. Both Statement I and Statement II are correct
B. Both Statement I and Statement II are incorrect
C. Statement I is correct but Statement II is incorrect
D. Statement I is incorrect but Statement II is correct

321. Which family of proteins has the greatest likelihood of containing a Leucine-zipper motif?

A. Serine proteases
B. Map kinases
C. Transcription factors
D. Sugar binding proteins

322. Which one of the following types of mutations can lead to a major change in the encoded protein?

(*a*) Insertion of a single nucleotide near the end of the coding sequence.
(*b*) Removal of a single nucleotide from the beginning of the coding sequence.
(*c*) Deletion of three consecutive nucleotides of a codon in the middle of the coding sequence.
(*d*) Deletion of four consecutive nucleotides in the middle of the coding sequence.

A. A, D   B. B, D
C. B, C   D. A, E

323. The most likely sub-cellular localization of NAC transcription factors is:

A. Nucleus
B. Cytoplasm
C. Mitochondria
D. Plastid

324. Which enzyme will digest RNA in a DNA-RNA Hybrid?

A. RNase A
B. BamHI
C. Reverse transcriptase
D. RNAse H

325. Which one of the molecular processes utilize 2', 3' Dideoxy-ribonucleoside triphosphates?

A. DNA synthesis for primers
B. Okazaki fragment formation during lagging strand synthesis.
C. DNA sequencing by synthesis
D. Transcript chain elongation

326. Given below are two statements:

Statement I: RNA secondary structure is composed primarily of double-stranded RNA regions formed by folding of the single-stranded molecule back on itself.

Statement II: Like protein secondary structure, RNA secondary structure can be conveniently viewed as an intermediate step in the formation of a three-dimensional structure.

In the light of the above statements, choose the most appropriate answer from the options given below

A. Both Statement I and Statement II are correct
B. Both Statement I and Statement II are incorrect
C. Statement I is correct but Statement II is incorrect
D. Statement I is incorrect but Statement II is correct

327. Which one of the following DOES NOT represent known interactions of RNA secondary structural elements?

A. Pseudo knot
B. Kissing hairpins
C. Hairpin-bulge contact
D. Helix-turn-helix

328. In the Table given below, the column (A) lists three eukaryotic RNA Polymerases and column (B) lists group of genes they transcribe. Identify the correct match from the options below:

A	B
(*a*) RNA polymerase I	(*i*) mRNA, miRNA, snRNA genes
(*b*) RNA polymerase II	(*ii*) tRNA and 5S rRNA genes
(*c*) RNA polymerase III	(*iii*) rRNA genes

	(*a*)	(*b*)	(*c*)
A.	(*iii*)	(*ii*)	(*i*)
B.	(*ii*)	(*iii*)	(*i*)
C.	(*ii*)	(*i*)	(*iii*)
D.	(*iii*)	(*i*)	(*ii*)

329. How many different kinds of post translational modifications are present in this peptide?

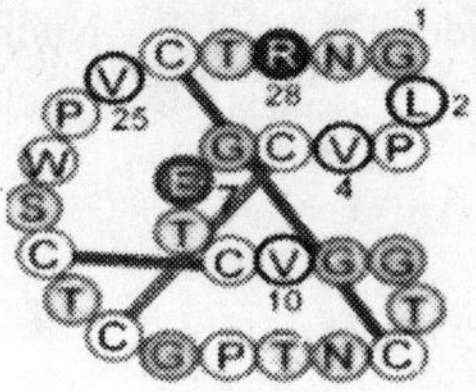

A. One B. Two
C. Four D. Nine

330. Which one among the following is an important constituent of RNA induced silencing complex inplants?
A. Argonaute
B. LHP1
C. RNaseP
D. RNA dependent RNA polymerase

331. Green Fluorescent Protein (GFP) emits green light due to the presence of a:
A. prosthetic fluorophore that emits green light
B. group of amino acids that are not found in other proteins
C. metal cofactor that shifts the emission to green wavelength
D. post translational modification that generates a unique fluorophore

GATE (BIOTECHNOLOGY), 2022

332. Which of the following statement(s) is(are) CORRECT regarding the lac operon in E. coli when grown in the presence of glucose and lactose?
A. At low glucose level, the operon is activated
B. At high glucose level, the operon is activated to enable the utilization of lactose
C. The lac repressor binds to operator region inactivating the operon
D. Binding of lactose to the lac repressor induces the operon

333. Emerging viruses such as SARS-CoV2 cause epidemics. Which of the following process(es) contribute to the rise of such viruses?
A. Mutation of existing virus
B. Jumping of existing virus from current to new hosts
C. Spread of virus in the new host population
D. Replication of virus outside a host

334. Adenine can undergo a spontaneous change to hypoxanthine in a cell, leading to a DNA base pair mismatch. The CORRECT combination of enzymes that are involved in repairing this damage is
A. Nuclease, DNA polymerase, DNA ligase
B. Nuclease, DNA ligase, helicase
C. Primase, DNA polymerase, DNA ligase
D. Primase, helicase, DNA polymerase

335. In animal cells, the endogenously produced miRNAs silence gene expression by
A. base pairing with the 3'-untranslated region of specific mRNAs
B. blocking mRNA synthesis
C. binding to the operator site
D. base pairing with the 3' region of specific rRNAs

GATE (LIFE SCIENCE), 2022

Fundamental Process & Molecular Techniques

336. The bases present in DNA are
A. adenine, cytosine, guanine and thymine
B. adenine, guanine, thymine and uracil
C. adenine, cytosine, thymine and uracil
D. cytosine, guanine, thymine and uracil

337. Which one of the following statements about the DNA polymerase III of E. coli is NOT correct?
A. It catalyzes nick translation.
B. Its absence is lethal to E. coli.
C. It synthesizes a complementary DNA strand using a single-stranded template.
D. It possesses 32 '→ 52 exonuclease activity.

338. Which one of the following compounds is NOT a translation inhibitor?
A. Chloramphenicol B. Cycloheximide
C. Puromycin D. Rifampicin

339. Two RNAs shown below were used separately as templates in an in vitro translation system, which can generate proteins in all possible reading frames.

RNA_1 : 5' – $(AG)_n$ – 3'
RNA_2 : 5' – $(AAG)_n$ – 3'

The RNA_1 translated product contained Arg and Glu. The RNA_2 translated product contained Arg, Glu, and Lys.

Which one of the following codons directs the incorporation of Arg?

A. AAG B. AGA
C. GAA D. GAG

340. Which one of the following mutagens convert DNA's adenine to hypoxanthine?

A. Ultraviolet light
B. Mitomycin C
C. Methyl methanesulfonate
D. Nitrous acid

341. Nonsense suppressor mutation is found in ....

A. rRNA
B. tRNA
C. start codon of mRNA
D. stop codon of mRNA

342. Which one of the following organic compounds is composed of only (*i*) a nitrogen containing base, (*ii*) a single five-carbon sugar, and (*iii*) a triphosphate?

A. Nucleoside B. Nucleotide
C. Base D. Nucleic acid

ANSWERS

1	2	3	4	5	6	7	8	9	10
C	B	C	B	C	D	B	B	C	B
11	12	13	14	15	16	17	18	19	20
B	B	D	C	B	C	B	C	C	D
21	22	23	24	25	26	27	28	29	30
C	B	C	B	C	B	A	D	A	D
31	32	33	34	35	36	37	38	39	40
B	C	D	D	B	C	B	B	C	C
41	42	43	44	45	46	47	48	49	50
B	B	D	A	B	C	B	B	D	D
51	52	53	54	55	56	57	58	59	60
A	D	A	C	C	A	D	C	B	C
61	62	63	64	65	66	67	68	69	70
B	A	B	C	C	C	B	B	A	B
71	72	73	74	75	76	77	78	79	80
A	C	B	B	D	C	B	D	D	B
81	82	83	84	85	86	87	88	89	90
C	C	B	A	A	A	A	B	C	B
91	92	93	94	95	96	97	98	99	100
B	D	D	D	B	C	C	D	C	D
101	102	103	104	105	106	107	108	109	110
C	B	A	A	D	A	C	B	B	C
111	112	113	114	115	116	117	118	119	120
C	D	D	B	D	D	D	B	B	C
121	122	123	124	125	126	127	128	129	130
C	C	A	A	B	A	A	A	C	C
131	132	133	134	135	136	137	138	139	140
C	B	D	C	B	D	A	B	C	B
141	142	143	144	145	146	147	148	149	150
B	D	A	C	B	B	C	A	D	A
151	152	153	154	155	156	157	158	159	160
B	A	B	B	B	A	B	B	A	B

161	**162**	**163**	**164**	**165**	**166**	**167**	**168**	**169**	**170**
B	B	B	A	C	D	A	C	A	B
171	**172**	**173**	**174**	**175**	**176**	**177**	**178**	**179**	**180**
B	C	B	A	A	D	D	A	C	D
181	**182**	**183**	**184**	**185**	**186**	**187**	**188**	**189**	**190**
D	B	A	C	A	D	D	C	C	B
191	**192**	**193**	**194**	**195**	**196**	**197**	**198**	**199**	**200**
A	A	A	B	B	B	C	B	B	C
201	**202**	**203**	**204**	**205**	**206**	**207**	**208**	**209**	**210**
A	B	A	D	C	D	B	D	B	C
211	**212**	**213**	**214**	**215**	**216**	**217**	**218**	**219**	**220**
B	A	C	C	C	A	C	A	A	D
221	**222**	**223**	**224**	**225**	**226**	**227**	**228**	**229**	**230**
A	D	D	A	D	A	B	A	C	A
231	**232**	**233**	**234**	**235**	**236**	**237**	**238**	**239**	**240**
A	B	B	B	B	D	D	B	D	A
241	**242**	**243**	**244**	**245**	**246**	**247**	**248**	**249**	**250**
D	C	C	D	A	D	B	A	A	A
251	**252**	**253**	**254**	**255**	**256**	**257**	**258**	**259**	**260**
D	A	D	D	C	D	B	A	A	B
261	**262**	**263**	**264**	**265**	**266**	**267**	**268**	**269**	**270**
A	B	D	A	A	A	C	C	A	B
271	**272**	**273**	**274**	**275**	**276**	**277**	**278**	**279**	**280**
B	A	A	B	C	B	D	C	A	A
281	**282**	**283**	**284**	**285**	**286**	**287**	**288**	**289**	**290**
C	D	A,B,D	C	A	A	A	D	C	C
291	**292**	**293**	**294**	**295**	**296**	**297**	**298**	**299**	**300**
B	B	C	A	C	B	C	C	D	B
301	**302**	**303**	**304**	**305**	**306**	**307**	**308**	**309**	**310**
A	A	D	D	D	B	C	D	A	C
311	**312**	**313**	**314**	**315**	**316**	**317**	**318**	**319**	**320**
A	C	C	A	D	A	D	A	C	A
321	**322**	**323**	**324**	**325**	**326**	**327**	**328**	**329**	**330**
C	B	A	D	C	A	D	D	D	A
331	**332**	**333**	**334**	**335**	**336**	**337**	**338**	**339**	**340**
D	A,C	A,B,C	A	A	A	A	D	B	D
341	**342**								
B	B								

CHAPTER

4

GENETICS

CSIR-NET, JUNE, 2017

Mendelian Principles

1. A recessive inherited disease is expressed only in individuals of blood group O and not expressed in blood groups A, B or AB. Alleles controlling the disease and blood group are independently inherited. A normal woman with blood group A and her normal husband with blood group B already had one child with the disease. The woman is pregnant for second time. What is the probability that the second child will also have the disease?

A. 1/2 B. 1/4
C. 1/16 D. 1/64

2. The following is a schematic representation of a hypothetical pathway involved in formation of eye color in an insect species.

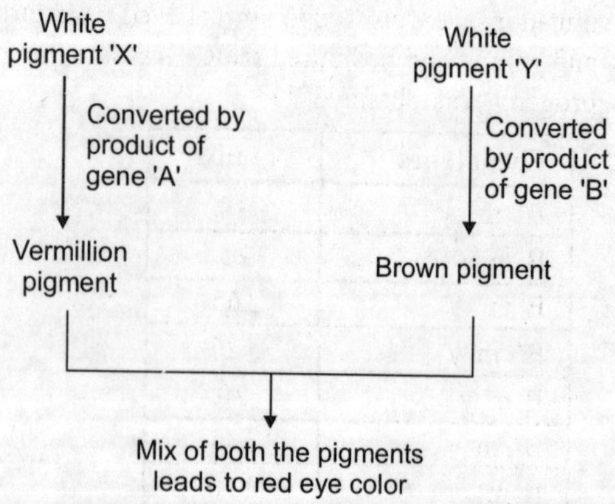

Genes A and B are linked and have a map distance of 10cM. Females with genotypes $a^+ ab^+ b$ are test crossed. Further, in these females, the two genes are linked in cis. a^+ and b^+ represent wild type alleles, while a and b are null alleles. The progeny of the test cross have individuals with four different eye colours.

What is the expected ratio of individuals with eye color Red: Vermillion: Brown: White in the progeny?

A. 9 : 3 : 3 : 1 B. 1: 1: 1 : 1
C. 9 : 1 : 1 : 9 D. 1 : 9 : 9 : 1

3. A phenotypically normal fruit fly was crossed to another fly whose phenotype was not recorded. Of the progeny, 3/8 were wild type, 3/8 had ebony body color, 1/8 had vestigeal wings and 1/8 had ebony body color and vestigeal wings. Ebony body color and vestigeal wings are recessive characters and their genes are located on two different autosomes. Based on this information which one of the following is the likely genotype of the parents?

A. ee vg vg and e^+e^+ vg^+vg
B. ee vg^+ vg and e^+e vg^+vg
C. e^+e vg vg and e^+e^+ vg^+vg
D. e^+e vg^+ vg and e^+e vg^+vg

Microbial Genetics

4. In a transduction experiment using $a^+ b^+ c^+$ genotype as a donor and $a^- b^- c^-$ as the recipient, a^+ transductants were selected and screened for b and c. The data obtained are shown below.

Genotype	No. of Recombinant
$a^+ b^- c^-$	573
$a^+ b^+ c^-$	98
$a^+ b^- c+$	11
$a^+ b^+ c^+$	68

The co-transduction frequencies for a^+b^+ and b^+c^+, respectively, are:

A. 17% and 12% B. 22% and 9%
C. 22% and 17% D. 17% and 9%

CSIR-NET, DECEMBER, 2017

Mendelian Principles

5. A researcher exposed *Drosophila* larvae to 37°C during their growth. One of the adult flies that emerged had a crossveinless phenotype. Crossveinless is a known mutant in *Drosophila.* When this crossveinless fly was crossed to a known crossveinless mutant fly all the progeny had normal phenotype.
The observed phenotype can be best explained as an example of

A. Conditional mutant B. Phenocopy
C. Penetrance D. Pleiotropy

6. Two inbred lines of beans were intercrossed. In F1 the variance in bean length was measured as 2.0. The F1 was selfed to obtain F2 and the variance in bean length in F2 was 7.0. The broad heritability of bean length in the F2 population will be:

A. 0.75 B. 9.0
C. 5.0 D. 0.71

Non-mendelian Genetics

7. Two mutant plants, both bearing white flowers, were crossed. All F1 plants had red coloured flowers. When an F1 plant was selfed it produced progeny with either red or white coloured flowers in 9:7 ratios. Based on this information, which one of the following conclusions is correct?

A. The mutations in the parents do not complement each other
B. The mutations in the parents are allelic
C. The mutations in the parents are nonallelic
D. The mutations in the parents are linked

Gene Mapping

8. In a linkage map, two genes A and B, are 70 cM apart. If individuals heterozygous for both the genes are test crossed number of progeny with parental phenotype will be:

A. Equal to the number of progeny with recombinant phenotype
B. More than the number of progeny with recombinant phenotype.
C. Less than the number of progeny with recombinant phenotype
D. Could be more or less than the number of progeny with recombinant phenotype depending on whether the genes are linked in *cis* or *trans*, respectively.

9. The following table shows mapping data from three interrupted mating experiments using three different Hfr strains and an F-strain:

Appearance of genes in F^- cells

Hfr 1	Genes	e^+	f^+	c^+	d^+	b^+
	Time	6	24	34	49	54
Hfr 2	Genes	b^+	d^+	c^+	f^+	g^+
	Time	1	6	21	31	63
Hfr 3	Genes	d^+	c^+	f^+	e^+	g^+
	Time	4	19	29	47	61

(Time is Represented in Minutes)

The following answers are derived:

The order of genes is
(*a*) e g b d c f
(*b*) f g b d c e

The distance between
(*c*) f and g is 32 min and between f and b is 30 min
(*d*) c and e is 28 min and between b and c is 20 min

The correct combination of answers is

A. (*a*), (*c*) and (*d*) B. (*b*) and (*c*)
C. (*a*) and (*b*) D. (*b*) and (*d*)

10. In *Drosophila*, Bar eye (B) is a dominant mutation while miniature wing (m) and yellow body colour (y) are recessive mutations. Heterozygous females for these mutations were crossed to normal eyed miniature winged and yellow body coloured males. Assume the following progeny was obtained:

Phenotypes	Number
$B^+ m^+ y^+$	30
$B\ m\ y^+$	25
$B\ m^+ y^+$	165
$B^+ m\ y^+$	120
$B\ m\ y$	20
$B^+ m\ y$	185
$B\ m^+ y$	110
$B^+ m^+ y$	45

Based on the results obtained, the order of genes will be:

(*a*) B m y (*b*) m B y

The genetic distance between B and y will be:

(*c*) 40 cM (*d*) 17.1cM

The correct combination of answer is

A. (*a*) and (*c*) B. (*b*) and (*c*)
C. (*a*) and (*d*) D. (*b*) and (*d*)

Microbial Genetics

11. Phages are collected from an infected *E. Coli* donor strain of genotype $cys^+leu^+thr^+$ and used to transduce a recipient of genotype $cys^-leu^-thr^-$. The treated recipient population is plated on a minimal medium supplemented with leucine and threonine. Many colonies grew. Which one of the following combinations of genotypes is appropriate for the colonies that grew?

A. $cys^+\ leu^+\ thr^+$, $cys^+\ leu^-\ thr^+$, $cys^-\ leu^+\ thr^-$
B. $cys^-\ leu^+\ thr^+$, $cys^+\ leu^-\ thr^-$, $cys^+\ leu^+\ thr^-$
C. $cys^-\ leu^-\ thr^-$, $cys^-\ leu^-\ thr^+$, $cys^-\ leu^+\ thr^-$
D. $cys^+\ leu^-\ thr^-$, $cys^+\ leu^-\ thr^+$, $cys^+\ leu^+\ thr^-$

Pedigree Analysis

12. The inheritance of a given disorder is recorded in three small families shown below:

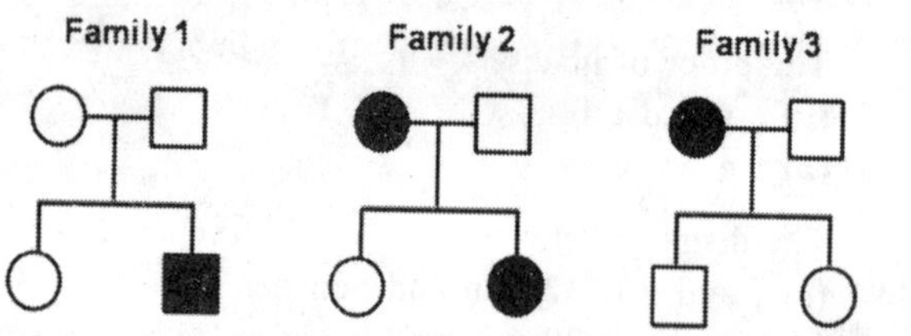

Based on the above limited information, which one of the following inheritance pattern best explains the observations?

A. X-linked recessive
B. X-linked dominant
C. Autosomal recessive
D. Autosomal dominant

Mutation & Chromosomal Aberration

13. In Burkitt's Lymphoma a reciprocal translocation between chromosome 8 and 14 is observed. If an individual is heterozygous for this translocation, the consequence in meiosis will be as follows:

(*a*) Four chromosomes, *i.e.*, normal chromosome 8 and 14, and translocated chromosome 8 and 14, pair together
(*b*) The two normal chromosomes 8 and 14, and two translocated chromosomes pair separately
(*c*) All gametes produced from this meiosis are non-viable as they have deletions and duplications
(*d*) In one of the cross configurations called "alternate segregation" all gametes having normal or translocated chromosomes, survive
(*e*) The gametes having normal chromosomes only survive while all gametes having translocated chromosomes are non-viable, hence the translocations are used as crossover suppressors.

Which of the following combinations best describes the meiotic consequences for the translocation described above?

A. (*b*) and (*e*) B. (*b*), (*c*) and (*e*)
C. (*a*), (*c*) and (*e*) D. (*a*) and (*d*)

DBT-JRF, 2017

Genetics, Phylogeny & Evolution

14. What is the minimum number of edges that meet at every branch node in a phylogenetic tree?

A. 1 B. 2
C. 3 D. 4

Molecular and Human Genetics

15. The phenomenon of transfer of traits from a man to his grandson through his daughter is known as:

A. Sex influenced inheritance
B. Criss-cross inheritance
C. Y-linked inheritance
D. Sex-limited inheritance

16. Which of the following is a reason that geneticists use mtDNA to study the relatedness of animal populations?

A. mtDNA mutates at a slower rate than nuclear DNA
B. mtDNA transmitted from mother to child, is free from recombination
C. All mitochondrial proteins are coded by mitochondrial genes
D. There are only a few single nucleotide polymorphisms in the mtDNA

17. In a Multi-Locus Variable number tandem repeat Analysis (MLVA) for *Salmonella enterica* subspecies, three tandem repeats loci have been identified inside *yohM* gene of *S. typhimurium LT2, S.typhi* CT18 and *S.typhi* Ty2 strains. Motif lengths for the loci are 2,3 and 5 respectively. Motif AT and ATG are found to be repeated by 13 and 5 times respectively in all the strains. Motif ATGTC is repeated 13 times in *S. typhimurium* LT2, 15 times *S.typhi* CT18 and 12 times *S.typhi* Ty2 strains. Which locus is Variable Number Tandem Repeat (VNTR)?

A. AT B. ATG
C. ATGTC D. GTCA

18. Of a population of cells undergoing meiosis, 1% of the cells undergo recombination between genes A and B. What is the distance between the two genes?

A. 0.25 cM B. 0.75 cM
C. c.0.50 cM D. 1.00 cM

19. Two independent transgenic plants, one with single copy of gene A and another with single copy of gene B were expressed under the same seed-specific promoter. In transgenic plants, seed formation on self-pollination was similar to that of untransformed plants. When homozygous plants with gene A (male parent) were crossed with homozygous plants with gene B (female parent), viable seed formation did not occur although, pollen production was normal. What could be the possible reason for this observation?

A. Product of gene A is lethal to the male gametophyte.
B. Interaction between products of genes A and B is lethal to the zygote
C. Interaction between products of genes A and B is lethal to the male gametophyte.
D. Product of gene B is lethal to the zygote.

20. In inbred lines, gene and genotypic frequencies are maintained by growing them in isolation followed by:

A. self-pollination
B. self-pollination and selection
C. pair-wise crossing
D. random mating without selection.

21. Homozygous plants from biparental mating for development of mapping populations can be obtained in a short time by:

A. development of RILs
B. development of doubled haploids
C. random mating in F2 followed by selfing in subsequent generations
D. chromosome elimination technique

22. Which one of the following is NOT required for QTL analysis in association mapping?

A. Phenotypic data from multi-location trials
B. Polymorphic markers
C. Genetic linkage map
D. Diverse germplasm lines

23. In transgenic plant, the phenomenon of Co-suppression is due to:

A. transgene integration within the endogenous gene
B. transgene integration at a locus very close to the endogenous gene
C. similarity between the transgene and endogenous gene sequences
D. lack of similarity between the transgene and endogenous gene sequences

24. Which one of the following types of mutation would usually NOT be detected in a molecular diagnostic test that is based on sequencing each exon of a gene individually from a male suspected of having an X-linked disorder?

A. Missense mutation
B. Nonsense mutation
C. Deletion of an exon
D. Inversion of a part of the gene.

25. A couple came for counselling following three first-trimester miscarriages and underwent chromosomal analysis. The man was found to have pericentric inversion with the karyotype 46, XY, inv8(p12q22). Which one of following would be a correct conclusion?

A. This is a normal variant, likely of no significance
B. This is an abnormal chromosome that would cause congenital anomalies if transmitted to a child.
C. This rearrangement might lead to chromosomal imbalance in an offspring and could explain multiple miscarriages.
D. This rearrangement might cause dicentric or acentric chromosomes in an offspring, which would probably not be compatible with survival.

26. Unequal crossing over between two *Alu* repeats can lead to an LDL receptor gene with an internal deletion or duplication. Based on this information, which of the following must be true?

A. The LDL receptor gene contains one and only one *Alu* repeat sequence.
B. The LDL receptor gene does not contain *Alu* repeat sequences.
C. The genome contains only one copy of the *Alu* repeat sequence.
D. The LDL receptor gene contains at least two Alu repeat sequences

27. Linkage analysis is performed in a large family with an autosomal dominant hemolytic anemia, using a polymorphic marker within the β-globin locus. The LOD score at $q = 0$ is negative infinity. The LOD score at $q = 0.01$ is –4.5. You conclude that the disorder in this family is:

A. not due to a beta-globin gene mutation
B. due to a beta-globin gene mutation
C. an acquired disorder, due to a somatic gene mutation
D. due to a mutation in a gene on chromosome 11, 10 cM centromeric of beta-globin

28. The following pedigree shows the inheritance of a very rare human disease. What is most likely mode of inheritance for the disease trait and what is the probability that second child of III-2 and III-3 be a son and will also have the disease

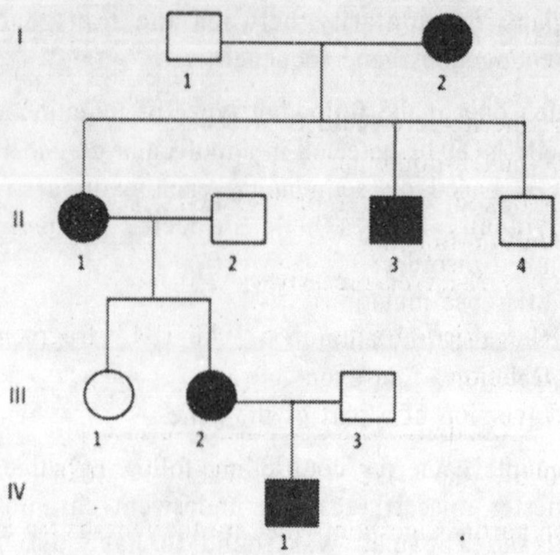

A. Sex-linked recessive; 0.5
B. Autosomal recessive; 0.25
C. Autosomal dominant: 0.75
D. Autosomal dominant; 0.25

29. The range of transformation frequencies obtained in independent transformation experiments using four different constructs with different combinations of promoters (Pr) and selection marker genes, is given below:

Construct	Transformation frequency
CaMV35S Pr – *bar* – nos polyA	20% – 35%
Nos Pr – *bar* – nos polyA	2% – 4%
CaMV35S Pr – *NPTII* – nos polyA	46% – 49%
Nos Pr – *NPTII* – nos polyA	24% – 28%

In the absence of any other factors, which one of the following statements is NOT acceptable as a logical conclusion based on the above data?
A. Use of stronger promoters for expression of selection marker genes can increase transformation frequencies.
B. Variations in expression levels between the *NPTII* and *bar* genes is not influenced by the nos poly A signal.
C. Production of herbicide resistant plants at high frequency can be achieved with lower expression levels of the transgene.
D. Use of kanamycin as a selection marker appears to be more favorable for production of larger number of transgenic plants.

30. In a randomly breeding population, an autosomal recessive condition affects 1 newborn in 10,000. The expected frequency of carriers will be nearly:
A. 1 in 25 B. 1 in 50
C. 1 in 100 D. 1in 1,000

31. There are reports of more than 100 mutations at different sites of Factor IX that manifests Haemophilia B. This is an example of:
A. clinical heterogeneity
B. allelic heterogeneity
C. protein heterogeneity
D. locus heterogeneity

32. In a diploid organism, loss of function mutations produces dominant phenotypes when there is:
A. pleiotropy
B. epistasis
C. multiple allelism
D. haploinsufficiency

33. In Mendel's dihybrid cross experiment, if the two selected traits were on the same chromosome (linked) and assuming that there is no recombination, what would be the expected genotypic ratio in the F_2 generation?
A. 1:2:1
B. 9:3:3:1
C. 1:3
D. 1:1

34. Huntington disease is caused by:
A. Expanded dinucleotide repeats sequence in coding region
B. Expanded trinucleotide repeats in non-coding region
C. Expanded trinucleotide sequence in coding sequence
D. Expanded dinucleotide sequence in non-coding sequence.

Genomics and Proteomics

35. A gene was cloned into a unique HindIII restriction site present in the ampicillin resistance gene of a vector that contains both ampicillin and kanamycin resistance genes. To select for only recombinant clones, the transformation mixture should be plated on which of the following plates?
A. Ampicillin containing plate
B. Ampicillin plus Kanamycin containing plate
C. Ampicillin containing plate followed by replica-plating on kanamycin containing plate
D. Kanamycin containing plate followed by replica-plating on ampicillin containing plate

36. Pyrosequencing derives its name from the fact that:
A. the bases are detected by pyrolysis
B. it detects pyrophosphate released during base incorporation
C. it uses apyrase to detect the bases
D. it generates a pyrogram as an output.

GATE (BIOTECHNOLOGY), 2017

Genetics and Evolutionary Biology

37. If the nucleotide composition (%) of a viral genome is A = 10, U = 20, C = 40. and G = 3, which one of the following is this genome?
A. Double stranded DNA
B. Single stranded RNA
C. Single stranded DNA
D. Double stranded RNA

38. A pedigree of an inheritable disease is shown below

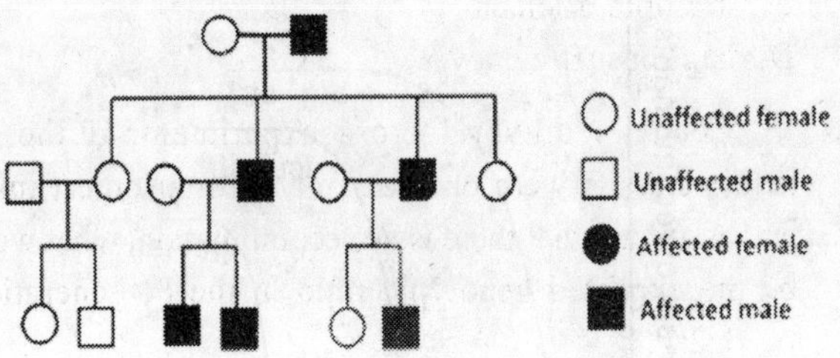

This inheritable disease is:
A. X-linked dominant
B. X-linked recessive or Y-linked
C. Only Y-linked
D. Only X-linked recessive

39. EcoRI restriction sites on a 10kb DNA fragment are shown below:

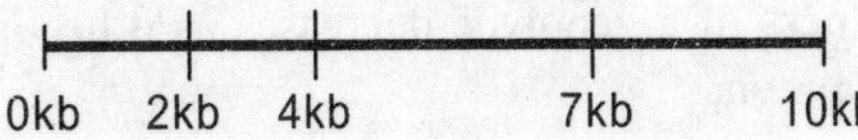

Upon partial digestion, what are the lengths (in kb) of all the possible DNA fragments obtained?
A. 2,3,4,5,6,7,8, and 10
B. 2,3,4,5,6, and 7
C. 2,3,4, and 7
D. 2 and 3

GATE (LIFE SCIENCE), 2017

Genetics and Genomics

40. Among the following, which genetic material is naturally inherited through maternal inheritance in higher plants?
A. Nuclear DNA B. Plasmid DNA
C. Chloroplast DNA D. T-DNA

41. Two independent non-segregating recessive mutants (*m1* and *m2*) display similar defects in petal formation. When they were crossed with each other (*m1* × *m2*), all the F1 plants developed normal petals. In view of this observation, which of the following conclusions is CORRECT?
A. Mutations in both *m1* and *m2* are in the same gene
B. Mutations in both *m1* and *m2* are in two separate genes
C. Inheritance in non-Mendelian
D. None of the above

42. In a hypothetical trihybrid cross of three loci (viz. A, B, C), all were inherited in a complete dominant manner over their recessive alleles a, b, c, respectively. When a test cross between F1 and parent 'aabbcc' was performed, following genotypes of eight phenotypically distinct classes were observed with respective numbers The genetic distance (up to one decimal) between A and C loci will be cM.

Class	Genotype	Number
1	ABC	412
2	abc	406
3	Abc	85
4	aBC	80
5	ABc	08
6	abC	07
7	AbC	01
8	aBc	01

A. 18.3 cM B. 28.3 cM
C. 13.3 cM D. 8.3 cM

CSIR-NET, JUNE, 2018

Mendelian Principles

43. In an organism, allele for red eye colour is dominant over the allele for white eye colour. A cross is made between a white eyed male and a red eyed female. In the progeny all males are red eyed while the females are white eyed. The reciprocal cross leads to all red eyed progeny. Based on the above information which one of the following conclusions is correct?
A. This is a sex-limited trait, and the male is the homomorphic sex
B. This is a sex-linked trait, with male being the homomorphic sex

C. This is a sex-linked trait, with female being the homomorphic sex

D. This is a case of autosomal inheritance, with incomplete penetrance

44. Which one of the following statements is TRUE for positive-frequency dependent selection?

A. Fitness of a genotype increases as it becomes less common.

B. Fitness of a genotype increases as it becomes more common.

C. Fitness of a genotype decreases as it becomes less common.

D. Fitness of a genotype decreases as it becomes common and gets fixed.

45. Inclusive fitness of an animal can be measured as a sum of direct fitness and indirect fitness. Imagine you have 10 off springs. Through diligent parental care, 5 survive to reproduce. You give your life in a heroic deed to save a total of 5 of your nieces and nephews. What is your inclusive fitness?

A. 15 B. 12.5

C. 7.5 D. 3.75

Extra chromosomal Inheritance

46. A male snail homozygous for dextral alleles is crossed with a female homozygous for sinistral alleles. All the F1 individuals showed sinistral phenotype. When F1 progeny snails were self-fertilized all individuals of F2 progeny had dextral coiling. This experiment demonstrated

A. dominant epistasis as dextral allele is dominant over sinistral allele

B. recessive epistasis as in F2 dextral allele appeared in homozygous condition

C. maternal effect as the nuclear genotype of the F1 mother has governed the phenotype of the F2 individuals.

D. maternal inheritance as the mitochondrial genes of the F1 mother has governed the phenotype of the F2 individuals.

Microbial Genetics

47. Uracil containing plasmid was constructed and was used in transformation into the wild type (*ung*$^+$) and uracil-N-glycosylase mutated (*ung*$^-$) *E. coli* cells and scored for transformants in the presence of appropriate antibiotics. Which one of the following statements correctly describes the experimental outcome?

A. *ung*$^+$ cells will have fewer transformants compared to *ung*- cells.

B. *ung*$^-$ cells will give fewer transformants compared to *ung* cells.

C. No transformants will be obtained in ung- cells as uracil excision repair will not occur and the plasmid would not replicate.

D. Presence of uracil in DNA is unnatural and the plasmid DNA with uracils in it will not produce transformants in either *ung*$^+$ or *ung*$^-$ cells.

48. Two Hfr strains, Hfr-1 (arg$^+$ leu$^+$ gal$^+$ str^s) and Hfr-2 (arg$^+$ his$^+$ gal$^+$ pur$^+$ str^s) were mated with a F-strain (arg$^-$ leu$^-$ gal$^-$ his$^-$ pur$^-$ str^s). The results of the interrupted mating experiment are shown as plots '*a*' and '*b*', respectively.

a

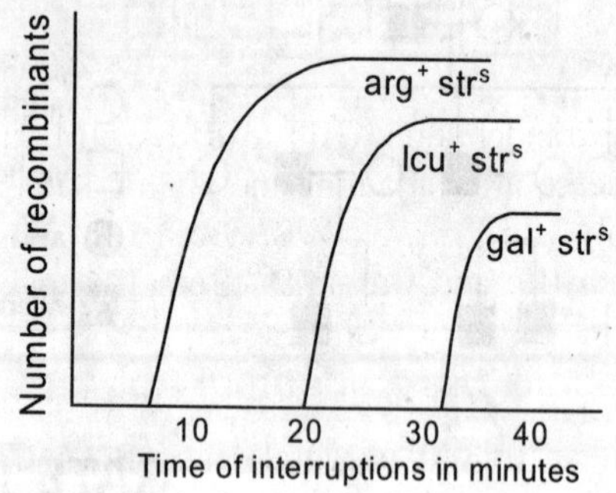

b

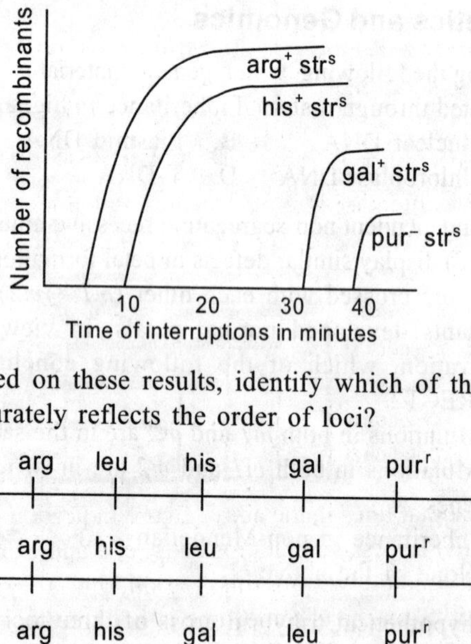

Based on these results, identify which of the options accurately reflects the order of loci?

A. arg — leu — his — gal — pur^r

B. arg — his — leu — gal — pur^r

C. arg — his — gal — leu — pur^r

D. arg — leu — gal — his — pur^r

Pedigree Analysis

49. The pedigree given below follows the inheritance pattern of a late-onset (after age of 30 years) genetic disease that is 100% penetrant. Affected individuals are indicated by a solid circle (woman) or solid square (males). RFLP analysis of DNA from each individual is shown below in the pedigree.

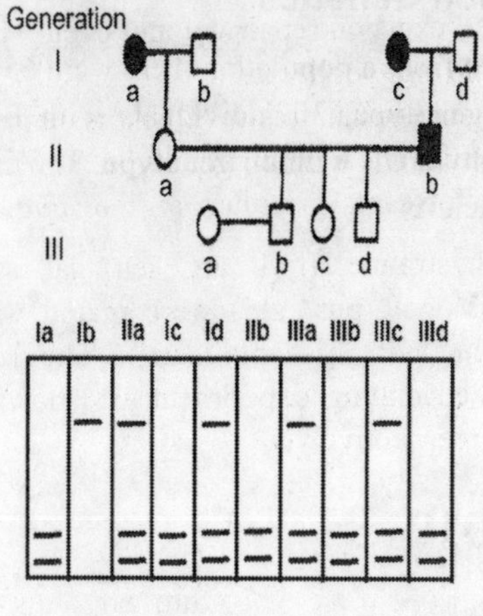

Which grandchildren (IIIb to IIId) will be affected by the disease after attaining the age of 30 years?

A. Only IIIb B. Both IIIb and IIIe

C. Both IIIc and IIId D. Both IIIb and IIId

Mutation & Chromosomal Aberration

50. Two near inbred parental lines P1 and P2 of an angiosperm species are crossed to produce F1 seeds in which, the ploidy of the endosperm is 6N. If plants generated from these F1 seeds are backcrossed with P1, what will be the ploidy of the somatic cells in the next generation?

A. 2N B. 4N

C. 5N D. 6N

51. The locations of five overlapping deletions have been mapped to a *Drosophila* chromosome as shown below

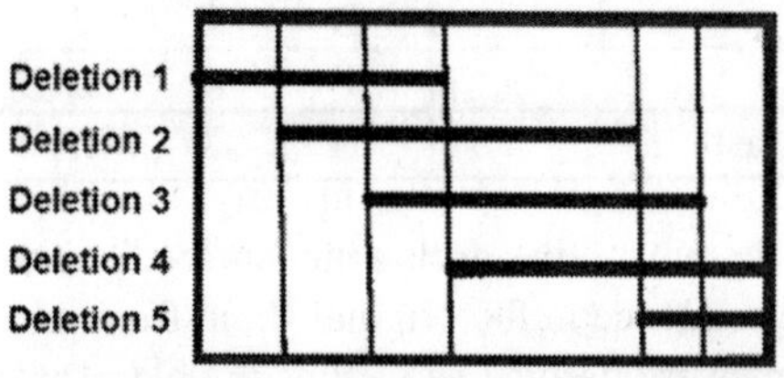

(Horizontal lines in the above figure indicate the deleted regions) Recessive mutations a, b, c, d and e are known to be located within this region, but the order of mutations on the chromosome is not known. When the flies homozygous for the recessive mutations are crossed with flies homozygous for the deletions, the following results are obtained (letter "m" represents mutant phenotype and "+" represents the wild type).

Deletion	Mutation				
	a	b	c	d	e
1	+	m	m	m	+
2	+	+	m	m	+
3	+	+	+	m	m
4	m	+	+	+	m
5	m	+	+	+	m

On the basis of the above data, the relative order of the five mutant genes on the chromosome is

A. b c d e a B. a b c d e

C. b c e a d D. c d b e a

52. A Chemist synthesizes three new chemical compounds in the laboratory and names them as X, Y and Z. After analyzing mutagenic potential of all these compounds, the geneticist observed that all are highly mutagenic. The geneticist also tested the potential of mutations induced by these compounds to be reversed by other known mutagens and obtained the following results

Mutation Produced by	Reversed by		
	Nitrous acid	Hydroxyl amine	Acridine orange
X	Yes	some	No
Y	No	No	No
Z	No	No	yes

Assuming that X, Y and Z caused any of the three types of mutations, transition, transversion or single base deletion, what conclusions can you make about the nature of mutations produced by these compounds?

A. X causes transversion; Y causes transition; Z causes single base deletion

B. X causes transition; Y causes transversion; Z causes single base deletion

C. X causes transition; Y causes single base deletion; Z causes transversion

D. X causes transversion; Y causes single base deletion; Z causes transition

53. An individual is having an inversion in heterozygous condition. The regions on normal chromosome are marked as (*a*), (*b*), (*c*), (*d*), (*e*), (*f*), (g) while the chromosome having inversion has the regions as *a*, *b*, *e*, *d*, *c*, *f*, *g*. The diagram given below shows pairing of these two homologous chromosomes during meiosis and the site of a crossing over is indicated:

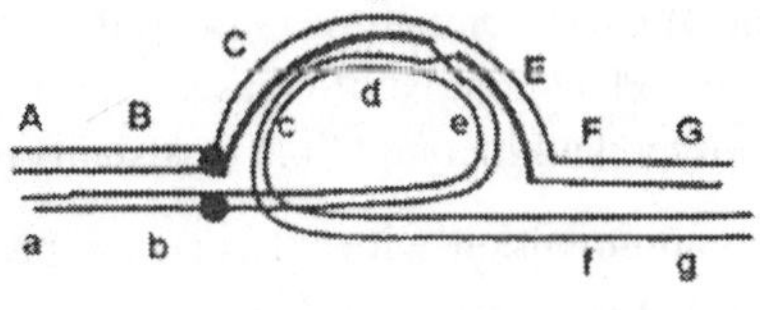

The following statements are given to describe the inversion and the consequence of crossing over shown in the above diagram:

(*a*) This is a pericentric inversion

(*b*) This will generate a dicentric and an acentric chromosome following separation of chromosomes after crossing over

(*c*) This will generate two monocentric recombinant chromosomes following separation of chromosomes after crossing over (*d*) All the gametes thus formed will have deletion and/ or duplication and will be non-viable

(*e*) 50% of the gametes having recombinant chromatid will be non-viable, while 50% gametes having non-recombinant chromatid will survive

(*f*) This is a paracentric inversion

Which combination of the above statements describes the inversion and meiotic consequences correctly?

A. (*a*), (*b*) and (*c*) B. (*a*), (*c*) and (*e*)
C. (*b*), (*e*) and (*f*) D. (*c*), (*d*) and (*f*)

Population Genetics

54. In a sample from a population there were 65 individuals with BB genotype, 30 individuals with Bb genotype and 15 individuals with bb genotype. The frequency of the '*b*' allele is

A. 0.59
B. 0.27
C. 0.41
D. 0.73

CSIR-NET, DECEMBER, 2018

Mendelian Principles

55. The allele *l* in Drosophila is recessive, sex- linked and lethal' when homozygous or hemizygous. If a female of the genotype *Ll* is crossed with a male, what is the ratio of females : males in the progeny?

A. 3 female: 1 male
B. 2 female: 1 male
C. 1 female: 1 male
D. 1 female: 2 male

56. A quadratic check of gene combinations and disease reaction types in a host-pathogen system where the gene-for-gene concept operates is represented below:

Virulence or avirulence genes in the pathogen	Resistance or susceptibility genes in the plant	
	R (resistant) dominant	r (susceptible) recessive
A(avirulent) dominant	AR	Ar
a(virulent) recessive	aR	ar

The following statements were made about. the above genotypes:

(*a*) AR genotype had incompatible (resistant) reactions.
(*b*) Ar genotype had compatible (susceptible) reactions.
(*c*) ar genotype had compatible (susceptible) reactions.
(*d*) aR genotype had incompatible (resistant) reactions.

Choose the combination with all correct statements

A. (*a*), (*b*) and (*d*)
B. (*a*), (*b*) and (*c*)
C. (*b*), (*c*) and (*d*)
D. (*a*), (*c*) and (*d*)

Extra Chromosomal Inheritance

57. Which of the following plastid coding region(s) have been recommended as a core barcode by Plant working group of the consortium for the Barcode of Life?

A. CO1 and rbcL
B. rbcL and matK
C. CO1 and matK
D. rbcL only

Microbial Genetics

58. Using interrupted mating, four Hfr strains were analysed for the sequence in which they transmitted a number of different genes to a F- strain. Each Hfr strain was found to transmit its genes in a unique order as summarized in the table (Only the first five genes were scored).

Order of transmission	*Hfr* strain 1	2	3	4
First	A	B	M	F
	B	A	K	H
	D	L	J	G
	F	M	G	J
Last	H	K	H	K

Which one of the following correctly represents the gene sequence in the original strain from which the Hfr strains were derived as well as the place of integration and polarity of the F plasmid?

A.
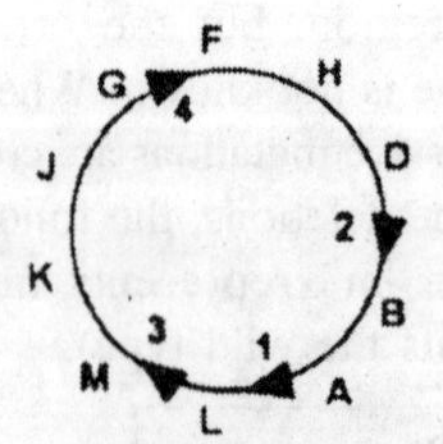

B.
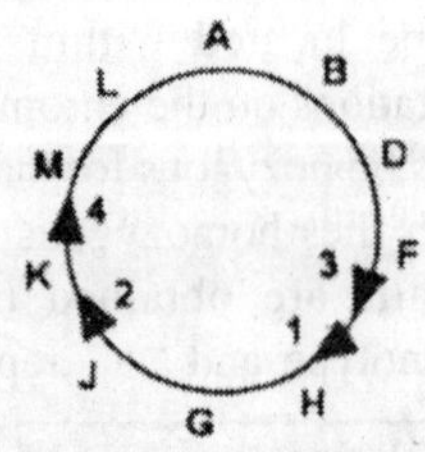

C.
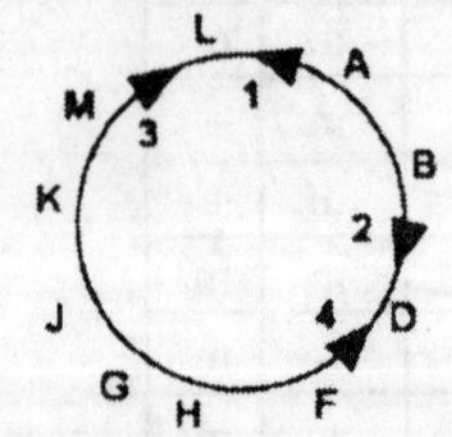

D.
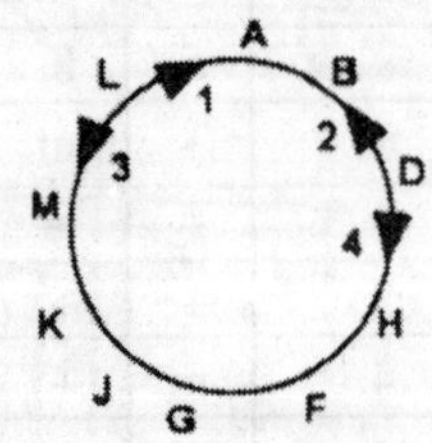

Pedigree Analysis

59. The pedigree below represents the inheritance of an autosomal recessive trait.

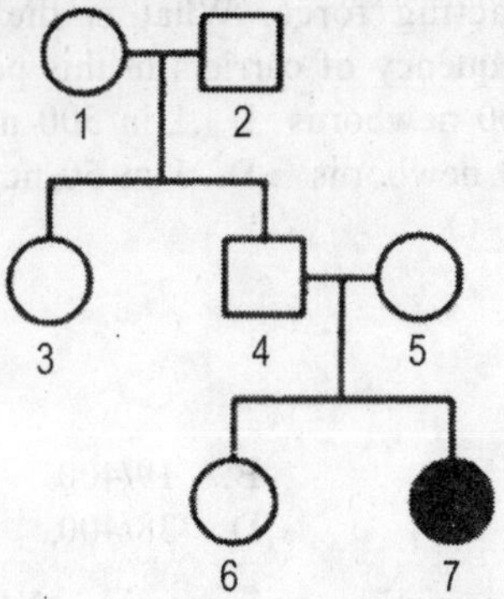

What is the probability that individual '6' is a heterozygote?

A. 1/4 B. 1/2
C. 2/3 D. 1/3

Mutation & Chromosomal Aberration

60. Several mutants (1-4) are isolated, all of which require compound E for growth. The compounds A to D in the biosynthetic pathway to E are known; but their order in the pathway is not known. Each compound is tested for its ability to support the growth of each mutant (l-4). In the following table, a plus sign indicates growth and a minus sign indicates no growth.

Mutants	Medium supplemented with compound				
	A	B	C	D	E
1	-	-	-	+	+
2	-	+	+	+	+
3	-	-	+	+	+
4	-	-	-	-	+

What is the order of the compounds (A to E) in the pathway?

A. E → D → C → B → A
B. A → C → D → B → E
C. E → B → D → C → A
D. A → B → C → D → E

61. Following is the picture of an inversion heterozygote undergoing a single crossing over event

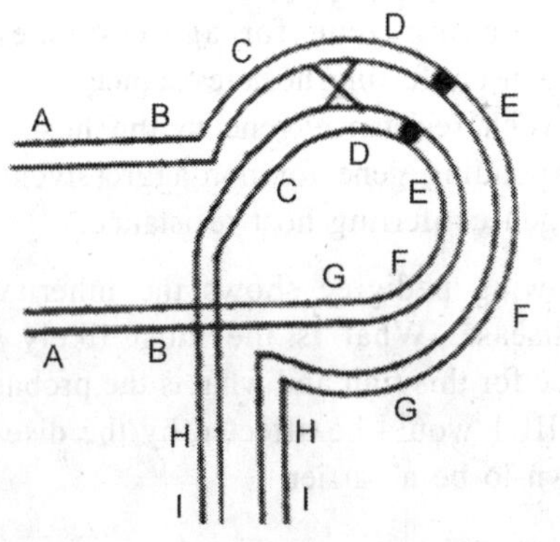

The following statements are given towards explaining the consequences at the end of meiosis.

(*a*) The resultant two chromosomes will have deletions and duplications.
(*b*) A dicentric and an acentric chromosome will be formed.
(*c*) The inversion does not allow crossing over to occur, so even if a crossing over is initiated, it will fail to occur.
(*d*) The crossing over is considered suppressed by inversion as the acentric chromosome will not segregate normally.
(*e*) All the gametes formed with cross-over chromatids at the end of meiosis will be non-viable as they carry large deletion or duplication.
(*f*) The gametes having non-crossover (parental) chromatid will survive.

Which combination of statements is correct?

A. (*b*) and (*e*) B. (*a*) and (*c*)
C. (*b*), (*d*) and (*f*) D. (*a*), (*e*) and (*f*)

62. Angelman syndrome (AS) and Prader-Willi Syndrome (PWS) have very distinct symptoms.

Factors responsible for the occurrence of these syndromes are given below:

(*a*) Microdeletion of1 5q 11-13 in paternal chromosome.
(*b*) Uniparental disomy of maternal chromosome 15.
(*c*) Lack of functional maternal copy of, ubiquitin ligase E3A.
(*d*) Lack of SNURF-Sl'-t'RPN transcript, which is produced only from paternal chromosome.
(*e*) Deficiencies of small nucleolar RNAs, which are encoded from the introns of SNURF'-SNRPN transcript from paternal chromosome.

Which of the following combination of answers is correct for Angelman and Prader Willi Syndromes?

A. Pws – A, c, D; AS – B, E
B. PWS – B only; AS – A, C, D E
C. PWS – A, B, D, E; AS – C only
D. PWS – A, B; AS – C, D, E

Population Genetics

63. In a population of 2000 individuals of a plant species, genetic difference at a single locus leads to different flower colours. The alleles are incompletely dominant. The population has 100 individuals with the genotype *rr* (white flowers), 800 individuals with the genotype *Rr* (pink flower) and the remaining have. Genotype *RR* (red flowers). What is the frequency of the r allele in the population?

A. 0.25 B. 0.50
C. 0.75 D. 1.00

64. Consider a single locus with 2 alleles which are at Hardy-Weinberg equilibrium. If the frequency of one of the homozygous genotypes is 0.64, what is the frequency of heterozygotes in the population?
A. 0.16 B. 0.20
C. 0.32 D. 0.36

65. Which one of the following will have the least impact on allele frequencies in small populations?
A. Inbreeding B. Random mating
C. Genetic drift D. Outbreeding

66. An autosomal recessive condition affects 1 newborn in 10,000 in a random mating population without any disruptive acting force. What is the approximate expected frequency of carriers in this population?
A. 1 in 1000 newborns B. 1 in 500 newborns
C. 1 in 100 newborns D. 1 in 50 newborns

DBT-JRF, 2018

Molecular and Human Genetics

67. In a cross between two black Labrador retrievers the phenotypic ratio of the offspring is 9 black puppies to 3 chocolate puppies to 4 yellow puppies; this is an example of
A. Partial recessiveness
B. Incomplete penetrance
C. Incomplete dominance
D. Epistasis

68. What will be the probability of obtaining a plant with AaBBCc genotype from trihybrid (AaBbCc) parents?
A. 4 out of 64
B. 1 out of 64
C. 8 out of 64
D. 0 out of 64

69. Parents who appear normal have a child with sickle cell anemia, which is an autosomal recessive trait. The woman becomes pregnant again and is told that she is carrying fraternal twins. What is the probability that both the twins will develop sickle cell anemia?
A. 1/16 B. 1/4
C. ½ D. 9/16

70. A 30 kb candidate gene linked to prostate cancer from a patient was digested with XhoI. Following Southern hydrization of the digested products with the full-length gene prob, three bands of 15, 10 and 5 Kb sizes were obtained. However, an identical experiment in normal individuals gave a 15 Kb fragment. This could be due to:
A. Presence of SNP in the candidate gene
B. Deletion of a fragment of DNA from the candidate gene
C. The probe could not identify the 10 and 5 Kb fragmented.
D. The probe could only identify the 15 Kb fragment.

71. In a given population, 1 out of 400 individuals has cancer caused by a recessive allele 'p'assuming the population is in Hardy-Weinberg equilibrium, what is the expected proportion of individuals who carry the '*p*' allele but do not develop cancer?
A. 1/400 B. 19/400
C. 20/200 D. 38/400

72. Color blindness in human beings is an X-linked trait. A color-blind man has a 45, X daughter who is also color-blind. The nondisjunction that leads to the 45, X daughter occurred in which parent and in which meiotic division?
A. Father; First meiotic division
B. Brother, father and mother; first meiotic division
C. Mother; first meiotic division
D. Father; second meiotic division

73. A marker present outside the targeted QTL used to check the crossing over is called:
A. Peak marker
B. Background marker
C. Recombinant marker
D. Foreground marker

74. Linkage disequilibrium (LD) decay is:
A. Much rapid in out-crossing than in selfing species
B. Much rapid in selfing than in out-crossing species
C. Equal in selfing and out-crossing species
D. Not dependent on selfing or out-crossing

75. 'Gene for Gene' hypothesis states
A. For each resistance gene in the host there is a corresponding gene for virulence in the pathogen conferring host resistance
B. For each resistance gene in the host there is a corresponding gene for a virulence in the pathogen conferring host resistance
C. For each resistance gene in the host there is a corresponding gene for aggressiveness in the pathogen conferring host resistance
D. For each resistance gene in the host there is a corresponding gene for non-aggressiveness in the pathogen conferring host resistance.

76. The following pedigree shows the inheritance of a human disease. What is the most likely mode of inheritance for this trait and what is the probability that a son of III 1 would be affected by the disease, if III 1 is known to be a carrier.

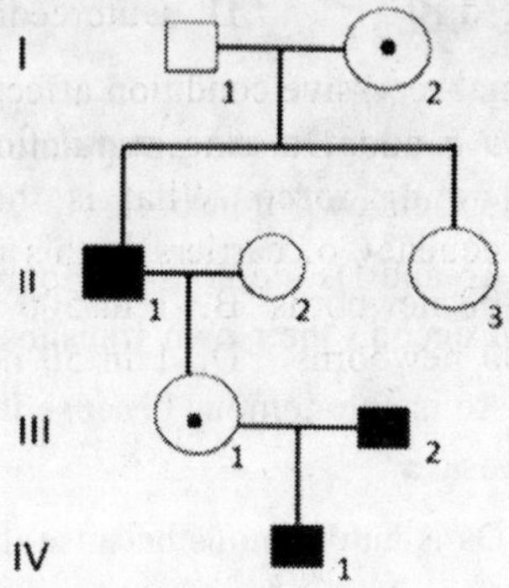

A. Sex-linked recessive; 0.75
B. Autosomal recessive; 0.5
C. Autosomal dominant; 0.75
D. Sex-linked recessive; 0.5.

77. 'In an ordered tetrad analysis, if the two genes are not linked, the .... will be almost equal.
A. Parental ditype and non-parental ditype
B. Parental ditype and tetratype
C. Tetratype and non-parental ditype
D. Parental ditype, non-parental ditype and tetratype

78. Assume that a marker M1 is present 5 cM away on one side of a gene "X" (a desirable allele of the gene), while marker M2 is present 10 cM away on the other side of the gene. The donor's genotype is M1M1XXM2M2, while the recipient has m1m1xxm2m2 genotype. A cross was made between these two individuals. The F1 is crossed to recipient. The progeny of this cross had 1000 plants. How many plants from this progeny will have both the markers (M1 & M2) present while the desired gene is absent? (Assume no interference)
A. 0
B. 5
C. 10
D. 15

79. In an experiment two different mutations in a single gene was observed. This gene was cloned. Northern and Western analysis of each mutant(1 and 2) and the wild type gave the following profiles:

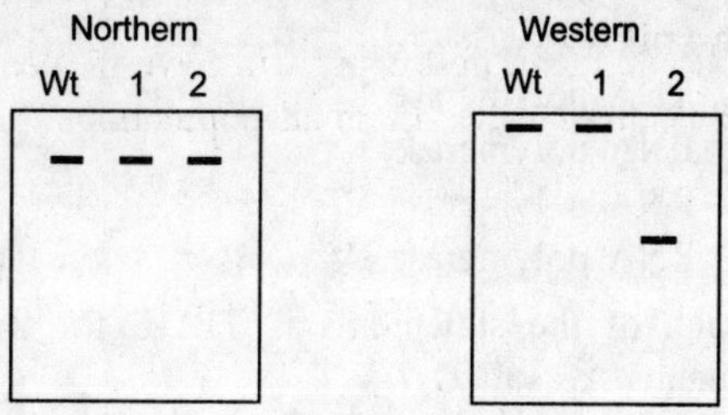

What will be the inference from the results?
A. Mutant 1 and 2 both have silent mutation at different positions.
B. Mutant 1 has missense mutation and 2 has silent mutation
C. Mutant 1 has missense mutation and 2 has nonsense mutation
D. Mutant 1 has silent mutation and 2 has missense mutation

80. Assume gene "A" is dominant over "a" and "B1" is codominant over "B2" in petunia. A cross is made between two individuals – AAB1B2 x aaB1B2. Assuming that there is no gene interaction, the progeny will segregate in a phenotypic ratio of:
A. 9:3:3:1
B. 1:1:1:1
C. 1:2:1
D. 3:1

81. Chromosome complement of river vs swamp domestic water buffalo is:
A. 50 vs 48
B. 52 vs 50
C. 60 vs 58
D. 48 vs 46

GATE (BIOTECHNOLOGY), 2018

Genetics and Evolutionary Biology

82. A pedigree of an inheritable disease is shown below:

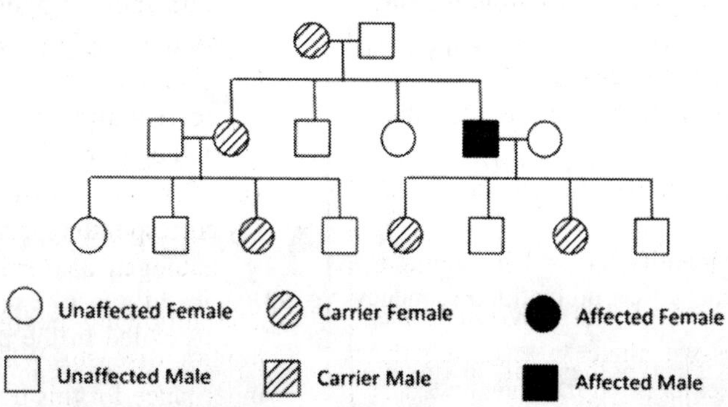

What type of inheritance does the disease follow?
A. Autosomal dominant
B. X-linked dominant
C. X-linked recessive
D. Autosomal recessive

GATE (LIFE SCIENCE), 2018

Genetics and Genomics

83. The genes for microRNA (miRNA) in plants are usually transcribed by
A. RNA polymerase I
B. RNA polymerase II
C. RNA polymerase III
D. RNA polymerase IV

84. Which of the statements is TRUE for transposable elements Ac and Ds?
A. Both Ac and Ds are autonomous because they encode their own transposase
B. Both Ac and Ds are non-autonomous because they do not encode their own transposase
C. Only Ac is autonomous because it encodes its own transposase
D. Only Ds is autonomous because it encodes its own transposase

CSIR-NET, JUNE, 2019

Mendelian Principles

85. Assuming that the A, B, C and D genes are not linked. The probability of a progeny being AaBBccDd from a corss between AABbccDd and aaBBccDD parents will be
A. 4/32 B. 3/16.
C. 1/4 D. 3/32

86. Two Yellow mice with straight hair were crossed and the following progeny was obtained:
1/2 Yellow, straight hair
1/6 Yellow, fuzzy hair
1/4 gray, straight hair
1/12 gray, fuzzy hair

In order to provide genetic explanation for the results and assign genotypes to the parents and progeny of this cross the following statements were given:
(*a*) The 6:2:3:1 ratio obtained here indicates recessive epistasis.
(*b*) This cross concerns two independent characteristics – body colour and type of hair.
(*c*) The deviation of dihybrid ratio from 9:3:3:1 to 6:2:3:1 may be due to one of the genes being a recessive lethal
(*d*) The lethal allele is associated with straight hair

The most appropriate combination of statements to provide genetic explanation for the result is:
A. (*b*) and (*c*) B. (*a*) Only
C. (*b*), (*c*) and (*d*) D. (*a*), (*c*) and (*d*)

Gene Mapping

87. A Lod score of 3 represents a Recombination Frequency (RF) that is
A. 3 times as likely as the hypothesis of no linkage
B. 30 times as likely as the hypothesis of no linkage
C. 100 times as likely as the hypothesis of no linkage
D. 1000 times as likely as the hypothesis of no linkage

88. Centromere postions can be mapped in linear tetrads in some fungi. A cross was made between two strains *ab* and $a^+ b^+$ and 100 linear tetrads were analysed. The genes *a* and *b* are located on two arms of the chromosome. The tetrad were divided into 5 classes as shown below.

Class	1	2	3	4	5
	$a\ b$	$a\ b$	$a\ b$	$a\ b$	$a\ b^+$
	$a^+\ b$	$a\ b^+$	$a\ b$	$a^+\ b^+$	$a^+\ b$
	$a\ b^+$	$a^+\ b$	$a^+\ b^+$	$a\ b$	$a^+\ b$
	$a^+\ b^+$	$a^+\ b^+$	$a^+\ b^+$	$a^+\ b^+$	$a\ b^+$
Linear tetrads	15	29	52	2	2

Based on the above observation the following conclusion were drawn:
(*a*) Class 1 is a result of a cross over between '*a*' and the centromere.
(*b*) Class 2 is result of double crossover involving 3 strands between '*a*' and the centromere.
(*c*) Class 5 is a result of a double crossover between '*a*' centromere and '*b*'- centromere.
(*d*) Class 4 is a result of a double cross over involving all the 4 strands.

Which one of the following options represents all correct statements?
A. (*a*) and (*b*) B. (*a*) and (*c*)
C. (*b*) and (*d*) D. (*c*) and (*d*)

Pedigree Analysis

89. A Family was examined for a given trait which is represented in the pedigree shown below. Further, the degree of expression of the trait is highly variable among members of the family; some are only slightly affected while others developed severe symptoms at an early stage

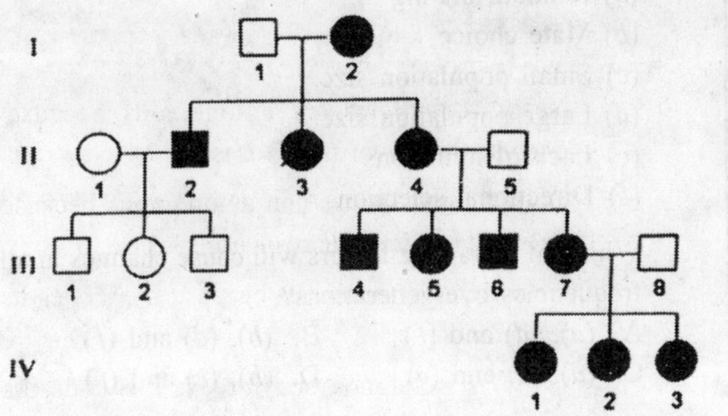

The following statements are made to explain the pattern of inheritance shown in the pedigree.

(*a*) X-linked dominant mutation
(*b*) X-linked recessive mutation
(*c*) Mitochondrial inheritance
(*d*) Vairiable expression can be due to heteroplasty

The best possible explanation for this inheritance is

A. (*a*) and (*d*) B. (*c*) and (*d*)
C. (*b*) only D. (*a*) only

90. In the following pedigree, individuals with shaded circle or shaded square show presence of a recessive autosomal trait.

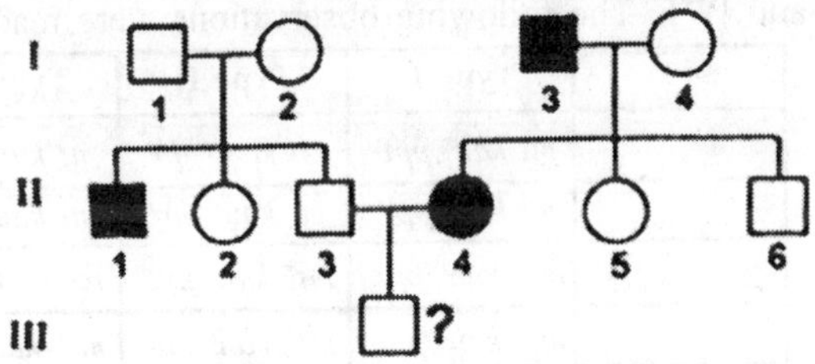

The calculated risk of occurance of this trait for III-I is

A. 1/2 B. 1/4
C. 1/8 D. 1/3

Mutation & Chromosomal Aberration

91. *E. coli* mutants isolated from a genetic screen showed following classes of mutations

(*a*) Point mutations in *lacI*
(*b*) Deletions immediately downstream of the transcription start site of the lacZYA mRNA
(*c*) Duplications of part or whole of lacY
(*d*) Duplications of part or whole of lac A

Choose the option which is likely to result in constitutive expression of the lac operon?

A. Both (*a*) and (*b*) B. Both (*b*) and (*c*)
C. Both (*c*) and (*d*) D. Only (*a*)

92. The location of six deletion (Shows as solid line underneath the chromosomes) has been mapped to the *Drosophila* chromosome as shown in the diagram given below:

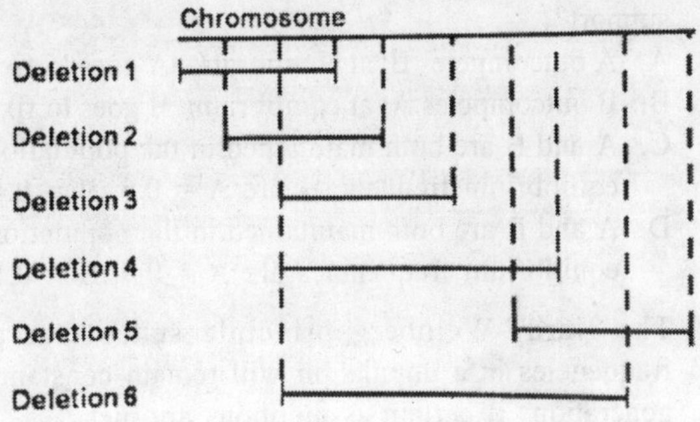

The recessive mutations *a, b, c, d, e f* and *g* are known to be located in the region of deletions, but order of mutations on the chromosome is not known. When flies homozygous for the recessive mutations are crossed with flies homozygous for the deletion, the following result were obtained where the letter '*m*' represents a mutant phenotype and '+' represents the wild type

	Mutations						
Deletion	*a*	*b*	*c*	*d*	*e*	*f*	*g*
1	+	M	M	M	+	+	+
2	+	+	M	M	+	+	+
3	+	+	+	M	M	+	+
4	M	+	+	M	M	+	+
5	M	+	+	+	+	M	M
6	M	+	+	M	M	M	+

The relative order of the seven mutant genes on chromosome is :

A. *b c e a f g d* B. *b c d f g e a*
C. *b c d e a f g* D. *c d e a g f b*

Population Genetics

93. Birds in a population show two foraging phenotypes: A and B. Birds of phenotype A search, attack and capture prey while birds of phenotype B steal prey from birds of phenotype A. A and B are maintained in the population through negative frequency-dependent selection. The graph below shows the fitness of A (broken line) and B (solid line) at different relative frequencies of A (frequency of B = 1-frequency of A).

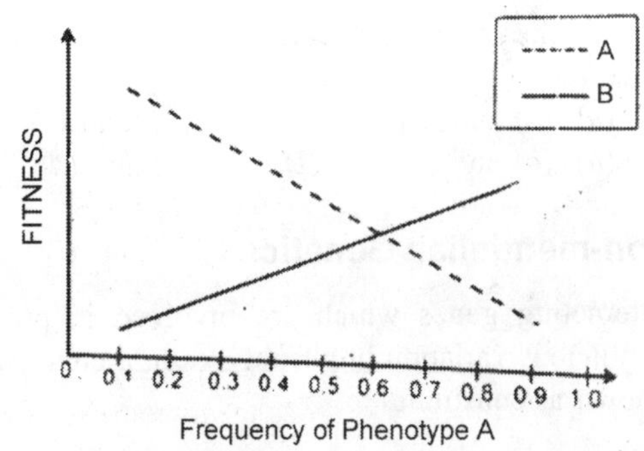

Which of the following statements does the grap support?

A. A outcompetes B; at equilibrium. A goes to fixation.
B. B outcompetes A: at equilibrium. B goes to fixation.
C. A and B are both maintained in the population; the equilibrium frequencies are A = 0.6, B = 0.4.
D. A and B are both maintained in the population; the equilibrium frequencies are A = 0.9, B = 0.1.

94. The Hardy-Weinberg principle states that allele frequencies in a population will remain constant over generations if certain assumptions are met.

(*a*) Random mating
(*b*) Mate choice
(*c*) Small population size
(*d*) Large population size
(*e*) Lack of mutations
(*f*) Directional selection

Which of the above factors will cause changes in allele frequencies overgenerations?

A. (*a*), (*d*) and (*f*) B. (*b*), (*d*) and (*f*)
C. (*a*), (*c*) and (*e*) D. (*b*), (*c*) and (*f*)

CSIR-NET, 15 DECEMBER, 2019

Mendelian Principles

95. Two strains of mice which are genetically identical except for a single genetic locus or region are said to be:

A. Syngenic B. Allogenic
C. Congenic D. Heterogenic

96. In summer squash, white colour fruit (*W*) is dominant over yellow colour (*w*) and disc-shaped phenotype (*D*) is dominant over sphere-shaped phenotype (*d*). Determine the genotype of the parents if the cross between white, sphere crossed with white, sphere gives ¼ white, sphere and 14 yellow, sphere.

A. WWDD × wwdd B. Wwdd × Wwdd
C. WwDd × wwdd D. WWDD × WWdd

97. What is the probability of getting a sum of 9 from simultaneously throwing two dice?

A. 1/6 B. 1/8
C. 1/9 D. 1/12

98. A disease-resistant plant was crossed with a susceptible plant and the resultant F_1 plants were disease resistant. The F_1 plant was selfed and the F_2 individuals were analysed for qualitative and quantitative disease resistance. The following statements were hypothesized

(*a*) Qualitative resistance follows Mendelian ratio.
(*b*) In the F_2 individuals demonstrating qualitative resistance, "resistance" is dominant
(*c*) Quantitative resistance is always monogenic
(*d*) Qualitative resistance can be polygenic

Which one of the following combination of statement is correct?

A. (*a*), (*c*) and (*d*) B. (*a*), (*b*), and (*c*)
C. (*a*), (*b*) and (*d*) D. (*b*), (*c*) and (*d*)

Non-mendelian Genetics

99. Interacting genes which are involved in producing continuous variation in phenotypes in a population are known as/constitute

A. codominant genes B. pseudogenes
C. alleles D. QTLs

Gene Mapping

100. A mutant mating type *mt* strain of *Chlamydomonas* thatwas resistant to the antibiotic kanamycin (kan^r) and herbicide PPT (ppt^r) was crossed to a wild type mating mt^+ kan^s ppt^s strain that was sensitive to kanamycin and PPT. Twenty tetrads of the progeny were analyzed for mating type and resistance/sensitivity to kanamycin and PPT. The following observations were made:

	Type I	Type II	Type III
	$mt\ kan^r\ ppt^r$	$mt\ kan^r\ ppt^r$	$mt\ kan^r\ ppt^r$
	$mt\ kan^r\ ppt^r$	$mt\ kan^r\ ppt^r$	$mt\ kan^r\ ppt^r$
	$mt^+\ kan^r\ ppt^r$	$mt^+\ kan^r\ ppt^r$	$mt^+\ kan^r\ ppt^r$
	$mt^+\ kan^r\ ppt^r$	$mt^+\ kan^r\ ppt^r$	$mt^+\ kan^r\ ppt^r$
Number of each type observed	8	9	3

The following statements were made to explain the observations:

(*a*) *mt* and *ppt* loci are on two different chromosomes
(*b*) Inheritance of mating type and *ppt*-resistance/sensitivity are demonstrating cytoplasmic inheritance
(*c*) Inheritance of kanamycin-resistance/sensitivity is demonstrating nuclear inheritance
(*d*) Nuclear inheritance is being demonstrated by mating type and *ppt*-resistance/sensitivity analysis

Which one of the combinations of above statements is correct?

A. (*a*) and (*b*) B. (*a*) and (*d*)
C. (*b*) and (*c*) D. (*c*) and (*d*)

Pedigree Analysis

101. The following pedigree three STR loci A, B and C are linked on the long arm of the X- chromosome in the order centromere-A-B-C- telomere. Further in the table, the STR alleles present in each individual is indicated.

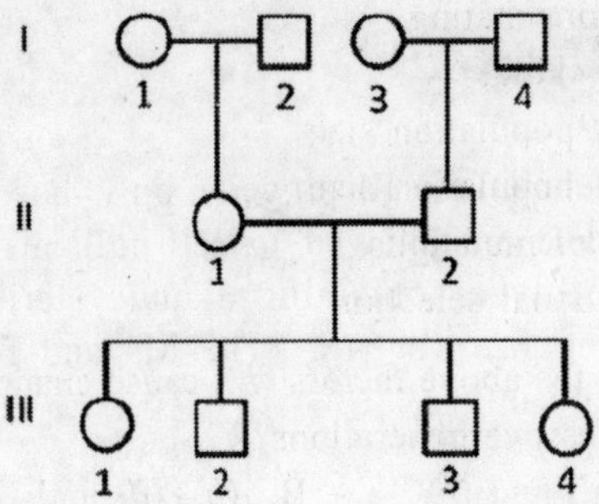

Loci	Generation									
	I				II		III			
	1	2	3	4	1	2	1	2	3	4
A	5.6	4	5.6	4	4.6	6	6	4	5	6
B	7.8	9	8.9	7	7.9	8	8.9	9	7	7.8
C	1.2	2	1.2	3	1.2	1	1.2	2	2	’

Based on the above, X-chromosome(s) in which of the following individuals are recombinant? [Hint: X-chromosome in males will help identify the phase of the alleles]

A. II – 1, III – 1 and III – 2
B. II – 2, III – 1 and III – 2
C. III – 1 and III – 3
D. III – 2 and III – 4

102. A pedigree shown below depicts that the individual I-1 is heterozygous for a dominant disease allele *D* and for molecular markers M1/M2. The paternal molecular markers present in the progeny individuals are indicated in the pedigree.

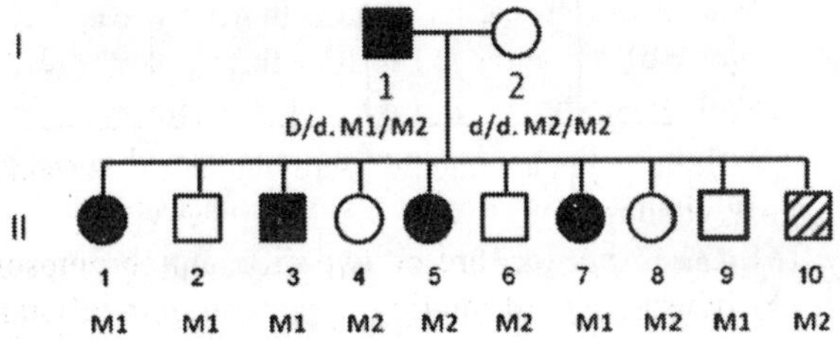

The following statements may be drawn from the above pedigree:

(*a*) The two loci D/d and M1/M2 appears to be linked
(*b*) The recombination frequency between the two loci is 20%
(*c*) If LOD score comes out to be 3, then it ensures that the two loci are independently assorting
(*d*) A LOD score < 1 would have ensured that the two Loci are linked

Which combination of the above statements can correctly interpret the depicted pedigree?

A. (*c*) and (*d*) B. Only (*c*)
C. (*a*) and (*b*) D. Only (*d*)

Mutation & Chromosomal Aberration

103. In an organism, a^+ allele governs grey body colour, while its mutant allele *a* gives yellow body colour. Further, presence of b^+ allele gives long and thin hairs while *b* allele gives rise to short and thick hairs. The alleles a^+ and b^+ are dominant over *a* and *b*, respectively. An individual with the genotype

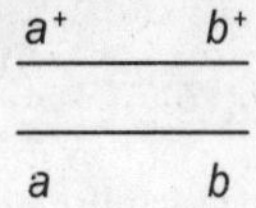

Has a patch of yellow cells with short and thick hairs. Which one of the following events is most likely to lead to the above?

A. Non disjunction of the homologous chromosomes during mitosis
B. Somatic recombination involving a and b
C. Translocation occurring in a few somatic cells
D. Mutation of both a^+ and b^+ alleles in the somatic cells

104. An individual is having a paracentric inversion (denoted by the region f-e-d, marked by arrows) in homozygous condition.

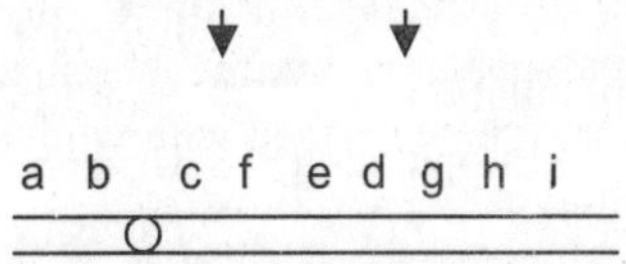

The meiotic consequences of inversion can be:

(*a*) generation of an acentric and a dicentric chromosome
(*b*) the recombinants will have long deletion or duplication and may be lethal
(*c*) the inversion will suppress crossing over
(*d*) all gametes will have complete genome and will survive normally

Which of the above statement or their combinations will explain the meiotic consequence of the given inversion logically?

A. (*a*), (*b*) and (*c*)
B. (*a*) and (*b*)
C. (*b*) and (*c*)
D. Only (*d*)

Population Genetics

105. The frequency of homozygotes in a diploid population is 0.68. Assuming that the population is in Hardy-Weinberg equilibrium, the frequencies of the two alleles are

A. 0.1 and 0.9
B. 0.2 and 0.8
C. 0.4 and 0.6
D. 0.5 and 0.5

CSIR-NET, 27 DECEMBER, 2019

106. A test cross was made with phenotypically wild type Drosophila flies having genes for sepia eye and curled wing in heterozygous condition. The following results were obtained:

Wild type	400 individuals
Sepia eyed	150 individuals
Curled winged	100 individuals
Sepia eyed curled winged	350 individuals

The Result Indicates

A. Independent assortment, as wild and the double mutant types are in almost equal proportion

B. Unequal segregation, as it is showing departure from 1:1:1:1 ratio

C. Complete linkage, as the two genes are very closely placed

D. Linkage, the two genes are separated by 25 cM distance

107. Which one of the following options is an INCORRECT match?

A. F2 population : Selfing or sib-mating F1 hybrid

B. F2:3 population : Immortal population

C. Backcross population : Difference in segregation pattern of dominant and recessive markers

D. F1 doubled haploids : Immortal population

108. Two petite yeasts, *Mat-a* and *Mat-α* are crossed. The diploid is grande. After a few mitotic divisions, the grande diploid is sporulated. The analysis of a large number of tetrads yielded a 2:2 ratio of petite: grande. A few potential scenarios describing the reason for this segregation pattern are stated below:

(*a*) The parental strains had two different mitochondrial rho- mutations

(*b*) One of the parents had a recessive nuclear petite mutation

(*c*) Only one of the mitochondrial petite mutation is inherited in the tetrads

(*d*) The mitochondria inherited are wild type.

Which one of the following options represents a combination of all correct statements?

A. (*a*), (*b*) and (*c*) B. (*b*) and (*d*) only

C. (*a*) and (*d*) only D. (*b*) and (*c*) only

109. In a plant, male sterility is caused by the presence of a dominant allele for a nuclear gene (Ms). There are also lines which carry a gene whose dominant allele (F) restores male fertility. These are called restorer lines. A cross is made between a male sterile line and a homozygous restorer line which does not contain the Ms allele. Of the F1 progeny, only those that carry the Ms allele are allowed to self-pollinate. What is the probability of obtaining a male sterile line in the resulting F2 progeny? (The Ms and F genes assort independently).

A. ¼ B. 2.3/16

A. ¾ B. 1/16

110. In a flower species, light pink locus is hypostatic to pigment development locus. R is for pigment development and W for light pink. The recessive allele (w)in light pink locus gives red colour and recessive allele in pigment locus (r) gives white colour. What will be the phenotype of W/-, r/r and w/w, r/r?

A. Red, Pink B. Pink, White

C. Red, Red D. White, White

Non-mendelian Genetics

111. A new trait was found to be highly variable in a population. It showed a bell-shaped distribution and is shown to be influenced by environmental factors. The trait can be

A. a monogenic trait

B. a polygenic trait

C. a non-quantitative trait

D. due to a point mutation in the regulatory region of a gene

Microbial Genetics

112. DNA from a bacterial strain with genotype at $b^+c^+d^+e^+f^+$ was isolated and used to transform a strain of bacteria with genotype $a^-b^-c^-d^-e^-f^-$. The transformed cells were tested for the presence of cotransformed genes and the following types of cotransformants were observed: a^+ and c^+ e^+ and d^+ d^+ and b^+ b^+ and f^+ c^+ and e^+

The correct order of genes will be:

A. *a b c d e f* B. *a c e b f d*

C. *a c e d b f* D. *a b f e d c*

Pedigree Analysis

113. The given pedigree shows the inheritance of a trait. The following derivations are made from the pedigree chart:

(*a*) The trait can be Y-linked because I-parent produced II-4 child

(*b*) The trait cannot be X-linked recessive because II-4 parent produced III-1 and III -3children

(*c*) The trait can be X-linked dominant because I-1 parent produced II-5 child

(*d*) The trait is unlikely to be autosomal recessive

because II-6 and II-7 parents producedIII-4 child.
(*e*) The trait may be autosomal dominant

Which one of the following options represents a combination of all correct statements?

A. (*b*), (*d*), (*e*)
B. (*a*), (*b*), (*d*)
C. (*b*), (*c*), (*d*)
D. (*a*), (*c*)

Mutation & Chromosomal Aberration

114. A protein has Gly at position 28 (wild type). On mutagenesis, a point mutation leads to conversion of Gly to Arg at position 28 (mutant 1). When mutant 1 is further rmutagenized, four different point mutants (mutants 2 to 5) were isolated where the Arg at position 28 was mutated to Ile, Thr, Ser or Gly as represented below:

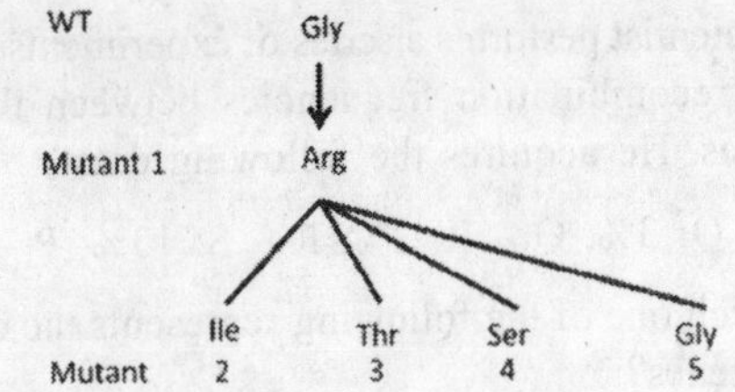

Gly	Thr	Ile	Ser	Arg
GGU	ACU	AUU	AGU	AGA
GGC	ACC	AUC	AGC	AGG
GGA	ACA	AUA		
GGG	ACG			

Based on the codons given in the table above, which one of the following codons codes for Gly at position 28 of the wild type protein?

A. GGU
B. GGC
C. GGA
D. GGG

DBT-JRF, 2019

Genetics, Phylogeny & Evolution

115. Which one of the following is a valid assumption regarding the molecular clock hypothesis in evolution?

A. For a given protein sequence, mutations accumulate at a constant rate in all lineages
B. For a given protein sequence, mutation rates are different in different lineages
C. All proteins evolve at the same constant rat
D. For a given lineage, mutation rates are the same for all proteins

116. Which one of the following statements about alleles is NOT TRUE?

A. They may occupy different loci in the same chromosome
B. There may be several at one locus
C. One may be dominant over another
D. They may show co-dominance

117. The figure represents a dot plot comparing two genomes X and Y. The portion marked N is a/an:

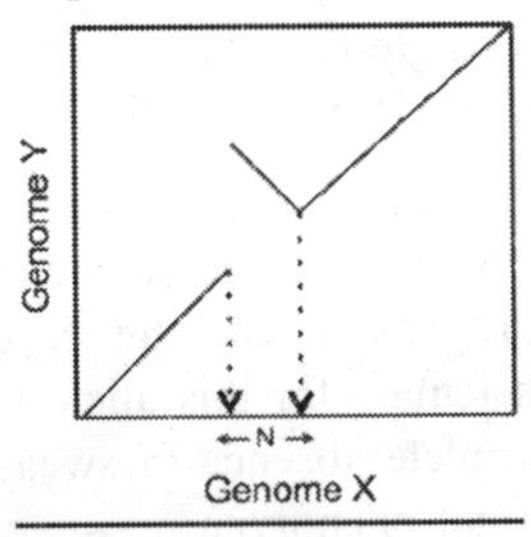

A. Translocation
B. Inversion
C. Repeat Sequence
D. Insertion or deletion (Indel)

118. Genes or proteins that display the same activity, but have different origins and are the product of convergent evolution, are called:

A. Analogs
B. Paralogs
C. Orthologs
D. Xenologs

Molecular and Human Genetics

119. A fetus with which one of the following karyotypes will NOT survive at birth.

A. 45, Y
B. 47, XY + 13
C. 45, X
D. 47, XY + 21

120. Allele 'A' is dominant over allele 'a' and results in dark skin pigmentation. In a mating of Aa with Aa, if 6 offspring are produced, the probability of all having dark pigment is:

A. 0.18
B. 0.75
C. 0.24
D. 0.12

121. A bacterial culture grown in a medium containing radioactive Sulphur would incorporate the radiolabel in the tetra-peptide:

A. serine-cysteine-tyrosine-methionine.
B. threonine-lysine-aspartic acid-glutamic acid.
C. alanine-proline-histidine-glycine.
D. tryptophan-phenylalanine-valine-isoleucine

122. The frequency of two alleles in a population is 0.19 (*B*) and 0.81(*b*). If the population is in Hardy-Weinberg equilibrium, what will be the percentage of heterozygous individuals in the population?

A. 62%
B. 38%
C. 31%
D. 19%

123. A scientist performs a series of experiments to determine the recombination frequencies between the following genes. He acquires the following data:

P – Q: 3%; Q – R: 2%; R – S: 13%; P – S: 8%

Which one of the following represents the correct order of genes?

A. PQRS B. QPSR
C. SPQR D. PRSQ

124. You have two tubes containing bacteriophage labelled with radioactive phosphorous (tube A) and radioactive Sulphur (tube B) that are devoid of bacteria. You use these bacteriophages to infect separate *E. coli* cultures. After infection you separate bacteria from the virus and check them for radioactivity. You will find:

A. Radioactivity in both bacterial samples.
B. Radioactivity in none of them as bacteria have been totally separated from the viruses.
C. Radioactivity in bacteria infected with viruses from tube A
D. Radioactivity in bacteria infected with viruses from tube B

125. Colour blindness (B) in human follows sex-linked recessive mode of inheritance. If a couple with normal colour vision have a colour-blind son. What will be the genotypes of the parents?

A. X^bXb and X^bY B. X^BXb and X^BY
C. X^bX^b and X^BY D. X^BX^B and X^bY

126. If the allele *A* is incompletely dominant over allele *a*, what is expected in a progeny of two heterozygous parents?

A. Same phenotypic and genotypic ratios
B. 2:1 phenotypic ratio
C. 3:1 phenotypic ratio
D. 2:1 ratio of homozygous dominant and intermediate phenotypes

127. A plant with orange flowers was self-pollinated. In the F1 progeny, we obtained 38 plants producing red flowers, 80 plants producing orange flowers and 41 plants producing yellow flowers. The likely explanation for the above observation is that:

A. the gene for flower colour shows incomplete dominance.
B. flower colour is a polygenic trait controlled by 3 genes.
C. the gene for flower colour is epistatic to another gen.
D. the trait of flower colour is maternally inherited.

128. Based on equal probability of any base occurrence in a genome, what should be the minimum length of a probe to bind specifically on a single locus on a bacterial genome of 1 Mbp?

A. 6 bases B. 15 bases
C. 10 bases D. 4 bases

129. The DNA gel picture shown below depicts the PCR banding pattern of two markers (M1 and M2).

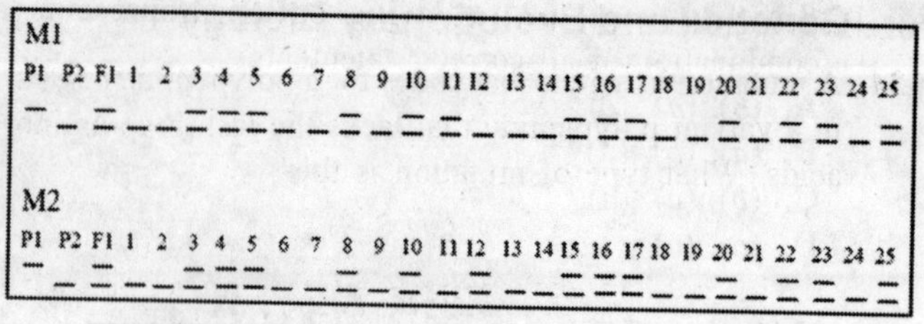

The linkage distance between the two markers from a test cross population is:

A. 4 cM B. 6 cM
C. 8 cM D. 10 cM

130. In rice, while pyramiding three genes for a trait, two donors were used. One donor carries two desirable genes, which are present on chromosome #2 and #4, while other donor has one desirable gene present on chromosome #3. Both the donors were crossed to produce a biparental F2 population. The theoretical expectations of an individual carrying all the desirable allele in homozygous condition is one out of:

A. 4 B. 16
C. 64 D. 256

131. The term 'co-suppression' was coined by Richard Jorgensen to explain:

A. Patchy flower colour in petunia.
B. Resistance to viral infection in tobacco.
C. Production of white flowers in Ipomea.
D. Silencing of actin gene in *C. elegans.*

132. A chemist synthesized a new chemical X which is highly mutagenic. He also tested the capacity of mutation induced by X to be reversed by other known mutagens and obtained the following results:

Mutation Produced by	Reversed by		
	Nitrous acid	Hydroxylamine	Acridine orange
X	Yes	Some	No

Which one of the following conclusions is appropriate?

A. X causes transversion
B. X causes transition
C. X causes single-base insertion
D. X causes single-base deletion

133. Anhidrotic dysplasia is a condition in which development of sweat glands is prevented. It is caused by mutation present on the X chromosome. A heterozygous female for this allele will:

A. Show complete absence of sweat glands.
B. Have normal phenotype
C. Show mosaic pattern of presence and absence of sweat glands
D. Show increased physiological activity of sweat glands

GATE (BIOTECHNOLOGY), 2019

Genetics and Evolutionary Biology

134. A mutation in a gene that codes for a polypeptide results in a variant polypeptide that lacks the last three amino acids. What type of mutation is this?

A. Synonymous mutation
B. Nonsense mutation
C. Missense mutation
D. Silent mutation

CSIR-NET, NOVEMBER (MORNING), 2020

Mendelian Principles

135. Mutation is essential for genetic variation. Which one of the following events can lead to variation amongst the gametes produced by males of *Drosophila melanogaster*? [Crossing over does not occur in (*d*) *melanogaster* males]

A. Segregation
B. Imprinting
C. Recombination
D. Independent Assortment.

Non-mendelian Genetics

136. In a mammal, coat colour is governed by gene B. The coat colour is either black or brown, depending on whether the genotype is BB or Bb. It is not known which of these genotypes lead to the black and brown colours. The genotype bb results in albino coat colour. Further, the genotype ce suppresses the expression of coat colour resulting in albino coat colour. An albino male was crossed with a brown female and the resulting progeny had individuals with either black or brown coats. From this observation it can be infered that the genotype of the male and female that were crossed are:

A. BB cc and Bb CC, respectively
B. Bb cc and Bb CC, respectively
C. bb CC and BB CC, respectively
D. bb Cc and BB CC, respectively

Gene Mapping

137. In D. Melanogaster, traits '*a*', '*b*' and '*c*' result from recessive alleles that are located on one of the autosomes. The resulting Fi females were test crossed and the following progeny (total of 1000) were obtained:

$a^+ \ b^+ \ c^+$	350
$a^+ \ b \ c$	25
$a \ b \ c$	380
$a \ b^+ \ c^+$	35
$a \ b^+ \ c$	100
$a \ b \ c^+$	10
$a^+ b \ c^+$	85
$a^+ \ b^+ c$	15

The following conclusions were made from the above data:

(*a*) The order of genes is a b c and the distance between a and b is 8.5 cM.
(*b*) The order of genes is a c b and the distance between a and c is 8.5 cM.
(*c*) The order of genes is b c a and the distance between b and c is 21 cM.
(*d*) The order of genes is c b a and the distance between b and c is 8.5 cM.

Which one of the following options represent statement(s) that is/are correct?

A. (*a*) only
B. (*a*) and (*d*)
C. (*b*) and (*c*)
D. (*d*) only

138. Given below are a few terms in column A and column B.

Column I	Column II
(*a*) Cisgenics	(*i*) Synteny studies
(*b*) Zinc-finger proteins	(*ii*) Linkage disquilibrium
(*c*) Comparative genomics	(*iii*) Site-specific
(*d*) Association mapping	(*iv*) Recombination
	Use of endogenous plant genes and regulatory elementgs

Which one of the following options represents all correct matches between terms of Column A and Column B?

	(*a*)	(*b*)	(*c*)	(*d*)
A.	(*iv*)	(*iii*)	(*i*)	(*ii*)
B.	(*iii*)	(*i*)	(*iv*)	(*ii*)
C.	(*ii*)	(*iii*)	(*iv*)	(*i*)
D.	(*i*)	(*iv*)	(*ii*)	(*iii*)

139. The data from an SI nuclease mapping experiment for a transcript mfgl using a 5'-end labelled probe are shown below.

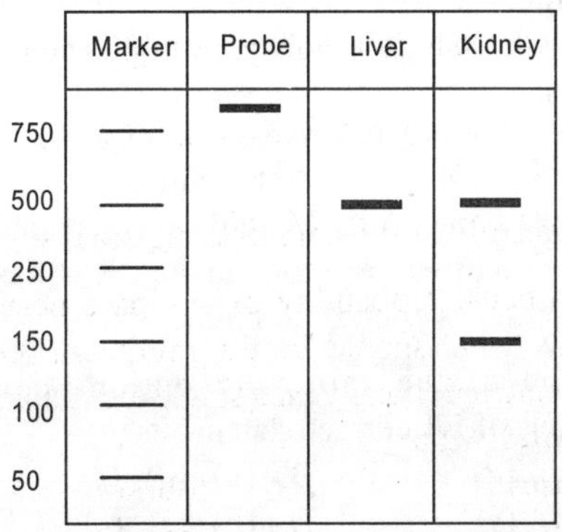

Following interpretations were made:
(*a*) The liver RNA is 500 bp in length
(*b*) The start site of the liver mfgl transcript is 500 bp downstream of the 5' end of probe.
(*c*) The kidney makes two mfg 7 transcripts, and the 3' end of one of these is shorter than the other.

Which one of the following options represents the correct combination of the interpretations?
A. (*a*), (*b*) and (*c*) B. (*a*) and (*c*) only
C. (*b*) and (*c*) only D. (*b*) only

Extra Chromosomal Inheritance

140. Cytoplasmic male sterility (CMS) in plants is caused by mutation in the mitochondrial genome. CMS can be restored by a nuclear gene, restorer of fertility (Rf), which is a dominant character. If a male sterile pea plant is pollinated by a fertile male pea plant with Rf in heterozygous condition, the progeny obtained will have
A. all male sterile progeny
B. all fertile progeny
C. 50% of the progeny fertile and 50% male sterile
D. 75% of the progeny fertile and 25% male sterile

141. Gene 'A' in mouse is needed for its normal growth [normal size]. Mouse strains with deletion in gene 'A' (A^{del}) have been developed. When the following cross is made
A^{del} A × AA
All progeny (both males and females) are of normal size.
When the F1, progeny with the following genotypes are crossed:A^{delA} × AA50% of the progeny obtained are small in size. The above observation can be explained by:
A. Maternal inheritance B. Maternal imprinting
C. Paternal imprinting D. Maternal effect

142. Following statements were made about human mitochondrial genome:
(*a*) The replication of both the H and L strands is unidirectional and begins at specific origins.
(*b*) Majority of the mitochondrial genes encode for protein products.
(*c*) Though the mitochondrial genome is extremely compact, the genes never show any sequence overlap.
(*d*) The CR/D-loop region of mitochondrial genome exhibits triple stranded structure.
(*e*) Transcription of mtDNA starts bi-directionally from a common promoter region in the CR/D-loop region and continues round the circle.

Which one of the following options contains a combination of all correct statements?
A. (*a*), (*b*), (*d*) B. (*a*), (*d*), (*e*)
C. (*b*), (*d*), (*e*) D. (*b*), (*c*), (*d*)

Microbial Genetics

143. Which one of the following is correct statement about the difference between a F^{+} cell and Hfr cell?
A. In F^{+} cell F factor is an integral part of bacterial chromosome, while in Hfr cell F factor is present as an episome.
B. F+and Hfr are synonymous.
C. In F^{+} cell a bacteriophage carries F factor, while in Hfr cell F factor is an integral part of bacterial chromosome.
D. In F^{+} cell F factor is in the form of an episome while in Hfr cell, F factor is integrated into the bacterial chromosome.

Pedigree Analysis

144. What kind of inheritance is indicative in the pedigree chart shown below?

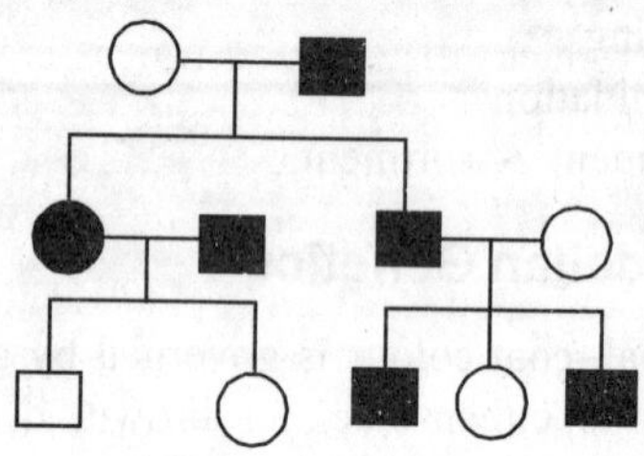

A. Y-linked B. X-linked dominant
C. X-linked recessive D. Autosomal dominant

Mutation & Chromosomal Aberration

145. A scientist synthesized four new chemicals which had mutagenic potential and named then as Cl, C2, C3 and C4. He tried to analyse the nature of mutations caused by them and obtained the following results:

Mutains produced by mutagen	Mutation reversed by			
	2-Amino purine	Nitrous Acid	Hydroxyl Amine	Acridine Orange
C1	Yes	Yes	Some	No
C2	No	No	No	No
C3	Yes	Yes	No	No
C4	No	No	No	Yes

Which one of the following answers describes the mutagenic potential of the chemicals?
A. Cl causes transitions, C2 causes transversions or large deletions, C3 causes transitions and C4 causes single base insertions or deletions
B. Cl causes transversions, C2 causes transitions, C3 causes transversions and C4 causes large deletions
C. Cl cause large deletions, C2 causes transitions, C3 causes transversions and C4 causes s ngle base insertions
D. Cl and C3 causes transversions while C2 and C4 causes transitions

146. Fertilization of gametes containing chromosome with duplications or deletions often results in children with disabilities. What is the probability of a couple where the male is karyotypically normal and the female has a pericentric inversion in heterozygous condition producing a child with disabilities if crossing over took place within the pericentric inversion in 26% of meiotic divisions?

In this case consider that fertilization with a gamete containing chromosomes with duplications or deletion will result in disabilities.

A. 26% B. 13%
C. 25% D. 50%

Population Genetics

147. In a population that is in a Hardy-Weinberg equilibrium, 40% of the plants are recessive homozygotes and produce white flowers (WF). If the total number of individuals in the population is 14000 plants, the numbers of homozygous dominant red flowered (RF) plants and heterozygous pink flowered (PF) plants would be:

A. RF-5600 PF-1891
B. RF-1891 PF-6508
C. RF-5600 PF-6508
D. RF-5145 PF-8855

CSIR-NET, NOVEMBER (AFTERNOON), 2020

Mendelian Principles

148. A plant that produces disc-shaped fruit is crossed with another plant that produces long fruit. All the FI plants gave disc-shaped fruits. When the F1 were intercrossed, F2 progeny were produced in the following ratio: 9/16 plants with disc–shaped fruits; 6/16 plants with spherical fruits and 1/16 plants having long fruits. Which one of the following options gives correct genotype of spherical fruits obtained in F2?

A. A_bb only B. aaB_ only
C. A_bb and aaB D. A_B_ and aabb

Non-mendelian Genetics

149. In some sheep, horns are produced by an autosomal allele, 'H', that is dominant in males and recessive in females. H^+H^+ individuals are hornless. A horned female is crossed with a hornless male. One of the resulting F1 females is crossed with a hornless male. What proportion of the male and female progeny of F1 will have horns?

A. 50% of male and 50% of female progeny will be horned
B. 50% of male progeny but none of the female progeny will be horned
C. 25% of male and 25% of female progeny will he horned
D. 100% of male progeny and 50% of female progeny will be horned

150. Body weight of rabbits is determined by pairs of alleles at two loci, 'a' and 'b', that are additive and equal in their effects. Rabbits with genotype $a^-\ a^-\ b^-\ b^-$ have average 1 kg body weight, whereas individuals with genotype $a^+\ a^+\ b^+\ b^+$ have animals that average 3.4 kg in weight. A male rabbit with a $a^-\ a^-\ b^-\ b^-$ is crossed with a female of genotype $a^+\ a^+\ b^+\ b^+$.

What will be predicted average weight of F1 progeny of this cross?

A. 2.2 kg B. 1.6 kg
C. 1.2 kg D. 2.8 kg

Gene Mapping

151. The maximum frequency of recombination that can occur between two loci is

A. 25% B. 50%
C. 75% D. 100%

152. A panel of six hybrid cell lines, each containing a different subset of human chromosomes, was examined for the presence of the gene product as shown below:

Cell line	Gene product present	Human chromosomes present 1	2	3	4	5	6	7	8	9	10
A	+	+	+	+	+	–	–	–	–	–	–
B	+	–	–	+	+	+	+	+	–	–	–
C	–	–	+	+	–	–	–	–	+	+	+
D	–	–	+	–	–	–	+	+	+	+	–
E	–	–	+	–	–	–	+	–	–	–	–
F	+	+	+	–	+	+	+	–	–	–	–

The gene which codes for the given gene product is located on which chromosome?

A. Chromosomes 3, 4 or 5
B. Chromosome 3
C. Chromosome 3 or 4
D. Chromosome 4

153. E coli cells were simultaneously infected with two strains of phage λ

One strain of λ had a mutant host range, is temperature sensitive and known to produce clear plaques (genotype h st c); another strain of λ carried the wild type alleles (genotype $h^+st^+c^+$). Progeny phages were collected from the lysed cells and were plated on bacteria. The following numbers of different progeny were obtained:

Number of plaques	Progeny phage genotype
$h^+ c^+ st^+$	350
h^+ cst	86
$h^+ c^+$ st	4
h c st	300
h^+ c st^+	90
h c st^+	6
h $c^+ st^+$	114
h c^+ st	50

What will be the order of the three genes and the map distance between them? (anc-c)

A. h —(36cM)— c —(15cM)— st B. c —(21cM)— h —(15cM)— st

C. h —(21cM)— st —(15cM)— c D. h —(36cM)— c —(∞cM)— st

154. Curled wing (cu), ebony body colour(e) and sepia eye (se) are three recessive mutations that occur in fruit flies. The loci for these mutations have been mapped and they are separated by the following hypothetical map distances:

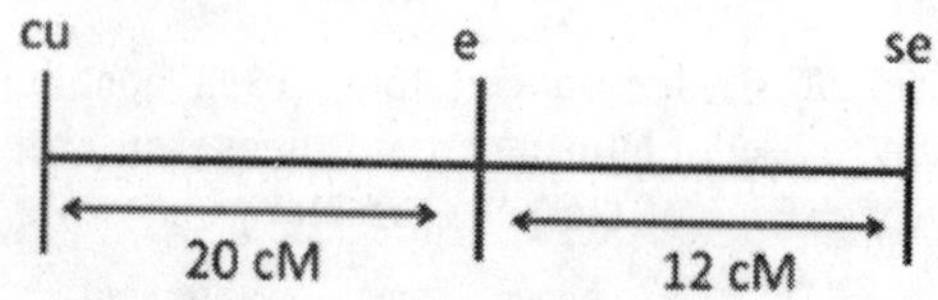

The interference between these genes is 0.4.

A mutant cuese fly was crossed with a homozygous wild type fly. The resulting F1 females were test crossed that produced 1800 progeny. What number of flies in each phenotype class is likely to be obtained in the progeny of the test cross?

A. Non recombinants will be 1250; single crossover between cu and e 334; single cross over between e and se 190; double cross over 26
B. Non recombinants 1181; single crossover between cu and e 360; single cross over between e and se 216; double cross over 43
C. Non recombinants 1198; single crossovers 576; double cross overs 26
D. Non recombinants 1233; single crossover 524; double cross over 43

155. The figure below represents a profile of DNA markers in two parents (PI and P2), progeny (F1) from a cross between P1 and P2 and that of gametes produced from F1. Eight different patterns (DH1 to DH8) were observed in case of gametes. The numbers below, DH1 to DH8 indicate the number of individuals observed in each case

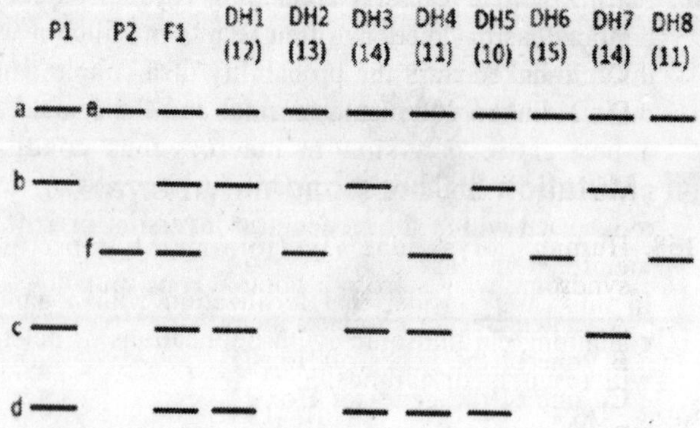

Based on the above observations, the following statements were made:

(*a*) Markers 'b' and 'f are likely to be allelic in nature
(*b*) Markers 'c' and'd' are linked intrans with a map distance of 24 cM C Marker 'b' assorts independently from marker 'c'

Which one of the following have a combination of all correct statements?

A. (*a*), (*b*) and (*c*) B. (*a*) and (*b*)
C. (*a*) only D. (*c*) only

156. Given below are some terms in column A and their corresponding properties/related terms in column B

Column A	Column B
(*a*) Bulk segregant analysis	(*i*) QTL analysis of wider genetic diversity using fewer individuals
(*b*) NILs	(*ii*) Mapping monogenic qualitative trails
(*c*) Association mapping	(*iii*) Co-dominant markers
(*d*) SNPs	(*iv*) Repeated back-crossing of F_1 to recurrent parent

Which one of the following options represents the most appropriate match between all terms of column A and B.?

	(*a*)	(*b*)	(*c*)	(*d*)
A.	(*ii*)	(*iv*)	(*i*)	(*iii*)
B.	(*iii*)	(*i*)	(*iv*)	(*ii*)
C.	(*iv*)	(*iii*)	(*ii*)	(*i*)
D.	(*iii*)	(*iv*)	(*i*)	(*ii*)

Pedigree Analysis

157. The trait shown in the below pedigree is

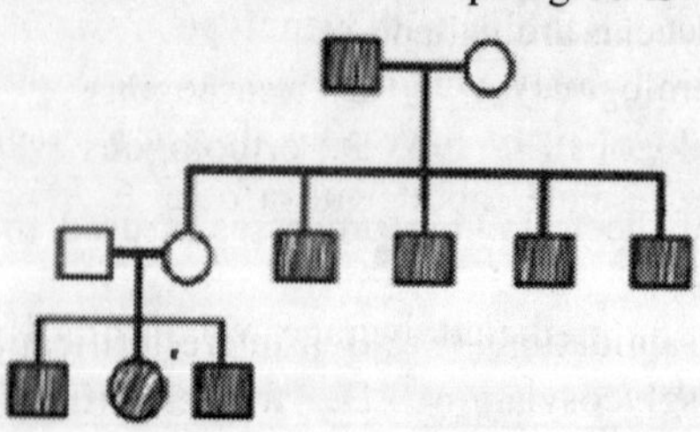

A. X-linked recessive trait
B. autosomal recessive trait
C. Y-linked trait
D. X-linked dominant trait

Mutation & Chromosomal Aberration

158. Human polysyndactyly (joining of extra digits) syndrome results from a homozygous mutation at
A. antennapedia complex locus
B. one of the genes of Hox D
C. one of the genes of Hox C
D. β-catenin locus

159. A species of plant (species 1) is diploid (2n = 6) with chromosomes AABBCC and a related species (species 2) is also diploid (2n = 4) with chromosomes PPQQ. The following statements were given by students regarding the chromosome numbers involving these plant species:
(*a*) Autotriploid of species 1 will have 12 chromosomes
(*b*) Allotetraploid involving species 1 and 2 will have 16 chromosomes
(*c*) A monosomy in species 1 will generate 5 chromosomes
(*d*) A double trisomy in species 1 will generate 8 chromosomes
(*e*) A nullisomy in species 2 will generate 2 chromosomes

The combination of statements with all correct answers is:
A. A, (*b*) and (*c*) B. (*b*), (*c*) and (*d*)
C. (*c*), (*d*) and (*e*) D. (*d*), (*e*) and (*a*)

Population Genetics

160. In Africa "AS" represents a carrier of sickle cell anaemia, where A is the allele for normal haemoglobin and S for sickle cell haemoglobin. If the allele S is maintained at a high frequency in some populations, this represents a case of
A. homozygote advantage
B. heterozygote advantage
C. dominance
D. genetic drift

DBT-JRF, 2020

Genetics, Phylogeny & Evolution

161. The fruit of a particular tree species formed the predominant diet of the dodo. After dodo became extinct, that tree species also became extinct. Which of the following is the most likely cause for the tree's extinction?
A. the dodo habitat was destroyed
B. the seeds of that tree required passage through the digestive system of the dodo for germination
C. by living close to the tree, the dodo protected the tree from other birds
D. other birds ate the fruit of that tree, as well as fruit of other trees, and dispersed more seeds than the dodo did.

162. Phylogenetic tree provides information about
A. evolution relationships between organisms
B. environmental relationships between organisms
C. ecological relationships between organism
D. none of the given options

163. Genes related through vertical descent from a common ancestral gene are called
A. heterologous B. xenologous
C. paralogous D. orthologous

164. Which of the following processes is used to produce biodiesel?
A. transamidation B. interesterification
C. transglycosylation D. transesterification

Molecular and Human Genetics

165. The genetic codon is a triplet and there are 64 codons. How many codons would be possible if the codon is a doublet?
A. 24 B. 16
C. 8 D. 64

166. Fragile X syndrome is caused by a fragile site at the end of the long arm of X chromosome. Such a disorder is
A. X-linked
B. all the given options
C. dominant
D. caused by loss-of-function of FMR1 gene

167. One centimorgan is defined as the genetic distance between two loci with a statistically corrected recombination frequency of
A. 10% B. 1%
C. 0.5% D. 0.1%

168. The sequence CGAATTTGG is matched globally with four sequences in a database. The sequence that will give the highest similarity score taking match = 1, mismatch = 0 and gap penalty = minus 1 is
A. CGTATCG B. CGTTTGG
C. CGATTCG D. CAATGAG

169. How many linkage groups would be there in a plant with 2*n* = 20?
A. 20 B. 5
C. 40 D. 10

170. A combination of gametes that can be formed by the genotype AaBbCcDdEeFfGg are

A. 32 B. 64
C. 16 D. 128

171. Only 10% of babies with Edward syndrome survive beyond 5 years. This is a genetic disease arising due to

A. absence of chromosome 18
B. absence of chromosome Y
C. Trisomy 18
D. Trisomy 13

172. What is Single Nucleotide Polymorphism (SNP)?

A. variation at a single nucleotide position observed in 100% population
B. variation at a single nucleotide position observed in at least 1% population
C. variation at a single nucleotide position observed in more than 10% population
D. variation at a single nucleotide position observed in at least 10% population

173. A class of temperature sensitive E. coli mutants defective in DNA replication were identified that ceased replication immediately upon increase in temperature. Which of the following processes are likely to be defective in these mutants?

A. elongation step of DNA replication
B. segregation step of DNA replication
C. initiation of DNA replication
D. termination of DNA replication

174. A set of closely linked genetic markers present on a single chromosome, which are not easily separable by recombination and tend to be inherited together are termed as

A. haplotypes B. allotypes
C. isotypes D. alleles

175. Which of the following disorders does not show sex-linked inheritance?

A. Haemophilia B
B. Duchenne muscular dystrophy
C. Haemophilia A
D. Tay-Sachs disease

GATE (BIOTECHNOLOGY), 2020

Genetics and Evolutionary Biology

176. In tomato plant, red (R) is dominant over yellow (r) for fruit color and purple (P) is dominant over green (p) for stem color. Fruit color and stem color assort independently, The number of progeny plants of different fruit/stem colors obtained from a mating are as follows:

Red fruit, purple stem-145
Red fruit, green stem-184
Yellow fruit, purple stem-66
Yellow fruit, green stem-47

What are the genotypes of the parent plants in this mating?

A. RrPp X Rrpp B. RrPp X RrPp
C. RRPP X rrpp D. RrPP X Rrpp

GATE (LIFE SCIENCE), 2020

Genetics and Genomics

177. Which of the following chemicals is used for doubling of chromosome numbers during production of 'doubled haploids' in crop plants?

A. Hygromycin B. Kanamycin
C. Colchicine D. Glufosinate

Genetics

178. Match the following genetic disorders in column I with associated typical chromosomal changes mentioned in Column II

Column I	Column II
P. Klinefelter syndrome	*(i)* 45,XO
Q. Down syndrome	*(ii)* 5p minus
R. Turner syndrome	*(iii)* 47,XXY
S. Cri du chat syndrome	*(iv)* Trisomy 21

A. P-*(iv)*, Q-*(iii)*, R-*(ii)*, S-*(i)*
B. P-*(iv)*, Q-*(ii)*, R-*(i)*, S-*(iii)*
C. P-*(iii)*, Q-*(iv)*, R-*(ii)*, S-*(i)*
D. P-*(iii)*, Q-*(iv)*, R-*(i)*, S-*(ii)*

CSIR-NET, JUNE (MORNING), 2021

Mendelian Principles

179. Wheat plant can have kernels of white color or in shades of red *i.e.* light red, red, dark red and very dark red (purple).

A researcher made the following cross:

P	Wheat plant with white kernel	Wheat plant with purple (very dark red) kernel
F1	All plant with red kernel	

F2	1/16	plant with purple kernel
	4/16	plant with dark red kernel
	6/16	plant with red kernel
	4/16	plant with light red kernel
	1/16	plant with white kernel

The following conclusions are made from the results obtained:

(*a*) It is a dihybrid cross where white color is coded by gene A and the purple color is coded by gene B

(*b*) Two genes, both coding for the color of kernel and each gene having two alleles, one that produced red pigment and the other that produced no pigment.

(*c*) Four genes, one coding for no pigment, which is epistatic over the other genes. The remaining three genes have 2 alleles each, one of that produce red pigment and the other that produced no pigment.

(*d*) The trait is influenced the environment leading to the observed variation in kernels color.

Which of the above conclusion(s) is/are correct?

A. (*a*) only B. (*b*) only
C. (*c*) only D. (*c*) and (*d*) only

Non-mendelian Genetics

180. A fly with apricot coloured eye was crossed with a sepia eyed fly of opposite sex. In F1 all flies were wild type. The genes responsible for the two phenotypes were

A. Allelic B. Non-allelic
C. Pseudo-allelic D. Paralogous genes

181. Following statements were made about imprinting in the human genome

(*a*) Imprinting control center harbors part of the SNRPN gene.

(*b*) Imprinting of gene in an individual cannot be tissue specific

(*c*) Sperms and eggs exhibit identical pattern of genome methylation, except in the sex chromosome

(*d*) At imprinted loci, expression depends on the parental origin.

Select the options with all the correct statements?

A. (*a*) and (*d*) B. (*b*) and (*d*)
C. (*a*) and (*c*) D. (*b*) and (*c*)

Gene Mapping

182. A *Drosophila* mutant (line A) with vestigial wings is isolated in a laboratory. The vestigial wing phenotype was observed to be recessive and mapped to gene 'X'. Three other laboratories also isolated vestigial mutants, called line B, C and D. In order to test if the mutation in line B-D also mapped to gene 'X', the following crosses were made and phenotype of F1 progeny observed.

Cross	F1 progeny (wing morphology)
A × B	Vestigial
A × C	Vestigial
A × D	Normal
B × C	Vestigial
B × D	Normal
C × D	Normal

Based on the above identity the line (s) which is the most likely NOT to have a mutation on gene 'X'.

A. Both lines B and C
B. Line C only
C. Line D only
D. Both lines B and D

Microbial Genetics

183. DNA was isolated from a strain of bacterium with genotype $a^+ b^+ c^+ d^+ e^+$ and transformed into a bacterium strain $a^- b^- c^- d^- e^-$. The transformants were tested for the presence of the donated gene. The cotransformed genes were found as follows, a^+ and b^+; c^+ and e^+; d^+ and c^+; b^+ and d^+

What is the order of genes on the bacterial chromosome?

A. a b c d e B. a c b e d
C. a b c e d D. a b d c e

184. 22 transduction was used to map the fadl gene. The result of teo-factor crosses between fadl and two linked marker, purF and aroC are show below.

Donar	Recipient	Recombinants		Numbers obtained
		Selected marker	Second marker	
fadL purF+	fadL+purF	purF+	fadL	200
			$fadL^+$	800
fadL aroC+	fadL+aroC	aroC+	fadL	400
			$fadL^+$	600
aroC+ purF	aroC purF+	aroC+	purF	500
			$purF^+$	500

Which one of the following is the correct map for the three gene

A. 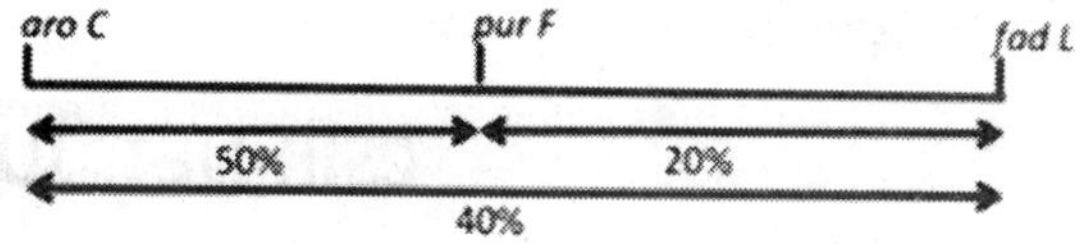

B. 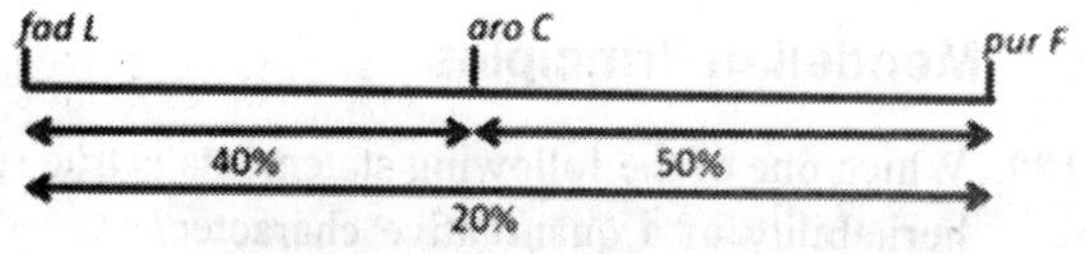

C. 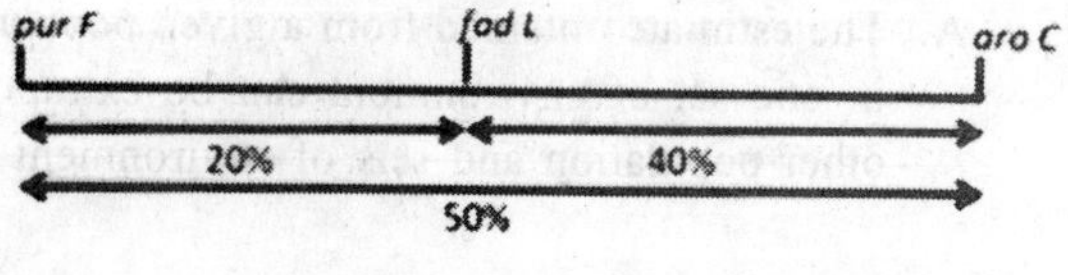

D. 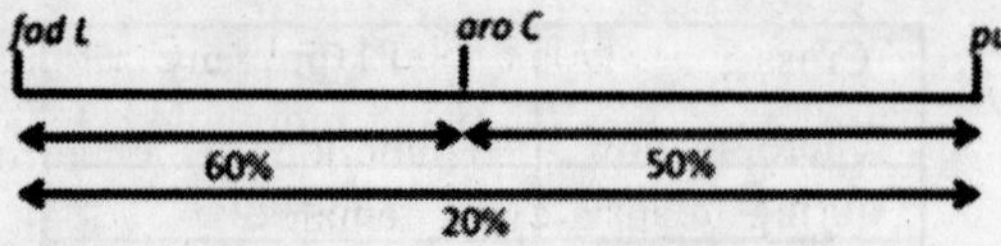

Pedigree Analysis

185. The pedigree given below represents the genotype at Four different loci for the children in generation III

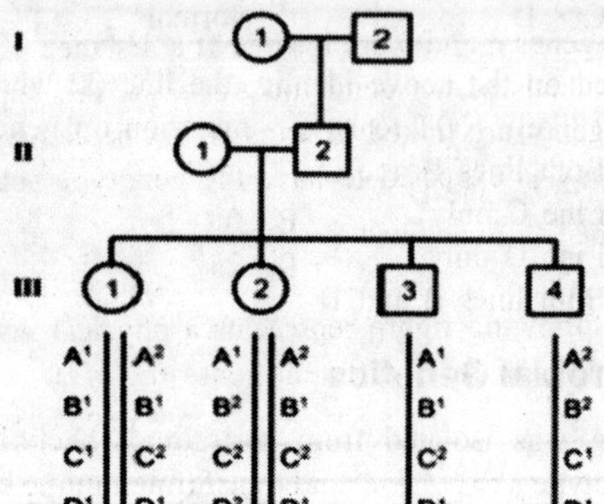

Which one of the given genotype is likely to represent the genotype of individual II-1

A. 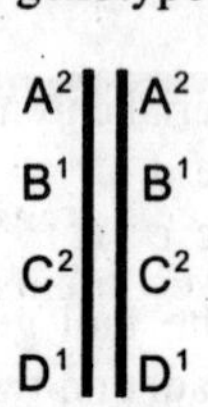

B. 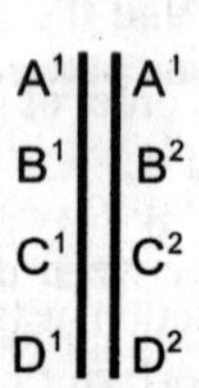

C. 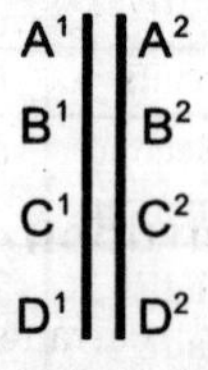

D. 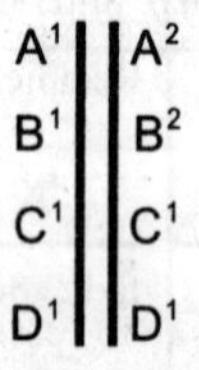

Mutation & Chromosomal Aberration

186. Human polydactyly traits having extra fingers of toes are caused by a dominants allele. In a screening it was found that out of 42 individuals having an allele for polydactyly only 38 of them were polydactyly. Which of the following is the correct interpretation of the observation?

A. The penetrance of polydactyly is estimated to be 90%

B. The expressivity of polydactly is 90%

C. This is an example of variable expressivity

D. The polydactly trait is show complete penetrance.

187. Given below are graphs depicting two possible dynamics of gene duplication events over a period of time during genome evolution.

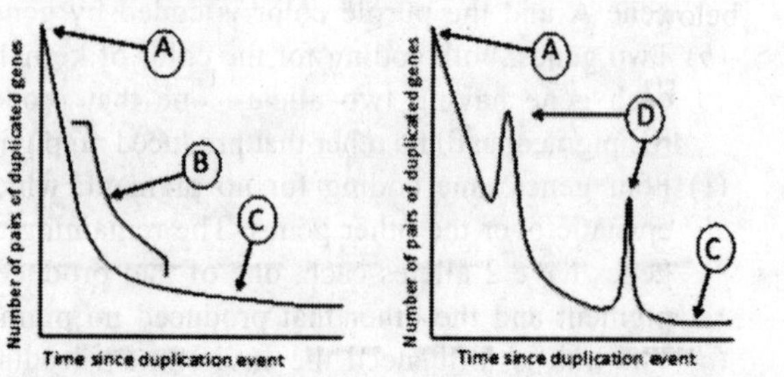

Based on the above figures, which one of the following options correctly represents the identity of A, B, C and D?

A. A-gene duplication event, B-rqndom loss od duplicated genes,C-remaining pairs of duplicated genes, D-additional gene duplication events

B. A-remaining pairs of duplicated genes, B-gene duplication event, C-random loss of duplicated genes, D-additional gene duplication event

C. A-additional gene duplication events B-random Loss of duplicated genes C-remaining pairs of duplicated genes D-gene duplication events

D. A-random Loss of duplicated genes, B-additional gene duplication events , C-gene duplication events, D-remaining pairs of duplicated genes

Population Genetics

188. In a population that is in Hardy-Weinberg equilibrium, the frequency of the recessive homozygous genotype of trait q is 0.04. The percentage of individual homozygous for the dominant allele is

A. 64 B. 40
C. 32 D. 16

CSIR-NET, JUNE (AFTERNOON), 2021

Mendelian Principles

189. Which one of the following statements is true regarding heritability of a quantitative character?

A. The estimate obtained from a given population and in one set of environment can be extrapolated to other population and sets of environment

B. The estimate is a population as well as an individual parameter.

C. Heritability measures the proportion of the phenotypic variation that is the result of genetic factors

D. Heritability indicates the degree to which a trait is genetic.

Non-mendelian Genetics

190. Doubled haploids (DH) are plants derived from single immature pollen and doubled artificially to form diploids. A DH population was created from F1 Progeny derived from a cross between two parents (P1 and P2), one resistant (R) and the other sensitive (S) to white rust. The parents, F1 and DH population were profiled with a set of co-dominate markers, which is represented below.

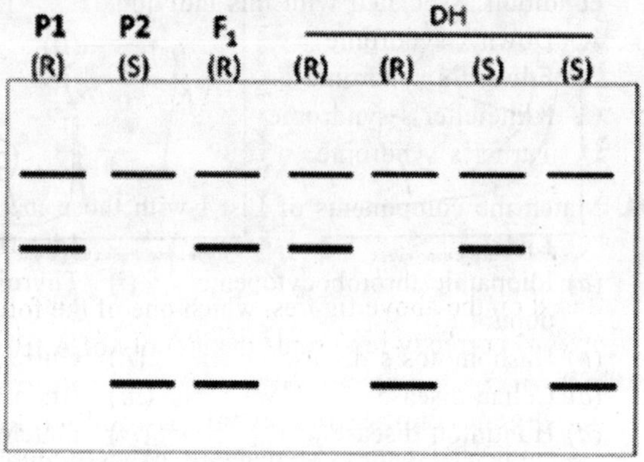

The following table summarizes the proposed percentage of the 4 different types (1 to 4) of DH progeny, assuming that the DNA marker is (*i*) unlinked to the gene governing the trait and (*ii*) linked at a distance of 10cM.

Expected % of progeny with profiles(1 to 4)									
	Unliked					Linked			
Profile	1	2	3	4		1	2	3	4
A.	25	25	25	25	i.	45	5	5	45
B.	37.5	37.5	12.5	12.5	ii	5	45	45	5
					iii.	37.5	12.5	12.5	37.5

Which one of the following options correctly represents the expected ratio for unlinked and linked, respectively?

A. A, ii B. A, i
C. B, i D. A, iii

191. A cross is made between Drosophilla stocks, each with an independent mutant alleles resulting in white eye color. The mutant alleles are recessive, X-linked and caused by a deletion in the w+ alleles. The type phenotype is red eye color.

The F1 females are then cross are then crossed with type males. In the progeny, all females have red eye colour, 1 out of 10,000 males was observed to have red eye color, while the remaining had white eyes.

Which one of the following could possibly explain occurrence of red eyed males in the progeny?

A. One of the mutant alleles has a high rate of spontaneous reversion
B. There is an intragenic recombination between the w1 and w2 alleles during meiosis of.
C. There is non – disjunction of X-choromosome during meiosis of F1 females.
D. The w1 and w2 alleles show intragenic complementation in red eyed males though it is a rare event.

Gene Mapping

192. Two genes *a* and *b* are located at a distance of 10 CM. Individuals of the genotype AaBb are sib-mated. The two genes are linked in trans. What percentage of the progeny is expected to have the genotype aabb?

A. 0.25 B. 0.1
C. 6.25 D. 25

193. The following figure represents a physical map and a genetic map for 5 different genes (*a* to *e*).

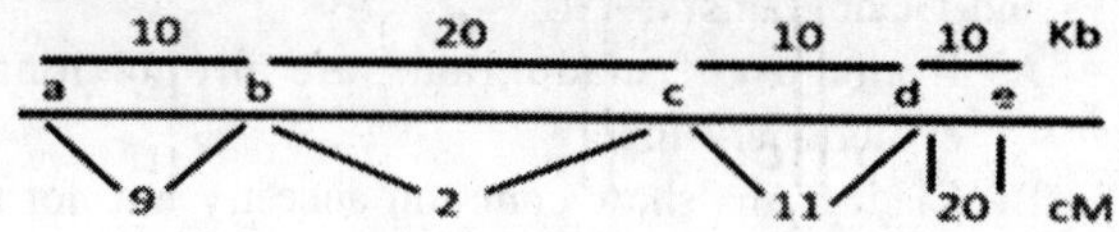

Which one of the following statements based on the above is correct?

A. The region between *b* and *c* is more recombinogenic than the other loci.
B. In comparison to the region between *a* and *b*, the region between d and e is more recombinogenic.
C. 1 cM is equal to 1 kb 1 cM
D. If more markers were mapped between *d* and *e*, the genetic distance between *d* and *e* is likely to decrease.

Mutation & Chromosomal Aberration

194. Chromosomal inversions are balanced rearrangements and thus do not change the overall amount of genetic material. While inversions can exist in homozygous condition, some only exist as heterozygotes. In the latter condition, the breakpoint disrupts:

A. Pairing of the homologous chromosomes
B. A non-coding region of the genome
C. A coding region of the genome
D. a gene with an essential function

Population Genetics

195. Sampling of 200 persons for their ABO blood group was done from an urban area. The types of blood group observed in the given population are as follows:

A = 60, B = 32, AB = 10 and O = 98

Which of the following gives the correct frequency of blood group determining alleles I^A = I^B = I^A I^B and I^O in the given population?

A. $I^A = 0.10$, $I^B = 0.11$, $I^O = 0.7$
B. $I^A = 0.27$, $I^B = 0.63$, $I^O = 0.09$

C. $I^A = 0.16$, $I^B = 0.14$, $I^O = 0.7$
D. $I^A = 0.38$, $I^B = 0.22$, $I^O = 0.7$

196. Colour blindness affects approximately 1 in 12 men (8%). In a population that is in Hardy-Weinberg Equilibrium where 8% of men are colourblind due to a sex-linked recessive gene. What propogation of women are expected to be carriers?
A. 0.92 B. 0.85
C. 0.78 D. 0.15

DBT-JRF, 2021

Genetics, Phylogeny & Evolution

197. Genes that are related through gene duplication events are:
A. Analogs B. Homologs
C. Orthologs D. Paralogs

198. Which one of the following is true about Phylograms and Cladograms?
A. Branches of cladograms are proportional to evolutionary time
B. Cladograms show common ancestry but not time
C. Phylograms show common ancestry but not time
D. There is no difference between cladograms and phylograms

Molecular and Human Genetics

199. You are performing a PCR reaction in which you need to use 20 pmoles of each primer. If both the primers are 20 nucleotides long and the average molecular weight of each nucleotide is 300 Da, the amount of each primer required for 100 ul reaction is:
A. 1.2 ng B. 1.2 ng
C. 120 ng D. 1200 ng

200. A mutation that generate termination codon is known as
A. Missense Mutation B. Nonsense Mutation
C. Reverse Mutation D. Silent Mutation

201. Breeding of Aa and AA genotype resulted in five offspring. What is the probability that exactly four offspring will have AA genotype
A. 1/16 B. 1/32
C. 5/16 D. 5/32

202. A geneticist interested in immune function induces random mutations in a number of specific genes in mice and then determines which of the resulting mutant mice have impaired immune function. This approach is an example of:
A. Both forward and reverse genetics
B. Forward genetics
C. Neither forward nor reverse genetics
D. Reverse genetic

203. Karyogram of an individual shows presence of 45 chromosomes (44 + X) and one sex chromosome is missing. The individual has a female appearance and dwarfism. Which of the following is the most probable condition associated with this individual?
A. Down's syndrome
B. Edward's syndrome
C. Klinefelter's syndrome
D. Turner's syndrome

204. Match the components of List I with those in List II

List I	List II
(*a*) Idiopathic thrombocytopenic pupura	(*i*) Thyroid
(*b*) Hashomotos's disease	(*ii*) Gut
(*c*) Celiac disease	(*iii*) Brain
(*d*) Huntinton disease	(*iv*) Platelets

Choose the correct answer from the options given below:

	(*a*)	(*b*)	(*c*)	(*d*)
A.	(*i*)	(*iii*)	(*ii*)	(*iv*)
B.	(*ii*)	(*i*)	(*iv*)	(*iii*)
C.	(*iii*)	(*iv*)	(*ii*)	(*i*)
D.	(*iv*)	(*i*)	(*ii*)	(*iii*)

205. Which one of the following diseases is caused due to a point mutation in the coding region of the associated gene?
A. Hemolytic anemia B. Sickle cell anemia
C. thalassemia D. α-thalassemia

206. Tay-Sachs disease is a:
A. Autosomal recessive genetic disorder
B. Sex-linked inherited disorder
C. Transposition disorder
D. Trinucleotide repeat disorder

Genomics and Proteomics

207. Chip-on-chip, a technique that combines chromatin immune precipitation with microarrays, is used to identify:
A. microRNA coding genes
B. Protein motifs involved in protein-protein interaction
C. Protein-coding regions in the genome
D. Transcription factor binding regions in the promoters

208. For sequencing DNA by Sanger's method, the chain elongation is terminated by:
A. 1', 4' dideoxy nucleotides
B. 2', 3' dideoxy nucleotides
C. 2', 4' dideoxy nucleotides
D. 4', 3' dideoxy nucleotides

209. The fragments obtained from a Sanger sequencing experiment are as follows:

5′ – GAATTA – 3′
5′ – GAATTAT – 3′
5′ – GAATTATC – 3′
5′ – GAATTATCA – 3′
5′ – GAATTATCAC – 3′

Please identify the template sequence from the above given data:

A. 3′ – CTTAATAGTG – 5′
B. 3′ – GAATTATCAC – 5′
C. 5′ – CACTATTAAG – 3′
D. 5′ – GAATTATCAC – 3′

210. In genomics, a contig means:

A. A set of fragments generated through digestion with restriction enzymes
B. A set of molecular markers used in genetic mapping
C. A set of overlapping fragments that form a continuous stretch of DNA
D. A small DNA fragment used in next generation sequencing

211. Copy number variation (CNV) signifies:

A. A short (1-4 nucleotide) highly polymorphic DNA sequence, widely distributed in the genome
B. DNA segments > 1 Kb repeated multiple times in the genome
C. Increase in the number of some of the chromosomes
D. Series of short tandem repeat sequences (10 – 100 nucleotides) occurring frequently in the genome

212. DNA fingerprinting for forensic investigation is based on

A. Exon sequence
B. Intron sequence
C. Promoter sequence
D. Repetitive sequence

213. Which one of the following CANNOT be used for differential gene expression analysis?

A. EST data analysis
B. Microarray data analysis
C. mRNA sequencing data sequencing
D. Whole genome sequencing data analysis

214. Which one of the following is NOT true for local alignment of protein sequences?

A. Gap penalty is not used for insertions and deletions
B. It is generally used for analyzing distantly related sequences
C. It looks for regions/blocks of high similarity between the two sequences
D. Smith-Waterman algorithm is used to locally align the two sequences

215. Given below are two statements: one is labelled as Assertion (A) and the other is labelled as Reason (R).

Assertion (A): Gene Sequences are aligned using identity matrices instead of substitution matrices.

Reason (R): The four bases in DNA cannot be replaced with each other.

In light of the above statement, choose the correct answer from the options given below:

A. (A) is false but (R) is true
B. (A) is true but (R) is false
C. Both (A) and (R) are true and (R) is the correct explanation of (A)
D. Both (A) and (R) are true but (R) is not the correct explanation of (A)

216. Match the components of List I with List II

List I	List II
(*a*) Sequence alignment	(*i*) PUBMED
(*b*) Structural alignment	(*ii*) BLAST
(*c*) Fold prediction	(*iii*) ROSETTA
(*d*) Review of literature	(*iv*) DALI

Choose the correct answer from the options given below:

	(*a*)	(*b*)	(*c*)	(*d*)
A.	(*i*)	(*iv*)	(*iii*)	(*ii*)
B.	(*i*)	(*iii*)	(*iv*)	(*ii*)
C.	(*ii*)	(*iii*)	(*iv*)	(*i*)
D.	(*ii*)	(*iv*)	(*iii*)	(*i*)

217. CASP judges one of the following:

A. Experimental techniques of structure determination
B. Quality of protein structures
C. Suitability of drug
D. Techniques of protein structure prediction

218. The in vitro ADMET analysis cannot provide information about:

A. Cytochrome P450 inhibition
B. Adverse reaction to the drug
C. Blood – brain barrier penetrability
D. Metabolic Stability,

219. The motif D[TS]x (2) {GH}-L motif will have sequence:

A. DRRRRL
B. DSARRL
C. DSRRGL
D. DTRRHL

220. Gene of different species consisting sequencal and functional relationship to each other is called

A. Paralog
B. Synteny
C. Ortholog
D. Microarray

GATE (BIOTECHNOLOGY), 2021

Genetics and Evolutionary Biology

221. The order of genes present in a chromosome is as follows

Which one of the following rearrangements represents a paracentric inversion?

A. 

B. 

C. 

D. 

222. In Neurospora crassa, a mutation in the poky gene results in a slow growth phenotype (poky). The results of four crosses are given below.

(*a*) wild-type ♀ × wild-type ♂ → All progeny are wild-type

(*b*) wild-type ♀ × poky ♂ → All progeny are wild-type

(*c*) poky ♀ × wild-type ♂ → All progeny are poky

(*d*) poky ♀ × poky ♂ → All progeny are poky

Which one of the following explains the inheritance mode of poky?

A. Episomal inheritance
B. Mendelian inheritance
C. Mitochondrial inheritance
D. X-linked inheritance

GATE (LIFE SCIENCE), 2021

Genetics and Genomics

223. To understand the mechanism of systemic acquired resistance (SAR), a team of researchers isolated a mutant with reduced SAR response. Sequencing of this mutant revealed homozygous mutations in two genes, X and Y. Which of the following experiment(s) would test whether the mutant phenotype is caused by mutation in either or both the genes?

A. Complement the mutant with X or Y and analyze the phenotype in each case.
B. Complement the mutant with both X and Y and analyze the phenotype.
C. Cross the mutant with wild-type and analyze the segregation pattern of the phenotype.
D. Compare the expression of X and Y in mutant and wild-type plants.

224. Which of the following option(s) is/are CORRECT in the context of hybrid plant generation using Barnase/ Barstar-based male sterile lines?

A. Barnase inhibits Barstar.
B. Barstar inhibits Barnase.
C. Barnase and Barstar are used to generate the male sterile line and the restorer line, respectively.
D. Barnase and Barstar are used to generate the restorer line and the male sterile line, respectively.

Genetics

225. The expression of holandric genes causes which of the following genetic trait in humans?

A. Haemophilia
B. Sickle cell anaemia
C. Down's Syndrome
D. Hypertrichosis

CSIR-NET, SEPTEMBER (MORNING), 2022

Mendelian Principles

226. In Drosophila, balancer chromosomes are used to keep all the alleles on one chromosome together. A balancer contains multiple inversions; so that when it recombines with the corresponding wild type chromosome, no viable cross products are formed. Balancers also carry an allele for a dominant phenotype. A Drosophila male with sepia eye color is crossed to a female carrying a third chromosome balancer (TM6B). The allele for sepia phenotype (se) is located on chromosome 3 and is recessive to the wild type eye color. The dominant marker for TM6B is a tubby phenotype. Further, an individual homozygous for TM6B balancer does not survive. F_1 progeny with tubby phenotype is sib-mated. The F_2 progeny is expected to have:

A. only sepia eye color
B. sepia, tubby and wild type flies in a ratio of 1:2:1
C. sepia and tubby flies in a ratio of 1:2
D. sepia and wild type flies in ratio of 3:1

Gene Mapping

227. The additive nature of a genetic map as suggested by Alfred Sturtevant and T. H. Morgan is possible if
A. no interference in crossovers
B. complete interference in crossovers
C. partial interference in crossovers
D. variable interference in crossovers dependent on the genetic distances

Microbial Genetics

228. In a conjugation experiment between Hfr strain 'X' and F-cell, lac gene enters the recipient in F-cells remain auxotrophic for Leu, Trp, Ura, Glu, Phe and Gly. The mating is then allowed to proceed for 20 minutes and lac^+ exconjugants are selected. Of the lac^+ cells

35% are leu^+
98% are trp^+
10% are ura^+
65% are glu^+
0% are phe^+
81% are gly^+

Select the correct order of the genes as they enter, from the choices given below:
A. trp^+, gly^+, glu^+, leu^+, ura^+, phe^+, lac^+
B. lac^+, phe^+, ura^+, leu^+, glu^+, gly^+, trp^+
C. phe^+, ura^+, leu^+, glu^+, gly^+, trp^+, lac^+
D. lac^+, trp^+, gly^+, glu^+, leu^+, ura^+, phe^+

Pedigree Analysis

229. Given below is a pedigree indicating a pattern of inheritance:

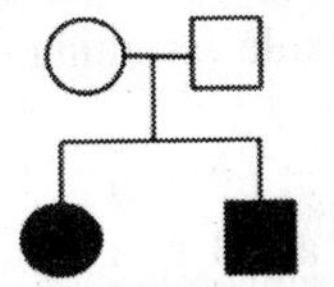

Which one of the following options correctly describes the pattern of inheritance shown in the above pedigree?
A. X-linked recessive
B. Autosomal recessive
C. X-linked dominant
D. Autosomal dominant

230. Given below is a pedigree indicating a pattern of inheritance:

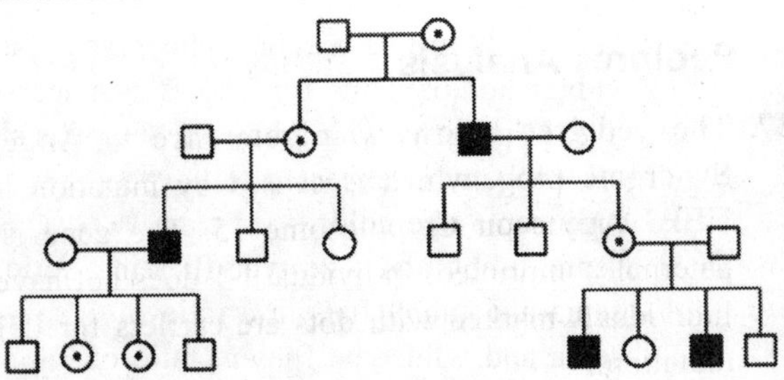

The following statements are drawn from the above pedigree towards understanding the pattern of inheritance:
(*a*) An affected male does not appear to pass the trait to his sons
(*b*) An affected male appears to pass the allele to a daughter who is unaffected
(*c*) All affected individuals have at least one affected parent
(*d*) The given trait appears to be a recessive one
(*e*) The given trait appears to be an autosomal recessive one

Select the option from the following that has all correct statements:
A. (*c*) and (*e*) only
B. (*a*), (*b*) and (*d*) only
C. (*e*) only
D. (*a*), (*b*), (*c*), (*d*) and (*e*)

Mutation & Chromosomal Aberration

231. Which one of the following conditions represents autopolyploidy?
A. More than two sets of chromosomes, both of which are from the same parental species
B. More than two sets of chromosomes, both of which are from the different parental species
C. More than two sets of chromosomes only from a single parent
D. Duplication of a chromosomal locus leading to spontaneous increase in the copy number of a gene

232. The following represents sequences of different alleles of a gene found in a family represented by mothe father (allele1/allele 2) and their two sons: Son1 (allele1/allele 2) and Son 2 (allele1/allele2). Further, observed in one of the alleles of the son, which is marked with a triangle.

Mother allele 1 CAGCATAGTCATTCGTCCATGGACTAG
Mother allele 2 CAGCATTGTCATTCGTCCATGGACTAG
Father allele 1 CAGCATTGTCATTCGTCCATGGGCTAG
Father allele 2 CAGCTTAGTCATTCGTCCATGGTACTAG
Son 1 allele 1 CAGCATAGTCATTCGTCCATGGACTAG
Son 1 allele 2 CAGCTTAGTCATTCGTCCATTGTACTAG
Son 2 allele 1 CAGCATTGTCATTCGTCCATGGACTAG
Son 2 allele 2 CAGCTTAGTCATTCGTCCATTGTACTAG

The following statements were made about the mutation:
(*a*) The mutation arose in the germline of the father.
(*b*) The mutation arose in the son.
(*c*) The given DNA sequences are present on the X chromosome.
(*d*) There is a possibility to use RFLP for tracking this variation.

Which one of the following options presents a combination of correct statements?

A. (*b*) only B. (*a*) and (*d*)

C. (*a*) and (*c*) D. (*b*) and (*d*)

233. Two new chemical compounds X and Y are synthesized in a laboratory and tested for their potency as a nature of the mutation produced by these compounds is tested for reversal by other known mutagens an results were obtained:

New compounds	Reversed by			
	5-Bromouracil	EMS	Hydroxylamine	Acridine orange
X	Yes	Yes	No	No
Y	No	No	No	Yes

Which statement best describes the nature of the two mutagens?

A. Compound X produces single base substitutions that generate CG to TA transitions and Compound Y produces insertions or deletions

B. Compound X produces insertions or deletions and Compound Y produces single base substitutions that generate CG to TA transitions

C. Compound X produces single base substitutions that generate CG to TA transitions and Compound Y produces TA to GC transitions

D. Compound X produces single base substitutions that generate insertions and Compound Y produces deletions

CSIR-NET, SEPTEMBER (AFTERNOON), 2022

Non-mendelian Genetics

234. In a plant r^+ and a^+ genes encode for a regulatory and a structural protein, respectively. These genes are responsible for blue color of flower. Mutation in either of the genes leads to white flowers, which is a recessive character. The two genes assort independently. When two homozygous white flowered plants are crossed, the F_1 plants have blue colored flowers. If the F_1 plant is backcrossed, the progeny will have plants with blue and white flowers in the ratio of :

A. 9 : 7 B. 1 : 1

C. 3 : 1 D. 1 : 0

Extra Chromosomal Inheritance

235. During development, many gene products are provided by the females to the eggs which are needed for normal development of the zygote. Such genes are called as maternal effect genes. The following are a set of crosses between parents carrying a recessive mutant allele (m) and the offspring obtained:

Cross No	Genotype of Parents	Phenotype of offspring
I	*m* /+♂ X *m* /+♀	All normal
II	*m* /*m*♂ X *m* /+♀	All normal
III	*m* /+♂ X *m* /*m*♀	All mutants
IV	*m* /*m*♂ X *m* /*m*♀	All mutants
V	*m* /+♂ X *m* /+♀	Both normal and mutant

Which of the above cross(es) is/are indicative that the mutation is in a maternal-effect gene?

A. Cross III only

B. Cross V only

C. Cross I, II and III

D. Cross II and V

Microbial Genetics

236. Four different Hfr strains of E. coli were mated with F— recipients, and the time of entry of various donor markers were found to be as below:

Hfr 1: met [15 min] thr [30 min] phe [42 min] mal [57 min]

Hfr 2: bio [50 min] thy [51 min] his [60 min] mal [77 min]

Hfr 3: cys [10 min] phe [26 min] his [58 min]

Hfr4: his [12 min] bio [22 min] azi [27 min] thi [44min]

Based upon the above observations, the following statements were made assuming met to be at 0 min and thr at 15 min:

(*a*) his is located at 59 min

(*b*) azi is located at 74 min

(*c*) cys is located at 11 min

(*d*) mal is located at 76 min

Which one of the following options represents all correct statements?

A. (*a*) and (*d*) only

B. (*b*), (*c*) and (*d*)

C. (*a*), (*b*) and (*c*)

D. (*c*) and (*d*) only

Pedigree Analysis

237. The pedigree below is in reference to Angelman Syndrome (AS), which is caused by mutation in the UBE3A gene on Chromosome 15. The gene is also paternally imprinted. Individual I-1 does not have AS. Individuals marked with dots are carriers for UBE3A mutation.

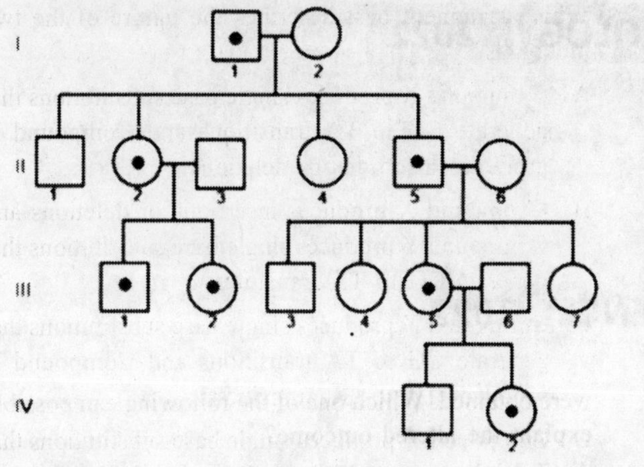

Which one of the following options lists individuals all of whom are likely show AS?

A. II-1, III-1 and IV-1
B. III-1, III-2 and IV-2
C. II-2, III-2, III-5 and IV-2
D. II-1 and II-V II-1

Mutation & Chromosomal Aberration

238. How many complementation groups do the following mutants m1 to m6 come under?

Results of complementation between different mutants						
	m1	m2	m3	m4	m5	m6
m1	–	–	+	+	–	+
m2		–	+	+	–	+
m3			–	–	+	+
m4				–	+	+
m5					–	+
m6						–

A. Two
B. Four
C. Five
D. Three

239. In which one of the following human disorders, parents or grandparents are said to carry premutations?

A. Down syndrome
B. Fragile X syndrome
C. Klinefelter syndrome
D. Alkaptonuria

240. If a gamete produced following non-disjunction of a chromosome at second meiotic division was fertilized by a normal gamete, what is the expected frequency of trisomic progeny?

A. 1/4
B. 2/4
C. 3/4
D. 1

DBT-JRF, 2022

241. Which regions of the genome are best suited for generating DNA Barcodes for species identification?

A. Organellar genes
B. Ribosomal genes
C. Histone genes
D. Non coding regions of the genome

242. Differential expression of the genetic material depending on its parentage of inheritance is known as:

A. Penetrance
B. Expressivity
C. Epistasis
D. Genomic imprinting

243. One centimorgan is defined as the genetic distance between two loci with a statistically corrected recombination frequency of:

A. 0.1%
B. 0.5%
C. 1.0%
D. 5.0%

244. A haploid sperm from one species and a haploid egg from another species may form a diploid interspecies hybrid. Meiosis in these plants generally fails but can also lead to rare duplicated gametes called:

A. Allopolyploid
B. Aneuploid
C. Autopolyploid
D. Heteroployploid

245. Match items in List-I with items in List-II

List-I	List-II
(*a*) Down Syndrome	(*i*) Trisomy 18
(*b*) Edward Syndrome	(*ii*) XXY
(*c*) Klinefelter Syndrome	(*iii*) Female with one X
(*d*) Turner Syndrome	(*iv*) XX+21

	(*a*)	(*b*)	(*c*)	(*d*)
A.	(*i*)	(*iv*)	(*ii*)	(*iii*)
B.	(*iv*)	(*ii*)	(*iii*)	(*i*)
C.	(*iv*)	(*i*)	(*ii*)	(*iii*)
D.	(*iii*)	(*i*)	(*iv*)	(*ii*)

246. Which one of the immunodeficiency is caused by a mutation in BTK gene:

A. X-linked SCID
B. X-linked agammaglobulinemia
C. DiGeorge syndrome
D. Chronic granulomatous disease

247. Which one of the following markers is NOT routinely used for DNA fingerprinting?

A. Amplification short tandem repeats
B. Analysis of copy number variations
C. Restriction fragment length polymorphism
D. Amplification variable number tandem repeats

GATE (BIOTECHNOLOGY), 2022

248. The type of nucleic acid present in λ-phage is

A. Double stranded DNA
B. Single stranded circular DNA
C. Single stranded DNA
D. Single stranded RNA

GATE (LIFE SCIENCE), 2022

Genetics and Genomics

249. Mendel deduced the genetic principle of inheritance by experimenting on sweet pea plants. One of the experiments involved crossing plants with two contrasting characters, tall (dominant) and dwarf (recessive), which yielded all tall plants in the first generation. When the same genetic cross was independently repeated by a researcher, only short plants were obtained. Which one of the following can possibly explain the altered outcome?

A. Tall plants were heterozygous
B. An enhancer for the tall allele is present in the dwarf plant
C. A suppressor for the tall allele is present in the dwarf plant
D. Dwarf plants are homozygous

ANSWERS

1	2	3	4	5	6	7	8	9	10
C	C	D	B	B	D	C	A	A	B
11	**12**	**13**	**14**	**15**	**16**	**17**	**18**	**19**	**20**
D	C	D	C	A	B	C	D	B	D
21	**22**	**23**	**24**	**25**	**26**	**27**	**28**	**29**	**30**
B	C	C	D	C	D	A	D	C	B
31	**32**	**33**	**34**	**35**	**36**	**37**	**38**	**39**	**40**
B	D	A	C	D	B	B	C	A	C
41	**42**	**43**	**44**	**45**	**46**	**47**	**48**	**49**	**50**
B	A	B	B	D	C	A	B	D	B
51	**52**	**53**	**54**	**55**	**56**	**57**	**58**	**59**	**60**
A	B	C	B	B	B	B	C	C	D
61	**62**	**63**	**64**	**65**	**66**	**67**	**68**	**69**	**70**
D	C	A	C	B	D	D	A	A	A
71	**72**	**73**	**74**	**75**	**76**	**77**	**78**	**79**	**80**
D	C	C	A	B	D	B	A	C	C
81	**82**	**83**	**84**	**85**	**86**	**87**	**88**	**89**	**90**
A	C	B	C	C	A	D	B	B	D
91	**92**	**93**	**94**	**95**	**96**	**97**	**98**	**99**	**100**
A	C	C	D	C	B	C	C	D	B
101	**102**	**103**	**104**	**105**	**106**	**107**	**108**	**109**	**110**
C	C	B	D	B	D	B	B	B	D
111	**112**	**113**	**114**	**115**	**116**	**117**	**118**	**119**	**120**
B	C	A	C	B	A	B	A	A	A
121	**122**	**123**	**124**	**125**	**126**	**127**	**128**	**129**	**130**
A	C	C	C	B	A	A	C	C	C

131	132	133	134	135	136	137	138	139	140
A	B	C	B	D	A	C	A	D	C
141	**142**	**143**	**144**	**145**	**146**	**147**	**148**	**149**	**150**
B	B	D	D	A	B	C	C	B	A
151	**152**	**153**	**154**	**155**	**156**	**157**	**158**	**159**	**160**
B	D	C	A	C	A	B	B	C	B
161	**162**	**163**	**164**	**165**	**166**	**167**	**168**	**169**	**170**
B	A	D	D	B	B	B	B	D	D
171	**172**	**173**	**174**	**175**	**176**	**177**	**178**	**179**	**180**
C	B	A	A	D	A	C	D	B	B
181	**182**	**183**	**184**	**185**	**186**	**187**	**188**	**189**	**190**
A	C	D	B	D	A	A	A	C	B
191	**192**	**193**	**194**	**195**	**196**	**197**	**198**	**199**	**200**
B	A	B	D	A	D	D	B	C	B
201	**202**	**203**	**204**	**205**	**206**	**207**	**208**	**209**	**210**
D	D	D	D	B	A	D	B	A	C
211	**212**	**213**	**214**	**215**	**216**	**217**	**218**	**219**	**220**
B	D	D	A	C	D	D	B	B	C
221	**222**	**223**	**224**	**225**	**226**	**227**	**228**	**229**	**230**
B	C	A, B, C	B, C	D	C	B	D	B	B
231	**232**	**233**	**234**	**235**	**236**	**237**	**238**	**239**	**240**
A	B	A	B	B	C	B	D	B	A
241	**242**	**243**	**244**	**245**	**246**	**247**	**248**	**249**	
B	B	C	A	C	B	B	A	C	

■■■■■

CHAPTER

5

MICROBIOLOGY

CSIR-NET, JUNE, 2017

Microbes

1. Which one of the following pairs is NOT matched correctly?

A. Glycocalyx-adherence
B. Fimbriae-motility
C. Pili-conjugation
D. Peptidoglycan-cell wall

2. Which one of the following is NOT a bacterial disease?

A. Tuberculosis B. Typhoid
C. Tetanus D. Small pox

3. Which of the following is NOT true for the Anammox bacteria?

A. They convert nitrate and ammonium into dinitrogen
B. They are responsible for 30-50% of the dinitrogen gas produced in the ocean
C. They belong to the bacterial phylum Planctomycetes
D. Membranes of these bacteria contain ladderane lipids

4. The table given below lists organisms (column A) and characteristic features (column B).

A	B
(*a*) Caulobacter	(*i*) Multicellular fruiting body
(*b*) Myxobacteria	(*ii*) Endospore
(*c*) Methylotroph	(*iii*) Non-free living, Penicillin resistant
(*d*) *Bacillus subtilis*	(*iv*) Immortal stalk cells
(*e*) Mycoplasma	(*v*) Can use formate, cyanide and carbon monoxide as a source of carbon

Choose the option that correctly matches organisms with their characteristic features.

	(*a*)	(*b*)	(*c*)	(*d*)	(*e*)
A.	(*i*)	(*v*)	(*iv*)	(*ii*)	(*iii*)
B.	(*iv*)	(*i*)	(*v*)	(*ii*)	(*iii*)
C.	(*iv*)	(*v*)	(*i*)	(*iii*)	(*ii*)
D.	(*ii*)	(*i*)	(*v*)	(*iv*)	(*iii*)

DBT-JRF, 2017

5. In a bacterial growth experiment, the concentration of cells increased from 10,000 cells/ml to 30,000 cells/ml in 3 h during the exponential growth phase. The doubling time (h) of the bacteria is:

A. 2.5 B. 3.0
C. 1.0 D. 1.9

6. A cell suspension (1.5 × 105 cells per ml) was treated with 1mM $HgCl_2$ for 30 min. After treatment, the cell suspension was diluted 10-fold and 100 microliters was plated which gave 5 colonies. Calculate the percentage of cells that survived?

A. 0.00033 B. 3.3
C. 0.033 D. 0.33

7. Equal volumes of cell suspensions of *Escherichia coli, Saccharomyces cerevisiae, Streptococcus lactis* and *Mycoplasma pneumoniae,* all have the same $OD_{600nm} = 0.50$. Which cell suspension would have the minimum and maximum number of cells, respectively?
A. *Saccharomyces cerevisiae* and *Mycoplasma pneumoniae*
B. *Saccharomyces cerevisiae* and Streptococcus *lactis*
C. *Escherichia coli* and *Mycoplasma pneumoniae*
D. *Mycoplasma pneumoniae* and *Streptococcus lactis*

GATE (BIOTECHNOLOGY), 2017

8. Which one of the following organisms is an indicator of faecal contamination?
A. *Escherichia coli*
B. *Streptococcus lactis*
C. *Bacillus subtilis*
D. *Lactobacillus acidophilus*

9. Assertion (A): Gram negative bacteria show staining with safranin
Reason (R): Gram negative bacteria have ab outer membrane with lipopolysaccharides.
A. Both (A) and (R) are true and (R) is the correct reason for (A).
B. Both (A) and (R) are true and (R) is not the correct reason for (A).
C. Both (A) and (R) are false.
D. (A) is true but (R) is false.

10. Match the proteins in Column I with cellular processes in Column II

Column I	Column II
P. *Methanococcus*	1. Halophile
Q. *Dunaliella*	2. Acidophile
R. *Sulfolobus*	3. Mesophile
S. *Escherichia*	4. Barophile

A. P-4, Q-3, R-2, S-1
B. P-3, Q-2, R-4, S-1
C. P-2, Q-1, R-4, S-3
D. P-4, Q-1, R-2, S-3

11. An immunocompetent person becomes infected with pathogenic strain of bacteria. Which one of the following graphs correctly depicts bacterial load in this person over time?

A. 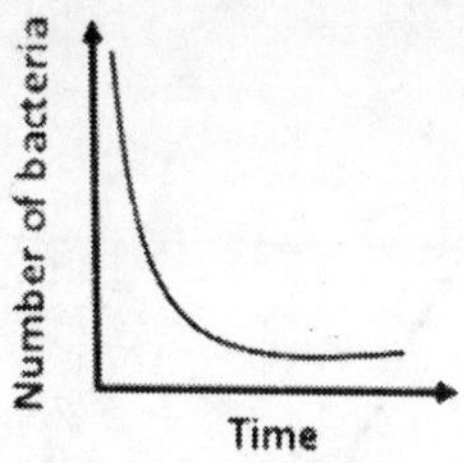

B. 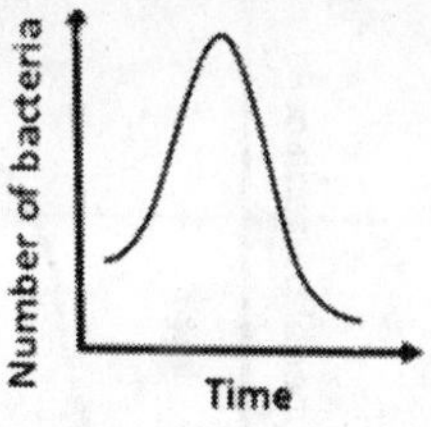

C. 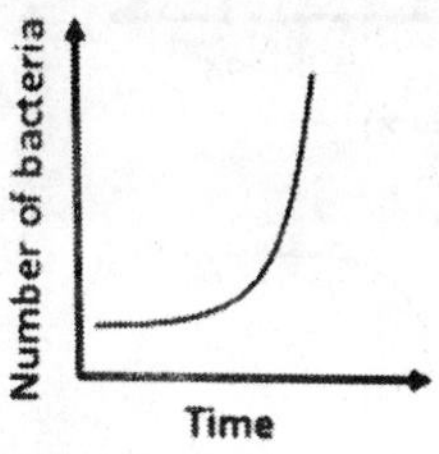

D. 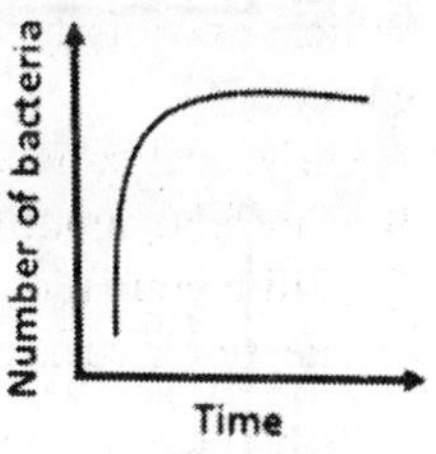

GATE (LIFE SCIENCE), 2017

Historical Perspective

12. Which one of the following is NOT a contribution by Robert Koch?
A. Identification of causative agent of anthrax
B. Discovery of causative agent of tuberculosis
C. Discovery of causative agent of leprosy
D. Identification of causative agent of cholera

Microbial Taxonomy and Diversity

13. Unicellular eukaryotic organisms belongs to which one of the following kingdoms of classification?
A. Monera B. Plantae
C. Protista D. Animalia

Prokaryotic Cells: Structure and Function

14. The inner mitochondrial membrane comprises of a series of folds known as
A. cristae B. thylakoids
C. cisterns D. cilia

Microbial Growth

15. Microbes that have their optimal growth rate near 15°C but can still grow at 0°C to 20°C are known as
A. mesophiles B. psychrotrophs
C. psychrotolerant D. psychrophiles

16. Which one of the following statements is TRUE about MacConkey (MAC) agar medium?
A. MAC agar medium is a selective and differential medium for Gram-positive bacteria.
B. MAC agar medium is a selective and differential medium for Gram-negative bacteria.
C. MAC agar medium is an enriched medium for Gram-positive bacteria.
D. MAC agar medium is a synthetic medium for Gram-positive and Gram-negative bacteria.

17. A bactericidal agent X is added after 3 hours of growth of a bacterial culture. Following the addition of X, the bacterial growth was measured using the standard plate count method till 24 hours. Which one of the following figures is the most accurate representation of the action of X?

A. 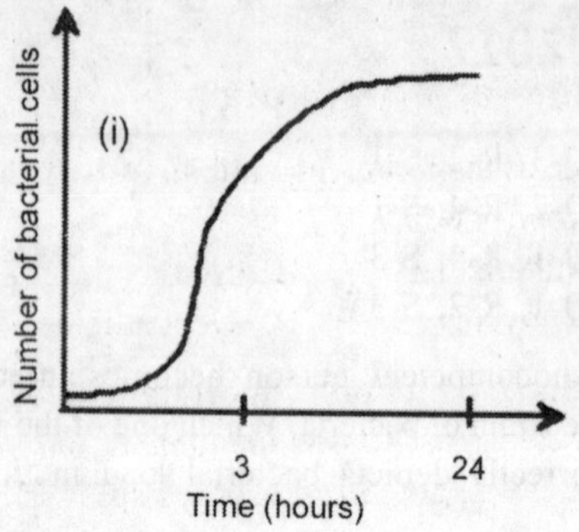

B. 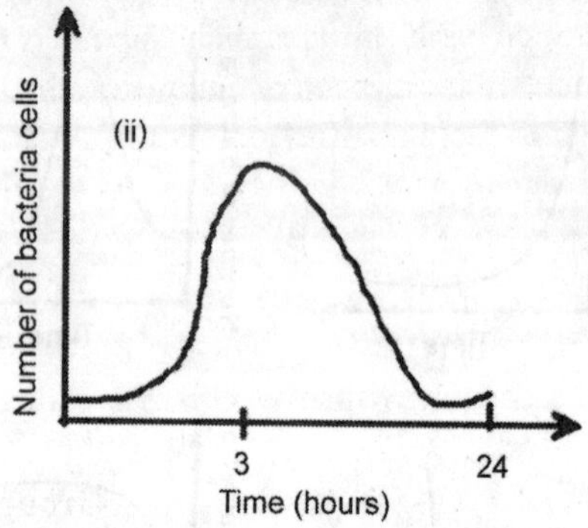

C. 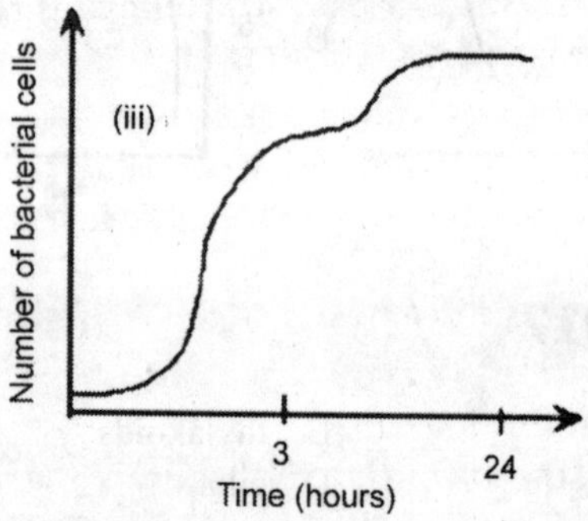

D. 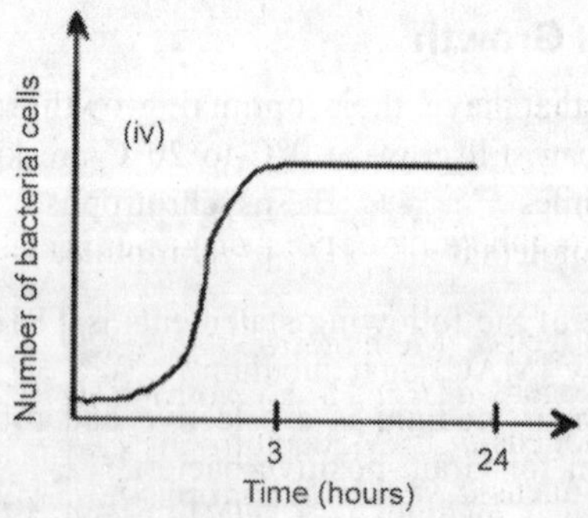

Control of Micro-organisms

18. As an antiseptic, alcohol is effective against
A. bacteria and non-enveloped viruses
B. bacterial endospores and fungi
C. bacteria and fungi
D. fungi and non-enveloped viruses

19. Match the terms given in Group I with the descriptions from Group II.

Group I	Group II
(*a*) Photoautotrophs	(*i*) Use inorganic chemical reaction for energy production
(*b*) Chemoautotrophs	(*ii*) Use organic compound for energy production
(*c*) Photohetrotrophs	(*iii*) Use sunlight as energy source and carbon dioxide as carbon source.
(*d*) Chemoheterotrophs	(*iv*) Use sunlight as energy source and organic compounds as carbon source.

	(*a*)	(*b*)	(*c*)	(*d*)
A.	(*ii*)	(*i*)	(*iv*)	(*iii*)
B.	(*iii*)	(*i*)	(*iv*)	(*ii*)
C.	(*iv*)	(*iii*)	(*i*)	(*ii*)
D.	(*ii*)	(*iv*)	(*iii*)	(*i*)

Microbial Metabolism

20. Which one of the following is the end product of dissimilatory sulfate reduction bacteria?
A. Hydrogen sulphide B. Sulfur dioxide
C. Sulfur D. Thiosulfate

21. Which one of the following is the terminal electron acceptor in the given metabolic reaction catalyzed by methanogens

$4H_2 + CO_2 \rightarrow CH_4 + 2H_2O$

A. H_2 B. CO_2
C. CH_4 D. H_2O

Microbial Diseases and Host Pathogen Interaction

22. Which one of the following is a contagious disease?
A. Chickenpox B. Tetanus
C. Malaria D. Filariasis

23. An antigen X was injected into a rabbit for the first time at time P. Then the rabbit was given a booster dose of X at time Q. Which one of the following figures accurately depicts the adaptive immune response by the rabbit against X?

A. 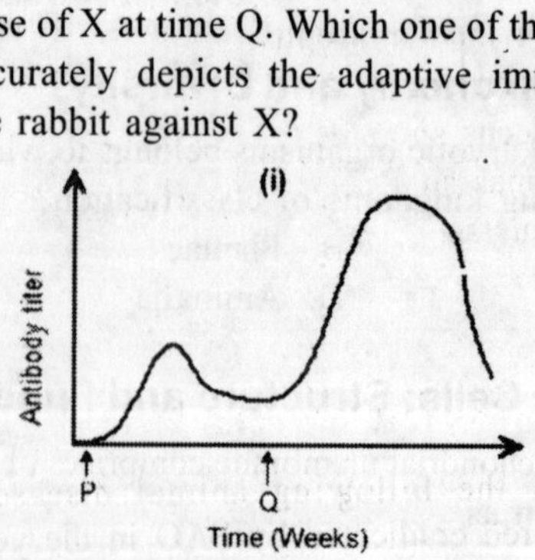

B. 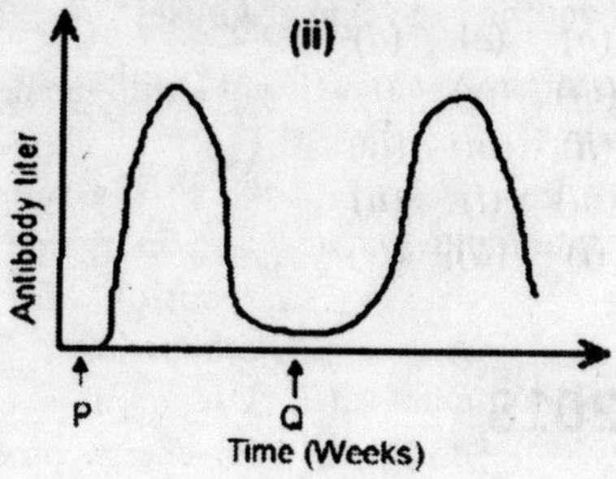

C. 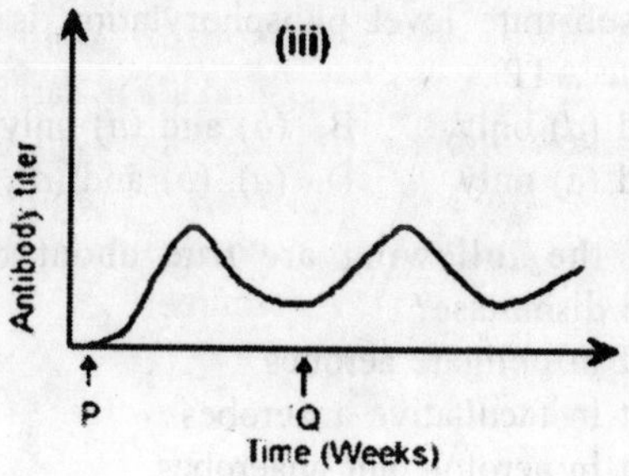

D. 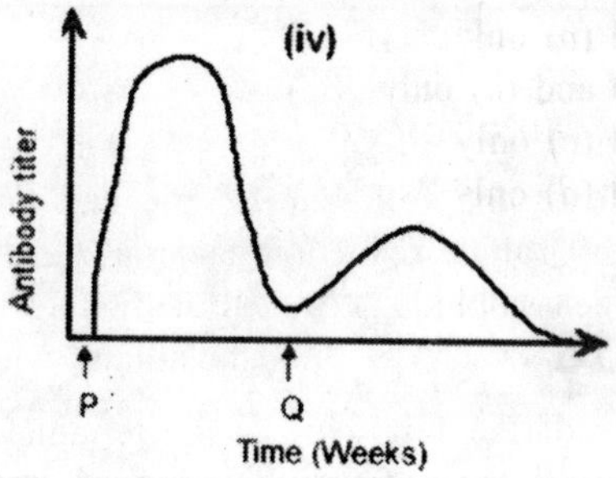

24. Match the diseases given in Group I with their causative agents from Group II

Group I	Group II
(*a*) Plague	(*i*) Coxiella burnetii
(*b*) Rabies	(*ii*) Plasmodium spp.
(*c*) Q fever	(*iii*) Yersinia pestis
(*d*) Malaria	(*iv*) Lyssavirus

	(*a*)	(*b*)	(*c*)	(*d*)
A.	(*iii*)	(*iv*)	(*i*)	(*ii*)
B.	(*iii*)	(*i*)	(*ii*)	(*iv*)
C.	(*iv*)	(*iii*)	(*i*)	(*ii*)
D.	(*iii*)	(*i*)	(*iv*)	(*ii*)

Chemotherapy/Antibiotics

25. Which one of the following antibiotics is NOT produced by *Streptomyces sp.*?

A. Amphotericin B
B. Neomycin
C. Vancomycin
D. Gentamicin

26. The minimal inhibitory concentration (MIC) of an antibiotic X against *Clostridium tetani, Staphylococcus* sp., *Shigella* sp., and *Streptococcus* sp. is 25, 15, 2 and 1 μg/ml, respectively. Assuming that the bioavailable concentration of X in an animal model is 20 μg/ml, which one of these bacteria may develop resistance against X in the animal model?

A. *Clostridium tetani*
B. *Staphylococcus* sp.
C. *Shigella* sp.
D. *Streptococcus* sp.

Microbial Genetics

27. Match the enzymes given in Group I with the events from Group II

Group I	Group II
(*a*) Uvr ABC endonuclease	(*i*) Retrovirus replication
(*b*) Reverse transcriptase	(*ii*) Base excision repair
(*c*) AP endonuclease	(*iii*) Nucleotide excision repair
(*d*) ATP sulfurylase	(*iv*) Pyrosequencing

	(*a*)	(*b*)	(*c*)	(*d*)
A.	(*ii*)	(*i*)	(*iv*)	(*iii*)
B.	(*iii*)	(*i*)	(*ii*)	(*iv*)
C.	(*iv*)	(*iii*)	(*i*)	(*ii*)
D.	(*ii*)	(*i*)	(*iii*)	(*iv*)

CSIR-NET, DECEMBER, 2018

28. Given below is a list of bacteria either functioning as methanogens or methanotrophs:

(*a*) Methanobacterium sp
(*b*) Methanococcus sp
(*c*) Methylomonas sp
(*d*) Methylosinus sp

Which of the following options classifies the above list correctly?

A. Methanogen-*a*; Methanotrophs-*b*, *c*, *d*
B. Methonogens-*a*, *b*, *c*; Methanotroph-*d*
C. Methanogens-*a*, *b*; Methanotrophs *c*, *d*
B. Methonogens-*a*, *d*; Methanotrophs-*b*, *c*

DBT-JRF, 2018

29. Which one of the following animal diseases was officially declared eradicated by FAO in the year?

A. CBPP
B. Dourine
C. African horse sickness
D. Rinderpest

30. Mtach the genus listed in A with the features in B

A	B
(*a*) Clostridium	(*i*) Nosocomial infection
(*b*) Streptococcus	(*ii*) Growth in Thioglycollate broth
(*c*) Shigella	(*iii*) Growth in Blood agar
(*d*) Pseudomonas	(*iv*) Dysentery

	(*a*)	(*b*)	(*c*)	(*d*)
A.	(*ii*)	(*iii*)	(*iv*)	(*i*)
B.	(*i*)	(*ii*)	(*iii*)	(*iv*)
C.	(*iv*)	(*iii*)	(*i*)	(*ii*)
D.	(*iii*)	(*i*)	(*ii*)	(*iv*)

GATE (BIOTECHNOLOGY), 2018

31. Which one of the following is an example of a neurotoxin?

A. Cholera toxin B. Streptolysin-O
C. Botulinum toxin D. Diphtheria toxin

32. Which of the following are true with regard to anaerobic respiration in bacteria?

(*a*) The final electron acceptor is an inorganic substance other than molecular oxygen.
(*b*) The number of ATP molecules produced per glucose molecule is more than that produced in aerobic respiration.
(*c*) The number of ATP molecules produced per glucose molecule is less than that produced in aerobic respiration.
(*d*) Only substrate level phosphorylation is used to generate ATP.

A. (*a*) and (*d*) only B. (*b*) and (*d*) only
C. (*a*) and (*c*) only D. (*a*), (*b*) and (*d*) only

33. Which of the following are true about bacterial superoxide dismutase?

(*a*) Present in obligate aerobes
(*b*) Present in facultative anaerobes
(*c*) Present in aerotolerant anaerobes
(*d*) Absent in obligate aerobes

A. (*a*) and (*b*) only
B. (*a*), (*b*) and (*c*) only
C. (*a*) and (*c*) only
D. (*b*) and (*d*) only

GATE (LIFE SCIENCE), 2018

Historical Perspective

34. Match the scientists to their area of major contribution

Scientists	Area of major contribution
(*a*) Antonie van Leeuwenhoek	(*i*) Taxonomy
(*b*) Carl Linnaeus	(*ii*) Antimicrobial agents
(*c*) Sir Alexander Fleming	(*iii*) Vaccination
(*d*) Louis Pasteur	(*iv*) Microscopy

	(*a*)	(*b*)	(*c*)	(*d*)
A.	(*iv*)	(*ii*)	(*i*)	(*iii*)
B.	(*iv*)	(*i*)	(*ii*)	(*iii*)
C.	(*i*)	(*iv*)	(*iii*)	(*ii*)
D.	(*ii*)	(*i*)	(*iii*)	(*iv*)

Methods in Microbiology

35. Which of the following combinations would improve the resolution of a microscope?

(*a*) Increasing the half aperture angle of the objective lens
(*b*) Decreasing the wavelength of the illumination source
(*c*) Decreasing the numerical aperture of the objective lens
(*d*) Decreasing the refractive index of immersion medium

A. (*a*) and (*b*) B. (*b*) and (*c*)
C. (*b*) and (*d*) D. (*a*) and (*c*)

Microbial Taxonomy and Diversity

36. David Baltimore's classification of viruses is based on differences in

A. host cell receptors used by viruses
B. the pathways required to synthesize virus mRNA
C. the modes of transmission of viruses
D. the envelope proteins on the surface of viruses

37. Analysis of DNA sequences suggest that eukaryotic mitochondrial genomes primarily originated from

A. fungi B. protozoa
C. algae D. bacteria

38. Binomial nomenclature has NOT yet been adopted for

A. bacteria B. fungi
C. viruses D. protozoa

39. Accumulating evidence suggest that Domain Archaea is more closely related to Domain Eukarya than to Domain Bacteria. Which of the following properties are shared between eukaryotes and archaea?

(*a*) Protein biogenesis

(b) Presence of sterol containing membranes
(c) Ribosomal subunit structures
(d) Adaptation to extreme environmental conditions
(e) Fatty acids with ester linkages in the cell membrane
A. (b), (c) and (e) B. (a), (b), (d), and (e)
C. (a) and (c) D. (c) and (d)

Prokaryotic Cells: Structure and Function

40. Which of the following eukaryotic cellular components carries out intracellular degradation during autophagy?
A. Nucleus B. Golgi bodies
C. Ribosomes D. Lysosomes

Control of Micro-organisms

41. Which of the following is NOT an accepted method for sterilization?
A. Autoclaving B. X-rays
C. Gamma rays D. UV rays

Microbial Metabolism

42. The primary product of nitrogen fixation is
A. N_2 B. NH_4^+
C. NO_2^- D. NO_3^-

43. Match the precursors/intermediates with the corresponding metabolic pathways.

Scientists	Area of major contribution
(a) Inosine monophosphate	(i) L-methionine biosynthesis
(b) Orinithine	(ii) L-tryptophan biosynthesis
(c) Chorismate	(iii) Purine biosynthesis
(d) Homocysteine	(iv) L-arginine biosynthesis

	(a)	(b)	(c)	(d)
A.	(ii)	(iii)	(iv)	(i)
B.	(i)	(iii)	(iv)	(ii)
C.	(iii)	(i)	(iv)	(ii)
D.	(iii)	(iv)	(ii)	(i)

Microbial Diseases and Host Pathogen Interaction

44. Which of the following immune system components can function as an opsonin?
A. Antibodies B. T-cell receptors
C. Histamines D. Interferons

45. The oral polio vaccine (OPV) consists of
A. live attenuated virus
B. killed virus
C. viral toxin
D. viral capsid subunit

46. In humans, the key stages in the life cycle of malarial parasites occur in
A. red blood cells and the liver
B. red blood cells and platelets
C. red blood cells and the pancreas
D. red blood cells and the gut

47. Match the microorganisms to their predominant modes of transmission.

Microorganism	Mode of transmission
(a) Bordetella pertusis	(i) Vector borne
(b) Dengue virus	(ii) Blood borne
(c) Entamoeba histolytica	(iii) Droplet infection
(d) Hepatitis B virus	(iv) Contaminated food

	(a)	(b)	(c)	(d)
A.	(iii)	(i)	(iv)	(ii)
B.	(iv)	(ii)	(i)	(iii)
C.	(ii)	(i)	(iv)	(iii)
D.	(iv)	(iii)	(i)	(ii)

Chemotherapy/Antibiotics

48. Match the antimicrobial agents in group I with their category/mode of action in group II.

Group I	Group II
(a) Fluoroquinolones	(i) beta lactam antimicrobial
(b) Amphotericin B	(ii) inhibition of protein synthesesis
(c) Tetracyclin	(iii) inhibition of nucleic acid synthesis
(d) Amoxicillin	(iv) antifungal agent

	(a)	(b)	(c)	(d)
A.	(ii)	(iv)	(iii)	(i)
B.	(iv)	(iii)	(i)	(ii)
C.	(iii)	(iv)	(ii)	(i)
D.	(iv)	(iii)	(ii)	(i)

CSIR-NET, 15 DECEMBER, 2019

49. For bacterial growth, a single cell elongates in size before it divides into two, in a process called binary fission. During cell growth,
A. new peptidoglycan synthesis is required along with the hydrolysis of bonds linking the old peptidoglycan chains.
B. new peptidoglycan synthesis is required but no hydrolysis of the old peptidoglycan occurs.
C. the old peptidoglycan is completely degraded and replaced with the newly synthesized longer polymer.
D. newly synthesized peptidoglycan is utilized to deposit a new layer of the peptidoglycan in the cell wall.

50. During the exponential phase of growth, if *No*, *Nt*, and *n* define the initial population number, population number at time *t*, and the number of generations in time *t*, respectively, then

A. $Nt = No \times 2n$
B. $No = Nt/2$
C. $Nt/No = 2^n$
D. $No/Nt = 2^n$

GATE (BIOTECHNOLOGY), 2019

51. Which of the following processes can increase genetic diversity of bacteria in nature?

(*a*) Conjugation (*b*) Transformation
(*c*) Transduction (*d*) Transfection

A. (*a*) only
B. (*a*) and (*b*) only
C. (*a*), (*b*) and (*c*) only
D. (*a*), (*b*), (*c*) and (*d*)

GATE (LIFE SCIENCE), 2019

Microbial Taxonomy and Diversity

52. Microbes make up about ________ of earth's living material by weight.

A. 1/4th B. 2/3rd
C. 3/4th D. 4/5th

53. Which of the following is a symbiotic bacterial genus that converts nitrogen into nitrogen containing compounds that are utilized by legume plants to synthesize amino acids?

A. Spirillum B. Azotobacter
C. Rhizobium D. Clostridium

Prokaryotic Cells: Structure and Function

54. Among the following characteristics listed below, select those that are the most appropriate for archaebacteria.

(*a*) Peptidoglycan containing muramic acid and D-amino acids are present in cell wall
(*b*) Long chain branched alcohols (phytanols) bound to glycerol by ether linkages are found in the lipids of cytoplasmic membrane
(*c*) First amino acid to initiate new polypeptide chain is N-Formyl methionine
(*d*) Translation process is sensitive to the action of diphtheria toxin

A. (*a*), (*c*) B. (*b*), (*c*), (*d*)
C. (*b*), (*d*) D. (*a*), (*b*), (*d*)

55. Which of the following cellular structures are absent in eukaryotes and are present at least in some prokaryotic organisms?

(*a*) Respiratory enzymes
(*b*) Ribosomes
(*c*) Nucleoid
(*d*) Internal membranes
(*e*) Pili

A. (*c*) and (*e*) B. (*a*) and (*d*)
C. (*a*), (*c*) and (*e*) D. (*c*), (*d*)

56. Granules are inclusion bodies found in bacteria. Which of the following statements are true about granules?

(*a*) Granules can be storage vessels for carbohydrates/lipids
(*b*) Some granules supply substances for a variety of metabolic processes
(*c*) Granules are dissolved in cytoplasm
(*d*) Granules are membrane-enclosed structures

A. (*b*) and (*c*) B. (*c*) and (*d*)
C. (*a*) and (*b*) D. (*a*) and (*c*)

Microbial Growth

57. Secondary metabolites such as penicillin from mold are produced during the ________ .

A. lag phase B. idiophase
C. log phase D. decline phase

58. Match the culture media to their uses

Culture Media		Uses
(*a*) Complex media	(*i*)	identifying certain bacteria from mixed culture
(*b*) Selective media	(*ii*)	chemically undefined media for growing bacteria
(*c*) Differential media	(*iii*)	cultivating fastidious bacteria
(*d*) Enriched media	(*iv*)	distinguishing one bacteria from another

	(*a*)	(*b*)	(*c*)	(*d*)
A.	(*iv*)	(*iii*)	(*ii*)	(*i*)
B.	(*ii*)	(*i*)	(*iv*)	(*iii*)
C.	(*ii*)	(*iii*)	(*i*)	(*iv*)
D.	(*i*)	(*iv*)	(*ii*)	(*iii*)

Control of Micro-organisms

59. Which of the following radiation methods is used in preserving food from spoilage by microorganisms?

A. Radio waves B. Microwaves
C. Non-ionizing D. Ionizing

Microbial Metabolism

60. What is the enzyme involved in the following reaction?
Triglyceride + 3H2O Glycerol + fatty acids
A. Glycerol phosphate dehydrogenase
B. Glycerol kinase
C. Lipase
D. Zymase

61. Folic acid synthesis in bacteria is competitively inhibited by sulfonamides. Which of the following essential components is replaced by sulfonamides during the process of folic acid synthesis?
A. Pteridine
B. Glutamic acid
C. Para-amino benzoic acid
D. Sulfamethaxazole

Microbial Diseases and Host Pathogen Interaction

62. Which part of the lipopolysaccharides has toxic properties that make some bacterial infections a potentially serious medical problem?
A. Polysaccharide side-chains
B. Lipid A portion
C. Repeat carbohydrate units
D. Core region of polysaccharides

63. Dick test is used to assess the susceptibility to ______.
A. diphtheria B. scarlet fever
C. typhoid fever D. tuberculosis

64. Match the class of antibodies to appropriate description or function

Antibodies	Description/function
(a) IgA	(i) Mucosal immunity
(b) IgG	(ii) Immunity to parasitic infections
(c) IgD	(iii) Most abundant antibody in the blood
(d) IgE	(iv) Found on the B cell membrane

	(a)	(b)	(c)	(d)
A.	(iv)	(iii)	(ii)	(i)
B.	(i)	(ii)	(iv)	(iii)
C.	(i)	(iii)	(iv)	(ii)
D.	(i)	(iv)	(ii)	(iii)

65. Match the diseases with the appropriate causative agents

Disease	Causative agents
(a) Rheumatic heart disease	(i) Candida ablicans
(b) Syphilis	(ii) Group A Streptococcus
(c) Genital warts	(iii) Human pappiloma virus
(d) Oral thrus	(iv) Treponema pallidum

	(a)	(b)	(c)	(d)
A.	(i)	(ii)	(iv)	(iii)
B.	(ii)	(iv)	(iii)	(i)
C.	(iii)	(iv)	(i)	(ii)
D.	(iv)	(ii)	(i)	(iii)

Chemotherapy/Antibiotics

66. Chloramphenicol and tetracycline are broad spectrum antibiotics which inhibit bacterial growth by targeting ______.
A. cell wall synthesis B. protein synthesis
C. RNA synthesis D. DNA synthesis

Microbial Genetics

67. The highly contagious viral disease measles is caused by a
A. double-stranded DNA virus
B. single-stranded DNA virus
C. single-stranded RNA virus
D. double-stranded RNA virus

68. Which of the following processes are involved in horizontal gene transfer (HGT)?
(a) Conjugation (b) Transduction
(c) Binary fission (d) Transformation
(e) Translesion synthesis (f) Transversion
A. (a), (c), (d) B. (a), (d), (f)
C. (b), (d), (e) D. (a), (b), (d)

CSIR-NET, NOVEMBER (MORNING), 2020

69. The total number of cells in 1 ml of a bacterial culture was estimated to be 2.7 × 10s. The culture was diluted 27-fold and 100 ul seeded per well of a 96-well plate. What is the final cell number per well?
A. 1×10^5 B. 2.7×10^4 C. 2.7×10^5 D. 1×10^4

CSIR-NET, NOVEMBER (AFTERNOON), 2020

70. For an exponentially growing culture of bacteria where JV0 is the initial population number and Nt is the population number at time *t*, the mean growth rate constant (K) is expressed as,

A. $\frac{\log N_t - \log N_0}{0.301t}$ B. $\frac{\log N_t - \log N_0}{0.301}$ C. $\frac{\log N_t - \log N_0}{t}$ D. $\frac{\log N_t}{0.301t}$

GATE (BIOTECHNOLOGY), 2020

71. A microorganism isolated from salt-rich (salt concentration ~ 2M) lake was found to be possess diglycerol tetraethers, with polyisoprenoid alcohol side chains as the major lipid component of its cell membrane. The isolated organism is

A. a planctomycete B. a cyanobacteria
C. a unicellular amoeba D. an archaea

72. A list of pathogens (Group I) and list of anti-microbial agents (Group II) used to treat their infection are given below. Match the pathogens with the corresponding anti-microbial agents.

Group I	Group II
(*a*) Influenza A virus	(*i*) Isoniazid
(*b*) Fungus	(*ii*) Amantadine
(*c*) Plasmodium	(*iii*) Fluconazole
(*d*) *Mycobacterium*	(*iv*) Artemisinin
	(*v*) Iodoquinol

	(*a*)	(*b*)	(*c*)	(*d*)
A.	(*iv*)	(*iii*)	(*ii*)	(*v*)
B.	(*v*)	(*ii*)	(*iv*)	(*i*)
C.	(*ii*)	(*iii*)	(*iv*)	(*i*)
D.	(*ii*)	(*iii*)	(*i*)	(*v*)

GATE (LIFE SCIENCE), 2020

Historical Perspective

73. The technique of microbial "pure culture" was pioneered by

A. Edward Jenner B. Louis Pasteur
C. Robert Hooke D. Robert Koch

Methods in Microbiology

74. Which one of the following does NOT provide three-dimensional images?

A. Atomic force microscopy
B. Confocal scanning laser microscopy
C. Differential interference contrast microscopy
D. Phase-contrast microscopy

75. Which one of the following will increase the resolution of a light microscope?

A. Decreasing the numerical aperture of the objective lens
B. Using an objective lens with a longer distance
C. Using a medium of higher refractive index
D. Increasing the wavelength of light

Microbial Taxonomy and Diversity

76. Choose the correct taxonomical hierarchy among the following:

A. Species, Genus, Family, Order, Class, Phylum, Domain
B. Species, Genus, Order, Class, Family, Phylum, Domain
C. Species, Genus, Order, Family, Class, Phylum, Domain
D. Species, Genus, Family, Class, Order, Phylum, Domain

Prokaryotic Cells: Structure and Function

77. Match the cellular organelle in Group I with its function in Group II

Group I	Group II
(*a*) Golgi apparatus	(*i*) Lipid degradation
(*b*) Nucleolus	(*ii*) Protein degradation
(*c*) Peroxisome	(*iii*) Protein sorting
(*d*) Proteasome	(*iv*) Ribosomal RNA synthesis

	(*a*)	(*b*)	(*c*)	(*d*)
A.	(*iii*)	(*ii*)	(*i*)	(*iv*)
B.	(*iii*)	(*iv*)	(*i*)	(*ii*)
C.	(*i*)	(*ii*)	(*iv*)	(*iii*)
D.	(*iii*)	(*i*)	(*iv*)	(*ii*)

Microbial Growth

78. An example of a differential and selective medium in which colonies of Gram-negative bacteria produce large amounts of acidic products and appear green with a metallic sheen is

A. Blood agar B. EMB agar
C. MacConkey agar D. Mannitol salt agar

79. Which one of the following statements about control of microbial growth is NOT correct?

A. Nonionizing radiation leads to thymine dimers formation in DNA
B. Spirochetes and mycoplasma can pass through membrane filters (0.22-0.45 μm)
C. Use of high concentration of salts and sugars to preserve food is a chemical method of microbial control
D. Thermoduric bacteria can survive pasteurization

Control of Micro-organisms

80. The antibacterial trimethoprim is an inhibitor of

A. dihydrofolate reductase

B. dihydropteroate synthetase
C. N5, N10-methenyl tetrahydrofolate synthetase
D. serine hydroxymethyl transferase

Microbial Metabolism

81. Match the process involved in nitrogen or sulfur cycle in Group I with the corresponding microbe in Group II

Group I	Group II
(*a*) Denitrification	(*i*) Azotobacter
(*b*) Nitrogen fixation by free-living microbe	(*ii*) Beggiatoa
(*c*) Oxidation of H_2S to sulfur	(*iii*) Pseudomonas
(*d*) Nitrogen fixation by a symbiotic microbe	(*iv*) Rhizobium

	(*a*)	(*b*)	(*c*)	(*d*)
A.	(*ii*)	(*iii*)	(*iv*)	(*i*)
B.	(*ii*)	(*i*)	(*iii*)	(*iv*)
C.	(*iii*)	(*iv*)	(*i*)	(*ii*)
D.	(*iii*)	(*i*)	(*ii*)	(*iv*)

82. Which one of the following is an example of substrate level phosphorylation.
A. Glucose to Glucose 6-phosphate
B. Fructose 6-phosphate to Fructose 1,6-bisphosphate
C. 1,3-bisphosphoglycerate to 3-phosphoglycereate
D. 2-phosphoglycerate to Phosphoenolpyruvate

Microbial Diseases and Host Pathogen Interaction

83. Digestion of an immunoglobulin G(IgG) molecule with pepsin will NOT
A. generate a bivalent antigen binding fragment
B. generate monovalent antigen binding fragments
C. destroy the complement binding site
D. cleave the heavy chain of IgG molecule

84. Determine the correctness or otherwise of the following Assertion (A) and the Reason (R).
Assertion (A): Diphtheria exotoxin is an example of A-B type toxin
Reason (R): The A component of the toxin is released from the host cell while the B component inhibits protein synthesis and kills the host cell.
A. Both (A) and (R) are true and (R) is the correct reason for (A)
B. Both (A) and (R) are true and (R) is not the correct reason for (A)
C. Both (A) and (R) are false
D. Both (A) and (R) are false

Chemotherapy/Antibiotics

85. Which one of the following diseases is treated by a neuraminidase inhibitor?
A. Chickenpox B. Polio
C. Influenza D. Japanese encephalitis

Microbial Genetics

86. Which one of the following conditions favours maximum expression of *lac* operon genes in *E.coli*?
A. Glucose-low, Lactose-low, cAMP-high
B. Glucose-high, Lactose-low, cAMP-high
C. Glucose-low, Lactose-high, cAMP-high
D. Glucose-high, Lactose-high, cAMP-low

CSIR-NET, JUNE (MORNING), 2021

Microbial Physiology

87. Which one of the following is valid with respect to, one step grwoth experiment developed by Ellis and Delbruck in 1939?
A. The reproduction of large phage population is synchronize.
B. A culture is directlt developed by inoculation of single bacterial colony from the agar plate to liquid midum.
C. Involves only a single step of overnight culture development followed by inoculation of fresh medium with 1% inoculum.
D. Only single carbon sorce such as giucose is used in the midum.

88. A culture was strsted by inoculating the medium with 100 cells having a generation time of 2 hours. Assuming the culture growes in ideal synchrony for at least 24 hours, what will be the number of the cells in the culture at 2 hour and 9 hours?
A. 2.0×10^2 cells, 1.6×10^3 cells, respectivrly
B. 2.0×102 cells, 2.4×103 cells, respectivrly
C. 2.0×104 cells, 3.2×103 cells, respectivrly
D. 2.0×104 cells, 1.6×108 cells, respectivrly

89. The table given below lists types of extremophiles and the environmental that they are adapted to.

List-I Types of extremophile	List-II Environment
(*a*) Psychrophile	(*i*) High salinity
(*b*) Hyperthermophile	(*ii*) High Pressure
(*c*) Alkaliphile	(*iii*) High alkaline environment
(*d*) Hyperpiezophile	(*iv*) Extreme high temperature
(*e*) Halophile	(*v*) Extreme cold temperatures

Which one of the following options represents the correct match of the columns?

	(*a*)	(*b*)	(*c*)	(*d*)	(*e*)
A.	(*i*)	(*ii*)	(*iii*)	(*iv*)	(*v*)
B.	(*v*)	(*ii*)	(*iii*)	(*iv*)	(*i*)
C.	(*v*)	(*iv*)	(*iii*)	(*ii*)	(*i*)
D.	(*v*)	(*ii*)	(*iv*)	(*iii*)	(*i*)

DBT-JRF, 2021

90. At which phase of the growth curve are bacteria more sensitive to ampicillin?
A. Declining phase
B. Lag phase
C. Log Phase
D. Stationary phase

GATE (BIOTECHNOLOGY), 2021

91. Which one of the following is CORRECT about microbial growth medium?
A. Luria-Bertani broth is a synthetic medium
B. Nutrient broth is a defined medium
C. Sabouraud dextrose agar is a differential medium
D. Trypticase soy agar is a complex medium

92. Coronavirus genome consists of
A. Double-Stranded DNA
B. Double-Stranded RNA
C. Negative-Sense Single-Stranded RNA
D. Positive-Sense Single-Stranded RNA

93. Which of the following antimicrobial agent(s) is/are growth factor analog(s)?
A. 5-Fluorouracil
B. Isoniazid
C. Sulfanilamide
D. Tetracycline

GATE (LIFE SCIENCE), 2021

Historical Perspective

94. Antonie van Leeuwenhoek observed several microscopic organisms under his hand-made microscope. He described them as
A. Bacteria
B. Fungi
C. Animalcules
D. Bacteriophages

Methods in Microbiology

95. *Nocardia spp.* are not amenable to the classical method of Gram staining due to the presence of
A. N-acetyltalosaminuronic acid in the cell wall
B. thick peptidoglycan
C. mycolic acid
D. keto-deoxy-octulosonic acid

96. Which of the following method(s) can be applied to identify a bacterial species?
A. Fluorescent in situ hybridization (FISH)
B. Polymerase chain reaction (PCR) followed by sequencing of the amplicon
C. Gram staining
D. Acid-fast staining

Microbial Growth

97. The order of abundance of quinones (ubiquinone [UQ], menaquinone [MQ] and demethylmenaquinone [DMQ]) in *E. coli* growing anaerobically onfumarate is
A. UQ > DMQ > MQ
B. MQ > DMQ > UQ
C. MQ = DMQ > UQ
D. MQ > UQ > DMQ

Microbial Metabolism

98. Which of the following is/are used as electron donor/s for CO2 reduction during photosynthesis in purple sulfur bacteria?
A. Hydrogen sulfide
B. Thiosulfates
C. Methane
D. Sulfates

99. Which of the following catalyze(s) substrate-level phosphorylation?
A. ATP synthase
B. Succinate thiokinase
C. Phosphofructokinase
D. Pyruvate kinase

100. What is the number of ATPs generated per molecule of NADH during oxidative phosphorylation in E. coli via (*i*) NDH-1 and cytochrome bo complex or (*ii*) the NDH-2 and cytochrome bd complex? (Assume H+/ATP = 3)
A. (*i*) 2.00 and (*ii*) 3.67
B. (*i*) 3.00 and (*ii*) 2.67
C. (*i*) 2.70 and (*ii*) 0.67
D. (*i*) 2.50 and (*ii*) 0.50

101. Which ONE of the following pathways oxidizes 1 mole of glucose to 2 moles of pyruvic acid along with one mole each of ATP, NADH and NADPH, in *Pseudomonas spp.*, but not in *Bacillus spp.*?
A. Gluconeogenesis
B. Embden-Meyerhoff Pathway (EMP)
C. Entner-Doudoroff (ED) Pathway
D. Pentose Phosphate Pathway (PPP)

102. Under anaerobic fermentative growth conditions, one mole of glucose yields 22 grams of *Streptococcus faecalis* or 8.6 grams of *Zymomonas mobilis*. The molar growth yield (YATP) for (*i*) S. faecalis and (*ii*) Z. mobilis will be

A. (*i*) 11 and (*ii*) 4.3
B. (*i*) 22 and (*ii*) 4.3
C. (*i*) 22 and (*ii*) 8.6
D. (*i*) 11 and (*ii*) 8.6

Microbial Diseases and Host Pathogen Interaction

103. Match the Immunoglobulin classes with their function

Immunoglobulin		Function
(*a*) IgE	(*i*)	protects the fetus
(*b*) IgG	(*ii*)	first antibody to be produced in response to infection
(*c*) IgM	(*iii*)	provides localized protection of mucosal surfaces
(*d*) IgA	(*iv*)	mediates allergic reaction
	(*v*)	directly lyses the target cells

	(*a*)	(*b*)	(*c*)	(*d*)
A.	(*iv*)	(*i*)	(*ii*)	(*iii*)
B.	(*i*)	(*v*)	(*ii*)	(*iii*)
C.	(*ii*)	(*i*)	(*v*)	(*iii*)
D.	(*iii*)	(*i*)	(*v*)	(*iv*)

104. The figure shows the profiles of quantitative real-time PCR (qRT-PCR) tests for SARS-CoV-2 conducted on the throat swab samples of three individuals (X, Y and Z). Tests were carried out under identical conditions. Dotted line represents the threshold fluorescent value. Identify the correct statement on the status of the COVID-19 tests of the individuals based on their qRT-PCR profiles.

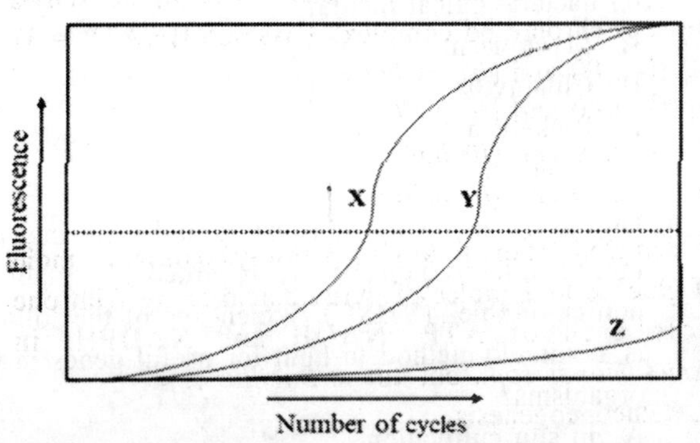

A. X and Y are negative; Z is positive
B. X and Y are positive; There is no apparent difference in their viral load
C. X and Y are positive; X has the highest viral load
D. X and Y are positive; Y has the highest viral load

Microbial Genetics

105. Which of the following event(s) would contribute to the induction of lacoperon in a wild-type strain of E. coli?

A. Accumulation of allolactose in the cell
B. Direct binding of cAMP to the promoter DNA
C. Binding of cAMP to a specific protein leading to its interaction with the promoter
D. Elimination of cAMP from the cell

106. The rate of appearance of recombinant *E. coli* strains containing different genes after a mating between Hfr and F^- strains is shown in the graph (left). The approximate location of different genes (*p, q, r, s, t, x,* and *y*) along the Hfr chromosome is also shown (right). Based on this information, identify the recombinants X, Y and Z.

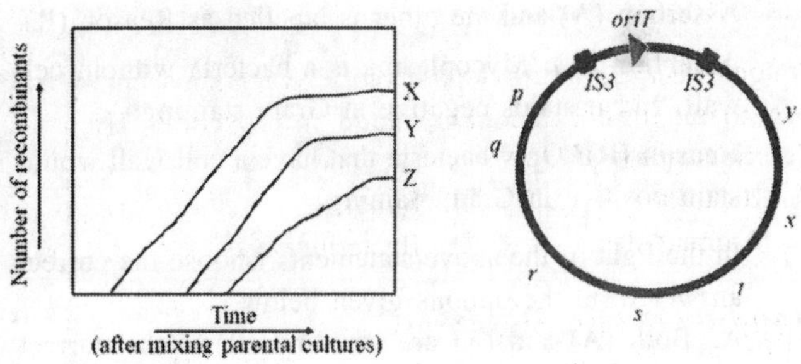

A. X is x^+, Y is r^+ and Z is p^+
B. X is p^+, Y is r^+ and Z is x^+
C. X is x^+, Y is p^+ and Z is r^+
D. X is p^+, Y is x^+ and Z is r^+

Microbial Ecology

107. Water balance in extreme halophiles such as *Halobacterium* is maintained by cell surface glycoproteins consisting of

A. glycine and lysine
B. lysine and histidine
C. glycine
D. aspartate and glutamate

108. Protists belonging to the genus *Trichonympha* thrive in the gut of termites. They help the termites use wood as a food source. This relationship is an example of

A. Parasitism
B. Competition
C. Commensalism
D. Mutualism

DBT-JRF, 2022

109. A growing bacterial culture doubles in 1 hr; the increase in cell mass in 30 minutes will be:
A. Zero B. 50%
C. Less than 50% D. More than 50%

110. The principle microorganism for yogurt is:
A. Streptococcus thermophilus
B. Lactobacillus acidophilus
C. Streptococcus lactis
D. Leuconostoc citrovorum

111. A bacterial signaling system that regulates population density-dependent gene expression using secreted chemical signals is known as :
A. G protein-coupled receptor signalling
B. Quorum sensing
C. Receptor-mediated signalling
D. Two component system

112. Given below are two statements: one is labelled as Assertion (A) and the other is labelled as Reason (R).

Assertion (A): Mycoplasma is a bacteria without cell wall, and it stains negative in Gram staining.

Reason (R): Only bacteria that have a cell wall would stain positive in Gram staining.

In the light of the above statements, choose the correct answer from the options given below:
A. Both (A) and (R) are true and (R) is the correct explanation of (A).
B. Both (A) and (R) are true but (R) is not the correct explanation of (A).
C. A is true but (R) is false
D. A is false but (R) is true

113. Given below are two statements:

Statement I: MacConkey agar is a media used for recovery of Gram positive bacteria from mixed bacterial culture.

Statement II: The bile salts and crystal violet in MacConkey agar inhibit growth of some bacteria.

In the light of the above statements, choose the correct answer from the options given below :
A. Both Statement I and II are true and Statement II is the correct explanation of Statement I
B. Both Statement I and II are true but Statement II is not the correct explanation of Statement I
C. Statement I is true but Statement II is false
D. Statement I is false but Statement II is true

114. Identify the correct statement about Fucoidans:
A. Fucoidans are iron containing proteins, found in blue green algae
B. Fucoidans are sulphur containing amino acids found in marine derived proteins
C. Fucoidans are iron containing lipopolysaccharides found in algal biomass
D. Fucoidans are sulfated polysaccharides, found in brown algae, that contain L-fucose among their constituent sugars

115. The term Dysbiosis is associated with:
A. Kinome B. Immunome
C. Genome D. Microbiome

116. A probiotic is a live microorganism that is claimed to confer a health benefit by altering the indigenous microflora of the intestinal tract. Which one of the following bacteria has been used widely in probiotics?
A. Klebseilla pneumonie
B. Pseudomonas putida
C. Lactobacillus lactis
D. Escherichia coli

117. Latency is a characteristic of which one of the following viruses?
A. Herpes virus
B. Polio virus
C. Rhino virus
D. Influenza virus

118. Which one of the following is the drug of choice for sexually transmitted diseases urethritis and cervicitis caused by Chlamydia trachomatis?
A. Ampicillin
B. Ciprofloxacin
C. Rifampin
D. Azithromycin

119. Which one of the following organisms is NOT an obligate intracellular parasite and, therefore, can grow on bacteriological media?
A. Mycoplasma
B. Chlamydia
C. Rickettsia
D. Adenovirus

120. Due to the difficulty of isolating and culturing, many marine microorganisms are regarded as "viable but non-culturable" (VBNC). Which one of the following is a suitable method to hunt for useful genes in these organisms?
A. in situ cultivation
B. growing them in a large bioreactor
C. barcode sequencing
D. metagenomic analysis

GATE (LIFE SCIENCE), 2022

Microbial Diseases and Host Pathogen Interaction

121. Which of the following plant diseases is/are caused by bacteria?

A. Angular leaf spot of cotton
B. Citrus canker
C. Apple scab
D. Leaf curl of papaya

122. Match Group I (plant disease), Group II (causal organism) and Group III (affected plant) in CORRECT combination.

Group-I	Group-II	Group-III
P. Karnal Bunt	I. Phytophthora infestans	(*a*) Rice
Q. Ergot	II. Blumeria graminis	(*b*) Potato
R. Late blight	III. Neovossia indica	(*c*) Rye
S. Powdery mildew	IV. Puccinia recondita	(*d*) Wheat
	V. Claviceps purpurea	(*e*) Barley
	VI. Alternaria solani	(*f*) Brinjal

A. P-II-(*a*), Q-V-(*b*), R-III-(*d*), S-I-(*e*)
B. P-III-(*d*), Q-V-(*c*), R-II-(*e*), S-IV-(*f*)
C. P-III-(*d*), Q-V-(*c*), R-I-(*b*), S-II-(*e*)
D. P-V-(*c*), Q-I-(*d*), R-VI-(*b*), S-II-(*e*)

123. Which of the following are present in Gram-negative bacteria?

A. Lipopolysaccharide
B. Teichoic acid
C. Periplasm
D. Endotoxin

124. Choose the correct match for structural components of bacteria to their function.

Structural component	Function
(*a*) Flagella	(*i*) prevent cell lysis
(*b*) Cell wall	(*ii*) chemotaxis
(*c*) Metachromatic granules	(*iii*) storage for ATP
(*d*) Magnetosomes	(*iv*) cell orientation

	(*a*)	(*b*)	(*c*)	(*d*)
A.	(*ii*)	(*iii*)	(*i*)	(*iv*)
B.	(*ii*)	(*i*)	(*iii*)	(*iv*)
C.	(*ii*)	(*i*)	(*iv*)	(*iii*)
D.	(*i*)	(*iv*)	(*iii*)	(*ii*)

125. Match the pathogen with the appropriate disease.

Pathogen	Disease
(*a*) Streptococcus pyogenes	(*i*) Scarlet fever
(*b*) Brucella species	(*ii*) Pott's disease
(*c*) Mycobacterium tuberculosis	(*iii*) Traveler's diarrhea
(*d*) Escherichia coli	(*iv*) Undulant fever

	(*a*)	(*b*)	(*c*)	(*d*)
A.	(*ii*)	(*iii*)	(*i*)	(*iv*)
B.	(*ii*)	(*i*)	(*iii*)	(*iv*)
C.	(*i*)	(*iv*)	(*ii*)	(*iii*)
D.	(*i*)	(*iv*)	(*iii*)	(*ii*)

126. Match the correct mode of cell division with respective bacteria.

(*a*) Streptomyces species
(*b*) Rhodopseudomonas acidophila
(*c*) Bacillus subtilis
(*d*) Nocardia species

Mode of Cell Division

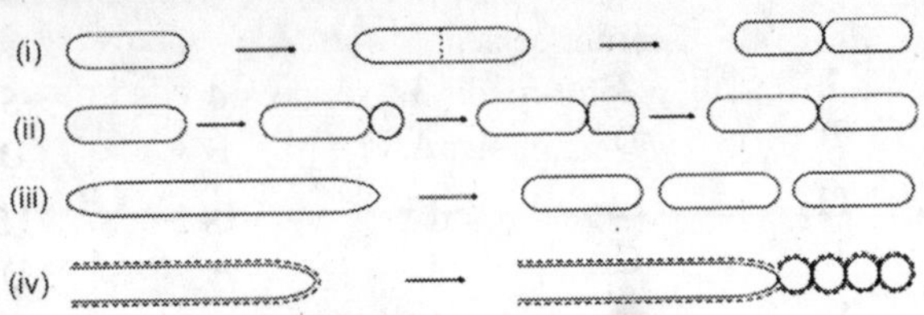

	(*a*)	(*b*)	(*c*)	(*d*)
A.	(*ii*)	(*iii*)	(*i*)	(*iv*)
B.	(*ii*)	(*i*)	(*iii*)	(*iv*)
C.	(*iv*)	(*ii*)	(*i*)	(*iii*)
D.	(*i*)	(*iv*)	(*iii*)	(*ii*)

Methods in Microbiology

127. Which of the following methods are used for the identification of microorganisms?

A. Nucleic acid hybridization
B. Southern blotting
C. 16s rRNA sequencing
D. Percentage G-C content

Control of Micro-organisms

128. The antimicrobial activity of vancomycin is due to the ___________.

A. inhibition of nucleic acid synthesis
B. damage to the cytoplasmic membrane
C. inhibition of cell wall synthesis
D. regulation of DNA supercoiling

129. Phenolics act as disinfectant by ___________.

A. rupturing plasma membrane followed by leakage of cellular contents
B. bond formation between adjacent pyrimidine bases
C. forming adduct with amino acid and unsaturated fatty acids
D. alkylation of proteins

Microbial Metabolism

130. The terminal acceptor of electron during anaerobic respiration in *Methanococcus* is ________.

A. Nitrate ion B. Sulfate ion
C. Carbon dioxide D. Oxygen

131. The site of photosynthesis in cyanobacteria is ________.

A. Chloroplast B. Chromatophores
C. Thylakoids D. Chlorosomes

132. Which of the following Gram-positive cocci are found in biofilm of dental plaque?

A. Gonococcus
B. Streptococcus mutans
C. Streptococcus sobrinus
D. Fusobacterium species

133. Which of the following statements are TRUE for archaea?

A. Cell wall in archaea contains muramic acid and D-amino acid
B. N-Formylmethionine is the first amino acid to initiate new polypeptide chain synthesis in archaea
C. Methionine is the first amino acid used during protein synthesis in archaea
D. Membrane of archaea contains phytanyl rather than fatty acids

ANSWERS

1	2	3	4	5	6	7	8	9	10
B	D	A	B	D	D	A	A	A	D
11	**12**	**13**	**14**	**15**	**16**	**17**	**18**	**19**	**20**
B	C	C	A	D	B	B	C	B	A
21	**22**	**23**	**24**	**25**	**26**	**27**	**28**	**29**	**30**
B	A	A	A	D	A	A	C	D	A
31	**32**	**33**	**34**	**35**	**36**	**37**	**38**	**39**	**40**
C	C	C	B	A	B	D	C	C	D
41	**42**	**43**	**44**	**45**	**46**	**47**	**48**	**49**	**50**
D	B	D	A	A	A	A	C	A	C
51	**52**	**53**	**54**	**55**	**56**	**57**	**58**	**59**	**60**
C,D	B	C	C	A	C	B	B	D	C
61	**62**	**63**	**64**	**65**	**66**	**67**	**68**	**69**	**70**
C	B	B	C	B	B	C	D	D	A
71	**72**	**73**	**74**	**75**	**76**	**77**	**78**	**79**	**80**
D	C	D	D	C	A	B	B	C	B
81	**82**	**83**	**84**	**85**	**86**	**87**	**88**	**89**	**90**
D	C	B	D	C	C	A	A	C	C
91	**92**	**93**	**94**	**95**	**96**	**97**	**98**	**99**	**100**
D	D	A,B,C	C	C	A,B	B	A,B	B,D	C
101	**102**	**103**	**104**	**105**	**106**	**107**	**108**	**109**	**110**
C	D	A	C	A,C	B	D	D	C	A
111	**112**	**113**	**114**	**115**	**116**	**117**	**118**	**119**	**120**
B	C	D	D	D	C	A	D	A	D
121	**122**	**123**	**124**	**125**	**126**	**127**	**128**	**129**	**130**
A,B	C	A,C,D	B	C	C	A,B,C	C	A	C
131	**132**	**133**							
C	B,C	C,D							

CHAPTER

6

FERMENTATION AND BIOPROCESS TECHNOLOGY

DBT-JRF, 2017

Fermentation and Bioprocess Engineering

1. For a cell growth process, the units for yield, productivity and titer are:

A. gl^{-1},$gl^{-1}h^{-1}$ and gl^{-1}

B. gg^{-1},$gl^{-1}h^{-1}$ and g $g^{-1}l^{-1}$ h^{-1}

C. gl^{-1},$gl^{-1}h^{-1}$ and gg^{-1}

D. gg^{-1}, $gl^{-1}h^{-1}$ and gl^{-1}

2. In a fermentor the impeller diameter is increased from 0.5 m to 1 m and the rpm is increased from 100 rpm to 400 rpm. Reynolds number will increase by?

A. 16 fold B. 8 fold

C. 2 fold D. 4 fold

3. Zymomonas *mobilis* is cultivated in a 60 l chemostat. The μ_{max} and K_s values are 0.2 h^{-1} and 0.5 gl^{-1} respectively. The flow rate (l h^{-1}) required for a steady state substrate concentration of 0.5 g l^{-1} in the reactor is:

A. 6 B. 9

C. 4 D. 12

4. Which one of the following statements is WRONG for conventional batch filtration of a mycelial fermentation broth?

A. Blockage of the membrane pores by cell debris

B. The specific cake resistance remains constant

C. compressible cake deposition on the membrane

D. medium resistance remain constant

5. Acetobacter *aceti* converts alcohol to acetic acid according to the stoichiometric relation

$$CH3COOH + H2O \rightarrow C_2H_5OH + O_2$$

In a vigorously agitated and aerated reactor containing 20 g/l ethanol, the organism produces 16 g/l acetic acid and 2 g/l was the residual ethanol concentration. What are the theoretical and observed yields of acetic acid expressed in g/g ethanol?

A. 60/46 and 16/18 B. 50/46 and 18/16

C. 46/60 and 18/16 B. 26/60 and 16/18

6. Match the native microbial sources in Group I with the products in Group II

Group I	Group II
(a) *Leuconostoc mesenteroides*	(i) Lysine
(b) *Lactococcus lactis*	(ii) Cheese
(c) *Brevibacterium brevis*	(iii) Dextran
(d) *Penicillium roqueforti*	(iv) Nisin

	(a)	(b)	(c)	(d)
A.	(ii)	(i)	(iv)	(iii)
B.	(i)	(ii)	(iii)	(iv)
C.	(iii)	(iv)	(i)	(ii)
D.	(iv)	(iii)	(ii)	(i)

7. Anchorage dependent CHO cells are grown by aeration using micro carrier beads. The maximum detrimental effect of shear occurs due to agitation if the size (Kolmogorov scale) of eddies is:

A. lesser than the size of the beads

B. equal to the size of beads
C. larger than the size of beads
D. independent of the size of beads

8. With progress in the growth of E. coli in a minimal medium (constant aeration and agitation), the dissolved oxygen (DO) initially declined and then started to increase. If the DO again starts to decrease on addition of glucose, then the most probable explanation is:
A. growth is limited by glucose
B. growth is limited by oxygen
C. decrease in solubility of oxygen occurred due to glucose addition
D. decrease in the number of cells takes place due to cell lysis

9. An organism obeys Andrews model for growth inhibition with K_s and K_i values of 0.01 g/l and 1.0 g/l respectively. If the substrate is present at an initial concentration of 1.0g/l, the specific growth rate of the culture upon entering log phase would be approximately:
A. 1/5th of μ_{max}
B. 1/4th of μ_{max}
C. 1/3rd of μ_{max}
D. ½ of μ_{max}

10. In a stirred tank reactor when the agitation rate is increased, the k_L and k_La values will:
A. increase and decrease respectively
B. decrease and increase respectively
C. both increase
D. both decrease

11. Which one of the following is correct regarding cell damage in an agitated and sparged mammalian cell bioreactor?
A. High shear stress arising during mixing of the cell culture is the major cause of cell damage.
B. Shear stress arising from the breakup of bubbles at the liquid surface is a major cause of cell damage.
C. Shear stress between bubbles in the foam at the liquid surface is a major cause of cell damage
D. Using agitator blades of a radial flow type with mirror finish reduces shear and hence cell damage

12. Two organisms A and B with the same μ_{max} and Yx/s are cultivated independently in batch culture. They have Ks values of 1 g.l-1 and 3 g.l-1 respectively. Given that the initial substrate concentration was 5 g/l, which of the following is TRUE after complete exhaustion of the substrate?
A. Organism A will have lower average specific growth rate than B.
B. Organism A will have higher average specific growth rate than B.
C. Both the organisms would have same average specific growth rate.
D. The final biomass achieved in B would be higher than in A.

13. Pseudomonas with the elemental composition of CH3O0.5N0.5 (MW = 30) is grown in a bioreactor to a final cell mass of 30 g/l. The minimum concentration (g/l) of ammonia (NH3) (MW = 17) (as the sole nitrogen source) required is:
A. 17
B. 8.5
C. 14
D. 15

14. To reduce the level of deactivation of media components for culturing Lactobacillus spp., a high temperature and short time (HTST) regime is used for sterilization, PRIMARILY because:
A. Deactivation energy of contaminants > Deactivation energy of medium components
B. Deactivation energy of contaminants < Deactivation energy of medium components
C. Deactivation energy of contaminants = Deactivation energy of medium components
D. The time required for sterilization is reduced

15. A continuous stirred tank bioreactor produces 48 kg lysine day-1. If the volumetric productivity is 2 g.l-1.h-1, the volume of the reactor is:
A. 1 m^3
B. 1.5 m^3
C. 0.1 m^3
D. 2 m^3

16. Aqueous Two-Phase System (ATPS) is used to isolate a protease from a fermentation broth. The partition coefficient (K) is 2.5. For 80 % recovery of protease in a single step, the volume ratios of upper and the lower phases should be:
A. 1.6:1
B. 3.2:1
C. 2.4:1
D. 1.2:1

17. To have an overall yield of greater than 50% in a three-step purification process for a food additive, the minimum average step yield (%) necessary would be around:
A. 95
B. 80
C. 50
D. 20

18. In a fed batch process for the production of an antibiotic, the dissolved oxygen (DO) level was found to be falling below 30%. If the DO level of 30% is to be maintained in the reactor (without altering the composition of oxygen-air mixture, aeration rate and agitation) then we need to:
A. increase the feed rate
B. decrease the feed rate
C. increase the concentration of feed
D. decrease the volume of the broth by partial withdrawal.

19. In a batch sterilization process if ∇overall , ∇heating & ∇cooling are 32.2, 9.8 & 10.1 respectively, THEN the holding time at 121°C of the process is (given that the specific death rate (k) of microorganisms at 121°C is 2.54 min-1):

A. 4.84 min B. 6.75 min
C. 2.96 min D. 9.25 min

20. During a batch culture experiment, the following data was obtained

Time(h)	Substrate(g/l)	cell(g/l)	product(g/l)
2	40	1	2
8	20	5	7

What will be the product yield(g) per gram of substrate
A. 10 B. 0.25
C. 0.5 D. 2.2

21. The reason for the choice of *E. coli* for the production of ethanol from lignocellulose is because it:
A. grows efficiently in various hexoses and pentoses
B. can be grown to high cell density
C. can tolerate very high concentration of ethanol
D. is a GRAS organism

GATE (BIOTECHNOLOGY), 2017

22. Growth of a microbe in a test tube is modeled as dx/dt = rX (1-x/k), where, X is the biomass, r is the growth rate, and K is the carrying capacity of the environment ($\gamma \neq 0$; $K \neq 0$). If the value of startimg biomass id k/100, which one of the following = g graphs qualitatively represents the growth dynamics?

A. 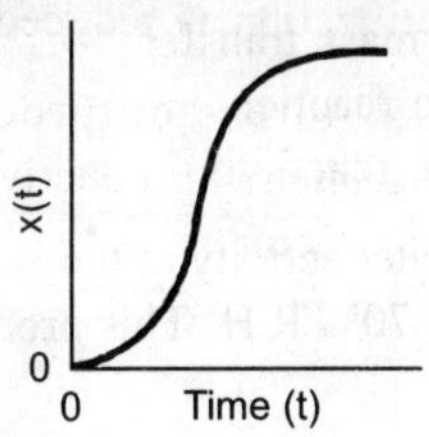

B. 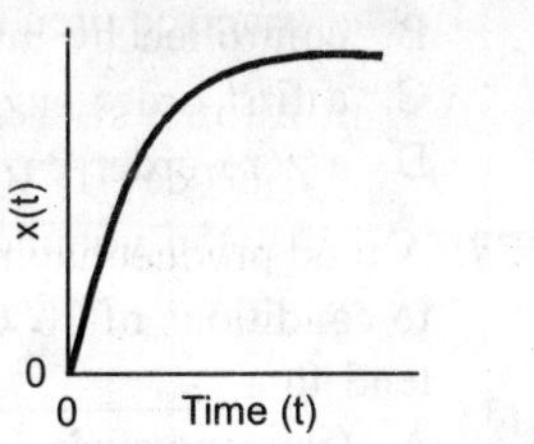

C. 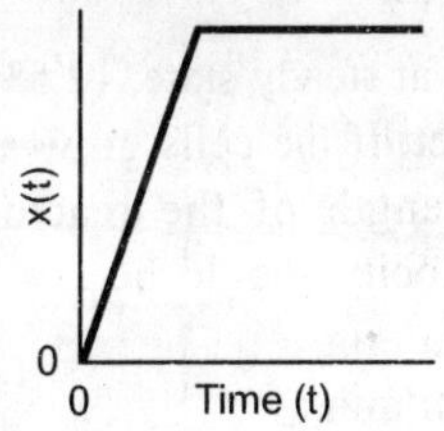

D. 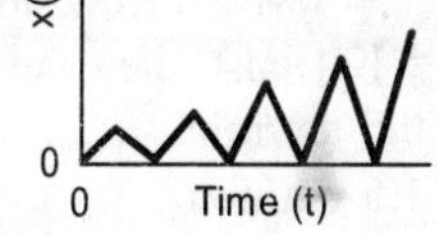

DBT-JRF, 2018

Fermentation and Bioprocess Engineering

23. In a fed-batch cultivation, a specific growth rate of 0.2/h needs to be maintained. At the start of fed-batch cultivation, 200 mL/h of media is fed to 1000 mL of working volume. Quasi-steady-state shall be obtained if:
A. flow rate/volume is kept constant at 0.2/h
B. flow rate/volume increases exponentially with time
C. flow rate increases linearly with time
D. flow rate is kept constant

24. The mean extracellular cellulase activity of 7 Bacillus strains isolated from soil was determined to be 12 IU/mL. A new hyper-producing Bacillus isolate was found to have an extracellular activity of 36 IU/mL. If equal volumes of the supernatants of all 8 strains are mixed together, the cellulase activity of the solution will be:
A. 13.5 B. 15
C. 16.5 D. 17.5

25. A microbial community has grown on starch anaerobically and it produced a mixture of metabolites with the following composition: glucose, disaccharides, acetate, butyric acid, butanol and carbon dioxide. This microbial community is comprised of:
A. E. coli, Clostridium, Methanosarcina
B. E. coli, Bacillus, Saccharomyces
C. Acetobacter, Bacillus, Methanosarcina
D. Methanosarcina, Methanococcus, E. coli

26. A recombinant protein is produced in Escherichia coli by two stage continuous cultivation at steady state. Upon induction of the culture in stage II, the specific growth rate of the culture decreased considerably. For an input flow rate in stage I of 100mL/h, a steady rate of product formation can only be obtained
A. when stage I is larger than stage II
B. when stage I is smaller than stage II
C. when both the stages are of the same size
D. for all possible ratios of the sizes of the two stages

27. Which one of the following is used for culturing Perna viridis?
A. Raft culture with hanging ropes.
B. Offshore cages and Pens.
C. Irrigated or flow through tanks.
D. Multitrophic recirculatory canal culture cage.

28. A mixture of food waste on inorganic analysis was found to contain Cl^-, $SO4^-$, $NO3^-$, $NH4^+$ ion. Successful anaerobic digestion by a mixed microbial community will result in biogas having the following gases
A. N_2, CO_2, O_2, H_2
B. CH_4, CO_2, N_2, H_2S
C. CH_4, CO_2, N_2, H_2S, H_2
D. H_2, CO_2, N_2, H_2S, Cl_2

29. A bioremediation mesocosm experiment has been carried out on a plot with 250 ppm aromatic molecules as contaminants. After 15 days the level of aromatic molecules came down to 100 ppm at a temperature of 48 ± 2°C. The electrical conductance of this site has increased over time because of the
A. Accumulation of NaCl
B. Evaporation of aromatics
C. Increase in organic acids
D. Production of CO_2

30. A microorganism following Monod kinetics is grown in a chemostat with working volume of 5 L and inlet substrate concentration of 1g/L. If the μ_{max} and Ks of the organism are 0.5 h^{-1} and 0.25g/L respectively, washout occurs when the flow rate (L.h^{-1}) exceeds
A. 0.5 B. 1
C. 2 D. 2.5

31. In a plug flow bioreactor running at steady state, 12.5% cells are recycled back to the inlet. If the cells grow at μ_{max} = 1 h^{-1} throughout the length of the reactor (L = 124 cm), then the flow velocity should be
A. 0.5 cm/min B. 1cm/min
C. 1.5 cm/min D. 2cm/min

32. Consider the scale up of a fermentation from a 10 L to 10,000 L while maintaining geometric similarity. Agitation speed, was maintained at 500 rpm in the 10 L fermenter. If scale up is done based on constant tip speed, then the agitation speed in the larger reactor should be .... rpm.
A. 5000 B. 500
C. 50 D. 5

33. A culture can grow independently in two carbon sources, glucose and hexadecane. Identify which one of the following statements is TRUE?
A. The biomass growth yield is more in hexadecane than in glucose
B. The biomass growth yield is lower in hexadecane than in glucose
C. The oxygen consumed is higher for glucose when compared to hexadecane
D. The CO_2 produced will be more in glucose than in hexadecane

34. In mammalian cell culture based monoclonal antibody production, perfusion culture is preferred over continuous stirred tank culture, because the process results in:
A. high volumetric productivity
B. high specific productivity per unit biomass
C. maintaining cells in active phase of production
D. retaining the product of interest in the reactor so that higher product concentration is obtained at the end of the process.

35. In a batch microbial fermentation process the dissolved oxygen concentration (DOC) remains almost zero during growth. Which of the following methods will you use for the estimation of oxygen transfer rate while the fermentation is in progress?
A. Static gassing out method
B. Dynamic gassing out method
C. Oxygen balance method
D. Sulfide oxidation method

36. Two columns of 1 m and 2 m height and of equal diameter are packed with beads containing immobilized enzyme. Substrate was fed to these two columns at flow rates of 10 mL/min (1 m column) and 20 mL /min (2 m column) and the corresponding conversion efficiencies obtained were 30% and 40% respectively. This demonstrates that the reaction is:
A. controlled by external mass transfer
B. controlled by internal mass transfer
C. a first order enzymatic reaction
D. a zero-order enzymatic reaction

37. A food product having a water activity of 0.6 is exposed to conditions of 30°C, and 70% R.H. This product will tend to ________
A. Gain moisture
B. Lose moisture
C. Neither gain, nor lose moisture
D. Initially lose, then gain moisture

38. 10 g of a plant material is extracted in 100 mL of a suitable buffer. On performing an assay for amylase activity, 100μ*l* extract produced 6μ moles glucose in 30 minutes of incubation. One unit of amylase activity is defined as the amount of enzyme required to produce 1μ mole of glucose per minute. The amylase activity (units/g) of the material is:
A. 60 B. 200
C. 20 D. 600

39. Water vapour transmission rate of a packaging film is 4g/m^2/day. A food product is packed in a rectangular pouch measuring 0.12m x 0.16m. The maximum amount of moisture lost in 90 days is:
A. 0.15 g B. 13.82 g
C. 0.04 g D. 18.34 g

40. An essential oil has antimicrobial activity with an MIC of 15 mg/Kg and can be used as a bio-preservative. This activity is lost at the rate of 1% of the remaining concentration, per day. The minimum amount of oil to be added (mg) to 1 Kg of food product that is stored for 30 days is:
A. 21.43 B. 17.65
C. 20.28 D. 19.50

41. The protein concentration and enzyme activity in 100 mL of a cell free extract is 5 mg/mL and 2 units/mL, respectively. After multiple steps of purification, the final 10 mL fraction contains 4 mg/mL of protein and 15 units/mL of enzyme activity. The fold purification and percentage recovery respectively is:

A. 10 and 75
B. 9.4 and 20
C. 9.4 and 75
D. 10 and 20

42. Solvent extraction using ethanol is used to purify a target metabolite from an aqueous broth. The partitioning coefficient is 3. The ratio of solvent to broth that is required to extract 80% of the metabolite in a single step is:

A. 0.8:1
B. 2.4:1
C. 2.67:1
D. 1.33:1

43. A litre of 18% glucose solution is converted anaerobically into methane and carbon dioxide. The theoretical maximum volume of gases at NTP assuming ideality, produced on complete conversion of the entire glucose would be:

A. 112 L
B. 67.2 L
C. 134.4 L
D. 22.4 L

44. A high cell density fermentation produces recombinant protein product which is 20% of the total cellular protein. The final cell density is 80 OD (1 OD = 0.4g of dry cell wt/L of which 50% is total cellular protein). Then the product concentration (g/L) is:

A. 2.4 g/l
B. 3.2 g/l
C. 4.8 g/l
D. 6 g/l

45. In a typical fermentation process the volumetric oxygen transfer coefficient (KLa) of the system was found to increase after the addition of antifoam agent. The most probable reason for this is:

A. the mass transfer coefficient of oxygen (KL) was increased
B. the interfacial area per unit volume (a) was decreased
C. The increase in the value of the oxygen transfer coefficient more than compensated the decrease in the interfacial area per unit volume so that the overall value of KLa was increased
D. The increase in the interfacial area per unit volume more than compensated the decrease in oxygen transfer coefficient so that the overall value of KLa was increased

46. In anaerobic lactic acid fermentation by bacteria, glucose is partially oxidized to pyruvate, followed by reduction to lactate

A. for maintaining proton motive force
B. for cofactor balancing
C. for cofactor balancing
D. to generate more ATP

GATE (BIOTECHNOLOGY), 2018

Upstream and Downstream Processing

47. Which one of the following bioreactor configurations is the basis for a trickling biological filter?

A. Stirred tank
B. Packed bed
C. Air lift
D. Fluidized bed

Instrumentation and Process Control

48. Shear stress versus shear rate behaviour of four different types of fluids (I, II, III and IV) are shown in the figure below.

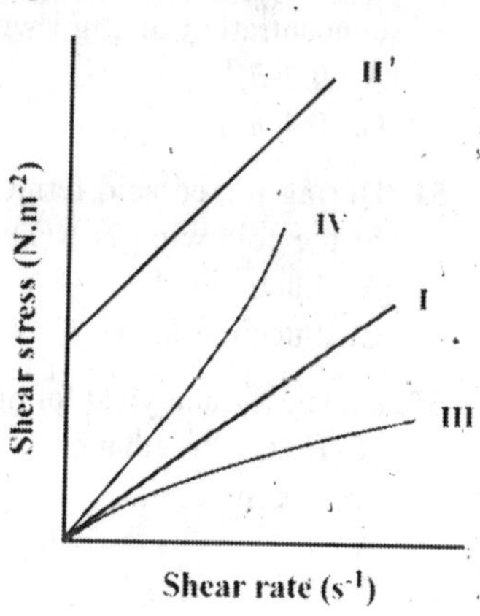

Which one of the following options is correct?

A. I-Newtonian, II-Bingham plastic, III-Dilatant, IV-Pseudoplastic
B. I-Pseudoplastic, II-Dilatant, III-Newtonian, IV-Bingham plastic
C. I-Newtonian, II-Pseudoplastic, III-Bingham plastic, IV-Dilatant
D. I-Newtonian, II-Bingham plastic, III-Pseudoplastic, IV-Dilatant

CSIR-NET, 15 DECEMBER, 2019

Downstream Processing

49. Which one of the following statements CANNOT be included while defining the fermentation process?

A. Alcohol is formed from sugar residues
B. Requires an electron transport system.
C. Utilizes an organic compound as the final electron acceptor
D. Produces lactic acid in oxygen deprived muscle

CSIR-NET, 27 DECEMBER, 2019

Industrially Important Microorganism

50. Which one of the following microorganisms is used for the fermentation of coffee beans?

A. *Candida krusei*
B. *Erwinia dissolvens*
C. *Lactobacillus delbrueckii*
D. *Lactobacillus plantarum*

51. Column A lists names of microorganisms and column B lists the pollutants that are degraded by the microbes.

Column A	Column B
(*a*) *Pseudomonas putida*	(*i*) Methyl tert-butyl ether
(*b*) *Methylicibium petroleiphilum*	(*ii*) Heavy metal detoxification
(*c*) *Alconivorax borkumensis*	(*iii*) Toluene, naphthalene
(*d*) *Deinococcus radiodurans*	(*iv*) Fuel hydrocarbon

Which one of the following options correctly matches the organism to the pollutant it most commonly degrades?

	(*a*)	(*b*)	(*c*)	(*d*)
A.	(*ii*)	(*iv*)	(*i*)	(*iii*)
B.	(*iii*)	(*iv*)	(*ii*)	(*i*)
C.	(*iii*)	(*i*)	(*iv*)	(*ii*)
D.	(*iv*)	(*iii*)	(*i*)	(*ii*)

Downstream Processing

52. Column A lists a set of nutrients and Column B lists some sources for these nutrients that are used in industrial fermentation.

Column A	Column B
(*a*) Nitrogen	(*i*) Soya meal
(*b*) Carbon	(*ii*) Yeast extract
(*c*) Micronutrient	(*iii*) Corn liquor
	(*iv*) Molasses
	(*v*) Tryptone

Choose the option that matches the nutrient with its most common source.

	(*a*)	(*b*)	(*c*)	(*d*)	(*e*)
A.	(*i*)	(*ii*)	(*iii*)	(*iv*)	(*v*)
B.	(*i*)	(*v*)	(*iii*)	(*iv*)	(*ii*)
C.	(*ii*)	(*v*)	(*iii*)	(*iv*)	(*i*)
D.	(*v*)	(*i*)	(*iii*)	(*ii*)	(*iv*)

DBT-JRF, 2019

Fermentation and Bioprocess Engineering

53. An organism exhibits Monod growth with the following growth parameters, $\mu_m = 0.6\ h^{-1}$ & $K_s = 4$ g/l. The specific growth rate, μ, of the organism at a substrate concentration of 2 g/l would be:

A. $0.2\ h^{-1}$ B. $0.3\ h^{-1}$
C. $0.4\ h^{-1}$ D. $1.2\ h^{-1}$

54. During mixed acid fermentation by *E. coli*, which one of the following is NOT produced?

A. Lactic acid B. Ethanol
C. Succinic acid D. Citric acid

55. The maximum yield for microbial conversion of Glucose ($C_6H_{12}O_6$) to ethanol (C_2H_5OH) on a mol/mol basis is approximately:

A. 1 B. 2
C. 3 D. 0.5

56. Antibiotic bleomycin is secreted by:

A. *Bacillus sp.* B. *Aspergillus sp.*
C. *Streptomyces sp.* D. *Acremonium sp.*

57. An anaerobic flask containing 50 ml of media with glucose as the sole carbon source was inoculated with a consortium consisting of *Methanosarcina* and *Bacillus.* After two weeks of incubation, there will be:

A. no growth
B. growth with methane production
C. growth with acetate and methane production
D. growth with CO_2 production

58. Combination of high temperature during processing, low temperature during storage, and increasing the acidity for prevention of food contamination is known as:

A. Stumbling technology
B. Mixed preservation approach
C. High pressure food preservation
D. Hurdle technology

59. The production of ethanol rather than biomass by yeast cells at high concentration of glucose is known as:

A. Warburg effect B. Simpson's effect
C. Crabtree effect D. Olivosky's effect

60. In a crossflow filtration process, if the volumetric flow rate of the feed is 10 times that of the retentate, the concentration factor is:

A. 9 B. 9/10
C. 1/10 D. 10

61. In a bioprocess, assume that only cell mass is formed. Due to a variation in process conditions, if the microbial cell yield has halved, what would be the rate of substrate consumption to maintain the same rate of cell mass production?

A. It would be doubled.
B. It would be halved
C. It would be unchanged
D. It would increase four folds

62. In a chemostat, which one of the following would increase the exit cell concentration?
A. Increase in inlet substrate concentration
B. Increase in dilution rate
C. Increase in inoculum size
D. Increase in impeller size

63. The ratio of gassed to ungassed powder (Pg/P) in a bioreactor will be in the range of:
A. 0.4 – 0.9 B. 1.0 – 2.0
C. 1.2 – 2.4 D. 4.0 – 8.0

64. Scale up of a fermenter is done based on constant impeller tip speed. If the diameter of the impeller is increased by 10 fold, the agitator speed will:
A. decrease by 10 fold
B. decrease by 100 fold
C. increase by 10 fold
D. increase by 100 fold

65. For an enzyme catalyzed reaction in a batch bioreactor, which one of the following is true under quasi-steady state conditions:
A. Enzyme-substrate complex concentration remains nearly constant
B. Substrate concentration remains nearly constant
C. Product concentration remains nearly constant
D. Both substrate and product concentration remain nearly constant

66. In a batch reactor, which one of the following is true regarding specific growth rate?
A. It remains constant with time.
B. It continuously increases with time.
C. It continuously decreases with time.
D. It reaches a maximum in the exponential phase.

67. For a Rushton turbine impeller (Reynold's number greater than 10,000) when RPM is doubled, the power absorption increases by:
A. 2 fold B. 4 fold
C. 8 fold D. 32 fold

68. Reynold's number is ratio of:
A. viscous force to inertial force.
B. inertial force to viscous force.
C. gravitation force to inertial force.
D. inertial force to gravitational force.

69. In developing a structured model for microbial cell growth, we:
A. separate the population by age.
B. compartmentalize the cell into different components.
C. separate the cells by age and also compartmentalize it.
D. treat cells to be composed of a single component only

70. The least used heat transfer-design in bioreactor is:
A. Jacket
B. Limpet coil
C. Internal cooling coil
D. External heat exchanger

71. The major drawback in using wild type *S. cerevisiae* for producing ethanol from biomass hydrolysate is:
A. Low biomass yield of hexose sugars
B. Presence of solid residues
C. Low concentration of sugars
D. Non utilization of Pentose sugars

GATE (BIOTECHNOLOGY), 2019

Engineering Principles Applied to Biological Systems

72. Which one of the following need NOT be conserved in a biochemical reaction?
A. Total mass
B. Total moles
C. Number of atoms of each element
D. Total energy

Classical thermodynamics and Bioenergetics

73. Which one of the following is the unit of heat transfer coefficient?
A. $W\ m^2\ K^{-1}$ B. $W\ m^{-2}\ K$
C. $W\ m^{-2}\ K^{-1}$ D. $W\ m^2\ K$

Bioreaction Engineering

74. Which one of the following can NOT be a limiting substrate if Monod's growth kinetics is applicable?
A. Extracellular carbon source
B. Extracellular nitrogen source
C. Dissolved oxygen
D. Intracellular carbon source

75. Which one of the following is catabolized during endogenous metabolism in a batch bacterial cultivation?
A. internal reserves
B. extracellular substrates
C. extracellular products
D. toxic substrates

Upstream and Downstream Processing

76. Which of the following factors can influence the lag phase of a microbial culture in a batch fermenter?
(*a*) Inoculum size
(*b*) Inoculum age
(*c*) Medium composition
A. (*a*) and (*b*) only B. (*b*) and (*c*) only
C. (*a*) and (*c*) only D. (*a*), (*b*) and (*c*)

77. Which of the following statements is ALWAYS CORRECT about an ideal chemostat?
(*a*) Substrate concentration inside the chemostat is equal to that in the exit stream
(*b*) Optimal dilution rate is lower than critical dilution rate
(*c*) Biomass concentration increases with increase in dilution rate
(*d*) Cell recirculation facilitates operation beyond critical dilution rate
A. (*a*) and (*b*) only
B. (*a*), (*c*) and (*d*) only
C. (*a*) and (*d*) only
D. (*a*), (*b*) and (*d*) only

Instrumentation and Process Control

78. Match the instruments in Group I with their corresponding measurements in Group II.

Group I	Group II
(*a*) Manometer	(*i*) Agitator speed
(*b*) Rotameter	(*ii*) Pressure difference
(*c*) Tachometer	(*iii*) Cell number
(*d*) Haemocytometer	(*iv*) Air flow rate

	(*a*)	(*b*)	(*c*)	(*d*)
A.	(*iv*)	(*i*)	(*ii*)	(*iii*)
B.	(*iii*)	(*iv*)	(*i*)	(*ii*)
C.	(*ii*)	(*iv*)	(*i*)	(*iii*)
D.	(*ii*)	(*i*)	(*iv*)	(*iii*)

DBT-JRF, 2020

Fermentation and Bioprocess Engineering

79. What will be the generation time of a culture with a specific growth rate constant of 0.01?
A. 1.155 h B. 11.55 h
C. 0.693 min D. 6.93 min

80. In an exponentially growing batch culture of Saccharomyces cerevisiae, the cell density is 30, the specific growth rate is and substate uptake rate (μ) is. The cell yield coefficient will be
A. 0.50 B. 0.32
C. 0.45 D. 0.67

81. A stirred tank bioreactor of is agitated using a Rushton turbine with diameter 0.5 m and stirrer speed of If the fermentation broth has viscosity and density of and respectively, the mixing time (in seconds) for the bioreactor will be
A. 33.3 B. 15.0
C. 66.7 D. 25.5

82. A fermentation medium is being cooled from 70°C to 32°C in a double pipe heat exchanger. Fluid flowing counter currently with this stream in heated from 20°C to 46°C. The log mean temperature difference (in°C) for the two streams is
A. 8.5 B. 17.3
C. 12.6 D. 4.8

83. Consider a bacterium that grows with doubling time of 20 min in the exponential phase of its growth cycle and acquire 10 random mutations in its genome in every generation. How many mutations will it acquire after 48 hr of growth in exponential phase?
A. 1440 B. 1404
C. 1000 D. 1044

84. A bacterial population, growing in batch culture, increases from 1000 cells to 10,00,000 cells in 5 hours. What is the generation time of the bacteria?
A. 9 min B. 30 min
C. 22 min D. 45 min

85. In large scale fermentation processes, corn steep liquor is mainly used as a
A. nitrogen source
B. carbon source
C. vitamin and micronutrient source
D. carbon and vitamin source

86. A dilution of a microbial culture was prepared by adding 1 ml of the culture to 9 ml of sterile blank. Further, 200 μL from the diluted culture was spread on an agar plate; and 150 colonies were observed after the incubation period. Calculate the CFU/mL of the original sample
A. 7500 B. 75000
C. 750 D. 75

87. At what condition does the specific growth rate of the microorganisms decline in a constant volume fed-batch culture
A. cell biomass increasing
B. cell biomass is equal to zero
C. cell biomass remains constant
D. cell biomass decreasing

88. In the design of a fermenter, which one of the following is NOT the intended use of baffles?
A. improves aeration efficiency
B. to reduce shear sensitivity of microorganism
C. prevents eddy/vortex formation
D. increases the effect of agitation.

89. During growth, the diameter of a Staphylococcus bacterial cell increases by 5%. The specific surface area (defined as surface area per unit volume)

A. increase approximately by 5%
B. decreases approximately by 5%
C. decreases approximately by 4%
D. increases approximately by 4%

90. The temperature of media post sterilization drops from 100°C to 60°C in 40 min by simply keeping it on the lab bench and allowing slow atmospheric cooling to take place at an ambient temperature of 20°C. In the next 40 min, the approximate temperature (°C) of the media would be around

A. 40°C B. 20°C
C. 50°C D. 30°C

91. The equation for aerobic production of acetic acid from ethanol is: $CH_2OH+O_2 \rightarrow CH_3CO_2H+H_2O$. (ethanol) (acetic acid) Acetobacter aceti bacteria are added to vigorously-aerated medium containing 10 g.14 ethanol. After some time, the ethanol concentration is 2 g.-2 and 7.5 g.11 of acetic acid is produced. What is the observed yield (Yoing-) and theoretical yield (Yting-8") of acetic acid from ethanol?

A. $Y_0 = 0.94, Y_T = 1.5$ B. $Y_0 = 0.69, Y_T = 1.0$
C. $Y_0 = 0.79, Y_T = 1.1$ D. $Y_0 = 0.94, Y_T = 1.3$

92. Which of the combination of gases is finally produced during anaerobic digestion?

A. $CH_4 + CO_2$ B. $N_2 + NH_3$
C. $CO + N_2$ D. $CO_2 + CO$

93. An energy generations process in which organic compounds act as both electron donors and terminal electron acceptor in a microbe is called

A. photosynthesis
B. biomass formation process
C. aerobic process
D. fermentation process

94. Aqueous two phase partitioning (ATPS) is used for the recovery of an enzyme from the cell free culture filtrate. On addition of PEG-2000 and dextran, the mixture separates into two phases with a partition coefficient for the enzyme as 4.2. The maximum possible enzyme recovery, when the volume ratio of the upper to lower phases in 5.0, will be

A. 95% B. 68%
C. 76% D. 85%

95. Match the polysaccharides (L.H.S.) with the microbial cultures (R.H.S.) associated with their industrial production

Polysaccharide	**Microbial culture**
(*a*) Cellulose	(*i*) Pseudomonas aeroginosa
(*b*) alginate	(*ii*) Alcaligenes faecalis
(*c*) curdalan	(*iii*) Gluconacetobacter hansenii
(*d*) Poly-hydroxy butyrate	(*iv*) Ralstonia eutropha

	(*a*)	(*b*)	(*c*)	(*d*)
A.	(*i*)	(*iii*)	(*ii*)	(*iv*)
B.	(*iii*)	(*i*)	(*ii*)	(*iv*)
C.	(*i*)	(*ii*)	(*iii*)	(*iv*)
D.	(*ii*)	(*i*)	(*iv*)	(*iii*)

96. Which of the following microorganism is used for commercial production of dextran?

A. Bacillus polymyxa
B. Streptomyces olivaceus
C. Leuconostoc mesenteroides
D. Bacillus thuringiensis

97. Which of the following is not a suitable material for a depth filter used in air sterilization?

A. glass fiber (pore size = 2 – 8 μm)
B. muslin cloth (pore size = 40 – 50 μm)
C. glass wool (pore size < 10 μm)
D. norite (pore size = 0.1 – 4 μm)

GATE (BIOTECHNOLOGY), 2020

Upstream and Downstream Processing

98. W, X and Y are the intermediates in a biochemical pathway as shown below:

$$S \ldots\ldots \rightarrow W \rightarrow X \rightarrow Y \rightarrow Z$$

Mutants auxotrophic for Z are found in four different complementation groups, namely Z1, Z2, Z3 and 4. The growth of these mutants on media

Supplemented with W, X, Y or Z is shown below (Yes: growth observed; No: growth not observed)

Mutants	Media supplemented with			
	W	X	Y	Z
Z1	No	No	Yes	Yes
Z2	No	Yes	Yes	Yes
Z3	No	No	No	Yes
Z4	Yes	Yes	Yes	Yes

What is the order of the four complementation groups in terms of the step they block?

A. $S\cdots \xrightarrow{Z1} W \xrightarrow{Z2} X \xrightarrow{Z3} Y \xrightarrow{Z4} Z$

B. $S\cdots \xrightarrow{Z4} W \xrightarrow{Z2} X \xrightarrow{Z1} Y \xrightarrow{Z3} Z$

C. $S\cdots \xrightarrow{Z3} W \xrightarrow{Z1} X \xrightarrow{Z2} Y \xrightarrow{Z4} Z$

D. $S\cdots \xrightarrow{Z4} W \xrightarrow{Z1} X \xrightarrow{Z2} Y \xrightarrow{Z3} Z$

CSIR-NET, JUNE(MORNING), 2021

Downstream Processing

99. A schematic of a metabolic pathway is shown below.

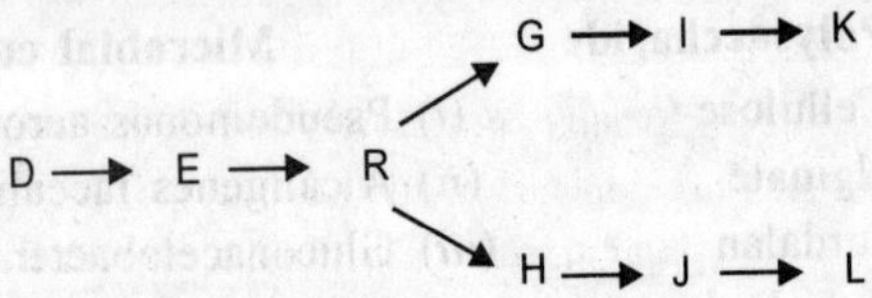

Under which of the following conditions would stoichiometric amounts of ends products K and L be obtained if a concerted feedback inhibition mechanism were in operation?

A. K inhibits F → G and L inhibits F → H; D → E is inhibited at equal amont of K & L

B. D → E is inhibited at equal amount of K & L; K inhibits F → G and L inhibits F → H

C. D → E is inhibited at equal amount of G & H; K inhibits F → H and L inhibits F → G

D. K inhibits F → H and L inhibits F → G

DBT-JRF, 2021

Fermentation and Bioprocess Engineering

100. If 180 gm of glucose is consumed during cell growth and 132 gm of carbon dioxide is produced, then the fractional carbon flux towards biomass (assuming no product is formed and glucose is the sole carbon source) is:

A. 0.5 B. 132/180

C. 2 /15 D. 48/180

101. S. cerevisiae produces ethanol at a yield of 0.5 g/g glucose. The strain ferments 20g/l glucose in 24 hours. Calculate productivity of ethanol in this fermentation.

A. 0.416 g/l/h B. 0.833 g/l/h

C. 108 g/l D. 20 g/l

102. *E. coli* was grown aerobically in batch fermentation. The initial concentration of cells was 1x 10^3/ml and it reached 1x10^6/ml in 10 hours. Calculate specific growth rate.

A. 0.3 h^{-1} B. 0.69 h^{-1}

C. 103 h^{-1} D. 3 h^{-1}

103. In a continuous culture of Saccharomyces cerevisiae, the cell density is 30 gL^{-1} (DCW), the dilution rate (D) is 0.4 h^{-1} and substrate uptake rate (q) is 18 gL^{-1} h^{-1}. The cell yield coefficient Yx/s will be:

A. 0.32 B. 0.67

C. 0.45 D. 0.50

104. Aqueous two-phase partitioning (ATPS) is used for the recovery of an enzyme from the cell free culture filtrate on addition of PEG2000 and dextran. The mixture separates into two phases with a partition coefficient for the enzyme = 4.2. The maximum possible enzyme recovery, when the volume ratio of the upper to lower phases is 5.0 will be:

A. 68% B. 76%

C. 85% D. 95%

105. A fermentation medium is being cooled from 70°C to 32°C in a double pipe heat exchanger. Cooling fluid flowing counter currently with this stream is heated from 20°C to 46°C. The log mean temperature difference (in Celsius) for the two streams is:

A. 12.6 B. 17.3

C. 4.8 D. 8.5

106. Which one of the following methods of controlling microbial contamination is the least preferred in food processing?

A. Autoclaving B. Dry heat

C. Pasteurization D. Preservatives

107. Which one of the following is NOT a fermented food?

A. Milk cream B. Cheese

C. Salami D. Sauerkraut

108. You have an assay method that can estimate compound A upto level 10 mg/ml. If you need to modify it so that you can estimate 0.1 mg/ml, you need to improve upon the:

A. Accuracy B. Reactivity

C. Sensitivity D. Specificity

109. In a two stage CSTR in series, the first reactor runs at a dilution rate D1 < μ_{max} and the inlet substrate concentration (S0) is two times greater than Ks, then:

A. Washout will never take place
B. Washout will take place when D2 > μ_{max} in the second reactor
C. Washout will take place when D2 < μ_{max} in the second reactor
D. Washout will take place when D2 = μ_{max} in the second reactor

110. To have an extended late log/ stationary phase so that secondary metabolites may be produced, you will prefer to use:
A. Batch reactor
B. Fed batch reactor
C. Fluidized bed reactor
D. Plug flow reactor

111. Given the pseudoplastic rheology of fungal fermentation broth, we can expect that:
A. The viscosity of the fungal broth to be uniformly high in the culture
B. The viscosity of the fungal broth to be uniformly low in the culture
C. The viscosity to be higher near the impeller but low near the walls of the bioreactor
D. The viscosity to be low near the impeller but high near the walls of the reactor

112. Given below are two statements: one is labelled as Assertion (A) and the other is labeled as Reason (R)

Assertion (A): In a plate & frame filter operated under constant pressure, the filtrate flow rate declines with time

Reason (R): In a plate & frame filter operated under constant pressure, the filtrate cake builds up on the filter membrane

In light of the above statements, choose the most appropriate answer from the options given below:
A. (A) & (R) are both true and (A) is due to (R)
B. (A) & R are both true but (A) is NOT due to (R)
C. (A) is false but (R) is true
D. (A) is true but (R) is false

113. Scaling up a reactor while keeping the power consumption per unit volume constant will lead to:
A. Decrease in RPM of the impeller of the larger reactor
B. Holding the RPM of the impeller at the same value
C. Increase in RPM of the impeller of the larger reactor
D. Increasing or decreasing the RPM of the impeller depending on the type of impeller

114. In a fed batch culture the feed rate of concentrated substrate is increased with time while the RPM of the impeller is kept constant. You will most likely observe one of the following:
A. A decline in the D.O. values of the culture
B. An increase in the D.O. values of the culture
C. An oscillation in the D.O. values of the culture
D. No change in the D.O. values of the culture

115. In an anaerobic fermentation producing ethanol, the ethanol yield (Yp/s) Options:
A. Decreases with increasing biomass yield (Yx/s)
B. Increases with increasing biomass yield (Yx/s)
C. Initially increases & then decreases with increasing biomass yield (Yx/s)
D. Is independent of biomass yield (Yx/s)

116. Doubling the substrate concentration in the inlet of a CSTR (with cells following Monod growth kinetics) will, after reaching the new steady state, lead to:
A. Higher biomass concentration but unchanged substrate concentration in the outlet
B. Higher substrate & biomass concentration in the outlet
C. Higher substrate concentration but unchanged biomass concentration in the outlet
D. Unchanged substrate & biomass concentration in the outlet

117. Match the components of List-I with List-II

List-I (Techniques)	List-II (Used in)
(*a*) Mosaic spheroids	(*i*) 3D aggregate of cells
(*b*) Micrcarrier matrix	(*ii*) Microgravity cell growth environment
(*c*) Organoids	(*iii*) Bystander effect
(*d*) Rotatory cell culture system	(*iv*) 3D growth environment

Choose the correct answer from the options given below:

	(*a*)	(*b*)	(*c*)	(*d*)
A.	(*iii*)	(*iv*)	(*i*)	(*ii*)
B.	(*iv*)	(*iii*)	(*ii*)	(*i*)
C.	(*ii*)	(*ii*)	(*iii*)	(*iv*)
D.	(*i*)	(*ii*)	(*iv*)	(*iii*)

118. In a fed batch process with a nongrowth product formation kinetics given by $q_p = \beta$(a constant), in order to maximize product concentration and enhance metabolic flux towards product formation, you will:
A. Maintain a slowly declining μ
B. Maintain a slowly increasing μ
C. Maintain highest possible μ
D. Maintain lowest possible μ

119. Given that Power number is constant; then increasing the RPM of the impeller 3fold will increase the power consumption due to agitation by:
A. 27 fold
B. 3 fold
C. 81 fold
D. 9 fold

120. If the maintenance coefficient (m) is significantly high, then with reduction in specific growth rate:
A. Biomass yield decreases
B. Biomass yield increases
C. Biomass yield remains constant
D. Sum of biomass & product yield remain constant

121. Increasing the agitation in a reactor increases oxygen transfer primarily because:

A. Gas hold up decreases

B. Good mixing takes place

C. Microbial cells move more energetically coming closer to gas bubbles

D. Specific surface area of bubbles increases

GATE (BIOTECHNOLOGY), 2021

Bioreaction Engineering

122. Which one of the following represents non-growth associated product formation kinetics in a bioprocess system? X and P denote viable cell and product concentrations, respectively.

A.

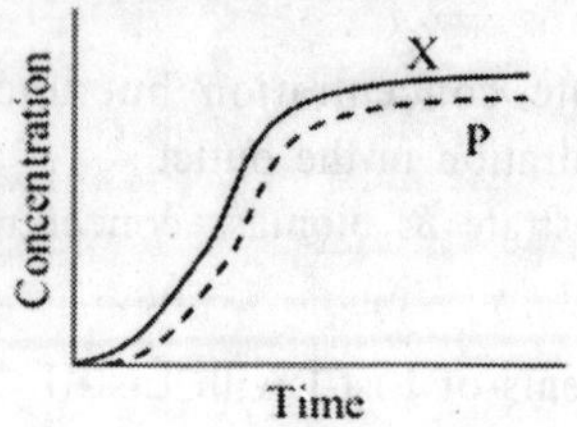

B.

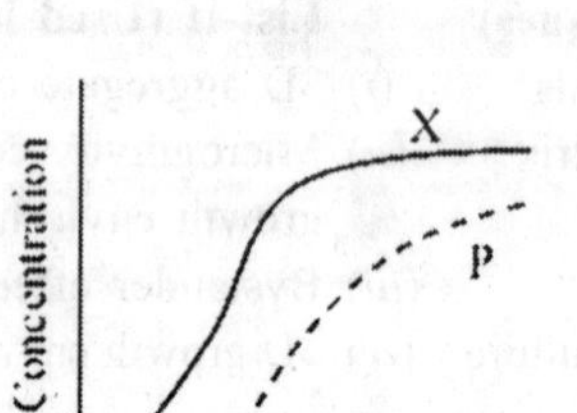

C.

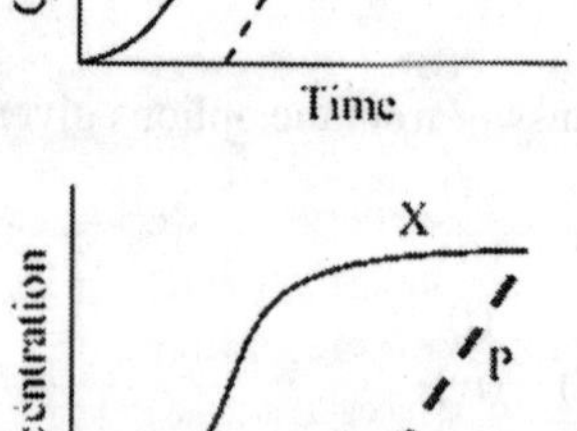

D.

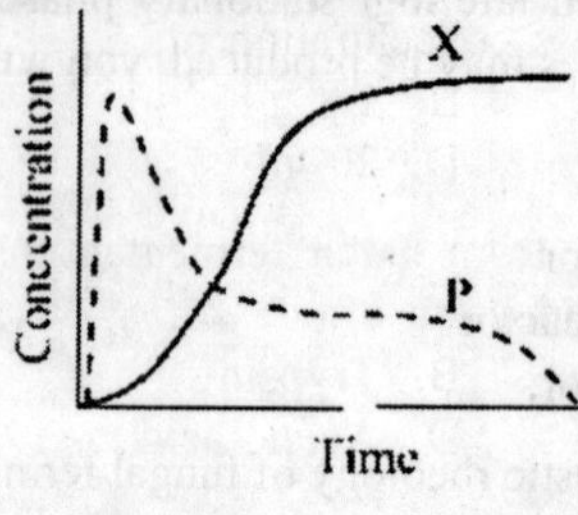

Instrumentation and Process Control

123. The process and instrumentation diagram for a feedback control strategy to maintain the level (h) of a liquid by regulating a valve (V) in a tank is shown below. F_1 is inlet liquid flow rate, F_2 is outlet liquid flow rate, LT is the liquid level transmitter, LC is the liquid level controller, h_{sp} is the setpoint value of the liquid level, h_m is the measured value of the liquid level and P_V is the valve pressure

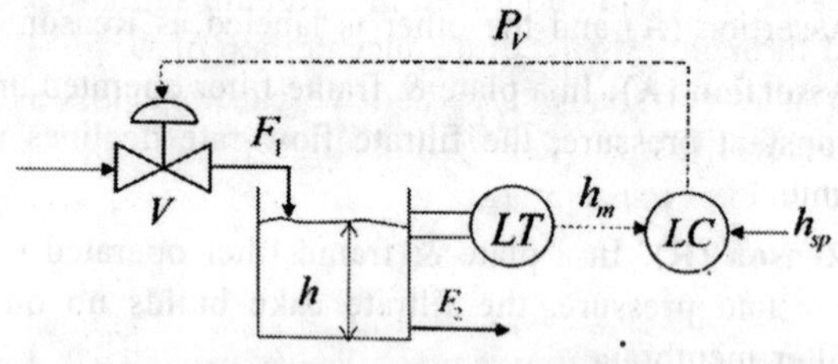

The manipulating variable(s) is/are

A. F_1 only

B. F_2 only

C. h_m and P_V only

D. h_{sp} and P_V only

CSIR-NET, SEPTEMBER(MORNING), 2022

124. The figure below depicts a hypothetical scheme for synthesizing a target product in plants. Ⓐ, Ⓑ, and Ⓒ of a target product Ⓓ, whereas Ⓔ is a by-product. The key enzymes of the pathway are indicated as E1–levels of target product Ⓓ, following strategies were tested:

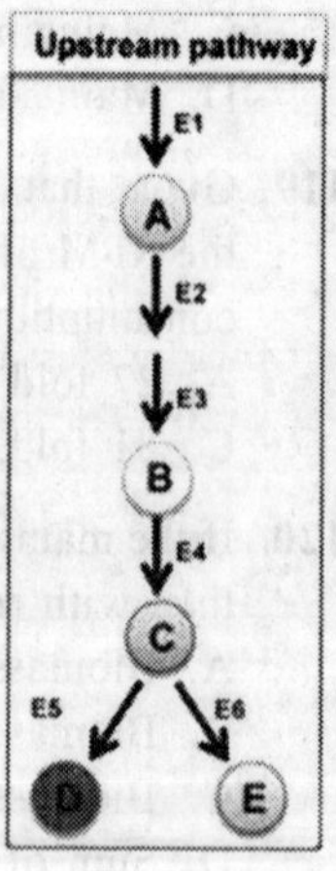

(*a*) Enhancing the activity of the enzyme E5 by over-expression and/or protein engineering.

(*b*) Enhancing the activity of the enzyme E4 by over-expression and/or protein engineering.

(*c*) Enhancing the levels of Ⓒ.

(*d*) Blocking the activity of E6 by RNA-interference or CRISPR/Cas-mediated knockout.

Which of the above mentioned strategies are likely to provide the maximum enhancement of the target the by-product, if no feedback regulation exists for any of the enzymes in the pathway?

A. (*a*) and (*b*)

B. (*b*) and (*c*)

C. (*c*) and (*d*)

D. (*a*) and (*d*)

DBT-JRF, 2022

Fermentation and Bioprocess Engineering

125. A Continuous Stirred Tank Reactor (CSTR) is running at a dilution (D) of 0.3 h-1 and the product formed is growth associated with YP/x = 0.2 g/g. In order to obtain productivity = 1.2 gl-1h-1 we need to have at steady state a biomass concentration of:
A. 0.8 g/l B. 1.8 g/l
C. 0.072 g/l D. 20 g/l

126. Yeast cells obtained from batch fermentation can be reutilized for the production of:
A. Beer B. Trypsin
C. Chloramphenicol D. Acetic acid

127. You wish to reduce the maximum shear rate in your reactor (given by impeller tip speed), without changing the power consumption (agitator power). For this, you will:
A. Increase the diameter of impeller and reduce the RPM
B. Reduce the diameter of impeller and increase the RPM
C. Reduce RPM only
D. Reduce diameter of impeller only

128. Yeast cells are immobilized in a column and glucose is fed through the inlet at a concentration of 90 g/l. If all the glucose is consumed and we can treat this as an anaerobic fermentation with negligible cell growth, then the ethanol concentration at the outlet will be:
A. 90 g/l B. 60 g/l
C. 36 g/l D. 46 g/l

129. In an ideal Continuous Stirred Tank Reactor (CSTR) at steady state:
A. All particles have the same residence time
B. Particles which enter the reactor earlier have a higher probability of leaving than those that enter later
C. Particles which enter the reactor later have a higher probability of leaving than those that enter earlier
D. All the particles have e27-200ual probability of leaving, independent of their time of entry into the Reactor

130. A continuous reactor has a productivity of 0.5 g/l/h. The volume of reactor re27-200uired to produce 1.2 ton/day of the product is:
A. 100 L B. 1 m^3
C. 10 m^3 D. 100 m^3

131. An exponentially increasing feed of concentrated substrate is fed into a fed batch reactor to maintain a constant specific growth rate 0.35 h-1. If the feed is 5 ml/hr at time, t = 0, then feed after 4 hrs will be approximately:
A. 5 ml/hr B. 10 ml/hr
C. 20 ml/hr D. 80 ml/hr

132. Commercial production of citric acid is done by fermentation using:
A. Aspergillus niger
B. Clostridium butyricum
C. Saccharomyces cerevisiae
D. Lactobacillus acidophilus

133. A concentrated feed of substrate is added at a constant rate in a fed-batch reactor. If all the substrate is utilized, the specific growth rate (μ) pattern will be:
A. Exponential growth with constant μ
B. Exponential growth with increasing μ
C. Growth with decreasing μ
D. Growth with fluctuating μ

134. If in a bioreactor, the gas hold up (ε) is 0.1 and the average diameter of the air bubbles is 1 mm;then the interfacial area (of the air bubble – liquid interface), per unit reactor volume is:
A. 6000 cm^3/l B. 600 cm^3/l
C. 60 cm^3/l D. 6 cm^3/l

135. If the respiratory quotient (R.Q) for growing cells is 1.1 and the exit gas analyzer of a bioreactor shows 3% CO_2 in the outlet gases; then given normal air as input to the reactor, you expect the outlet O_2 concentration to read approximately:
A. 3.3% B. 2.7%
C. 18.3% D. 17.7%

136. In a batch culture of cells following Monod Kinetics, the declining log phase lasts longer when:
A. Initial substrate concentration is high
B. Initial substrate concentration is low
C. Ks values are large
D. Ks values are small

137. In an external recycle reactor (CSTR with external recycle), the outlet stream is concentrated 20 fold with respect to biomass and half of this concentrated cells is fed back into the reactor. In such a situation, washout will take place when dilution rate (D) :
A. is equal to μ_{max}
B. is around 2 μ_{max}
C. is around 0.5 μ_{max}
D. Washout will never take place

138. Penicillin titers have been increased more than 1000 fold by classical mutagenesis from the original Fleming strain. The reason behind this increase in the titer is:
A. Increase in the promoter strength of the penicillin encoding genes
B. Increase in the stability of the mRNA of these genes
C. Increase in the stability of the proteins encoded by these genes
D. Removal of the regulatory controls in the penicillin pathway

GATE (BIOTECHNOLOGY), 2022

139. The overall stoichiometry for an aerobic cell growth is

$$3C_6H_{12}O_6 + 2.5NH_3 + O2 \rightarrow 1.5C_aH_bO_cN_d + 3CO_2 + 5H_2O$$

What is the elemental composition formula of the biomass?

A. $C_9H_{18}.2O_5N_{1.667}$
B. $C_9H_{22}.33O_6N_{1.667}$
C. $C_{10}H_{18}.2O_5N_{1.667}$
D. $C_{10}H_{22}.33O_6N_{1.667}$

ANSWERS

1	2	3	4	5	6	7	8	9	10
C	A	A	B	A	C	A	A	D	C
11	**12**	**13**	**14**	**15**	**16**	**17**	**18**	**19**	**20**
B	B	B	A	A	A	B	B	A	B
21	**22**	**23**	**24**	**25**	**26**	**27**	**28**	**29**	**30**
A	A	A	B	A	B	A	C	C	C
31	**32**	**33**	**34**	**35**	**36**	**37**	**38**	**39**	**40**
B	C	A	A	C	A	A	C	B	C
41	**42**	**43**	**44**	**45**	**46**	**47**	**48**	**49**	**50**
C	D	C	B	D	B	B	D	B	B
51	**52**	**53**	**54**	**55**	**56**	**57**	**58**	**59**	**60**
C	B	A	D	B	C	A	D	C	D
61	**62**	**63**	**64**	**65**	**66**	**67**	**68**	**69**	**70**
A	A	A	A	A	D	C	B	B	D
71	**72**	**73**	**74**	**75**	**76**	**77**	**78**	**79**	**80**
D	B	C	D	A	D	D	C	A	D
81	**82**	**83**	**84**	**85**	**86**	**87**	**88**	**89**	**90**
A	B	A	B	A	A	A	B	B	A
91	**92**	**93**	**94**	**95**	**96**	**97**	**98**	**99**	**100**
D	A	D	A	B	C	B	B	A	A
101	**102**	**103**	**104**	**105**	**106**	**107**	**108**	**109**	**110**
A	B	B	D	B	B	A	C	D	B
111	**112**	**113**	**114**	**115**	**116**	**117**	**118**	**119**	**120**
D	A	A	A	A	A	A	D	A	A
121	**122**	**123**	**124**	**125**	**126**	**127**	**128**	**129**	**130**
D	C	A	D	D	A	A	D	D	D
131	**132**	**133**	**134**	**135**	**136**	**137**	**138**	**139**	
C	A	C	A	C	C	B	D	D	

■■■■■

CHAPTER

7

IMMUNOLOGY

CSIR-NET, JUNE, 2017

Immunology & Disease

1. Which one of the following is NOT a bacterial disease?
   A. Tuberculosis B. Typhoid
   C. Tetanus D. Small pox

2. Which one of the following cells generally does NOT secrete IFN-γ?
   A. $CD8^+$ T cells B. TH_1 cells
   C. NK cells D. TH_2 cells

3. Toll-like receptors (TLR) present in mammalian macrophages are recognized by types of macromolecules that are not present in vertebrates but are present in certain groups of microbial pathogens. When these pathogens infect macrophages, TLR signalling is stimulated. Following are the list of macromolecules in column A and types of TLR in column B.

A	B
(*a*) Lipopolysaccharide (LPS)	(*i*) TLR3
(*b*) Flagellin	(*ii*) TLR4
(*c*) Double stranded RNA	(*iii*) TLR5
(*d*) Unmethylated CpG dinucleotides	(*iv*) TLR9

Which of the following is the best possible match of the pathogenic ligand with their corresponding TLR?

	(*a*)	(*b*)	(*c*)	(*d*)
A.	(*i*)	(*ii*)	(*iii*)	(*iv*)
B.	(*ii*)	(*i*)	(*iv*)	(*iii*)
C.	(*ii*)	(*iii*)	(*i*)	(*iv*)
D.	(*iii*)	(*iv*)	(*ii*)	(*i*)

4. The major histocompatibility complex (MHC) is referred to as the human leukocyte antigen (HLA) complex in humans and as the H-2 complex in mice. In an experiment, H-2k mice were primed with the lymphocytic choriomeningitis virus (LeMV) to induce cytotoxic T lymphocytes (CTLs) specific for the virus. Spleen cells from this LCMV-primed mouse were then added to target cells of the same (H-2k) or different H-2 haplotypes (H-2b) that were intracellularly radiolabelled with 51 Cr and either infected or not infected with LCMV. CTL mediated killing of target cells were then measured by the release of 51 Cr into the culture supernatant (Cr release assay). In which of the following cells, 51 Cr will be released into the culture supernatant?
   A. H-2k target cells
   B. H-2k LCMV-infected target cells
   C. H-2b target cells
   D. H-2b LCMV-infected target cells

5. There is evidence that following pyrogenic stimuli, cytokines produced by the CNS cause fever, possibly by local release of prostaglandins. Accordingly, the following statements have been proposed:
   (*a*) Cytokines act independently and directly on thermoregulatory centres
   (*b*) Intrahypothalamic injection of prostaglandin receptor agonists will prevent fever
   (*c*) Antipyretic effect of aspirin is exerted on the hypothalamus to prevent prostaglandin synthesis

(*d*) Aspirin blocks infections and eventually prevents fever.

Which one of the following combination of above statements is correct?

A. (*a*) and (*d*) B. (*b*) and (*c*)
C. (*b*) and (*d*) D. (*a*) and (*c*)

6. The table given below provides a list of diseases and causal organisms.

Disease	Causal Organism
(*a*) Sleeping sickness in humans	(*i*) *Trypanosoma cruzi*
(*b*) Chagas disease in humans	(*ii*) *Trypanosoma brucei*
(*c*) Blast disease of rice	(*iii*) *Magnaporthe graminis*
(*d*) Powdery mildew of grasses	(*iv*) *Magnaporthe oryzae*
	(*v*) *Blumeria oryzae*
	(*vi*) *Blumeria graminis*

Which of the following options represent the correct match between disease and the causal organism?

	(*a*)	(*b*)	(*c*)	(*d*)
A.	(*i*)	(*ii*)	(*v*)	(*vi*)
B.	(*ii*)	(*i*)	(*iii*)	(*v*)
C.	(*i*)	(*ii*)	(*vi*)	(*iv*)
D.	(*ii*)	(*i*)	(*iv*)	(*vi*)

CSIR-NET, DECEMBER, 2017

Immunology & Disease

7. Which one of the following human serum immunoglobulins takes part in classical complement fixation pathway?

A. IgD B. IgE
C. IgA D. IgG

8. Major histocompatibility complex (MHC) molecules are encoded by a cluster of genes called MHC locus. There are several reasons why an MHC molecule on the surface of a cell is important. Which one of the following reasons is INCORRECT?

A. To display self class I to demonstrate that the cell is normal and healthy.
B. To display foreign-peptide in class I to show that the cell is infected and to engage with T helper cells.
C. To display a self-peptide in class I and II to test developing T cells for autoreactivity.
D. To display a self-peptide in class I and II to maintain tolerance to self-proteins.

9. The below figure depicts the regulation of hypothalamo-pituitary-adrenal (HPA) axis. Changes in cortisol level in Addison's disease can lead to

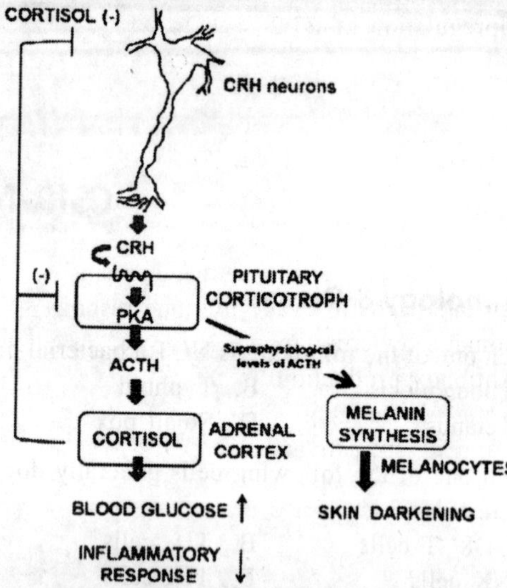

A. suppressed immune system and increased blood glucose level
B. gain of body weight and lightening of skin
C. loss of body weight, reduced blood glucose level and hyperpigmentation
D. increased blood glucose and activated immune system

DBT-JRF, 2017

10. Myeloma cells fused with spleen cells in hybridoma technology are:

A. Immortal and antibody producing cells
B. Mortal and antibody producing cells
C. Hypoxanthine guanine phosphoribosyl transferase lacking cells
D. Thymidine kinase lacking cells.

11. Detectable serum antibody against a T-independent pathogen is a good indication that:

A. A functional B-cell system exists
B. A functional T-cell system exists
C. The patient has immune suppression
D. Both T and B cell systems are not functional.

12. Which one of the following rearrangements is NOT permitted during somatic recombination in the heavy chain and light chain immunoglobulin loci?

A. D_H:J_H B. V_L:J_L
C. V_H:J_H D. V_H:D_H

13. Junctional diversity in CDR3 during gene rearrangement results from the addition of:
A. Switch region nucleotides
B. P and N nucleotides
C. V, D and J nucleotides
D. Recombination signal sequences.

14. The function of negative selection of thymocytes in the thymus is to eliminate:
A. Single-positive thymocytes
B. Double-positive thymocytes
C. Alloreactive thymocytes
D. Autoreactive thymocytes

15. Antigen recognition by T cells in the absence of co-stimulation results in:
A. Upregulation of B7.1
B. T-cell apoptosis
C. T-cell anergy
D. Upregulation of B7.2

16. Parasites numbers in the blood of a patient with Trypanosoma brucci (Sleeping sickness) shows the following pattern:

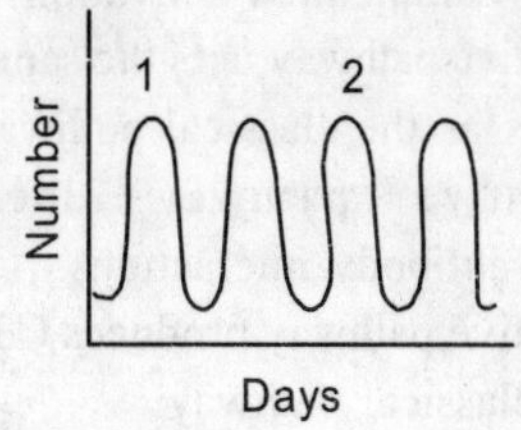

Parasites isolated from population 1 and 2 were found to be antigenecially non- cross reactive. The parasite distribuuion seen may be due to:
A. Change in gene expression
B. Loss of antigenic epitopes
C. Post-translational modification of antigen
D. Antigenic switching

GATE (BIOTECHNOLOGY), 2017

Immunology

17. Which one of the following mechanisms is used by human pathogens to evade immune responses?
A. Somatic hypermutation
B. Antibody production
C. Antigenic variation
D. Complement activation.

18. Which of the following conditions promote the development of human autoimmune disorders?
A. Inability to eliminate self- reactive lymphocytes
B. Generation of auto antibodies
C. Ability to eliminate self- reactive lymphocytes
D. Induction of regulatory T-cells in the thymus

GATE (LIFE SCIENCE), 2017

Immune System

19. Which one of the following features is NOT appropriate for Fab fragment of IgG?
A. Contains antigen binding site
B. Contains an intact L chain
C. Two fragments are formed from one IgG molecule
D. Mediates complement fixation in the intact IgG molecule

20. Which one of the following in NOT TRUE for class I MHC protein?
A. MHC class I protein are polymorphic
B. T-cell receptors recognizes MHC class I protein
C. MHC class I protein are displayed on the surfaces of nucleated vertebrate cells
D. β_2- macroglobulin is covalently associated with MHC class I protein

21. If a heavy chain of an antibody molecule weighs 65,000 Daltons (Da) and a light chain weighs 25,000 Da, the approximate calculated weight of an IgM antibody in Da will be
A. 90,000 B. 180,000
C. 360,000 D. 900,000

CSIR-NET, JUNE, 2018

Immunology & Disease

22. If a disease caused by an intracellular pathogen is associated with host anti-inflammatory response, which one of the following may lead to an effective therapeutic approach?
A. Treatment with TGF-β
B. Treatment with macrophage activating agent

C. Depletion of IFN-γ from the system
D. Treatment with IL-4 and IL-10

23. Which one of the following is NOT true for alternative pathway of complement activation?
A. Alternative pathway uses the same membrane-attack complex as the classical pathway
B. Alternative pathway does not require antigen-antibody interactions.
C. Alternative pathway produces C3 by the same route as the classical pathway
D. Certain microbial surfaces have physico-chemical properties that may result in activation of alternative pathway

24. Activation-induced cytidine deaminase (AID) is the key mediator of somatic hypermutation, gene conversion and class- switch recombination. In order to ascertain the role of AID in class-switch recombination, immune response against a target antigen was compared between AID knock-out mice (AID-/-) with that of mice retaining a functional copy of the AID gene (AID+/-). Development of IgM and IgG antibodies against the target antigen was then measured following successive immunization and plotted graphically.

Which one of the following is the most appropriate representation of the experiment?

—— AID +/–   **......** AID –/–

A. 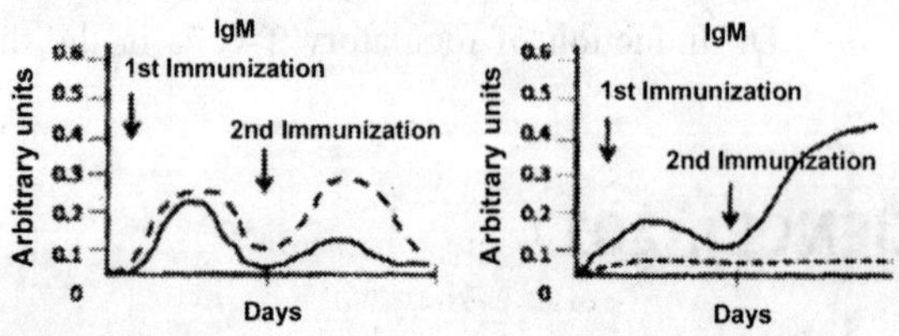

B. 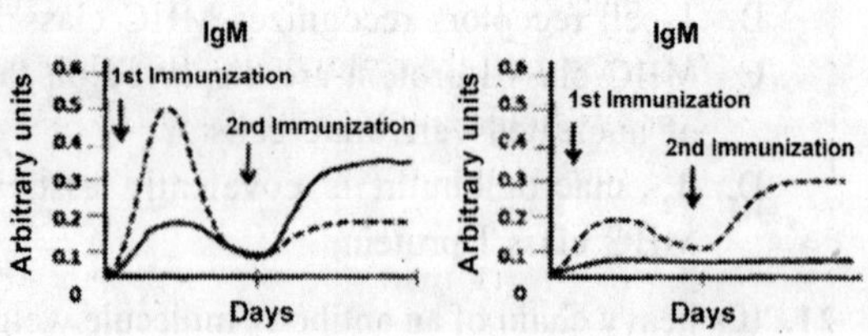

C. 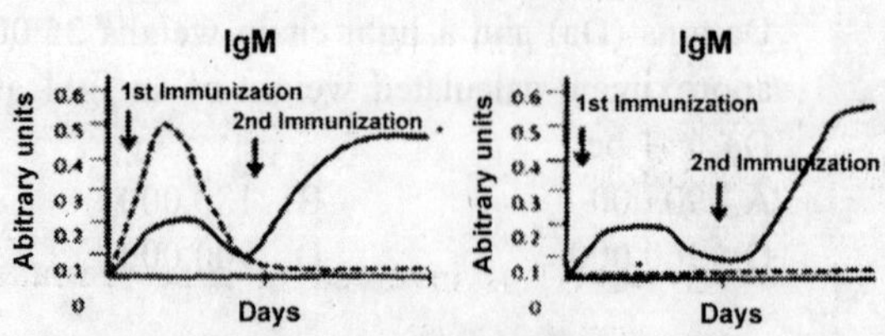

D. 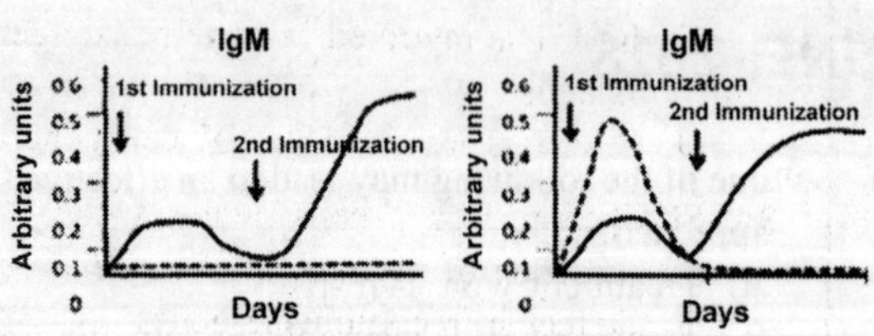

Vaccine and antibiotics

25. Actinomycin D inhibits the process of transcription in both prokaryotic and eukaryotic organisms. The following statements are made about actinomycin D-mediated inhibition of transcription:
(*a*) Actinomycin D inhibits transcription from a double stranded DNA template by either *E. coli* or yeast RNA polymerases.
(*b*) Actinomycin D inhibits transcription from a single stranded RNA template by eukaryotic viral RNA polymerases.
(*c*) Actinomycin D inhibits transcription from single stranded Φ × 174 DNA template by E. coli RNA polymerase, immediately after viral DNA entry.
(*d*) Actinomycin D inhibits transcription from double stranded RNA template by eukaryotic RNA polymerase II.

Which of the combinations of the above statements is a true representation of the mechanism of actinomycin D mediated inhibition?
A. (*a*) only
B. (*a*), (*b*) and (*d*)
C. (*a*), (*b*) and (*c*)
D. (*a*) and (*d*) only

26. Given below are the types of vaccination (column A), the diseases or conditions against which these vaccination types are used (column 8) and the advantages or disadvantages for using these vaccination types (column C).

A	B	C
(*a*) Live attenuated	(*i*) Rabies	(*x*) Strong immune response; often life-longimmunity with a few dose
(*b*) Inactivated or killed	(*ii*) Measles	(*y*) Stable immune response; cold Chain is not required
(*c*) Inactivated exotoxin	(*iii*) Diptheria	(*z*) Chance of untoward immunological reactions are very low; less successful in inducing long- term immunity; need to be administered repeatedly

Which one of the following combinations is the most appropriate match?

	(*a*)	(*b*)	(*c*)
A.	(*i*)-(*z*)	(*ii*)-(*y*)	(*iii*)-(*x*)
B.	(*ii*)-(*x*)	(*i*)-(*y*)	(*iii*)-(*z*)
C.	(*iii*)-(*y*)	(*ii*)-(*x*)	(*i*)-(*z*)
D.	(*ii*)-(*z*)	(*iii*)-(*x*)	(*i*)-(*y*)

CSIR-NET, DECEMBER, 2018

Immunology & Disease

27. Viruses adopt different strategies to suppress immune response of the host. Which one of the following statements is NOT correct?

A. Human Immunodeficiency Virus (HIV) destroys CD4+T cells.
B. Epstein-Barr Virus (EBV) produces a homolog of human IL-10.
C. Human influenza virus directly infects CD8+ T cells.
D. Human Cytomegalo Virus (CMV) establishes latent infection in bone marrow stem cells.

28. Many cytotoxic T lymphocytes initiate killing of target cells via delivery of molecules that could induce target-cell damage directly. Which one of the following is the most appropriate?

A. Interferon γ B. Peroxynitrite
C. Lysozyme D. Granzyme

29. Bacteria adopt different strategies to evade host defense mechanisms. From the lists of various different mechanisms and bacterial strategies against host defense given below, select the option representing all correct pairing.

Host Defence Mechanism	*Bacterial strategies against host defence*
(*a*) Phagocytosis	(*i*) Change of bacterial surface charge, making it more positive
(*b*) Release antibodies, like IgG	(*ii*) Capsular polysaccharides, such as that of *Klebsiellapneumoniae*
(*c*) Antibody mediated agglutination	(*iii*) Release of soluble proteins like protein A of *Staphyloccusaureus*
(*d*) Anti-microbial peptides	(*iv*) Secretion of elastase to inactivate C3a and C5a

	(*a*)	(*b*)	(*c*)	(*d*)
A.	(*i*)	(*ii*)	(*iii*)	(*iv*)
B.	(*ii*)	(*iii*)	(*iv*)	(*i*)
C.	(*iv*)	(*iii*)	(*ii*)	(*i*)
D.	(*iii*)	(*i*)	(*iv*)	(*ii*)

30. Which one of the following statements regarding clonal selection hypothesis is NOT CORRECT?

A. Mature B lymphocytes bear lg receptors on their cell surface and all receptors on a single B cell have variable specificity for antigen.
B. On antigen stimulation, B cell matures, migrates to lymphoid organs and replicates. Its clonal descendents bear the same receptor as parental B cell and secrete antibodies with identical specificity.
C. After immune response, more B cells bearing receptors will remain in the host and act as memory cells for mounting enhanced secondary response.
D. B cells with receptors for self-antigens are deleted during embryonic development.

31. Monoclonal antibodies can be modified for better research and therapeutic applications. Several such approaches are mentioned below (Column A) along with their possible applications (Column B).

Column A	Column B
(*a*) Binding site of the original mouse mAa are placed onto the Fe regions of human antibodies	(*i*) Abzymes
(*b*) Antibodies are modified by conjugation to toxins designed to kill cells to which the antibody will bind	(*ii*) Reduce side effect of xenogenic antibodies in immunotherapy
(*c*) Generation of mAb that specifically bind and stabilize the transition state of a chemical reaction	(*iii*) Immunotoxins

Which one of the following options represents a correct combination of terms in Column A and column B?

	(*a*)	(*b*)	(*c*)
A.	(*i*)	(*ii*)	(*iii*)
B.	(*ii*)	(*i*)	(*iii*)
C.	(*iii*)	(*ii*)	(*i*)
D.	(*ii*)	(*iii*)	(*i*)

DBT-JRF, 2018

32. Aminopterin in HAT medium inhibits:

A. Thymidine kinase
B. Hypoxanthine - guanine phosphoribosyl transferase
C. Ribonucleotide reductase
D. Dihydrofolate reductase

33. RAG1 null mice are susceptible to infection because:

A. RAG1 is a protein involved in innate immune response
B. RAG1 is involved in gene rearrangement in all somatic cells
C. RAG1 is involved in gene rearrangement in T and B cells
D. RAG1 is involved in NK cell generation

34. SCID mice lack T-cells owing to the:

A. Absence of thymus
B. Defect in recombinase genes

C. Defect in expression of pre-TCR
D. Absence of terminal deoxynucleotide transferase.

35. During infection by single stranded RNA viruses, host immune system distinguishes viral RNA from the host RNA based on:
A. differences in the length of the RNAs
B. specific signals at the 5′ end of the RNs
C. localization of viral RNA to a particular region in the cell
D. phosphorylation of viral RNA

36. Anti-human μ chain antibody is specific for epitopes present in the:
A. Constant region of the Ig molecule
B. Variable region of the Ig molecule
C. CDR region of the Ig molecule
D. Framework region of the Ig molecule

37. Hapten-carrier hypothesis was useful in the designing of the vaccine for:
A. Polio myelitis
B. Vibrio cholerae
C. Haemophilus influenzae B
D. Corynebacterium diphtheriae

38. Tetanus toxoid is a protein that has been chemically treated to retain its:
A. Toxicity and antigenicity
B. Toxicity and immunogenicity
C. Immunogenicity and not its toxicity
D. Antigenicity and not its toxicity

39. Hemolytic disease of the new born called erythroblastosis fetalis commonly develops in mothers with repeated pregnancies owing to the activation of:
A. IgG-secreting memory cells
B. IgE-secreting memory cells
C. Cytotoxic T-cells
D. Natural killer cells

40. Which one of the following is NOT a part of the recombination signal sequence in VDJ recombination?
A. A conserved 7 bp consensus sequence
B. Locus control regions (LCR)
C. A less conserved spacer of either 12 or 23 bp
D. A conserved 9 bp consensus sequence.

41. The mechanism that permits immunoglobulins to be synthesized either in a membrane bound or secreted form is:
A. Allelic exclusion
B. Co-dominant expression
C. Differential RNA processing
D. Class-switch recombination.

42. The transporter associated with antigen processing (TAP) complex is for loading of peptides onto class I MHC molecules. The cellular compartment harboring the TAP complex is:
A. Mitochondria
B. Golgi apparatus
C. Endoplasmic reticulum
D. Lysosome

43. Peste des petits ruminants (PPR) also known as "goat plague", a viral disease of goats and sheep is caused by:
A. Morbilli virus B. Flavi virus
C. Reo virus D. Astro virus

44. In utero microcephaly is caused by:
A. Rota virus
B. HIV
C. Borna disease virus
D. Zika virus

45. Labels on the tubes containing Fab and F(ab')2 fragments of anti-SRBC were dislodged. Recommend one of the following techniques to identify the correct fragments in the tube:
A. Agglutination with SRBC
B. Complement fixation assay with SRBC
C. Rocket electrophoresis with SRBC
D. Reducing SDS-PAGE followed by immunoblotting

GATE (BIOTECHNOLOGY), 2018

46. Which one of the following is NOT a principal component of innate immunity?
A. Mucosal epithelia B. Dendritic cells
C. Complement system D. Memory B-cells

47. Which of the following cytokines are endogenous pyrogens?
(*a*) Tumour necrosis factor-α
(*b*) Interleukin-1
(*c*) Transforming growth factor-β
(*d*) Interleukin-10
A. (*a*) and (*b*) only B. (*a*) and (*c*) only
C. (*c*) and (*d*) only D. (*b*) and (*d*) only

48. Which one of the combinations of the following statements is true about antibody structure?
(*a*) Limited proteolysis of rabbit IgG with the enzyme pepsin generates two antigen-binding regions (Fab) and an Fc fragment
(*b*) Limited proteolysis of rabbit IgG with the enzyme papain generates a single bivalent antigen-binding region F(ab')2 and peptide fragments
(*c*) The Fc fragment of IgG can self-associate and crystallize into a lattice
(*d*) The F(ab')2 fragment of IgG is composed of both light and heavy chains

A. (*a*) and (*b*) only B. (*a*) and (*c*) only
C. (*c*) and (*d*) only D. (*b*) and (*d*) only

49. Which one of the following statements is true with regard to processing and presentation of protein antigens?
A. In the class II MHC pathway, protein antigens in the cytosol are processed by proteasomes
B. In the class I MHC pathway, extracellular protein antigens are endocytosed into vesicles and processed
C. In the class I MHC pathway, transporter associated antigen processing (TAP) protein is required for translocating processed peptides generated in the cytosol
D. Invariant chain in endoplasmic reticulum is involved in transport of peptides and loading of class.I MHC.

GATE (LIFE SCIENCE), 2018

50. Which one of the following properties of the myeloma cells is used in the hybridoma technology to generate monoclonal antibody?
A. lack of thymidylate synthase
B. over-expression of hypoxanthine-guanine phosphoribosyl transferase
C. over-expression of inosine 5′-monophosphate cyclohydrolase
D. lack of hypoxanthine-guanine phosphoribosyl transferase

51. Among the reagents given below which one of the combination of reagents will NOT break the disulphide bonds in the immunoglobulin molecules?
(P) Reduced glutathione
(Q) Dithiothreitol
(R) Sodium dodecyl sulphate
(S) Methionine
A. R & S B. P & R
C. P & S D. Q & R

52. The type-II hypersensitivity reaction is mainly mediated by____.
A. IgE B. IgM
C. IgA D. T cells

CSIR-NET, JUNE, 2019

Immunology & Disease

53. Which one of the following does NOT belong to human antimicrobial proteins and peptides at epithelial surface forming part of innate immunity?
A. Lactoferrin B. Defensin
C. Calprotectin D. Vimentin

54. Fruit bats are known to harbor and spread several viruses that can infect other animals and humans. Which one of the following viruses NOT reported to spread by fruit bats?
A. Ebola B. Nipah
C. SARS D. HIV

55. In a type I hypersensitivity- mediated asthmatic response, which one of the following is thought to contribute significantly to the prolonged bronchospasm and build-up of mucous seen in asthmatics?
A. Thromboxane B. Leukotriene
C. TGFβ D. Chondroitin

56. Which one of the following influenza A virus subtypes caused severe avian flu and was responsible for disease outbreak in the year 1997 in Hong Kong?
A. H1N1 B. H7N7
C. H3N2 D. H5N1

57. The newborn baby of a mother having blood group AB, Rh^+ and father having blood group O, Rh^-, got mixed with other babies in the hospital. The baby with which of the following blood groups is expected to be of the said couple?
A. O, Rh^+ B. O, Rh^-
C. AB, Rh^- D. B, Rh^+

58. There are number of specific T cell surface molecules involved in various functions of adaptive immune response. Column X represents a list of T cell surface molecules and Column Y with the possible functional characteristics:

Column X	Column Y
(*a*) T cell receptor	(*i*) binds to CD40 on B cells and APCs and triggers activation of APCs and activation/ differentiation of B cells.
(*b*) CD 28	(*ii*) binds to MHC class I molecules and restricts T cytotoxic cells to recognizing only peptide presented on MHC class I
(*c*) CD8	(*iii*) binds to B7-1,2 or CD80/86 on B cells and APCs, which triggers T cell activation.
(*d*) CD154	(*iv*) consists of two polypeptide chains a and α and β and some consist of polypeptide chains γ and δ.

Which of the following option has all correct matches?

	(a)	(b)	(c)	(d)
A.	(i)	(ii)	(iii)	(iv)
B.	(iv)	(i)	(ii)	(iii)
C.	(iii)	(iv)	(i)	(ii)
D.	(iv)	(iii)	(ii)	(i)

59. Column X lists two diseases and column Y lists name of proteins which are commonly used for routine clinical diagnosis of these diseases

Column-X	Column-Y
(a) Myocardial infarction	(i) Amylase
(b) Pancreatitis	(ii) Creatine kinase
	(iii) Lipase
	(iv) Troponin

Find out correct combination.

A. A-(ii); B-(i); A-(iv); B-(iii)

B. A-(iii); B-(iv); A-(ii); B-(i)

C. A-(i); B-(ii); A-(iii); B-(iv)

D. A-(iv); B-(iii); A-(i); B-(ii)

CSIR-NET, 15 DECEMBER, 2019

Immunology & Disease

60. Some statements regarding the process of autophagy are given below:

(a) Autophagy occurs when cells contain aggregated proteins

(b) Autophagosomes fuse with any organelles

(c) Autophagosome is a single membrane structure

(d) Autophagosomes fuse with lysosomes to form autophagolysosomes

Which one of the following combination of the above statements is correct?

A. (a) and (b)

B. (b) and (c)

C. (c) and (d)

D. (d) and (a)

61. Listeria is a food-borne pathogen that causes mild gastro-intestinal symptoms. To move from one host-cell to another, it polymerizes actin into a comet tail like structure. Listeria can assemble host-cell actin at its rear end because:

(a) Listeria has on its surface a protein called Act A

(b) Listeria can activate Arp 2/3 complex

(c) Listeria has on its surface γ-tubulin

(d) Listeria has on its surface myosin II motor

Which one of the following options represents all correct statements?

A. (a) and (d)

B. (a) and (b)

C. (a) and (c)

D. (c) and (d)

62. Bacterial infections are generally divided into two broad classes: intracellular and extracellular bacterial infections. Given below are some of the properties, which are applicable for bacterial infections.

(a) Humoral immune response is the main protective response against extracellular bacteria.

(b) Innate immunity is not effective against intracellular bacterial pathogens.

(c) Bacterial endotoxins do not induce an innate immune response.

(d) Intracellular bacterial infections generally induce a cell-mediated immune response resulting in secretion of cytokines which activate macrophages.

Which one of the following combination of statements is correct?

A. (a) and (b)

B. (b) and (c)

C. (c) and (d)

D. (a) and (d)

63. Strain A mice were crossed with strain B mice and first generation F_1 mice were obtained, *i.e.* (A × B)F_1. A scientist then implanted thymectomized and irradiated (A × B)F1 mice with a B-type thymus and then reconstituted the animals immune system with an intravenous infusion of (A x B)F_1 bone marrow cells. The chimeric mice were infected with lymphocytic choriomeningitis virus (LCMV) and the spleen T cells were then tested for their ability to kill LCMV-infected target cells from the strain A or strain B mice. Which one of the following is the correct outcome of the experiment?

A. LCMV-infected target cells from strain A only will be killed

B. LCMV-infected target cells from strain B only will be killed

C. LCMV-infected target cells from both strain A and B will be killed

D. Neither cells from strain A nor from strain B will be killed

CSIR-NET, 27 DECEMBER, 2019

Immunology & Disease

64. Which one of the following pathogens cannot survive and replicate within phagocytic cells?
A. Listeria monocytogenes
B. *Mycobacterium tuberculosis*
C. *Leishmania donovani*
D. *Streptococcus pneumoniae*

65. Which one of the following immunoglobulin isotypes plays a primary role in protecting against pathogens that invade through the gut or respiratory mucosa?
A. IgE B. IgM
C. IgD D. IgA

66. The most common cause of blindness induced by microbial infection in humans is:
A. *Chlamydia psittaci*
B. *Chlamydia pneumonia*
C. *Chlamydia muridarum*
D. *Chlamydia trachomatis*

67. Given below are some of the major characteristics of inflammatory responses against bacterial infections in general:
(*a*) TGF β levels are elevated
(*b*) Phagocytic capacity of macrophages is increased
(*c*) Complement system may get activated
(*d*) Self-reactive CD8+ T cells may get activated

Which one of the following combinations of above characteristics is most appropriate for inflammatory response against extracellular bacterial infections?
A. (*a*) and (*b*) B. (*b*) and (*c*)
C. (*c*) and (*d*) D. (*a*) and (*d*)

68. Given below are some properties that are applicable for T cell receptors:
(*a*) It is associated with a multi-component signal transducing complex, CD3, on the membrane
(*b*) It is divalent in nature
(*c*) It contains domains which are similar to the immunoglobulin fold structure
(*d*) It exhibits diversity generated by somatic mutation

Which one of the following combinations represents correct statements?
A. (*a*) and (*b*) B. (*a*) and (*c*)
C. (*c*) and (*d*) D. (*b*) and (*d*)

DBT-JRF, 2019

69. A patient suffering from allergy has been advised to take anti-histamine drugs. Which one of the following biological processes is most likely to be the reason for the allergy?
A. Mast cell degranulation
B. Thymocyte maturation
C. Somatic hypermutation
D. Bystander lysis

70. Lack of reactivity to self HLA is known as?
A. Autoimmunity
B. Complement fixation
C. Clonal selection
D. Tolerance

71. Bovine spongiform encephalopathy is a disease caused by:
A. Fungus B. Bacteria
C. Prions D. Viroids

72. Cytotoxic T cells generally recognize antigen in association with:
A. class II MHC determinants
B. class I MHC determinants
C. class III MHC determinants
D. HLA-DR determinants

73. A patient is suffering from an autoimmune disorder. Exome analysis has revealed a mutation in the gene '*AIRE*'. Which one of the following biological processes is likely to be affected in this patient?
A. Positive selection of thymocytes
B. Negative selection of thymocytes
C. Affinity maturation
D. Dendritic cell development

74. Under which of the following circumstances do T cells develop anergy?
A. With the expression of CD69 on T cells.
B. When the CD4/ CD8 molecules present on T cell surfaces do not recognize self MHC II/MHC I molecules.
C. When the MHCII molecules present on antigen presenting cells bind to the peptides with less avidity.
D. When co-stimulatory molecules present on the antigen presenting cells fail to interact with T cells.

75. Match the common antibody origin with appropriate generic name/brand name of the antibody
(*a*) Mouse (*i*) Binatumomab
(*b*) Chimeric (*ii*) Herceptin
(*c*) Humanized (*iii*) Pantimumab
(*d*) Human (*iv*) Retuxan

	(a)	(b)	(c)	(d)
A.	(ii)	(i)	(iv)	(iii)
B.	(i)	(iv)	(iii)	(ii)
C.	(i)	(iv)	(ii)	(iii)
D.	(iv)	(i)	(ii)	(iii)

76. The first humanized monoclonal antibody approved by the US-FDA for targeted treatment of breast cancer was:
A. Trastuzumab B. Paliviuzmab
C. Gemtuzumab D. Natalizumab

77. Which one of the following statements is INCORRECT with regard to DNA vaccines?
A. No risk of infection
B. Proteins produced are likely to be correctly post translationally modified
C. It can persist for an extended time period in the cell
D. Introduced DNA stimulates a protective immune response

78. Antigen-activated B cells differentiate into antibody-producing plasma cells in:
A. Lymphoid follicles B. Hassall's corpuscles
C. Lamina propria D. Phagosome

79. Allergenicity of a protein refers to its capacity to activate:
A. Mast cells B. B cells
C. Dendritic cells D. M cells

80. Secondary immune response to a hapten depends on the:
A. Hapten immunization alone
B. Carrier immunization alone
C. Both hapten and carrier used in the primary immunization
D. Hapten and is independent of the carrier used during immunization

81. Ig class specific antigenic determinants are known as:
A. Allotypic determinants
B. Isotypic determinants
C. Idiotypic determinants
D. Gm determinants

82. Isotypic determinants of the Ig molecule are located in the:
A. HC
B. LC
C. Constant region of HC and LC
D. Variable region of HC and LC

83. Which one of the following genes is mutated in nude mice?
A. Foxn1 B. Foxp3
C. Foxp1 D. Prkdc

84. Zinc deficiency among children primarily results in the atrophy of:
A. Thymus B. Spleen
C. Lymph nodes D. Peyer's patches

GATE (BIOTECHNOLOGY), 2019

85. Which one of the following is coded by the ABO blood group locus in the human genome?
A. Acyl transferase
B. Galactosyltransferase
C. Transposase
D. β-Galactosidase

86. Which one of the following enzymes is encoded by human immunodeficiency virus (HIV) genome?
A. Reverse transcriptase B. Phospholipase
C. Phosphatase D. ATP synthase

87. Which one of the following is NOT a part of the human nonspecific defence system?
A. Interferon B. Mucous
C. Saliva D. Antibody

88. Antibody-producing hybridoma cells are generated by the fusion of a
A. T cell with a myeloma cell
B. B cell with a myeloma cell
C. macrophage with a myeloma cell
D. T cell and a B cell

GATE (LIFE SCIENCE), 2019

Immune System

89. RAG recombinase is responsible for the formation of specific immune receptors. This process occurs in
A. T cells & B cells
B. Natural killer cells
C. Macrophages
D. Neutrophils

90. Allergies are due to a hyper immune response. Drugs given to counter allergies target
A. Glycine B. Histamine
C. Insulin D. Cellulose

91. A mixture of the following purified proteins, IgG, IgM and Fab fragment of immunoglobulins, is separated using gel filtration chromatography. The order of elution of these proteins (first to last) is
A. Fab fragment, IgM and IgG
B. IgM, IgG and Fab fragment
C. Fab fragment, IgG and IgM
D. IgG, IgM and Fab fragment

CSIR-NET, NOVEMBER (MORNING), 2020

Immunology & Disease

92. Leishmanai major, the causative protozoan paratiste of cutaneous leishmaniasis, resides and multiplies within the phagosomes of macrophages. Resistance to the infection correlated verv well with the development of a Thl response. In order to prove this hypothesis, three groups of BALB/c mice were taken: control group, IFN$\gamma^{(-/-)}$ group and IL-4 (-/-) group. All the groups were infected with L. Major and then parasite load was meausred in each group after 4 weeks, Which one of the following result will justify the experimental outcome confirming the hypothesis?

A.

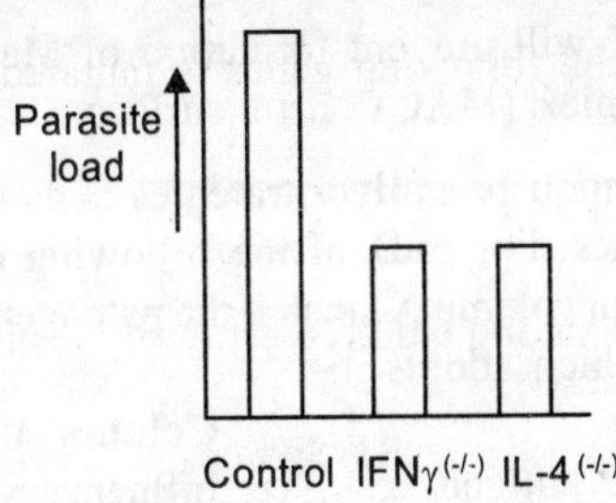

B.

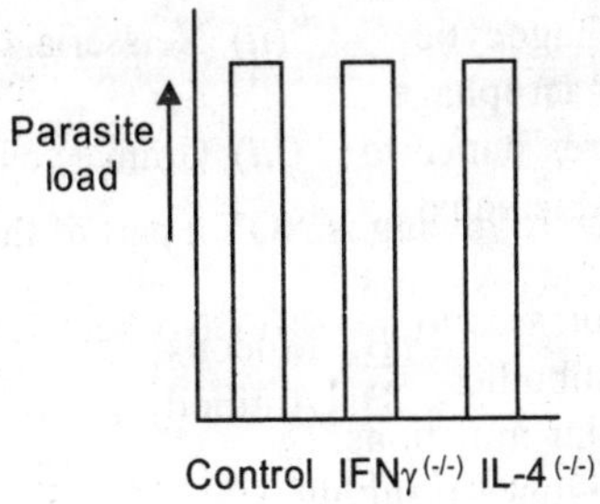

C.

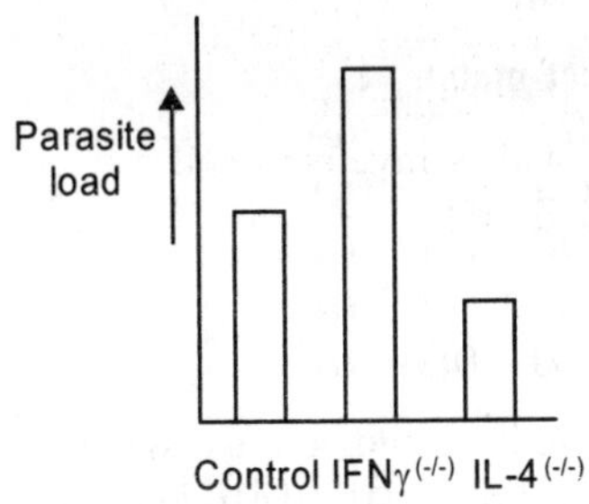

D.

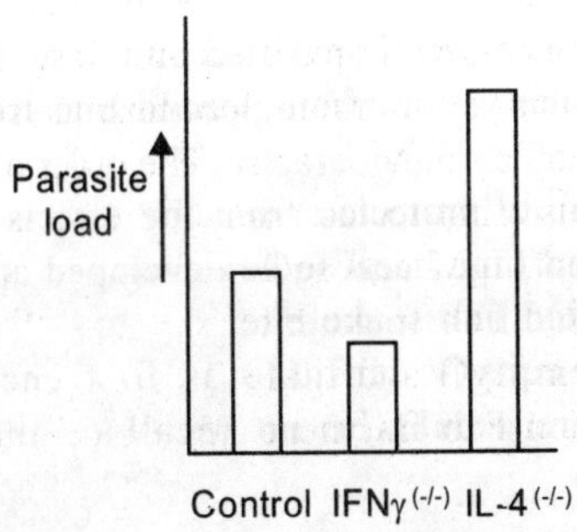

93. If you require to generateanergy in T cells, which of the following conditions will you use?

A. Stimulate naive T cells with antibodies that bind both T cell receptor and CD28

B. Stimulate naive T cells with antibodies that bind only the T cell receptor

C. Stimulate naive T cells with antibodies that bind both T cell receptor and CD28 in presence of IL-4

D. Permit naive T cell interactions with activated macrophages in presence of IL-4

94. A transgenic mouse was generated for both heavy and light chain specific for MHC molecule H-2K^{m} so that all the B cells in this mouse therefore had BCRS specific only for H-2K^{m} and made only anti- H-2K^{M} specific antibodies. By appropriate breeding, the H-2K^{m} specific immunoglobulin transgene was introduced into mice bearing different MHC genotypes H-2K^{n} and H-2K$^{m/n}$. With respect to selection of B-cells within the bone marrow of H-2K^{n} and H-2k$^{m/n}$ mice,

Which of the following statements is correct?

A. In H-2K^{n} mice, the transgenic antibodies will not be detected on the surface of any of the B cells

B. In H-2K$^{m/n}$ mice, the transgenic antibodies will not be detected on the surface of any of the B cells.

C. In H-2K^{n} mice, the transgenic antibodies will be detected on the surface of some of the B cells but not released in the serum.

D. In H-2K$^{m/n}$ mice, the transgenic antibodies will be detected on the surface of some of the B cells.

95. Following diagram displays the MHC haplotype of a heterrozygous H-2k/d mouse.

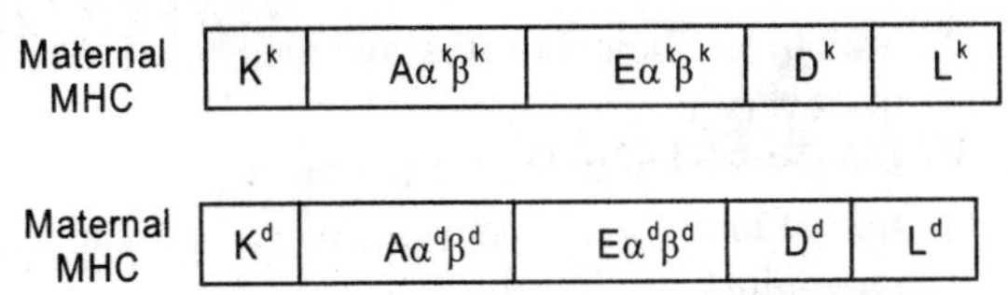

How many types of MHC molecules will be expressed on activated macrophage (MCP) and a normal fibroblast (IMF)?

A. MCP 8; NF 14

B. MCP 4; NF 6

C. MCP 14; NF 14

D. MCP 14; NF8CP

CSIR-NET, NOVEMBER (AFTERNOON), 2020

Immunology & Disease

96. The immunoglobulin heavy-chain that is rearranged first and is displayed on the surface of early stages of B-cell development is associated with:

A. class-II associated invariant chain peptide (CLIP).
B. a surrogate light chain.
C. β_2-macroglobulin.
D. Immunoglobulin-like cell adhesion molecule.

97. Given Below are plots that show changing titres of natural killer cells (NK cells), cytotoxic T-lymphocytes specific to the virus (virus-specific CTLs) and interferon α/β during a virus infection. (increasing titres)

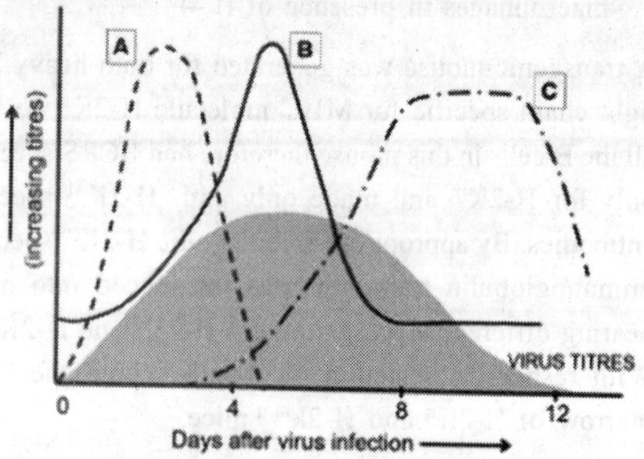

With respect to changing virus titers, select the plots that represent these factors correctly from the option given below.

A. A: Interferon; B: virus-specific CTLs; C: NK cells.
B. A: NK cells; B: Interferon; C: virus-specific CTLs.
C. A: Interferon; B: NK cells; C: virus-specific CTLs
D. A: virus-specific CTLs; B: Interferon; C: NK cells.

98. Which one of the following systems forms a chemical mediator that is involved in the mechanism of pain during inflammation?

A. Activated blood clotting cascade
B. Plasmin - Fibrinolytic system
C. Kininogen - Bradykinin system
D. B-cell activation

99. Dr. Ralph M. Steinman was awarded Nobel Prize for his discovery on:

A. acquired immunological tolerance.
B. role of major histocompatibility complex in antigen recognition by T-cells
C. chemical structure of antibody
D. role of dendritic cells in adaptive immunity

100. Three strains of pathogenic bacteria were found to express proteins mimicking human proteins associated with complement pathway. Bacterium 'X' expressed on its surface proteins mimicking Decay Accelerating Factor (DAF) and Complement Receptor 1 (CR1). Bacterium T secreted a protein that mimicked protein of humans and bacterium Z secreted protein that mimicked Factor I activity.

Given below are statements on the possible effect of complement activation on these pathogenic bacteria. Select the INCORRECT statement

A. Bacterium X will prevent formation of C3 convertase on its surface by alternate and classical pathways.
B. Bacterium Y will prevent formation of C3 convertase on its surface by lectin pathway.
C. Bacterium Z will be susceptible to complement attack by Membrane Attack Complex (MAC) despite secreting Factor I-like protein to cleave C3b and C4b.
D. Bacterium Y will prevent formation of Membrane Attack Complex (MAC) on its surface.

101. Pathogens continuously evolve strategies to evade host immune responses. For each of the following evasion strategies (listed in column X) match the pathogen (listed in column Y) which adopts it:

Column X	Column Y
(*a*) Changing the antigen expressed on their surface	(*i*) Influenza virus
(*b*) Increasing phagocytic activity of macrophage	(*ii*) Neisseria
(*c*) Developing resistance to complement-mediated lysis	(*iii*) Gram +ve bacteria
(*d*) Secreting proteases to inactivate antibodies	(*iv*) No bacteria
(*e*) Allowing point mutations in surface epitopes resulting in antigenic drift	

Choose the correct match

	(*a*)	(*b*)	(*c*)	(*d*)	(*e*)
A.	(*i*)	(*iii*)	(*ii*)	(*iv*)	(*i*)
B.	(*i*)	(*iv*)	(*iii*)	(*ii*)	(*i*)
C.	(*iv*)	(*iii*)	(*iv*)	(*ii*)	(*i*)
D.	(*ii*)	(*iv*)	(*iii*)	(*ii*)	(*i*)

102. Suresh was bitten by a poisonous snake and was immediately treated with anti-venom human immunoglobulin and was saved. A year later he was bitten by the same type of snake second time. Predict his response to the venom from second bite from the following:

A. He will be fully protected from the effects of the poison second time because he developed adaptive immunity after first snake bite.
B. He will be equally sensitive as first encounter because there would be no recall of the first encounter.

C. There are residual cells or anti-venom antibodies that were involved in the original/first encounter, hence he will be protected.
D. There will be memory cells made after the first encounter hence he will be more sensitive.

103. An antigen was injected into a mouse. Macrophages and antigen primed T_H cells were isolated from this mouse to perform the following in vitro experiments:
(*a*) Macrophages were treated with the antigen for an hour and then incubated with T_H cells.
(*b*) Macrophages were treated with paraformaldehyde first and then treated with the antigen for an hour. These macrophages were then incubated with T_H cells.
(*c*) Macrophages were treated with paraformaldehyde first then treated with the digested (proteolytically cleaved) antigen for an hour. These macrophages were then incubated with T_H cells.
(*d*) Macrophages were treated with the antigen for an hour and then treated with paraformaldehyde. These macrophages were then incubated with T_H cells.

Which of the above experiments would lead to T_H cells proliferation?
A. (*a*) and (*d*) only B. (*b*) only
C. (*a*), (*c*) and (*d*) only D. (*c*) and (*d*) only

104. Following are the statements which explain why patients with a-linked hyper-IgM syndrome express normal genes for other antibody subtypes but fail to produce IgG, IgA, or IgE:
(*a*) CD40 expressed on B cells is defective
(*b*) CD40L mediates binding of B-cells to T-cells and sends co-stimulatory signals to the B-cells for class switching
(*c*) Without CD40 on macrophage, class switching does not occur
(*d*) CD40L mediates binding of B-cells to macrophages and sends co-stimulatory signals to the B-cells for class switching

Select the option with correct combination.
A. (*a*), (*c*) and (*d*) B. (*a*), (*b*) and (*c*)
C. (*a*) and (*b*) D. (*a*) and (*d*)

DBT-JRF, 2020

105. The biological sample used for diagnosis of Giardiasis is
A. blood B. sputum
C. urine D. stool

Parasites

106. The malarial parasite that has caused recent outbreaks of Monkey malaria in humans is
A. Plasmodium berghei
B. Plasmodium vivax
C. Plasmodium knowlesi
D. Plasmodium malariae

107. Using only random VDJ recombination, from 40 V, 30 D and 6 J gene segments, the number of possible variable regions of the resulting antibody would be
A. 7,200 B. 76
C. 40 D. 1.4×10^6

108. The Freund's complete adjuvant is a mixture of
A. oil, water, dried bacterial spores
B. oil, water and dried Mycobacterium cells
C. amino acids, detergent and dried S. aureus cells
D. glucose, oil and dried E. coli cells

109. Opsonization is the process of
A. coating of foreign substances by antibody
B. coating of foreign substances by MHC
C. coating of foreign substances by TCR
D. none of the given options is correct

110. The enzyme-linked immunospot (ELISPOT) assay is highly sensitive because it can measure
A. total concentration of secreted cytokine
B. RNA copy number of the secreted cytokine
C. size of the cytokine secreting cells
D. frequency of cytokine secreting cells at the single cell level

111. Which of the following is associated with SARS-CoV-2 infection?
A. lymphopenia
B. all of the given option are correct
C. cytokine storm
D. pneumonia

112. Which of the following is NOT an arboviral infection?
A. Dengue fever B. COVID-19
C. Chikungunya fever D. Zika virus disease

113. The Innate immune system recognizes Pathogen Associated Molecular Patterns (PAMPs) through activation of
A. B cell recpetors B. Fc recpeptor
C. Toll-like receptor D. T cell receptor

114. The beta-sheet rich structure of prion protein represents the
A. abnormal disease-causing protein
B. soluble form of the protein
C. normal functional protein
D. intermediator state of the protein

115. What is the use of Aminopterin in hybridoma production?
A. to kill unfused myeloma cells
B. to kill non-antibody secreting hybrids
C. to kill unfused splenic cells
D. to kill non-specific antibody secreting hybrids

116. All the vaccines mentioned below are attenuated or inactivated whole pathogen except
A. oral polio vaccine B. Hepatitis A vaccine
C. rotavirus vaccine D. Tetanus vaccine

117. Cyclosporine, as immunosuppressive drug, given to avoid transplant rejection acts by
A. complement inhibition
B. B cell inhibition
C. T cell inhibition
D. NK cell inhibition

118. Which autoimmune disease is caused by production of autoantibodies and autoreactive T cells against DNA and chromatin proteins?
A. Systemic lupus erythematosus
B. Graves' Disease
C. Sjögren syndrome
D. Multiple Sclerosis

119. A humanized antibody is one in which the
A. antibody heavy chain is from human and light chain is from mouse
B. antibody heavy and light chains are from human
C. complementarity-determining regions (CDRs) are from mouse and the rest is from human
D. antibody light chain is from human and heavy chain is from mouse

120. Hepatitis B is caused by a
A. fungal infection B. viral infection
C. protozoan infection D. bacterial infection

121. The probe used to analyse glycoproteins is
A. interferons B. cytokine
C. lectins D. glutens

122. Which of the following represents the correct sequence of steps in pathogenesis?
A. adhesion, exposure, infection, invasion
B. adhesion, infection, exposure, invasion
C. invasion, infection, adhesion, exposure
D. exposure, adhesion, invasion, infection

GATE (BIOTECHNOLOGY), 2020

123. Which class of antibody is first made by developing B cells inside bone marrow?
A. IgD B. IgE
C. IgA D. IgM

124. Which of the following statements about immune response are correct?
(*a*) T cells are activated by antigen presenting cells.
(*b*) Foreign peptides are not presented to helper T cells by Class II MHC protein.
(*c*) Dendritic cells are referred to as professional antigen -presenting cells.
A. (*a*) and (*c*) only B. (*a*) and (*b*) only
C. (*b*) and (*c*) only D. (*a*), (*b*) and (*c*)

GATE (LIFE SCIENCE), 2020

125. The human major histocompatibility (MHC) is
A. Polygenic and monomorphic
B. Polygenic and polymorphic
C. Monogenic and polymorphic
D. Monogenic and polymorphic

126. Binding of an antibody to its cognate antigen does NOT involve
A. Covalent bonds
B. Electrostatic forces
C. Van der Waals forces
D. Hydrogen bond

127. Match the items in Group I with the most appropriate items in Group II and choose the correct option

Group I	Group II
(*a*) Integrin	(*i*) Phagocytosis in the neural tissue
(*b*) Microglial cell	(*ii*) Antigen processing by cross-presentation
(*c*) TLR-7	(*iii*) Single stranded RNA recognition
(*d*) Dendritic cell	(*iv*) Binding of cells to endthelial

	(*a*)	(*b*)	(*c*)	(*d*)
A.	(*ii*)	(*i*)	(*iii*)	(*iv*)
B.	(*iv*)	(*i*)	(*iii*)	(*ii*)
C.	(*i*)	(*ii*)	(*iii*)	(*iv*)
D.	(*iv*)	(*i*)	(*ii*)	(*iii*)

128. Which ONE of following leucocytes is phagocytic and has clear cytoplasm?
A. Eosinophil B. Monocyte
C. TH-lymphocyte D. Basophil

129. Digestion of an immunoglobulin G (IgG) molecule with pepsin will NOT
A. Generate a bivalent antigen binding fragment
B. Generate monovalent antigen binding fragments
C. Destroy the complement binding site
D. Cleave the heavy chain of IgG molecule

CSIR-NET, JUNE(MORNING), 2021

Immunology & Disease

130. The population that is an highest risk influenza infection should be immunized annually which one of the following is the most important reason for this?
A. Influenza virus can change its surface antigen very frequently.
B. Influenza virus has a very short incubation period.
C. Influenza virus has a reasonably longer incubation period Giving memory B cells time to respond by producing high levels of serums antibody
D. Repeated immunization interferes with the diffraction of plasma cells from memory cells thereby decreasing levels of neutralizing antibody.

131. Which one of the statement given below regarding generation of monoclonal antibodies is INCORRECT?
A. Monoclonal antibodies are the product of a single stimulated B-lymphocyte
B. To generate large quantity of monoclonal antibodies, a normal stimulated antibody producing B-cell is fused with a long lived B-cell tumor
C. The hybridoma generated for antibody production is selected on HAT medium
D. For HAT selection of hybridoma, the antibody producing B-cells are pretreated with 8-azaguanine to block salvage pathway of DNA synthesis.

132. Which of the following is/are associated with the presentation of endogenous antigens by class 1 MHC molecule by an antigen presenting cell(APC), given the condition that there is no cross presentation of antigens by the APC?
A. TAP1 and TAP2 proteins only
B. Invariant chain
C. Proteosome-like subunits LMP2 and LMP7 only
D. TAP1, TAP2 proteins and proteosome-like subunits LMP2, LMP7 TAP1,TAP2

CSIR-NET, JUNE (AFTERNOON), 2021

133. If TLR2 is knocked out from human monocyte-derived macrophages, PAMP recognition by which one of the following TLRs will most probably get affected?
A. TLR 95　B. TLR 3
C. TLR 6　D. TLR 5

134. A newborn baby got mixed up with other babies in a hospital. If the mother is of O blood group and is Rh +ve and the father is of AB blood group and is Rh -ve, which one of the following can be their baby?
A. AB and Rh +ve AB　B. O and Rh –ve o a
C. A and Rh +ve A　D. B and Rh –ve B

135. Which one of the following pathogens does not have the ability to survive within macrophages?
A. Schistosoma mansoni
B. Mycobacterium tuberculosis
C. Listeria monocytogenes
D. Leishmania donovani

136. What is the nature of India's indigenous COVID-19 vaccine?
A. It is an mRNA vaccine (for expression of viral spike protein)
B. It is a preparation of inactivated whole virus
C. It is a preparation of attenuated SARSCov2 virus
D. It is recombinant, replication-deficient chimpanzee adenovirus vector encoding the SARS-CoV-2 Spike

137. Bone marrow cells were sorted using 4 cell-surface markers, CD45R (B220), CD43 (leukosialin), membrane assay Immunoglobulin D (mIgD). The sorted cells were then analyzed for immunoglobulin (Ig) gene rearrangements for the heavy chain. With this information, the sorted cells were categorized into different stages of B-Cell development. The observation the inferences drawn are given below

Sr. No.	Status of cell surface markers	Status of Ig gene rearrangement with respect to heavy chain	Inference drawn
(*a*)	$CD45R^+$,$CD43^-$, $mIgM^{hi}$, $mIgD^{hi}$	V_HDJ_H-Cμ	Mature B-cell
(*b*)	$CD45R^+$,$CD43^+$, $mIgM^-$, $mIgD^-$	Germline arrangement of Ig heavy chain locus	Pro B-cell
(*c*)	$CD45R^+$,$CD43^-$, $mIgM^{low}$, $mIgD^-$	V_HDJ_H-Cμ	Pre B-cell (small Pro B-cell)
(*d*)	$CD45R^+$,$CD43^+$, $mIgM^-$, $mIgD^-$	V_HDJ_H	Immature B-cell
(*e*)	$CD45R^-$, $CD43^+$, $mIgM^-$, $mIgD^-$	Germline arrangement of Ig heavy chain locus	May not be precursor of B-cell

Which of the above inferences are correct?
A. (*b*) and (*d*) only

B. (*a*), (*b*) , (*c*) and (*e*) only
C. (*a*), (*c*) and (*e*) only
D. (*b*), (*d*) and (*e*) only

138. Virus infected cells are cleared by cytolysis by natural killer (NK) cells and CD8+ Cytotoxic T lymphocytes (CTLs). Which of the following graphs correctly represent the changes in the cell number of the two cell types during the course of a viral infection, considering that the virus is cleared by 14th day?

A.

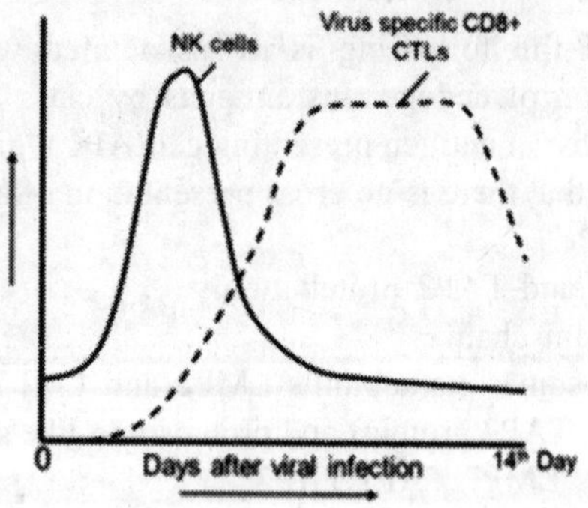

B.

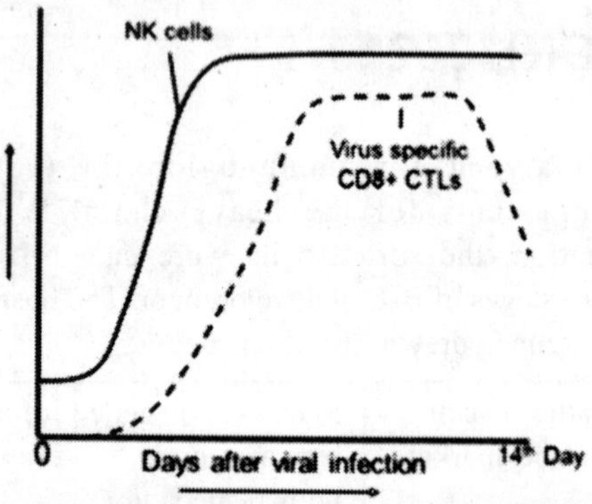

C.

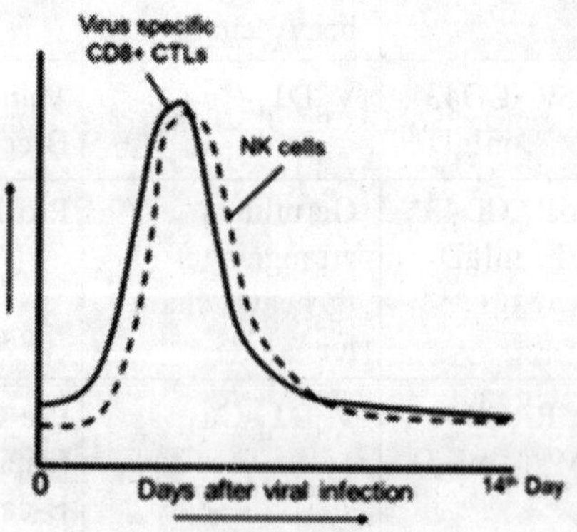

D.

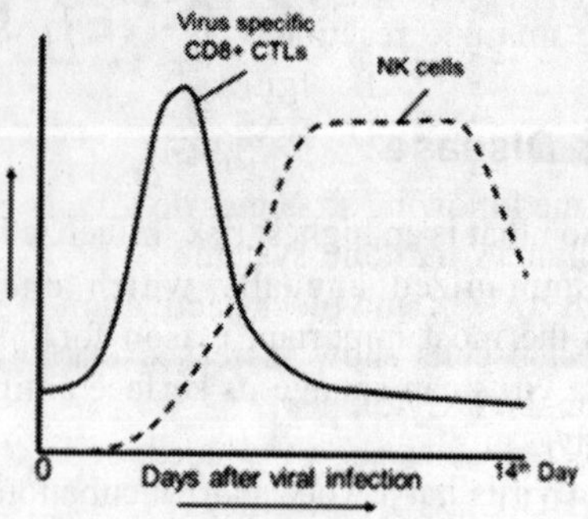

139. Column "X" represents a list of

X	Y
(*a*) Hepatitis -C	(*i*) By inhibiting antigen delivery to Class I MHC receptor on virus infected cell thus preventing presentation of viral antigen to CD8+ T cell
(*b*) Herpes simplex virus (HSV)	(*ii*) By evading antibody mediated distruction through complement activation.
(*c*) Vaccinia virus	(*iii*) By constantly chaning their antigen called antigenic variation.
(*d*) Human Immuno-deficiency Virus (HIV)	(*iv*) By evading the action of IFN-α/β, the major antiviral cytokine.

different viruses and column "Y" represents the mechanisms generally adopted by viruses to evade host defense.

Identfy the correct match:

	(*a*)	(*b*)	(*c*)	(*d*)
A.	(*i*)	(*ii*)	(*iii*)	(*iv*)
B.	(*ii*)	(*iii*)	(*iv*)	(*i*)
C.	(*iii*)	(*iv*)	(*i*)	(*ii*)
D.	(*iv*)	(*i*)	(*ii*)	(*iii*)

140. When species express a suite of correlated traits (e.g., behavior, morphology, function), within a given context or across contexts, it is referred to as
A. A syndrome
B. Trait flexibility
C. Plasticity taal
D. Character displacement

DBT-JRF, 2021

141. Which one among the following can be effectively transmitted from person to person due to coughing?
A. AIDS and Tuberculosis
B. Dengue and COVID-19
C. Malaria and Typhoid
D. Swine Flu and Adenovirus

142. Enzyme linked immunospot (ELISPOT) assay measures:
A. Cytokine concentration in culture supernatant
B. Expression of cytokinc gene
C. Intracellular cytokine concentration
D. Number of cytokines releasing cells at single cell level

143. Which one of the Immunoglobulins (Ig) cause type-I hypersensitive immune reaction?
A. IgA
B. IgE
C. IgG
D. IgM

144. Which one of the following strategies do viruses employ to evade the human immune system?
A. Virus binds to TCR and blocks activation of T cells
B. Virus infected cells show increased expression of proinflammatory Cytokines
C. Virus infected cells show reduced expression of surface MHC Class I molecules
D. Viruses bind to surface Ig on B-cells and neutralize them

145. Single chain variable fragment (ScFV) are fusion proteins composed of:
A. FC region
B. VH + VL (joined by a flexible linker)
C. VH only
D. VL only

146. Which one of the following is the most common adjuvant composed of water in oil emulsion with Mycobacterium tuberculosis components?
A. Alum
B. Complete Freund's adjuvant
C. Incomplete Freund's adjuvant
D. Montanide

147. Which statement is TRUE for pathogenicity islands?
A. These are large segments of bacterial genome encoding virulence factors
B. They coordinate gene expression to make the biofilm
C. They generate signals that activate global response regulators
D. They interfere with the antibody response of the host

148. Protein A, which has strong affinity for Fc region of immunoglobulin, is extracted from:
A. Saccharomyces cerevisae
B. Staphlyococcus pyogenes
C. Staphylococcus aureus
D. Staphylococcus sanjuis

149. What is the role of macrophage activating factor (MAF) in an animal cell culture media?
A. Antiviral
B. Epithelial cell mitogen
C. Inhibits differentiation of embryonic stem cells
D. Support growth of activated T cells

150. Match the components of the List I with those in List II

List I	List II
(*a*) Neutrophil	(*i*) Make antibodies
(*b*) Platelets	(*ii*) Phagocytose and destroy bacteria
(*c*) B-cell	(*iii*) Kill virus infected cell
(*d*) T-cell	(*iv*) Initiate blood clotting

	(*a*)	(*b*)	(*c*)	(*d*)
A.	(*ii*)	(*iv*)	(*i*)	(*iii*)
B.	(*iv*)	(*ii*)	(*i*)	(*iii*)
C.	(*iv*)	(*ii*)	(*i*)	(*iii*)
D.	(*ii*)	(*i*)	(*iv*)	(*iii*)

151. What types of bonds generally stabilize the antigen-antibody interactions?
A. Covalent bonds and hydrogen bonds
B. Disulphide bonds
C. Glycosidic bonds
D. Weak hydrogen bonds and Van der Waals forces

GATE (BIOTECHNOLOGY), 2021

152. Match the autoimmune diseases in Group I with the corresponding primarily affected organ in Group II.

Group I	Group II
(*a*) Hashimoto's disease	(*i*) Brain
(*b*) Juvenile diabetes	(*ii*) Pancreas
(*c*) Multiple sclerosis	(*iii*) Skeletal muscle
(*d*) Myasthenia gravis	(*iv*) Thyroid

	(*a*)	(*b*)	(*c*)	(*d*)
A.	(*i*)	(*ii*)	(*iii*)	(*iv*)
B.	(*iii*)	(*i*)	(*ii*)	(*iv*)
C.	(*iv*)	(*ii*)	(*i*)	(*iii*)
D.	(*i*)	(*ii*)	(*iv*)	(*iii*)

153. Which one of the following statements is INCORRECT about hybridoma production
A. Hybridoma cells can use hypoxanthine and thymidine
B. DNA synthesis in myeloma cells is blocked by aminopterin
C. Hybridoma cells are made to produce polyclonal antibodies
D. Polyethylene glycol is used to fuse myeloma cells to B-cells

154. CRISPR-Cas system is associated with
A. Adaptive Immunity in Eukaryotes
B. Adaptive Immunity in Prokaryotes
C. Innate Immunity in Eukaryotes
D. Innate Immunity in Prokaryotes

155. Match hypersensitivity types in Group I with their corresponding condition in Group II.

Group I	Group II
(*a*) Type I	(*i*) Erythroblastosis fetalis
(*b*) Type II	(*ii*) Host reaction to bee venom
(*c*) Type III	(*iii*) Systemic lupus erythematosus
(*d*) Type IV	(*iv*) Tuberculin reaction

	(*a*)	(*b*)	(*c*)	(*d*)
A.	(*ii*)	(*iii*)	(*i*)	(*iv*)
B.	(*iii*)	(*i*)	(*iv*)	(*ii*)
C.	(*ii*)	(*iii*)	(*iv*)	(*i*)
D.	(*ii*)	(*i*)	(*iii*)	(*iv*)

GATE (LIFE SCIENCE), 2021

Immune System

156. Which one of the following cells lack hypoxanthine-guanine phosphoribosyl transferase (HGPRT)?

A. B Cell B. T Cell
C. Macrophage D. Myeloma Cell

157. Anti-B antibodies are present in the serum of ________

A. Blood group A B. Blood group B
C. Blood group AB D. Blood group O

158. Match the autoimmune diseases in Column I for the self-antigens in Column II

Column I	Column II
(*a*) Rheumatoid arthritis	(*i*) Myelin
(*b*) Systemic lupus erythematosus	(*ii*) Connective tissue
(*c*) Myasthenia gravis	(*iii*) DNA
(*d*) Multiple sclerosis	(*iv*) Acetylcholine receptors

	(*a*)	(*b*)	(*c*)	(*d*)
A.	(*i*)	(*ii*)	(*iii*)	(*iv*)
B.	(*ii*)	(*iii*)	(*iv*)	(*i*)
C.	(*iii*)	(*i*)	(*iv*)	(*ii*)
D.	(*iv*)	(*i*)	(*ii*)	(*iii*)

CSIR-NET, SEPTEMBER (MORNING), 2022

159. The immune system of thymectomized and lethally irradiated (A X B) F_1 mice (H-$2^{a/b}$) were reconstitute thymus from Strain B mice (H-2^b) and with (A X B) F_1 bone marrow cells. These mice were then infected with lymphocytic choriomeningitis virus (LCMV). The CD8+ cytotoxic T lymphocytes from the reconstituted mice were then co-cultured with the following cells:

(*a*) Uninfected fibroblast cells from (A X B) F_1 mouse
(*b*) Uninfected fibroblast cells from strain-A mouse
(*c*) Uninfected fibroblast cells from strain-B mouse
(*d*) LCMV infected fibroblast cells from (A X B) F_1 mouse
(*e*) LCMV infected fibroblast cells from strain-A mouse
(*f*) LCMV infected fibroblast cells from strain-B mouse

Which of the options below indicate the cells that will be lysed by the CD8+ cytotoxic T lymphocytes from the reconstituted mice?

A. (*a*), (*c*), (*d*) and (*f*) only
B. (*d*), (*e*) and (*f*) only
C. (*d*) and (*f*) only
D. (*b*) and (*f*) only

160. Interferons α, β and γ are cytokines produced and secreted by animal cells after infection by viruses. Which one of the following statements about interferons is INCORRECT?

A. When mammalian cells are incubated with different interferons, activation of STATs (Signal Transducers and Activators of Transcription) links stimulation of cell surface receptors with gene expression
B. Increase in the expression of genes after addition of IFNα results only after activation of the interferon-stimulated response element (ISRE)
C. The receptors of all three interferons belong to the Ig superfamily of receptors and do not lead to downstream phosphorylation events
D. An important feature of interferon-STAT signaling pathway is its specificity: each type of interferon induces transcription of a unique subset of genes

161. Mouse IgM (whole molecule) was injected into rabbit to generate antiserum. Which one of the following components (the same mouse from which IgM molecules were used for immunization) has the possibility using the rabbit antiserum in Western blotting?

A. IgG F(ab')2 fragment only
B. J chain only
C. IgG Fc fragment only
D. Both IgG F(ab')2 fragment and J chain

162. Which one of the following combinations of CD molecules and their associated functions is matched INC

A. CD1: Antigen-presenting proteins that present antigenic peptides to T-cell receptors on natural killer T
B. CD8: Thymic differentiation marker for T cells
C. CD11a: A membrane glycoprotein that provides cell-cell adhesion by interaction with ICAM 1 (intercell molecule 1)
D. CD14: Activates innate immune responses by transferring LPS-LBP complex to TLR4

163. While studying pathogenic bacteria, a protein with the following features was identified:

(*a*) It was secreted during infection conditions, but not in in-vitro cultures
(*b*) It was also observed to be present in the membranous fraction in traces, which was released upon ba
(*c*) It had a heat labile N-terminal enzymatic domain that binds MHC molecules, stimulating T cells non-s
(*d*) It had a C-terminal non-enzymatic domain which was highly antigenic and heat-stable

How will you best classify the toxic nature of this protein?

A. An endotoxin B. Superantigen
C. Pore-forming toxin D. A-B toxin

CSIR-NET, SEPTEMBER (AFTERNOON), 2022

164. What is the nature of the successful anti-cancer Human Papilloma Virus (HPV) vaccine?

A. Chemically inactivated virus
B. Live attenuated mutant form of HPV
C. L1 major capsid proteins self-assembled into virus-like particles (VLP)
D. mRNA vaccine expressing viral L1 protein mixed with recombinant viral proteins

165. Inbred mouse strains with different MHC haplotypes (homozygous H-2^m MHC haplotype and homozygous for the H-2^n haplotype) were mated resulting in F1 progeny (H-$2^{m/n}$). Skin transplantation experiments were performed between these mouse strains (parents with H-2^m and H-2^n MHC haplotypes and progeny with H-$2^{m/n}$ MHC haplotype). Which one of the following statements with respect to acceptance and rejection of the skin graft is correct?

A. Skin graft from the progeny will be accepted by any of the parents (recipient).
B. Skin graft from one parent (donor) will be accepted by the other parent (recipient).
C. Skin graft from progeny will be accepted by the parent homozygous for the H-2^m haplotype, but not by the parent homozygous for the H-2^n haplotype.
D. Skin graft from any of the parents will be accepted by the progeny recipient.

166. For an experiment, the hapten DNP was conjugated with the carrier protein BSA or with the carrier protein OVA. A set of mice were primed with either DNP-BSA conjugate or with OVA which was not conjugated to DNA. The following experiments were then performed.

(*a*) X-ray irradiated syngeneic mice were injected with spleen cells from both DNP-BSA– primed mice and OVA-primed mice and then challenged with DNP-OVA conjugate.
(*b*) X-ray irradiated syngeneic mice were injected with T-cell depleted spleen cells from DNP-BSA–primed mice and spleen cells from OVA-primed mice and then challenged with DNP-OVA conjugate.
(*c*) X-ray irradiated syngeneic mice were injected with spleen cells from DNP-BSA–primed mice and T-cell depleted spleen cells from OVA-primed-mice and then challenged with DNP-OVA conjugate.

Which one of the following options of mice will generate secondary anti-hapten response to DNP?

A. The mice in experiment (*a*) only
B. The mice in experiment (*b*) only
C. The mice in experiment (*c*) only
D. The mice in experiments (*a*) and (*b*)

167. Consider the defects in human macrophage cell lines (antigen presenting cells, Column A) and their possible consequence on T cell activation (Column B).

Column A	Column B
(*a*) β2-microglobulin knockout macrophages	(*i*) Cannot activate $CD4^+$ or $CD8^+$ T cells.
(*b*) TLR4 knockout macrophages	(*ii*) Cannot activate $CD4^+$ T cells
(*c*) Macrophages with HLA region for DP, DQ and DR deleted	(*iii*) Cannot activate $CD8^+$ T cells
(*d*) B7 knockout macrophages	(*iv*) Can activate $CD4^+$ or $CD8^+$ T cells.

Select the option that represents all the correct matches

	(*a*)	(*b*)	(*c*)	(*d*)
A.	(*i*)	(*iii*)	(*ii*)	(*iv*)
B.	(*iv*)	(*ii*)	(*iii*)	(*i*)
C.	(*iii*)	(*iv*)	(*ii*)	(*i*)
D.	(*ii*)	(*i*)	(*iv*)	(*iii*)

168. In fever caused by bacterial infection, the set-point of the thermoregulatory mechanism is changed to a new point above 37°C. The following statements were proposed by a researcher to explain the pathogenesis of this fever:

(*a*) The infection induced cytokines inhibit PGE2 in the hypothalamus, and that increases the body temperature.
(*b*) The increased levels of circulating TNFα and IL 1β after infection are not able to induce fever.
(*c*) The endotoxins of bacteria act on the macrophages and monocytes of the infected person to initiate the process that results in the rise of body temperature.
(*d*) The cytokines produced from the macrophages by endotoxins act as endogenous pyrogens in the infected person.
(*e*) The infection induced circulating cytokines act on the organum vasculosum of lamina terminalis (OVLT) which activates preoptic area of hypothalamus resulting in the increase of body temperature.
(*f*) The inhibition of COX2 gene expression by the increased level of circulating cytokines causes the rise of body temperature in the infected person.

Choose the option with all correct statements:

A. (*a*), (*b*) and (*c*)
B. (*b*), (*c*) and (*d*)
C. (*c*), (*d*) and (*e*)
D. (*d*), (*e*) and (*f*)

DBT-JRF, 2022

169. T-cell clones in an individual recognize peptides only when bound and displayed by that individual's MHC molecules on the surface of antigen presenting cells. This process is known as:
A. MHC selection B. MHC restriction
C. MHC interaction D. MHC display

170. AIDS is caused by a human retrovirus that kills:
A. B lymphocytes
B. Lymphocytes stem cells
C. CD4-positive T-lymphocytes
D. CD8-positive T-lymphocytes

171. Short Chain variable fragments (ScFv) of antibody are composed of :
A. VH and VL domains with CH domain
B. VH and VL domains along with Fc region
C. VH and VL domains
D. Only Complementarity Determining Regions

172. RTS,S vaccine for malaria consists of the central repeat (R) region derived from Plasmodium falciparum circumsporozoite protein (CSP) that is genetically fused to the T-cell epitope (T) and surface antigen (S) regions derived from:
A. Vaccinia virus
B. Hepatitis B virus
C. Adenovirus
D. Influenza virus

173. Which one of the following Immunoglobulins cause type 1 allergic reaction?
A. IgG B. IgM
C. IgE D. IgA

174. Sleep loss may induce:
A. increased learning ability and increased body weight
B. increased memory loss and reduced infection
C. increased memory retention, increased infection and reduced cognitive ability
D. increased memory loss, compromised immune system, and deceased cognitive ability

175. Which one of the immunodeficiency is caused by a mutation in BTK gene:
A. X-linked SCID
B. X-linked agammaglobulinemia
C. DiGeorge syndrome
D. Chronic granulomatous disease

GATE (BIOTECHNOLOGY), 2022

176. Match the cell type (Column I) with its function (Column II)

Column I	Column II
(*a*) B cells	(*i*) Humoral immunity
(*b*) Neutrophils	(*ii*) Cytotoxicity
(*c*) T cells	(*iii*) Histamine-associated allergy
(*d*) Mast cells	(*iv*) Phagocytosis

	(*a*)	(*b*)	(*c*)	(*d*)
A.	(*i*)	(*ii*)	(*iii*)	(*iv*)
B.	(*i*)	(*iv*)	(*ii*)	(*iii*)
C.	(*iv*)	(*iii*)	(*i*)	(*ii*)
D.	(*iv*)	(*iii*)	(*ii*)	(*i*)

GATE (LIFE SCIENCE), 2022

Immune System

177. Which of the immune cells listed below are a granular?
(*a*) Eosinophils
(*b*) Mast cells
(*c*) Monocytes
(*d*) T-cells
A. (*a*) and (*b*) only
B. (*b*) and (*c*) only
C. (*c*) and (*d*) only
D. (*d*) and (*a*) only

178. Which of the following statements about IgA is/are correct?
A. It is secreted into colostrum.
B. It is transported across the cell by transcytosis.
C. Its secretion is facilitated by poly-Ig receptor.
D. It primarily exists as a dimer in serum.

179. Which of the following diseases are caused by family of DNA viruses?
A. Hepatitis B B. Smallpox
C. Influenza D. Rabies

180. In the human body, which of the following is/are involved in processing of a foreign antigen?
A. B-cells
B. Macrophages
C. Red blood cells
D. Platelets

ANSWERS

1	**2**	**3**	**4**	**5**	**6**	**7**	**8**	**9**	**10**
D	D	C	B	D	D	D	B	C	C
11	**12**	**13**	**14**	**15**	**16**	**17**	**18**	**19**	**20**
A	C	B	D	C	D	C	C	D	D
21	**22**	**23**	**24**	**25**	**26**	**27**	**28**	**29**	**30**
D	B	C	A	A	B	C	D	B	A
31	**32**	**33**	**34**	**35**	**36**	**37**	**38**	**39**	**40**
D	D	B	B	B	A	C	C	A	B
41	**42**	**43**	**44**	**45**	**46**	**47**	**48**	**49**	**50**
C	C	A	D	A	D	A	C	C	D
51	**52**	**53**	**54**	**55**	**56**	**57**	**58**	**59**	**60**
A	B	D	D	B	D	D	D	A	D
61	**62**	**63**	**64**	**65**	**66**	**67**	**68**	**69**	**70**
B	D	C	D	D	D	B	B	A	D
71	**72**	**73**	**74**	**75**	**76**	**77**	**78**	**79**	**80**
C	B	B	D	C	A	D	A	A	C
81	**82**	**83**	**84**	**85**	**86**	**87**	**88**	**89**	**90**
B	C	A	A	B	A	D	B	A	B
91	**92**	**93**	**94**	**95**	**96**	**97**	**98**	**99**	**100**
B	C	B	D	D	B	C	C	D	B
101	**102**	**103**	**104**	**105**	**106**	**107**	**108**	**109**	**110**
B	B	C	C	D	C	A	B	A	D
111	**112**	**113**	**114**	**115**	**116**	**117**	**118**	**119**	**120**
B	B	C	A	A	D	C	A	C	B
121	**122**	**123**	**124**	**125**	**126**	**127**	**128**	**129**	**130**
C	D	D	A	B	A	B	B	B	B
131	**132**	**133**	**134**	**135**	**136**	**137**	**138**	**139**	**140**
D	D	C	C	A	B	C	A	D	A
141	**142**	**143**	**144**	**145**	**146**	**147**	**148**	**149**	**150**
D	D	B	C	B	B	A	C	A	A
151	**152**	**153**	**154**	**155**	**156**	**157**	**158**	**159**	**160**
D	C	C	B	D	D	A,D	B	C	C
161	**162**	**163**	**164**	**165**	**166**	**167**	**168**	**169**	**170**
D	A	B	C	D	D	C	C	A	D
171	**172**	**173**	**174**	**175**	**176**	**177**	**178**	**179**	**180**
C	B	C	D	B	B	C	A,B,C	A,B	A,B

CHAPTER

8

INSTRUMENTATION & TECHNIQUE

CSIR-NET, JUNE, 2017

Instrumentation

1. In order to separate red and white blood cells, which of the following methods can be used?
A. Ion-exchange chromatography and FACS
B. Hydrophobic chromatography and density gradient centrifugation
C. Density gradient centrifugation and FACS
D. Hydrophobic chromatography and FACS

2. α-bungarotoxin binds to acetylcholine receptor (AChR) protein with high specificity and prevents the ion-channel opening. This interaction can be exploited to purify AChR from membrane using:
A. Ion-exchange chromatography
B. Gel filtration chromatography
C. Affinity chromatography
D. Density gradient centrifugation

3. The Nuclear Magnetic Resonance (1D and 2D) spectrum of a 30-residue peptide were recorded at 25°C. The following observations were made.
(*a*) The NH and CαH resonances were well resolved
(*b*) The NOESY spectra showed extensive Ni-Ni+1 connectivities
(*c*) The NH resonances showed slow exchange with deuterium

The spectra indicates that the peptide adopts
A. Helical conformations
B. Anti-parallel β-strand conformations
C. Polyproline conformation
D. β-turn conformation with four amino acids participating in the tum. Rest of the amino acids are unstructured

Biophysical Methods

4. Denaturation of a highly helical protein having disulfide bridges and two phenylalanines can be monitored as a function of temperature by which one of the following techniques?
A. Recording circular dichroism spectra at various temperatures
B. Monitoring the absorbance at 214 nm at various temperatures
C. Estimating the -SH content during heat denaturation
D. Monitoring the ratio of absorbance at 214 nm and at 250 nm at various temperatures

5. Point group symmetry operations such as inversion and mirror plane are not applicable to protein crystals. This is because
A. protein molecules assemble in highly ordered fashion
B. protein molecules have handedness.
C. protein molecules form a lattice plane that do not diffract X-rays
D. hydrogen atoms in proteins diffract weakly.

Electrophysiological Methods

6. Membrane potential in mitochondria critical for oxidative phosphorylation and is monitored by

A. Patch clamping

B. Measuring internal sodium ions after lysing the mitochondria

C. Measuring distribution of labelled ions across the mitochondrial membrane

D. Measuring the consumption of ATP.

CSIR-NET, DECEMBER, 2017

Molecular Technique, Marker, Immunotechnique

7. A new mutant called early ripening (EL) is identified in a plant. The wild type phenotype is late ripening (LR). Further DNA marker(s) is/are observed to be polymorphic between EL and LR plants. A cross was made between pure lines of LR and ER. The F1 progeny was test crossed and its progeny was analyzed. The parental, F1 and progeny of test cross were also analyzed for the DNA marker. The table below summarizes the phenotype of the progeny and the pattern of DNA marker observed in each case.

Based on the below information, the following statements were made:

(*a*) LR is dominant to ER

(*b*) The DNA marker used is a dominant marker

(*c*) The DNA marker is linked to the phenotype

Generation	Parent		F_1	Progeny of test cross			
Phenotype	ER	LR	LR only	LR		ER	
No. of progeny				52		48	
Pattern of DNA marker on gel electrophoresis	— 	 —	— —	— —	 —	— —	 —
No. of progeny for each pattern				25	27	23	25

Which of the above statements are correct?

A. (*a*)

B. (*a*) and (*b*) only

C. (*a*) and (*c*) only

D. (*a*), (*b*) and (*c*) only

8. Match the technique with its appropriate application/use from the list of options given below

Technique		Application
(*a*) ChIP	(*i*)	Analysis of methylation sites
(*b*) Bisulphite sequencing	(*ii*)	Identification of 5′ and/or 3′ ends of transcripts
(*c*) ELIS	(*iii*)	Identification of binding sites of transcription factors
(*d*) RLMRACE	(*iv*)	Quantification of transgene expression

	(*a*)	(*b*)	(*c*)	(*d*)
A.	(*iii*)	(*i*)	(*iv*)	(*ii*)
B.	(*ii*)	(*iii*)	(*i*)	(*iv*)
C.	(*iv*)	(*i*)	(*iii*)	(*ii*)
D.	(*iii*)	(*iv*)	(*ii*)	(*i*)

9. Diagnosis of influenza virus infections can be done using some of the following techniques:

(*a*) Western blot and Southern blot

(*b*) Northern blot and western blot

(*c*) ELISA and RT-PCR

(*d*) PCR and electron microscopy

Choose the combination of techniques that correctly lists the detection methods.

A. (*a*) and (*b*) only B. (*c*) and (*d*) only

C. (*b*) and (*c*) only D. (*a*) and (*d*) only

Instrumentation

10. Which one of the following microscopes would you use to visualize a protein fused to an appropriate reporter in a living cell?

A. Fluorescence microscope

B. Scanning electron microscope

C. Differential interference contrast microscope

D. Phase contrast microscope

11. Which one of the following statements regarding proteins is CORRECT?

A. $n \rightarrow \sigma^*$ transition requires less energy than $n \rightarrow \pi^*$ transition and can be monitored by mass spectrometry.

B. $n \rightarrow \pi^*$ transition requires more energy than $p \rightarrow \pi^*$ transition and can be monitored by UV-V is spectroscopy.

C. $n \rightarrow \pi^*$ transition requires less energy than $n \rightarrow \sigma^*$ transition and can be monitored by CD spectroscopy.

D. $\sigma \rightarrow \sigma^*$ transition requires less energy than $n \rightarrow \pi^*$ transition and can be monitored by CD spectroscopy.

12. A polymer is synthesized from an achiral amino acid. Conformation of the polymer can be investigated by the following techniques.

(*a*) Fibre diffraction

(*b*) Nuclear magnetic resonance spectroscopy

(*c*) Circular dichroism spectroscopy

(*d*) Differential scanning calorimetry

Choose the combination which would indicate that the polymer adopts a helical conformation

A. (*a*), (*c*) B. (*b*), (*d*)
C. (*a*), (*b*) D. (*c*), (*d*)

Biophysical Methods

13. In an intact cell patch-clamp experiment,

A. two electrodes are inserted into the cytosol but at different depths.
B. one electrode is applied to the plasma membrane in a region containing only lipids and one into the cytosol.
C. two electrodes are applied to the plasma membrane, one in a region containing only lipids and the other in a region containing one or few ion channels.
D. one electrode is applied to the plasma membrane containing one or few ion channels and one electrode inserted into the cytosol.

14. Following observations are made regarding a peptide sequence.

– The peptide is inert to Ellman's reagent. However, on reacting with β-mercaptoethanol, the peptide gives a positive Ellman's test.
– The peptide sequence gives a broad minimum around 211 nm in the CD spectrum.
– With increasing concentration of the peptide, the melting temperature of the peptide increases.
– On treating the peptide with D_2O, half the total number of amides gets exchanged.

Which one of the following statements is correct?

A. It is an α-helical peptide that undergoes aggregation
B. It is an α-helical disulfide bridged peptide that undergoes aggregation
C. It is an β-hairpin peptide, which is stabilized by a disulfide bridge
D. The peptide is composed of an α-helix and β-sheet connected by a disulfide bridge

15. If a metabolically active cell is challenged with 55Fe radioisotope label, which of the following proteins CANNOT be detected by autoradiography?

A. Aconitase and lipoic acid synthase
B. Cytochrome C and DNA primase
C. Calmodulin and Calcineurin
D. Myoglobin and Homoaconitase

Microscopic Techniques

16. To achieve a best resolution using a fluorescence microscope, what combination of wavelength of emitted light (λ), refractive index and the angle (2θ) by which light enters into the microscope would be the best choice for the user:

A. λ = 405; refractive index = 1.33; 2θ = 90°
B. λ = 420; refractive index = 1.51; 2θ = 180°
C. λ = 520; refractive index = 1.51; 2θ = 90°
D. λ = 405; refractive index = 1.51; 2θ = 180°

17. From the following Statements:

(*a*) Coloured images can be obtained by transmission electron microscopy by fluorescent labelling of the specimen
(*b*) Scanning electron microscopy requires sectioning of the sample
(*c*) Confocal microscopy uses optical methods to obtain images from a specific focal plane and excludes light from other planes
(*d*) Differential-interference microscopy relies on interference between polarized light due to differences in the refractive index of the object and surrounding medium
(*e*) Visualization in epifluorescence microscopy requires staining by heavy metal atoms

Choose the combination with two correct and one incorrect statement.

A. (*b*), (*c*), (*e*) B. (*a*), (*b*), (*e*)
C. (*a*), (*c*), (*d*) D. (*b*), (*d*), (*e*)

Electrophysiological Methods

18. Given below are spatial and temporal techniques (column I) used to detect brain activity (column II)

Column I		Column II
(*a*) Functional magnetic resonance imaging	(*i*)	Uses short-lived radioactive material to map functional processes in brain
(*b*) Positron emission tomography	(*ii*)	Measure the fluctuation of dipole voltage in neurons of brain
(*c*) Computed tomography	(*iii*)	Detects changes in blood oxygenation and flow due to neural activity
(*d*) Electroence phalogram	(*iv*)	Images of brain obtained by differential absorption of X rays

Select the correct set of combination

	(*a*)	(*b*)	(*c*)	(*d*)
A.	(*i*)	(*ii*)	(*iii*)	(*iv*)
B.	(*iii*)	(*i*)	(*iv*)	(*ii*)
C.	(*iv*)	(*iii*)	(*ii*)	(*i*)
D.	(*ii*)	(*iv*)	(*i*)	(*iii*)

19. When the electrical response of the two receptors A1 and A2 in a noctuid moth that was exposed to a variety of sounds was measured, it produced the following patterns

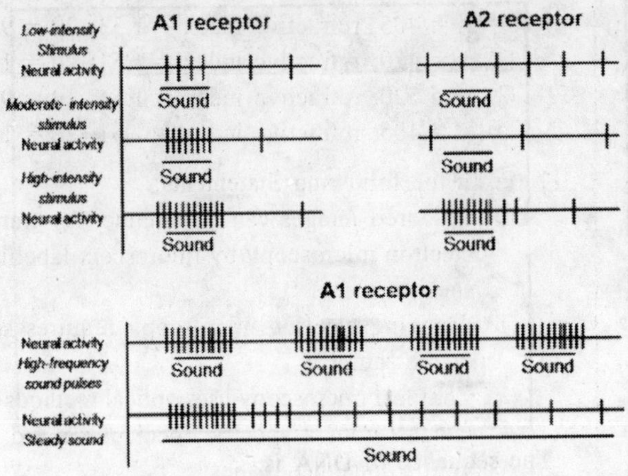

Given this, which one of the following statements is INCORRECT:

A. The A1 receptor is sensitive to sound of low to high intensity.
B. A2 receptor begins to produce action potentials only when a sound is loud.
C. Both the receptors have similar response to high intensity sound.
D. The A1 receptor fires much more frequently to steady, uninterrupted sounds than to high frequency pulses of sound.

DBT-JRF, 2017

Methods in Biotechnology

20. Resolution in adsorption chromatography is achieved at:

A. Elution stage only
B. Binding stage only
C. Equilibration stage only
D. Both binding and elution stage.

21. Which one of the following techniques cannot be used to remove salt from a protein solution?

A. Ultrafiltration
B. Ion exchange chromatography
C. Gel filtration chromatography
D. Dialysis

22. To achieve complete separation of two pharmaceutical compounds (shown as two peaks in the chromatogram), the relative separation (RS) should be:

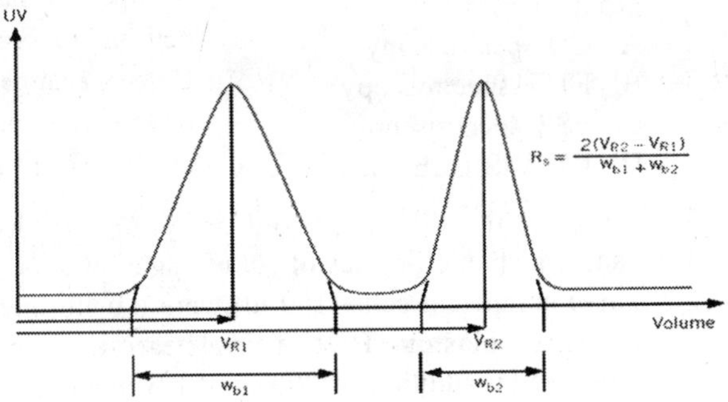

A. ≤ 1
B. ≥ 1.5
C. < 0.5
D. $= 0.8$

23. The following figure shows the electrophoretic migration of a secretory protein in SDS-PAGE from the time of its synthesis (0 min) to its secretion (90 min) from the cells.

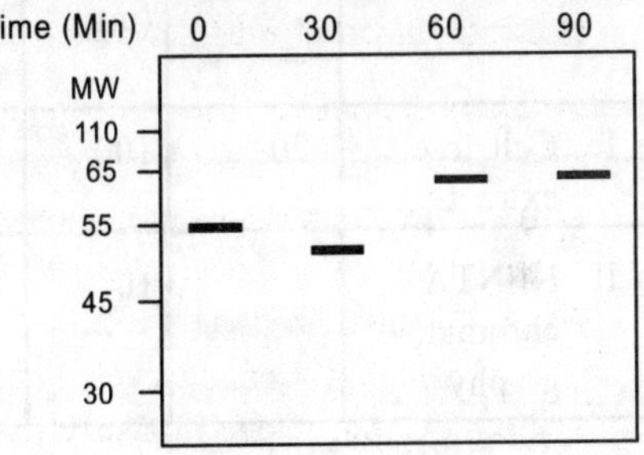

Assuming that there was no problem in sample preparation and SDS-PAGE, the reason for a lower band at 30 min and a higher band at 60 and 90 min compared to that at 0 min be due to:

A. Changes in the rate of protein synthesis at various time points
B. The protein was associated with other proteins at different time points resulting in change in its migration
C. The protein underwent processing and posttranslational modifications as a function of time
D. Small changes observed in the migration of the protein do not give enough

24. Match the Matrices in Group I with appropriate gradient elution condition from Group II

Group I	Group II
(*a*) DEAE-Sephacel	(*i*) Isocratic gradient
(*b*) Phenyl-Sepharose	(*ii*) Increasing concentrations Of sodium chloride
(*c*) Chromatofocusing	(*iii*) Decreasing concentrations of ammonium sulphate
(*d*) Sephadex-G100	(*iv*) pH gradient

	(*a*)	(*b*)	(*c*)	(*d*)
A.	(*ii*)	(*iii*)	(*iv*)	(*i*)
B.	(*ii*)	(*iii*)	(*i*)	(*iv*)
C.	(*iii*)	(*ii*)	(*i*)	(*iv*)
D.	(*iv*)	(*i*)	(*ii*)	(*iii*)

25. Match the techniques in Group I with applications given in Group II

Group I	Group II
(*a*) Salting out	(*i*) pI determination
(*b*) Ultracentrifugation	(*ii*) Protein precipitation
(*c*) Dialysis	(*iii*) Sedimentation coefficient
(*d*) Isoelectric focusing	(*iv*) Removal of low molecular weight impurities

	(*a*)	(*b*)	(*c*)	(*d*)
A.	(*ii*)	(*iii*)	(*iv*)	(*i*)
B.	(*i*)	(*iii*)	(*ii*)	(*iv*)
C.	(*iv*)	(*i*)	(*iii*)	(*ii*)
D.	(*ii*)	(*iv*)	(*iii*)	(*i*)

26. Purification data for an enzyme is given below:

	Purification Step	Volume (ml)	Total protein (mg)	Total activity (micromole/min)
Step I	Cell free extract	20	100	150
Step II	Ni-NTA chromatography	4	10	120

What is the fold-purification?

A. 8 B. 13.5
C. 10.5 D. 18

27. Asynchronous animal cells were stained with a fluorescent DNA binding dye and analyzed by flow cytometry. The histogram of cell count versus fluorescence intensity is shown below with or without treatment.

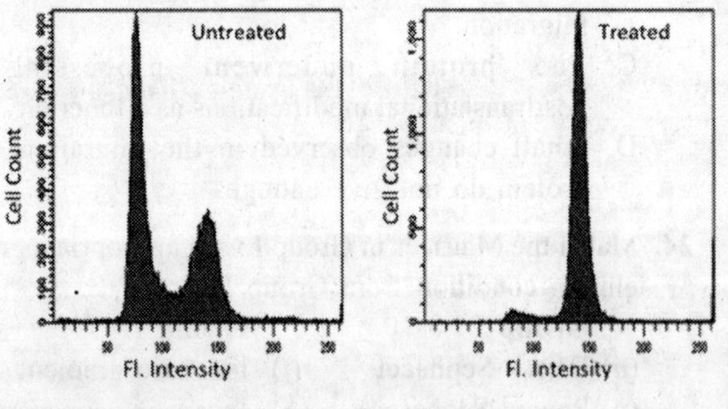

It can be concluded from the histogram that:

A. The treatment inhibits the cells from entering the S-phase
B. The treatment increases the proportion of G1 phase
C. The treatment increases the proportion of G2/M phase
D. The treatment increases the proportion of S phase

28. A student sequenced a DNA using Sanger's method and obtained the following autoradiogram.

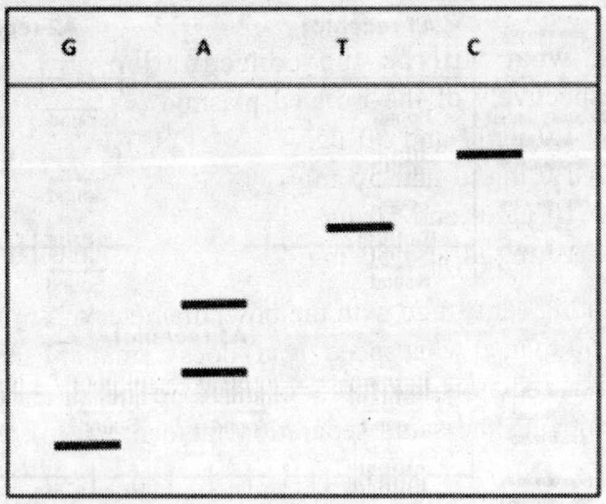

The sequence of DNA is:

A. 5'CTTAG'3 B. 5'GAATC'3
C. 5'CTAAG'3 D. 5'AATTG'3

29. Bindin is a protein that is expressed in the tip of sperm head (acrosome) and is important for sperm-egg interaction. Its distribution pattern changes during sperm maturation. Which one of the following methods may be used to monitor the expression pattern of bindin in a simple light microscope?

A. Phase contrast microscopy
B. Normarski-contrast microscopy
C. Immuno cytochemistry
D. Immunofluorescence

30. Lyophilization is a method used for preservation of microbes because:

A. moisture is removed by sublimation
B. moisture is removed by very slow evaporation
C. ice crystals formed at low temperature improves cell viability
D. removal of air during lyophilization prevents formation of free radicals

31. The spectroscopic method for detection of functional groups is:

A. CD spectroscopy
B. FTIR spectroscopy
C. ESR spectroscopy
D. UV-VISIBLE spectroscopy

32. Competent cells prepared in your lab have a transformation efficiency of 10^8 cfu/μg of plasmid DNA. These competent cells (100 μl) were transformed with 10 ng of plasmid DNA using heat shock method followed by addition of 900 μl of LB medium. 100 μl of transformed cells were plated on antibiotic containing plates. The number of colonies expected to be on the plate would be:

A. 10^5 B. 10^4
C. 10^3 D. 10^2

33. The A_{260} of a plasmid solution after 100-fold dilution is 0.2. Given that A_{260} of 1.0 represents 50 μg/ml of DNA and the total volume of isolated plasmid solution is 50 µl, what will be the concentration and amount respectively of the isolated plasmid?

A. 1.0 µg/µl and 50 µg
B. 1.0 mg/µl and 50 mg
C. 10 µg/µl and 50 µg
D. 10 mg/µl and 50 mg

34. If a big centrifuge with the bowl diameter of 1m rotates at 60 rpm, at what speed (rpm) does a smaller centrifuge with a diameter of 0.5 m need to be operated for achieving the same separation factor?

A. 85
B. 120
C. 30
D. 42

35. What is the linear flow rate (superficial velocity in cm/h) in a chromatographic column of 1.0 cm inner diameter with a bed porosity of 0.8 when the volumetric flow rate is 1 ml/min?

A. 61.1
B. 76.4
C. 38.2
D. 15.2

GATE (BIOTECHNOLOGY), 2017

Analytical Tools

36. Which one of the following techniques can be used to determine the structure of a 15 KDa globular protein at atomic resolution?

A. Raman spectroscopy
B. IR spectroscopy
C. UV spectroscopy
D. NMR spectroscopy

37. Enzyme linked immunosorbent assay (ELISA) is used for

A. quantifying antibody levels in blood
B. determining the molecular weight of an antigen.
C. purifying proteins from biological fluids.
D. determining the molecular weight of an antibody.

38. A proto-oncogene is suspected to have undergone duplication in a certain type of cancer. Of the following techniques, which one would be verify gene duplication?

A. Northern blotting
B. Southern blotting
C. South western blotting
D. Western blotting

GATE (LIFE SCIENCE), 2017

39. The molecular weight of a protein as determined by native PAGE is 400 kDa. This protein when run on a non-reducing SDS-PAGE gave a band of 200 kDa, and on a reducing SDS-PAGE, gave a band of 100 kDa. The protein has

A. Four subunits of which two sets are linked by two disulphide bridges
B. Four subunits which are linked by four disulphide bridges
C. Two subunits only and none are linked by disulphide bridges
D. Two subunits which are linked by disulphide bridges

40. Which one of the following techniques CANNOT be used to determine the sequence of a novel protein?

A. De novo sequencing by ESI-MS/MS
B. Edman degradation
C. Sanger sequencing
D. Peptide mass fingerprinting

41. Which type of polyacrylamide gel can be used for analysing the four different proteins listed below?

Protein P: 60 kDa, pI 4
Protein Q: 45 kDa, pI 8
Protein P: 60 kDa, pI 6
Protein P: 45 kDa, pI 7.5

A. 20% gel, pH 4-7
B. 20% gel, pH 3-10
C. 12% gel, pH 3-10
D. 12% gel, pH 4-7

CSIR-NET, JUNE, 2018

Molecular Technique and Marker

42. Scientists discovered two new plant species. "A" and "B" that look similar except that, species "A" bears flowers and leaves that are twice the size of those in species "B''. Which method should the scientists use to appropriately investigate if species "A" is a result of gene duplication in species "B''?

A. Sequence similarity, gene structure and gene size.
B. Plant size, physical proximity of gene and genome size.

C. Sequence similarity, physical proximity of gene, genome size.
D. Sequence length, gene structure and chromosome count.

43. From the various techniques listed below, which one CANNOT be used to precisely map the transcription start-site of a gene?
A. S1 Mapping
B. Sequencing the region downstream of promoter
C. 5' RACE
D. Primer Extension Method

44. Three students (P, Q, R) in a research lab were trying to identify proteins that interact with a transcription factor X. P performed gel filtration experiments and identified that X was found along with proteins A, B, C and D. Q performed coimmunoprecipitation experiments using antibodies to X and identified A, B and C. R did a yeast-2-hybrid screen and identified only B.

The following are likely conclusions that may explain all the results:
(*a*) A, B, C and D are in a complex with X.
(*b*) X directly interacts with B.
(*c*) Only A, B and C are in complex with X.
(*d*) D is probably weakly associated with X.

Which of the above conclusions best explains all the results?
A. (*a*), (*b*) and (*c*)
B. (*a*), (*b*) and (*d*)
C. (*a*), (*c*) and (*d*)
D. (*b*), (*c*) and (*d*)

45. A certain protein has been assumed to play an indispensable role in the survival of an intracellular parasite inside the host cells. Which one of the following techniques will best prove the assumption to be correct?
A. Treat the parasite-infected host cells with an inhibitor of the protein and check the number of parasites per host cell under the microscope.
B. Check the expression of the protein in parasite-infected host cells.
C. Check the activity of the protein in parasite-infected host cells.
D. Treat the parasite-infected host cells with an activator of the protein and check the number of parasites per host cell under the microscope.

46. Which one of the following set of essential components are required for Sanger method of DNA sequencing in a required buffer containing MgCl2 and Tris-HCl?
A. DNA template, a primer, 4 deoxyribonucleotides, 4 labelled dideoxyribonucleotides, DNA polymerase
B. DNA template, a primer, 4 labelled dideoxyribonucleotides, DNA polymerase, DNA ligase
C. DNA template, 4 deoxyribonucleotides, 4 labelled dideoxyribonucleotides, DNA polymerase, DNA ligase
D. DNA template, a primer, 4 labelled dideoxyribonucleotides, DNA polymerase, telomerase

Instrumentation

47. The MALDI mass spectrum of a peptide gave a single peak with M/z of 2000. The ESI mass spectrum of the same peptide gave multiple peaks. These observations indicate that
A. degradation has occurred while acquiring ESI mass spectrum
B. multiple charged species of the same compound are observed in the ESI spectrum
C. the sample is impure
D. ESI induces polymerization of the peptide

48. Protein conformational dynamics CANNOT be determined by which one of the following techniques
A. NMR spectroscopy
B. Differential scanning calorimetry
C. Mass spectroscopy
D. Fluorescence microscopy

49. From the following statements,
(*a*) Surface plasmon resonance can be used to determine binding constants only in the range of 10^2-10^3 M.
(*b*) *de novo* sequencing is not possible by mass spectral methods.
(*c*) The position of hydrogen atoms in proteins is not directly determined by X-ray, diffraction.
(*d*) Circular dichroism and nuclear magnetic resonance spectroscopy do not give the same information on protein structure.

Choose the option with all correct statements.
A. (*a*), (*b*), (*c*)
B. (*a*), (*c*), (*d*)
C. (*b*), (*d*)
D. (*c*), (*d*)

Biophysical Methods

50. A group of palaeontologists digging in an area discovers a pre-historic human burial site. The same group, while exploring a nearby area, discovered fossil remains of what appeared to be more than 100 million year old dinosaur bones. Which of the following combinations of modern radiometric dating techniques should they use to calculate the age of these fossils most accurately?
A. ^{14}C dating for human remains and ^{235}U dating for dinosaur remains
B. ^{87}Rb dating for both human and dinosaur remains
C. ^{14}C dating for both human and dinosaur remains
D. ^{129}I dating for human remains and ^{129}Xe for dinosaur remains

51. Given below is a table with information on isotopes, their half-life and type of particle(s) they emit.

Symbol and atomic weight	Half life	Type of particle(s) emitted
(*a*) ^{11}C	(*i*) 5700 yrs	(X) β
(*b*) ^{14}C	(*ii*) 15.1 hours	(Y) γ
(*c*) ^{24}Na	(*iii*) 20 min	

Choose the correct combination from the options given below.

	(*a*)	(*b*)	(*c*)
A.	(*iii*) (Y)	(*ii*) (X) (Y)	(*i*) (Y)
B.	(*iii*) (X)	(*i*) (X)	(*ii*) (X),(Y)
C.	(*ii*) (X),(Y)	(*iii*) (X),(Y)	(*i*) (X)
D.	(*i*) (X)	(*ii*) (X)	(*iii*) (X), (Y)

Microscopic Techniques

52. Sub-cellular fractionation-based assays have been used to identify various organelles in the mammalian cells. In order to characterize such organelles in a living mammalian cell, which of the following microscopy-based method would be the most accurate?

A. use of fluorescent probes specific for organelles.
B. use of organelle specific fluorescent probes followed by microinjection of fluorescent antibodies against organelle specific protein.
C. use of fluorescent probes in permeabilized cells.
D. use of organelle specific fluorescent probes followed by cryo-electron microscopy

53. In order to visualize the intracellular organization of a cell, one can utilize various microscopy-based techniques. These include:

(*a*) Differential interference contrast (DIC) microscopy
(*b*) Phase contrast microscopy
(*c*) Dark field microscopy
(*d*) Epifluorescence microscopy
(*e*) Scanning electron microscopy
(*f*) Transmission electron microscopy
(*g*) Confocal microscopy

Which of the above mentioned microscopes can be used to study the intracellular dynamics using live cell imaging?

A. (*a*), (*b*), (*e*), (*f*), (*g*)
B. (*a*), (*b*), (*c*), (*d*), (*g*)
C. (*a*), (*d*), (*e*), (*f*), (*g*)
D. (*c*), (*d*), (*e*), (*f*), (*g*)

Immunotechniques

54. In order to detect minor variations in antigen concentration, the following procedures were suggested. Which one will likely be the best option?

A. Antigen coated microtitre well → add antibody → add enzyme conjugated secondary antibody → add substrate and measure colour.
B. Antibody coated microtitre well → add antigen → add enzyme conjugated secondary antibody → add substrate and measure colour.
C. Preincubate antigen with fixed amount of antibody → add to antigen coated well → add enzyme conjugated secondary antibody → add substrate and measure colour.
D. Preincubate antigen with fixed amount of antibody → add to antibody coated well → add enzyme conjugated secondary antibody → add substrate and measure colour.

CSIR-NET, DECEMBER, 2018

Molecular Technique and Marker

55. Given below is a marker profile for two parental lines (P1 and P2) and their derived F1 progeny:

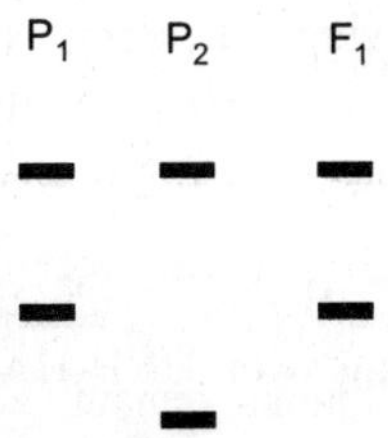

The marker that is represented in the above figure is most likely to be

A. RFLP or SSR
B. SSR only
C. SSR or RAPD
D. RAPD only

56. In an experiment, intact chromatin was isolated and digested with micrococcal nuclease in independent tubes for 30 min, 1 h, 2h, and 4h. Further, the DNA was purified from each tube, separated on agarose gel and Southern hybridization was performed with rRNA gene probe and a centromeric DNA probe. Which one of the following patterns of signal intensity from both of the probes is likely to be obtained following Southern hybridization?

A. With increasing time, compared to centromeric probe, a rapid increase in signal intensity of rRNA gene probe was observed.
B. With increasing time, compared to centromeric probe, a rapid decrease in signal intensity of rRNA gene probe was observed.

C. Irrespective of incubation period, both probes produced identical band intensities.
D. Treatment with micrococcal nuclease would instantly degrade the DNA, hence, no hybridization signal would be obtained in any of the samples.

57. In a genetic assay, randomly generated fragments of yeast DNA were cloned into a bacterial plasmid containing gene '*X*' essential for yeast viability on minimal media. The recombinant plasmid was used to transform a yeast strain deficient in recombination and lacking '*X*' gene. Transformants, which survive on minimal media and form colonies should essentially have:
A. Yeast centromeric sequence which ensures integrity of the plasmid after transformation.
B. Enhancers for the essential gene missing in the transformed strain.
C. sequence similar to bacterial origin of replication
D. Yeast autonomous replicating sequence.

58. A western blot analysis after treating cancer cells with a prospective anti-cancer drug is shown below:

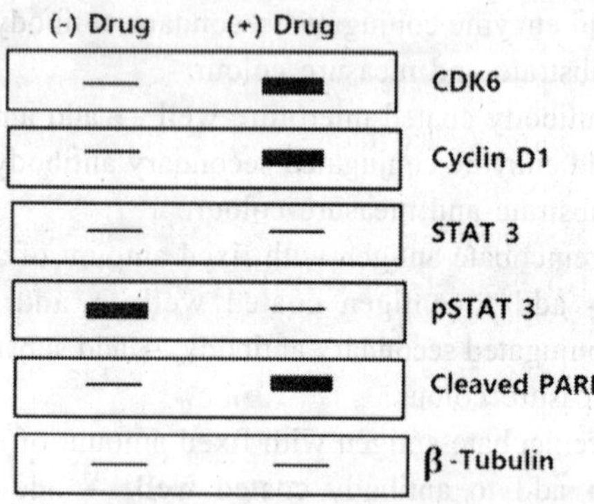

The following assumptions were made:
(*a*) The drug may have arrested the growth of cells at the G1 phase.
(*b*) The drug targeted the JAK-STAT signalling pathway.
(*c*) The drug led to apoptosis of the cells.
(*d*) Drug-induced apoptosis was through the extrinsic or mitochondrial-independent pathway.

Which one of the following combination is correct?
A. Only (*b*) and (*d*)
B. (*a*), (*b*) and (*c*)
C. Only (*a*) and (*b*)
D. (*b*), (*c*) and (*d*)

59. Polymorphic DNA sequences are used for molecular identification. Short tandem repeats (STRs) and Single Nucleotide Polymorphism (SNPs) are used as polymorphic markers. The table below summarizes the status of autosomal. SNP, autosomal STR, mitochondrial SNP, Y- linked STR for four individuals related to each other, representing parents and their two children.

	Autosomal		Mt DNA		Y-linked
Individual	SNP	STR	SNP 1	SNP 2	STR
A	C/C	13/12	C	G	13
B	C/G	13/13	C	A	13
C	C/G	14/13	C	A	–
D	C/C	13/14	C	A	–

Based on the above data, identify the individuals representing the two parents.
A. Individuals A and D
B. Individuals A and C
C. Individuals B and C
D. Individuals C and D

Instrumentation

60. Given below are names of techniques (Column A) and their characteristic features/applications (Column B):

Column A	Column B
(*a*) Hybridoma technology	(*i*) Separation of technology proteins according to charge
(*b*) MALDI-TOF	(*ii*) Identification of protein complexes in cells
(*c*) Ion-exchange chromatography	(*iii*) Production of identical antibodies
(*d*) Co-immunoprecipitation	(*iv*) Determination of molecular weight of proteins and/or peptides

Which one of the following represents a correct match between Column A and Column B:

	(*a*)	(*b*)	(*c*)	(*d*)
A.	(*ii*)	(*iii*)	(*iv*)	(*i*)
B.	(*iii*)	(*iv*)	(*i*)	(*ii*)
C.	(*iv*)	(*i*)	(*ii*)	(*iii*)
D.	(*ii*)	(*iv*)	(*i*)	(*iii*)

61. Detailed NMR spectra of a 20-residue peptide were recorded using a 600 MHz instrument.

If the peptide adopts an α-helical conformation, which one of the following statements is correct?
A. Prominent NHi-NHi+1 NOE peaks would be observed along with 3JNH-HA coupling constants 8.5 Hz
B. Prominent CαHi-NHi+1 NOE peaks would be observed along with 3JNH-HA coupling constants 4.8 Hz
C. Prominent CαHi-NHi+1 NOE peaks with 3JNH-HA coupling constants 8.5 Hz
D. Prominent NHi-NHi+1 NOE peaks along with 3JNH-HA coupling constants 4.8Hz.

62. Highly purified peptides Pl, P2 and P3 were subjected to MALDI mass spectral analysis. The following observations were made:

P1: Showed a m/z of 16 more than the expected value.

P2: Showed a m/z of 80 more than the expected value. MS/MS spectra of the peptide resulted in a precursor ion with m/z 98 less than the expected m/z.

P3: Showed a m/z that was double the expected value.

[Note: z = + 1 for all the mass spectra.]

Which one of the options given below comprises all correct interpretations?

A. P1: Cys is oxidized; P2: has undergone oxidation at multiple Met residues; P3: is a non-covalent dimer.

B. P1; Met is oxidized; P2: is phosphorylated; P3: is a covalent dimer.

C. P1: Met is oxidized; P2: multiple Cys are oxidized; P3 is a covalent dimer.

D. P1: Cys is oxidized; P2: phosphorylated and oxidized at Met; P3: is a noncovalent dimer.

Microscopic Techniques

63. Which one of the following is used as a source of excitation in a confocal microscope?

A. Lasers B. Electron beam

C. Mercury lamp D. Masers

64. The most important property of any microscope is its resolution. Which one of the following 125. Wavelengths (nm) would be used to achieve the best resolution using a light microscope with lenses having numerical aperture (NA) of 1.4?

A. 450

B. 480

C. 560

D. 700

DBT-JRF, 2018

Methods in Biotechnology

65.

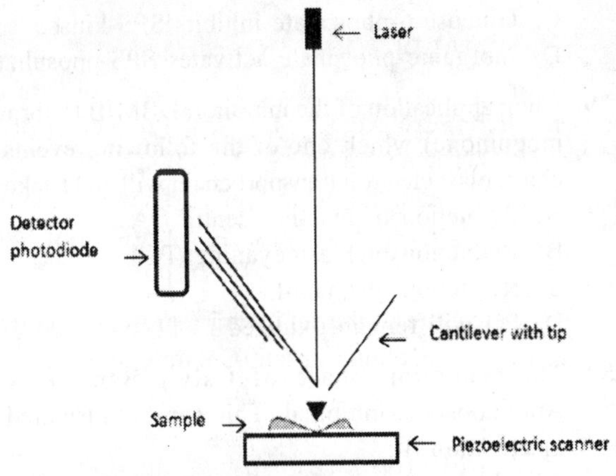

The schematic represents the basic structural components of a

A. Cryo electron microscope

B. Confocal microscope

C. Atomic force microscope

D. Dark field microscope

66. DNA with the sequence 5′ CGC TCG TC TGCCCTG GTCCC TT G TGCC3′ needs to be PCR amplified. The reverse primer will have the following sequence:

A. 5′ GGCATCTA3′

B. 5′ TAGATGCC3′

C. 5′ GGACTCTA3′

D. 5′ CGCATCGA3′

67. Hot start PCR is performed to:

A. Expedite the PCR reaction

B. Prevent mutations

C. Prevent primer-dimer formations

D. Minimize non-specific amplification

68. A scientist aims to identify a binding site for a new transcriptional anti-terminator protein. Which one of the following techniques will be most appropriate for this experiment?

A. Microarray B. RNA Sequencing

C. RIP Sequencing D. ChIP Sequencing

69. In which one of the following PCR assays only one primer is used for amplification?

A. SSR B. SCAR

C ISSR D. CAPS

70. The result of an in vitro phosphorylation assay of a protein using γ-^{32}P ATP in the presence of various kinases is shown below. The bands represent phosphorylated proteins detected.

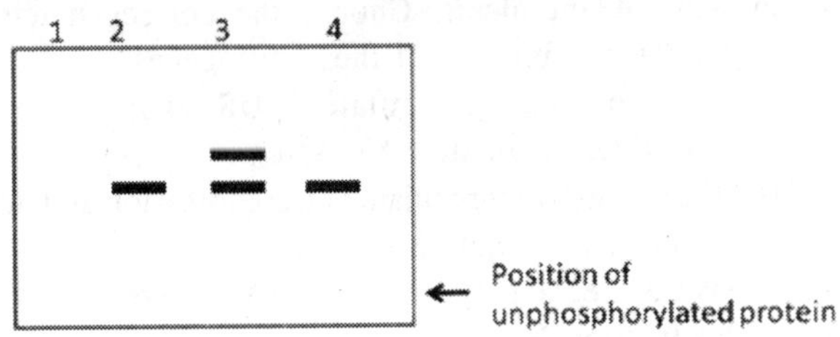

1. Lane 1: No kinase
2. Lane 2: Kinase 2
3. Lane 3: Kinase 2 followed by inactivation of kinase and subsequent addition of kinase 3
4. Lane 4: Kinase 3 followed by inactivation of kinase and subsequent addition of kinase 2

Based on the autoradiograph shown above it can be concluded that:

A. The protein cannot be phosphorylated by any kinase

B. Kinase 3 phosphorylates two sites on the protein

C. Kinase 2 can phosphorylate the protein independent of kinase 3
D. Kinase 3 can phosphorylate the protein independent of kinase 2

71. Hemoglobin is made up of two copies each of α and β globin subunits. The techniques used to establish the stoichiometry of α and β subunits are:
A. SDS-PAGE and hydrophobic interaction chromatography
B. Gel filtration chromatography and Ion-exchange chromatography
C. SDS-PAGE and gel filtration chromatography
D. Isoelectric focusing and Native PAGE

72. Sedimentation efficiency depends on the relative strength of
A. Drag versus centrifugal force
B. Drag versus gravitational force
C. Gravitational versus centrifugal force
D. Gravitational versus electrostatic force

73. Which one of the following is NOT used for partition-based bioseparation?
A. Solvent extraction
B. Electrodialysis
C. Salting out
D. Adsorption chromatography

Agricultural Biotechnology

74. Flower development in plants is regulated by the ABC model of gene regulation. Members of this gene family are characterized by which one of the following domains.
A. C box
B. MADS box
C. WRKY
D. NAC

75. In CLAVATA (clv) mutant of Arabidopsis, Shoot Apical Meristem (SAM) size and expression of WUSCHEL (WUS) is increased. SAM size is reduced in wus mutant plants. Choose the correct statement regarding the function of these two genes:
A. CLV positively regulate WUS expression and negatively regulate SAM size
B. CLV negatively regulate WUS expression and WUS positively regulate SAM size
C. WUS negatively regulate SAM size and CLV expression
D. WUS and CLV independently regulate SAM size

76. The bacterial flagellin activates a typical MAPK cascade consisting of MEKK1-MKK4-MPK6 leading to the activation of ACS6 enzyme involved in ethylene biosynthesis in plants.

Which one of the following events will be true in a transgenic Arabidopsis plant overexpressing the constitutively active form of MKK4?
A. Ethylene-responsible genes will be less transcribed in the presence of flagellin stimuli
B. MPK6 will not get activated in the absence of flagellin
C. Flagellin stimuli are not required for the activation of ACS6
D. Flagellin stimuli will be required for ethylene biosynthesis

77. Which one of the following statements is correct during gibberellic acid (GA) signal transduction in plants?
A. DELLA protein stimulates GA response
B. GID1 does not make complex with DELLA protein
C. Degradation of DELLA protein by 26S proteasomal pathway
D. GID1 proteins get degraded by 26S proteasomal pathway

78. Sucrose-phosphate synthase (SPS) is inhibited by SPS-kinase and activated by SPS-phosphatase. It is known that a high ratio of Glucose-6-phosphate to inorganic phosphate maintains SPS in its active form. Which one of the following statements is true?
A. Glucose-6-phosphate inhibits SPS-phosphatase
B. Inorganic phosphate activates SPS-kinase
C. Glucose-6-phosphate inhibits SPS-kinase
D. Inorganic phosphate activates SPS-phosphatase

79. Upon application of the inhibitor, DBMIB (Dibromothymoquinone) which one of the following events in the chloroplast electron transport chain will NOT take place?
A. Reduction of reaction centre QA
B. Reduction of Plastocyanine (PC)
C. Reduction of Cytb6f
D. PQ will remain oxidized

80. The reduction phase of Calvin-Benson cycle in Arabidopsis is inhibited. This can be attributed to the inactivation of:
A. Aldolase
B. Triose phosphate isomerase
C. Fructose-1, 6-bisphosphatase
D. 3-Phosphoglycerate kinase

81. Oat seeds will usually NOT germinate when exposed to Red (R) and Far red (FR) light in the following order:
A. R → FR → R
B. FR → R → FR
C. R → FR → R → FR → R
D. FR → R → FR → R

82. Maize transgenic for bacterial CspA (a RNA chaperone) imparts tolerance to:
A. Water Stress
B. High Temperature Stress
C. Salt Stress
D. Nutrient Stress

83. A multiline variety is:
A. a mixture of isogenic lines that usually confer resistance to a specific disease
B. a single genotype with stacked multiple genes conferring resistance to a specific disease
C. a mixture of pure lines having different traits
D. a collection of germplasm lines

84. Variety "X" is a donor for resistance to blast, but it has an undesirable gene for lodging susceptibility that is tightly linked to the blast resistant gene. The best breeding method which has high probability of breaking this linkage is
A. Pedigree method
B. Bulk method
C. Single seed decent method
D. Backcross method

85. One of the most popular genes used for developing rice tolerant to flooding stress is:
A. Sub1A B. LEA
C. HSP70 D. DREB1A

86. "Refugia" is a practice commonly employed to control
A. Diptera
B. Coleoptera
C. Development of resistance in insects
D. Bacillus thuringiensis

87. Vir genes are necessary for the transfer of the T-DNA into the host genome. The product of which one of the following genes is tightly associated with the 5′ end of the T-strand and helps in nuclear targeting?
A. Vir A B. Vir G
C. Vir E D. Vir D2

GATE (BIOTECHNOLOGY), 2018

Molecular Tools

88. An analysis of DNA-protein interactions was carried out using all DNA-protein complexes in the protein data bank (PDB). The frequency distribution of four amino acid residues, represented as P, Q, R and S, occurring in non-covalent interactions between the protein and DNA backbone is shown below:

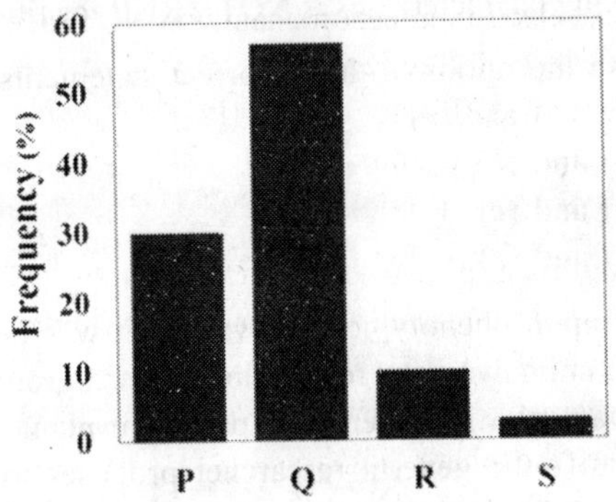

Which one of the following is correct?
A. P-Lys, Q-Arg, R-Gln, S-Glu
B. P-Gln, Q-Glu, R-Lys, S-Arg
C. P-Asn, Q-Asp, R-Arg, S-Lys
D. P-His, Q-Glu, R-Gln, S-Lys

89. Which one of the following techniques is used to monitor RNA transcripts, both temporally and spatially?
A. Northern blotting B. In situ hybridization
C. Southern blotting D. Western blotting

Analytical Tools

90. A mixture contains three similarly sized peptides P, Q and R. The peptide P is positively charged, Q is weakly negative and R is strongly negative. If this mixture is passed through an ion-exchange chromatography column containing an anionic resin, their order of elution will be
A. P, Q, R
B. R, Q, P
C. Q, R, P
D. P, Q and R elute together

91. Which of the following technique(s) can be used to study conformational changes in myoglobin?
(*a*) Mass spectrometry
(*b*) Fluorescence spectroscopy
(*c*) Circular dichroism spectroscopy
(*d*) Light microscopy
A. (*a*) only B. (*a*) and (*d*) only
C. (*b*) and (*c*) only D. (*d*) only

GATE (LIFE SCIENCE), 2018

Biochemical Separation Techniques

92. Match the protein elution condition given in Group I with the appropriate chromatography matrices from Group II.

Group I	Group II
(*a*) Increasing concentration of sodium chloride	(*i*) Phenyl-Sepharose
(*b*) Increasing concentration of histidine	(*ii*) Chromatofocusing
(*c*) Decreasing concentration of ammonium sulphate	(*iii*) DEAE-Sephacryl
(*d*) Decreasing concentration of H^+	(*iv*) Ni-NTA

	(a)	(b)	(c)	(d)
A.	(iii)	(iv)	(i)	(ii)
B.	(ii)	(iv)	(i)	(iii)
C.	(i)	(ii)	(iii)	(iv)
D.	(iv)	(ii)	(iii)	(i)

Instrumental Analysis & Technique

93. A zoologist recovered some tissue from preserved skin of a woolly mammoth. Further genetic analysis requires DNA isolation and increasing its amount. Which ONE of the following techniques would be most useful for increasing the amount of DNA?

A. RFLP analysis
B. Polymerase chain reaction (PCR)
C. Electroporation
D. Chromatography

CSIR-NET, JUNE, 2019

Molecular Technique and Marker

94. Which one of the following DNA markers can be used to distinguish between a homozygote and heterozygote?

A. RAPD
B. AFLP
C. RFLP
D. ISSR

95. To test the impact of cAMP on protein kinase A conformation in cells, an investigator made FRET biosensor by fusing two fluorescent protein at the N and C terminus of protein Kinase A. In the absence of cAMP in the cellular milieu, no FRET signal was detected. However, upon c-AMP addition, a strong emission at 530 nm was observed. What could be the best configuration of fluorophores that were used by the investigator?

A. Green fluorescent protein (GFP) and Red fluorescent protein (RFP).
B. CYAN fluorescent protein (CFP) and Yellow fluorescent protein (YFP)
C. Yellow fluorescent protein (YFP) and Red fluorescent protein (RFP)
D. Red fluorescent protein (RFP) and CYAN fluorescent protein (CFP)

96. A multimeric protein when run on SDS gel showed 2 bands at 20 kDa and 40 kDa. However, when the protein was run on a native gel, it showed a single band at 120 k Da. The native form of the protein would be

A. homotrimer
B. heterotetramer
C. heterodimer
D. heterotrimer

97. Orientation of a cloned DNA fragment (gene) in a plasmid vector can be checked by

A. PCR using two genes – specific primers
B. Restriction digestion with an enzyme that has a single restriction site within the cloned gene and none in the vector
C. PCR using a combination of one gene specific primer and one vector – specific primer.
D. Restriction digestion with an enzyme that has two restriction sites within the vector sequence and none in the cloned gene.

98. In a laboratory experiment it was observed that both 'Virus A' and 'Virus B' could infect a mammalian host cell, when infected individually. Interestingly, if the cell were first infected with Virus A (with large MOI), Virus B failed to infect the same cell. If the Virus B (with large MOI) is added first followed by Virus A, both the virus can infect the cells. However, infection with 'Virus A' was found to be in lesser extent. Considering X and Y are the receptors/co-receptors which may be involved for the virus entry, following are few possibilities that can explain the observation.

(a) 'Virus A' uses 'X' as receptor and Y as coreceptor.
(b) 'Virus B' uses exclusively 'Y' as receptor for entry:
(c) Both 'Virus A' and 'Virus B' need X as receptor.

Protein of this kind is fibronectin. Which one of the following characteristics is NOT TRUE for fibronectin?

Choose the option with all correct statements.

A. (a), (b) and (c)
B. (a) and (b)
C. (b) and (c)
D. (a) and (c)

99. Based upon phenotypic observation, it was concluded that an unknown gene responsible for an agronomically important trait is present in a particular plant. In order to identify the gene, a researcher proposes to use the following strategies:

(a) PCR amplification of the gene.
(b) Map based cloning of the gene.
(c) Subtractive DNA hybridization
(d) Genome sequencing
(e) Develop molecular markers linked to the trait

Which one of the following options is most suitable for identifying unknown gene?

A. (a) and (c)
B. (b) and (e)
C. (c) only
D. (a) and (d)

100. Run off transcription assays were performed to establish the specificity of three novel sigma factors for their promoters. Result of the experiments are shown below:

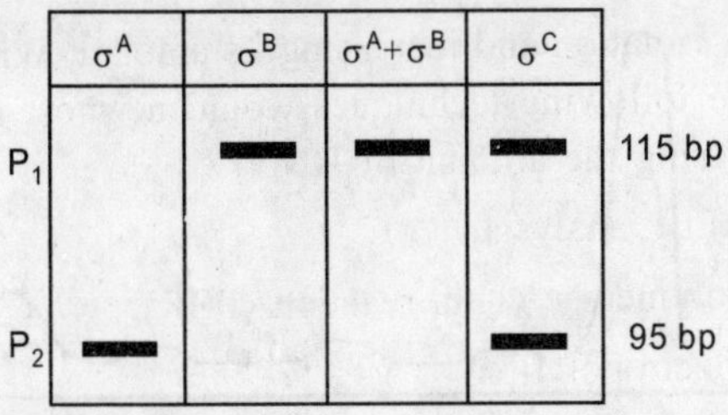

Following inferences were made from these results:
(*a*) σ^A intiates transcription from P_2 and σ^B from P_1
(*b*) σ^C can intiates transcription from both promoters.
(*c*) σ^B Prevents intiation of transcription from P_2
(*d*) σ^A Intiates transcription from P_1

Choose the option that correctly interprets that results?
A. (*a*), (*b*) and (*c*) only
B. (*a*), (*b*) only
C. (*c*) and (*d*) only
D. (*b*), (*c*) and (*d*) only

Instrumentation

101. A solution contains NADH and NAD^+, BOTH AT 0.1 mM concentration. If NADH has a molar extinction co efficient of 6220 and that of NAD^+ is negligible, the optical density measured in a cuvette of 5mm path length will be
A. 0.62 B. 0.062
C. 0.31 D. 0.031

102. The structure of a protein with 100 residues was determined by X-ray analysis at atomic resolution and NMR spectroscopy. The following observations are possible.
(*a*) The dihedral angles determined from the X-ray structure and NMR will be identical.
(*b*) The dihedral angles determined from the X-ray structure will be more accurate.
(*c*) β-turns can be determined only by NMR.
(*d*) β-sheets can be more accurately determined from the X-ray structure.

Indicate the combination with ALL correct answers
A. (*a*) and (*c*) B. (*b*) and (*d*)
C. (*b*) and (*c*) D. (*a*) and (*d*)

103. The blood plasma proteins (albumin and globulins) from a healthy person were separated by electrophoresis as shown above. The diagnosis of acute inflammation can be done based on one of the following observations.
A. Increase in both αl and α2; decrease in Albumin
B. Increase in albumin; decrease in αl, α2 and α.
C. Increase in albumin and decrease in γ globulin
D. Only decrease in albumin.

104. The below figure shows the fluorescence emission spectra of three different proteins; Protein (X), Protein (Y), and Protein (Z) excited at 280 nm. Which one of the following statements gives the correct interpretation?
A. Proteins (Y) and (Z) have tryptophan while protein (X) has only phenylalanine.
B. Protein (X) has only tyrosine and protein (Y) has tryptophan on the surface while protein (Z) has tryptophan buried inside.
C. Protein (X) has tryptophan buried insidechile proteins (Y) and (Z) have tryptophan on the surface
D. Protein (X) has only tyrosine and protein (Y) has tryptophan buried and protein (Z) has tryptophan on the surface.

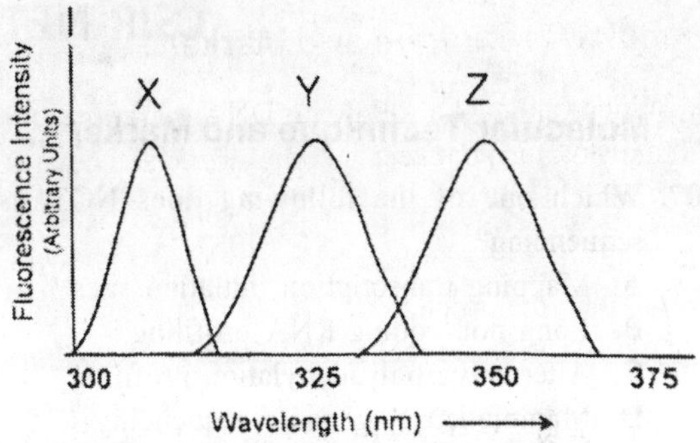

Microscopic Techniques

105. Specimens for light microscopy are commonly fixed with a solution containing chemicals that crosslink/ denature cellular constituents. Commonly used fixatives such as formaldehyde and methanol could act in various ways as described below:
(*a*) Formaldehyde crosslinks amino groups on adjacent molecules and stabilizes protein- protein and protein-nucleic acid interactions.
(*b*) Methanol acts as a denaturing fixative and acts by reducing the solubility of protein molecules by disrupting hydrophobic interactions.
(*c*) Formaldehyde crosslinks lipid tails in biological membranes.
(*d*) Methanol acts on nucleic acids. crosslinks nucleic acids with proteins and thus stabilizes protein-nucleic acid interactions.

Which one of the following combinations represents all correct statements?
A. (*a*) and (*c*)
B. (*b*) and (*c*)
C. (*b*) and (*d*)
D. (*a*) and (*b*)

Electrophysiological Methods

106. A neurophysiolgist was interested in using the patch-clamp technique. Following statements are related to this technique:

(*a*) Intracellular movement of ion channels.
(*b*) Post–translational modification of the ion channel protein
(*c*) Ligand that controls the opening or closing of ion channels.
(*d*) Change in current flow in a single ion channel.

Which one of the following combinations will be achievable using the patch-clamp technique?

A. (*a*) and (*b*) B. (*c*) and (*d*)
C. (*b*) and (*c*) D. (*d*) and (*a*)

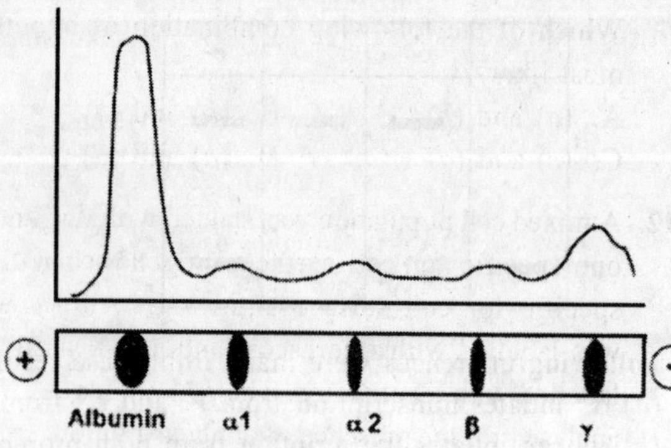

CSIR-NET, 15 DECEMBER, 2019

Molecular Technique and Marker

107. Which one of the following does NOT use RNA-sequencing?

A. Mapping transcription initiation sites
B. Long non-coding RNA profiling
C. Alternative polyadenylation profiling
D. Mammalian epigenome sequencing

108. Given below are various types of molecular markers in Column A and properties of these markers in Column B.

Column A	Column B
(*a*) RFLP	(*i*) Single locus
(*b*) SSR	(*ii*) Multi-allele
(*c*) AFLP	(*iii*) Co-dominant
(*d*) RAPD	(*iv*) Single allelic
	(*v*) Multi-locus
	(*vi*) Dominant

Which one of the options given below correctly matches the molecular markers with their properties?

	(*a*)	(*b*)	(*c*)	(*d*)
A.	(*vi*)	(*i*)	(*ii*)	(*v*)
B.	(*v*)	(*ii*)	(*iv*)	(*iii*)
C.	(*i*)	(*ii*)	(*v*)	(*vi*)
D.	(*ii*)	(*iii*)	(*i*)	(*ii*)

109. Given below are a few statements on use of plant breeding to develop improved varieties of a crop plant

(*a*) Genotypic/phenotypic variation in the desired trait should be available in the germplasm resources of the crop plant.
(*b*) Availability of molecular markers linked to the trait of interest would decelerate the process of trait introgression into desired varieties.
(*c*) Breeding procedures to improve plant varieties are generally more successful among sexually compatible species as compared to sexually incompatible species.
(*d*) Co-dominant molecular markers cannot be used for selection of plants with the desired trait

Which of the above statement(s) is/are INCORRECT?

A. (*a*) and (*c*) B. (*b*) only
C. (*c*) and (*d*) D. (*b*) and (*d*)

110. Given below are two sets of terms related to various methods used in biological science.

Column A	Column B
(*a*) RACE	(*i*) DNA-protein interactions
(*b*) South-Western blotting	(*ii*) FAM
(*c*) Recursive PCR	(*iii*) Determining the ends of mRNA
(*d*) TaqMan	(*iv*) Construction of synthetic DNA

Which one of the following options correctly matches terms of Column A and Column B?

	(*a*)	(*b*)	(*c*)	(*d*)
A.	(*iv*)	(*iii*)	(*i*)	(*ii*)
B.	(*iii*)	(*i*)	(*iv*)	(*ii*)
C.	(*ii*)	(*iv*)	(*i*)	(*iii*)
D.	(*ii*)	(*i*)	(*iv*)	(*iii*)

Instrumentation

111. Analysis of a homotetrameric protein and a double stranded DNA (that had been incubated in standard buffer) on native gels revealed that they migrated true to their physical states (tetrameric nature of the protein and double stranded nature of the DNA). Following hypotheses were made for the effect of adding high salt to the incubation mix and subsequent analysis on native gels.

(*a*) The protein would migrate as a homotetramer and DNA in double stranded form.
(*b*) The protein would migrate as a monomer but DNA in double stranded form.
(*c*) The protein would migrate as a homotetramer but the DNA in single stranded form.
(*d*) The protein would migrate as a monomer and the DNA in single stranded form.

Which of the following combination of hypotheses is most likely?

A. (*a*) and (*b*) B. (*b*) and (*c*)
C. (*c*) and (*d*) D. (*a*) and (*d*)

112. A mixed cell population was stained with two antibodies, one specific for cell surface antigen A and the other specific for cell surface antigen B. Anti-A antibody was labelled with fluorescein and anti-B antibody was labelled with Rhodamine. The cell population was then analysed for the presence of antigens by flow cytometry. Which one of the following is the correct out come for this cell population?

A.
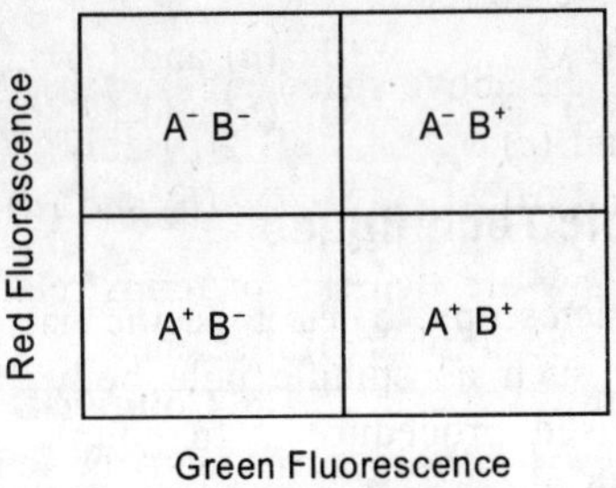

B.
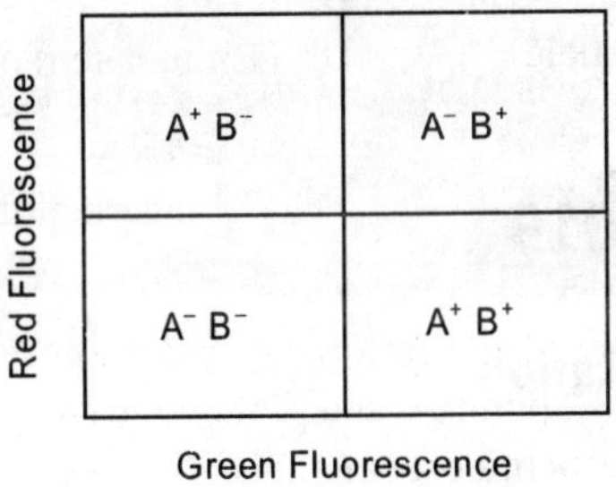

C.
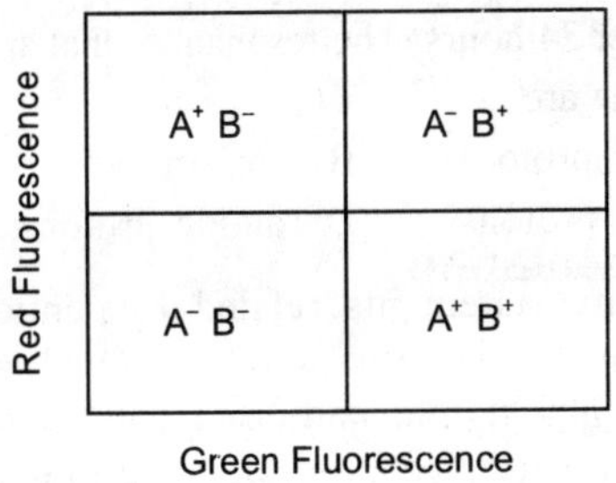

D.
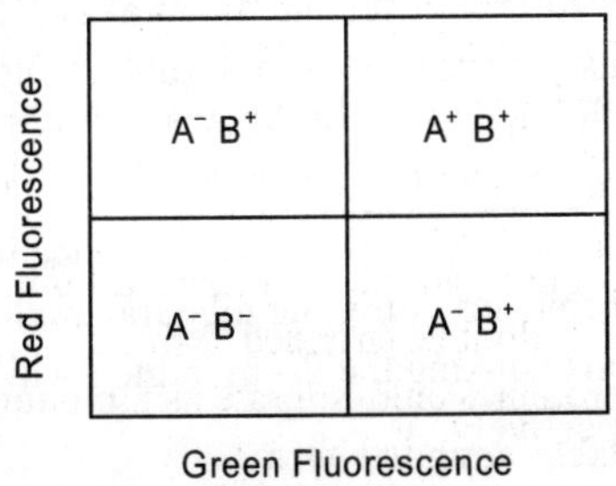

113. Absorption spectra of L-tyrosine in acidic (continuous line) and basic (dotted line) medium was estimated and plotted on a graph as depicted below:

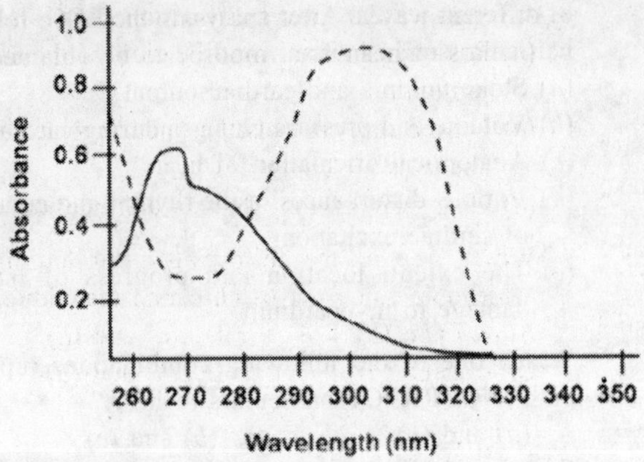

Following interpretations were made:

(*a*) Change in the pH from acidic to basic results in shift in the lowest energy absorption maximum and decrease in the molar absorptivity.
(*b*) Shifting of the absorption band to longer wavelength signifies a shift to lower energy, also known as red shift
(*c*) Shifting of the absorption band to shorter wavelength signifies a shift to higher energy, also known as blue shift.
(*d*) Wavelength shift is always accompanied by change in intensity of the absorption band.

Select the combination with correct interpretations.

A. (*a*) and (*b*) B. (*a*) and (*c*)
C. (*b*) and (*c*) D. (*b*) and (*d*)

Biophysical Methods

114. If you inject a mouse with radioactive material of current activity of 256 Bq, what will be the activity after completion of 6 half-lives?

A. 4 Bq B. 8 Ba
C. 16 Ba D. 24 Bq

115. Given below are some physicochemical properties (column X) and their manifestations (column Y).

X	Y
(*a*) Pauling electronegativity	(*i*) Charge separation
(*b*) Isolated-orbital overlap	(*ii*) Solvation of atoms
(*c*) Aromaticity	(*iii*) Restricted rotation
(*d*) Dielectric constant	(*iv*) Planarity of molecules

Which one of the following is the most appropriate match?

	(*a*)	(*b*)	(*c*)	(*d*)
A.	(*i*)	(*iv*)	(*ii*)	(*iii*)
B.	(*iii*)	(*ii*)	(*iv*)	(*i*)
C.	(*ii*)	(*iii*)	(*iv*)	(*i*)
D.	(*iv*)	(*ii*)	(*i*)	(*iii*)

116. The ECG recorded by different leads is analysed on the basis of variation of electrical potential at various loci on the surface of the body, and the time scale relation of different waves. After analysing the ECG, following particulars of heart are proposed to be obtained

(*a*) Stoke volume and cardiac output

(*b*) Volume and pressure changes during cardiac cycle

(*c*) Anatomical orientation of heart

(*d*) Various disturbances in the rhythm and conduction of cardiac excitation

(*e*) The extent, location and progress of ischemic damage to myocardium

Which one of the following combinations represents both INCORRECT particulars of heart?

A. (*a*) and (*b*) B. (*b*) and (*c*)
C. (*c*) and (*d*) D. (*d*) and (*e*)

117. To investigate the dynamic nature of two unrelated centrosome-localized GFP-tagged proteins (GFP-A; GFP-B), a team of scientists conducted fluorescence recovery after photo bleaching (FRAP) experiment. The FRAP profile of these two proteins is given below:

The following statements for this FRAP analysis were made

(*a*) GFP-B shows faster exchange rate than GFP-A

(*b*) GFP-A shows faster exchange rate than GFP-B

(*c*) GFP-A has more immobile fraction than GFP-B

(*d*) GFP-B has more immobile fraction than GFP-A

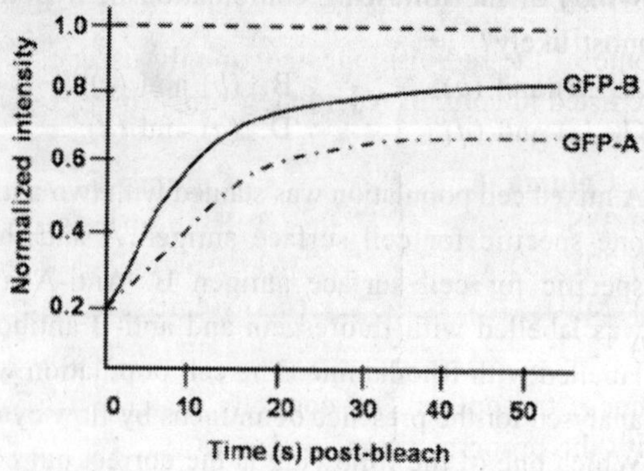

Which of the above mentioned statements for GFP-A and GFP-B are correct?

A. (*a*) and (*c*) B. (*a*) and (*d*)
C. (*b*) and (*c*) D. (*b*) and (*d*)

Microscopic Techniques

118. In electron microscopy, to detect specific macromolecule or structure such as spindle pole body (SPB), the frequently used procedure is to couple secondary antibody with

A. Alexa 568 B. Cy5
C. Gold particle D. Osmium tetraoxide

CSIR-NET, 27 DECEMBER, 2019

Molecular Technique and Marker

119. Which one of the following techniques/approaches CANNOT be used to analyse expression pattern of a gene?

A. Western blotting B. qRT-PCR
C. Northern blotting D. Southern blotting

120. Given below are four statements regarding the use of marker assisted selection (MAS) in plant breeding.

(*a*) Markers that are not linked to target traits cannot be used to test accumulation of the desired recurrent parent's genetic background in a backcross breeding program.

(*b*) Co-dominant markers are more effective for marker assisted backcrossing since they facilitate selection of heterozygous progeny.

(*c*) MAS can be used to facilitate backcrossing of recessive genes that influence traits of interest.

(*d*) Use of tightly linked flanking makers for a trait of interest increases linkage drag in a breeding program.

Which one of the following options represents a combination of all INCORRECT statements?

A. (*a*) and (*b*) B. (*b*) and (*c*)
C. (*a*) and (*d*) D. (*c*) and (*d*)

Instrumentation

121. A 30-residue peptide containing Phe, Tyr and Trp is dissolved in D2O and the high field proton NMR is recorded after 24 hours. The resonances that are unlikely to be present are

A. aromatic protons B. Cα protons
C. aliphatic protons D. amide protons

122. Following are statements related to peptide/protein conformation.

(*a*) The circular dichroism spectra of collagen and a protein in α-helical conformation will be identical.

(*b*) The allowed region for the dihedral angles φ, ψ in Gly, spans a large area in the Ramachandran map. This can be drastically reduced by substituting the two hydrogens with methyl groups.

(*c*) Proline has high frequency of occurrence in β-turns.

(*d*) In a β-hairpin structure, the dihedral angles φ, ψ of amino acids flanking the β-turn region will be ~-60°, -30°, respectively.

Choose the combination with both INCORRECT statements.

A. (*b*) and (*c*) B. (*a*) and (*b*)
C. (*a*) and (*d*) D. (*c*) and (*d*)

Biophysical Method

123. Some of the radioisotopes commonly used in biology are listed in column A and their properties are listed in Column B.

Column A	Column B
(*a*) 35S	(*i*) High energy ß
(*b*) 32P	(*ii*) α-particle
(*c*) 238U	(*iii*) γ-emission
(*d*) 125I	(*iv*) Low energy ß

Choose the option that correctly matches the isotope with the property listed.

	(*a*)	(*b*)	(*c*)	(*d*)
A.	(*iv*)	(*iii*)	(*ii*)	(*i*)
B.	(*iii*)	(*ii*)	(*iv*)	(*i*)
C.	(*ii*)	(*i*)	(*iv*)	(*iii*)
D.	(*iv*)	(*i*)	(*ii*)	(*iii*)

124. When two atoms are linked by a covalent bond, vanderwaals interaction between then contributes substantially to the bond energy

(*a*) When solute is dissolved in a solvent, the increase in boiling point is independent of the number of particles into which the solute dissociates and dependent only on the molarity of solute.

(*b*) When two atoms are linked by a covalent bond, van der Waals interaction between then contributes substantially to the bond energy

(*c*) If a plot of reactant concentration versus time is not linear, but a plot of 1/reactant concentration versus time is linear, the reaction is second order.

(*d*) Glucose, tyrosine and tryptophan can be easily distinguished by analyzing their UV spectra at equimolar concentration.

Choose the combination with correct statements

A. (*a*) and (*c*) B. (*b*) and (*d*)
C. (*a*) and (*b*) D. (*c*) and (*d*)

125. A and B Two cell surface receptors, A and B with a single binding site specifically bind with their respective ligands, X and Y. In the table below are the values for the association constant, K_a of the respective ligand-receptor interactions. K_a is also called the affinity constant.

Recepter	Ligand	K_a
A	X	1×10^8
B	Y	1×10^{11}

Based on these values, which one of the following statements is INCORRECT?

A. Kd for B-Y binding is smaller than that for A binding

B. K1 for A-X binding is lesser than that for B-Y binding

C. K-1 for B-Y binding is smaller than that for A-X binding

D. K-1/K1 for B-Y binding is higher than that for A-X binding (K1 is the forward rate constant, K-1 is the reverse rate constant and K_d is the dissociation constant)

126. The first few steps of the tryptophan biosynthetic pathway in plants along with the available mutants is provided below:

Chlorismate $\xrightarrow{trp4}$ Anthranilate $\xrightarrow{trp1}$ PR-anthranilate $\xrightarrow{pai}$ CDRP

Column X represents genotypes and Column Y summarizes the anthranilate fluorescence phenotype in UV light.

Column X Genotype	Column Y Phenotype in UV Light
(*a*) wild type	(*i*) Strong fluorescence
(*b*) *trp*1	(*ii*) No fluorescence
(*c*) *trp*1; *trp*4	(*iii*) Weak fluorescence
(*d*) *pai*	

Which of the following combinations represent the correct match between column X and column Y?

	(*a*)	(*b*)	(*c*)	(*d*)
A.	(*i*)	(*ii*)	(*i*)	(*iii*)
B.	(*ii*)	(*i*)	(*ii*)	(*iii*)
C.	(*ii*)	(*ii*)	(*iii*)	(*i*)
D.	(*iii*)	(*i*)	(*iii*)	(*ii*)

127. Following are statements related to spectroscopic investigation of proteins.

(*a*) Tryptophan fluorescence in a protein is not sensitive to its environment.

(*b*) Observation of a large number of N;-Ni+1 connectivity's in the NOESY spectrum of a protein suggests the presence of helical conformation.

(*c*) Only proteins with masses less than 5000 daltons can be identified by MALDI mass spectrometry.

(*d*) Protein conformation can be investigated by ESI mass spectrometry.

Which one of the following options consists of both correct statements?

A. (*a*) and (*c*) B. (*b*) and (*d*)
C. (*a*) and (*b*) D. (*b*) and (*c*)

Microscopic Techniques

128. To spatiotemporally detect the localization of two proteins A and B using a confocal microscope, an investigator plans to utilize a few fluorescent proteins (X, Y, Z and T). The excitation and emission spectra of these fluorescent proteins are shown below.

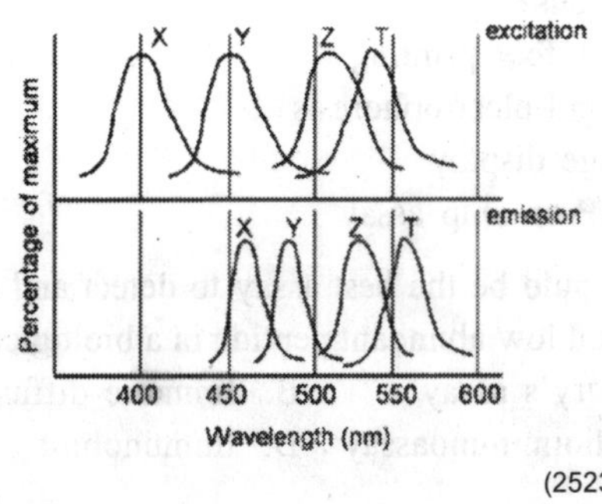

Which one of the following options comprises of a fluorescent pair that is best suited to conduct such an experiment?

A. X and Y B. Y and Z
C. X and T D. Z and T

Immunotechniques

129. Given below are a few factors that influence the sensitivity of immunoassays:

(*a*) Affinity of the antibody used
(*b*) Epitope density on the antigen
(*c*) Epitope distribution on the antigen

Which one of the following options represents the correct factor(s)?

A. (*a*) only B. (*b*) only
C. (*b*) and (*c*) only D. (*a*), (*b*) and (*c*)

130. For ELISPOT measurements of interferon γ (IFN-γ) secretion by mouse NKT cells, the following steps were performed in an ELISA plate:

(*a*) Addition of purified spleenocytes
(*b*) Stimulation of spleenocytes by peptide pulsed antigen presenting cells (APCs)
(*c*) Addition of biotin-conjugated anti IFN-γ antibody
(*d*) Addition of capture antibody specific to IFN-γ
(*e*) Addition of avidin-conjugated colour changing substrate.

Which one of the following options lists the correct sequence of steps performed?

A. A → D → B → C → E
B. D → B → A → C → E
C. D → A → B → C → E
D. B → A → D → C → E

131. A student hypothesized that protein Yfg100 interacted with protein Yfr70 in a tissue-specific manner. To test this, an immune precipitation experiment was performed using antibodies to Yfg100 and the samples were subjected to western blot using antibodies to both Yfg100 and Yfr70. The results obtained are shown below:

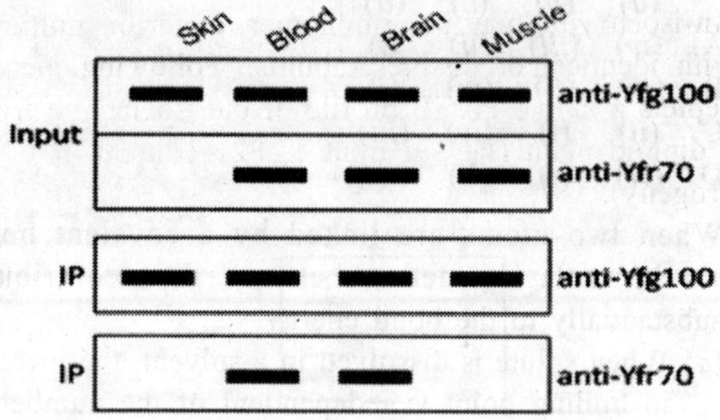

Based on the results shown, identify the INCORRECT statement

A. Protein Yfg100 is expressed in all tested tissues
B. Yfg100 does not interact with Yfr70 in muscle
C. Yfg100 interacts with Yfr70 in muscle but not in other tissues.
D. Yfr70 is not expressed in skin

DBT-JRF, 2019

Methods in Biotechnology

132. Which one of the following techniques can be used to study transient protein – protein interactions in a live cell?

A. Pull-down assay
B. Immunoprecipitation
C. Surface Plasmon Resonance
D. Forster Resonance Energy Transfer

133. Which one of the following techniques can be utilized to study both protein–peptide and protein–DNA interactions?

A. DNA foot printing
B. 2D-gel electrophoresis
C. Phage display
D. ChIP-on-chip assay

134. What would be the best assay to detect and quantify a small and low abundant peptide in a biological sample?

A. Lowry's assay B. Immuno-diffusion
C. Radioimmunoassay D. Immunoblot

135. The molecular mass of a protein CANNOT be determined by:

A. MALDI-TOF
B. Gel filtration Chromatography.
C. Chromatofocusing
D. SDS-PAGE

136. Protein X exists in both GTP-bound and GDP-bound forms. When this protein was purified, it was always GDP-bound. Proteins Y, W and V were added separately in an experiment along with GTP. The results of the experiment are depicted in the following figure:

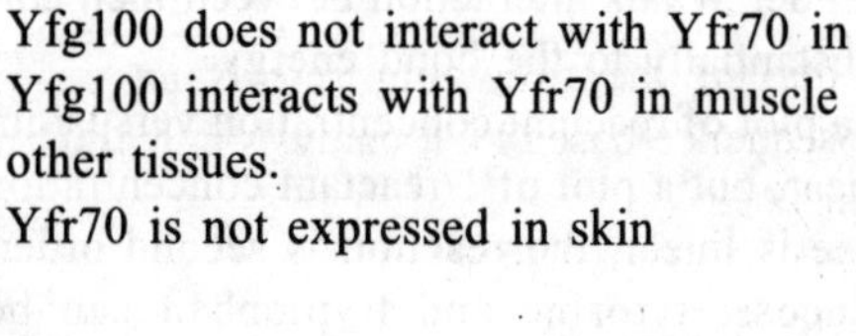

Which one of the following could be the right conclusion of the results?

A. Protein Y is GAP for protein X
B. Protein Y is GEF for protein X

C. Protein W is GEF for protein X
D. Protein V is GEF for protein X

137. Which one of the following statements is INCORRECT in relation to reverse phase chromatography?
A. The solutes elute with decreasing order of polarity.
B. The stationary phase surface covering the silica particles involves non-polar functional groups.
C. The solutes elute with increasing order of molecular weight.
D. The pH of the mobile phase has a profound influence on retention, selectivity and separation.

138. An isoenzyme may be a monomer, dimer or multimer with identical or distinct subunits. Following picture depicts a native PAGE profile of the isoenzyme from a diploid plant (P1 – Parent 1, P2 – Parent 2, F1 – Progeny).

P1 P2 F_1

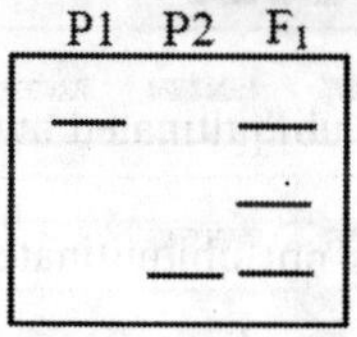

This isoenzyme is a:
A. monomer B. homodimer
C. homotrimer D. homopentamer

139. Which one of the following sets is an example of specific sequence-based PCR analysis in marker assisted selection?
A. RAPD, DAF, AP-PCR
B. SCAR, SSR, COS
C. SCAR, SSR, DAF
D. RAPD, SSR, COS

140. A recombinant therapeutic protein is intracellularly produced in soluble form using *E. coli*. Which one of the following sequences of chromatographic separation methods is preferable for obtaining clinical grade protein?
A. Hydrophobic interaction followed by ion-exchange
B. Dye-ligand followed by ion-exchange
C. Ion-exchange followed by gel-filtration
D. Gel-filtration followed by metal-affinity

141. What property is involved in the separation of a mixture of analytes using gas chromatography?
A. Partitioning B. Conductivity
C. Mass D. Polarity

142. Match the physical/chemical property with the corresponding unit operations used for separation:

(*a*) Density difference	(*i*) Distillation
(*b*) Partition coefficient	(*ii*) Filtration
(*c*) Relative coefficient	(*iii*) Liquid-liquid extraction
(*d*) Praticle size	(*iv*) Centrifugation

	(*a*)	(*b*)	(*c*)	(*d*)
A.	(*iii*)	(*iv*)	(*i*)	(*ii*)
B.	(*i*)	(*iii*)	(*ii*)	(*iv*)
C.	(*iv*)	(*ii*)	(*iii*)	(*i*)
D.	(*iv*)	(*iii*)	(*i*)	(*ii*)

143. Which one of the following experimental methods is NOT used to determine three-dimensional structures of biological macromolecules?
A. Nuclear Magnetic Resonance Spectroscopy
B. Fluorescence spectroscopy
C. X-ray crystallography
D. Cryo-Electron microscopy

144. Which one of the following is used to study the structural details of biological tissues using freeze-fracture technique
A. Scanning electron microscopy
B. Transmission electron microscopy
C. Atomic force microscopy
D. Phase contrast microscopy

145. For identifying the distribution of a specific protein in a tissue, which one of the following types of immunofluorescence microscopic methods has attained the highest level of resolution?
A. Indirect immunofluorescence microscopy
B. Confocal microscopy
C. Confocal microscopy with deconvolution
D. Wide angle microscopy with deconvolution

146. The taxonomic method of identifying an organism to its species is:
A. Genetic speciation B. DNA barcoding
C. RFLP D. AFLP

147. Variable number of tandem repeats (VNTR) in DNA molecule are highly useful in:
A. Fingerprinting B. Foot printing
C. Gene annotation D. DNA repair

GATE (BIOTECHNOLOGY), 2019

Molecular Tools

148. For site-directed mutagenesis, which one of the following restriction enzymes is used to digest methylated DNA?
A. KpnI B. DpnI
C. XhoI D. MluI

149. Which one of the following techniques can be used to compare the expression of a large number of genes in two biological samples in a single experiment?
A. Polymerase chain reaction
B. DNA microarray
C. Northern hybridization
D. Southern hybridization

Analytical Tools

150. Group I list spectroscopic methods and Group II lists biomolecular applications of these methods. Match the methods in Group I with the applications in Group II.

Group I	Group II
(*a*) Infrared	(*i*) Identification of functional groups
(*b*) Circular Dichroism	(*ii*) Determination of secondary structure
(*c*) Nuclear Magnetic Resonance	(*iii*) Estimation of molecular weight
	(*iv*) Determination of 3-D structure

	(*a*)	(*b*)	(*c*)
A.	(*iv*)	(*iii*)	(*i*)
B.	(*ii*)	(*i*)	(*iii*)
C.	(*i*)	(*ii*)	(*iv*)
D.	(*iii*)	(*ii*)	(*iv*)

151. The hexapeptide P has an isoelectric point (pI) of 6.9. Hexapeptide Q is a variant of P that contains valine instead of glutamate at position 3. The two peptides are analysed by polyacrylamide gel electrophoresis at pH 8.0. Which one of the following statements is CORRECT?

A. P will migrate faster than Q towards the anode
B. P will migrate faster than Q towards the cathode
C. Both P and Q will migrate together
D. Q will migrate faster than P towards the anode

CSIR-NET, NOVEMBER (MORNING), 2020

Molecular Technique and Marker

152. Which one of the following approaches /markers would be typically used for discovering polymorphism between two closely related accessions of a crop plant?

A. AFLP B. GBS
C. SSR D. RAPD

153. Which one of the following statements is TRUE?

A. Nick translation cannot be used for radiolabeling DNA fragments for use in Soutnern hybridization
B. RACE can be used to obtain sequence information of the ends of a cDNA
C. In a 2-D gel electrophoresis for separating proteins, analytes are first separated on the basis of their size and then on the basis of their pi.
D. AFLP markers are typically used to screen heterozygotes from homozygotes

154. A protein found in the golgi compartment was found to be degraded rapidly at mitosis. Golgi extracts (isolated from Gi and M phase cells treated with deubiqutination inhibitors) were treated with glycosidase and western blots done using antibodies against the protein. The following pattern was obtained.

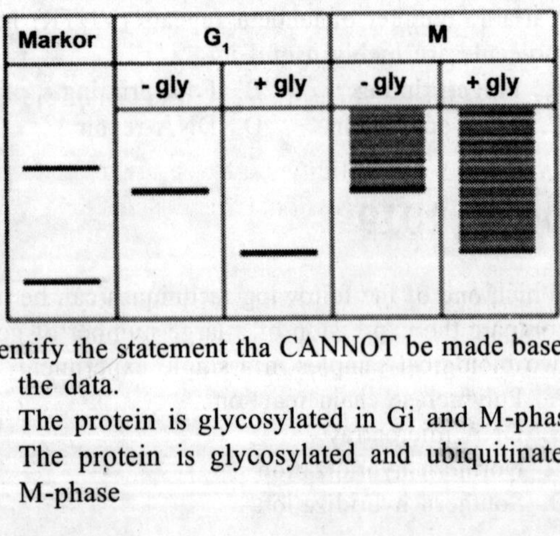

Identify the statement tha CANNOT be made based on the data.

A. The protein is glycosylated in Gi and M-phase
B. The protein is glycosylated and ubiquitinated in M-phase
C. The protein is ubiquitinated but not glycosylated in M-phase
D. The protein is not ubiquitinated in Gi

155. Given below is a schematic representation of the T-DNA region of a transgene construct and the Southern blot analysis (using Pst I digested genomic DNA) of five independent transgenic lines (labelled as A to E) developed using the construct. The probe used for hybridization is shown as a black box below the construct (UT: Untransformed Plant)

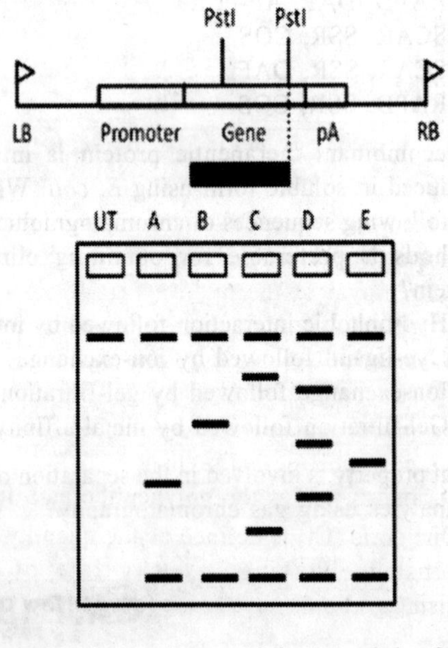

Based on the above data, which one of the following options gives the correct list of single insertion transgenic events?

A. (*b*) and (*c*) only
B. (*a*), (*b*) and (*e*) only
C. (*a*) and (*b*) only
D. (*e*) only

Instrumentation

156. The mechanism of oxygen transport by hemocyanin (containing Cu) is describe by $Cu^{+}.Cu^{+} + O_2$ which one of the following techniques can be used to monitor the change in the oxidation stae of copper?

A. Mass spectrometry
B. Circular dichrosim
C. Absorption spectroscopy
D. Fluorescence spectroscopy

157. Which one of the following sets of terms is matched correctly?

A. Fluorescence microscopy: Use of dyes that absorb and emit light of the same wavelength
B. Confocal microscopy: Use of pinpoint illumination and detection apertures
C. Confocal microscopy: Use of pinpoint illumination and detection apertures
D. Gas Chromatography: Used for analysis of non-volatilized carbohydrate molecules

158. A 100 residue long protein has a single chromporic residue (tyrosine). The UV absorption of this protein and a homologous protein (also with a single tyrosine residue) was monitored at 280 nm at different pH conditions. A plot of the absorbance as a function of pH is shown below. The locations of the tyrosine residue in the context of the protein sequences is also shown in the figure.

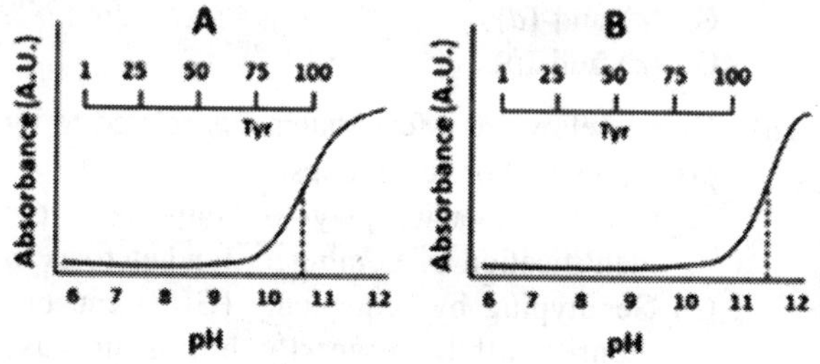

Which one of the following rationalises the difference in the two pH titra..s?

A. removal of the hydroxyl group of tyrosine above pH 11
B. location of the tyrosine residue in the protein structure
C. pH dependent changes in the absorption in the polypepetide main chain
D. hydrolysis of the polypeptide as a function of pH

159. One curie (Ci) is defined as the quantity of radioactive substance having a decay rate of 2.22×10^{12} disintegratioins per minute (dpm). How much of counts per minutes (cpm) will be recorded for 100μCi of ^{32}P when measured in a scintillation counter working at 50% efficiency?

A. 1.11×10^8
B. 1.11×10^6
C. 2.22×10^8
D. 2.22×10^6

160. Following are the typical dot plots of cytometric data obtained from peripheral white blood cells:

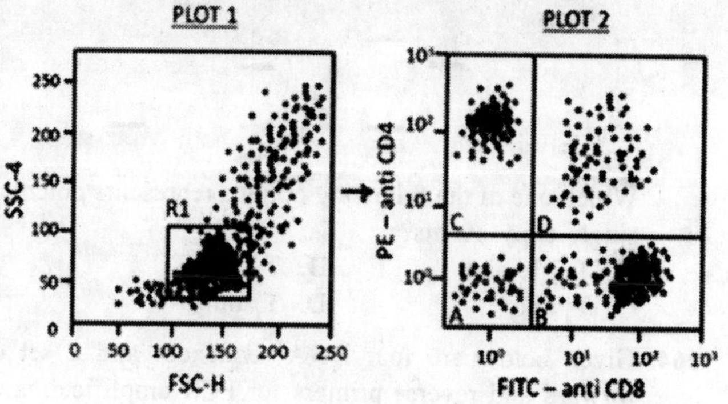

R1 in plot 1 shows the selection window of cells which were further analysed based on immunostaining (plot 2). Analyze the given data and choose the correct option representing the type of cell population in plot 1 selected and segregated in various quadrants of plot 2.

A. Plot 1 → lymphocytes; Plot 2 → (A) $CD4^- CD8^-$ (B) $CD4^- CD8^+$ (C) $CD4^+ CD8^-$ (D) $CD4^+ CD8^+$
B. Plot 1 → neutrophils; Plot → 2(A) $CD4^+ CD8^+$ (B) $CD4^- CD8^+$ (C) $CD4^+ CD8^-$ (D) $CD8^- CD4^-$
C. Plot 1 → lymphocytes; Plot 2 → (A) $CD8^+ CD4^-$ (B) $CD4^+ CD8^-$ (C) $CD4^- CD8^+$ (D) $CD8^- CD4^+$
D. Plot 1 → lymphocytes; Plot 2 → (A) $CD4^- CD8^+$ (B) $CD4^- CD8^+$ (C) $CD4^+ CD8^-$ (D) $CD8^+ CD4^-$

161. The ^1H NMR spectrum of $^{13}CH_3Cl$ in $CDCl_3$ shows two lines (doublet, 1:1 intensity) spaced 140 Hz apart. The carbon (^{13}C) NMR spectrum of the same molecule shows four lines (quartet, intensity ratio 1:3:3:1). Both ^1H and ^{13}C have nuclear spin quantum numbers I = 1/2 Based on the above information which one of the following options is correct?

A. The multiplicity pattern observed follows the 2n/+1 rule.
B. The ^1H-^{13}C coupling constant is different in the 1H (Proton) and ^{13}C (Carbon) spectra.
C. The multiplicity patterns are a consequence of the difference in gyromagnetic ratios of the ^1H and ^{13}C nuclear spins.
D. The multiplicity patterns are dependent on the Larmor precessional frequencies.

CSIR-NET, NOVEMBER (AFTERNOON), 2020

Molecular Technique and Marker

162. Amongst the following, which one is the most appropriate strategy to sequence and assemble highly repeated regions of a genome?

A. Shot gun sequencing
B. Illumina sequencing
C. 454 sequencing
D. Sequencing of BAC libraries

163. Given below is a schematic representation of a Southern blot performed to identify single copy integration events of the T-DNA among six transgenic plants (T_1-T_6).

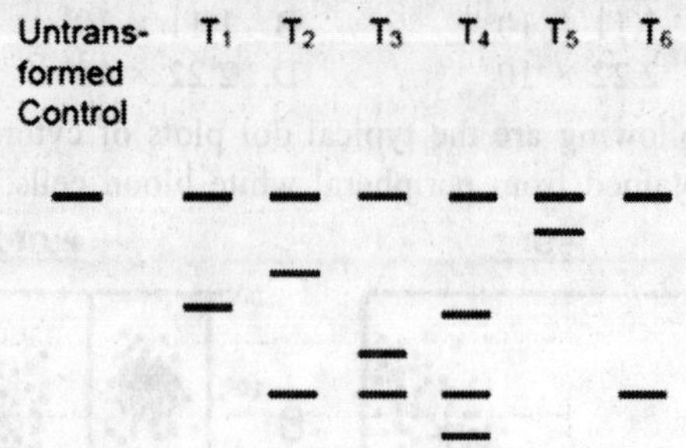

Which one of the following options represents potential single copy events?

A. T_1, T_5 and T_6 B. T_2 and T_3
C. T_4 only D. T_1 only

164. Given below are four DNA sequences and a set of forward and reverse primers for PCR amplification.

Sequence	Primes
(*a*) 5'-ACAATCGT .... ACTAGTAC-3'	FP: 5'-TGTTAG-3' RP: 5'-TAGTAC-3'
(*b*) 5'-AGTCTTAG .... ATGCCAGT-3'	FP: 5'-AAGACT-3' RP: 5'-ACTGGC-3'
(*c*) 5'-CTTGACTA .... GTACAGTCA-3'	FP: 5'-CTTGAC-3' RP: 5'-TGACTG-3'
(*d*) 5'-GATCTAGC .... TCAAGCAGAC-3'	FP: 5'-GATCTA-3' RP: 5'-CAGACG-3'

In the absence of any other factors such as (but not restricted to) T_m, length, percent GC, etc., which one of the above template-primers combinations would produce an amplified fragment?

A. Both (*a*) and (*c*) B. B only
C. Both (*c*) and (*d*) D. (*c*) only

165. Expression of gene 'A' is regulated by Mg^{2+}. The expression of gene 'A' is untreated (UN) and cells treated with Mg^{2+} (T) was analysed by Northern hybridization (N) and Western blotting (W). A similar exercise was done for a mutant (Mut) which was isolated with a 6 bp deletion in 5'UTR of the transcript of gene 'A'. The following are summary of four possible results that are hypothesized to be obtained

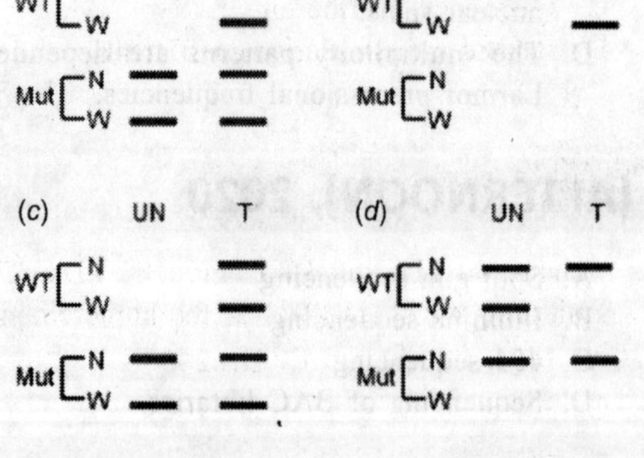

UN = Untreated Cells, WT = Wild type cells, T = Cells treated with Mg^{2+}, Mut = Cell with mutation in gene A, N = Northern hybridization, W = Western blotting

If the regulation of gene 'A' expression is controlled ONLY at the level of translation, which of the above profile/s are possible correct representation of the experimental results.

A. (*a*) only B. (*d*) only
C. (*a*) and (*d*) D. (*b*) and (*c*)

166. Given below are statements related to various molecular techniques

(*a*) During molecular cloning of DNA fragments, a vector and insert molecule digested with two different enzymes can never be ligated with each other.

(*b*) Only 3' → 5' exonucleases and not 5' → 3' exonucleases can be used for digesting nucleic acids to generate blunt-ended fragments for cloning.

(*c*) In Sanger's dideoxy sequencing method, each reaction consists of a mixture of three dNTPs and one ddNTP.

(*d*) Self-ligation of a vector with compatible ends can be prevented by treatment with alkaline phosphatase.

Which one of the following options represents a combination of correct statements?

A. (*b*) and (*c*)
B. (*a*) and (*d*)
C. (*c*) and (*d*)
D. (*a*) and (*b*)

167. Given below are a few statements related to biological principles and/or techniques:

(*a*) Genetic diversity plays an important role in the identification of combiners for heterosis breeding

(*b*) Genotyping by sequencing (GBS) can be used to identify allelic diversity but is not useful for construction of linkage maps.

(*c*) Genome editing by sequence specific nucleases (SSNS) in the presence of guide RNAs would result in NHEJ-mediated knock outs and loss of function mutations.

(*d*) In a comparison of synteny and colinearity between diploid and polyploid plant genomes, colinearity is high but synteny is low.

Which one of the following options represents all correct statements?

A. (*a*) and (*c*) only
B. (*b*) and (*d*) only
C. (*a*), (*c*) and (*d*)
D. (*b*) only

Immunotechniques

168. For a given immunological application [column X], select the type of antibody [column Y] that should be used:

Column X	Column Y
(a) Bacterial agglutination	(i) Only monoclonal
(b) Western blotting	(ii) Only polyclonal
(c) Detection of a cytokine using a solid phase ELISA	(iii) Either monoclonal or polyclonal
(d) Diagnostic tissue typing	

Choose the option with correct matches between terms of Columns X and Y.

	(a)	(b)	(c)	(d)
A.	(ii)	(i)	(iii)	(i)
B.	(iii)	(iii)	(i)	(i)
C.	(iii)	(ii)	(i)	(i)
D.	(i)	(iii)	(i)	(ii)

Electrophysiological Methods

169. A researcher intends to stimulate neurons via glutamate receptors in medial septum of an experimental animal. The following apparatus/instruments are available in the laboratory:

(a) Stereotaxic apparatus
(b) Slow perfusion pump
(c) Microcannula
(d) Radiofrequency lesion maker
(e) Electrical stimulator
(f) Nichrome coated bipolar steel electrode

Which one of the following options contains all the correct items required for the experiment?

A. (a) and (b) only B. (a), (b) and (c)
C. (d) and (e) only D. (d), (e) and (f)

170. The electrical response of the afferent nerve terminal in a Pacinian corpuscle (PC), after application of different grades of pressure, are proposed in the following statements:

(a) A non-propagated depolarizing potential or receptor potential is elicited when small magnitude of pressure is applied to PC.
(b) The magnitude of receptor potential is increased as the pressure to PC is increased.
(c) An action potential is generated when receptor potential attains a critical value.
(d) The receptor potential shows all-or-none response.
(e) The receptor potential is not a graded potential.

Choose the option with both INCORRECT statements:

A. (a) and (b) B. (b) and (c)
C. (c) and (d) D. (d) and (e)

171. The discharge patterns in a single afferent nerve fibre from carotid sinus at various levels of mean arterial pressure (MAP) are plotted against changes in aortic pressure with time in the following figure:

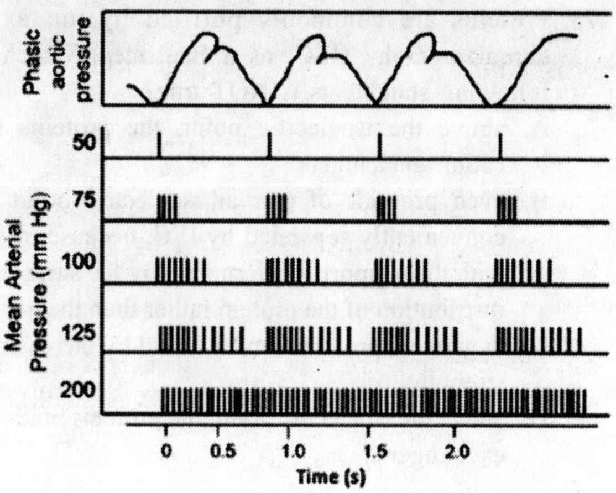

The following statements were proposed from the above figure:

(a) Baroreceptors are more sensitive to phasic change of aortic pressure at normal MAP
(b) The baroreceptor firing rate is reduced at lower MAP than in normal MAP
(c) The phasic change in baroreceptor fibre is less prominent at lower MAP
(d) A burst of action potentials appear in a single baroreceptor fibre during diastole at normal MAP
(e) The discharge of baroreceptors even extends to systole at higher MAP

Choose the option with both CORRECT statements:

A. (a) and (b) B. (b) and (c)
C. (c) and (d) D. (d) and (e)

Field Biology

172. A field biologist is sampling tree species in a forest area to estimate tree diversity. What method can be employed to decide if his sampling effort is adequate to estimate the tree diversity in the area?

A. Quadrat method of sampling
B. Saturation using species accumulation curves
C. Frequency distributions
D. Jaccard's dissimilarity coefficient

DBT-JRF, 2020

Methods in Biotechnology

173. A mixture of homotetramer 'X' and heterodimer 'Y' with identical molecular weight were resolved on SDS-PAGE. It gives three bands on a gel with molecular weights 40 kDa, 60 kDa, and 100 kDa, The native molecular wight (in kDa) of the homotetramer 'X' is

A. 160 B. 240
C. 320 D. 100

174. Single stranded DNA can be separated from double stranded DNA efficiently using
A. hydrophobic interaction chromatography
B. RP-HPLC
C. hydroxyapatite chromatography
D. urea PAGE

175. Proteins are commonly purified by ion exchange chromatography (IEC) as a final step. Which of the following statements is NOT true?
A. above the isoelectric point, the proteins bind to cation exchangers
B. even proteins of similar isoelectric point can be conveniently separated by IEC, because interaction with the support is determined by the surface charge distribution of the protein rather than the net charge.
C. in general, proteins can be eluted by increasing ionic strength
D. above the isoelectric point, the proteins bind to anion exchangers

176. The method utilized to determine the three-dimensional structure of proteins are
A. Cyro-Electron Microscopy
B. X-ray Crystallography
C. all the given options
D. Nuclear Magnetic Resonance

177. The location of a proteins in cells can be studied using
A. X-ray crystallography
B. western blotting
C. fluorescent microscopy
D. NMR spectroscopy

178. Which of the following methods first ionizes a protein before separation and detection?
A. mass spectrometry
B. nuclear magnetic resonance
C. reverse phase chromatography
D. fluorescence spectroscopy

179. A mixture of three proteins (X, Y, and Z) was loaded on a size exclusion column. The molecular weight (<W) and pl of the proteins are as follows

Protein	MW (KD)	PI
X	140.75	5.5
Y	22.3	10.1
Z	88.6	2.8

A. X, Z, Y B. X, Y, Z
C. Y, X, Z D. Y, Z, X

180. Two proteins of molecular weights 1.0×10^5 and 1.0×10^4 Daltons were eluted from a gel filtration column at 220 ml and 300 ml respectively. The molecular weight of an unknown protein that elutes at 140 ml under the same conditions, will be
A. 1.00×10^6 B. $2.5.00 \times 10^5$
C. $3.1.00 \times 10^5$ D. $4.5.00 \times 10^6$

181. In Transmission Electron Microscope (TEM), a beam of electrons interacts with the specimen to form image as
A. reflection B. diffraction
C. shadow D. scattering

182. Which of the following is a method of investigating the sequence specificity of DNA- binding proteins in vitro?
A. gene targeting
B. DNA foot printing
C. polymerase chain reaction
D. Southern hybridization

183. The temperature of liquid nitrogen used for cryopreservation of plant samples is
A. –170°C B. –120°C
C. –196°C D. –100°C

184. The first organic acid to be produced industrially is
A. aspartic acid
B. gibberellic acid
C. acetic acid
D. lactic acid

185. While working in the lab, you forgot to keep enzymes back in the fridge. Which of the following enzyme will be least affected on being left outside at room temperature?
A. Topoisomerase
B. Taq DNA polymerase
C. DNA ligase
D. BamHI restriction enzyme

186. Nucleosides isolated from a Caribbean sponge, Cryptotethyacrypta, were the basis for the synthesis of the antiviral
A. Avarol
B. Amantadine
C. Abacavir
D. Acyclovir

187. Which of the following is NOT used for producing vitamins industrially?
A. Ashbyagossypii
B. Corynebacterium sp.
C. Propionibacterium freudenreichii
D. Pseudomonas aeruginosa

188. Which of the following yeast is used for the production of riboflavin?
A. Saccharomyces rouxii
B. Saccharomyces cerevisiae
C. Eremothecium ashbyi
D. Candida utilis

GATE (BIOTECHNOLOGY), 2020

Molecular Tools

189. The DNA sequences shown below is to be amplified by PCR:

5'GCTAAGATCTGAATTTTCC.......
TTGGGCAATAATGTAGCGC3'

3'CGATTCTAGACTTAAAAGG........
AACCCGTTATTACATCGCG5'

Which one of the following pair of primers can be used for this amplification?

A. 5'GGAAATTCAGATCTTAGT3' and 5'TGGGCAATAATGTAGCGC3'
B. 5'GCTAAGATCTGAATTTTC3' and 5'TGCGCTACATTATTGCCCA3'
C. 5'CGGAAATTCAGATCTTAG3' and 5'GCGCTACATTATTGCCCA3'
D. 5'GCTAAGATCTGAATTTTC3' and 5'TGGGCAATAATGTAGCGC3'

Analytical Tools

190. Two monomeric His-tagged proteins if identical molecular weight is present in a solution. pIs of these two proteins are 5.6 and 6.8. Which one of the following techniques can be used to separate them?

A. Denaturing polyacrylamide gel electrophoresis
B. Size-exclusion chromatography
C. Ion-exchange chromatography
D. Nickel affinity chromatography

GATE (LIFE SCIENCE), 2020

191. A globular protein of molecular weight 50kDa exists as a mixture of monomers and dimers in solution. The most appropriate technique for the separation of these two forms of the protein is

A. Thin layer chromatography
B. Ion exchange chromatography
C. Gel filtration chromatography
D. Paper chromatography

CSIR-NET, JUNE (MORNING), 2021

Molecular Technique and Marker

192. Which one of the following options represents a combination of terms that are matched INCORRECTLY?

A. ddNTPs : Chain termination
B. South Western blot: Physical interaction between DNA and protein
C. 5'-3' exonuclease activity: Proof reading polymerase for PCR
D. Yeast two hybrid system : Interaction between proteins

193. Which one of the following combinations of terms is matched INCORRECTLY?

A. nanopore : DNA sequencing
B. Pyroseqencing: protein primary structure
C. homologus recombination: chloroplast transformation
D. SSRs: Co-dominant markers SSRs

194. Given below are a few terms related to map-based sequencing of genomics:;

(*a*) Partial digestion with restriction enzymes.
(*b*) Assembly of contigs
(*c*) Pulsed field gel electrophoresis
(*d*) Cloning in cosmid/YACs/BACs
(*e*) Sub cloning and sequencing.

Which one of the following options represents the correct order of steps(based on the above terms) in map-based sequencing?

A. (*c*), (*b*), (*d*), (*e*), (*a*)
B. (*c*), (*a*), (*d*), (*b*), (*e*)
C. (*e*), (*a*), (*b*), (*d*), (*c*)
D. (*a*), (*c*), (*b*), (*d*), (*e*)

195. Given below are the various protein cleaving reagents (List I) and their recognition sites (List II) in the target protein

List I	List II
(*a*) CNBr	(*i*) -Asp-Ala
(*b*) Trypsin	(*ii*) *-Phe-Ala-*
(*c*) Caspase	(*iii*) -Met-Ala-
(*d*) Chymotrypsin	(*iv*) -Arg-Gly-

Which one of the following options represents the correct combination of items

	(*a*)	(*b*)	(*c*)	(*d*)
A.	(*iii*)	(*ii*)	(*i*)	(*iv*)
B.	(*iv*)	(*ii*)	(*i*)	(*iii*)
C.	(*iv*)	(*i*)	(*ii*)	(*iii*)
D.	(*iii*)	(*iv*)	(*i*)	(*ii*)

196. Inverse PCR is performed for site-directed mutagenesis with complementary primers using a plasmid having the cloned gene as template. The following statements were made regarding the above experiment.

(*a*) PCR is followed by transformation of bacterial cells directly with the reaction mixture. A large number of the transformants will have the wild type gene.

(*b*) The PCR mixture is treated with Dpn I and then used to transform bacterial cells. Most of the transformants will have the mutant gene.

(*c*) PCR is followed by transformation of bacterial cells directly with the reaction mixture. None of the transformants will have the mutant gene.

(*d*) The PCR mixture is treated with Dpn I and then used to transform bacterial cells. Half of the transformants will have the mutant gene.

Which one of the following options represents a combination of all correct statements?

A. (*a*) and (*b*)
B. (*a*) and (*d*)
C. (*b*) and (*c*)
D. (*b*) only

Instrumentation

197. Historical frequencies of fires in an area can be determined by ?

A. Radioactive dating of the tree remains.
B. Examining the fire scars in growth rings of living trees.
C. Measuring carbon content on the soil surface after fire.
D. Examining records of evacuation history of the nearby villages.

198. For a nuclear Spin of spin quantum no. (I = 1/2) Processing in a magnetic field at a larger frequency of 300 mhz the wavelength of incident radiation required to excite the nuclear spin must be approximately.

A. 1 nm   B. 1 cm
C. 1 m   D. 10 m

199. The molecular ion peak $[M]^{+}$ of an analyte as measured by electron ionization mass spectroscopy has an m/z of 149 and a relative abundance of 100%. The $[M]^{+}$ has a relative abundance of 6.7% and the $[M^{+2}]^{+}$ peak has a relative abundance of 5%. The abundance of the major isotope of H, C, N, O and S are ^{1}H-100%, ^{12}C-98.9%, ^{13}C-1.1%, ^{14}N-99.6%, ^{15}N-0.4%, ^{16}O-99.8%, ^{18}O-0.2%, ^{32}S-95.0%, ^{33}S-0.75% and ^{34}S-4.2%. The most probable molecular formula of the compound is

A. $C_7H_{21}N_2O$
B. $C_5H_{11}NO_2S$
C. $C_6H_{13}O_2S$
D. $C_6H_{15}NOS$

200. Optical remote sensing has been increasingly used to monitor vegetation globally. The table below lists different regions of the electromagnetic radiation (EMR) spectrum as well as different vegetation characteristics,

List I (*Part of the EMR spectrum)*	List II (*Vegetation characteristics)*
(*a*) Ultraviolet	(*i*) Plant water content
(*b*) Visible	(*ii*) Foliage density
(*c*) Near Infrared	(*iii*) Plant photosynthetic pigments
(*d*) Shortwave Infrared	

Which one of the following combinations correctly matches the EMR region with the vegetation character analyzed?

	(*a*)	(*b*)	(*c*)
A.	(*i*)	(*ii*)	(*iii*)
B.	(*i*)	(*iii*)	(*ii*)
C.	(*ii*)	(*iii*)	(*i*)
D.	(*iii*)	(*ii*)	(*i*)

201. A circular dichorim spectrum in the far-UV region informs on the kind and content of secondary structure in a protein. Near- UV and tryptophan emission spectra inform on the tertiary structure. Shown in the panels above are (A) Intrinsic fluorescence emission spectra of protein X, (B) Far-UC CD spectra of protein X, (C) Near-UV CD spectra of protein X recorded under different conditions.

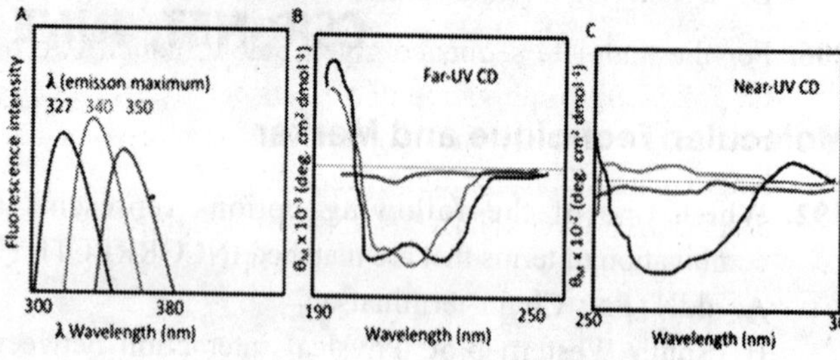

Curve represents the spectra of protein X at PH 7.0 (black), PH 3.0 (green) and PH 7.0 in the presence of 6.0M guanidine hydrochloride (red).

What does the experiment report?

A. Protein is fully folded at pH 7, acid-indud = sed molten globule at pH 3 and unfolded in 6M guanidine HCL
B. Protin is 2 str. Is reduced at pH 7 & the protein has formed b fibers at other 2 condition
C. The charges in flurosance and near-UV CD indicates increase in hydrodynamic radiusat pH3 in gunidine HCl
D. There is extensive denaturation of these protein both at pH 3 and in 6 M guanidine HCl

202. The table below lists the biochemical characteristics of protein and experimental procedure used to determine them. Match the characteristics with the experimental procedure.

Biochemical characteristics	Experimental procedure
(*a*) 3-dimensional structure	(*i*) Nuclear magnetic resonance
(*b*) Ionic charge	(*ii*) Isoelectric focusing
(*c*) Binding specificity	(*iii*) Affinity chromatography
(*d*) Molecular size	(*iv*) Ultracentrifugation

Which one of the following match is correct?

	(*a*)	(*b*)	(*c*)	(*d*)
A.	(*iii*)	(*i*)	(*ii*)	(*iv*)
B.	(*i*)	(*ii*)	(*iii*)	(*iv*)
C.	(*iv*)	(*i*)	(*iii*)	(*iii*)
D.	(*iv*)	(*ii*)	(*i*)	(*iii*)

Microscopic Techniques

203. Fluorescence microscope that requires photoactivatable probes to obtain super- resolution is
A. Structured illumination microscope (SIM)
B. dSTORM-stochastic optical reconstruction microscopy
C. Stimulated emission depletion microscopy (STED)
D. Laser scanning confocal microscope

Immunotechniques

204. Widal test, a widely used serological test for enteric fever is a type of
A. Precipitation reactio
B. Agglutination reaction
C. complement fixation test
D. immunofluresence detection

CSIR-NET, JUNE (AFTERNOON), 2021

Molecular Technique and Marker

205. Which one of the following techniques CANNOT be used for separation, detection or visualization of DNA?
A. Western Blotting
B. Polyacrylamide gel electrophoresis
C. Fluorescence microscopy
D. Denaturing high performance liquid chromatography

206. For the template sequence given below, which one of the following combination of primers can hypothetically be used to amplify the target region (Ignore Tm and length parameters for the primers)?
5'ATCGACTAGNNNNNNNNNNNNNNNNNN
CCTAATGCAG – 3'

	Primer 1	Primer 2
A.	5'-T A G C T G -3'	5'-G A C G T A -3'
B.	5'-C T G C A T -3'	5'-A T C G A C -3'
C.	5'-A T C G A C -3'	5'-G A C G T A - 3'
D.	5'-T A G C T G -3'	5'-C T G C A T -3'

207. Two experiments were performed on a peptide sample 'X'. In experiment 1, treatment of 'X' with dithiothreitol (DDT), followed by blocking of free sulphydryl groups, yielded two polypeptides whose amino acid sequences are as shown below :
I : Ala-Phe- CysA3-Met-Try-CysA6-Leu-Trp-CysA9-Asn
II : Val-CysB2-Trp-Val-Ile-Phe-Gly-CysB8-Lys

In experiment 2,'X' was treated with chymotrypsin, a protease that cleaves the carboxy-terminal of aromatic residues. The amino acid composition of five peptides obtained from this experiment are shown below

I. ([Ala], [Phe])
II. ([Asn], 2[Cys], [Met], [Try])
III. ([Cys], [Gly], [Lys])
IV. (2[Cys], [Leu], 2[Trp], [Val])
V. ([Ile], [Phe], [Val])

Based on the above results, which cysteine/s are linked by disulfide bond in peptide 'X'?
A. A6-B2 and B8-A3 B. A3-A9 and B2-A6
C. A3-B2 and A3-B2 D. A3-B2 and A3-B8

208. Sequencing of the human genome has identified 67 putative gene encoding K+ channels. To characterize the function of one of these genes, a researcher would typically carry out the following experiments :
(*a*) In vitro transcription of the cloned cDNA for this gene in a cell – free system to produce the corresponding mRNA
(*b*) Injecting above mentioned mRNA into frog oocytes.
(*c*) Measuring channel protein activity using a patch – clamping techniques.
(*d*) Knocking out the gene encoding the homolog of this channel in frog oocytes and measuring channel activity using a patch clamping techniques.

Choose the correct combination of experiments that would help in the characterization of the K+ channel.
A. (*a*), (*b*) and (*c*) B. (*b*), (*c*) and (*d*)
C. (*c*), (*d*) and (*a*) D. (*d*), (*a*) and (*b*)

209. In 1990, Bhattacharya et al identified that the wrinkled seed character of pea as described by mendal is caused by a transposon-like insertion in a gene enconding starch Branching Enzyme. This leads to an RFLP pattern, when genomic DNA of round and wrinkled seed is digested with Eco r I and probed with the c-DNA of the R gene product. The following is a represent of the hybridization pattern.

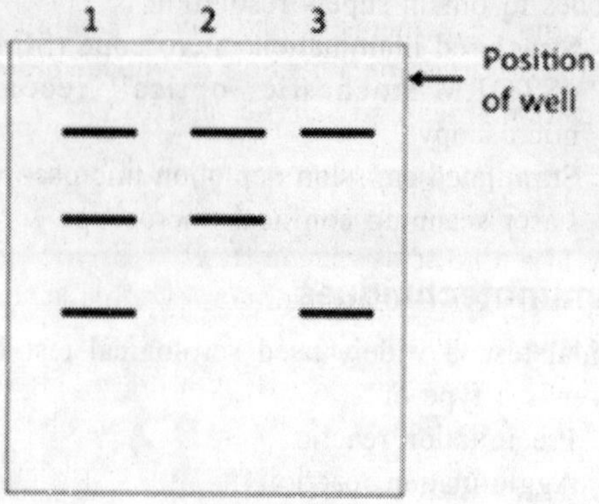

Based on the above, which one of the following statement is INCORRECT

A. Lane 3 reprent genomic DNA from plant with wrinkled seeds.
B. These DNA markers are co-dominance in nature
C. Lane 1 represent genomic DNA from plant with round seeds
D. If genomic DNA from F2 progeny as obtained in Mendel's work was analysed by RFLP the ratio of progeny with pattern in lane 1,2,3 will be

210. In recent decades, the use of genetic markers has allowed the rapid introgression and selection of desired breeding stocks in advance generations. In this regard, following statements are given:

(*a*) AFLP markers can discriminate between homozygote and heterozygous genotypes.
(*b*) Microsatellites are capable of detecting higher level of polymorphism than RFLP.
(*c*) SNPs are more prevalent in the coding regions of the genome.
(*d*) SNPs markers are the most suitable markers for both foreground and background selection.

Which one of the following combination of the above statements is correct?

A. (*a*), (*b*) and (*c*) B. (*a*), (*b*) and (*d*)
C. (*b*) and (*c*) only D. (*b*) and (*d*) only

Instrumentation

211. The unit of molar extinction coefficient are

A. L mol^{-1} cm^{-1}
B. Cm^{-1} mg ml^{-1}
C. Mol^{-1} mm
D. Mol cm ml^{-1}

212. The green fluorescent protein from the deep -sea jellyfish Aquaria victoria has excitation peaks at 395 nm and 475 nm. Its emission peak is at 509 nm, which is in the green portion of the visible spectrum. In the deep sea habitat of this marine organism, what is the source of light for excitation of GFP?

A. Blue -light emitted from the oxidation of the cofactor coelentrazine is energy transferd to GFP.
B. Blue light emitted by aequorin present in A.
C. Light emitted by other organism in ocean seabed is absorbed by GFP in jellyfish
D. Ocean currents provide electrical energy that is conveted to light

Microscopic Techniques

213. Which of the following components is typically NOT utilized while capturing images using a confocal laser scanning microscope(CLSM) ?

A. CCD camera B. Pinhole
C. Laser D. Detectors

214. To investigate the relationship between microtubules and centrioles in fixed heLa cells using an epifluorescent microscope, a researchers plans to (centriolar protein). After the incubation with the primary antibodies. Below is a list of secondary antibodies carrying various fluorophores (dye) available to the researcher?

(*a*) Alexa 568 (*b*) FITC
(*c*) Alexa 488 (*d*) Alexa 647

Select the correct combination of the appropriate dyes that the researcher should typically utilize of observe co-localization in an epifluorescence microscope?

A. (*a*) and (*c*) B. (*b*) and (*c*)
C. (*a*) and (*d*) D. (*c*) and (*d*)

Immunotechniques

215. Which one of the following is the most sensitive immunoassay?

A. Immuno-electrophoresis
B. Rocket electrophoresis
C. Immunofluorescence
D. Passive agglutination

216. A researchers raised antibodies against sheep red blood cells (SRBCs) and purified the IgG fraction. Some of the IgG antibodies were then subjected to enzymatic digestion to have Fab, Fc and F(ab')2 fractions. He placed each preparation in a separate tube (1 to 3), labeled the three tubes to indicate their contents, and incubated them on ice. After a while he noticed that the label on two of the tubes (1 and 2) had gotten erased. He did a test for tube 1 and found that the preparation in the tube agglutinated SRBCs but did not lyse them in presence of complement. Which preparation was in tube 1?

A. Fab B. Fc
C. F(ab') 2 D. IgG

DBT-JRF, 2021

Methods in Biotechnology

217. You have isolated a hypothetical protein X. When X is run on a gel filtration column, the apparent size of the protein is 80kDa. When X is run on an SDS-PAGE with 2-mercaptoethanol present in the loading buffer, the size is around 40kDa

A. X is a dimer of two units together by disulfide bond(s) with a molecular weight of 40kDa per monomeric unit.
B. X is a dimer of two units of X held together by electrostatic interaction with a molecular weight of 80kDa per monomeric unit.
C. X is a monomer with at least one disulfide and molecular weight of 40 kDa
D. X is a monomer with at least one disulfide bond and a molecular weight of 80 kDa

218. A scientist chose Nickel–NTA affinity chromatography to purify a recombinant protein. Which one of the following tag was present in his recombinant protein?

A. Flag
B. Glutathione-S-transferase
C. Hexa-histidine
D. Maltose binding protein,

219. Gel filtration chromatography separates proteins on the basis of:

A. Affinity tag
B. Charge
C. Hydrodynamic volume
D. Hydrophobicity

220. Fake medicines are a nuisance that shatter the faith of patients in medicine and enhance the emergence of drug resistance. A medicine is likely to be fake if:

A. HPLC retention time (RT) of standard and test sample is same
B. Melting point of standard and test are same
C. Rf of standard and test sample on TLC is same
D. Same peak intensity and same retention time are not observed on injection of equal amount of the test and standard sample on HPLC

221. A 20-mer peptide composed of all 20 coded standard amino acids was hydrolyzed with 6N HCl. However, only 17 amino acids were detected when the hydrolysate was analyzed by chromatography. The three missing amino acids will be:

A. Gln, Asn, Trp   B. Glu, Asp, Trp
C. Glu, Asp, Tyr   D. Tyr, Trp, Phe

222. Two immobilized enzyme columns with equal enzyme loading and same column volume are run at the same feed rate and same inlet substrate concentration. It is observed that the taller and thinner column gives better conversion. This demonstrates that:

A. Column packing efficiency is not good
B. Enzyme deactivation is taking place
C. Immobilized enzyme has external diffusion which reduces the enzymatic conversion rate
D. Immobilized enzyme has internal pore diffusion which reduces the enzymatic conversion rate,

223. You have purified a protein X and observed the following:

(*a*) When run on a native PAGE, it gives rise to a single band.
(*b*) When run on a nonreducing SDSPAGE, you obtain two bands-corresponding to 40kDa and 60kDa.
(*c*) When run on a reducing SDS page you get three bands-corresponding to 60kDa, 30kDa, and 10kDa.

What can you conclude about the purified protein X?

A. X contains 2 polypeptide chains that form a complex
B. X contains at least 3 polypeptide chains that from a complex
C. X has 3 polypeptide that have intramolecular disulfide bonds X is a complex of 3 polypeptide chains all of which are linked to each other by disulfide bonds

GATE (BIOTECHNOLOGY), 2021

Molecular Tools

224. Which one of the following techniques/tools is NOT used for inserting a foreign gene into a cell?

A. DNA microarray   B. Electroporation
C. Gene gun   D. Microinjection

225. The cellular process which utilizes RNA-induced silencing complex to block gene expression is

A. RNA editing
B. RNA interference
C. RNA polyadenylation
D. RNA splicing

Analytical Tools

226. Tertiary structure of a protein consisting of α-helices and β-strands can be determined by

A. Circular Dichroism Spectroscopy
B. Mass Spectrometry
C. Nuclear Magnetic Resonance Spectroscopy
D. UV Spectroscopy

227. Match separation methods in Group I with associated properties in Group II.

Group I	Group II
(*a*) Centrifugation	(*i*) Density
(*b*) Dialysis	(*ii*) Diffusivity
(*c*) Solvent extraction	(*iii*) Size
(*d*) Ultrafiltration	(*iv*) Solubility

	(*a*)	(*b*)	(*c*)	(*d*)
A.	(*iv*)	(*ii*)	(*i*)	(*iii*)
B.	(*iii*)	(*i*)	(*ii*)	(*iv*)
C.	(*i*)	(*iii*)	(*ii*)	(*iv*)
D.	(*i*)	(*ii*)	(*iv*)	(*iii*)

228. Which of the following nucleus/nuclei is/are NMR active?

A. ^{1}H B. ^{13}C
C. ^{16}O D. ^{32}S

GATE (LIFE SCIENCE), 2021

Biochemical Separation Techniques

229. The stationary phase used in gel filtration chromatography is composed of ____

A. Blue dextran
B. Carboxymethyl (CM) cellulose
C. Diethylaminoethyl (DEAE) cellulose
D. Sepharose

230. With respect to sodium dodecyl sulphate-polyacrylamide gel electrophoresis (SDS-PAGE), which of these statement(s) is/are true?

A. Ethidium bromide is used to track the progress of electrophoretic mobility
B. β-mercaptoethanol is used to reduce disulphide bonds
C. The protein migrates towards the anode
D. The lower molecular weight protein migrates slower than the larger molecular weight protein

231. Which one of the following enzymes is used in Polymerase Chain Reaction?

A. *Klenow* fragment B. *Taq* polymerase
C. *T7* polymerase D. Primase

CSIR-NET, SEPTEMBER (MORNING), 2022

Molecular technique, Marker, Immunotechnique

232. The following table enlists different ways of carrying out reverse genetics (Column X) and different strategies (Column Y)

Column X	Column Y
(*a*) Random mutagenesis	(*i*) RNAi
(*b*) Targeted mutagenesis	(*ii*) Transposable elements
(*c*) Phenocopying	(*iii*) Homologous recombination
	(*iv*) UV mutagenesis
	(*v*) CRISPR

Which one of the following options is a correct match between Column X and Y?

	(*a*)	(*b*)	(*c*)
A.	(*i*) and (*iv*)	(*iii*)	(*ii*) and (*v*)
B.	(*ii*) and (*iv*)	(*iii*) and (*v*)	(*i*)
C.	(*i*) and (*iv*)	(*iii*) and (*v*)	(*ii*)
D.	(*ii*) and (*iv*)	(*i*) and (*iii*)	(*v*)

Instrumentation

233. Protein 'A' was subjected to different experiments:

(*a*) SDS-PAGE with/without β-mercaptoethanol (β-ME)
(*b*) Fluorescence
(*c*) Far-UV and
(*d*) Near-UV CD spectra at pH 7.0 (blue) and 3.0 (red)

The results are shown below:

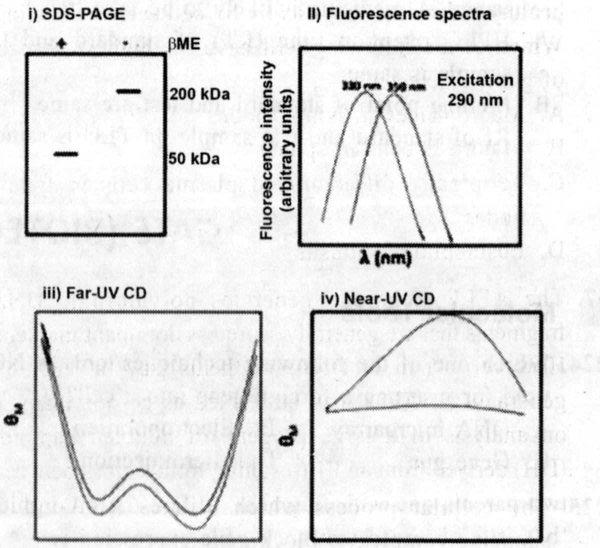

Which one of the following options provides the correct inference?

A. Protein 'A' is an S-S bonded homotetramer and each subunit has a molecular mass of 50 kDa, folded at pH 7.0 and molten globule at pH 3.0
B. Protein 'A' has a molecular mass of 200 kDa, βME degrades the protein, low pH changes the conformation α helix to β sheet
C. SDS denatures protein 'A' into different oligomeric states, low pH changes the conformation from α helix to β sheet
D. SDS promotes the formation of different oligomeric states of Protein 'A', low pH changes the conformatation from β sheet to α helix

Microscopic Techniques

234. Following statements are made regarding the properties of two-photon microscopy over traditional confocal microscopy:

(*a*) By using longer wavelength, two-photon microscopy induces less photobleaching of the tissue preparation.
(*b*) By using shorter wavelength, two-photon microscopy induces less photobleaching of the tissue preparation.
(*c*) The intensity of fluorescence emitted by the sample will remain the same even if only one of the two impinge on the sample.
(*d*) No fluorescence is detected unless two exciting photons simultaneously impinge on the sample.

A. (*a*) and (*c*).
B. (*a*) and (*d*)
C. (*b*) and (*c*)
D. (*b*) and (*d*)

Electrophysiological Methods

235. Different waves of EEG (Column A) are listed with their frequencies (Column B) below:

Column A *(EEG waves)*	**Column B** *(Frequencies)*
(*a*) α	(*i*) 4-7 Hz
(*b*) β	(*ii*) Less than 4 Hz
(*c*) θ	(*iv*) 8-13 Hz
(*d*) δ	(*v*) 13-30 Hz

Choose the option with all correct matches of the wave with its frequency

	(*a*)	(*b*)	(*c*)	(*d*)
A.	(*i*)	(*ii*)	(*iii*)	(*iv*)
B.	(*ii*)	(*iii*)	(*iv*)	(*i*)
C.	(*iii*)	(*iv*)	(*i*)	(*ii*)
D.	(*iv*)	(*i*)	(*ii*)	(*iii*)

CSIR-NET, SEPTEMBER (AFTERNOON), 2022

Molecular Technique, Marker, Immunotechnique

236. An anti-idiotypic antibody with fluorescent tag was used for detection of immune cells in tissue sections from a healthy individual specifically by cell surface labeling. Which of the following will have the highest chances of getting detected?

A. Macrophages in lymph nodes
B. Mature B cells in spleen
C. Terminally differentiated plasma cells in lymph nodes
D. Eosinophils in tonsils

237. The AFLP technique generates polymorphic DNA fragments that are generally scored as dominant markers. However, a pair of DNA fragments (say 'a' and 'b') generated by AFLP can be termed as co-dominant, if on analysis of a large progeny of doubled haploids (DH) derived from an F1 (resulting from a cross between two parents one with fragment 'a' and the other with 'b'), it is observed that:

A. 50% of the progeny has both 'a' and 'b' fragments and the rest have none.
B. 50% of the progeny has fragment 'a' and the remaining have fragment 'b'.
C. 25% of the progeny has fragment 'a', 50% both 'a' and 'b' and the rest fragment 'b'.
D. 75% of the progeny has both the fragments, while 25% has either 'a' or 'b'.

238. An in vitro translation system capable of incorporating ~8 amino acids s-1 was programmed to translate a single mRNA that codes for an alanine-rich (~35% alanine with uniform distribution of alanine) protein of 275 amino acids (~30kDa) including a hexahistidine tag at the C-terminal end of the protein. The protein possesses three methionine residues at amino acid positions 1, 135 and 230 and generates polypeptides of ~15 kDa, ~10 kDa and ~5 kDa upon degradation with cyanogen bromide. The translation reaction was initiated and the ongoing reaction was supplemented with 14C Ala after 5 min. Soon after addition of 14C Ala, aliquots were drawn at 2, 20, and 200 s, and reactions in the aliquots were instantaneously stopped. The translated proteins were purified on Ni-NTA columns, processed for degradation by CNBr, resolved on SDS-PAGE, and visualized by nonquantitative autoradiography. Which of the following autoradiograms represents the expected pattern of the bands?

A. 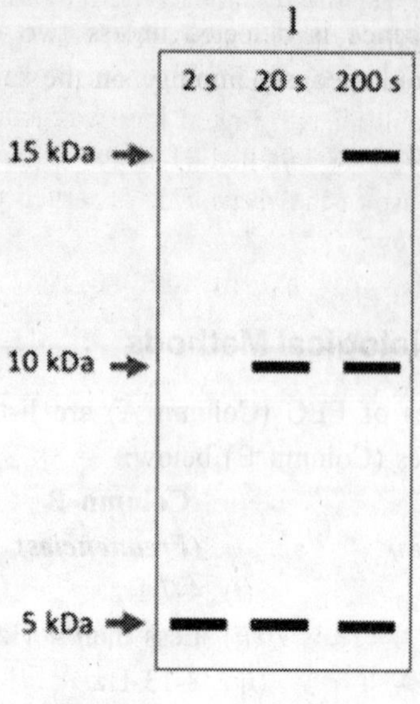

B. 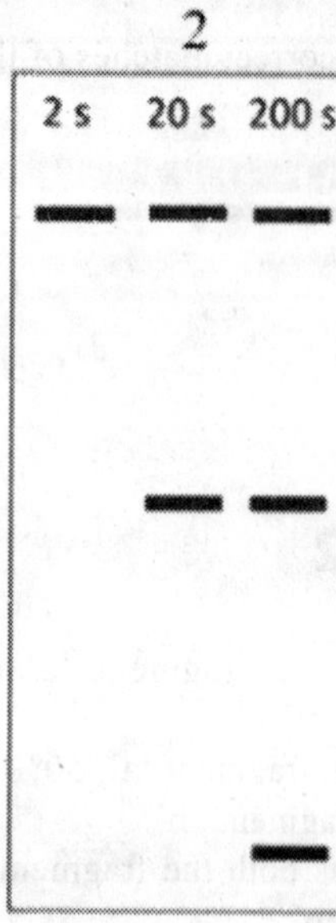

C. 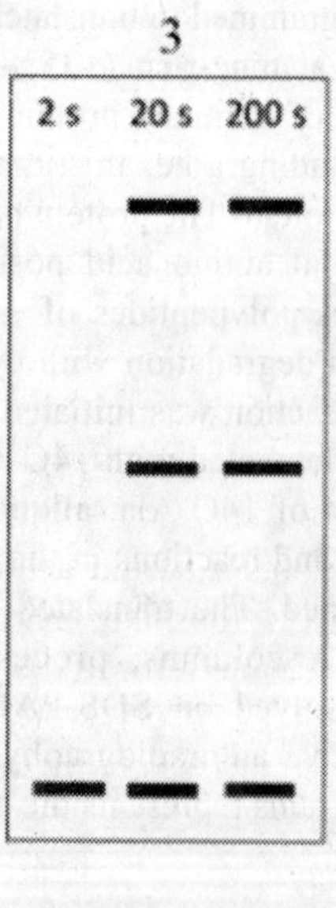

D. 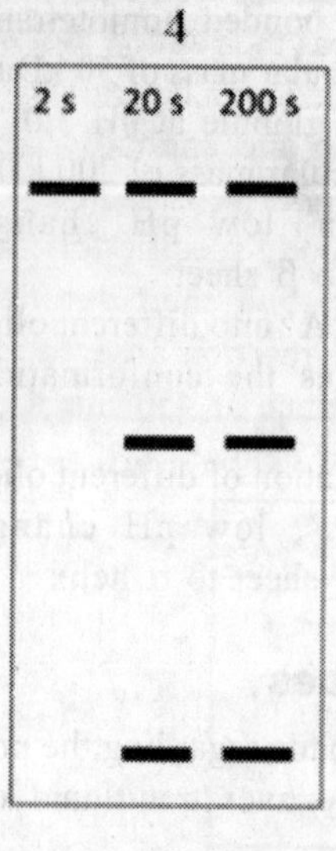

239. Cervical cancer cells were untreated(–) or treated(+) with compound 'X', a putative anticancer drug. The cell extracts were analyzed by immunoblotting for the level of specific markers as indicated by the band thickness. The following results were obtained:

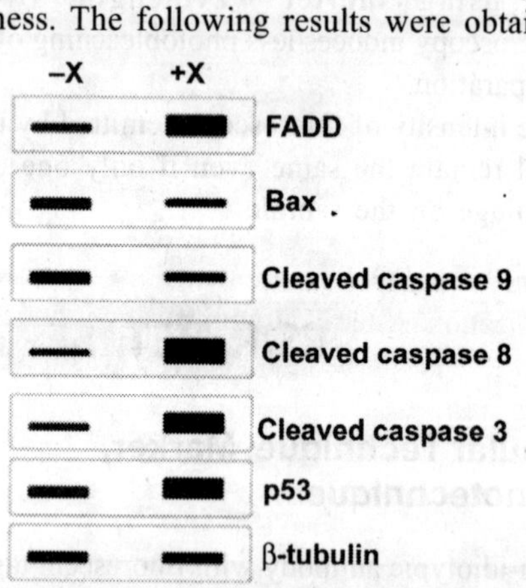

Which one of the following options best describes the action of compound 'X'?

A. Compound 'X' induced cell death via the intrinsic pathway by activating caspase 8 and apoptosis was p53 independent

B. Compound 'X' induced cell death via the extrinsic pathway by inducing the F as ligand associated death domain (FADD) and apoptosis was p53 dependent

C. Compound 'X' induced cell death by reducing the expression of Bax in a p53 dependent manner and consequently increasing the expression of caspase 9

D. Compound 'X' induced cell death by activating the death domain together with increasing the expression of the pro-apoptotic protein in a p53 independent manner

240. In a modified version of ELISA, a student first incubated antibody against the Pseudomonas aeruginosa exotoxin A (Pa-exotoxin A) with culture samples in a 0.5 mL tube to check for Pseudomonas contamination. Each antibody-culture mixture was then added to a microtiter plate whose wells were coated with Pa-exotoxin A. This was followed by removing the antibody-culture mix from the wells, washing the wells, adding enzyme-conjugated secondary antibody specific for the isotype of the primary antibody, and then detection with enzyme- specific substrate reaction absorbance at 450 nm. The values of absorbance at 450 nm for each of four samples A-D is given below:

Samples	A_{450}
(A)	0.323
(B)	0.582
(C)	0.098
(D)	0.220

Select the option that arranges the samples from having highest to least contamination.

A. (C), (D), (A), (B) B. (B), (A), (D), (C)
C. (C), (D), (B), (A) D. (B), (A), (C), (D)

241. Three reactions were performed to detect a 150 bp DNA fragment rich in GC content, using PCR amplification method and the following radiolabeled material (*i*) 5'^{32}P-labelled primers (*ii*) α-^{32}P-labelled dCTP and, (*iii*) γ-^{32}P-labelled dATP. All the reactions had the remaining components for a successful PCR amplification. After PCR amplification the samples were run on a 2% Agarose gel. The gel was then exposed to radiographic film. From the radiographs given below, which is the correct representation of the reactions (*i*), (*ii*) and (*iii*) in lanes A, B and C respectively.

A. 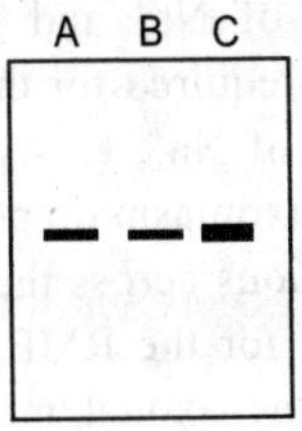

B. 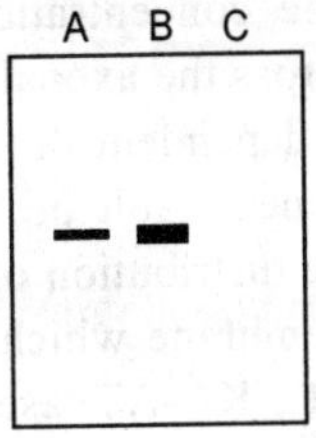

C. 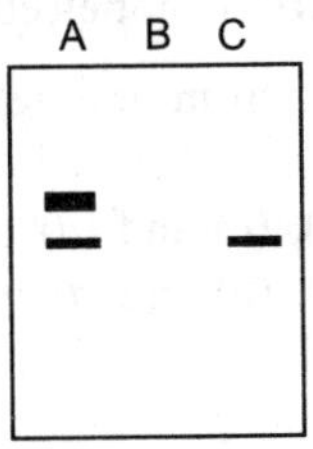

D. 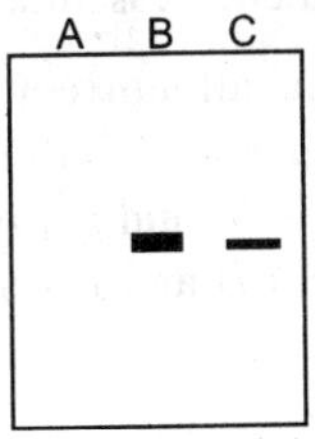

E. 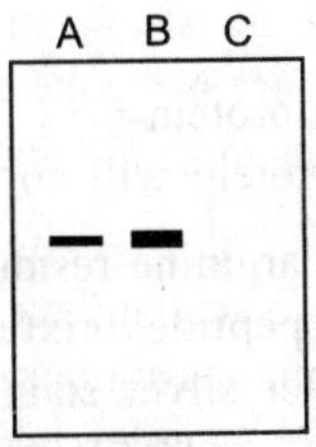

242. Fertilization between two mating types (P1 and P2) of Neurospora, led to a diploid ascus cell, which gave rise to ascus containing 8 haploid ascospores. A set of DNA markers representing two linked loci was analyzed in P1, P2 and the octads labelled 01 to 08 arranged from the tip to the base of the ascus. The observed profile is represented below:

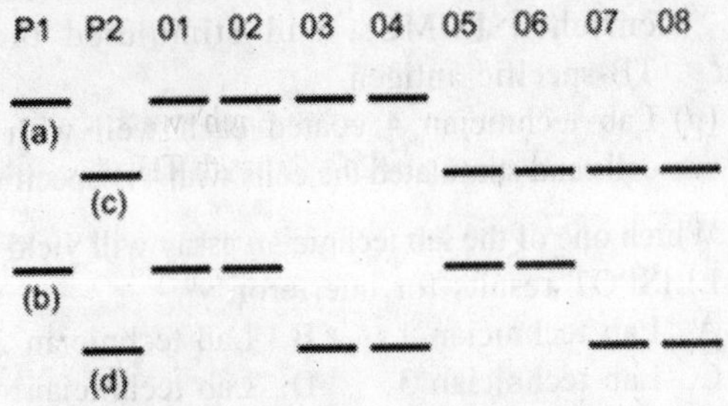

Which one of the following is a correct conclusion of the above observation?

A. Bands labeled (*a*) and (*c*) are allelic and segregation occurred during meiosis II
B. Bands labeled (*b*) and (*d*) are allelic and segregation occurred during meiosis II
C. Bands labeled (*a*) and (*d*) are allelic and segregation occurred during meiosis II
D. Bands labeled (*c*) and (*d*) are allelic and segregation occurred during meiosis I

243. Given below are terms related to Genome-editing tools in Column A and their feature in Column B.

Column A	Column B
(*a*) ZFN	(*i*) Homing endonuclease (I-SceI)
(*b*) Meganuclease	(*ii*) Repeat of near 35 amino acid length, each amino acid binding a specific DNA base in the target sequence
(*c*) CRISPR/Cas9	(*iii*) Fusion of Zinc finger DNA binding domain with endonuclease domain of FokI restriction enzyme
(*d*) TALEN	(*iv*) Target specificity using guide RNA

Which one of the following options is the most appropriate match between terms of Column A and Column B?

	(*a*)	(*b*)	(*c*)	(*d*)
A.	(*iv*)	(*iii*)	(*ii*)	(*i*)
B.	(*iii*)	(*i*)	(*iv*)	(*ii*)
C.	(*ii*)	(*iv*)	(*i*)	(*iii*)
D.	(*iii*)	(*iv*)	(*ii*)	(*i*)

244. PBMCs from the blood collected from a tuberculosis (TB) patient were given to four lab technicians to perform ELISPOT assay for interferon γ(IFN γ). While all steps recommended for ELISPOT were followed, the first step was performed differently by the four lab technicians, as detailed below.

(*a*) Lab technician 1 coated each well with 250,000 formaldehyde-treated cells and stimulated the cells with TB-specific antigen.
(*b*) Lab technician 2 coated each well with 250,000 cells and did not stimulate the cells with TB-specific antigen.
(*c*) Lab technician 3 depleted T cells from PBMCs completely, coated the wells with monocyte-enriched PBMCs, and stimulated them with TB-specific antigen.
(*d*) Lab technician 4 coated each well with 250,000 cells and stimulated the cells with TB-specific antigen.

Which one of the lab technician assay will yield a correct ELISPOT results for interferon γ?
A. Lab technician 1 B. Lab technician 2
C. Lab technician 3 D. Lab technician 4

Instrumentation

245. Emission maximum of a fluorophore is shifted to longer wavelength when compared to the wavelength of excitation. What is the reason?
A. Non-radiative loss of excitation energy
B. Partial absorbance of incident light
C. Scattering of light by molecules
D. Radiative loss of excitation energy

246. What will be the percentage transmission when absorbance is 1, 2 and 3, respectively?
A. 10, 1, 0.1 B. 1, 10, 100
C. 0.2, 0.1, 0 D. 20, 10, 0

Biophysical Methods

247. The functions of some components used for magnetic resonance imaging (MRI) technique are proposed in the following statements:
(*a*) The static magnetic field used by MRI causes all the magnetically sensitive particles to align themselves in same direction.
(*b*) The pulse sequence used by MRI is an oscillating magnetic field which causes perturbation of static magnetic field.
(*c*) The receiver coil placed near a portion of subject's body is a radiofrequency coil that records the relaxation time of protons.
(*d*) Various parameters of pulse sequence cannot be adjusted to maximize the ability to image certain substances.
(*e*) The signal intensity received by the receiver coil can provide the location of brain from which it is coming

Choose the option with all INCORRECT statements.
A. (*a*) and (*b*) B. (*b*) and (*c*)
C. (*c*) and (*d*) D. (*d*) and (*e*)

248. Given below are radio-imaging technologies with the type of radiation/radioisotope that is used for the same.
(*a*) Computed tomography scanner uses UV-rays
(*b*) Magnetic resonance imaging [MRI] uses non-ionization radiation
(*c*) Thyroid scintigraphy uses Iodine-123 (I123)
(*d*) Phase-contrast radiography uses X-rays
(*e*) Fluoroscopy uses X-rays

Which of the options represents all correct statements?
A. (*b*) and (*e*) only
B. (*a*), (*c*) and (*d*) only
C. (*a*), (*b*), (*d*) and (*e*) only
D. (*b*), (*c*), (*d*) and (*e*) only

Electrophysiological Methods

249. A potential difference of about -70 mV between inside and outside of a single axonal membrane in resting condition may be recorded by suitable electrodes and amplifier. The physico-chemical and biological basis of the origin of this resting membrane potential (RMP) are suggested below:
(*a*) The RMP is close to the equilibrium of Na^+ ion.
(*b*) There must be an unequal distribution of diffusible ions across the axonal membrane for the RMP.
(*c*) The axonal membrane must be permeable to one or more species of ions for the RMP.
(*d*) The concentration gradient of Na^+ and K^+ ions across the axonal membrane required for the RMP, is dependent on the activity of Na^+, K^+-ATPase.
(*e*) Impermeable proteins in the axoplasm do not affect the distribution of diffusible ions across the axonal membrane which is required for the RMP.
(*f*) Na^+, K^+-ATPase pump in the axonal membrane which is essential for the RMP, is not electrogenic.

Choose all correct statements from the following options:
A. (*a*), (*b*) and (*c*) only B. (*b*), (*c*) and (*d*) only
C. (*c*), (*d*) and (*e*) only D. (*d*), (*e*) and (*f*) only

DBT-JRF, 2022

Methods in Biotechnology

250. In Reverse Phase chromatography of a mixture of protein and sodium chloride:
A. The salt will elute before the protein
B. The salt and protein will co-elute
C. The salt will elute after the protein
D. The salt will elute but the protein will not

251. A protein with 10 lysines and 2 arginine residues was digested with trypsin and the peptide mixture was resolved on an SDS-PAGE. After silver staining, 10

bands were detected instead of 13. Select the plausible reasons from the following:
(*a*) Some of the Arginines and Lysines were inside the protein core.
(*b*) Some of the Arginines and Lysines were followed by a Proline residue.
(*c*) Some of the Arginines and Lysines were followed by a negatively charged residue.
(*d*) Some of the Lysines were modified at the epsilon Nitrogen atom.
(*e*) One of the Lysine or Arginine was at the extreme C-terminus.

Choose the correct answer from the options given below:
A. (*a*), (*b*), (*c*) and (*d*) B. (*a*), (*b*), (*c*) and (*e*)
C. (*b*), (*c*), (*d*) and (*e*) D. (*a*), (*b*), (*d*) and (*e*)

252. A laboratory is trying to purify a Histone-binding protein from its native source. Which one of the following purification techni27-200ues should be used for one-step purification of the protein?
A. Cation exchange chromatography
B. Immuno affinity chromatography
C. Gel exclusion chromatography
D. Metal affinity chromatography

253. The color of emitted light of quantum dots used in fluorescence microscopy depend on:
A. The antibody they are coupled with
B. The size of the nanocrystal
C. Time at which they are visualized
D. The material that coats them

254. What will be the absorbance of a 1 mM solution of molecule X whose molar extinction coefficient is 1000 M-1cm-1 & path length of the cuvette used is 1 cm?
A. 1.0 B. 0.1
C. 0.5 D. 2.0

255. Given below are two statements one is labelled as Assertion (A) and the other is labelled as Reason (R):
Assertion (A): In size exclusion chromatography, larger proteins elute earlier and smaller proteins elute later.
Reason (R): When matrices like sephadex are used, the partitioning of protein molecules between liquid and solid phases is a function of protein size.

In the light of the above statements, choose the correct answer from the options given below:
A. Both (A) and (R) are true and (R) is the correct explanation of (A)
B. Both (A) and R are true and R is not the correct explanation of (A)
C. (A) is true but (R) is false
D. (A) is false but (R) is true

256. A diafiltration process is used to remove salts from a protein solution of 1L. After 1L of make-up buffer (without salts) has been added to this system, the residual salt concentration would be__________ of the original.
A. 50% B. 36%
C. 10% D. 5%

257. A protein sample isolated from natural source was electrophoresed on a non-reducing SDSPAGE. It migrated as a band corresponding to 60 kDa. When the same protein was electrophoresed on a native-PAGE its migration corresponded to a 120 kDa marker protein. What is a reasonable inference?
A. The protein is a dimer of 60 kDa subunits that are not linked with disulfides
B. The protein has two 60 kDa subunits that are linked with disulfides
C. No inference concerning protein size can be drawn since proteins don't run according to their masses in native PAGE
D. The protein is unusually rich in aspartic and glutamic acid

258. Protein A used for the purification of IgG is isolated from:
A. Staphylococcus aureus
B. Streptomyces lividans
C. Streptomyces pyogenes
D. Staphylococcus carnosus

259. A conventional light microscope allows us to magnify cells up to 1000 times and to resolve details as small as __________.
A. 200 μm B. 200 nm
C. 0.2 nm D. 20 nm

260. Which one of the following cell separation techniques allows cells from different stages of the cell cycle to be separated simultaneously with minimal perturbation to their physiology?
A. counterflow centrifugal elutriation
B. fluorescent activated cell sorter
C. size exclusion chromatography
D. ultracentrifugation

261. A spectrum that depicts the magnitude of response of a biological system to light as a function of wavelength is called:
A. Action spectrum B. Absorption spectrum
C. Visible spectrum D. Hypothetical spectrum

262. You are measuring blood glucose level by glucose oxidase method. Following are the absorbance values that you got for the standard and the test sample. Determine the glucose concentration in the test sample:

Sample	Concentration	A505
Standard 1	0.4 mmol/L	0.120
Standard 2	0.6 mmol/L	0.180
Standard 3	0.6 mmol/L	0.240
Unknown	?	0.210

A. 0.65 mM B. 0.70 mM
C. 0.725 mM D. 0.75 mM

GATE (BIOTECHNOLOGY), 2022

263. Which of the following spectroscopic technique(s) can be used to identify all the functional groups of an antibiotic contaminant in food?

(*a*) Infrared
(*b*) Circular dichroism
(*c*) Nuclear magnetic resonance
(*d*) UV-Visible

A. (*a*) only
B. (*a*) and (*c*) only
C. (*a*), (*b*) and (*c*) only
D. (*a*), (*b*), (*c*) and (*d*)

264. Match the stationary phase (Column I) with its corresponding chromatography technique (Column II).

Column I	Column II
(*a*) Protein A	(*i*) Size exclusion chromatography
(*b*) Sephadex	(*ii*) Ion-exchange chromatography
(*c*) Phenylsepharose	(*iii*) Affinity chromatography
(*d*) Diethylaminoethyl cellulose	(*iv*) Hydrophobic interaction chromatography

	(*a*)	(*b*)	(*c*)	(*d*)
A.	(*i*)	(*iv*)	(*ii*)	(*iii*)
B.	(*iii*)	(*i*)	(*iv*)	(*ii*)
C.	(*iii*)	(*iv*)	(*ii*)	(*i*)
D.	(*iv*)	(*i*)	(*iii*)	(*ii*)

GATE (LIFE SCIENCE), 2022

Biochemical Separation Techniques

265. Purification of 6 × His-tagged protein using Ni-NTA column is an example of ________.

A. affinity chromatography
B. hydrophobic-interaction chromatography
C. ion-exchange chromatography
D. size-exclusion chromatography

266. According to Abbe's equation on microscopy, the ability to resolve two entities inside a cell by light microscopy depends on which of the following factor/s?

A. Magnification of the objective lens
B. Intensity of incident light
C. Wavelength
D. Numerical aperture of the objective lens

ANSWERS

1	2	3	4	5	6	7	8	9	10
C	C	A	A	B	C	A	A	C	A
11	**12**	**13**	**14**	**15**	**16**	**17**	**18**	**19**	**20**
C	C	C	C	C	D	C	B	D	D
21	**22**	**23**	**24**	**25**	**26**	**27**	**28**	**29**	**30**
B	B	C	A	A	A	A	B	C	A
31	**32**	**33**	**34**	**35**	**36**	**37**	**38**	**39**	**40**
B	D	A	A	B	D	A	B	A	D
41	**42**	**43**	**44**	**45**	**46**	**47**	**48**	**49**	**50**
C	C	B	B	A	A	B	B	D	A
51	**52**	**53**	**54**	**55**	**56**	**57**	**58**	**59**	**60**
B	B	B	C	D	B	D	D	B	B
61	**62**	**63**	**64**	**65**	**66**	**67**	**68**	**69**	**70**
D	B	A	A	C	A	D	C	C	C
71	**72**	**73**	**74**	**75**	**76**	**77**	**78**	**79**	**80**
C	B	B	B	B	C	C	C	C	D
81	**82**	**83**	**84**	**85**	**86**	**87**	**88**	**89**	**90**
B	A	A	D	A	C	D	A	B	B
91	**92**	**93**	**94**	**95**	**96**	**97**	**98**	**99**	**100**
C	A	B	C	B	B	C	B	B	A

101	102	103	104	105	106	107	108	109	110
C	B	A	D	D	B	D	C	D	B
111	112	113	114	115	116	117	118	119	120
A	C	C	A	C	A	A	C	D	C
121	122	123	124	125	126	127	128	129	130
D	C	D	D	D	B	B	C	D	C
131	132	133	134	135	136	137	138	139	140
C	D	C	C	C	B	C	B	B	A
141	142	143	144	145	146	147	148	149	150
A	D	B	B	C	B	A	B	B	C
151	152	153	154	155	156	157	158	159	160
A	B	B	C	B	C	B	B	A	A
161	162	163	164	165	166	167	168	169	170
A	C	A	D	C	C	A	B	B	D
171	172	173	174	175	176	177	178	179	180
A	B	A	C	A	C	C	A	A	A
181	182	183	184	185	186	187	188	189	190
C	B	C	D	B	D	D	C	B	C
191	192	193	194	195	196	197	198	199	200
C	C	B	B	D	A	C	C	B	D
201	202	203	204	205	206	207	208	209	210
A	B	B	B	A	B	B	A	A	D
211	212	213	214	215	216	217	218	219	220
A	A	A	A	D	C	A	C	C	D
221	222	223	224	225	226	227	228	229	230
A	C	B	A	B	C	D	A,B	D	B,C
231	232	233	234	235	236	237	238	239	240
B	B	A	B	C	B	B	C	B	A
241	242	243	244	245	246	247	248	249	250
B	B	B	D	A	A	D	D	B	A
251	252	253	254	255	256	257	258	259	260
D	B	B	A	A	B	C	A	B	A
261	262	263	264	265	266				
A	B	B	B	A	C,D				

CHAPTER 9

RECOMBINANT DNA TECHNOLOGY

CSIR-NET, JUNE, 2017

Genetic Engineering

1. In normal individuals, there are three *MstII* restriction sites, two flanking the β-globin gene and one within the gene. In individuals affected by a disease, a single nucleotide polymorphism in the β-globin gene abolishes the internal *MstII* recognition site. The RFLP pattern for this locus, obtained by hybridization using a probe internal to the flanking *MstII* sites, from three siblings of a family is shown below:

Size (kb)	Normal Son	Normal Daughter	Affected Son
1.35	—		—
1.15	—	—	
0.2	—	—	

Based on the above profile, what is the nature of the genetic disorder?
A. X-linked Recessive
B. Autosomal Dominant
C. Autosomal Recessive
D. X-linked Dominant

2. In an experiment designed to clone a PCR-amplified fragment in a cloning vector digested with XhoI (C/TCGAG) and SmaI (CCC/GGG), which one of the following combinations of restriction enzymes can be used in the PCR primer to generate compatible ends for cloning?
('/' indicates the site of cleavage within the recognition sequence)
A. XbaI (T/CT AGA) and SpeI (A/CT AGT)
B. EcoRI (G/ AA TIC) and SmaI (CCC/GGG)
C. SalI (G/TCGAC) and EcoRV (GAT/ATC)
D. HindIII(A/AGCTT) and PvuII (CAG/TAG)

Molecular Technique and Marker

3. In order to check whether a protein has been phosphorylated during treatment with a drug, you would perform
A. Southern hybridization
B. Western blot analysis
C. ChIP assay
D. RFLP

4. Several fusion constructs were developed to purify heterologous protein in *E. coli*. The table below lists fusion partners and ligands

Partner	Ligand
(*a*) Maltose binding protein	(*i*) Specific monoclonal antibody
(*b*) Streptavidin	(*ii*) Nickel
(*c*) Glutathione-S-transferase	(*iii*) Glutathione
(*d*) Flag-tag	(*iv*) Amylose
(*e*) 6-Histiden tag	(*v*) Biotin

Which one of the following is the correct match off fusion partner with the ligand?

	(a)	(b)	(c)	(d)	(e)
A.	(ii)	(iv)	(iii)	(i)	(v)
B.	(iv)	(ii)	(v)	(iii)	(i)
C.	(iv)	(v)	(iii)	(i)	(ii)
D.	(iii)	(iv)	(i)	(ii)	(v)

5. In a breeding experiment; two homozygous parental lines (P1 and P2) were crossed to produce F1 hybrids. Due to an experimental error, seeds of these hybrids got mixed up with the seeds of two other germplasm lines (P3 and P4) and hybrid seeds derived from them.

A marker-based fingerprinting exercise was performed using six randomly selected seeds (F1-F6) from the mixed material and the four parental lines. Results of this analysis are shown below:

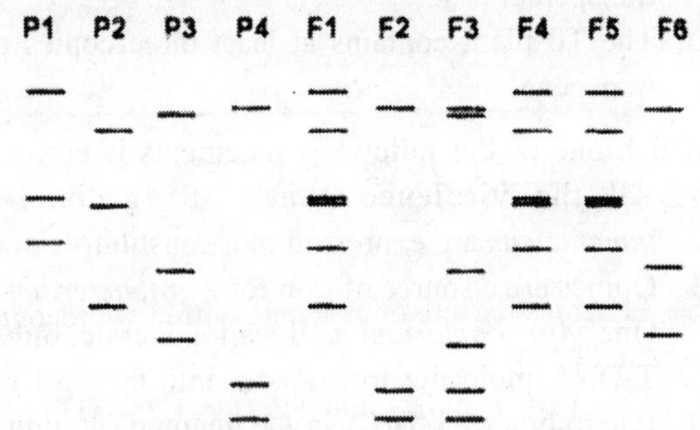

Based on the above data, which one of the following options represents the correct set of parents and their F1 progeny?

A. P1 × P2 = F3 B. P3 × P4 = F2
C. P1 × P2 = F1 D. P3 × P4 = F6

6. A researcher was working with three proteins, A, B and C which may have potential roles in gene expression. In order to validate the hypothesis, EMSA (electrophoretic mobility shift assay) was performed. The purified proteins were allowed to bind with a labelled DNA and the results obtained after autoradiography as shown below.

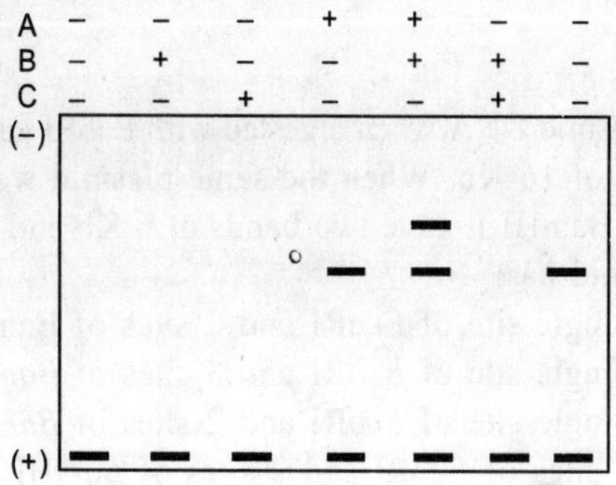

The following interpretations were made
(*a*) Protein A possesses the DNA binding motif
(*b*) Protein B possesses the DNA binding motif
(*c*) Protein B binds to DNA -protein A complex
(*d*) Protein-C binds to DNA only when protein A is bound

Choose the correct combination of interpretations.
A. (*a*) and (*d*) B. (*a*) and (*c*)
C. (*b*) and (*c*) D. (*c*) and (*d*)

CSIR-NET, DECEMBER, 2017

7. Which one of the following statements regarding use of hybrid nucleases for plant genome engineering is INCORRECT?
A. For gene knock out experiments, the nuclease is expressed without a donor DNA template.
B. Hybrid nucleases typically comprise two protein subunits that dimerize at their nuclease domain.
C. Zinc finger nucleases (ZFNs) can efficiently target all nuclear genes with equal efficiency.
D. Both ZFNs and TALENs are fused with cleavage domains of FokI endonuclease.

8. Which of the following host systems is best suited to express large amounts of glycosylated protein for structural studies?
A. GST fusion protein in *E. Coli*
B. His-tagged protein in *E. Coli*
C. Native protein in baculovirus
D. Native protein in *Pseudomonas fluorescens*

9. Which of the following statements about YACs is FALSE?
A. YACs can carry DNA fragments of 1Mb
B. A single yeast may contain more than one YAC
C. Rearrangements in YACs are rare because recombination is poor in yeast
D. YACs have to be transferred to bacteria for subsequent DNA manipulations

10. A researcher attempted to clone a 630bp coding sequence of a gene downstream to a bacterial promoter (500bp in length) for over expression and purification of the encoded protein. The gene sequence was isolated as a SmaI fragment (Recognition sequence: CCC↓GGG; arrow indicates the site of restriction) and cloned at a SmaI site located downstream to the promoter. The gene sequence contained a single site for EcoRI located 30bp downstream to the start codon. A schematic representation of the plasmid along with locations(s) of some restriction enzyme sites of the vector is given below.

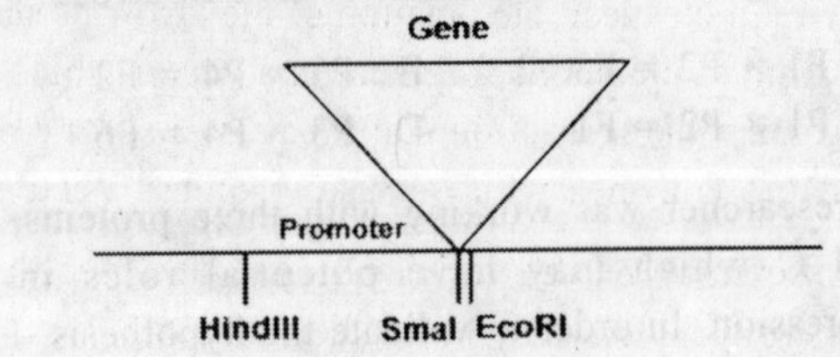

The researcher screened the obtained colonies by a double digestion using HindIII and EcoRI. Which one of the following restriction digestion patterns would represent the restriction profile of the desired clone that could be used for overexpression?

A. ~530bp + ~600bp + vector backbone
B. ~1100bp + ~30bp + vector backbone
C. ~500bp + vector backbone
D. ~1130bp + vector backbone

DBT-JRF, 2017

11. A plasmid DNA when digested with EcoRI gave a single band of 16 Kb. When the same plasmid was digested with BamHI it gave two bands of 6 Kb and 4 Kb. The plasmid has:
A. Single site of EcoRI and 2 sites of BamHI
B. Single site of *Eco*RI and 3 sites of *Bam*HI
C. Single site of *Eco*RI and 2 sites of *Bam*HI
D. 2 sites of *Eco*RI and 2 sites of *Bam*HI

12. The use of guide RNA to bind to DNA and target the double strand break at a specific site is a feature of:
A. Gene knockout by homologous recombination
B. Gene knock down by RNAi
C. Genome editing by CRISPR/Cas system
D. Gene silencing by siRNA

13. Which one of the following combinations of marker genes and promoters CANNOT be used for selection of transgenic plants under *in vitro* conditions?
A. positive selection marker genes under the *Agrobacterium*-derived NOS promoter
B. conditional negative selection marker genes under an inducible promoter
C. positive selection marker genes under CaMV 35S promoter
D. non-conditional negative selection marker genes under CaMV 35S promoter

14. Several experiments have shown leaky/deregulated expression of reporter genes viz., *GUS* from plant promoters in *Agrobacterium* cells. Which one of the following approaches would be most useful in restricting transgene expression in transformed plant cells and prevent their expression in *Agrobacterium*?
A. Use of weak promoters to express the transgene
B. Use of 5' and 3' UTRs flanking the transgene
C. Avoiding use of the polyA signal
D. Use of intron(s) within the transgene sequence

15. A T0 transgenic plant showing two copies of T-DNA on Southern analysis, segregated in a 3:1 ratio for the transgenic:non-transgenic phenotype among T1 progeny obtained by self-pollination. Which one of the following statements best explains this observation?
A. The T0 plant contains a single copy of the transgene.
B. The T0 plant contains two linked copies of the transgene.
C. The T0 plant contains two unlinked copies of the transgene.
D. The T0 plant contains at least three copies of the transgene

16. Which one of the following statements is correct?
A. All the virulence genes of *Agrobacterium tumefaciens* are expressed in a constitutive manner.
B. Opines are a source of iron for *Agrobacterium* cells.
C. One *Agrobacterium* cell can generate only one T-DNA molecule for transfer into the host cell.
D. Integration of T-DNA in the genome can mutate or modulate endogenous plant genes.

17. Which one of the following statements related to transgene silencing in plants is INCORRECT?
A. Transgene silencing is usually accompanied by methylation of cytosine residues in "CG" and/or "CNG" sites.
B. Events with multi-copy integrations of the T-DNA are more susceptible to transgene silencing.
C. Transgene silencing always occurs in T0 individuals and never in subsequent generations.
D. Transgene silencing may lead to silencing of endogenous plant gene homologs.

18. Which one of the following is NOT a feature of Agrobacterium VirE protein?
A. Its synthesis is induced by VirG protein
B. It contains a nuclear localization signal
C. It protects T-DNA from being destroyed by plant defense mechanism
D. It is a component of T-pilus.

19. Transgenic potato plants with high amylose starch were developed by:
A. suppression of starch branching enzymes
B. over-expression of starch branching enzymes
C. over-expression of ADP-glucose pyro phosphorylase
D. suppression of granule-bound starch synthase

20. Developing cisgenic disease resistant apple is advantageous over conventional breeding because:

A. genes cannot be transferred from sexually compatible species through pollination due to hybridization barriers

B. there is no linkage drag.

C. apple is vegetatively propagated and produces sterile seeds

D. cisgenes will not disrupt endogenous genes when introduced by *Agrobacterium* mediated transformation

21. For development of selection marker-free transgenic plants by co-transformation using Agrobacterium, the marker genes are:

A. segregated out in T_0 generation

B. excised out in T_0 generation

C. segregated out in T_1 generation

D. excised out in T_1 generation

22. Breakdown of Bt- mediated insect resistance in crops can be delayed by:

A. Refugia strategy

B. Cultivation of different Bt cotton varieties with same Bt gene

C. Application of Bt Bio-pesticides

D. application of systemic insecticides

23. Which one of the following is matched INCORRECTLY?

A. Nanopore–DNA sequencing

B. beta-carotene–golden rice

C. *bar* gene–resistance to viruses

D. Figwort Mosaic Virus–constitutive promoter

24. DNA fragment was digested with a restriction enzyme X with the recognition sequence

5'G↓GATCC 3'

3'CCTAG↑G 5'

that would cleave at the position of the arrow as shown. You want to clone this fragment in a vector which does not contain the restriction site for X. Which one of the following enzymes will you use to digest Vector

The sequence of the restriction site and position of cleavage for each enzyme is shown below

A. Restriction enzyme A

5'G↓AATTC 3'

3'CTTAA↑G 5'

B. Restriction enzyme B

5'C↓TCGAG 3'

3'GAGCT↑C 5'

C. Restriction enzyme C

5'A↓GATCT 3'

3'TCTAG↑A 5'

D. Restriction enzyme D

5'G↓TCGAG 3'

3'CAGGT↑C 5'

25. To prepare a DNA probe of high specific activity for detecting a single copy gene in a Zoo-blot experiment, which one of the following procedures would be preferred?

A. 5' end labelling

B. 3' end labelling

C. In vitro transcription

D. Random primer labelling

26. A recombinant protein is found to be expressed very poorly in E. coli. It is hypothesized that the expression is blocked at the translational step. The first experimental technique to test this is:

A. PCR followed by sequencing

B. Quantitative RT PCR

C. Western Blot

D. EMSA

GATE (BIOTECHNOLOGY), 2017

27. Which one of the following CANNOT be a recognition sequence for a TYPE II Restriction Enzyme?

A. GAATTC B. AGCT

C. GCGGCCGC D. ATGCCT

28. The transcription factor X binds to 20 base pair DNA stretch. In the DNA of an organism X was found to bind at 20 distinct sites. An analysis of these 20 binding sites showed the following

Base	Position in the binding site									
	1	2	3	4	5	6	7	8	9	10
A	11	0	0	0	16	2	4	0	4	3
T	3	0	19	0	1	3	4	20	2	4
G	4	20	0	0	2	4	6	0	12	2
C	2	0	1	20	1	11	6	0	2	11

What is the consensus sequence for the binding site of X?

A. NGTCNNNTNN

B. AGTCACNTGC

C. CACCTANCTG

D. ANNNACGNGC

29. Given below is a plasmid vector (P) and an insert (Q). The insert was cloned into *Bam*HI site of the vector. The recombinant plasmid was isolated and digested with *Bam*HI or *Xho*I. The results from the digestion experiments are shown in (R).

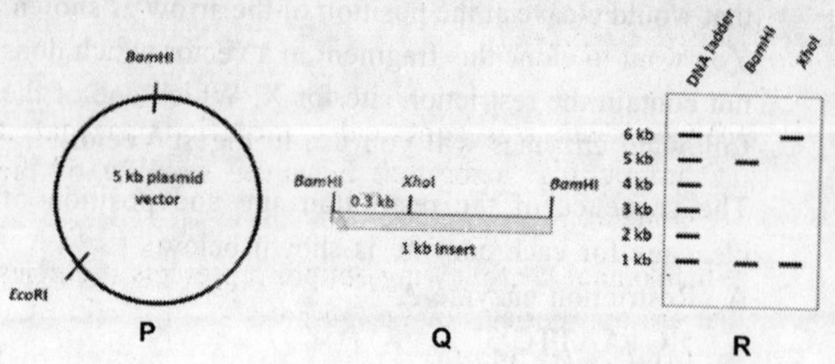

Which one of the following explains the digestion results shown in (R)?

A. The insert did not ligate to the vector.

B. One copy of the insert ligated to the vector

C. The insert ligated to the vector as two tandem copies

D. The insert ligated to the vector as two copies but not in tandem

GATE (LIFE SCIENCE), 2017

30. A newly isolated circular plasmid gave two bands of 3.2 and 3 kb on digestion with EcoRI and two bands of 5.0 kb and 1.2 kb digestion with BamHI. Double digestion with EcoRI and BamHI, yielded four bands of 2.6 kb, 2.4 kb, 0.8kb and 0.4 kb. Digestion with Sa1I led to disruption of ampicillin resistance gene cassette. The correct restriction map is

A.

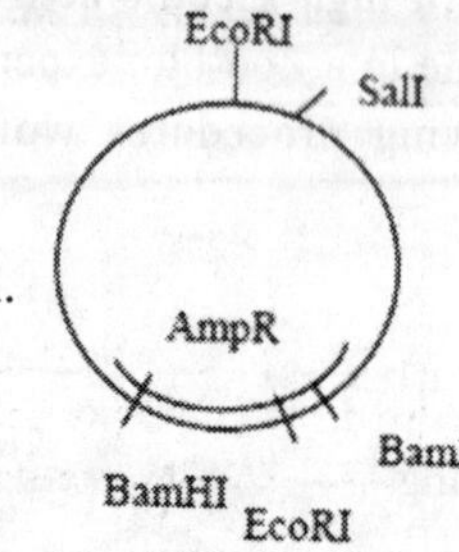

B.

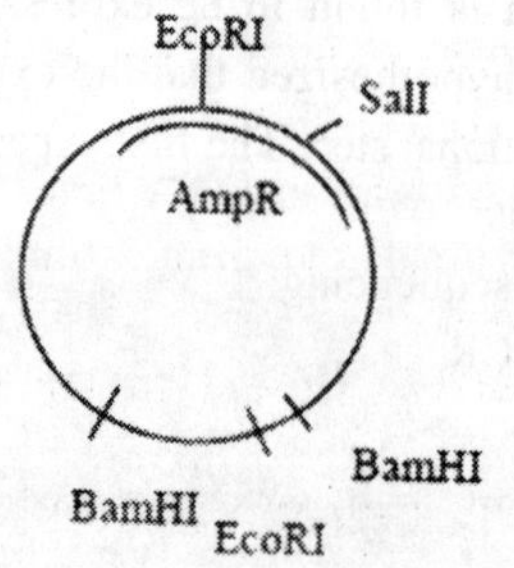

C.

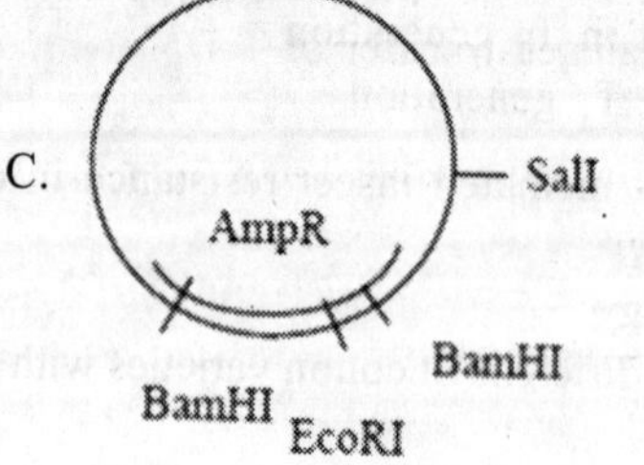

D.

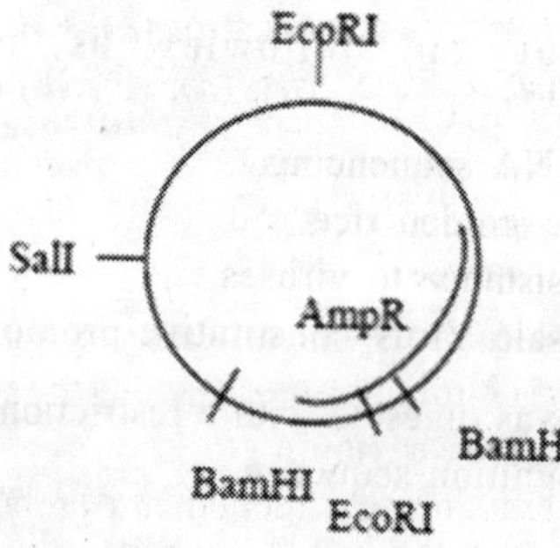

CSIR-NET, JUNE, 2018

31. A researcher attempted to clone two genes (*X* and *Y*) independently in a plasmid vector for over expression and purification in *E. coli.* All attempts to clone gene *X* were unsuccessful whereas gene '*Y*' could be cloned easily. When the, researcher attempted to clone gene '*X*' in the plasmid clone containing gene '*Y*', gene '*X*' could be cloned. The following statements were proposed to explain the above results.

(*a*) Protein encoded by gene '*Y*' is not lethal to the cell.

(*b*) Gene '*X*' has introns, which prevents its expression in *E. coli*

(*c*) Expression of '*X*' protein is lethal to the cell.

(*d*) The '*Y*' gene product inhibits the activity of '*X*' protein

Which one of the following options represents a combination of correct statements to explain the observations?

A. Only (*a*) and (*b*)

B. (*b*), (*c*) and (*d*)

C. Only (*a*) and (*d*)

D. (*a*), (*c*) and (*d*)

CSIR-NET, DECEMBER, 2018

Genetic Engineering

32. Which one of the following statements regarding restriction/modifying enzymes used in recombinant. DNA technology is correct?

A. Endonucleases remove nucleotides, one at a time, from the ends of a sequence.
B. Type II class of restriction enzymes do not recognise palindromic sequences.
C. Mung bean nuclease acts on double stranded DNA or RNA termini.
D. Type II class of restriction enzymes can generate either "sticky" (staggered) or "blunt" ends

33. Given below are four statements related to Agrobacterium-mediated transfer of T-DNA into plant cells:

(*a*) Production of single-stranded T-DNA by VirD1 and VirD2 proteins.
(*b*) Interaction of VirE2 with VIP1 and VirE3.
(*c*) Use of VirB/VirD4 type IV secretion system.
(*d*) Activation of VirA-VirG complex.

The correct sequence of events (from earliest to latest) is:

A. (*a*), (*b*), (*d*), (*c*) B. (*b*), (*c*), (*a*), (*d*)
C. (*c*), (*a*), (*b*), (*d*) D. (*d*), (*a*), (*c*), (*b*)

34. In an attempt to increase the yield of a commercially important enzyme from natural isolate several strategies were adopted as follows:

(*a*) Genome was selectively modified to increase yield.
(*b*) Reappraisal of culture requirements of the modified organism to increase yield.
(*c*) Induced mutants were screened and selected for organism synthesizing improved levels of the enzyme.
(*d*) Organism was genetically modified, so that it produces a factor that enhances stability of the enzyme.

Which one of the following options represents strategies that are appropriate for the purpose?

A. (*a*), (*b*), (*c*) and (*d*)
B. (*b*) and (*c*) only
C. (*a*), (*c*) and (*d*) only
D. (*a*) and (*b*) only

35. Three proteins*Blm 1, Blm 2, Blm 3* were shown to be involved in repair of DNA double strand breaks. A chromatin immunoprecipitation experiment was performed for the three proteins.

The pattern of results obtained is shown below

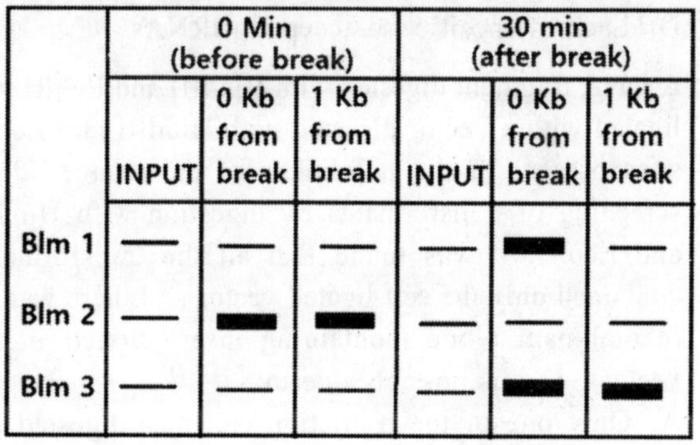

Based on the above figure, choose the option that correctly interprets the data.

A. Blm 1, Blm 2, Blm 3 bind to DNA break sites
B. Blm 1 binds to the break site; Blm 3 binds to the break site and beyond
C. Blm 2 remains bound to DNA after the break is induced
D. Blm 3 binds to DNA irrespective of the break

DBT-JRF, 2018

36. A recombinant plasmid is introduced with adenovirus to specifically label liver cells with GFP. Which gene promoter will be most optimal for specific expression of GFP

A. Catalase
B. α-Mannosidase
C. Cytochrome-P_{450}
D. Amylase

37. The graph below shows the excitation and emission spectra of three flurophores: CFP,GFP and YFP, If you were to design an experiment to image two fluorescently labelled proteins inside the same cell, which is the best combination to use

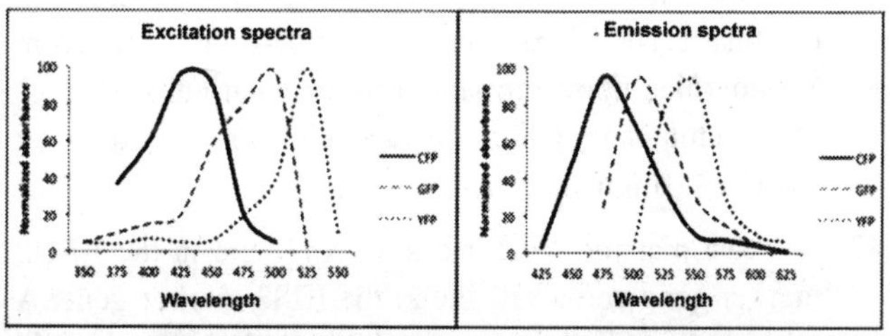

A. CFP-GFP as they have overlapping excitation and emission spectra
B. CFP-YFP as they have maximally separate excitation and emission spectra
C. GFP-YFP as they have overlapping excitation and emission spectra

D. Any combination of CFP-GFP-YFP is suitable for imaging two proteins

38. A 1 Kb insert (I) is ligated to a 5 Kb vector (V) in a molar ratio of I:V of 5:1, in a reaction volume of 1 mL at a final DNA concentration at 10 μ g/mL. How much of the insert and vector was used in the ligation mixture?

A. 5 μg I and 5 μg V
B. 2 μg I and 8 μg V
C. 8 μg I and 2 μg V
D. 3 μg I and 7 μg V

39. A human gene is cloned in an E. coli expression vector. However, extremely poor protein expression is detected on SDS-PAGE despite high levels of specific mRNA. The most likely explanation is:

A. Formation of inclusion bodies
B. Lack of human translation initiation factors
C. Lack of human elongation factors
D. Lack of specific iso-accepting tRNAs

40. A DNA fragment digested with HindIII and EcoRI was ligated with a vector digested with HindIII and EcoRI sites present in the polylinker of the vector. Upon screening of transformants by digestion with HindIII and EcoRI, it was found that all the transformants contained only the self-ligated vector and there was no recombinant clone (containing insert cloned in the vector). This is possibly due to:

A. Only one of the restriction enzymes digested the vector
B. Both the restriction enzymes digested the vector
C. Only one of the restriction enzymes digested the insert
D. Both the restriction enzymes digested the insert

41. In a cloning experiment, alkaline phosphatase is generally used to dephosphorylate a plasmid vector rather than insert DNA fragments because:

A. Alkaline phosphatase can only dephosphorylate plasmid vector and not insert DNA fragments
B. Vector can self-ligate and form colonies upon introduction into host cells
C. Insert DNA fragments can self-ligate and form colonies upon introduction into host cells
D. Vector cannot ligate to a dephosphorylated insert DNA fragment

42. A Yeast plasmid Vector has an XhoI site in the LEU2 marker gene and a salI site in the HIS3 marker gene. A student cloned a gene using the SalI site. How should the student select for the recombinant clone?

A. Plate the transformation mixture on leu^- his^- medium
B. Plate the transformation mixture on leu^+ his^+ medium, followed by replica plating on leu^+ his^- medium
C. Plate the transformation mixture on his^+ leu^- medium, followed by replica plating on leu^- his^- medium
D. Plate the transformation mixture on leu^+ his^- medium

43. Which of the following statements about IPTG and lactose is NOT correct?

A. IPTG is an analog of lactose
B. Both IPTG and lactose are inducers of the lac operon
C. IPTG is not metabolized while lactose is metabolized by the cells
D. Both IPTG and lactose need permease for entry into the cell.

44. Any DNA fragment can be used as a STS marker provided it fulfills one of the following conditions:

A. Multilocus nature
B. Single copy
C. Present in repeat regions
D. Telomeric region

45. Which one of the following transposition events would increase the DNA content in a given cell?

A. Ac/Ds elements
B. Mu elements
C. P elements
D. LINEs

46. A 30 Kb linear DNA was digested with HindIII and BamH1. The fragments obtained on complete digestion were as follows

The appropriate restriction map of DNA is

HindIII; 14 Kb, 20 Kb
BamHI; 4 Kb, 12 Kb, 18 Kb
HindIII + BamHI: 4 kB, 10 Kb, 8 Kb, 12 Kb

A. 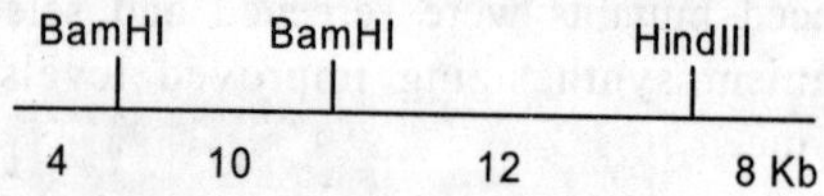

B. 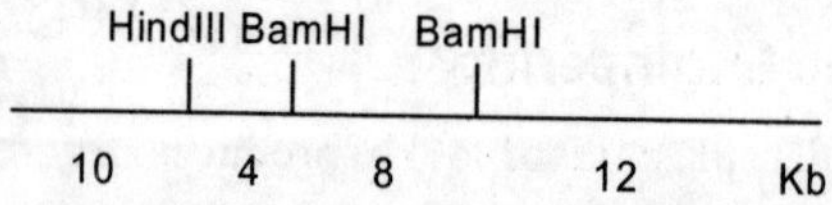

C. 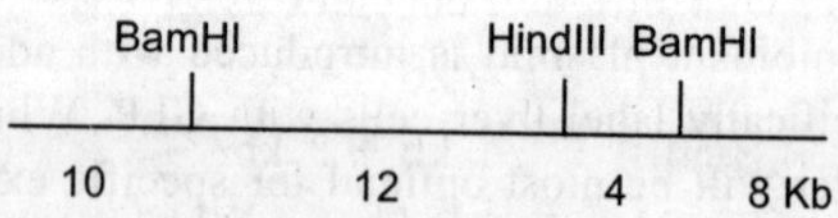

D. 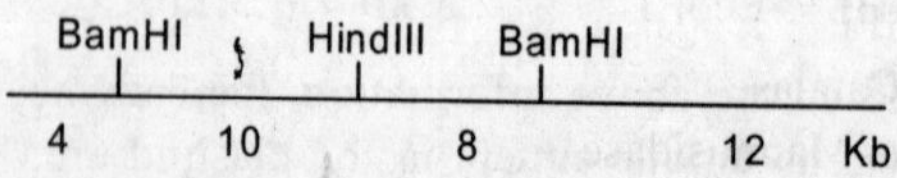

47. The restriction site for Van91I is 5' CCANNNN↓NTGG 3'. How many times can Van91I cut a 4 Mb bacterial genome with 50% GC content?

A. ~1000 times
B. ~10 times
C. Once
D. ~100 times

GATE (BIOTECHNOLOGY), 2018

48. 5' capping of mRNA transcripts in eukaryotes involves the following events:

(*a*) Addition of GMP on the 5' end

(*b*) Removal of 5'-phosphate of the triphosphate on first base at the 5' end

(*c*) 5'-5' linkage between GMP and the first base at 5' end

(*d*) Addition of methyl group to N7 position of guanine

Which one of the following is the correct sequence of events?

A. (*a*), (*b*), (*c*), (*d*)
B. (*a*), (*c*), (*b*), (*d*)
C. (*b*), (*a*), (*c*), (*d*)
D. (*b*), (*a*), (*d*), (*c*)

CSIR-NET, 15 DECEMBER, 2019

Genetic Engineering

49. Which one of the following statements related to molecular cloning procedures is INCORRECT?

A. 5' overhangs of restricted DNA fragments can be blunt-ended by Klenow polymerase but not by DNaseI.

B. A DNA fragment obtained as an XhoI fragment (C↓TCGAG) may be ligated at the SalI site (G↓TCGAC) in a vector.

C. To prevent self-ligation of a vector digested with KpnI (GGTAC↓C), alkaline phosphatase enzyme is used to remove 3'-PO4 groups from the ends of fragments

D. α-complementation/blue-white screening may produce blue coloured recombinant colonies (containing cloned fragments) in case of translational fusion with the β-galactosidase gene.

50. In an experiment, a 1 kb fragment with a single BamHI site (as shown below in figure "A") is to be cloned in the SmaI (CCC ↓ GGG) site of a cloning vector of 3kb length (figure 'B'). None of the other enzymes of the multiple cloning sites are present in the fragment to be cloned.

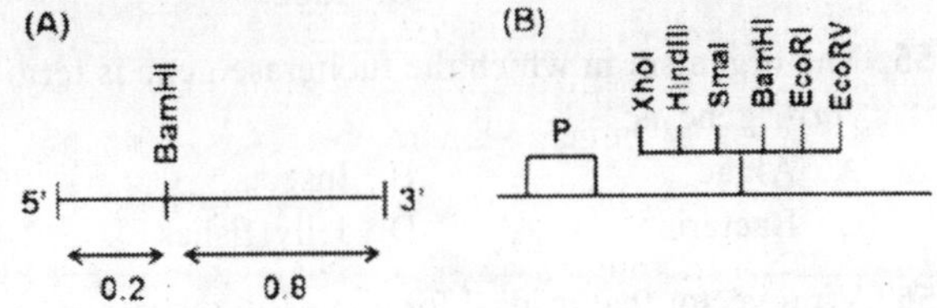

Based on the information given above, a series of digestions were set up for the potential clones and their fragment profiles are given below:

(*a*) BamHI : 200bp + 3.8 kb
(*b*) BamHI : 800bp + 3.2 kb
(*c*) HindIII + EcoRI : 1 kb + 3kb
(*d*) XhoI + BamHI : 200bp + 800bp + ≈ 3kb

Which one of the above digestion profiles confirms successful cloning of the fragment in the vector in an orientation wherein the 5' end of the cloned fragment is towards P?

A. (*a*) only
B. (*b*) only
C. (*a*) and (*c*)
D. (*c*) and (*d*)

CSIR-NET, 27 DECEMBER, 2019

Genetic Engineering

51. A circular plasmid of 4 kb produces fragments on digestion with different enzymes as given below:

BamHI	– 4 kb
BamHI + HindIII	– 1 kb + 3 kb
BamHI + EcoRI	– 2.5 kb + 1.5 kb

Based on the above information, the enzymes that are present as unique cutters in the plasmid are:

A. BamHI and HindIII only
B. BamHI only
C. HindIII and EcoRI only
D. BamHI, HindIII and EcoRI

52. Given below are four statements on various methods used in molecular biology and recombinant DNA studies:

(*a*) Orientation of a cloned DNA fragment in a plasmid vector can be determined by using primers specific to the cloned fragment.

(*b*) Transcriptome sequencing cannot be used to identify differential expression profiles of mRNA in an organism.

(*c*) A DNA fragment with 5' overhangs can be converted into a blunt-ended fragment by using a nuclease but not by a DNA polymerase.

(*d*) Oligonucleotide probes can be labelled at their 5 and 3' ends by using T4polynucleotide kinase and terminal transferase, respectively

Which one of the following options consists of only correct statement/s?

A. (*a*) and (*c*) only
B. (*b*) only
C. (*c*) and (*d*) only
D. (*d*) only

DBT-JRF, 2019

53. Which one of the following transgenes expressed in transgenic fish by an appropriate inducible promoter, may be used for detecting environmental toxicants?
A. Super oxide dismutase
B. Green Fluorescent Protein
C. Antimicrobial peptide
D. Aromatic hydrocarbon decarboxylase

54. A researcher wants to ectopically express protein X exclusively in the seeds of Arabidopsis. Which one of the following promoters is most suitable for this purpose?
A. CaMV 35S   B. Maize ubiquitin
C. Napin   D. rd22

55. The organism in which the luciferase gene is termed as "*lux*" gene is:
A. Algae   B. Insects
C. Bacteria   D. Jelly fishes

56. Viral vector that is ideal for expressing therapeutic gene in non-dividing cells is:
A. Lentiviral vector
B. Retroviral vector
C. Adeno-associated viral vector
D. Adenoviral vector

57. Identify the product(s) obtained when luciferin undergoes the following reaction:

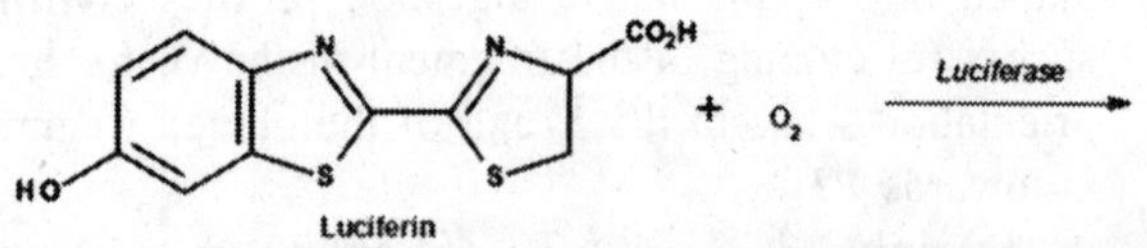

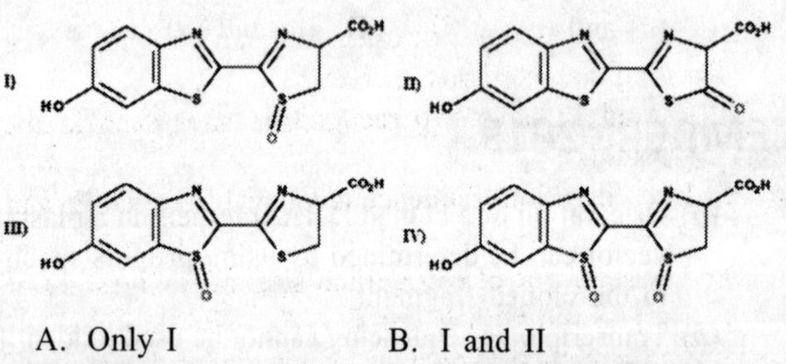

A. Only I   B. I and II
C. Only IV   D. I, II and III

58. CRISPR/Cas9 is an example of bacterial adaptive immunity. The transcription of *CRISPR* loci generates small crispr-RNAs (crRNA) to specifically target viral DNA, but not *CRISPR* loci, by forming complex with guide RNA and Cas9 nuclease. This prevention of autoimmunity is due to the:
A. absence of protospacer adjacent motif sequence in *CRISPR* loci.
B. absence of DNA sequence complementary to crRNA in *CRISPR* loci.
C. absence of DNA sequence complementary to guide RNA in *CRISPR* loci.
D. methylation of *CRISPR* loci.

59. An experiment involves formation of RNA-DNA hybrid. Which one of the following enzymes could be utilized to degrade only the RNA strand from the RNA-DNA hybrid?
A. Micrococcal nuclease
B. S1 nuclease
C. RNase H
D. RNase P

60. For engineering virus resistance in plants, which one of the following viral components is commonly targeted?
A. coat protein   B. replication protein
C. satellite RNA   D. movement protein

61. The Bt protein employed for raising insect-resistant plants is not toxic to humans because:
A. it is inactive under acidic pH
B. it is inactive under basic pH
C. it is inactive at 37°C
D. it is rendered inactive by inhibitors

62. *Opaque2* gene in maize and *Wx* gene in rice affects the .... and .... content, respectively.
A. protein quality, amylose
B. oil, wax
C. protein quality, wax
D. oil, starch

63. Which one of the following is associated with RNA-induced gene silencing in plants?
A. DNA methylation   B. DNA acetylation
C. DNA degradation   D. DNA restriction

64. In genetically modified Dhara Mustard Hybrid – 11, male sterility is conferred by ...., while .... restores fertility.
A. barnase, barstar   B. barstar, barnase
C. bar, barnase   D. barnase, bar

65. If the pulse input response curve for a CSTR shows a long tail, it means:
A. Strong internal circulation in the reactor
B. Dead space in the reactor
C. Short circuiting in the reactor
D. Parallel flow in the reactor

66. A chimeric organism is generated when:
A. Cells of different genetic constitutions appear in the same organism
B. Union of two different genomes occur within a cell
C. A genome of another individual is injected into an adult organism
D. A part of the genome is inactivated by chromosomal rearrangement

CSIR-NET, NOVEMBER (MORNING), 2020

Genetic Engineering

67. In the context of plant breeding and genetic engineering, which one of the following statements is correct?

A. To achieve high expression level of a heterologous gene in a transgenic plant a promoter of bacterial origin is often used.

B. FI progeny derived by crosses between inbred lines with low genetic diversity is more likely to show heterosis.

C. In Agrobacterium mediated plant transformation, always a single copy of the transgene is inserted in the host genome.

D. Qualitative traits are typically characterized by discontinuous phenotypic variation while quantitative traits often generate continuous phenotypic variation.

68. In a cloning experiment, a DNA molecule isolated as a Pst I fragment was inserted into the Pst I site of a cloning vector that is Bkb in length. Digestion of the CONFIRMED clones with Pst resulted in the appearance of a single band corresponding to 3kb in an agarose gel. Based on this information, what is the probable size of the cloned fragment?

A. 6 kb B. 1.5 kb

C. 3 kb D. 4.5 kb

69. Which one of the following proteins produces a dark blue/purple color in the presence of 5- bromo-4-chloro-3-indolyl phosphate and nitroblue tetrazolium?

A. Polynucleotide kinase

B. Alkaline phosphatase

C. β-glucuronidase

D. β-galactosidase

70. RNA silencing is an important strategy to control viral infection in plants. The following statements were made regarding RNA silencing.

(*a*) It is driven by small interfering RNA (SiRNA) derived from double-stranded form of viral RNA.

(*b*) siRNA requires RISC for it function.

(*c*) Many plant viruses encode proteins that act as suppressors of RNA silencing.

(*d*) Viral P19 protein activates RNA induced silencing complex

Which one of the following combination of statements is correct?

A. (*a*), (*b*) and (*c*) B. (*b*), (*c*) and (*d*)

C. (*a*), (*c*) and (*d*) D. (*a*), (*b*) and (*d*)

71. Given below is a schematic representation of a few restriction sites in the multiple cloning site of a plasmid:

The recognition sequences of the above enzymes and their digestion patterns are shown below:

HindIII : A▼AGCTT / TTCGA▲A SmaI : CCC▼GGG / GGG▲CCC

XhoI : C▼TCGAG / GAGCT▲C PstI : C▼TGCAG / GACGT▲C

Which one of the following combinations of enzymes from the vector can be used for cloning a DNA fragment obtained as a Sal I (GVTCGAC) - Hind II (GTYVRAC) fragment.

A. Sma I - Hind III B. Xho I - Pst I

C. Xho I - Sma I D. Hind III - Pst I

72. Given below are the restriction profiles obtained upon digestion of a 4.8 kb plasmid with four different enzymes (E_1, E_2, E_3 and E_4).

E_1 : 4.8kb $E_1 + E_2$ = 500 bp + 4.3 kb

E_2 : 4.8kb $E_2 + E_3$ = 400 bp + 4.4 kb

E_3 : 4.8kb $E_3 + E_4$ = 2 kb + 2.8 kb

E_4 : 4.8kb $E_1 + E_4$ = 1.9 kb + 2.9 kb

Based on the above information, which one of the following statements is correct?

A. E_1 and E_4 have two recognition sites each in the plasmid.

B. E_2 recognitioin sequence is located between E_1 and E_3.

C. The sequence of recognition sites after digestion of the plasmid with E_3 is: $E_4 - E_2 - E_1$.

D. The sequence of recognition sites after digestion of the plasmid with E_2 is $E_1 - E_3 - E_4$

CSIR-NET, NOVEMBER (AFTERNOON), 2020

Genetic Engineering

73. An experiment was performed to introduce a transgenic trait in a crop plant by Agrobacterium - mediated transformation using a transgene construct in which the transgene was expressed using the CaMV 35S promoter. It was observed that expression levels of the transgenic protein were very low in all transgenic plants while transgene mRNA levels were high and variable among different plants. Further, different transgenic lines contained different numbers of the T-DNA insert. The following statements were made to explain the above observation:

(*a*) Variations in the number of T-DNA inserts in different transgenic plants is due to more number of host cells getting infected with the T-DNA

(*b*) Low expression levels of the transgenic protein in all transgenic plants could be due to codon usage variations between the host plant and the heterologous source of the transgene

(*c*) The coding sequence of the transgene contained sequences that destabilized the transgene mRNA

(*d*) Variation in copy number of T-DNA in different transgenic plants is due to variation in the promoter used to express the transgene.

Which one of the following options represents all correct statements?

A. (*a*) only
B. (*b*) and (*c*)
C. (*a*) and (*d*)
D. (*b*) only

DBT-JRF, 2020

74. A protein with 1000 amino acids was tagged with GFP. The molecular weight of GFP is 26 KDa What will be the most likely molecular weight of the fused target protein?

A. 100 KDa B. 126 KDa
C. 136 KDa D. 150 KDa

75. The most important step of an automated DNA sequencing reaction is

A. specific and systematic termination of the amplified DNA
B. ligation of DNA template
C. addition of calcium chloride
D. cleavage of template DNA

76. How many peptide fragments can be generated from the complete digestion of the polypeptide AGRCDKCQANRSLMNF with trypsin?

A. 6 B. 4
C. 3 D. 2

77. Digestion of a 5 Kb linear DNA with BamHi leads to the generation of two fragments of size 2 Kb and 3 Kb, while digestion of the same DNA with Hindill generates 3 fragments of 0.7, 0.8 and 3.5 Kb. When the same DNA is cut with both BamHI and Hindill enzymes the fragments generated are of 0.7, 0.8, 1.3 and 2.2 Kb. The right order of the recognition sites for the two enzymes is

A. one Hindill site between two BamHl sites
B. two Hindill sites followed by one BamHl site
C. one BamHI site between two Hindill sites
D. two BamHl sites followed by one Hindill si

78. A shuttle vector is a vector that

A. can replicate in the cells of more than one organism
B. helps in transporting proteins from one cell to the adjacent cell
C. helps in conjugation of bacterial cells
D. moves between two organisms automatically

79. During genome engineering process, the role of flippase enzyme in the next round of modification in the target gene is to

A. add frt sequence
B. remove frt sequence
C. remove the antibiotic cassette
D. add the antibiotic cassettd

80. A student added a 5' exonuclease enzyme instead of a restriction enzyme to digest his purified plasmid DNA sample. What is he likely to observe when he runs his plasmid digest on an agarose gel?

A. free nucleotides from the 5' end only
B. free nucleotides from both ends
C. no digestion of plasmid DNA
D. plasmid DNA will be digested similar to the restriction enzyme

81. A CDNA encoding a human protein of interest was cloned in a bacterial expression vector and introduced into bacterial cells for expression. However, no expression of the human protein of interest was obtained. This could be because of

A. Bacterial ribosomes were unable to bind to the mRNA corresponding to the Human protein of interest
B. Presence of introns in the gene encoding the human protein
C. E. coli RNA polymerase cannot transcribe the sequence encoding the human protein of interest
D. Codon bias

82. Which one of the following approaches is generally not used for identifying an SNP?

A. protein sequencing
B. molecular beacons
C. microarrays
D. RNA Seq

83. Ananda Chakrabarty received the first U.S. patent for a GM organism. This organism was

A. cloned E. coli
B. Dolly the cloned sheep
C. transgenic mouse expressing the growth hormone gene
D. Pseudomonas engineered to degrade petroleum

GATE (BIOTECHNOLOGY), 2020

84. The schematic of a plasmid with a gap in one of the strands is shown below:

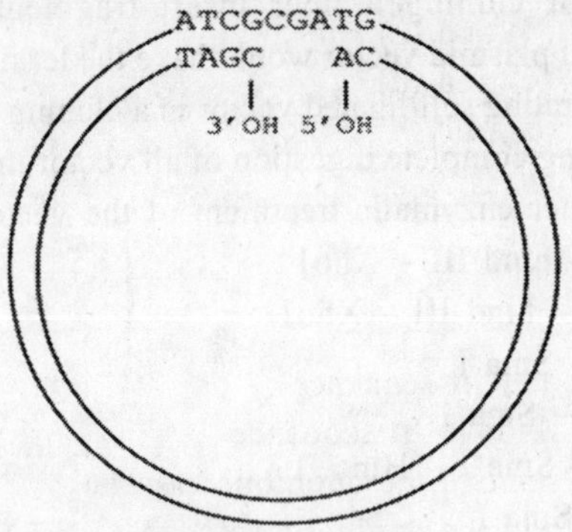

Which of the following enzyme(s) is/are required to fill the gap and generate a covalently closed circular plasmid?
(*a*) DNA ligase
(*b*) Alkaline Phosphatase
(*c*) DNA polymerase
(*d*) Polynucleotide kinase

A. (*a*) only
B. (*a*), (*c*) and S only
C. (*a*) and (*c*) only
D. (*a*), (*b*) and (*c*) only

85. A vector derived from which one of the following viruses is used for high frequency genomic integration of a transgene in animal cells?
A. Adenovirus
B. Adeno-associated virus
C. Lentivirus
D. Herpes simplex virus

86. Which one of the following statements about *Agrobacterium* Ti plasmid is CORRECT?
A. Vir genes located within the T-DNA segment.
B. Phytohormone biosynthesis genes are located outside the T-DNA segment
C. Opine catabolism genes are located within the T-DNA segment.
D. Opine biosynthesis genes are located within the T-DNA segment.

CSIR-NET, JUNE (MORNING), 2021

Genetic Engineering

87. *Pichia pastoris* is a good host for producing human proteins for therapeutic use. Given below are some statements on the reason for its utility.
(*a*) It produces large amount of recombinant protein
(*b*) It has the property of secreting proteins into the medium
(*c*) It allows the formation of disulphide bonds similar to those in humans
(*d*) It carries out proteins glycosylation identical to those found in humans

Which one of the following combination of the statement is correct?
A. (*a*) and (*b*)
B. (*a*), (*b*) and (*c*)
C. (*a*), (*b*) and (*d*)
D. (*b*), (*c*) and (*d*)

CSIR-NET, JUNE (AFTERNOON), 2021

Genetic Engineering

88. Which one of the following statements related to genetic transformation of plants is correct?
A. Negative selection markers need to be expressed only under strong constitutive promoters for development of transgenic plants
B. A transgenic plant containing two linked copies of the transgene in heterozygous condition would segregate in a 3:1 (transgenic : non transgenic) ratio for the transgenic phenotype on self pollination.
C. Agrobacterium -mediated transfer of T-DNA into a host plant does not require host plant proteins.
D. In a binary vector system of Agrobacterium tumefaciens, the oncogenes are located on the Helper plasmid.

89. In a forward genetic screen to investigate the heat stress response in Arabidopsis, a team of researchers identified an uncharacterized gene 'x' that shows some sequence homology to alpha-subunit of hetrotrimeric G-protein. Since a typical alpha-subunit of hetrotrimeric G-protein localizes at the membrane in a eukaryotic cell, researchers sought to validate whether the protein coded by gene 'X' localizes to membrane in tobacco protoplasts. To achieve this, they cloned the gene in fusion with GGP at its N-terminus, under the control of the CaMV promoter; however, upon expression of this GFP-gene 'X' fusion construct, they did not observe any membrane localisation of GFP- signal in tobacco protoplasts. Based on this, they made a few assumptions:

(*a*) N-terminally tagging of protein 'X' with GFP may block membrane localization of protein X

(*b*) Tagging of protein 'X' with GFP may alter the conformation of protein X because of its bigger size

(*c*) Tobacco protoplasts are a herterologous system for the expression of gene 'X', and thus, the protein X does not localize to the membrane

(*d*) Gene 'X' is not getting transcribed because of the wrong promoter choice

Which one of the following options represents all correct assumptions?

A. (*a*) and (*b*) only
B. (*b*) and (*d*) only
C. (*c*) and (*d*) only
D. (*a*), (*b*) and (*c*)

90. Given below is a figure representing expression levels of transgenic protein in ten independent transgenic plants generated using the same transformation vector by Agrobacterium – mediated transformation.

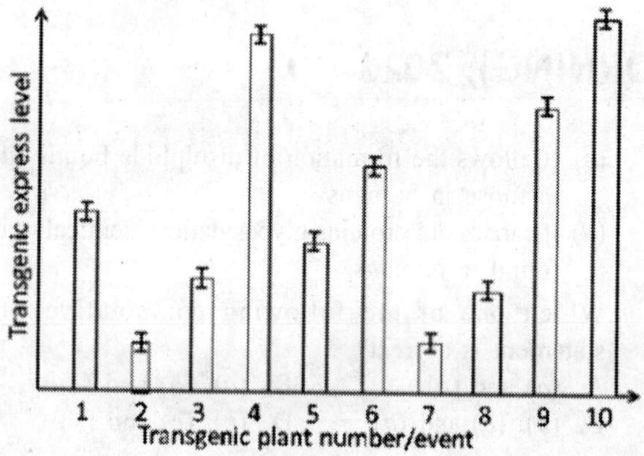

Given below are a few statements to explain the above data:

(*a*) Plant nos. 4. 9 and 10 that show high expression levels of the transgene.

(*b*) Plant nos. 2 and 7 contain mutations in the coding sequence of the transgene in the construct.

(*c*) The transgenic plants may contain varying number of transgene copies inserted at different locations in the host genome.

(*d*) The host genome has no role in influencing expression levels of the transgene. Response Sheet E. The stability of the transgenic mRNA and its translatability would not be different among the independent transgenic plants.

Which one of the following options represents all correct statements?

A. (*a*) and (*d*) only
B. (*b*) and (*c*) only
C. (*c*) and (*e*) only
D. (*a*), (*d*) and (*e*) only

91. Which one of the following combination of enzymes used for cloning a liner insert fragmenting into a digested plasmid vector would have the least probability of generating self ligated vector in a cloning experiment following complete digestion of all vector mlecules and no further enzymatic treatment of the vector?

Insert – hind III – Xho1
Vector – hind III – Xho1
Insert – Sma I
Vector – Sma I
Insert – Sma I – Hinc II
Vector Sma I
Insert – Eco RI
Vector – Eco RI

	Insert	Vector
A.	Sma I (CCC↓GGG)	Sma I(CCC↓GGG)
B.	Sma I .... Hinc II (CCC↓GGG) (GTY↓RAC)	Sma I (CCC↓GGG)
C.	Hind III ...... Xho I (A↓AGCTT) C↓TCGAG)	Hind III .... Xho I (A↓AGCTT) (C↓TCGAG)
D.	Eco RI(G↓AATTC)	Eco RI(G↓AATTC)

92. Given below are names and recognition sequences of a few restriction enzymes that are used for cloning experiments. The cleavage site of each enzyme

EcoRI – G*AATTC
HincII – GTY*RAC
EcoRV – GAT*ATC
BamHI – G*GATCC
BglII – A*GATCT

Given below are different vector (Column A) and insert (Column B) fragments generated by digestion using the above enzymes:

Column A (*Vector fragment*)	Column B (*Insert fragment*)
(*a*) EcoRI	(*i*) EcoRV
(*b*) EcoRV	(*ii*) HincII
(*c*) BamHI	(*iii*) EcoRI
(*d*) BglII	(*iv*) BamHI
(*e*) HincII	(*v*) BglII

Which one of the following options represents the correct combinations of the vector and insert, respectively, which generate compatible ends for ligation

A. (*a*)-(*ii*) (*b*)-(*v*) (*c*)-(*iv*)
B. (*b*)-(*ii*) (*d*)-(*iv*) (*e*)-(*i*)
C. (*a*)-(*v*) (*c*)-(*i*) (*e*)-(*iii*)
D. (*c*)-(*iv*) (*d*)-(*i*) (*e*)-(*ii*)

DBT-JRF, 2021

93. A 2Kb insert has to be ligated to a 8Kb Plasmid in a ligation mix where we want to keep the vector insert molar ratio as 1:2. If ug of vector is used, the amount of insert to be used is:
A. 0.25 ug B. 0.5 ug
C. 1 ug D. 2 ug

94. The enzyme used to prevent unwanted self-ligation of DNA molecules during cloning experiments are:
A. Alkaline phosphatase
B. Reverse transcriptase
C. Terminal peroxidase
D. Terminal phosphatase

95. A student clones a gene of interest within the ampicillin resistance gene of pBR322 vector for transformant selection, the student will use
A. Ampicillin plates
B. Both Ampicillin plates and Tetracycline plates
C. Neither Ampicillin plates nor Tetracycline plates
D. Tetracycline plates

96. Type IIP restriction endonucleases will always:
A. Bind to double strand RNA
B. Cleave outside the recognition sequence
C. Generate blunt ends
D. Recognize palindromic sequence

97. The GA2oxidase gene from bean is overexpressed in a wheat plant by genetic engineering. Which one of the following phenotypes correctly describes the resultant transgenic plant?
A. The height of the plant will not be affected
B. The plant will be shorter than the wild type
C. The plant will be taller than the wild type
D. The plant will not survive

98. Which nuclease of bacteria is responsible for degrading the genome of the invading lambda phage?
A. Exonuclease
B. Phagodegradase
C. Restriction endonuclease
D. Topoisomerase

GATE (BIOTECHNOLOGY), 2021

99. The enzyme which adds phosphate group to the free 5' terminus of a DNA sequence is
A. Adenosine kinase
B. Alkaline phosphatase
C. Polynucleotide kinase
D. Terminal deoxynucleotidyl transferase

100. The possible number of SalI restriction sites in a 9 kb double-stranded DNA, with all four bases occurring in equal proportion (rounded off to the nearest integer) is?
A. 1 B. 2
C. 3 D. 4

DBT-JRF, 2022

101. A plasmid has three sites for EcoRI. When digested by this enzyme, incidentally partial digestion took place, though no uncut or nicked plasmid remained in the digestion mixture. The maximum number of bands that can be visualized in an agarose gel would be:
A. 1 B. 3
C. 7 D. 10

GATE (BIOTECHNOLOGY), 2022

102. The recognition sequences of four Type-II restriction enzymes (RE) are given below. The symbol (↓) indicates the cleavage site. Identify the RE that generates sticky ends.
A. RE1 - 5' G↓GATCC 3'
B. RE2 - 5' CTG↓CAG 3'
C. RE3 - 5' CCC↓GGG 3'
D. RE4 - 5' AG↓CT 3'

103. Among individuals in a human population, minor variations exist in nucleotide sequences of chromosomes. These variations can lead to gain or loss of sites for specific restriction enzymes. Which of the following technique is used to identify such variations?
A. Polymerase dependent fragment insertion
B. Real-time polymerase chain reaction
C. Restriction fragment length polymorphism
D. Reverse transcriptase polymerase chain reaction

ANSWERS

1	2	3	4	5	6	7	8	9	10
C	C	B	C	C	B	C	C	C	A
11	**12**	**13**	**14**	**15**	**16**	**17**	**18**	**19**	**20**
B	C	D	D	B	D	C	D	A	B
21	**22**	**23**	**24**	**25**	**26**	**27**	**28**	**29**	**30**
C	A	C	C	D	B	D	B	C	A
31	**32**	**33**	**34**	**35**	**36**	**37**	**38**	**39**	**40**
D	D	D	A	B	C	B	A	D	A
41	**42**	**43**	**44**	**45**	**46**	**47**	**48**	**49**	**50**
B	C	D	B	D	D	A	C	C	B
51	**52**	**53**	**54**	**55**	**56**	**57**	**58**	**59**	**60**
D	D	B	C	C	A	A	A	C	A
61	**62**	**63**	**64**	**65**	**66**	**67**	**68**	**69**	**70**
A	A	A	A	B	A	D	C	B	A
71	**72**	**73**	**74**	**75**	**76**	**77**	**78**	**79**	**80**
C	B	D	C	A	B	C	A	C	C
81	**82**	**83**	**84**	**85**	**86**	**87**	**88**	**89**	**90**
D	A	D	B	C	D	B	B	D	C
91	**92**	**93**	**94**	**95**	**96**	**97**	**98**	**99**	**100**
C	B	B	A	D	D	B	C	C	B
101	**102**	**103**							
C	A	C							

CHAPTER

10

ANIMAL BIOTECHNOLOGY

CSIR-NET, JUNE, 2017

Animal Tissue Culture

1. Somatic cell hybridization is used to assign a gene to a particular chromosome. When two cell lines from two different species are fused, they form a heterokaryon which tends to Jose chromosomes as they divide, preferentially from one species. A panel of cell lines was created from mouse-monkey somatic cell fusions. Each line was examined for the presence of monkey chromosomes and for the production of a given enzyme. The following results were obtained:

Cell line	Presence of Enzyme	Presence of Monkey chromosomes									
		1	2	3	4	5	6	7	8	9	10
A	+	+	+	+	+	+	–	+	–	+	+
B	+	–	+	+	–	+	+	+	–	+	–
C	–	–	+	–	–	–	–	–	+	+	+
D	+	+	+	+	–	–	+	+	+	+	–
E	–	–	–	–	+	+	–	–	–	+	+
F	+	+	+	–	+	+	+	+	–	+	–

On the basis of these results, which chromosome has the gene that codes for the given enzyme?

A. Chromosome 10

B. Chromosome 7

C. Chromosome 1

D. Chromosome 5

Stem Cell & Gene Therapy

2. The following are certain statements regarding stem cells:

(*a*) All types of stem cells have the ability to give rise to a complete embryo.

(*b*) Multipotent stem cells are those whose commitment is limited to a relatively small subset of all possible cell types.

(*c*) Stem cell niches allow controlled self-renewal and also survival of the cells that leave the niche.

(*d*) The pluripotency of the stem cells in an embryo is essentially maintained by Fgf8, Nanog and TGFβ.

(*e*) Adult cells may be reprogrammed to gain pluripotency by modifying the following genes: Oct 3/4, Sox2, c-myc, Klf-4.

Which one of the following combinations of statements is correct?

A. (*a*), (*b*) and (*d*)

B. (*b*) and (*e*)

C. (*c*) and (*e*)

D. (*a*), (*c*) and (*d*)

DBT-JRF, 2017

3. In commercial farms, embryos are routinely recovered by non-surgical methods. On which day are the embryos recovered from the donor cow after the onset of estrus?

A. 21 B. 7
C. 14 D. 5

4. Midblastula transition (MBT) is a characteristic process that occurs in early embryogenesis of organisms (like Amphibians) whose eggs are large. MBT refers to:

A. Transition of structures from early embryonic to late embryonic
B. Transition of gene expression from maternal to zygotic
C. Regulation of transition of primordial germ cells to Gonadal structure
D. Epigenetic modification of gene regulation

5. Which one of the following is an inhibitory neurotransmitter

A. GABA B. Glutamate
C. Acetylcholine D. Dopamine

6. Heparin is a:

A. Glycosylated lipid
B. Glycoprotein
C. Lipopolysaccharide
D. Sulphated polysaccharide

7. Epinephrine is used along with local anaesthetic because of its:

A. alpha-adrenergic receptor agonist properties
B. β2 adrenergic receptor agonist properties
C. β1 adrenergic receptor agonist properties
D. nicotinic receptor agonist properties

8. Huntington's disease is clinically characterized by chorea (abnormal involuntary movements). Which part of the brain is responsible for this phenotype?

A. Basal Ganglia B. Cerebellum
C. Hippocampus D. Brain stem

9. Which one of the following promoters is most efficient for transgene expression in mammary gland of livestock?

A. Beta-casein B. Prolactin
C. Uromodulin D. Immunoglobulin.

10. The genes that have been used for reprograming somatic cells of an adult mammal to stem cells called induced pluripotent stem cells (IPSC) are KLF4, SOX2, OCT4 and c-MYC. These code for:

A. Transcription factors
B. Both transcription factors and RNA binding proteins
C. Chaperone proteins
D. Growth factors

11. Human mesenchymal stem cells:

A. Can differentiate into only one type of cell
B. Can differentiate into few types of cells
C. Can differentiate into all types of cells
D. Do not differentiate at all

12. A primary cell culture can be transformed into a cell line by all EXCEPT:

A. Simian Virus 40
B. Hepatitis B virus
C. Human Papillomavirus
D. Epstein-Barr Virus.

CSIR-NET, JUNE, 2018

13. The following cassette was designed to create estrogen receptor knock-out mice:

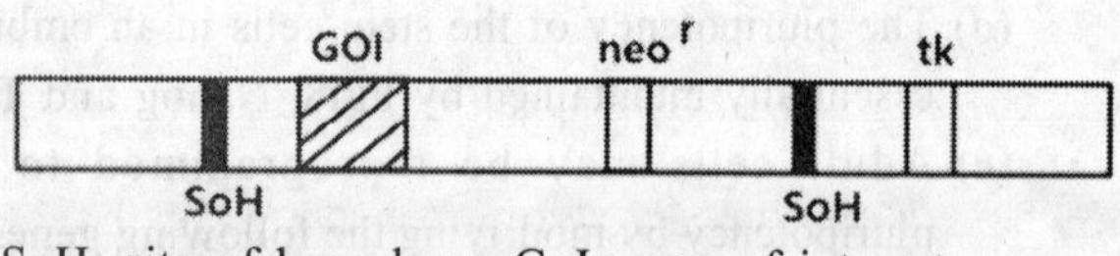

SoH: site of homology; GoI: gene of interest

What would ensure that proper recombination has taken place?

A. Cells survive when cultured in presence of only G418
B. Cells survive when cultured in presence of G418 followed by ganciclovir
C. Cells die when cultured in presence of G418
D. Cells survive when cultured with G418 and die when cultured with ganciclovir

Stem Cell & Gene Therapy

14. The following assumptions were derived from the below experiment:

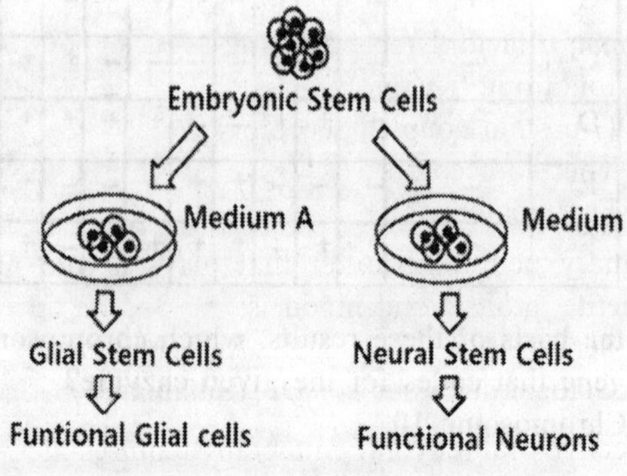

(*a*) Medium A contained FGF and PDGF.

(*b*) Medium B contained retinoic acid.
(*c*) Cells cultured in Medium B were determined to become functional neurons prior to addition of the medium.

Which one of the following combinations represents correct statements?

A. (*a*) and (*b*) only B. (*a*), (*b*) and (*c*)
C. (*b*) and (*c*) only D. (*a*) and (*c*) only

Vaccine and Antibiotics

15. DNA vaccines offer several advantages over other existing vaccine approaches. Which one of the following statements related to DNA vaccine is NOT correct?

A. The immune response is directed to the antigen encoded by the DNA and able to induce both humoral and cell-mediated immunity.
B. DNA vaccine can induce prolonged expression of the antigen, enhancing the induction of immunological memory.
C. DNA vaccine could remain stable and potent for long storage and transportation time without refrigeration, eliminating the challenges of
D. DNA vaccine construct can be engineered to carry several antigens to infect host and replicate in neuronal cells.

16. Susceptible individuals were infected with pathogen A and pathogen B separately. Pathogen A has a very short incubation period and disease symptoms are already underway by the time memory cells are activated. Pathogen B on the other hand has a long incubation period which allows the memory cells to be activated and respond. Which one of the following will be the most appropriate vaccination strategy against both pathogens A and B?

A. Repeated vaccination against both A and B for maintaining high levels of neutrallizing antibodies.
B. Repeated vaccination against A and a single injection of pathogen B vaccine for maintaining high levels of neutrallizing antibodies.
C. Singleinjection of pathogen A vaccine and repeated vaccination against pathogen B for maintaining high levels of neutrallizing antibodies.
D. Single injection of both pathogens A and B vaccine so that memory cells can respond by producing high levels of serum antibodies.

CSIR-NET, DECEMBER, 2018

Stem Cell & Gene Therapy

17. The following demonstrates proposed functions of different genes which determine the decision to become either trophoblast or inner cell mass (ICM) blastomere during early mammalian development:

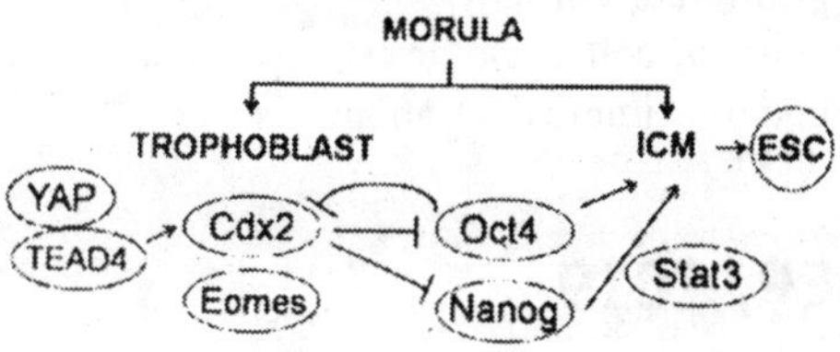

Based on the above figure, which one of the following assumptions is correct?

A. The interplay between Cd × 2 and Oct4 can influence the formation of ICM
B. The ICM would form even if expression of Oct4 was inhibited.
C. YAP and TEAD4 are upstream components of Cd × 2 and can be inhibited by Nanog.
D. The expression of Stat 3 is optional for maintaining pluripotency of the ICM.

DBT-JRF, 2018

18. Human olfactory receptors are:

A. Ionotropic receptors
B. G-protein coupled receptors
C. Thermoreceptors
D. Fc receptors

19. Primary neurotransmitter that plays a role in sleep, appetite, arousal and mood is:

A. Serotonin B. Acetylcholine
C. Octopamine D. Glutamate

20. Effective oral rehydration therapy requires the presence of both Na^+ and glucose because the intestinal epithelial cells express a:

A. Na^+-glucose symporter on their basolateral membrane
B. Na^+-glucose antiporter on their basolateral membrane
C. Na^+-glucose symporter on their apical membrane
D. Na^+-glucose antiporter on their apical membrane

21. Helicobacter pylori survives in the acidic environment of the stomach because it:

A. has acid resistant cell wall
B. releases alkaline compounds
C. produces urease enzyme
D. uses acid as a nutrient

22. Dental formula of cattle older than 4 years is:
A. 0/2,0/0,3/3,3/3
B. 0/4,0/0,3/3,3/3
C. 2/2,0/0,2/2,4/4
D. 1/1, 0/0, 3/3, 2/2

23. Normal bilirubin (4Z, 15Z isomer) undergoes structural isomerisation on absorption of blue-green light (460 - 490 nm). For this reaction, which one of the following statements is TRUE?
A. It is fast and reversible
B. It is slow but reversible
C. It is fast but irreversible
D. It is slow and irreversible

24. For some people it is a popular herb added in food for flavour, but for others it tastes like soap due to a mutation in OR6A2 receptor. The herb is:
A. Basil B. Mint
C. Cilantro D. Parsley

25. Which of these is used as a preferred inhalation anaesthetic for laboratory animals?
A. Isoflurane
B. Nitrous oxide
C. Anaesthetic ether
D. Methoxyflurane

26. A1/A2 cow milk are genetic variants of the beta casein milk protein that differ by a single amino acid at position 67. The variants for A1 and A2 are:
A. A1-Histidine vs A2-Proline
B. A1-Proline vs A2-Histidine
C. A1-Histidine vs A2-Tyrosine
D. A1-Tyrosine vs A2-Proline

27. Gynogenesis in fishes is achieved by:
A. Heat shock treatment at 42°C for 5 min after normal fertilization.
B. Cold shock treatment at 5°C for 10 min after normal fertilization.
C. Fertilization of egg with UV-irradiated sperm followed by heat shock treatment.
D. Treatment of fertilized eggs with cytochalasin.

28. Two cell lines (Vero and SP2/O-Ag14) were cross-contaminated. In order to confirm the homogeneity of the cell lines, which of the following approaches would you use?
A. Comparative morphological examination of unstained or stained cells
B. Comparative assessment of chromosome number of the cell lines
C. Comparative cell-cycle analysis of the cell lines
D. Comparative flow cytometric analysis of the cell lines

29. Recently US FDA approved CAR-T treatment is a
A. Monoclonal antibody therapy
B. Cell therapy
C. Small molecule therapy
D. Photoactive agent-based therapy

GATE (BIOTECHNOLOGY), 2018

30. If serum is removed from the growth medium of human embryonic kidney cell line (HEK), then the cells will
A. proliferate faster
B. proliferate normally
C. undergo cell cycle arrest
D. undergo immediate apoptosis

CSIR-NET, 15 DECEMBER, 2019

Transgenics-application

31. The following statements are made regarding developing a transgenic mouse:
(*a*) The transgenic mouse thus born will be a homozygous transgenic animal and can be maintained by crossing with another transgenic animal.
(*b*) The fertilized transgenic eggs are allowed to develop in vitro.
(*c*) The desired gene is preferably microinjected in male pronucleus after sperm entry in oocyte.
(*d*) For best efficiency, the desired gene is always microinjected in the male gametes and then they are allowed to fertilize the female gametes.
(*e*) Blastocyst stage embryos are transferred to the uterus of hormonally prepared mother.
(*f*) The fertilized eggs are collected from specific strain of mouse.
(g) The female mouse of specific strain is super ovulated, oocytes are collected and allowed to fertilize in vitro.

Choose the combination of statements arranged in the correct sequence for developing transgenic mouse.
A. (*g*) → (*c*) → (*e*)
B. (*f*) → (*b*) → (*a*)
C. (*g*) → (*d*) → (*a*)
D. (*d*) → (*f*) → (*b*) → (*a*)

DBT-JRF, 2019

32. Which one of the following sets of protein factors, named as Yamanaka factors, can be used to convert mammalian somatic cells into induced pluripotent stem cells?
A. Oct3/4, Sox2, Klf4, c-Myc
B. c-fos, nestin, TGF-β, c-jun
C. Oct3, snail, FGF, nanos
D. Hstf, vimentin, ets, ras

33. Which one of the following assures prevention of polyspermy in an egg?
A. Activation of PI3 kinase
B. Cortical reaction
C. Acrosome reaction
D. Cross-linking between ZP1 and ZP3

34. Midblastula transition is a phenomenon that occurs during early development in certain organisms. It refers to:
A. Transition from maternal to zygotic gene expression
B. Transition of morphology during midblastula stage
C. Transition from two germ layer embryo to three germ layer embryo
D. Transition of blastula to gastrula

35. The major difference between hormones that have intracellular receptors and those that have cell membrane receptors is that the former is usually:
A. Charged B. Hydrophilic
C. Glycosylated D. Hydrophobic

36. Neurotransmitter at the neuromuscular junction is:
A. Epinephrine B. Serotonin
C. Acetylcholine D. Dopamine

37. Which one of the following amino acids can be used as a diuretic because of its importance in metabolism of ammonia?
A. Asparagine B. Leucine
C. Tryptophan D. Isoleucine

38. Which one of the following contributes to the development of the reproductive tract in a male foetus?
A. Anti-diuretic hormone
B. Inhibin
C. Anti-Mullerian hormone
D. Activin

39. When dissolved oxygen is lower than the critical concentration in mammalian cell culture systems, cell viability declines because of:
A. Complete glutamine oxidation
B. Decrease in specific lactate production from glucose
C. Incomplete glutamine oxidation and increase in lactate production from glucose
D. Accumulation of ammonia

GATE (BIOTECHNOLOGY), 2019

40. Which one of the following is used as a pH indicator in animal cell culture medium?
A. Acridine orange B. Phenol red
C. Bromophenol blue D. Coomassie blue

41. Which of the following statements are CORRECT about the function of fetal bovine serum in animal cell culture?
(*a*) It stimulates cell growth
(*b*) It enhances cell attachment
(*c*) It provides hormones and minerals
(*d*) It maintains pH at 7.4
A. (*a*) and (*b*) only B. (*a*) and (*d*) only
C. (*a*), (*b*) and (*c*) only D. (*a*), (*b*), (*c*) and (*d*)

CSIR-NE , NOVEMBER (AFTERNOON), 2020

Animal Tissue Culture

42. A student added DMEM culture medium which was pink in colour to growing liver cells. Three days later the medium colour was yellow. This indicated
A. change in cell morphology
B. change in pH of the medium
C. depletion of nutrients in the medium
D. lack of antibiotics in the culture

Stem Cell & Gene Therapy

43. Gene therapy is a promising tool for addressing several diseases in humans. With respect to the above, which one of the following statements is FALSE?
A. Gene therapy involves the direct genetic modification of the cells/model to achieve a therapeutic goal.
B. Current gene therapy is directed at modifying somatic cells.
C. The only successful gene therapies are those in which cells are removed from a patient, genetically modified, and then reintroduced into patients.
D. Recessively inherited disorders are good targets for gene therapy.

DBT-JRF, 2020

44. Embryonic stem cells are

A. unipotent B. totipotent

C. pluripotent D. differentiated

45. Which of these procedures poses the least risk to an unborn child?

A. embryoscopy & fetoscopy

B. amniocentesis

C. alpha-feto protein sampling

D. chronic villi sampling

46. Baroreceptors are responsible for sensing human

A. temperature

B. blood pressure

C. oxygen saturation

D. heart rate

47. The first drug approved by FDA of USA, that was produced through genetic engineering was

A. Somatotropin B. insulin

C. penicillin D. interferon

GATE (BIOTECHNOLOGY), 2020

48. Which of the following statements about gene therapy are correct?

(*a*) Affected individuals, but not their progeny, can be cured through germline gene therapy.

(*b*) Affected individuals, as well as their progeny, can be curd through germline gene therapy.

(*c*) Affected individuals, but not their progeny, can be cured through somatic gene therapy.

(*d*) Affected individuals, as well as their progeny, can be cured through somatic gene therapy

A. (*a*) and (*c*) only

B. (*a*) and (*d*) only

C. (*b*) and (*c*) only

D. (*b*) and (*d*) only

49. During a positive – negative selective process, transformed animal cells expressing ....are killed in presence of ganciclovir in the medium.

A. pyruvate kinase

B. viral thymidine kinase

C. viral serine/threonine kinase

D. viral tyrosine kinase

50. Which one of the following media components is used to maintain pH in mammalian cell culture?

A. $CaCl_2$ B. $MgSO_4$

C. NaCl D. $NaHCO_3$

51. Determine the correctness or otherwise of the following Assertion (A) and the Reason (R)

Assertion (A): Embryonic stem cells are suitable for developing knockout mice.

Reason (R): Homologous recombination is more frequent in embryonic stem cells than in somatic cells.

A. Both (A) and (R) are true and (R) is the correct reason for (A).

B. Both (A) and (R) are true and (R) is the not correct reason for (A).

C. Both (A) and (R) are false

D. (A) is false but (R) is true.

52. Determine the correctness or otherwise of the following Assertion (A) and the Reason (R)

Assertion (A): A zygote and its immediate descendant cells are unspecialized and are called totipotent

Reason (R): Totipotent cells retain the capacity to differentiate into only a few cell types.

A. Both (A) and (R) are false

B. Both (A) and (R) are true and (R) is the not correct reason for (A).

C. Both (A) and (R) are true and [r] is the correct reason for (A).

D. (A) is true but (R) is false.

CSIR-NET, JUNE (MORNING), 2021

Stem Cell & Gene Therapy

53. A breakthrough in cancer therapy is expected where T-cell are taken from a patient are modified in the laboratory to attack cancer cells before reinfusion in the patient. These T-cells are called,

A. Cancer associated receptor T-cell

B. Chimeric antigen-receptor T-cell

C. Chimeric B and T-cells

D. Cancer antigen recognition T-cells

CSIR-NET, JUNE (AFTERNOON), 2021

Stem Cell & Gene Therapy

54. Which one of the following statements about stem cells is correct?
A. Stem cells cannot be maintained in culture since they require a distinct in micro environment known as niches.
B. During asymmetric steam cell division, only one of the daughter cell is retained as stem cell.
C. Stem cell derived transit - amplifying cells are differentiated cells which retain the capacity to divide further.
D. Hematopoietic stem cell (HSCs) are totipotent stems cells.

55. The embryonic stem cells in mammals arew derived from:
A. Blastocoel B. Inner cell mass
C. Trophoectoderm D. Trophoendoderm

DBT-JRF, 2021

56. The hypothalamus protects the body against hypoglycemia by:
A. Increasing epinephrine release
B. Increasing glucagon release
C. Increasing thyroxin release
D. Inhibiting insulin release

57. Chemical transmitters in basal ganglia include all the following, EXCEPT:
A. Dopamine
B. GABA
C. Glutamate
D. Glycine

58. Double pain sensation that is occasionally felt following painful stimulation of the skin is due to:
A. Application of two painful stimuli simultaneously at two different sites
B. Perception of pain at two different higher centers
C. Presence of dual pain pathways
D. Repetition of the painful stimulus

59. Interneurons:
A. Influence the rate of discharge from the alpha motor neurons
B. Participate in ascending sensory pathways
C. Provide communication between dendrites of the efferent neurons
D. Provide communication between the central ends of afferent neurons

60. Which one of the statements is TRUE regarding chemical synapses in the nervous system?
A. Allow diffusion of chemical substances form the presynaptic neuron into the postsynaptic neuron
B. Allow transmission of potential changes in one direction only; from the presynaptic to the postsynaptic neurons
C. Are more numerous in the peripheral nervous system than the central nervous system
D. Have potential-gated ionic channels

61. Match the components of List I with List II.

List I (Inducers of Cell differentiation)	List II (Cell type)
(a) Hydrocortisone	(i) Neuroblastoma
(b) Retinoids	(ii) Endothelium
(c) Prolactin	(iii) Glia,glioma
(d) Interferon-γ	(iv) Mammary epithelium

Choose the correct answer from the options given below:

	(a)	(b)	(c)	(d)
A.	(i)	(ii)	(iii)	(iv)
B.	(ii)	(i)	(iv)	(iii)
C.	(iii)	(ii)	(iv)	(i)
D.	(i)	(iii)	(ii)	(iv)

62. Digitalis is used for the treatment of congestive heart failure because:
A. It can dissolve clots to release congestion
B. It can increase the force of contraction of heart muscle
C. It can increase the volume of the heart chambers
D. It clears the lungs to release congestion

63. Beta-lactam ring is present in:
A. Chloramphenicol
B. Erythromycin
C. Penicillin
D. Tetracycline

64. Given below are two statements: one is labelled as Assertion (A) and another one is labelled as Reason (R)

Assertion (A): It is essential that the animal cell cultures be maintained in antibiotic free conditions otherwise cryptic contaminations will persist

Reason (R): The constant use of antibiotics favours development of chronic contamination. Many organisms are inhibited but not killed by antibiotics, which may resurface when conditions are favorable.

In light of the above statements, choose the correct answer from the options below:
A. (A) is false but (R) is true
B. (A) is true but (R) is false
C. Both (A) and (R) is true and (R) is NOT the correct explanation of (A)
D. Both (A) and (R) is true and (R) is the correct explanation of (A)

65. In induced pluripotent stem cells:
A. Germ cells are transformed and passaged continuously in culture to maintain a state conducive to future pluripotent cell formation
B. Oncogenes are added to embryonic stem cells to help them retain stemness for prolonged cultures.
C. Somatic cells are continuously cultured to generate a cell line that is mutagenized to produce pluripotent cells when required
D. Somatic cells are transduced with viral vectors coding for transcription factors that induce a pluripotent state in the recipient cells

66. You have recently observed a mutation in gene X in patients with lung cancer. You have sequenced the gene X in these patients and have observed that (*i*) both the copies of gene X are mutated, and (*ii*) the mutation leads to absence of the protein X in the patients. The gene is most likely:
A. A metastasis inducer
B. A stem cell associated gene
C. A tumor suppressor
D. An oncogene

67. Human embryonic stem cells (hESCs) can be obtained from:
A. Inner cell mass of blastocyst
B. Morula stage
C. Teratoma
D. Trophoblast of blastocyst

68. Which gene is often been inserted in an adenoviral vector to treat cancer by suicide gene therapy?
A. GMCSF B. HSV-TK
C. IL2 D. VSVG

69. Which one of the following diseases can be treated with dopamine producing neurons generated from stem cells?
A. Alzheimer's disease
B. Amyotrophic lateral sclerosis
C. Brain tumor
D. Parkinson's disease

70. Given below are two statements:
Statement I: Tissues that are nonregenerative, such as neurons in the brain, do have stem cells.
Statement II: Tissue localization does not necessarily mean lineage commitment and reduced potency, as liver stem cells can generate neurons.
In light of the above statements, choose the most appropriate answer from the options given below:
A. Both statement I and II are correct
B. Both statement I and II are incorrect
C. Statement I is correct but statement II is incorrect
D. Statement I is incorrect but statement II is correct

71. Which family does HIV belong to?
A. Paramyxoviridae B. Retroviridae
C. Rhabdoviridae D. Togaviridae

72. Kuru disease in human is caused by:
A. Bacteria B. Mycoplasma
C. Prions D. Virus

GATE (LIFE SCIENCE), 2021

73. Match the therapeutic factors in Column I with the applications in Column II

Column I	Column II
(*a*) Humulin	(*i*) Cancer therapy
(*b*) Erythropoietin	(*ii*) Diabetes
(*c*) Plasminogen activator	(*iii*) Osteoporosis
(*d*) Cathepsin K inhibitor	(*iv*) Anaemia
(*e*) Leptin	(*v*) Myocardial infraction
	(*vi*) Obesity

	(*a*)	(*b*)	(*c*)	(*d*)	(*e*)
A.	(*ii*)	(*iv*)	(*v*)	(*iii*)	(*vi*)
B.	(*ii*)	(*v*)	(*i*)	(*iv*)	(*iii*)
C.	(*v*)	(*vi*)	(*iv*)	(*iii*)	(*i*)
D.	(*iii*)	(*iv*)	(*ii*)	(*v*)	(*vi*)

CSIR-NET, SEPTEMBER (MORNING), 2022

74. If you want to selectively kill the newly dividing mammalian cells in a cell culture assay, which of the following methods will you use?
A. Exposure to UV radiation at 250 nm
B. Treatment with 5-ethynyl-2′ -deoxyuridine (EdU), followed by doxorubicin hydrochloride treatment
C. Treatment with 5-bromo-2′-deoxyuridine (BrdU), followed by UV-A exposure
D. Tritiated thymidine treatment followed by vinblastine treatment

CSIR-NET, SEPTEMBER (AFTERNOON), 2022

75. Which of the following methods can be used to selectively lyse newly dividing cells?

A. MTT (3-(4,5-Dimethylthiazol-2-yl)-2,5-diphenyl-tetrazolium bromide) treatment of dividing cells followed by UVB irradiation MTT
B. Treatment of dividing cells with caspase inducers
C. Bromodeoxyuridine (BrdU) labeling of dividing cells followed by exposure to light
D. Treatment of dividing cells with ^{51}Cr and measuring its release over a period of time.

76. From a newly fertilized mouse egg, maternal pronucleus was removed and replaced with a second paternal pronucleus. Following observations/ statements were made:

(*a*) This will result in formation of an androgenetic embryo.
(*b*) This will result in formation of a gynogenetic embryo.
(*c*) The embryo will not survive beyond mid-gestation since parental genomes serve distinct complementary functions due to variable imprinting pattern.
(*d*) The adult originating from the embryo will be a clone of the father.
(*e*) The embryo will develop as adult but will die early due to rapid shortening of the telomeres.

Which one of the following represents correct combination of above statements?

A. (*a*), (*b*), (*c*)
B. (*b*), (*c*), (*e*)
C. (*a*) and (*c*) only
D. (*a*) and (*e*) only

DBT-JRF, 2022

77. For monoclonal antibody production, mammalian expression systems are preferred over bacterial expression systems, primarily because:

A. mammalian cultures have better productivity
B. mammalian cultures produce extra-cellular product simplifying the purification steps
C. mammalian system provide necessary post-translational modifications
D. mammalian genes can only be expressed in mammalian systems

78. The animal embryonic stem cells that can differentiate into any embryonic cell type are known as:

A. Pluripotent stem cells
B. Multipotent stem cells
C. Oligopotent stem cells
D. Unipotent stem cells

79. In animal cloning protocol, while performing enucleation, which chemical is used for relaxing the cellular cytoskeleton?

A. Phytohaemagglutinin
B. Cytochalasin B
C. Pronase
D. Heparin

80. The technique used in animal biotechnology for rapid multiplication and production of animals with a desired genotype is:

A. Protoplast fusion and embryo transfer
B. Hybrid selection and embryo transfer
C. In vitro fertilization and embryo transfer
D. Nuclear injection of genetic material and embryo transfer

81. In a neuronal culture experiment, the effect of a chemical (under study) was prevented by pretreating the cells with prazosin, an alpha1 adrenoceptor antagonist but not by propranolol, a beta adrenoceptor antagonist. The chemical under study is likely to be:

A. Acetylcholine or carbachol
B. Orexin or serotonin
C. GABA or glutamate
D. Noradrenaline or methoxamine

GATE (BIOTECHNOLOGY), 2022

82. Match the media component used in mammalian cell culture (Column I) with its respective role (Column II).

Column I	Column II
(*a*) Hydrocortisone	(*i*) Mitogen
(*b*) Fibronectin	(*ii*) Vitamin
(*c*) Epidermal growth factor	(*iii*) Hormone
(*d*) Riboflavin	(*iv*) Cell attachment

	(*a*)	(*b*)	(*c*)	(*d*)
A.	(*iii*)	(*iv*)	(*i*)	(*ii*)
B.	(*iii*)	(*iv*)	(*ii*)	(*i*)
C.	(*iv*)	(*iii*)	(*i*)	(*ii*)
D.	(*iv*)	(*iii*)	(*ii*)	(*i*)

ANSWERS

1	2	3	4	5	6	7	8	9	10
B	B	A	B	A	D	A	A	A	A
11	**12**	**13**	**14**	**15**	**16**	**17**	**18**	**19**	**20**
B	B	B	A	D	B	A	B	A	C
21	**22**	**23**	**24**	**25**	**26**	**27**	**28**	**29**	**30**
C	B	D	C	A	A	C	B	B	C
31	**32**	**33**	**34**	**35**	**36**	**37**	**38**	**39**	**40**
A	A	B	A	D	C	A	C	C	B
41	**42**	**43**	**44**	**45**	**46**	**47**	**48**	**49**	**50**
C	B	C	C	C	B	B	C	C	D
51	**52**	**53**	**54**	**55**	**56**	**57**	**58**	**59**	**60**
A	D	B	B	B	A	D	C	D	B
61	**62**	**63**	**64**	**65**	**66**	**67**	**68**	**69**	**70**
B	B	C	D	D	C	D	C	D	A
71	**72**	**73**	**74**	**75**	**76**	**77**	**78**	**79**	**80**
B	C	A	C	C	C	C	A	B	C
81	**82**								
D	A								

CHAPTER

11

PLANT BIOTECHNOLOGY

CSIR-NET, JUNE, 2017

Transgenic Plant

1. A T0 transgenic plant containing a transgene for herbicide resistance shows two bands on Southern blot analysis using a probe that is internal to the restriction sites used for genomic DNA digestion. However, it segregates in a 3:1 ratio for herbicide resistance: sensitivity in the T1 progeny obtained by self pollination. Which one of the following statements is correct?

A. The T0 plant is a single-copy event

B. The T0 plant is a double-copy event and the two transgene copies are tightly linked

C. The T0 plant is a double-copy event and the two transgene copies are integrated in two different chromosomes

D. The T0 plant contains two unlinked copies of the transgene, both of which are truncated versions of the herbicide resistance gene.

2. Given below are four statements regarding genetic transformation of plants in the laboratory:

(*a*) Planes incapable of sexual reproduction cannot be transformed by *Agrobacterium tumifaciens*

(*b*) Integration of transgene in organellar (chloroplast) genome occurs primarily by homologous recombination

(*c*) An enhancer trap construct used in Agrobacterium-mediated transformation would contain a functional coding sequence of a reporter gene and a minimal promoter

(*d*) A To transgenic plant containing two unlinked copies of a selection marker gene (*hpt*) and one copy of the passenger gene (*gfp*) would segregate in a 1 : 1 ratio for hygromycin resistance: sensitivity in the backcrossed progeny grown on selection media

Which one of the combinations of above statements is correct?

A. (*a*) and (*d*) B. (*b*) and (*c*)

C. (*a*) and (*c*) D. (*b*) and (*d*)

3. *Agrobacterium* mediated transformation was used to generate transgenic plants using a construct with a selection marker gene "X" and a passenger gene "Y". Expression levels of "Y" protein in eight independent transgenic plants are given below

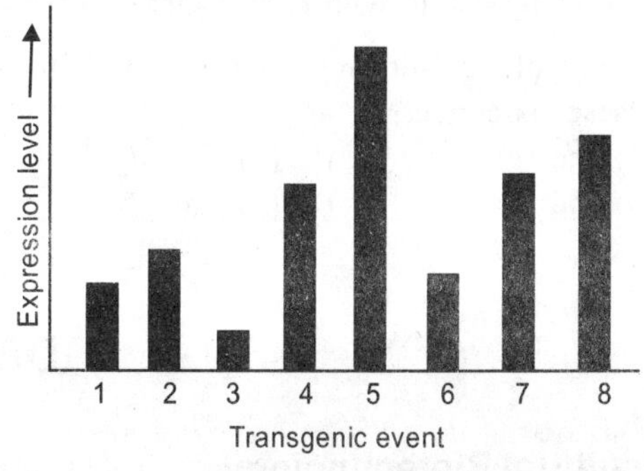

The following could represent probable reasons for the observed variability in transgene expression levels

(*a*) Position effects on passenger gene
(*b*) Transgene silencing of the marker gene
(*c*) Variation in copy number of passenger gene
(*d*) mRNA instability of marker gene

Which one of the following combinations of above statements is correct?

A. (*a*) and (*c*) B. (*c*) and (*d*)
C. (*b*) and (*d*) D. (*a*) and (*b*)

CSIR-NET, DECEMBER, 2017

Transgenic Plant

4. Identification of genes that are associated with the development of male and/or female gametophyte and embryogenesis in plants is facilitated by T-DNA mediated insertional mutagenesis. In an experiment, a transgenic plant was generated by insertion of T-DNA (containing a Kanamycin-resistance gene) into a gene "A". Self pollination of the T0 plant generated F1 progeny that segregated in a 2 : 1 ratio for resistance: sensitivity to Kanamycin. These observations indicate that

A. the mutant allele did not segregate from the wild type allele.
B. mutation in gene "A" induces lethality in the male gametophyte.
C. mutation in gene "A" induces lethality in the female gametophyte.
D. mutation in gene "A" induces zygotic lethality.

5. Transgenic tobacco plants over-expressing isopentenyl transferase (*IPT*) under the control of promoter region of Senescence Associated Receptor kinase (PSARK) were exposed to drought for 15 days followed by re-watering for 7 days. The following hypotheses were proposed regarding changes in the transgenic plants at the end of 7 days of re-watering:

(*a*) The plants would be wilted and fail to survive.
(*b*) The plants would be healthy and survive.
(*c*) The plants would show higher production of cytokinin compared to wild type plants.
(*d*) The plants would show higher production of absicic acid compared to wild type plants.

Which one of the following combinations of the above hypotheses is correct?

A. (*a*) and (*c*) B. (*a*) and (*d*)
C. (*b*) and (*c*) D. (*b*) and (*d*)

6. Some of the following transgenic approaches could be used for functional characterization of endogenous genes in plants:

(*a*) Transformation using a binary vector containing a strong enhancer element and lacking the right border of T-DNA
(*b*) Transformation using a binary vector containing a promoter-less reporter gene sequence and a selction maker gene cassette within the T-DNA.
(*c*) Transformation using a binary vector containing only a strong enhancer element and a selection marker gene cassette within the T-DNA.
(*d*) Transformation using a binary vector lacking a reporter gene as well as both the left and right borders of T-DNA.

Which one of the following combinations can be used?

A. (*a*) and (*b*) only
B. (*b*) and (*c*) only
C. (*c*) and (*d*) only
D. (*a*) and (*d*) only

7. Match the following Vir proteins with their correct function during *Agrobacterium* mediated transfer of T-DNA to plant cells.

(Vir protein)	***(Function)***
(*a*) Vir G	(*i*) Nucleus targeting of T-DNA
(*b*) Vir D2	(*ii*) Component of membrane structure (transfer apparatus) for T-DNA transfer
(*c*) Vir B1	(*iii*) Proteasome mediated destruction of proteins coating T-DNA complex
(*d*) Vir F	(*iv*) Induction of *Vir* genes

	(*a*)	(*b*)	(*c*)	(*d*)
A.	(*i*)	(*ii*)	(*iii*)	(*iv*)
B.	(*iv*)	(*i*)	(*ii*)	(*iii*)
C.	(*i*)	(*iii*)	(*iv*)	(*ii*)
D.	(*iii*)	(*ii*)	(*i*)	(*iv*)

DBT-JRF, 2017

Agricultural Biotechnology

8. Callus-mediated regeneration is NOT preferred for micropropagation because:

A. it takes longer time for regeneration
B. plant regeneration is problematic due to poor organogenesis
C. it leads to generation of variants
D. hardening of plants is difficult to achieve

9. Which one of the following would produce androgenic haploids in anther culture?

A. Anther wall B. Tapetal layer
C. Connective tissue D. Young microspores

10. Male sterility in plants is induced by expression of the TA29-*barnase*-pA cassette in:

A. Pollen mother cell B. Stamen
C. Tapetum D. Pollen grain.

11. Which one of the following hormones promote production of seedless grapes?

A. IAA B. IBA
C. BAP D. GA_3

12. Which one of the following molecular markers is associated with bacterial blight resistance in rice?

A. PiB B. Rar
C. Xa21 D. Pi9

GATE (LIFE SCIENCE), 2017

Botany

Plant development; cell and tissue morphogenesis

13. A typical floral meristem differs from shoot apical meristem on the basis of

A. Determinate growth
B. Presence of auxin
C. Presence of stem cells
D. Negative geotropism

Plant Breeding, Genetic Modification, Genome Editing

14. Two of the *vir* operons of Ti plasmid in *Agrobacterium tumefaciens* are constitutively expressed. Identify the CORRECT pair.

A. *virA* and *virG* B. *virF* and *virH*
C. *virC* and *virD* D. *virB* and *virE*

15. Choose the CORRECT set of matches between group I and group Ii in relation to plant genetic transformation methods

Group I	Group II
(*a*) Helium	(*i*) Agrobactor tumefaciens
(*b*) Acetocyringone	(*ii*) Microinjection
(*c*) Polyethylene glycol	(*iii*) Particle bombardment
(*d*) Agarose embedding	(*iv*) Protoplasr

	(*a*)	(*b*)	(*c*)	(*d*)
A.	(*iv*)	(*iii*)	(*ii*)	(*i*)
B.	(*ii*)	(*i*)	(*iv*)	(*iii*)
C.	(*iii*)	(*iv*)	(*i*)	(*ii*)
D.	(*iii*)	(*i*)	(*iv*)	(*ii*)

CSIR-NET, JUNE, 2018

Transgenics-application

16. Given below are a few statements on *Agrobacterium* mediated transformation of plants. Which one of the following statements is CORRECT?

A. T-DNA transfer occurs from left border to right border.
B. The *gfp* reporter gene can never be used for selection of transgenic plants.
C. Transformation frequencies will decrease on overexpression of *virulence* genes.
D. Host plant genes play an important role in influencing transformation frequencies.

17. To characterize the mechanism/s by which heat-stress is perceived in Arabidopsis, a team of researchers fused a Heat Shock promoter with luciferase gene. Transgenic plants having promoter: luciferase fusion were raised. Such plants revealed strong luciferase expression upon heat-stress but they showed no expression under unstressed control condition. Subsequently, these transgenic plants were mutagenized by EMS and seeds from F2 generation were obtained. To analyze the downstream positive regulators of heat-stress, the researchers should analyze seedlings that are

A. expressing luciferase in the presence of heat-stress
B. not expressing luciferase in the presence of heat-stress
C. expressing Iuciferase in the absence of heat-stress
D. not expressing luciferase in the absence of heat-stress

DBT-JRF, 2018

Agricultural Biotechnology

18. Which one of the following conditions eliminates the possibility of horizontal gene transfer from a transgenic plant?

A. Single copy nuclear events
B. Multicopy nuclear events
C. Plastid transformation event
D. Marker free events

GATE (BIOTECHNOLOGY), 2018

Plant, Animal and Microbial Biotechnology

Animals

19. Which one of the following statements is true for actin?
A. Actin filament is structurally polarized and the two ends are not identical
B. De novo actin polymerization is a single-step process
C. The pointed end of the actin filaments is the fast-growing end
D. Actin forms spindle fibres during mitosis

20. Cell type A secretes molecule X into the culture medium. Cell type B in the same culture responds to the molecule X by expressing protein Y. Which one of the following modes of signalling represents the interaction between A and B?
A. Autocrine B. Juxtacrine
C. Paracrine D. Intracrine

Microbes

21. Match the industrial products mentioned in Group I with their producer organisms in Group II

Group I	Group II
(*a*) Citric acid	(*i*) *Trichoderma viride*
(*b*) Cellulase	(*ii*) *Clostridium acetobutylicum*
(*c*) Vitamin B12	(*iii*) *Aspergillus niger*
(*d*) Butanol	(*iv*) *Propionibacterium freudenreichii*

	(*a*)	(*b*)	(*c*)	(*d*)
A.	(*iv*)	(*iii*)	(*i*)	(*ii*)
B.	(*iii*)	(*i*)	(*ii*)	(*iv*)
C.	(*ii*)	(*i*)	(*iv*)	(*iii*)
D.	(*iii*)	(*i*)	(*iv*)	(*ii*)

GATE (LIFE SCIENCE), 2018

Plant Development; Cell and Tissue Morphogenesis

22. Statements given below are either TRUE (T) or FALSE (F). Select the CORRECT combination.
(*a*) Mitosis occurs exclusively in diploid mother cell
(*b*) Mitosis occurs both in diploid and haploid mother cells
(*c*) Meiosis occurs exclusively in diploid mother cell
(*d*) Meiosis occurs both in diploid and haploid mother cells

	(*a*)	(*b*)	(*c*)	(*d*)
A.	T	F	T	F
B.	F	T	F	T
C.	T	F	F	T
D.	F	T	T	F

23. Identify the CORRECT statement.
A. Receptor-like kinases play role in gametophytic self-incompatibility in Brassicaceae
B. Receptor-like kinases play role in sporophytic self-incompatibility in Solanaceae
C. Ribonucleases play role in sporophytic self-incompatibility in Brassicaceae
D. Ribonucleases play role in gametophytic self-incompatibility in Solanaceae

Plant Breeding, Genetic Modification, Genome Editing

24. You are asked to design a genetic construct for high-level expression of a gene encoding the therapeutic protein 18 (TP18) via plastid transformation. Select the CORRECT set of genetic elements for this construct.
A. Actin1 promoter → TP18 coding sequence → Actin1 transcription terminator
B. Ubiquitin1 promoter → TP18 coding sequence → Ubiquitin1 transcription terminator
C. rbcS promoter → TP18 coding sequence → rbcS transcription terminator
D. rbcL promoter → TP18 coding sequence → rbcL transcription terminator

Economic and Applied Botany

25. Which of the following plants produces Ylang-ylang oil?
A. Cananga odorata
B. Carcum copticum
C. Pandanus odoratissimus
D. Pimenta racemose

26. Match the plant alkaloids with their uses and source species

Alkaloid	Use	Source species
(*a*) Codeine	1. Stimulant	(*i*) *Hyoscyamus niger*
(*b*) Caffine	2. Analgesic	(*ii*) *Catharanthus roseus*
(*c*) Scopolamine	3. Antineoplastic	(*iii*) *Cola nitida*
(*d*) Vinblastin	4. Anticholinergic	(*iv*) *Papaver somniferum*
		(*v*) *Coptis japonica*
		(*vi*) *Senecio jacobaea*

	(*a*)	(*b*)	(*c*)	(*d*)
A.	2-(*iv*)	1-(*iii*)	4-(*i*)	3-(*ii*)
B.	4-(*iii*)	2-(*v*)	1-(*vi*)	3-(*i*)
C.	2-(*v*)	1-(*vi*)	3-(*iv*)	4-(*ii*)
D.	3-(*ii*)	4-(*iii*)	1-(*iv*)	2-(*i*)

CSIR-NET, JUNE, 2019

Transgenics-application

27. Most of the plant disease resistance (R) gene products contain:

A. G-Box domains
B. Transcription repression domains
C. Leucine-rich repeats
D. Enzymatic activities

28. A To transgenic plant contains two unlinked copies of the T- DNA of which one is functional and the other is silenced. Segregation of the transgenic to non transgenic phenotype would occur in a

(*i*) Ratio in progeny obtained by backcrossing and in a (*ii*) ration in F1 progeny obtained by self pollination.

Fill in the blanks with the correct combination of (*i*) and (*ii*) from the options given below:

A. (*i*)— 3:1 and (*ii*) — 15 : 1
B. (*i*)— 1:1 and (*ii*) — 3 : I
C. (*i*)—3:1 and (*ii*) — 3 : 1
D. (*i*) —1:1 and (*ii*) — 15 : 1

29. Following statements were given regarding factors influencing variation in expression levels of transgene in transgenic plants:

(*a*) Difference in restriction enzyme sites within the T- DNA
(*b*) Difference in copy number of the transgene.
(*c*) Variations in site of integration of the T-DNA within the plant genome.
(*d*) Presence of multiple promoters within the T-DNA region.

Which one of the following options represents combinations of statements that would NOT lead to variations in transgene expression levels in transgenic plants generated using the same T-DNA/ binary vector?

A. (*a*) and (*c*)only
B. (*b*) only
C. (*c*) and (*d*) only
D. (*a*) and (*d*) only

CSIR-NET, 15 DECEMBER, 2019

Transgenics-application

30. *Agrobacterium tumefaciens* is frequently used as a vector to create transgenic plants. Under laboratory conditions *Agrobacterium* - mediated plant transformation does not require

A. host plant genes
B. bacterial type IV secretion system
C. *vir* genes
D. opine catabolism genes

31. The T-DNA region of the Ti plasmid of *Agrobacterium tumefaciens* harbours two genes: X and Y. Mutation of gene 'X' produces a rooty tumour while mutation of gene 'Y' produces shoots in the tumor. Based on the above information, which one of the following statements is correct?

A. Gene 'X' encodes auxins and gene 'Y' encodes cytokinins
B. Gene 'X' encodes cytokinins and gene 'Y' encodes auxins
C. Gene 'X' and gene 'Y' both encode auxins
D. Gene 'X' encodes opines while gene 'Y' encodes cytokinins

32. Given below are schematic representations of the T-DNA regions of four constructs that are to be used for Agrobacterium – mediated transformation to silence an endogenous plant gene represented as XYFP that is expressed constitutively in the plant.

A. B. C. D.

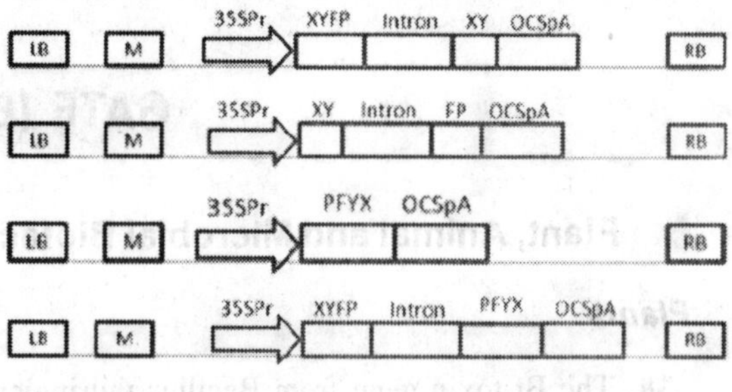

M: Selectable marker gene expression cassette LB Left Border

RB: Right Border

Which of the four constructs depicted above could be used to silence the target gene XYFP?

A. (*a*) and (*b*) only
B. (*b*) and (*d*) only
C. (*a*) and (*c*) only
D. (*c*) and (*d*) only

CSIR-NET, 27 DECEMBER, 2019

Transgenics-application

33. "In *Agrobacterium*-mediated transformation of a plant using a binary vector construct," Complete the above statement with the correct option.

A. All transgenic plants generated would show similar levels of transgenic expression".
B. The Agrobacterium cells lose the binary vector after the transfer of T-DNA".

C. Some transgenic plants generated may contain partial or truncated versions of the T-DNA".
D. Proteins of the host plant do not play any role".

34. In a gene stacking experiment, a transgenic plant generated using bar as a selection marker was crossed with another transgenic line containing hpt as the selection marker. Analysis of the F_1 progeny of this cross showed that 50% of the progeny was resistant to both selection agents (Basta and hygromycin) while the remaining 50% of the progenywas resistant to only hygromycin.

Which one of the following statements is a possible explanation of the above results?

A. Both the transgenic lines used as parents for the cross are single-copy events that arehomozygous for the transgenes.
B. The Basta-resistant transgenic plant is a single-copy, homozygous event and thehygromycin-resistant plant is a double-copy event that is homozygous for twounlinked copies of the transgene.
C. The bar containing transgenic plant is a hemizygous single-copy event and the hptcontaining transgenic plant is a homozygous, single-copy event
D. Both the transgenic plants used as parents for the cross are hemizygous, single-copy

DBT-JRF, 2019

Agricultural Biotechnology

35. 'Dichogamy' refers to a phenomenon in which anther dehiscence and stigma receptivity are:

A. temporally separated
B. spatially separated
C. temporally coinciding
D. spatially coinciding

36. Fusicoccin promotes cotyledon growth by promoting:

A. cell division
B. cell wall biosynthesis
C. tonoplast acidification
D. cell wall acidification

Transgenics-application

37. Disarmed Ti plasmid of *Agrobacterium tumefaciens* does not result in crown gall phenotype since it does not possess:

A. *ipt* and *iaaH* genes
B. *Vir D* gene
C. *Vir A* gene
D. *Vir G* gene

GATE (BIOTECHNOLOGY), 2019

Plant, Animal and Microbial Biotechnology

Plants

38. The Bt toxin gene from Bacillus thuringiensis used to generate genetically modified crops is

A. cry B. cro
C. cdc D. cre

Animals

39. Match the human diseases in Group I with the causative agents in Group II.

Group I	Group II
(*a*) Amoebiasis	(*i*) *Leishmania donovani*
(*b*) African sleeping sickness	(*ii*) *Trypanosoma cruzi*
(*c*) Kala azar	(*iii*) *Entamoeba histolytica*
(*d*) Chagas' disease	(*iv*) *Trypanosoma gambiense*

	(*a*)	(*b*)	(*c*)	(*d*)
A.	(*iii*)	(*iv*)	(*ii*)	(*i*)
B.	(*iii*)	(*ii*)	(*i*)	(*iv*)
C.	(*iii*)	(*iv*)	(*i*)	(*ii*)
D.	(*iv*)	(*iii*)	(*i*)	(*ii*)

40. Determine the correctness or otherwise of the following Assertion (A) and the Reason (R)

Assertion (A): It is possible to regenerate a whole plant from a single plant cell.

Reason (R): It is easier to introduce transgenes in to plants than animals.

A. Both (A) and (R) are true and (R) is the correct reason for (A)
B. Both (A) and (R) are true but (R) is not the correct reason for (A)
C. Both (A) and (R) are false
D. (A) is true but (R) is false

GATE (LIFE SCIENCE), 2019

Plant Development; Cell and Tissue Morphogenesis

41. Which one of the following combinations of polysaccharides is present in plant cell wall?
A. Only cellulose, hemicellulose and fibroin
B. Only cellulose, hemicellulose and lignin
C. Only cellulose, hemicellulose and pectin
D. Only cellulose, pectin and lignin

Plant Breeding, Genetic Modification, Genome Editing

42. The plant cells are considered totipotent. The phenomenon of a mature cell reverting to the meristematic state and forming undifferentiated callus tissue is called
A. redifferentiation
B. dedifferentiation
C. organogenesis
D. recalcitrancy

Economic and Applied Botany

43. Cybrids may arise through the
A. fusion of a normal protoplast with another nucleated protoplast of different origin
B. fusion between a normal protoplast and a protoplast containing viable nucleus
C. elimination of one of the nuclei from heterokaryon formed from two protoplasts of different origin
D. fusion of a normal cell with another nucleated cell

44. Which one of the following statements is CORRECT with respect to endosperm development? It originates
A. from the fusion product of three haploid nuclei - one from male gametophyte and two from the female gametophyte
B. from the fusion product of three haploid nuclei - two from male gametophyte and one from the female gametophyte
C. from the fusion product of two haploid nuclei - one from male gametophyte and one from the female gametophyte
D. by a phenomenon called apomixis

45. Which one of the following methods is INCORRECT with respect to haploid plant production? It can be produced
A. from an unfertilized egg cell
B. from nucellar tissue
C. from isolated pollen culture
D. by distant hybridization, followed by selective elimination of chromosomes of one of the parents

CSIR-NET, NOVEMBER (MORNING), 2020

Plant Tissue Culture

46. A group of researchers are testing two new agents, Ml and M2 for their efficacy in selecting transgenic plants. When they performed tissue culture experiments using three explants, A, B, and C without Agrobacterium transformation, and selected the regenerated plants on Ml and M2, the following regeneration frequencies were obtained.

Regeneration frequencies (%) in presence of different concentration of agents						
Explants Type	M1 conc. (mg/L)			M2 conc. (mg/L)		
	20	60	100	10	15	20
A	44%	21%	Nil	8%	Nil	Nil
B	53%	30%	10%	Nil	Nil	Nil
C	71%	42%	18%	15%	9%	4%

Based on the above data, which one of the following conclusions is incorrect?
A. M2 is a stronger selection agent than Ml for explant types A and B.
B. A concentration of 100 mg/L of Ml and 15 mg/L of M2 can be used for selection of transformed cells using explant type A.
C. Among the three explants, type C is least suitable at the tested concentrations of Ml and M2
D. Use of Ml with explant type B is the most ideal combination for selection of transformants.

Transgenics-application

47. Given below are a few approaches/ techniques used in the analysis of plants:
(*a*) Phenotype linked to the marker gene.
(*b*) PCR using primers specific to the host genome.
(*c*) Southern hybridization
(*d*) PCR using transgene-specific primers.

Which one of the following combination of approaches/ techniques can be used to differentiate between transgenic and non- transgenic plants of a particular variety if the site of insertion is unknown?
A. (*b*) and (*c*) only
B. (*a*) and (*d*) only
C. (*a*), (*c*) and (*d*)
D. (*a*), (*b*) and (*c*)

CSIR-NET, NOVEMBER (AFTERNOON), 2020

Transgenics-application

48. In Agrobacterium mediated transformation, which one of the following approaches is more likely to generate transgenic plants with INCOMPLETE transfer of the passenger gene?

A. Placement of selection marker gene towards left border and passenger gene towards right border of T-DNA

B. Expression of selection marker gene under constitutive promoter and passenger gene under tissue-specific promoter

C. Placement of passenger gene towards left border and marker gene towards right border of T-DNA

D. Expression of both selection marker gene and passenger gene under constitutive promoters

49. Suppression of VPE (Vascular Processing Enzymes) gene- expression in Nicotiana benthamiana plants will NOT

A. abolish hypersensitive response

B. enhance TMV (Tobacco Mosaic Virus) infection

C. reduce caspase-like activity

D. reduce DNA fragmentation

DBT-JRF, 2020

Plant Tissue Culture

50. Which part of a plant would be most suitable for raising virus-free plants for micropropagation?

A. node B. bark

C. vascular tissue D. apical meristem

51. Synthetic are mostly derived from

A. zygotic embryos

B. fruit of coconut

C. avocado seeds

D. somatic embryos

52. 'Cybrids' are produced by

A. in vitro fusion of cytoplasm

B. in vitro fusion of gametes

C. fusion of plastids

D. fusion of nuclear genomes

Agricultural Biotechnology

53. Which of the following plant horomones employs a phosphorelay system to regulate gene expression?

A. barassinosteroid B. cytokinin

C. auxin D. ethylene

Transgenics-application

54. During Agrobacterium infections, plant cell begins to synthesize Arginine derivatives called

A. Acetobenzylpurine B. Opines

C. Acetosyringone D. Hygromycin

55. 'Golden rice' is genetically engineered by altering the biosynthetic pathway for the production of

A. carotenoids B. chlorophylls

C. flavonoids D. Phycocyanins

GATE (LIFE SCIENCE), 2020

Plant Development; Cell and Tissue Morphogenesis

56. In a typical angiosperm under natural condition, primary meristems are usually established during

A. Gametogenesis

B. Embryogenesis

C. Vegetative phase development

D. Secondary growth

Plant Breeding, Genetic Modification, Genome Editing

57. In relation to agrobacterium mediated genetic engineering in plants, match the following in CORRECT combination

Gene name	Function
(*a*) virA	(*i*) Acetosyringone receptor
(*b*) virB	(*ii*) Conjugal tube formation
(*c*) virD1	(*iii*) Topoisomerase
(*d*) virG	(*iv*) Inducer of all vir operon
	(*v*) Octapine synthesis

	(*a*)	(*b*)	(*c*)	(*d*)
A.	(*iv*)	(*iii*)	(*ii*)	(*v*)
B.	(*ii*)	(*i*)	(*iii*)	(*v*)
C.	(*i*)	(*ii*)	(*iii*)	(*iv*)
D.	(*iii*)	(*i*)	(*ii*)	(*iv*)

58. Selection markers and the corresponding genes used in plant genetic engineering are given below

Selectable marker	Gene
(*a*) Kanamycin	(*i*) htpIV
(*b*) Hygromycin	(*ii*) bar
(*c*) Bialaphos	(*iii*) pmi
(*d*) Mannose	(*iv*) nptII

Choose the CORRECT combination

	(*a*)	(*b*)	(*c*)	(*d*)
A.	(*ii*)	(*i*)	(*iv*)	(*iii*)
B.	(*iv*)	(*ii*)	(*i*)	(*iii*)
C.	(*iv*)	(*i*)	(*ii*)	(*iii*)
D.	(*iii*)	(*iv*)	(*ii*)	(*i*)

CSIR-NET, JUNE (MORNING), 2021

Plant Tissue Culture

59. Which of the following 'R' gene products do not contain NBS-LRR domain

A. RPS2 Protein of arabidopesis
B. Xa1 protein of rice
C. N Protein of tobacco
D. MIo protein of barley

60. In which of the following stages of arabidopesis embryogrnsis do the visible distinction between the ataxia tissues of the cotyledons becomes initially appa rent?

A. globulqr stage B. zygotic stages
C. torpedo stages D. mature stages

Transgenics-application

61. Given below are a few statements on technology concept related to development of transgenic plants.

(*a*) Frequency of genetic transformation is influenced is only by the genes of agrobacterium and not by those of the host plants
(*b*) Transgenic plants contain multiple transgenic copy of the translated are preferred over those that contain multiple transgene copies for subsequent genetic analysis.
(*c*) Supervirulent strains of agrobacterium can be generated by increasing the copy number of violence gence.
(*d*) A nonconditional negative selection marker has to be necessarily used with a strong constitute promoter Forthe development of transgenic plants

Which one of the following options represent a combination of all incorrect statements?

A. (*a*) and (*d*) only B. Only (*c*)
C. (*b*) and (*c*) only D. (*d*) only

DBT-JRF, 2021

62. Seeds of Arabidopsis thaliana placed on Murashige and Skoog (MS) media without any hormones germinates faster than in the medium that contains:

A. Abscisic acid B. Auxin
C. Cytokinin D. Jasmonic acid

63. Which one of the following statements are TRUE for gibberellins?

(*a*) Gibberellins promote seed germination
(*b*) Gibberellins cannot stimulate leaf growth
(*c*) Gibberellins cannot stimulate stem growth
(*d*) Gibberellins can be exogenously used to increase plant growth
(*e*) GA3 is predominantly used in agronomic and horticultural practices

Choose the most appropriate answer from the options given below:

A. (*a*), (*b*) and (*c*) only
B. (*a*), (*c*) and (*e*) only
C. (*a*), (*d*) and (*e*) only
D. (*b*), (*c*) and (*d*) only

64. The GA2oxidase gene from bean is overexpressed in a wheat plant by genetic engineering. Which one of the following phenotypes correctly describes the resultant transgenic plant?

A. The height of the plant will not be affected
B. The plant will be shorter than the wild type
C. The plant will be taller than the wild type
D. The plant will not survive

65. The TDNA of Agrobacterium must be cut out from its circular plasmid for its transfer into plant cells. Which one of the following Vir proteins are involved in this process?

A. Vir A /Vir C B. Vir B6 /Vir B7
C. Vir D1 /Vir D2 D. Vir E2 /Vir G

66. Which one of the following can be used as a selection marker for developing transgenic plants?

A. galactosidase,
B. glucuronidase
C. Green fluorescent protein
D. Hygromycin phosphotransferase

67. A plant species nearing its extinction due to viral infection has been chosen for micropropagation by tissue culture. Which explants will be the most appropriate to produce virus free plants?
(*a*) Shoot apical meristem
(*b*) Stem
(*c*) Leaf disc
(*d*) Root tip

Choose the most appropriate answer from the options given below:
A. (*a*) and (*c*)   B. (*a*) only
C. (*b*) and (*d*)   D. (*c*) only

68. The first alkaloid to be isolated and characterized from plants is:
A. Caffeine   B. Cocaine
C. Morphine   D. Quinine

GATE (BIOTECHNOLOGY), 2021

Plant, Animal and Microbial Biotechnology

Plants

69. Which of the following statement(s) is/are CORRECT about Agrobacterium tumefaciens?
A. It contains tumour inducing plasmid
B. It causes crown gall disease in dicotyledonous plants
C. It is a Gram-positive soil bacterium
D. It is used in generating transgenic plants

Animals

70. Which of the following layer(s) is/are formed from the inner cell mass of the blastocyst?
A. Ectoderm   B. Endoderm
C. Mesoderm   D. Trophectoderm

Microbes

71. Match enzymes in Group I with their corresponding industrial application in Group II.

Group I	Group II
(*a*) Amylase	(*i*) Laundry detergent
(*b*) Invertase	(*ii*) Fruit juice clarification
(*c*) Pectinase	(*iii*) Liquefaction of sucrose
(*d*) Xylanase	(*iv*) Pulp and paper processing

	(*a*)	(*b*)	(*c*)	(*d*)
A.	(*ii*)	(*iii*)	(*iv*)	(*i*)
B.	(*i*)	(*iii*)	(*ii*)	(*iv*)
C.	(*i*)	(*ii*)	(*iii*)	(*iv*)
D.	(*i*)	(*iv*)	(*ii*)	(*iii*)

GATE (LIFE SCIENCE), 2021

Plant Breeding, Genetic Modification, Genome Editing

72. Match the genetically modified crop in GROUP I with the corresponding genetic element in GROUP II.

Group I	Group II
(*a*) Tomato with delayed fruit ripening	(*i*) EPSP synthase
(*b*) Herbicide-resistant soybean	(*ii*) Δ^{12}-Desaturase
(*c*) Insect-resistant cotton	(*iii*) Polygalacturonase
(*d*) Soybean with modified oil content	(*iv*) Bt-Cry protein

	(*a*)	(*b*)	(*c*)	(*d*)
A.	(*iii*)	(*i*)	(*iv*)	(*ii*)
B.	(*i*)	(*iii*)	(*ii*)	(*iv*)
C.	(*ii*)	(*i*)	(*iv*)	(*iii*)
D.	(*iii*)	(*ii*)	(*iv*)	(*i*)

73. Which of the following enzyme(s), when overexpressed, would result in rice grains with increased β-carotene content?
A. Phytoene synthase
B. Carotene desaturase
C. β-glucoronidase
D. Enolpyruvalshikimate-3-phosphate synthase (EPSPS)

CSIR-NET, SEPTEMBER (MORNING), 2022

74. Which one of the following is a small sulfated peptide that is secreted by a rice pathogenic bacterium, Xanthomonas oryzae to modulate motility, biofilm formation and virulence?
A. Coronatine
B. N-acylhomoserine lactones
C. Ax21
D. EPSS

75. Lr34, a broad-spectrum disease resistance gene in wheat, encodes for a putative:
A. Serine hydroxymethyl transferase
B. ABC transporter

C. Host-specific toxin
D. TIR-NB-LRR protein

76. Given below are a few statements about plant breeding and transgenesis:

(*a*) Recombinant inbred lines and double haploid populations have high levels of genetic homozygosity.
(*b*) Gene pyramiding involves introducing different genes for resistance to a specific pest in different gen species.
(*c*) Agrobacterium strains with a disarmed Ti plasmid do not require vir genes for transfer of T-DNA.
(*d*) Molecular breeding can be used for crop improvement if the trait of interest is present in naturally occurring of the plant.

Which one of the following options represents a combination of INCORRECT statements?

A. (*a*) and (*b*)
B. (*a*) and (*c*)
C. (*b*) and (*d*)
D. (*b*) and (*c*)

77. Given below is a schematic representation of the T-DNA region of a binary vector used for genetic transformation of plants

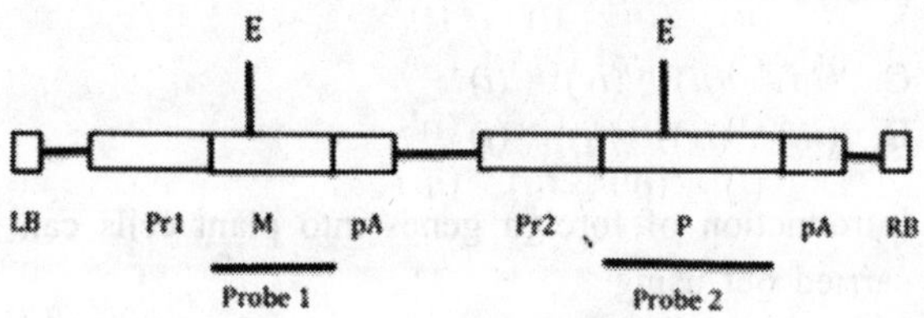

LB: Left Border, RB: Right Border, M: Marker gene, P: Passenger gene, pA: poly-adenylation signal, Pr1: Promoter of M gene, Pr2: Promoter of P gene, E: Restriction enzyme (sites) used for digestion of genomic DNA for Southern blotting, Probe 1 and Probe 2: probes used for Southern blotting. Transgenic plants generated using the above construct were subjected to Southern hybridization following digestion of genomic DNA with restriction enzyme 'E', to identify true single copy integration events from LB and RB flanks of the DNA.

Based on the above information, the following statements are made:

(*a*) Single copy events from the LB flank identified using Probe 1 would show two hybridization bands on the Southern blot.
(*b*) Single copy events from the RB flank identified using Probe 2 would show a single hybridization band on the Southern blot.
(*c*) For true single copy events, one hybridization band would be of the same length for each of the two probes used for hybridization.
(*d*) True single copy events would show two bands each for copy number on the left border and right border flanks.
(*e*) There would be no similar hybridization band obtained using Probe 1 and Probe 2.

Which one of the following options represents only correct statements?

A. (*a*), (*b*) and (*d*)
B. (*c*), (*d*) and (*e*)
C. (*b*), (*c*) and (*e*)
D. (*a*), (*c*) and (*d*)

DBT-JRF, 2022

78. VirA and VirG form a two component signaling system during Agrobacterium infection in plants. In an experiment, VirG was mutated resulting in nonfunctional VirG protein. Which one of the following conse 27-200uences is most likely?

A. Signaling leading to successful Agrobacterium infection will not be affected
B. Phenolic signal will be perceived but not transduced
C. Phenolic signal will not be perceived
D. VirD1 will take over the function of VirG

79. In plants, the overexpression of lectin genes confers resistance to:

A. Virus
B. Insects
C. Fungus
D. Bacteria

80. Given below are two statements one is labelled as Assertion (A) and the other is labelled as Reason (R):

Assertion (A): Phosphomannose isomerase (PMI) from E. coli was used as selection marker to develop 'golden rice 2'.

Reason (R): When mannose is added in the selection media, endogenous hexokinase converts mannose into mannose-6-phosphate which blocks glycolysis, ATP production, and represses transcription of photosynthetic genes, resulting in slower growth of non-transformed plants. PMI, on the other hand, converts mannose-6-phosphate to fructose-6-phosphate.

In the light of the above statements, choose the correct answer from the options given below:

A. Both (A) and (R) are true and (R) is the correct explanation of (A)

B. Both (A) and R are true but R is not the correct explanation of (A)
C. (A) is true but (R) is false
D. (A) is false but (R) is true

81. Which one of the following genes can be used to generate male sterile crop plants?
A. Barnase B. Bar
C. Lectinase D. Chalcone Synth

82. In a plant transformation vector, the selectable marker gene is ideally located next to the "left border" of T-DNA region, because:
(*a*) Left border of T-DNA enters last into the plant cell.
(*b*) Right border of T-DNA enters last into the plant cell.
(*c*) It ensures complete transfer of T-DNA into the plant cell.

Choose the most appropriate answer from the options given below:
A. (*a*) and (*b*) Only
B. (*b*) and (*c*) Only
C. (*a*) and (*c*) Only
D. (*c*) Only

83. Which one of the following is commonly used as a selection marker for developing transgenic plants?
A. Green fluorescent protein
B. β-lactamase
C. β-galactosidase
D. Hygromycin phosphotransferase

84. In a metabolic engineering experiment the flux from primary carbon metabolism was diverted towards methylerythritol phosphate (MEP) pathway. Which one of the following class of secondary carbon compounds do you think will accumulate more?
A. Alkaloids
B. Glucosinolates
C. Phenolics
D. Terpenes

GATE (BIOTECHNOLOGY), 2022

85. Match the media component (Column I) with its role (Column II).

Column I	Column II
(*a*) Sucrose	(*i*) Anti-foam agent
(*b*) Zinc chloride	(*ii*) Nitrogen source
(*c*) Ammonium sulphate	(*iii*) Carbon source
(*d*) Silicone oil	(*iv*) Trace element

	(*a*)	(*b*)	(*c*)	(*d*)
A.	(*i*)	(*ii*)	(*iii*)	(*iv*)
B.	(*ii*)	(*i*)	(*iii*)	(*iv*)
C.	(*iii*)	(*ii*)	(*iv*)	(*i*)
D.	(*iii*)	(*iv*)	(*ii*)	(*i*)

86. Introduction of foreign genes into plant cells can be carried out using
A. Agrobacterium
B. $CaCl_2$ mediated plasmid uptake
C. Electroporation
D. Gene gun

GATE (LIFE SCIENCE), 2022

Plant Breeding, Genetic Modification, Genome Editing

87. With reference to virulence (vir) region of nopaline type Ti plasmid of Agrobacterium tumefaciens, match Group-I (vir gene) and Group-II (coded protein) in CORRECT combination.

Group-I	Group-II
(*a*) *vir* A	(*i*) Single strand T-DNA binding protein
(*b*) *vir* B	(*ii*) Topoisomeras
(*c*) vir C	(*iii*) Membrane protein, channel for T-DNA
(*d*) *vir* D	(*iv*) Sensor protein, constitutive expression

	(*a*)	(*b*)	(*c*)	(*d*)
A.	(*iv*)	(*iii*)	(*ii*)	(*i*)
B.	(*iv*)	(*iii*)	(*i*)	(*ii*)
C.	(*iv*)	(*ii*)	(*i*)	(*iii*)
D.	(*i*)	(*iii*)	(*ii*)	(*iv*)

88. Match Group-I (selection agent) and Group-II (gene) in CORRECT combination.

Group I	Group II
(*a*) Kanamycin	(*i*) pmi
(*b*) Hygromycin	(*ii*) bar
(*c*) Phosphinothricin	(*iii*) nptII
(*d*) Mannose	(*iv*) ptxD
	(*v*) DHFR
	(*vi*) hpt

	(*a*)	(*b*)	(*c*)	(*d*)
A.	(*iii*)	(*vi*)	(*ii*)	(*i*)
B.	(*iv*)	(*iii*)	(*ii*)	(*i*)
C.	(*i*)	(*vi*)	(*iii*)	(*ii*)
D.	(*ii*)	(*i*)	(*v*)	(*vi*)

ANSWERS

1	2	3	4	5	6	7	8	9	10
B	B	A	D	C	B	B	C	D	C
11	**12**	**13**	**14**	**15**	**16**	**17**	**18**	**19**	**20**
D	C	A	A	D	D	B	C	A	C
21	**22**	**23**	**24**	**25**	**26**	**27**	**28**	**29**	**30**
D	D	D	D	A	A	C	B	D	D
31	**32**	**33**	**34**	**35**	**36**	**37**	**38**	**39**	**40**
B	D	C	C	A	D	A	A	C	B
41	**42**	**43**	**44**	**45**	**46**	**47**	**48**	**49**	**50**
C	B	C	A	B	D	C	C	B	D
51	**52**	**53**	**54**	**55**	**56**	**57**	**58**	**59**	**60**
D	A	B	B	A	B	C	C	D	C
61	**62**	**63**	**64**	**65**	**66**	**67**	**68**	**69**	**70**
A	A	C	B	C	D	B	C	A,B,D	B
71	**72**	**73**	**74**	**75**	**76**	**77**	**78**	**79**	**80**
B	A	A,B	C	B	D	D	B	B	A
81	**82**	**83**	**84**	**85**	**86**	**87**	**88**		
A	C	D	C	D	A,C,D	B	A		

■■■■■

CHAPTER

12

ENVIRONMENTAL BIOTECHNOLOGY

DBT-JRF, 2017

1. Application of the herbicide, phosphoinothricin, results in death of plants due to accumulation of:

A. CO_2 B. NH_3
C. CN D. Cl_2

2. Match the enzymes in Group I with their appropriate role in the environment from Group II

Group I	Group II
(*a*) Laccase	(*i*) Xenobiotic detoxification
(*b*) Catalse	(*ii*) Nitrogen fixation
(*c*) Nitrogenase	(*iii*) Lignin degradation
(*d*) Cytochrome P_{450}	(*iv*) Neutralization of toxic O_2 species

	(*a*)	(*b*)	(*c*)	(*d*)
A.	(*iii*)	(*iv*)	(*ii*)	(*i*)
B.	(*i*)	(*iii*)	(*ii*)	(*iv*)
C.	(*iv*)	(*i*)	(*iii*)	(*ii*)
D.	(*iii*)	(*ii*)	(*iv*)	(*i*)

3. Founder effects and bottlenecks are:

A. expected only in large populations
B. mechanisms that increase genetic variation in a population
C. two different modes of natural selection
D. forms of genetic drift

4. Heavy metal pollutants like Cd and Hg inactivate enzymes by interacting with:

A. cysteine B. glutamic acid
C. lysine D. histidine

5. Which of the following class of enzymes initiates aerobic degradation of aromatic pollutants (like naphthalene) in bacteria?

A. Oxido-reductases B. Hydrolases
C. Ligases D. Lyases.

6. The only naturally transformable marine cyanobacteria is:

A. *Agmenellum* sp. B. *Spirulina* sp.
C. *Oscillatoria* sp. D. *Nostoc* sp.

7. Marine chemosynthesis is mainly based on:

A. Oxygen B. Carbon dioxide
C. Sulphate D. Manganese nodules

8. Which one is a DNA replication blocking agent produced by sponges?

A. Clathesine B. Spongosides
C. Spongin D. Scleorin

9. Eutrophication in aquatic ecosystems is due to reduction of:

A. Carbon B. Oxygen
C. Sulphur D. Hydrogen

10. Halotolerant and halophilic microbes can be isolated from ——— and, respectively.

(*a*) Sea (*b*) River
(*c*) Lake (*d*) Estuary

A. (*d*) and (*a*) B. (*a*) and (*d*)
C. (*b*) and (*a*) D. (*c*) and (*d*)

11. Which one of the following organisms is NOT able to perform light harvesting reaction?
A. Azospirillum
B. Chlamydomonas
C. Rhodopseudomonas
D. Halobacterium

12. In the soil environment, which one of the following factors is responsible for the biotic stress on the microbial community?
A. Nutrients
B. Oxidation-reduction potential
C. Moisture
D. Microflora

DBT-JRF, 2018

13. A wastewater sample has COD of 1 g/L of which 80% is the BOD. During partial aerobic oxidation only 200 mg of COD was converted to CO2 and H2O. The remaining BOD (mg/L) is:
A. 800 B. 200
C. 600 D. 1000

14. In an air sample, 12% particulate matter is of around 25 nm size, 35% around 10 nm, 30% around 5 nm and remaining are 2.5 nm or smaller. The respiratory particulate matter in this sample is:
A. 53% B. 65%
C. 47% D. 23%

15. β-Glucans protect aquaculture organisms from various pathogenic strains because they:
A. resembles aminoglycoside antibiotics and cause misreading of pathogenic mRNA.
B. enhances immune response and promote growth of prebiotic gut bacteria in aquaculture organism.
C. adsorbs phosphorous and nitrogen from water hampering further proliferation of pathogen strain.
D. are degraded by pathogenic strains to form toxic intermediates.

16. Dead zones in oceans refer to:
A. Mariana trench, the deepest part of ocean where living organisms have not been found
B. Hydrothermal vents that have extreme temperatures
C. neritic zone at that are extremely end of continental shelf that is devoid of sunlight
D. oceanic regions that are extremely hypoxic due to substantial eutrophication.

17. From the table below, match the pellagic zones with their respective depths and choose the correct option:

Ocean Zone	Depth
(*a*) Mesopelagic	(*i*) >4000 to <6000m
(*b*) Bathypelagic	(*ii*) <6000m
(*c*) Abyssopelagic	(*iii*) >200 to <1000m
(*d*) Hadopelagic	(*iv*) >1000 to <4000m

	(*a*)	(*b*)	(*c*)	(*d*)
A.	(*ii*)	(*i*)	(*iii*)	(*iv*)
B.	(*i*)	(*ii*)	(*iv*)	(*iii*)
C.	(*iv*)	(*iii*)	(*ii*)	(*i*)
D.	(*iii*)	(*iv*)	(*i*)	(*ii*)

DBT-JRF, 2019

18. Which one of the following materials is a bioplastic?
A. Polypropylene
B. Alginate
C. Polyhydroxybutyrate
D. Dextran

19. Paralytic shellfish poisoning is a foodborne illness that typically develops after consumption of shellfish contaminated chiefly with the heat stable and acid stable toxin:
A. Okadaic acid B. Mitotoxin
C. Saxitoxin D. Aflatoxin

20. The antifreeze molecules that prevent intracellular ice formation in marine organisms are generally:
A. calcium salts
B. glycoproteins
C. membrane phospholipids
D. long-chain alcohols

21. Ballast water may be carried onboard by ships to maintain stability and improve maneuverability during transit. Introduction of which one of the following is regarded as the major threat in release of untreated ballast water?
A. pathogenic microbes
B. terrestrial inputs of pollutants
C. invasive marine species
D. algal blooms

22. Remote sensing of ocean-atmospheric parameters carried out in the microwave channels is based on the phenomenon of:
A. emission B. reflection
C. scattering D. diffraction

23. A starch containing wastewater sample with high BOD, $CaCl_2$ and NH_4NO_3 was subjected to aerobic oxidation using a designed bacterial consortium. The oxidised product(s) will have:

A. Cl_2, N_2, O_2, and CO_2
B. Cl_2, N_2, and O_2
C. O_2 and CO_2
D. CO_2

24. A wastewater has BOD of 1500 mg/L and COD of 2400 mg/L. Assuming 80% treatment efficiency in an activated sludge bioreactor, the BOD/COD ratio of treated effluent will be:
A. 0.25 B. 0.50
C. 0.625 D. 0.78

25. A slaughter house waste was subjected to anaerobic digestion. If the operation conditions are mesophilic then the biogas will have only:
A. H_2S, H_2, CH_4, and CO_2
B. H_2S, CH_4, and CO_2
C. CH_4, and CO_2
D. CH_4

26. A pilot plant treating organic waste in aerobic and continuous mode was running with a constant organic load. It was observed that after three days, the Dissolved Oxygen level had increased from 3mg/L to 4.5mg/L under the same operating conditions. This suggests that:
A. treatment system running efficiently
B. treatment system not running efficiently
C. treatment system not getting affected
D. activated biomass generating oxygen

DBT-JRF, 2020

27. 5th June is observed as
A. World Forest Day
B. World pollution Day
C. World Wildlife Day
D. World Environment Day

28. A major organism used in commercial bioleaching for copper recovery is
A. Thiobacillus ferrooxidans
B. Desulfovibrio desulfuricans
C. Pseudomonas aeruginosa
D. Aspergillus niger

29. Which of the following is NOT used as a biopesticide
A. Nuclear Polyhedrosis Virus
B. Bacillus thuringiensis
C. Trichoderma harzianum
D. Xanthomonas campestris

30. Wetlands are very rich and diverse ecosystems and must be preserved. Which convention signed in Iran protects this specific ecosystem (wetlands) on a global basis?
A. Ramsar Convention
B. Vienna Convention
C. Geneva Convention
D. Basel Convention

31. Which of the following is a chemotherapeutic drug obtained from marine source?
A. adriamycin B. avastin
C. trabectedin D. abraxane

32. Which of the following marine phototrophs can utilise carbon-dioxide as the carbon source?
A. Green sulfur bacteria
B. Halobacteria
C. Chloroacidobacteria
D. Hellobacteria

33. To maintain soil fertility, the most sustainable agricultural practice is
A. crop rotation
B. burning the crop waste in the field
C. repeated use of fertilizers
D. growing same crop

CSIR-NET, JUNE (MORNING), 2021

Industrially Important Microorganism

34. Given below are some terms and concepts related to phytoremediation in column A and column B

Column A	Column B
(*a*) Excluders	(*i*) Can absorb and transfer heavy metals to aerial parts without phytotoxicity symptoms
(*b*) Heavy metal protein transporter	(*ii*) Salix sp. and Populus sp.
(*c*) Hyperaccumulators	(*iii*) Transgenesis
(*d*) High biomass, non-accumulators	(*iv*) Can restrict heavy metal ions to the roots and detoxify them.

Which one of the following options represents the most appropriate match of all terms/concepts in column A and B?

	(*a*)	(*b*)	(*c*)	(*d*)
A.	(*ii*)	(*iv*)	(*ii*)	(*iii*)
B.	(*iii*)	(*iv*)	(*ii*)	(*i*)
C.	(*ii*)	(*iii*)	(*iv*)	(*i*)
D.	(*iv*)	(*iii*)	(*i*)	(*ii*)

DBT-JRF, 2021

35. Given below are two statements:

Statement I: Humans mainly obtain DHA and EPA by consuming fish whereas fish in turn obtain PUFAs from microalgae.

Statement II: Microalgae derived DHA and EPA can be used as a supplement for people who do not consume fish and seafood.

In light of the above statements, choose the most appropriate answer from the options given below:

A. Both Statement I and II are correct
B. Both Statement I and II are incorrect
C. Statement I is correct but statement II is incorrect
D. Statement I is incorrect but statement II is correct

36. The suitable method for treatment of municipal waste water and aqueous hazardous waste, which have less than 1% of suspended solids is:

A. Activated sludge process
B. Bioreactors
C. Lagoons & ponds
D. Trickling filter

37. Common indicators of water pollution with enteropathogens are following EXCEPT:

A. Bacillus spp
B. Clostridium spp
C. E.coli
D. Streptococcus spp.

38. "Dysbiosis" is a term associated with:

A. Genome
B. Metabolome
C. Microbiome
D. Proteome

39. Strong adhesives can be prepared using the constituents of one of the following:

A. Base of sea anemone
B. Byssus generated by sea mussel
C. Platform generated by sea urchin
D. Tentacles of hydra

40. Given below are two statements:

Statement I: Xenobiotic pollutants are biomagnified and accumulate in marine organisms.

Statement II: Pollutants can be quantified in tissue samples from key marine animals living in the environment where pollution monitoring is in place.

In light of the above statements, choose the most appropriate answer from the options given below:

A. Both Statement I and II are correct
B. Both Statement I and II are incorrect
C. Statement I is correct but statement II is incorrect
D. Statement I is incorrect but statement II is correct

41. Match the components of List I with List II

Choose the correct answer from the options given below:

List I	List II
(*a*) Chitolytic enzyme	(*i*) Digestive tract of fish, shellfish, squiad live, octopus saliva
(*b*) Gastric proteases	(*ii*) Pyloric ceca, pancreatic tissue, intestine of Sardine, cod and salmon.
(*c*) Polyphenol oxidases	(*iii*) Fish viscera from fishery source
(*d*) Serine and cysteine proteases	(*iv*) Crustaceans

	(*a*)	(*b*)	(*c*)	(*d*)
A.	(*i*)	(*ii*)	(*iii*)	(*iv*)
B.	(*i*)	(*iii*)	(*iv*)	(*ii*)
C.	(*ii*)	(*iii*)	(*iv*)	(*i*)
D.	(*iv*)	(*iii*)	(*ii*)	(*i*)

42. Spirulina is considered as a super food for human consumption because it contains:

A. All dietary phytochemicals
B. All essential amino acids vitamins and fatty acids
C. All known proteins, carbohydrates and lipids
D. No heavy metals or antinutritive compounds

CSIR-NET, SEPTEMBER (MORNING), 2022

43. The product of nahG gene of *Pseudomonas putida* catalyzes the metabolism of salicylic acid to which on compounds?

A. Benzoic acid
B. Methyl salicylate
C. Catechol
D. Benzoyl-CoA

44. In remote sensing, which one of the following formulae is used for the calculation of normalized difference (NDVI)?

A. RED / (NIR + RED)
B. RED / (NIR – RED)
C. (NIR + RED) / (NIR – RED)
D. (NIR – RED) / (NIR + RED

CSIR-NET, SEPTEMBER (AFTERNOON), 2022

45. Diclofenac toxicity has been suggested to be the cause for population decline in which one of the following animals?
A. Gyps vultures
B. Olive Ridley turtles
C. Honey bees
D. Oceanic sharks

46. Bioaugmentation refers to:
A. Developing microbial strains through genetic engineering which can degrade pollutants and toxic compounds efficiently.
B. Ex- situ bioremediation of toxins from soil or any other contaminant site by addition of selected microbes to enhance biodegradation.
C. Addition of nutrients at contaminated sites to enhance growth of indigenous microflora which will in turn degrade pollutants.
D. Addition of selected microbes both archaea and bacteria to the polluted site so that biodegradation is enhanced.

47. Which one of the following countries has contributed the maximum towards CO_2 emissions over the last decade?
A. India B. USA
C. China D. Russia

48. The table below lists terms used in bioremediation (column X) and explanations for the terms (column Y).

Column X	Column Y
(*a*) Bioventing	(*i*) Indigenous level of containment degradation without any treatment
(*b*) Natural attenuation	(*ii*) It is a technique of adding oxygen to the saturated zone below water table to stimulate degradation
(*c*) Air spraying	(*iii*) It is a technique to add oxygen directly to a site of contamination in an unsaturated zone which stimulates in situ aerobic degradation
(*d*) Biosimulaton	(*iv*) Modification of environmental conditional by adding nutrients to enhance biodegradation process

Which one of the following options is a correct match between terms in column X and explanations in column Y?

	(*a*)	(*b*)	(*c*)	(*d*)
A.	(*iii*)	(*i*)	(*iv*)	(*ii*)
B.	(*iv*)	(*iii*)	(*i*)	(*ii*)
C.	(*iii*)	(*iv*)	(*ii*)	(*i*)
D.	(*iii*)	(*i*)	(*ii*)	(*iv*)

49. The Montreal Protocol and its subsequent amendments have resulted in reduced ozon depletion. It is also observed that ozone depletion over the South Pole is much more severe than over the North Pole. In this regard, consider the following statements.
(*a*) A polar vortex is formed around the North Pole.
(*b*) Stratospheric temperatures over the South Pole are much lower compared to the North Pole.
(*c*) Emissions of ozone depleting substances are higher in the southern hemisphere compared to northern hemisphere.
(*d*) More extensive formation of polar stratospheric clouds over the South Pole compared to the North Pole.

Select the option which includes the correct combination of statements that explain the difference in the ozone depletion between the poles.
A. (*a*) and (*d*)
B. (*b*) and (*d*)
C. (*b*) and (*c*)
D. (*a*) and (*c*)

DBT-JRF, 2022

50. Arrange these soluble cations (Na, Ca, K, Mg) in ascending order of abundance of soluble cations found in saline water bodies:
A. Na > Mg > Ca > K B. Mg > Na > Ca > K
C. K > Mg > Ca > Na D. Na > Mg > K > Ca

51. In a water sample collected from an industrial cluster, the ratio of BOD:COD is found to be less than 0.3. Which one of the following may be presumed from this initial data?
A. There are numerous carbon-based compounds in the sample which are not utilizable by the microbial population
B. The microbial population efficiently utilizes all the organic compounds present in the sample

C. The water sample may contain carbohydrates that promote microbial growth
D. The sample contains lipids and fatty acids which require less oxygen for breakdown

52. Which one of the following is NOT extracted from seaweeds:
A. Agar B. Alginate
C. Calcium D. Aginomoto

53. For Bingham Plastics and pseudo plastic liquids, the apparent viscosity:
A. Increases with increase in shear force
B. Decreases with increase in shear force
C. Remains constant with increase in shear force
D. Changes in an unpredictable fashion with change in shear force

54. Which one of the following method can be used to treat crude sewage and nitrify secondary effluent?
A. Duck weed ponds B. Reed beds
C. Algal fish ponds D. Water hyacinth ponds

55. Which one of the following process is NOT used to convert the hydrocarbons present in the organic compounds to central metabolic intermediates?
A. Hydration
B. Extraction
C. Nitroreduction
D. Reductive dihydroxylation

56. Given below are two statements:
Statement I: Fungi are important degraders of polymers and are used in the composting and biodegradation of toxic organic substances.
Statement II: Fungi are able to selectively excrete toxins present in these polymers.
In the light of the above statements, choose the correct answer from the options given below:
A. Both Statement I and Statement II are true
B. Both Statement I and Statement II are false
C. Statement I is true but Statement II is false
D. Statement I is false but Statement II is true

GATE (BIOTECHNOLOGY), 2022

57. Match the microbial product (Column I) with its respective application (Column II).

Column I	Column II
(*a*) Methane	(*i*) Biosurfactant
(*b*) Glycolipids	(*ii*) Bioplastic
(*c*) Polyhydroxy alkanoate	(*iii*) Biofuel

	(*a*)	(*b*)	(*c*)
A.	(*i*)	(*ii*)	(*iii*)
B.	(*ii*)	(*i*)	(*iii*)
C.	(*iii*)	(*ii*)	(*i*)
D.	(*iii*)	(*i*)	(*ii*)

ANSWERS

1	2	3	4	5	6	7	8	9	10
B	A	D	A	A	A	B	B	B	A
11	**12**	**13**	**14**	**15**	**16**	**17**	**18**	**19**	**20**
A	D	C	D	B	D	D	C	C	B
21	**22**	**23**	**24**	**25**	**26**	**27**	**28**	**29**	**30**
C	A	D	A	A	B	D	A	D	A
31	**32**	**33**	**34**	**35**	**36**	**37**	**38**	**39**	**40**
C	A	A	D	A	A	A	C	B	A
41	**42**	**43**	**44**	**45**	**46**	**47**	**48**	**49**	**50**
B	B	C	D	A	D	C	D	B	A
51	**52**	**53**	**54**	**55**	**56**	**57**			
A	C	B	B	B	C	D			

CHAPTER

13

DEVELOPMENTAL BIOLOGY

CSIR-NET, JUNE, 2017

Basic Concepts of Development

1. Inward movement of an expanding outer layer spreading over the internal surface during gastrulation is termed as

A. invagination B. Ingression
C. involution D. delamination

2. Which kind of cleavage is shown in mammals?

A. Holoblastic rotational
B. Meroblastic rotational
C. Holobastic radial
D. Meroblastic radial

Morphogenesis and Organogenesis in Animals

3. The dorsal-most vegetal cells of the amphibian embryo that is capable of inducing the organizer is called as Nieuwkoop centre and is marked by the presence of

A. Chordin B. β-catenin
C. Goosecoid D. Nanos

4. When the 4 blastomere pairs of the 8-cell stage tunicate embryo are dissociated, each forms most of the structures it would have formed had it remained in the embryo. However, the notochord and nervous system get specified only if different blastomeres get the chance to interact. Given below are certain interpretations formulated from the above results:

(*a*) Each pair of blastomeres forming respective structures indicate autonomous specification
(*b*) Each pair of blastomeres forming respective structures indicate conditional specification
(*c*) The notochord and nervous system development indicate autonomous specification
(*d*) The notochord and nervous system development indicate conditional specification.

Which combination of interpretations is most appropriate?

A. (*a*) and (*c*) B. (*b*) and (*d*)
C. (*a*) and (*d*) D. (*b*) and (*c*)

5. The presence of β-catenin in the nuclei of blastomeres in the dorsal portion of the amphibian embryo is one of the determinants for laying down the dorso-ventral axis. What will be' the outcome of expressing a dominant negative form of GSK3 in the ventral cells of early embryo?

A. The dorsal cells will be ventralized
B. A second axis will be formed
C. The primary organizer will not be formed
D. The embryo will develop normally

6. Injection of Noggin mRNA in cells that will become the future ventral side of a frog embryo mimics the effect of an organizer graft to the ventral side. This experiment demonstrates that

(*a*) Noggin is a transcription factor
(*b*) Noggin induces ventral fates
(*c*) Noggin is involved in organizer fate
(*d*) Noggin is required to induce a secondary axis

Which one of the following options represents correct combination of statement/s?

A. (*a*) and (*c*) B. (*c*) and (*d*)
C. (*a*) and (*b*) D. (*b*) and (*c*)

7. In the following columns, certain terms and their descriptions are given in random order.

Column I	Column-II
(*a*) Protostome	(*i*) A fluid filled cavity lying inside the external body wall bathing the internal organs
(*b*) Deuterostome	(*ii*) Mouth forming from the blastopore
(*c*) Pseudocoely	(*iii*) Coelom formed by splitting the mesodermal tissue
(*d*) Schizocoely	(*iv*) Mouth forming from a second opening other than blastopore
(*e*) Enterocoely	(*v*) Coelom formed from pouches pinched off from the digestive tract

Which of the following combination gives correct match for the terms in column I from column II?

	(*a*)	(*b*)	(*c*)	(*d*)	(*e*)
A.	(*i*)	(*ii*)	(*iii*)	(*iv*)	(*v*)
B.	(*ii*)	(*iv*)	(*i*)	(*v*)	(*iii*)
C.	(*iv*)	(*ii*)	(*iv*)	(*i*)	(*iii*)
D.	(*ii*)	(*iv*)	(*i*)	(*iii*)	(*v*)

Morphogenesis and Organogenesis in Plants

8. During embryo germination in a grass family an absorptive organ that forms interface between the embryo and the starchy endosperm tissue is called

A. Coleorhiza B. Coleoptile
C. Scutellum D. Mesocotyl

9. Extensive molecular genetic studies on miR156, miR172, SPL genes and AP2- like genes have yielded the following functional model on the juvenile adult reproductive transition in Arabidopsis:

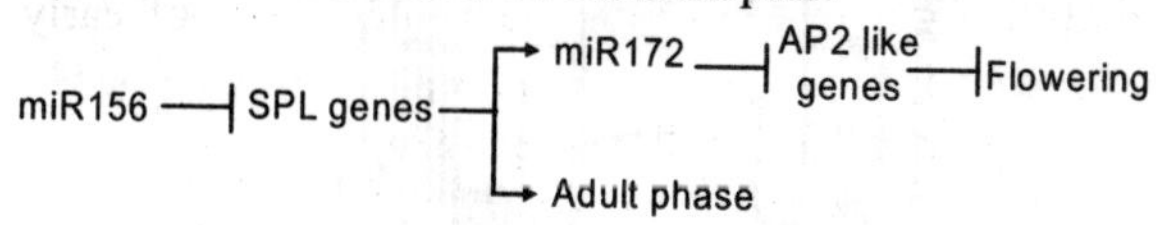

Based on these results, the following schematic diagram has been proposed to predict the expression kinetics of these genetic factors:

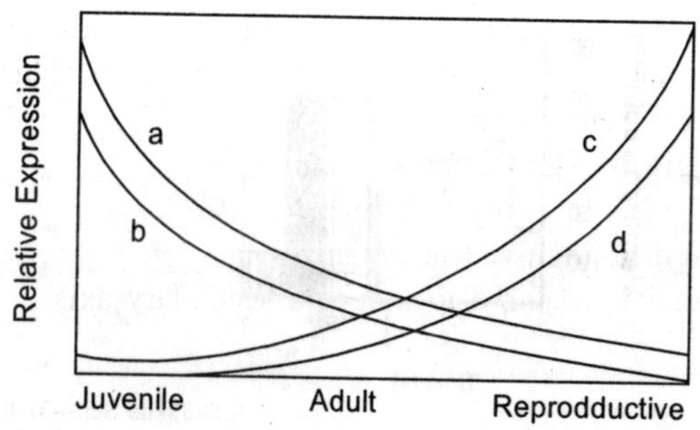

Which of the following combinations is most likely to be correct?

A. a-miR156; b-SPL genes; c -miR172; d - AP2 like genes
B. a-miR156; b-miR172; c-:-SPL genes; d - AP2 like genes
C. a-miR 172; b-SPL genes; c-AP2 like genes; d-miR156
D. a-miR156; b-AP2 like genes; c. miR172; d-SPL genes

10. Consider the following facts regarding the control of shoot apical meristem (SAM) size in Arabidopsis

(*a*) Loss of the CLAVATA1 (CLV1) gene leads to bigger SAM
(*b*) Loss of the CLAVATA3 (CLV3) gene leads to bigger SAM
(*c*) Loss of the WUSCHEL (WUS) gene leads to smaller SAM
(*d*) Loss of both CLV1 and WUS leads to smaller SAM
(*e*) Loss of both CLV3 and WUS leads to smaller SAM
(*f*) Loss of both CLV1 and CLV3 leads to bigger SAM
(*g*) Over expression of CLV3 leads to smaller SAM
(*h*) Over expression of CLV3 in the loss of function mutant of CLV1 leads to bigger SAM.

Based on the above information, which of the following genetic pathways describes the relationship among CLV1, CLV3 and WUS most appropriately?

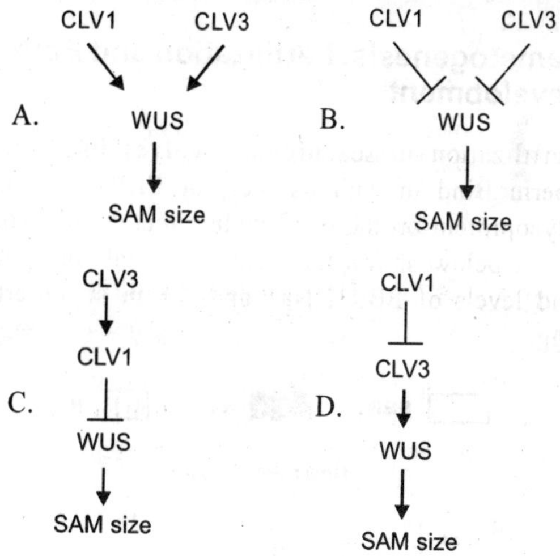

Developmental Gene Regulation in Drosophila

11. In *Drosophila melanogaster* males, homologous chromosomes pair and segregate during meiosis but crossing over does not occur. At which stage of meiosis does segregation of 2 alleles of a gene take place in these individuals?

A. Zygotene B. Diakinesis
C. Anaphase I D. Anaphase II

Apoptosis, Aging and Senescence

12. Following are list of some proteins

(*a*) BCL-2 (*b*) BCL-XL
(*c*) A1 (*d*) BAX

Which of the protein(s) is/are NOT anti-apoptotic?

A. (*d*) Only B. (*c*) only
C. (*a*) and (*b*) only D. (*b*) and (*d*) only

13. Given below is a list of some proteins known to be associated with apoptosis, their sub-cellular localization (but not in correct order) and possible role in apoptosis.

Proteins	Localisation	Role in apoptosis
(*a*) Effector caspase	A. Cytosol	(*i*) Promotes
(*b*) Apaf-1	B. Cytosol mitochondria	(*ii*) Inhibits
(*c*) Bax	C. Cytosol nucleus	

Choose the right combination which matches the proteins with their correct localization and role in apoptosis.

	(*a*)	(*b*)	(*c*)
A.	A-(*ii*)	B-(*ii*)	C-(*i*)
B.	C-(*i*)	A-(*ii*)	B-(*ii*)
C.	B-(*i*)	C-(*ii*)	A-(*i*)
D.	C-(*i*)	A-(*i*)	B-(*i*)

14. Antennapedia complex in Drosophila contains five genes, *lab, pb, dfd, scr* and *Antp* and they express in parasegments 1 to 5, respectively in a non-overlapping manner. In the larva or in later stages of development, the region of *Antp* (Antennapedia) expression corresponds to a part of second thoracic segment.

A mutation in *Antp* is known to cause transformation of antenna to leg-like structures. Below are certain statements made in respect to the functions of Antennapedia:

(*a*) In the above described *Antp* mutation, the gene ectopically expresses in the head region
(*b*) One of the functions of *Antp* is torepress genes that induce antenna development
(*c*) *Antp* expresses in thorax and forms a concentration gradient in the posterior-anterior direction, thus affecting head development
(*d*) A homozygous recessive mutation of *Antp* is expected to transform the leg to antenna in the second thoracic segment.

Which combination of the above statements correctly describes the function of Antennapedia?

A. (*a*), (*b*) and (*c*) B. (*b*) and (*c*)
C. (*c*) and (*d*) D. (*a*), (*b*) and (*d*)

CSIR-NET, DECEMBER, 2017

Gametogenesis, Fertilization and Early Development

15. Fertilization in sea urchin involves interaction of sperm Bind in with its receptor EBR1, a 350 kDa glycoprotein on the egg vitelline membrane. The plot given below shows the status of membrane potential and levels of EBR1, Na+ and K+ in an unfertilized egg.

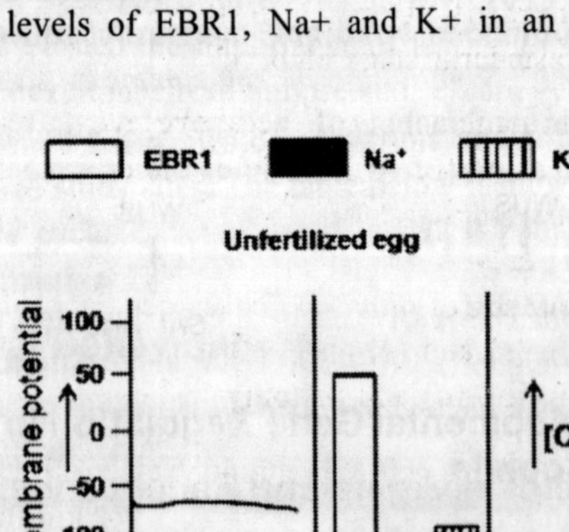

Which one of the following graphs best represents the condition within an egg 1-3 seconds after fertilization?

A.

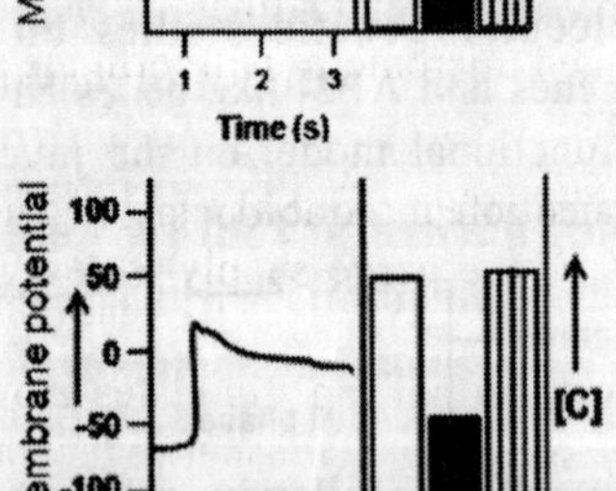

B.

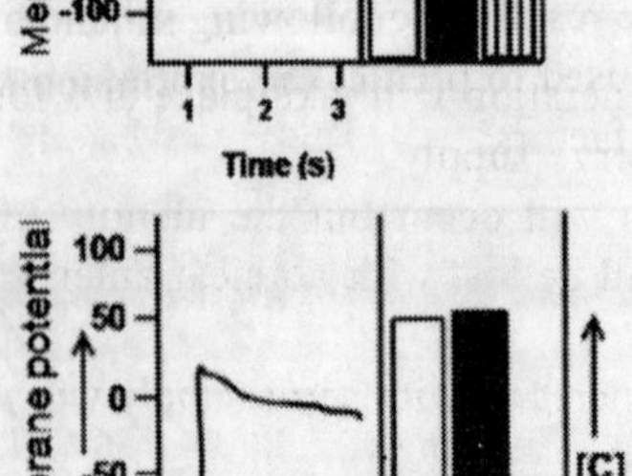

C.

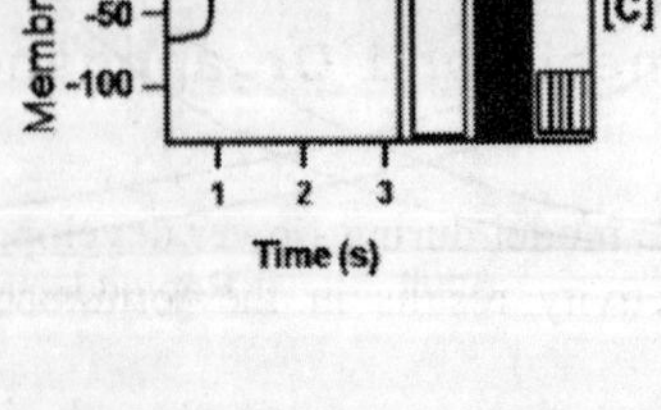

D. 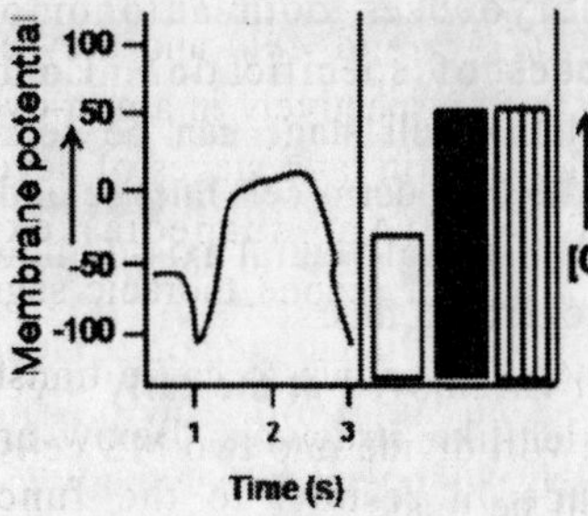

Morphogenesis and Organogenesis in Animals

16. Which one of the following statements regarding limb development in mice is true?

A. The gene encoding Tbx5 is transcribed in the limb fields of the hindlimbs.
B. The gene encoding Tbx4 is transcribed in the limb fields of the forelimbs.
C. Genes encoding Islet 1, Tbx4 and Pitx are expressed in the presumptive hindlimb.
D. Genes encoding Islet 1, Tbx4 and Pitx are expressed in the presumptive forelimb.

17. In a given experiment, transplantation of micromeres from the vegetal pole of a 16-cell sea urchin embryo onto the animal pole of a host 16-cell sea urchin embryo would initiate:

A. the transplanted micromeres to invaginate into the blastocoel to create a new set of skeletogenic mesenchyme cells
B. the transplanted micromeres to ingress into the blastocoel to create a new set of skeletogenic mesenchymal cells
C. the transplanted micromeres will mingle with the host micromeres to ingress into the blastocoel to create skeletogenic mesenchyme cells.
D. the transplanted micromeres will form the secondary archenteron.

18. What would be the effect on newt limb regeneration, if more than 90% of the nerve supply is severed before amputation?

A. The apical ectodermal cap stimulates growth of the blastema by secreting FGF8 but regeneration does not take place.
B. Limb regeneration will take place and form a limb with no nerve supply.
C. Outgrowth will occur but the identity of the limb formed will be lost with no clear anterior-posterior polarity.
D. Limb regeneration with nerve supply will take place.

Morphogenesis and Organogenesis in Plants

19. Based on ABC model during flower development, loss of class A activity results in the formation of only stamen and carpel. Which of the following floral organ identity genes controls the class A activity?

A. APETALA 1 and APETALA 2
B. APETALA 3 and PISTILLATA
C. Only PISTILLATA
D. Only AGAMOUS

20. A specific Mitogen Activated Protein Kinase (MAPK) cascade comprising MEKK1(a MAP3K), MKK1 (a MAP2K) and MPK6 (a MAPK) is activated sequentially in that order in Arabidopsis plants upon perceiving certain abiotic stress stimuli. The activated MPK6 phosphorylates and activates a transcription factor 'X', thereby making plant tolerant to the abiotic stress. Two different variants of MKK1 protein, a kinase inactive (KI) and a constitutively active (CA) forms were expressed independently in *mkk1* mutant Arabidopsis plant. Considering above facts, which one of the following statements is CORRECT?

A. 'X' will be activated even in the absence of stimuli in CA plants
B. 'X' will not be activated in the absence of stimuli in CA plants
C. 'X' will be activated in the absence of stimuli in KI plants
D. The KI plants will be tolerant to the abiotic stress

Developmental Gene Regulation in Drosophila

21. Following are the events that might take place during dorso-ventral axis specification in early embryonic development of *Drosophil*

(*a*) 'Torpedo' receptor activation
(*b*) 'Pipe' synthesis
(*c*) A cascade of protease activity
(*d*) 'Cactus' dephosphorylation
(*e*) Entry of 'Dorsal' in the nuclei of syncytial blastoderm stage embryo.

Which combination of the above events will occur in the presumptive dorsal side of the embryo deficient in maternal *gurken*?

A. (*a*) only
B. (*b*) and (*c*) only
C. (*b*), (*c*) and (*e*) only
D. (*b*), (*c*), (*d*) and (*e*) only

Apoptosis, Aging and Senescence

22. During vulva development in *C. elegans*, the anchor cell produces Lin-3 protein which interacts with the Let-23 protein present on the six vulval precursor cells (VPCs) that form an equivalence group. The central lineage cell (P6.p) adopts the primary fate, the adjacent VPCs (P5.p and P7.p) adopt the secondary fate and the rest VPCs adopt the tertiary fate. Few mutants

(Column A) and phenotypes (Column B) are listed in the table given below.

Column A	Column B
(*a*) Loss of function of *lin-3*	(*i*) P5.p, P6.p and P7.p adopt primary fate, P4.p and P8.p adopt secondary fate
(*b*) Loss of function of *lin-3* and gain of function of *let-23*	(*ii*) Multivulva
(*c*) Reduced function of *lin-3*	(*iii*) P6.p adopt primary fate and the rest of the VPCs adopt tertiary fate
(*d*) Overexpression of *lin-3*	(*iv*) All VPCs adopt tertiary

Match the correct mutant with the observed phenotype.

	(*a*)	(*b*)	(*c*)	(*d*)
A.	(*iv*)	(*ii*)	(*iii*)	(*i*)
B.	(*iv*)	(*iii*)	(*i*)	(*ii*)
C.	(*ii*)	(*iii*)	(*iv*)	(*i*)
D.	(*iii*)	(*i*)	(*ii*)	(*iv*)

23. *C. elegans* embryo uses both autonomous and conditional modes of specification. Conditional specification at the 4-cell stage can be seen in the development of the endoderm cell lineage and also in the establishment of dorsal-ventral axis. Following are few statements regarding this:

(*a*) If the P2 cell is removed at the early 4-cell stage, the EMS cell will divide into two MS cells and no endoderm will be made.

(*b*) In *pop-1* deficient embryos, both EMS daughter cells become E cells.

(*c*) When the position of ABa and ABp was reversed, their fates get reversed and no normal embryo forms.

(*d*) In embryos whose mother has mutant *glp-1*, ABp is transformed into ABa cell.

Which of the above statements are true?

A. (*a*), (*b*) and (*d*)
B. (*a*), (*b*) and (*c*)
C. (*b*), (*c*) and (*d*)
D. (*a*), (*c*) and (*d*)

DBT-JRF, 2017

24. Mutation of homeotic genes often result in which one of the following developmental defects in Drosophila?

A. Absence of a group of contiguous segments
B. Transformation of one segment to another
C. Tumor formation in imaginal discs
D. Absence of every other segment along the antero-posterior axis.

GATE (LIFE SCIENCE), 2017

Development Biology

25. MATCH the signalling pathways in Group I with their functions in Group II, during the process of development

Group I	Group II
(*a*) Hedgehog signaling	(*i*) Involve in signalling at 4-cell embryo stage in C. elegans through *glp 1* expression.
(*b*) Hox protein	(*ii*) Involves frizzeled receptor on target cell membrane and establish polarity in insects.
(*c*) Wnt signaling	(*iii*) Play critical role in facial morphogenesis in vertebrates and its mutation causes cyclopia
(*d*) Notch signaling	(*iv*) Required for T-bx transcription for vertebrate limb development.

	(*a*)	(*b*)	(*c*)	(*d*)
A.	(*iii*)	(*ii*)	(*iv*)	(*i*)
B.	(*iii*)	(*iv*)	(*ii*)	(*i*)
C.	(*iv*)	(*iii*)	(*ii*)	(*i*)
D.	(*iii*)	(*iv*)	(*i*)	(*ii*)

CSIR-NET, JUNE, 2018

Gametogenesis, Fertilization and Early Development

26. Fertilization in sea urchin eggs involves Ca^{2+} release from the endoplasmic reticulum for cortical granule reactivation. The major molecule responsible for releasing Ca^{2+} from intracellular stores is

A. zona pellucida glycoproteins
B. protamines
C. inositol 1, 4, 5-trisphosphate
D. N-acetylglucosaminidase

Morphogenesis and Organogenesis in Animals

27. Which one of the following statements with respect to amphibian development is correct?
A. The organizer is itself induced by the Nieuwkoop Centre located in the dorsal most mesodermal cells.
B. The organizer functions by secreting proteins like Noggin, Chordin and Follistatin that blocks BMP signal that would otherwise dorsalize the mesoderm.
C. In the presence of BMP activators the ectodermal cells form neural tissue.
D. Wnt signalling causes a gradient of β-catenin along the anterior-posterior axis of the neural tube that appears to specify the regionalization of the neural tube.

28. Eg5 is a well-studied protein in Xenopus. To understand the function of Eg5 in mammalian cells, a team of researchers treated mammalian cells during late G2 phase with Eg5-inhibitor. The following diagrams represent images of mitotic cells.

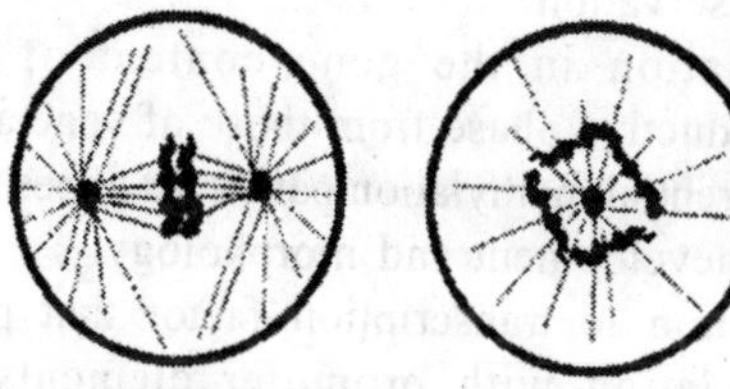

Based on the above observation, what function might be attributed to Eg5 during mitosis?
A. Eg5 inhibits actin dynamics.
B. Eg5 can activate GPCR signalling.
C. Eg5 has motor activity.
D. Eg5 can impact mitochondrial dynamics.

29. Following statements were made regarding vulval development in *Caenorhabditis elegans*:
(*a*) The six vulval precursor cells (VPCs) are influenced by the anchor cell to form an equivalence group.
(*b*) In the loss of function lin-12 mutants, both cells become uterine whereas in gain of function mutants, both become anchor cell.
(*c*) If the anchor cell is destroyed early in development, all the six VPCs divide once and contribute towards the formation of hypodermal cells.
(*d*) The anchor cell/ventral uterine precursor decision is due to Notch-Delta mediated mechanism of restricting adjacent cell fates.
(*e*) The paracrine factor secreted by the anchor cell directly activates the Notch-delta pathway.

Which one of the following options represents a combination of correct statements?
A. (*a*), (*c*) and (*d*) B. (*a*), (*b*) and (*d*)
C. (*c*), (*d*) and (*e*) D. (*b*), (*d*) and (*e*)

30. Given below are few statements regarding the role of Disheveled (Dsh) and β-catenin (β-cat) in the development of sea urchin.
(*a*) Dsh is localized in the vegetal cortex of the oocyte before fertilization and in the region of the 16-cell embryo about to become the micromeres.
(*b*) Dsh is localized in the cytosol of the oocyte during oogenesis and in the micromere forming blastomeres of a 16-cell embryo.
(*c*) β-cat accumulates predominantly in the micromeres and somewhat in the veg2 tier cells.
(*d*) Treatment of embryos with lithium chloride does not allow the accumulation of β-cat in the nuclei of all blastula cells, and the animal cells thus become specified as endoderm and mesoderm.
(*e*) When β-cat is prevented from entering the nucleus, the embryo develops as a ciliated ectodermal ball.

Which one of the following options represents a combination of correct statements?
A. (*b*), (*c*) and (*e*) B. (*a*), (*c*) and (*d*)
C. (*a*), (*c*) and (*e*) D. (*b*), (*d*) and (*e*)

31. Which one of the following statements regarding limb regeneration in Salamander is correct?
A. A normal limb is regenerated after amputation, irrespective of whether the cut was made below the elbow or through the humerus.
B. It occurs by compensatory regeneration and does not include formation of an apical ectodermal cap.
C. Regeneration occurs through formation of a blastema, which essentially consists of unspecified multipotential progenitor cells.
D. Proliferation of the blastema cells does not require nerves or factors secreted by the nerves.

32. cAMP signalling plays a very important role in the development of *Dictyostelium discoideum*. Below are few statements related to it.
(*a*) Every amoeba at the time of aggregation has the potential to make, receive and relay cAMA.
(*b*) acb- mutants develop normally but the spores formed appear glassy and arc unable to germinate.
(*c*) The spores formed by the acg- mutants germinate in the sorus itself.
(*d*) RegA is an extracellular phosphodiesterase.
(*e*) cAMP is continuously secreted in nanomolar amounts during aggregation.

Which combination of the above statements is correct?
A. (*a*) and (*d*) B. (*a*) and (*b*)
C. (*a*) and (*e*) D. (*b*) and (*d*)

33. Torpedo, is known to serve as a receptor for Gurken. Deficiencies of the *torpedo* gene in *Drosophila* cause ventralization of the embryo. In an experiment, the germ cell precursors from a wild type embryo were transplanted into embryos whose mother carried the *torpedo* mutation. Also, the reverse experiment, *i.e.*, transplantation of germ cell precursors from torpedo mutants into wild type embryos was done. The *torpedo* deficient germ cells developed in a wild type female showed normal dorso-ventral axis, while the wild type germ cells developed in a torpedo deficient female showed ventralized egg.

Some of the following statements are drawn from the above experiments and some from known facts to understand the functioning of Torpedo.

(*a*) Zygotic contribution of Torpedo is essential for the development of dorso- ventral axis.

(*b*) Maternal contribution of Torpedo is essential for the development of dorso- ventral axis.

(*c*) Since Torpedo is a receptor for Gurken and follicle cells surround the part of the oocyte where Gurken is expressed, it is likely that Torpedo is expressed in follicle cells.

(*d*) Gurken signalling initially dorsalizes the follicle cells, which in turn send signal to organize the dorso-ventral polarity in oocyte.

(*e*) Gurken signalling initially dorsalizes the nurse cells which help in generation of dorso-ventral polarity in oocyte.

Which one of the following combination of statements is most appropriate?

A. (*b*), (*c*) and (*d*) B. (*a*), (*c*) and (*d*)
C. (*b*), (*c*) and (*e*) D. (*a*), (*d*) and (*e*)

34. The figure below represents normal sex determination, differentiation and development in humans.

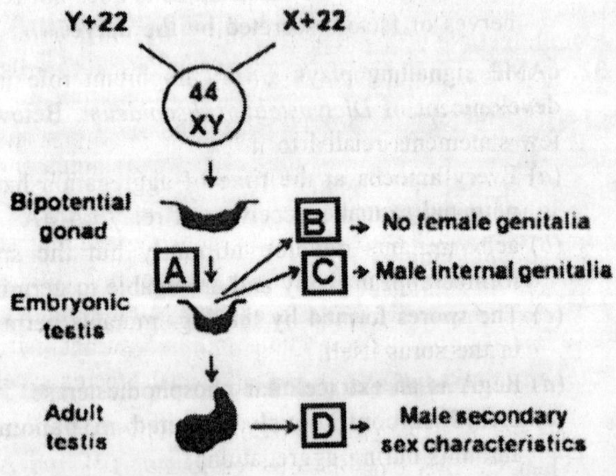

Identify A, B, C and D.

A. A = WTI (Wilm's Tumor 1), B = MIS (Mullerian Inhibitory Substance), C = SRY, D = Testosterone

B. A = GnRH, B = FSH, C = Testosterone, D = 5α Reductase

C. A = SRY, B = MIS, C = Testosterone, D = DHT (Dihydrotestosterone)

D. A = WT1, B = LH, C = ABP (Androgen Binding Protein), D = Inhibin

35. The following table shows names of bones (Column A) and specific features (Column B).

Column A	Column B
(*a*) Axis vertrebra	(*i*) Deltoid Ridge
(*b*) Humerus	(*ii*) Acromion Process
(*c*) Ulana	(*iii*) Odontoid process
(*d*) Pictorial girdle	(*iv*) Sigmoid Notch

Which one of the following options gives the correct match of the bones with their specific features?

	(*a*)	(*b*)	(*c*)	(*d*)
A.	(*iii*)	(*i*)	(*iv*)	(*ii*)
B.	(*ii*)	(*i*)	(*iii*)	(*iv*)
C.	(*iv*)	(*ii*)	(*i*)	(*iii*)
D.	(*i*)	(*iii*)	(*iv*)	(*ii*)

Morphogenesis and Organogenesis in Plants

36. Change in leaf morphology is observed during transition from vegetative to reproductive phase in several plants. The following statements are proposed to explain the above observation:

(*a*) Alteration in the gene content of leaves of reproductive phase from those of vegetative phase.

(*b*) Differential methylation pattern of genes influencing leaf development and morphology.

(*c*) Mutation in transcription factor that prevents its association with promoter elements of genes regulating leaf development.

(*d*) Small RNA mediated inhibition of gene expression of a homeotic gene.

Which one of the following options represents a correct combination of statements that could explain the observed changes?

A. (*b*) and (*c*) B. (*a*) and (*d*)
C. (*b*) and (*d*) D. (*a*) and (*c*)

Developmental Gene Regulation in Drosophila

37. What is the observed phenotype when the *ultrabithorax* gene is deleted in *Drosophila?*

A. The third thoracic segment is transformed into another second thoracic segment resulting in a fly with four wings.

B. Since it specifics the second thoracic segment, instead of antenna leg grows out of the head socket.

C. Since it specifies the third thoracic segment, a fly with two pairs of halters develop.

D. Since this gene fails to be expressed in the second thoracic segment, the antennae sprout in the leg position.

38. A virgin *Drosophila* female was crossed with a wild type male. The F1 progeny obtained had four types of males as shown below.

Phenotype	White eyed	Wild type	Cross veinless	White eyed and cross veinless
Number	50	3	44	3

Assuming that white eye and crossveinless mutations are X-linked and recessive, the following statements were made:

(*a*) F1 females were also of four types as that of males.

(*b*) The white eyed crossveinless male flies appeared due to independent assortment.

(*c*) The map distance between the genes for white eye and crossveinless is estimated to be 12 cM.

(*d*) The map distance between white eye and crossveinless is estimated to be 6 cM.

(*e*) All F1 females are expected to be wild type.

(*f*) The F1 wild type males appeared due to crossing over.

The combination with correct statements is:

A. (*c*), (*e*), (*f*) B. (*a*), (*b*), (*d*)
C. (*a*), (*d*), (*f*) D. (*b*), (*d*), (*e*)

Apoptosis, Aging and Senescence

39. Which one of the following statements related to components/features of senescence in plants is INCORRECT?

A. Programmed cell death in plants may generate functional cells or tissues.

B. Senescence can be induced by application of cytokinins and delayed by overexpression of salicylic acid.

C. Plants defective in autophagy demonstrate accelerated plant senescence.

D. Leaf senescence is regulated by NAC and WRKY genes families.

40. Which one of the following assay systems can specifically detect apoptotic cells?

A. Tetrazolium dye (MTT) based colorimetric assay
B. FITC-annexin V based FACS analysis
C. 51Cr release assay
D. Trypan blue exclusion assay

CSIR-NET, DECEMBER, 2018

Gametogenesis, Fertilization and Early Development

41. Human sperms are allowed to fertilize ova having non-functional ovastacin. The following possibilities may be of significance in the fusion of these gametes:

(*a*) The sperms will not fertilize ova.

(*b*) The sperms will bind and penetrate the zonapellucida but will not be able to fuse with ovum membrane.

(*c*) ZP2 will not be clipped by cortical granule protease.

(*d*) CD9 protein of egg membrane microvilli will not be able to interact with sperm membrane proteins in the absence of ovastacin.

(*e*) Polyspermy may occur frequently.

Which combination of statements represents the outcome of the above event?

A. (*a*) and (*b*) B. (*c*) and (*e*)
C. (*c*) and (*d*) D. (*b*) and (*c*)

Morphogenesis and Organogenesis in Animals

42. In case of Hydra, the major head inducer of the hypostome organizer is a set of Wnt proteins acting through the canonical β-catenin pathway. What would be the result, if a transgenic Hydra is made to globally mis-express the downstream Wnt effector β-catenin?

A. Ectopic buds will be formed all along the body axis and even on the top of the newly formed buds.

B. Ectopic tentacles form at all levels.

C. Both ectopic tentacles and buds would be formed along the body axis.

D. There would be no change observe

43. Temporal expression of N-cadherin is extremely important during early development of the mammalian embryos. Accordingly, which one of the following statements about N-cadherin is true?

A. Injection of N-cadherin antibodies just prior to condensation of mesenchymal cells will aid cartilage formation.

B. Presence of N-cadherin just prior to condensation will facilitate nodule formation and development of the limb skeleton.

C. The border between the nervous system and skin will form properly only if epidermal cells are experimentally made to express N-cadherin.

D. Expression of N-cadherin is redundant during separation of neural and epidermal precursor cells.

44. The zygote of *C. elegans* exhibits rotational cleavage. When the first two blastomeres formed (P1 and AB) are experimentally separated, the following outcomes may be possible:

(*a*) The P1 cell in isolation generates all the cells it would normally make, showing autonomous specification.

(*b*) The P1 cell in isolation generates all the cells it would normally make, showing conditional specification.

(c) The AB cell in isolation generates a small fraction of cell types it would normally make, showing conditional specification.
(d) The AB cell in isolation generates a small fraction of cell types it would normally make, showing autonomous specification.

Which one of the above combination of statements is true?

A. (a) and (c) B. (b) and (c)
C. (b) and (d) D. (a) and (d)

45. Given below are some of the statements regarding regeneration:

(a) The type of regeneration characteristic of mammalian liver is considered as compensatory regeneration.
(b) Regrowth of hair shaft from follicular cells exemplifies stem cell mediated regeneration.
(c) Regeneration occurring through the re-patterning of existing tissues with little new growth is known as morphallaxis.
(d) Adult structures undergoing dedifferentiation forming a blastema, that then re-differentiates to form the lost structure is called epimorphosis.

Choose the most appropriate combination of correct statements:

A. (d) only
B. (c) and (d) only
C. (a), (b) and (c) only
D. (a), (b), (c) and (d)

Morphogenesis and Organogenesis in Plants

46. In which stage of *Arabidopsis* embryogenesis is hypophysis first observed?

A. Octant
B. Dermatogen
C. Globular
D. Transition

47. Following are certain statements regarding apomixis in plants:

(a) Apomixis cannot be used to maintain hybrid vigor over many generations in plants.
(b) In sporophyticapomixis maternal genotype is maintained.
(c) There is an event of meiosis during gametophyticapomixis and is also referred as apomeiosis.
(d) In diplospory, meiosis of the megaspore mother cell is aborted, resulting in two unreduced spores, out of which one forms the female gametophyte.

Which one of the following combinations is correct?

A. (a) and (b)
B. (a) and (c)
C. (b) and (c)
D. (b) and (d)

Cell Differentiation

48. Both TGF β and Sonic hedgehog signals play important roles in both neurulation and cell-fate patterning of the neural tube. Which one of the following statements is true?

A. High levels of BMP specify the cells to become epidermis.
B. Very low levels of BMP specify the cells to become epidermis.
C. High levels of BMP specify the cells to become neural plate.
D. Intermediate levels of BMP do not effect the formation of neural crest cells.

GATE (LIFE SCIENCE), 2018

49. Cardiac and cerebral tissues are derived from the following germ layers respectively

A. Ectoderm and mesoderm
B. Mesoderm and ectoderm
C. Mesoderm and endoderm
D. Endoderm and ectoderm

50. In an experiment, nucleus from a Drosophila oocyte was transplanted into the anterior part of another oocyte, at a region opposite to the existing nucleus. Which ONE of the following phenotypes will the developing egg show?

A. A ventralized egg with no dorsal appendages
B. A dorsalized egg with two dorsal appendages
C. A ventralized egg with two dorsal appendages
D. A dorsalized egg with four dorsal appendages

51. In Drosophila melanogaster, a mutation in Ultrabithorax which defines the third segment of the thorax or T3 leads to development of four winged flies, as the halteres develop into a second pair of wings. Which ONE of the following phenotypes in fly will result from overexpression of Ultrabithorax in the second thoracic segment?

A. Four winged flies.
B. Two wings and two halteres flies.
C. Flies with four halteres.
D. Flies with two halteres.

CSIR-NET, JUNE, 2019

Morphogenesis and Organogenesis in Animals

52. In *Xenopus* embryos, β-catenin plays an important role in the Dorsal/Vental axis development. What would you expect if the endogenous glycogen synthase kinase 3 (GSK3) is knocked out by a dominant negative form of GSK3 in the ventral cells of the early embryos?

A. Blocking of GSK3 on the ventral side has no effect. A normal embryo will form.
B. The resulting embryo will only have ventral sides
C. 3A second axis will form
D. The dorsal fate is suppressed.

53. Homeobox transcription factor (Hox proteins), play important roles in specifying whether a particular mesenchymal cell will become stylopod, zeugopod or autopod. Based on the expression patterns of these genes, a model was proposed wherein these HOX genes specify the identity of a limb region. What would be the observed phenotype for human homozygous for a *HOXD13* mutation?

A. No zeugopod formation
B. Abnormalities of the hands and feet wherein the digits fuse
C. Deformities in stylopods
D. No femur of patella formation.

54. Irrespective of the chromosomal configuration, a single X chromosome remains active in all diploid human somatic cell lines. Which one of the following mechanisms best accounts for the above phenomenon.

A. A maternally inherited X–chromosome is developmentally programmed to remain active by avoiding DNA methylation.
B. Chromosome specific expression and binding of rox1 to one of the X-chromosomes protects it from Xist mediated silencing.
C. The T-six gene produces just enough of the Xist antisense RNA to block one Xic locus.
D. A cell produces just enough of the blocking factor to block one Xic locus.

55. When 8-cell embryo of tunicates is separated into 4 blastomere pairs and allowed to grow independently in culture medium, then each blastomere pair can form most the cell types; however, cells for nervous system are not developed. The following statements are formed from the above observations:

(*a*) Nervous system development demonstrated autonomous specification.
(*b*) The other tissue types are formed due to conditional specification.
(*c*) All the tissue types, except nervous tissues that developed demonstrated autonomous specification.
(*d*) Nervous system development demonstrated conditional specification.

The correct combination of statements that explains the above result is:

A. (*a*) and (*b*)
B. (*b*) and (*c*)
C. (*c*) and (*d*)
D. (*a*) and (*d*)

56. During wing development in chick, if Apical Ectodermal Ridge (AER) is removed, the limb development ceases, on the other hand placing leg mesenchyme directly beneath the wing AER, distal hindlimb structures develop at the end of the wing, and if replaced by non-limb mesenchyme sheath AER, the AER regresses. This may demonstrate that:

(*a*) the limb mesenchyme cells induce and sustain AER.
(*b*) the mesenchyme cells specify the type: wing or limb.
(*c*) the AER is responsible for specifying the type: wing or limb.
(*d*) the AER is responsible for sustained outgrowth and development of the limb.
(*e*) the AER does not specify the type: wing or limb.

Which combination of above statements is demonstrated by the experiment?

A. (*a*), (*b*), (*c*) and (*d*) only
B. (*a*), (*b*), (*d*) and (*e*) only
C. (*c*), (*d*) and (*e*) only
D. (*a*) and (*e*) only

Morphogenesis and Organogenesis in Plants

57. Given below are statements related to different aspects of plant growth and development.

(*a*) Leaf longevity is increased in ethylene insensitive mutants eir1-1 and ein2 of Arabidopsis.
(*b*) Programmed cell death (PCD) is responsible for the formation of prickles, thorns and spines in plants.
(*c*) Senescence and PCD occur only in the development of vegetative tissues and does not occur in reproductive tissues
(*d*) Redifferentiation of organelles is an integral component during initial stages of senescence in plants.

Which one of the following represents the combination of all correct statements?

A. (*a*), (*c*) and (*d*)
B. (*b*) and (*c*)
C. (*a*), (*b*) and (*d*)
D. (*c*) and (*a*)

Developmental Gene Regulation in Drosophila

58. The following statements regarding the generation of dorsal/ventral axis in Drosophila was made:

(*a*) Gurken protein moves along with the oocyte nucleus and signals follicle cells to adopt the ventral fate.

(*b*) Maternal deficiencies of either the gurken or torpedo gene cause ventralization of the embryo.

(*c*) Gurken is active only in the oocytes, Torpedo is active only in the somatic follicle cells.

(*d*) The Pipe protein is made in the dorsal follicle cells.

(*e*) The highest concentration of Dorsal is in the dorsal cell nuclei, which becomes the mesoderm.

Which one of the following combination of the above statements is true?

A. (*a*) and (*e*) B. (*c*) and (*d*)
C. (*b*) and (*c*) D. (*b*) and (*e*)

59. A specialized area of teratogenesis involves the misregulation of the endocrine system. Which one of the following statements regarding endocrine disruptors is true?

A. They can act as antagonist and inhibit the binding of a hormone to its receptors or block the synthesis of a hormone.
B. They do not affect the synthesis, elimination or transportation of a hormone in the body.
C. They do not mimic the effect of natural hormones.
D. Low dose exposure to endocrine disruptors is not sufficient to produce significant disabilities later in life.

Apoptosis, Aging and Senescence

60. Which one of the following best describes death-upon-detachment?

A. Necroptosis B. Anoikis
C. Extravasation D. Metastasis

CSIR-NET, 15 DECEMBER, 2019

Gametogenesis, Fertilization and Early Development

61. The cells of inner cell mass of a blastocyst stage mammalian embryo are

A. totipotent B. pluripotent
C. multipotent D. unipotent

Morphogenesis and Organogenesis in Animals

62. Following statements are being made regarding specification determination during animal development:

(*a*) During the course of commitment, the cell may not appear different from its nearest or most distant neighbours in the embryo and show no visible signs of differentiation; but its developmental fate is restricted.

(*b*) At the stage of specification, cell commitment is not labile.

(*c*) A cell or tissue is determined when it is capable of differentiating autonomously even when placed into another region of the embryo, or a cluster of differently specified cells in a petri- dish

(*d*) Cytoskeletal arrangements maintain positioning of nuclei in the syncytium, which enables specification of these nuclei by opposing morphogen gradients namely Bicoid and Caudal in Drosophila

(*e*) Capacity for "mosaic" development allows cells to acquire different functions as a result of interactions with neighbouring cells.

Which of the above statements are correct?

A. (*a*), (*b*) and (*c*) B. (*b*), (*c*) and (*d*)
C. (*c*), (*d*) and (*e*) D. (*a*), (*c*) and (*d*)

63. A "morphogen" can determine the fate of a cell by its concentration. Given below are some statements on the experiment performed to study the gradient- dependent effect of the morphogen, activin on cell fate by placing activin (4 nm)-secreting beads on unspecified cells from an early Xenopus embryo:

(*a*) Beads without activin did not elicit expression of either *Xbra* or *goosecoid* genes.

(*b*) Cells nearest to the beads getting highest concentration of activin induced *goosecoid* gene whose product is a transcription factor, specifies the frog's dorsal-most structures.

(*c*) Cells nearest to the beads getting highest concentration of activin induced *Xbra* gene whose product is a transcription factor, specifies the frog's dorsal-most structures.

(*d*) Cells farthest from the beads getting negligible activin activate *Xbra* gene and become blood vessels and heart

(*e*) Cells farthest from the beads getting negligible activin, activated neither *Xbra* nor *goosecoid* and the default gene expression instructed the cells to become blood vessels and heart.

Which of the above observations and conclusions drawn are correct?

A. (*a*), (*b*) and (*c*) B. (*b*), (*c*) and (*d*)
C. (*c*), (*d*) and (*e*) D. (*a*), (*b*) and (*e*)

64. Following statements were made about the events occurring during chick development.

(*a*) The fertilized chick egg undergoes discoidal meroblastic cleavage; however the cleavage does not extend into the yolk cytoplasm.

(*b*) Development of primary hypoblast is mediated by localized migration of a group of highly specified and connected cluster of 30-40 cells.

(*c*) By the stage XIII of chick embryogenesis and little prior to primitive streak formation, the formation of the hypoblast is just complete.

(*d*) Hansen's node of the chick embryo signifies a region at the anterior end of the primitive streak with regional thickening of cells.

(*e*) Inhibition of *Wnt* planar cell polarity pathway in the epiblast causes the mesoderm and endoderm to form centrally instead of peripherally.

Which one of the following combinations represents all correct statements?

A. (*a*), (*b*) and (*d*)　B. (*a*), (*c*) and (*e*)
C. (*a*), (*b*) and (*c*)　D. (*a*), (*c*) and (*d*)

Morphogenesis and Organogenesis in Plants

65. The following diagram represents a longitudinal section through an *Arabidopsis* shoot apical meristem (SAM) and leaf primordium at its flank. The dorsal (*D*) and ventral (*V*) domains are marked. The *D* and *V* genes are expressed in the dorsal and ventral domains, respectively.

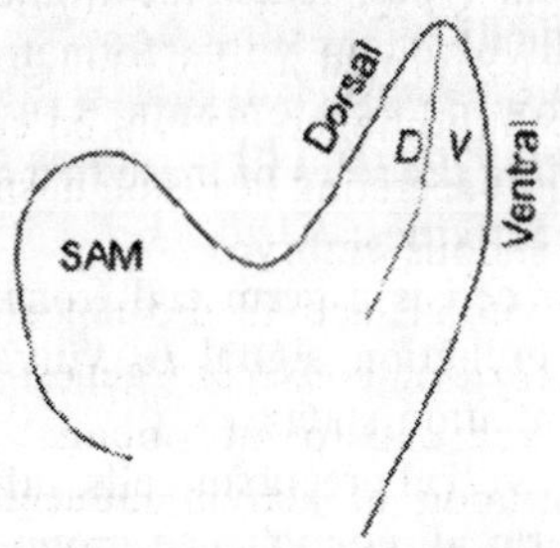

Consider the following statements describing the phenotypes of leaf polarity.

(*a*) Loss of *D* function makes the leaf ventralized whereas its overexpression dorsalizes the leaf.

(*b*) Loss of *V* function makes the leaf dorsalized whereas its overexpression ventralizes the leaf.

(*c*) Loss of microRNA *miR166* dorsalizes the leaf whereas its overexpression ventralizes the leaf.

(*d*) *miR166* functions by inhibiting its target mRNA

Which one of the following functional models best describes the above results?

A.
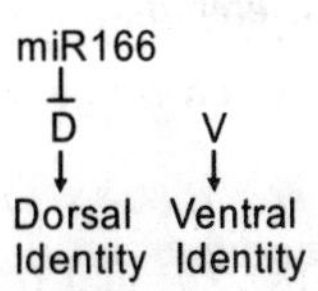

B.
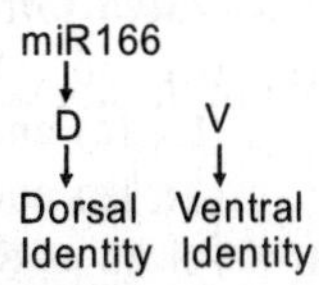

C.
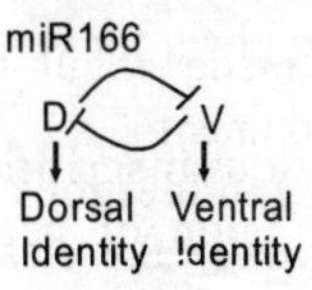

D.
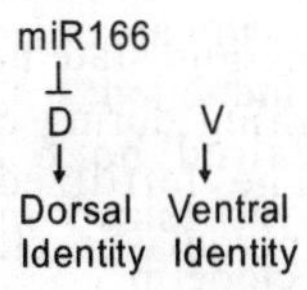

66. During fertilization in mammals proteins *Izumo* and *Juno* are required for recognition of sperm and egg. *Izumo* and *Juno* are found specifically in sperm and egg, respectively. Which one of the following in vivo experiments will demonstrate that *Izumo* and Juno interact with each other?

A. If sperms from a male mouse where *Izumo* has been knocked out is used to fertilize eggs from a normal female and no fertilization occurs.

B. Whole mount immunostaining for *Izumo* and Juno shows its presence on the sperm and egg respectively

C. If a CFP fused *Izumo* protein is mixed with YFP fused Juno protein in a tube, FRET occurs, *i.e.*, when CFP is excited, emission of YFP is observed.

D. Two independent kidney cell lines are developed, one expressing Izumo and the other Juno. If the two cells are mixed, they tend to aggregate with each other.

Developmental Gene Regulation in Drosophila

67. The anterior-posterior compartment of each segment of Drosophila is defined by wingless and engrailed genes. The following statements are given towards explaining their regulation:

(*a*) Wingless is a secretory factor

(*b*) Engrailed is a secretory factor and forms a long-range concentration gradient

(*c*) Engrailed regulates Wingless through Hedgehog which forms a short-range concentration gradient

(*d*) β-catenin homologue is the signalling molecule upstream of Engrailed, which gets cleaved by GSK3 homologue

(*e*) Cubitus interruptus is an intracellular signalling molecule in the Engrailed expressing cells.

Which one of the following options has all the correct statements towards the regulation of anterior- posterior compartment of segments?

A. (*b*) only　B. (*c*) only
C. (*b*) and (*e*)　D. (*a*), (*c*) and (*d*)

68. The individuals considered in this question are having two haploid sets of autosomes and no Y. chromosome. The X:A ratio of the individuals, the type of organisms chosen, their primary sex and number of Barr bodies expected in their cells are shown in the table below:

X: A ratio	Organism	Primary Sex	Number of Barr bodies
i. 0.5	A. Human	I. Male	a. Zero
ii. 2	B. *Drosophila*	II. Female	b. One
		III. Metafemale	c. Two
			d. Three

Select the option below with all correct matches:

A. i-A-II-a; ii-A-II-d; i-B-I-a; ii-B-III-a
B. i-A-I-a; ii-A-II-C; i-B-II-a; ii-B-I-a
C. i-A-II-c; ii-A-I-d; i-B-I-c; ii-B-II-b
D. i-A-II-a; ii-A-II-d; i-B-III-a; ii-B-I-a

CSIR-NET, 27 DECEMBER, 2019

Gametogenesis, Fertilization and Early Development

69. Which one of the following is NOT a typical movement pattern observed during gastrulation?

A. Involution B. Epiboly
C. Furrowing D. Delamination

70. Compaction during early embryonic development involves activation of actin filaments.
Which one of the following inhibitors would prevent formation of the blastula from the morula?

A. An inhibitor that would block the action of Glin.
B. A specific inhibitor for stabilizing the function of Axin.
C. A specific inhibitor for GSK3B
D. An inhibitor which would block Smad4.

Morphogenesis and Organogenesis in Animals

71. Which one of the following signalling pathways will best support the formation of the zone of polarizing activity (ZPA) during limb development in mice.

A. 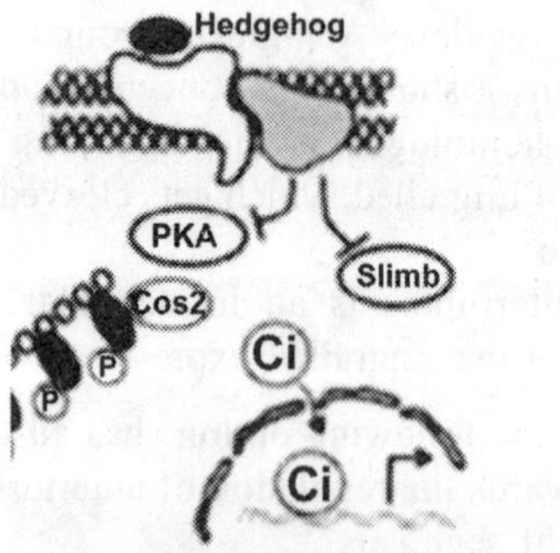

B. 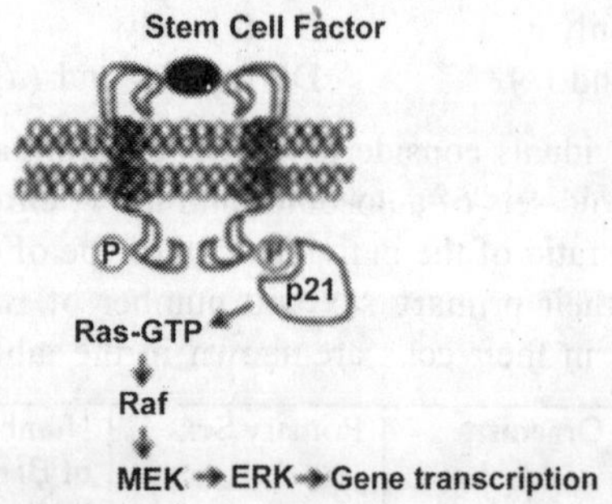

C. 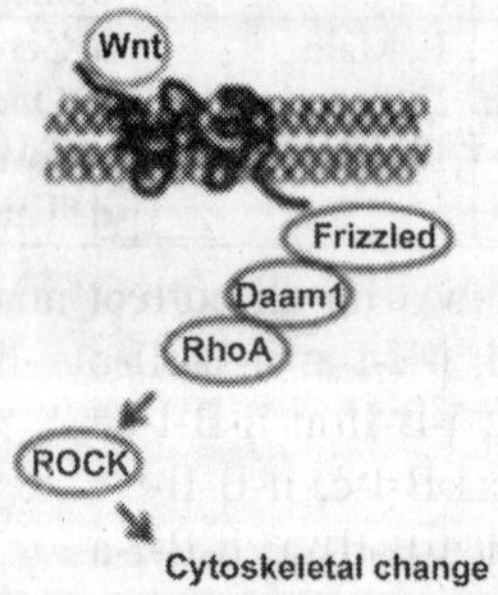

D. 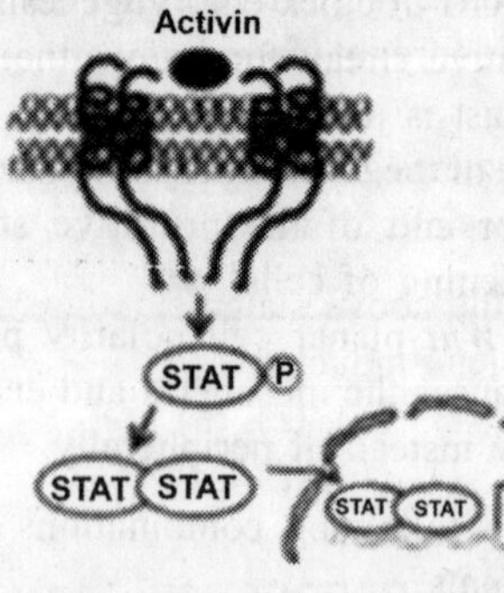

72. In sea urchins, successful fertilization can be ensured only after specific interaction between sperm proteins and their receptors on the egg vitelline envelope. Which one of the following will ensure proper fertilization of sea urchin eggs?

A. Expression of EBR1, a putative bindin receptor, on the surface of the acrosomal membrane
B. Expression of bindin just below the egg jelly
C. Expression of EBR1 on the egg vitelline envelope
D. Expression of bindin molecules on the egg vitelline envelope

73. The two cell types, Anchor cell and vulval precursor cells are involved in vulva formation in *C. elegans*. The following statements are given towards understanding the roles of these two cell types and their signalling activities:

(*a*) Anchor cell is a germ cell from the gonad, which sends induction signal to vulva for maintaining differentiation states.
(*b*) The six vulval precursor cells, influenced by anchor cell, form an equivalence group
(*c*) The cell directly beneath the anchor cell divides to form the central vulval cells, while the two flanking cells divide to become the lateral vulval cells
(*d*) The three cells further away from anchor cell generate hypodermal cells
(*e*) Lin3 signal from anchor cell forms a gradient and activates vulva forming genes in central and lateral cells
(*f*) The Notch-Delta mediated mechanism of restricting adjacent cell fates is called Lateral inhibition.

Which combination of the above statements is correct towards vulva formation in *C. elegans*?

A. (*a*), (*b*) and (*e*) only
B. (*a*), (*b*), (*e*) and (*f*)
C. (*a*), (*b*), (*c*) and (*d*)
D. (*b*), (*c*), (*d*), (*e*) and (*f*)

74. Following are some statements given for vertebrate eye lens induction:

(*a*) Paired box6 (Pax6) is a transcription factor synthesized in specific region of head surface ectoderm.

(*b*) Pax6 is secreted by optic vesicle.
(*c*) Optic vesicle serves as an inducer for competent head surface ectoderm.
(*d*) Studies on amphibians suggest that the first inducers of lens may be the foregut endoderm and heart forming mesoderm.
(*e*) The genes for lens proteins get induced in the surface ectoderm of optic vesicle.

Which combination of the above statements is correct towards vertebrate eye lens induction?

A. (*a*), (*c*), (*d*) B. (*a*), (*c*), (*e*)
C. (*b*), (*e*) D. (*b*), (*c*), (*d*)

Morphogenesis and Organogenesis in Plants

75. Which one of the following options related to plant growth and development is matched correctly?
A. LEAFY: regulator of genomic imprinting
B. Xylogenesis: wood formation
C. MET1: Inflorescence architecture
D. Caspases: inhibition of apoptosis

Developmental Gene Regulation in Drosophila

76. The table given below provides categories and names of genes involved in Drosophila development

Category	Gene Name
(*a*) Pair rule gene	(*i*) *abdominal A*
(*b*) Homeotic gene	(*ii*) *gooseberry*
(*c*) Gap gene	(*iii*) *fushi tarazu*
(*d*) Segment polarity gene	(*iv*) giant

Which one of the following options is a correct match between the categories and gene names?

	(*a*)	(*b*)	(*c*)	(*d*)
A.	(*i*)	(*ii*)	(*iii*)	(*iv*)
B.	(*iv*)	(*iii*)	(*ii*)	(*i*)
C.	(*ii*)	(*iv*)	(*i*)	(*iii*)
D.	(*iii*)	(*i*)	(*iv*)	(*ii*)

77. In *Drosophila* males, where no recombination occurs, segregation of the two alleles of a gene occurs at which stage of cell division?
A. Diplotene B. Anaphase I
C. Anaphase II D. Mitotic Telophase

Apoptosis, Aging and Senescence

78. The initiator caspase responsible for promoting cell death after specific activation of TRADD is
A. Caspase 1 B. Caspase 8
C. Caspase 7 D. Caspase 5

Cell Differentiation

79. Hippo pathway is responsible for the trophoblast and inner cell mass (ICM) differentiation during mammalian development. Which one of the following is true for ICM formation?
A. The Tead4 transcription factor, when active, promotes transcription of Cdx2 gene leading to ICM formation.
B. If LATS kinase phosphorylates the YAP transcriptional coactivator, the phosphorylated form of YAP does not enter the nucleus and gets degraded which leads to ICM formation
C. In the absence of functional LATS protein, the YAP transcriptional cofactor can bind to Tead4 to activate Cdx2 gene promoting ICM
D. Synthesis of Cdx2 upregulates Oct4 and Nanog leading to ICM formation.

GATE (LIFE SCIENCE), 2019

80. Closure of neural tube during neurulation is the process in which neural tube eventually forms a closed cylinder that separates from surface ectoderm. Which one of the following terms is linked to the failure in the closure of entire neural tube i.e. brain and spinal cord, over the body axis?
A. Craniorachischisis B. Spina bifida
C. Anencephaly D. Cleft palate

CSIR-NET, NOVEMBER (MORNING), 2020

Gametogenesis, Fertilization and Early Development

81. In echinoderms sperm direction is provided by
A. Calcineurin
B. Bindin
C. Resact
D. EBR1

Morphogenesis and Organogenesis in Animals

82. If an early cleavage stage wild type Drosophila embryo is injected with bicoid mRNA at the posterior pole then
A. head structures develop at posterior pole, while the same is inhibited at anterior pole
B. head structures form at both poles

C. head structures are not formed at posterior pole due to presence of posterior morphogens
D. duplication of usual posterior structures occurs

83. If the blastomeres of a 4 celled sea urchin embryo are isolated each blastomere can form a pluteus larvae. This is example of
A. Autonomous specification
B. Conditional specification
C. Determination
D. Mosaic development

84. In *C.* elegans the SKN-1 protein controls the fate of the EMS blastomere which generates the posterior pharynx. With reference to the above which one of the following statements is incorrect?
A. The MS blastomere is able to generate pharyngeal tissue even in isolation.
B. Embryos from skn-l (skin excess) deficient mothers lack both pharyngeal mesoderm and endoderm derivatives of EMS
C. Embryos which are skn-l null mutants will always make extra hypodermal (skin) and body wall tissue.
D. SKN-1 activates MED transcription factors whose level of activity controls the fate of EMS lineage

85. The hedgehog pathway is extremely important in vertebrate limb development, neural differentiation and facial morpho-genesis. In accordance with the above statement, what would happen in mice that are homozygous for a mutant allele of sonic hedgehog (shh)?
A. Limbs would form normally but the mice would have facial abnormalities.
B. Midline of the face would be reduced and a single eye would form in the center of the forehead.
C. Eyes would form normally but digits would be malformed.
D. Mutations of shh may activate tumor formation if Patched protein can inhibit the Smoothened protein.

86. In Xenopus, the Noggin protein, accomplishes two major functions of the organizer: it induces dorsal ectoderm to form neural tissues, and it dorsalizes mesoderm cells. Which one of the following observations is correct with respect to Noggin?
A. If a plasmid clone expressing Noggin protein is microinjected into a lithium chloride treated Xenopus gastrula, it should rescue the abnormalities induced by lithium chloride treatment.
B. If a plasmid clone expressing Noggin protein is microinjected into UV-treated embryo which does not give rise to neural tube, it will rescue the abnormality.
C. RNA in situ hybridization of noggin cDNA on Xenopus embryo will show its presence in all regions except the dorsal blastopore lip.
D. Microinjection of noggin mRNA into the embryo region fated to make the ventral part will promote its ventralization.

87. Antennapedia protein expresses in the thoracic segment of the fly and not in the head region. However, a dominant mutation of Antennapedia replaces antenna with leg-like structure.

The following statements were made with reference to Antennapedia:
A. In a dominant Antennapedia mutant, the Antennapedia gene is expressed in the head as well as in thorax.
B. In the Antennapedia mutants, the Antennapedia gene is expressed in head region only and thus promotes leg-like structure in head socket
C. In addition to promoting thoracic structures, Antennapedia protein binds to and represses the enhancer of homothorax and some other genes responsible for antenna specification.
D. Antennapedia has no role in thoracic region specification and thus recessive Antennapedia mutants show no phenotypic effect.

Which one of the following options represents correct statement(s)?
A. (*a*) only B. (*a*) and (*c*)
C. (*b*) and (*d*) D. (*b*) only

Morphogenesis and Organogenesis in Plants

88. Which one of the following plant homeotic genes does NOT encode MADS-domain transcription factor involved in floral organ specification?
A. AP2 B. API
C. AP3/P1 D. AG

89. The development of anthers and male gametophytes is highly conserved among angiosperms. Following are some of the events associated with pollen development, in random order.
(*a*) Microsporogenesis in pollen sac to produce a tetrad.
(*b*) Asymmetric division forming immature pollen grains.
(*c*) Archespore division.
(*d*) Division of generative cell to form two sperm cells.
(*e*) Callase digestion to form free microspheres.

Which of the following option represent the correct series of events during pollen development?
A. (*a*), (*b*), (*c*), (*d*), (*e*)
B. (*c*), (*a*), (*e*), (*b*), (*d*)
C. (*a*), (*c*), (*d*), (*b*), (*e*)
D. (*c*), (*e*), (*a*), (*b*), (*d*)

90. The gene encoding for mevalonate-3-kinase is disrupted in a certain plant. Which one of the following statements concerning the above plant is correct?
A. Mevalonic acid 3, 5-biphosphate will be synthesized, while there will be no synthesis of Mevalonic acid 5-phosphate.

B. Mevalonic acid 3, 5-biphosphate and Isopentenyl diphosphate will be synthesized.

C. There will be no synthesis of Mevalonic acid 3, 5-biphosphate but Mevalonic acid will be synthesized.

D. Acetoacetyl-coA and Mevalonic acid will not be synthesized.

Developmental Gene Regulation in Drosophila

91. Maternal effect genes are extremely important in establishing the anterior-posterior polarity of the Drosophila embryo. Mutant phenotypes arise when genes of this family are mutated. The following table enlists genes and phenotypes observed on mutation of these genes but not correctly matched.

Gene Mutant	Phenotype
(a) Torso	*(i)* No abdomen, no pole cells
(b) Vasa	*(ii)* Defective oogenesis
(c) Oskar	*(iii)* Head and thorax deleted
(d) Bicoid	*(iv)* No termini

Which one of the following combinations is correctly matched?

	(a)	*(b)*	*(c)*	*(d)*
A.	*(ii)*	*(i)*	*(iii)*	*(iv)*
B.	*(i)*	*(iii)*	*(iv)*	*(ii)*
C.	*(iv)*	*(ii)*	*(i)*	*(iii)*
D.	*(iii)*	*(iv)*	*(ii)*	*(i)*

92. Following statements were made about sex determination in Drosophila melanogaster

(a) It is achieved by a balance of female determinants on the X-chromosome and male determinants on the autosomes.

(b) A Drosophila with 0.66 value of X:A ratio would develop intersex type.

(c) Due to noninvolvement of Y chromosome in sex determination process, XO Drosophila develop as normal fertile male.

(d) The high value of X:A ratio facilitates activation of feminizing switch gene Sex - lethal (sxl).

(e) Sex specific expression of sxl causes selective activation of dosage compensation genes in female Drosophila.

Select the option with combination of all correct statements.

A. *(a)*, *(b)*, *(e)* B. *(a)*, *(b)*, *(d)*

C. *(b)*, *(c)*, *(e)* D. *(b)*, *(c)*, *(d)*

Apoptosis, Aging and Senescence

93. Prostate cancer cells were treated with Drug B and Drug B in order to check the efficacy of the drugs in arresting the growth of cells. The following results were obtained:

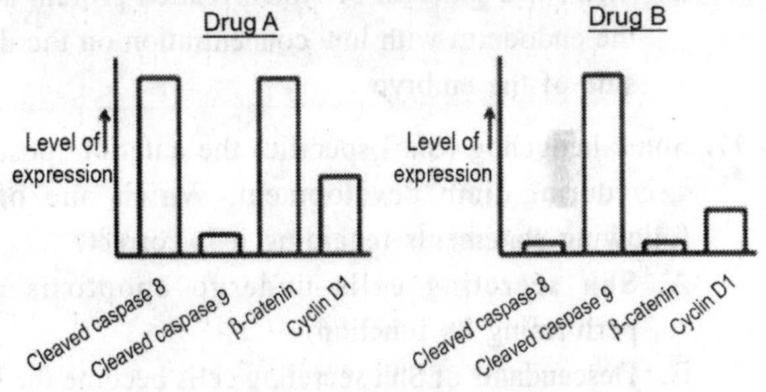

Which of the following statement is not correct?

A. Drug A targets the Wnt signaling pathway but does not lead to death of cells

B. Drug B targets the Wnt signaling pathway and leads to Gi cell cycle arrest.

C. Both drugs A and B lead to cell death but targets different apoptotic pathways.

D. Durg A kills cells via the mitochondrial-independent pathway.

CSIR-NET, NOVEMBER (AFTERNOON), 2020

Gametogenesis, Fertilization and Early Development

94. The major structural characteristic of avian gastrulation is the primitive streak, which becomes the blastopore lips of amniotic embryos. Migration through the primitive streak is controlled by Fgf8. What would happen if the Fgf8 protein, which repels migrating cells away from the streak, is over expressed in the primitive streak?

A. The yolk sac will be deformed.

B. Wnt signalling will be activated and orientation of the primitive streak will change.

C. Cells of the streak will not form the paraxial mesoderm.

D. Cells generate mesodermal portions of the embryo.

95. Several marine organism release their gametes into the environment, where sperm attraction and subsequent events lead to successful fertilization. With reference to sea urchins, which one of the following statements is NOT true?

A. Addition of resact into a drop of seawater containing sperms specifically attracts sperms of A. punctulata.

B. IP_3 is formed initially at the site of sperm entry and releases sequestered Ca^{2+}

C. Ca^{2+} prevents docking of cortical granules of the egg to the cell membrane.
D. Inhibitors that specifically block PLCγ can be circumvented by microinjection IP_3 into the egg.

Morphogenesis and Organogenesis in Animals

96. Which one of the following statements regarding amphibian development is correct?
A. The Nieuwkoop centre is formed on the dorsal side of the embryo due to accumulation of β-catenin which helps activate the siamois and twin genes
B. The ectodermal cells form neural tissues in the presence of BMP molecules.
C. Brain formation requires the activation of both Wnt and BMP pathway.
D. There is a gradient of Nodal-related protein across the endoderm with low concentration on the dorsal side of the embryo

97. Sonic hedgehog (Shh) specifies the anterior- posterior axis during limb development. Which one of the following statements regarding it is correct?
A. Shh secreting cells undergo apoptosis after performing its function.
B. Descendants of Shh secreting cells become the bone and muscle of the anterior limb
C. When the genes for Shh and Gli3 are conditionally knocked out in the mouse limb, the resulting limbs do not form any digit
D. Specification of the digit is primarily dependent on the amount of time the Shh gene is expressed and to a small extent on the concentration of the Shh protein that other cells receive.

98. In *C. elegans*, activation of the CED-3 and CED-4 proteins are essential for the apoptosis pathway. In addition, gain-of-function mutations in the ced-9 gene cause its protein to be made in cells that would normally die, resulting in survival of those cells. Given these facts, which one of the following diagrams correctly represents a cell death pathway?

A.
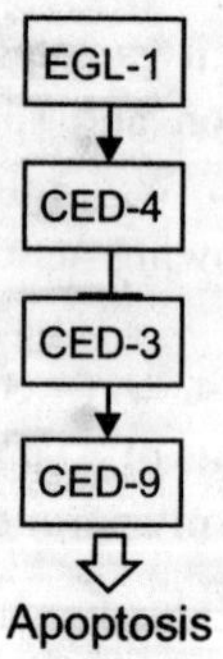

B.
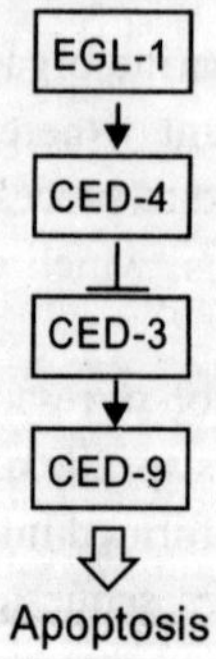

C.
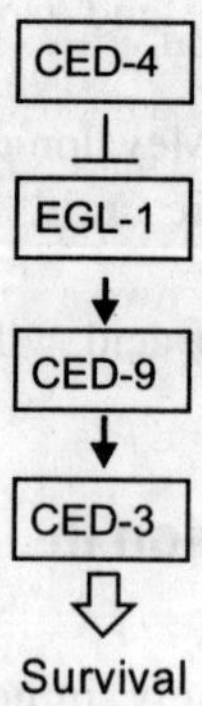

D.
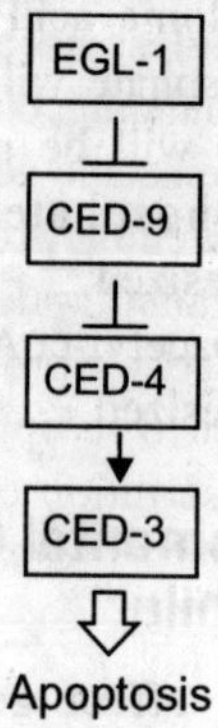

99. Kallmann syndrome generally exhibits gonadal dysfunctions in males. Following statements are made relating to such males.
(*a*) They mostly suffer from hypergonadism
(*b*) They mostly suffer from hypogonadism
(*c*) They have higher level of circulating gonadotropins
(*d*) They have lower level of circulating gonadotropins
Which one of the following combinations of statements is correct?
A. (*a*) and (*b*) B. (*b*) and (*c*)
C. (*b*) and (*d*) D. (*a*) and (*c*)

100. Driesch performed the "pressure plate experiment" to alter the distribution of nuclei in a 8-cell sea urchin embryo. He obtained normal larvae from these embryos. Following possible conclusions could be drawn:
(*a*) Prospective potency of the blastomeres is less than the actual prospective fate.
(*b*) Sea urchin embryo is a "harmonious equipotential system" implying that cell interaction is critical for normal development.
(*c*) Prospective potency of the blastomere is greater than the actual prospective fate.
(*d*) Prospective potency of the blastomere is equal to the prospective fate.

Which one of the following combinations of statements represents the correct inference from the experiment?
A. (*a*) and (*b*) B. (*b*) and (*c*)
C. (*b*) only D. (*d*) only

Developmental Gene Regulation in Drosophila

101. The continued expression of engrailed and wingless is maintained by interactions between the Engrailed- and Wingless-expressing cells. The following statements are given towards the initiation of the cascade of events that occur for this interaction:
(*a*) The engrailed gene is expressed in cells where neither even skipped nor fushi tarazu gene is active.
(*b*) The wingless gene is expressed in those cells that contain high concentration of either Even skipped or Fushi tarazu.

(*c*) Wingless is a secreted protein, diffuses to the surrounding, binds with the Frizzled and Lrpo receptor proteins and activates engrailed gene via Armadillo.
(*d*) Hedgehog protein activates the transcription of engrailed and also activates its own transcription.
(*e*) Hedgehog protein diffuses from cells and binds to Patched receptor on neighbouring cells and enables transcription of wingless gene.

Which combination of above statements correctly represent the maintenance of engrailed and wingless expression?
A. (*a*) and (*b*)
B. (*b*) and (*d*)
C. (*a*) and (*d*)
D. (*c*) and (*e*)

DBT-JRF, 2020

102. The mature anther wall comprises an epidermis followed by a layer of radially elongated cells with fibrous bands of callose called endothecium whose function is
A. mechanical B. protection
C. dehiscence D. Nutrition

103. Which of the following floral whorls are absent in agamous (ag) mutant of Arabidopsis?
A. petals and stamens B. sepals and petals
C. stamens and carpels D. sepals and carpels

104. In a plant, the cells adjacent to the egg cell in an ovule are known as
A. synergids B. antipodals
C. polar nuclei D. sperm cell

105. Pruning helps in making the hedge dense because
A. it frees axillary buds from apical dominance
B. more root growth supports more shoot branches
C. the apical shoot grows slower after pruning
D. it induces the differentiation of new shoots from the rootstock

106. In which organelle of seeds are stored oils converted to fatty acids and glycerol during germination?
A. endoplasmic reticulum
B. amyloplast
C. mitochondria
D. glyoxysome

GATE (LIFE SCIENCE), 2020

107. Which ONE of the following glial cells is NOT derived from the ectoderm?
A. Astrocytes B. Microglial cells
C. Oligodendrocytes D. Ependyma

108. Match the following components listed in Column I with their respective organs in Column II

Column I	Column II
(*a*) Endolymph	(*i*) Testes
(*b*) Vitreous humour	(*ii*) Ear
(*c*) Vas deferens	(*iii*) Ovary
(*d*) Corpus luteum	(*iv*) Eye

	(*a*)	(*b*)	(*c*)	(*d*)
A.	(*ii*)	(*iv*)	(*i*)	(*iii*)
B.	(*ii*)	(*i*)	(*iv*)	(*iii*)
C.	(*iii*)	(*iv*)	(*i*)	(*iii*)
D.	(*iii*)	(*iv*)	(*ii*)	(*i*)

109. Which ONE of the following is the precursor molecule for corticosteroids?
A. Androgen
B. Estrogen
C. Pregnenolone
D. Mineralocorticoids

CSIR-NET, JUNE (MORNING), 2021

Basic Concepts of Development

110. Which of the following combinations would best characterize the dominant phase of the life cycle of a pteridophyte?
A. Diploid gametophyte
B. Haploid gametophyte
C. Diploid sporophyte
D. Haploid sporophyte

Gametogenesis, Fertilization and Early Development

111. Which one of the following statements with respect to development in amphibians is correct?
A. Gastrulation begins with the invagination of bottle cells, followed by coordinated involution of the mesodermal precursors and the epiboly of the prospective ectoderm.

B. The organizer induces the Nieuwkoop centre
C. The organizer is formed by the accumulation of β-catenin
D. In the absence of BMP inhibitors ectodermal cells form neural tube.

112. What is the pattern of cleavage observed in mammals?
A. radial B. sprial
C. rotational D. bilate

Morphogenesis and Organogenesis in Animals

113. In a transplantation experiment, the area of presumptive ectoderm from an early frog gastrula was transplanted to a region of the newt gastrula destined to become parts of the mouth. The resulting salamander larvae had frog like mouth parts (frog tadpole suckers) instead of balancers as observed during development of wild type new embryo.
A. This is an example of Determination
B. Genetic specificity of interaction
C. Regional specificity of interaction
D. Autonomous specification

114. During normal development of sea urchin, β-catenin accumulates predominantly in the micromeres, which are fated to become endoderm and mesoderm. If GSK-3 is blocked in the developing embryo-
A. β-catenin accumulation in the nuclei of large mircomeres will be inhibited leading to formation of ectodermal ball.
B. β-catenin will accumulate in the nuclei of all blastula cells leading to an ectodermal ball.
C. β-catenin will accumulate in the nuclei of all blastula cells leading to animal cells getting specified as endoderm and mesoderm.
D. β-catenin which accumulate in the nuclei of large mircomeres will be inhibited leading to animal cell cells getting specified as endoderm and mesoderm.

115. Which one of the following is NOT correct regarding the tetrapod limb development?
A. As the limb grows outward, the stylops form first, then the zeugopod and the autopod is formed last. Each phas is characted by a specific pattern of Hox gene expression.
B. The zone of polarizing activity (ZPA) is maintained by the interaction of the FGFs from the AER and Shh expressed from the mesenchyme.
C. Although cell death in the limb is nasssary for the formation of the digits and joints, it is never madited by the BMPs, which only responsible for differentiation mesenchymal cell into cartilage
D. The dorsal-ventral axisis is formed inpart by the expression of Wnt7a in the dorsal potion of the limb ectoderm, which maintain expression level of Shh in the ZPA and Fgf4 in the posterior AER

116. Given below are some of the statements in connection with neural tube formation in vertebrates:
(*a*) In primary neurulation the cells surrounding the neural plate direct the neural plate cells to proliferate, invaginate and separate from the surface ectoderm to form an underlying hollow tube.
(*b*) In secondary neurulation the neural tube aries from the aggregation of mesenchyme cells into a solid cord that subsequently forms cavities to create a hollow tube
(*c*) In birds primary neurulation generates the neural tube from anterior up to the hind limb developing region
(*d*) In mammals, secondary neurulation begins at the level of sacral vertebrae
(*e*) Anencephaly results when a failure to close the neural tube occurs resulting in the forebrain remaining in contact with amniotic fluid.

Which one of the following options represents all correct statements?
A. (*a*), (*b*), (*c*), (*d*) and (*e*)
B. (*a*) only
C. (*b*) and (*e*) only
D. (*c*), (*d*) and (*e*) only

117. Match the terms used in vertebrate limb development in list I with their description in list II.

List I	List II
(*a*) EMT	(*i*) The cells found within the most posterior region of the limb bud
(*b*) Mesenchyme	(*ii*) The Thickening of ectoderm at the apex of the developing limb
(*c*) AER	(*iii*) A loosely organized, mainly mesodermal embryonic tissue
(*d*) Progress zone	(*iv*) Epithelial cells making up the mesoderm of the early somatopleure undergo this transition and get included in mesenchyme cell pool
(*e*) ZPA	(*v*) The proliferation mesenchyme that flues limb bud growth
(*f*) Autopod	(*vi*) The distal part of tetrahedron limb

Which one of the following combinations of the statements is correct?

	(*a*)	(*b*)	(*c*)	(*d*)	(*e*)	(*f*)
A.	(*iv*)	(*iii*)	(*ii*)	(*v*)	(*i*)	(*vi*)
B.	(*i*)	(*ii*)	(*iii*)	(*iv*)	(*v*)	(*vi*)
C.	(*v*)	(*iv*)	(*ii*)	(*vi*)	(*iii*)	(*i*)
D.	(*ii*)	(*v*)	(*i*)	(*iii*)	(*iv*)	(*v*)

Developmental Gene Regulation in Drosophila

118. The dorsal protein is involved in generating the dorsal-ventral (DV) polarity in Drosophila. The following statements were made regarding the activity of the Dorsal protein in establishing the DV polarity.

(*a*) In embryos that lack Gurken protein, the Dorsal protein is not translocated to the nucleus of the follicle cells which then causes ventralization of the embryo.

(*b*) Though Dorsal protein acts as a morphogen, it is found throughout the syncytial blastoderm of the early *Drosophila* embryo.

(*c*) In embryos that lack Cactus protein the Dorsal protein can be found in the nucleus of cells with a ventral fate.

(*d*) If the Dorsal protein is blocked from entering the nucleus, the genes responsible for specifying dorsal cell types are not described.

Which one of the above statements is correct?

A. (*a*) and (*b*) B. (*b*) and (*c*)
C. (*c*) and (*d*) D. (*a*) and (*c*)

CSIR-NET, JUNE (AFTERNOON), 2021

Basic Concepts of Development

119. Movement of epithelial sheet spreading as a unit to enclose deeper layers of the embryo is termed as

A. Epiboly B. Emboly
C. Involution D. Ingression

Morphogenesis and Organogenesis in Animals

120. What would be the effect of retinoic acid(RA) treatment on the 'positional information' of blastema cells present on the amputated newt limb?

A. RA will have no effect
B. The cells will become respecified to more proximal position
C. The cells will become respecified to more distal position
D. Cells will lose their positional information and remain as dedifferentiated

121. Induction is an extrinsic process that depends on the position of a cell in the embryo. It is a process whereby one cell or group of cells can influence the developmental fate of another, and is a common strategy to control differentiation and pattern formation in development. The following statements were made regarding induction in a developing embryo.

(*a*) The inductive signal can be a protein secreted from the inducing cells that binds to receptor of a responding cell.

(*b*) Response to inductive signals depends on competence of the inducing cell.

(*c*) Instructive induction occurs when the responding cell is already committed to a certain fate.

(*d*) Lateral inhibition is an induction that results in differentiation of individual cells in a regularly spaced pattern.

Which one of the following combination of statements is correct?

A. (*a*) and (*c*) B. (*b*) and (*d*)
C. (*a*) and (*d*) D. (*b*) and (*c*)

122. Given below are statements related to expression of some of the pattern forming genes in vertebrate limb bud :

(*a*) Lmx1b gene is expressed in dorsal mesenchyme.

(*b*) Shh is expressed in the posterior region.

(*c*) Wnt7a gene is expressed in dorsal ectoderm.

(*d*) Hoxa13 and Hoxd13 are expressed in the distal region.

(*e*) Tbx5 and FGF10 arr expressed in the lateral plate mesoderm involved in formation of limb bud.

The nail-Patella syndrome in human and the syndrome in mouse exhibiting foot-pads on both dorsal and ventral surfaces of limb are associated with which of the above mentioned gene functions?

A. (*b*), (*d*) and (*e*) B. (*b*) and (*d*) only
C. (*a*), (*b*) and (*d*) D. (*a*) and (*c*) only

123. The early embryonic development in amphibians and aves serve as two different model plans of development. In the former the germ layer formation is initiated from a fluid-filled ball like blastula, while in the latter the germ layer formation is initiated on a flat blastodisc. Given below are some of the terms for amphibian embryo in column I and from avian embryo in column II :

Column I	Column II
(*a*) Blastocoel	(*i*) Posterior marginal zone (PMZ)
(*b*) Blastocoel lip	(*ii*) Primitive streak
(*c*) Dorsal lip of blastopore	(*iii*) Hensen's node
(*d*) Blastopore	(*iv*) Between epiblast and hypoblast
(*e*) Nieuwkoop center	(*v*) Primitive groove

Which of the following is the all correct match of the terms in column I with that of column II?

	(a)	(b)	(c)	(d)	(e)
A.	(iv)	(iii)	(ii)	(v)	(i)
B.	(iv)	(ii)	(iii)	(v)	(i)
C.	(v)	(i)	(ii)	(iv)	(iii)
D.	(i)	(ii)	(iii)	(iv)	(v)

124. In an experiment, activin – secreting beads were placed on unspecified cells from an early Xenopus embryo. The activin then diffused from the beads. If the beads contained 1nM of activin, it elicited expression of Xbra gene in cells near to the beads. If the beads contained 4 nM activin, the expression of Xbra was elicited in cells, but only at a distance of several cell diameters away from the beads. In the latter case, expression of goosecoid gene was observed near the source bead. Beads with no activin did not elicit the expression of the two genes. Following statements were made regarding the observations and the role of activin in determining cell fate.

(*a*) High concentration of activin activates goosecoid, whereas lower concentrations activate Xbra.
(*b*) Lower concentrations of activin help specify the dorsal – most structures of the frog's embryo
(*c*) Concentrations of activin that do not lead to expression of the two genes
(*d*) specifies the cell to become blood vessels and heart

Which of the above statement (s) are correct?

A. (*a*) only B. (*c*) only
C. (*a*) and (*c*) D. (*a*) and (*c*)

125. The specification of sea urchin micrometers involves the activation of a repressor protein Pmr1 which represent the expression of hesC which also encoded a repressor proteins. one of the gene controlled by HesC is Delta whose expression is used as a marker for micromer lineage. The image below represent a sea urchin embryo on which whole mount in situ hybridization was performed using delta probe indicated by the area 'A'. The rest of the embryo is labelled 'B'.

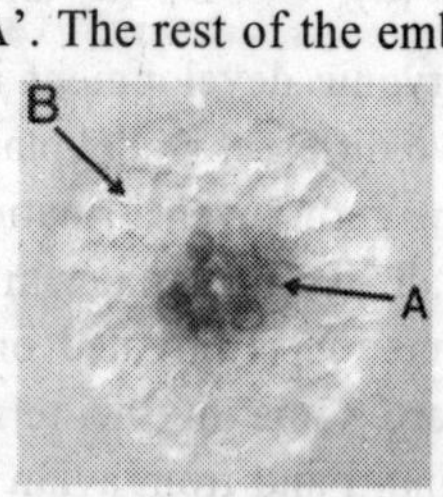

The table below summarizes a set of experiments column A and the area in which hybridization is observed column B

Column A	Column B
(*a*) WMISH with hesC probe	(*i*) A
(*b*) WMISH with delta probe following microinjection of pmr1 mRNA into fertilized egg.	(*ii*) B
(*c*) WMISH with delta probe following microinjection of antisense RNA to hesC into fertilized egg.	(*iii*) Both (*a*) and (*b*)
	(*iv*) Neither A nor B

Which of the following options is a correct match between column A and B?

	(a)	(b)	(c)
A.	(ii)	(iii)	(iii)
B.	(ii)	(iii)	(iv)
C.	(i)	(ii)	(iv)
D.	(i)	(ii)	(iii)

Morphogenesis and Organogenesis in Plants

126. Which one of the following transcription factors is important for delimiting the meristematic and elongation zones of roots?

A. SCARECROW (SCR)
B. SHORT ROOT (SHR)
C. PLETHORA (PLT)
D. SPEECHLESS (SPCH)

127. The high affinity ammonium uptake system in plant's roots involves transporters in the AMT/Rh family. Which of the following AMT genes is expressed in cortex and endodermis?

A. AMT1.1 B. AMT1.2
C. AMT1.3 D. AMT1.4

128. Following are certain statements related to seed maturation :

(*a*) Seed maturation involves mainly the accumulation of storage products, such as starch, lipids and proteins.
(*b*) A large number of chaperones including the family of LATE EMBRYO ABUNDANT (LEA) proteins, play a crucial role in desiccation process of seeds.
(*c*) Moisture content gets reduced with the maturation of seed.
(*d*) ABA and gibberellin both promote seed dormancy.

Which one of the following options has all correct statements?

A. (*a*) and (*c*) only B. (*b*) and (*d*) only
C. (*b*), (*c*) and (*d*) only D. (*a*), (*b*) and (*c*) only

Developmental Gene Regulation in Drosophila

129. A Drosophila male carrying an X - linked temperature sensitive recessive mutation that is lethal at 29°C but viable at 18°C is mated to : A. a normal female B. a female containing attached X-chromosome If the eggs laid in both the cases are reared at 29°C, what will be male female ratio in the given progeny?

A. A – 1:2, B – 1:1
B. A – 1:1 B – only females A – 1:1
C. A – 0:1 , B – 1:1
D. A – 1-0 , B – 1:2

DBT-JRF, 2021

130. E class homeotic genes in Arabidopsis thaliana are involved in the formation of:
A. Floral meristem
B. Petals and carpels
C. Sepals & petals
D. Shoot apical meristem

131. Lateral roots initiate from:
A. Endodermis
B. Pericycle
C. Root apical meristem
D. Root epidermis

132. Which one of the following is NOT a characteristic feature of skotomorphogenic development?
A. Apical hook   B. Closed cotyledons
C. Expanded leaves   D. Long hypocotyls

133. A plant with lateral branching, a main stem grow from:
A. Apical Bud
B. Terminal Bud
C. Both (A) and (B)
D. Cambium

134. Which one of the following statements are TRUE regarding specialized embryonic structures peculiar to the grass family?
(*a*) The cotyledon has been modified by evolution to form an absorptive organ called coleoptile
(*b*) Scutellum forms the interphase between the embryo and the starchy endosperm tissue
(*c*) Coleoptile covers and protect the first leaves while buried beneath the soil
(*d*) The base of the hypocotyl has elongated to form a protective sheath around the radicle called the scutellum

Choose the most appropriate answer from the options given below:
A. (*a*) and (*c*) only   B. (*a*) and (*d*) only
C. (*b*) and (*c*) only   D. (*c*) and (*d*) only

GATE (LIFE SCIENCE), 2021

135. Match the terms in Column I with the specific descriptions in Column II

Column I	Column II
(*a*) Zygote	(*i*) A hollow sphere of cells
(*b*) Morula	(*ii*) A newly born offspring
(*c*) Blastocyst	(*iii*) A cell that results from fertilization
(*d*) Ovum	(*iv*) An embryo
(*e*) Neonate	(*v*) An unfertilized egg
(*f*) Fetus	(*vi*) A compact mass of cells

	(*a*)	(*b*)	(*c*)	(*d*)	(*e*)	(*f*)
A.	(*iii*)	(*vi*)	(*i*)	(*v*)	(*ii*)	(*iv*)
B.	(*v*)	(*ii*)	(*iii*)	(*vi*)	(*i*)	(*iv*)
C.	(*ii*)	(*iv*)	(*vi*)	(*v*)	(*i*)	(*iii*)
D.	(*iii*)	(*vi*)	(*ii*)	(*v*)	(*iv*)	(*i*)

136. Match the types of cell movements during gastrulation in Column I with the descriptions in Column II

Column I	Column II
(*a*) Invagination	(*i*) Migration of individual cells from the surface into the embryo's interior
(*b*) Involution	(*ii*) Infolding of a sheet (epithelium) of cells during the formation of endoderm in sea urchin
(*c*) Ingression	(*iii*) Splitting of one cellular sheet into two nearly parallel sheets
(*d*) Delamination	(*iv*) Inward movement of an expanding outer layer of cells so that it spreads over the internal surface of the remaining external cells

	(*a*)	(*b*)	(*c*)	(*d*)
A.	(*ii*)	(*iii*)	(*iv*)	(*i*)
B.	(*iv*)	(*i*)	(*iii*)	(*ii*)
C.	(*ii*)	(*iv*)	(*i*)	(*iii*)
D.	(*iii*)	(*ii*)	(*iv*)	(*i*)

137. Match the cell/tissue types in GROUP I with their corresponding total DNA content in GROUP II of a typical diploid Angiosperm species and choose the CORRECT option (C denotes DNA content in haploid genome).

Group I	Group II
(*a*) Pollen tube	(*i*) 1C
(*b*) Megaspore mother cell	(*ii*) 2C
(*c*) Synergid	(*iii*) 3C
(*d*) Embryo sac prior to fertilization	(*iv*) 4C
	(*v*) 5C

	(*a*)	(*b*)	(*c*)	(*d*)
A.	(*i*)	(*ii*)	(*iii*)	(*v*)
B.	(*ii*)	(*ii*)	(*i*)	(*v*)
C.	(*i*)	(*ii*)	(*i*)	(*v*)
D.	(*ii*)	(*i*)	(*ii*)	(*iv*)

138. Which ONE of the following statements regarding spores and gametes is CORRECT?

A. Spores can directly undergo mitosis whereas gametes cannot.

B. Gametes can directly undergo mitosis whereas spores cannot.

C. Neither spores nor gametes can directly undergo mitosis.

D. Both spores and gametes can directly undergo mitosis.

139. The diagram describes the ABC model of flower patterning in Arabidopsis where the A, B and C functions are operational in the whorls (1 + 2), (2 + 3) and (3 + 4), respectively, in the wild-type flower. Removal of A or C function results in the floral organ arrangements as (carpel; stamen; stamen; carpel) or (sepal; petal; petal; sepal), respectively. Based on these observations, which ONE of the following molecular pathways is CORRECT for floral organ pattern generation? Arrow indicates activation and bar indicates inhibition.

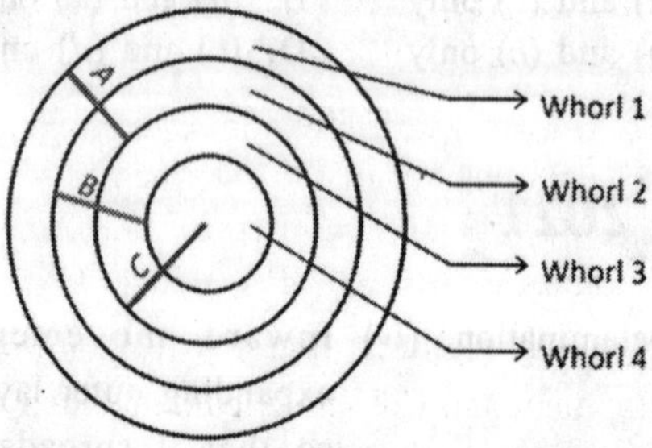

A. 

B. 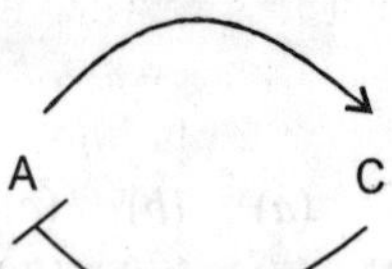

C. 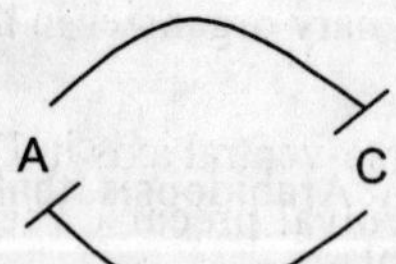

D. 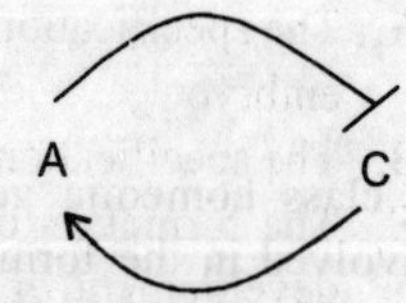

140. The observations of an experiment on seed germination in various genotypes under different light conditions are given, where √ and X indicate germination and the lack of it, respectively.

Genotype	Blue	Red	Far-red	White	Dark
Wild-type	√	√	√	√	X
cry1 mutant	X	√	√	√	X
phyA mutant	√	√	X	√	X
phyB mutant	√	X	√	√	X
vp1 mutant	√	√	√	√	√

Based on these observations, which of the following option(s) is/are CORRECT?

A. All the three light qualities– blue, red and far-red – are required for seed germination.

B. Any one of the three light qualities - blue, red and far-red – is sufficient to induce seed germination.

C. The CRY1, phyA and phyB proteins are required for blue, red and far-red light perception, respectively.

D. The VP1 protein is unlikely to be involved in light perception.

CSIR-NET, SEPTEMBER (MORNING), 2022

Basic Concepts of Development

141. The table below lists cleavage pattern and names of species

Cleavage pattern	Species
(*a*) Isolecithal bilateral	(*i*) Amphibians
(*b*) Mesolecithal radial	(*ii*) Birds
(*c*) Centrolecithal superficial	(*iii*) Tunicates
(*d*) Telolecithal discoidal	(*iv*) Insects

Match the cleavage patterns with the species

	(*a*)	(*b*)	(*c*)	(*d*)
A.	(*i*)	(*ii*)	(*iii*)	(*iv*)
B.	(*ii*)	(*iv*)	(*i*)	(*iii*)
C.	(*iv*)	(*i*)	(*iii*)	(*ii*)
D.	(*iii*)	(*i*)	(*iv*)	(*ii*)

Gametogenesis, Fertilization and Early Development

142. Which one of the following statements is INCORRECT?

A. Transient rise in Ca^{2+} is necessary for egg activation in mammals

B. Sperm induces egg activation and does not involve Ca^{2+}

C. In many organisms, eggs secrete diffusible molecules that attract and activate sperm

D. Capacitated mammalian sperm can penetrate the cumulus and bind the zona pellucid

Morphogenesis and Organogenesis in Animals

143. In which one of the following developmental events, the fate of maternal somatic cell is determined first, which then determines the fate of the developing embryo?

A. The specification of primary organizer in amphibian embryo
B. The specification of dorso-ventral axis in Drosophila
C. The formation of the vulval precursor cells during development of *C. elegans*
D. Specification of the micromeres in case of sea urchin

144. In mice, the gene encoding Tbx5 is transcribed in limb fields of the forelimbs, while the genes encoding Islet1, Tbx4 and Pitx1 are expressed in presumptive hindlimbs.

Following statements are made about limb development in mouse:

(*a*) Loss of Tbx5 gene results in complete failure of forelimb formation.
(*b*) Hindlimb bud growth and initial patterning appears normal when Tbx4 is knocked out, although leg development is arrested prematurely.
(*c*) Misexpression of Pitx1 in forelimb ceases development of muscles, bones and tendons.
(*d*) When Islet1 is inactivated specifically in the lateral plate mesoderm, the hindlimbs still develop.

Which one of the following options represents a combination of correct statements?

A. (*a*) and (*b*) B. (*a*) and (*c*)
C. (*b*) and (*c*) D. (*c*) and (*d*)

145. The following statements are made about mammalian development:

(*a*) Zygote is a totipotent stem cell.
(*b*) The cells of inner cell mass are said to be pluripotent.
(*c*) The three regulatory transcription factors, Oct4, Nanog and Sox2 help maintain pluripotency of the inner cell mass
(*d*) Cdx2 upregulates Oct4 and Nanog.

Which one of the following options represents the correct combination of the statements?

A. (*a*) and (*b*) B. (*b*) and (*c*)
C. (*c*) and (*d*) D. (*a*) and (*d*)

146. *C. elegans* embryo uses both autonomous and conditional modes of specification. The following statements are about specification of cell lineages:

(*a*) The signals from the P1 blastomere instructs the EMS cell for its further development.
(*b*) In the absence of the instructive signal, the EMS cell will divide into two MS cells.
(*c*) In the absence of the POP-1 signal, the prospective MS cell can take up the E fate.
(*d*) The MOM-2 protein from the blastomere neighbouring the EMS cell instructs the dividing EMS blastomere to take up MS fate.

Which one of the following options represent both correct statements?

A. (*a*) and (*b*) B. (*b*) and (*c*)
C. (*c*) and (*d*) D. (*a*) and (*d*)

147. The interactions that maintain polarity during Planaria regeneration is shown in the figure below:

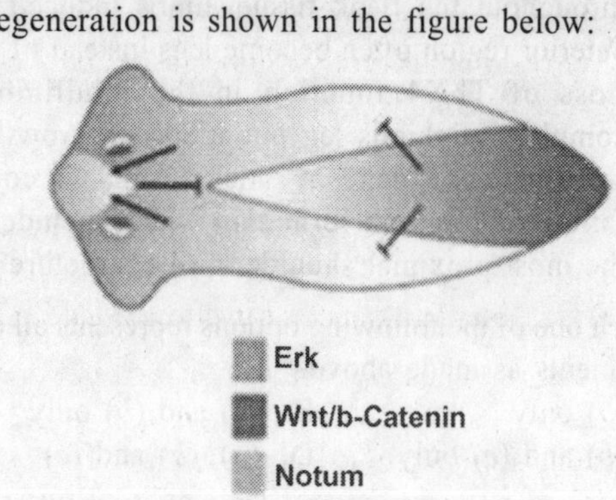

Following statements regarding these interactions were made:

(*a*) When Notum expression is knocked down, the anterior facing blastema will still form a head.
(*b*) When Notum is expressed in the posterior end, Planaria with two heads will be formed.
(*c*) When Wnt pathway is blocked, the resulting Planaria will have heads on both the ends.
(*d*) High levels of Erk inhibit head specification.

Which one of the following options represents the correct combination of the statements?

A. (*a*) and (*c*) B. (*b*) and (*c*)
C. (*c*) and (*d*) D. (*a*) and (*d*)

148. In the table below Column I lists terms related to development and Column II contains their descriptions not in a sequential manner:

Column I	Column II
(*a*) Koller's sickle	(*i*) The delaminated cells from epiblast forming islands
(*b*) Primary hypoblast	(*ii*) Homologous to amphibian blastopore
(*c*) Primitive groove	(*iii*) Local thickening of the epiblast formed at posterior edge of area pellucida
(*d*) Hensen's node	(*iv*) Equivalent of dorsal blastopore lip of amphibian embryo

Select the option with all correct matches between Column I and Column II

	(*a*)	(*b*)	(*c*)	(*d*)
A.	(*i*)	(*iii*)	(*ii*)	(*iv*)
B.	(*ii*)	(*i*)	(*iv*)	(*iii*)
C.	(*iii*)	(*i*)	(*ii*)	(*iv*)
D.	(*iv*)	(*ii*)	(*i*)	(*iii*)

149. Tbx4 and Tbx5 are critical in the specification of hindlimbs and forelimbs, respectively.

The following statements were made regarding experiments involving expression of Tbx4 or Tbx5 genes and their probable outcomes:

(*a*) When chick embryo was made to express Tbx4 throughout the flank tissue, limbs induced in the anterior region often become legs instead of wings.
(*b*) Loss of TbX4 function in the hindlimb field completely inhibits leg initiation and growth.
(*c*) Loss of Tbx5 gene in chick results in complete failure of forelimb formation which includes even the most proximal shoulder/girdle structure.

Which one of the following options represents all correct statements as made above?

A. (*a*) only
B. (*a*) and (*b*) only
C. (*b*) and (*c*) only
D. (*a*), (*b*) and (*c*)

150. The mammalian genital ridge is bipotential. Which one of the following statements regarding determination of the fate of genital ridge is INCORRECT?

A. The activation of Sox9 gene promotes testis determining pathway.
B. The accumulation of β-catenin is critical for activating ovarian development.
C. R-spondin 1 (Rspo1) stimulates the Disheveled protein, thus promoting testis determining pathway.
D. Though Wnt4 is expressed in the bipotential gonads, it is an important factor in ovary determination.

151. The table below summarizes the key signaling pathways that orchestrate development, their receptors, transcription effectors and output.

	Signaling pathway	Receptor	Transcriptional effector	Output
(*a*)	Wnt	Thick veins	β-catenin	Patterning
(*b*)	Hedgehog	Frizzled	Ci/Gli	Growth
(*c*)	RTK	EGFR	Pointed/Yan	Morphogenesis
(*d*)	TGFβ	Patched	NICD	Cell fate specification
(*e*)	JNK	TNF	Jun/Fos	Migration

Which of the above pathways is correctly depicted in one of the options given below?

A. (*a*), (*c*) and (*d*)
B. Only (*b*) and (*e*)
C. Only (*a*) and (*d*)
D. Only (*c*) and (*e*)

Morphogenesis and Organogenesis in Plants

152. Members of the WUSCHEL RELATED HOMEOBOX (WOX) transcription factor family play an important role during zygote elongation and division in Arabidopsis. Following are certain statements regarding the expression of different members of WOX gene family during zygote elongation.

(*a*) WOX2 and WOX8 are present in both the egg cell and the zygote.
(*b*) WOX2 is present in the apical and basal cell.
(*c*) WOX8 along with WOX9 regulates the development of basal lineage.
(*d*) WOX8 and WOX9 are directly activated in the zygote by the transcription factor WRKY2.

Which one of the following options represents combination of all correct statements?

A. (*a*), (*b*) and (*c*)
B. (*a*), (*b*) and (*d*)
C. (*a*), (*c*) and (*d*)
D. B, (*c*) and (*d*)

Cell Differentiation

153. Which one of the following floral mutants shows the pattern 'sepals-petals-petals' repeated several times?

A. agamous (ag)
B. apetala1 (ap1)
C. apetala 3 (ap3)
D. pistillata (pi)

CSIR-NET, SEPTEMBER (AFTERNOON), 2022

Basic Concepts of Development

154. A type of regeneration in which the differentiated cells divide, maintaining their differentiated function without dedifferentiation and production of undifferentiated mass, is known as

A. Epimorphosis
B. Morphallaxis
C. Compensatory regeneration
D. Stem cell mediated regeneration

Morphogenesis and Organogenesis in Animals

155. In mammals, autophagy is involved in specific cytosolic rearrangements needed for proliferation and differentiation during embryogenesis and postnatal development. Embryos have the ability to activate general protective strategy against many stress-inducing conditions. Which one of the following statements DOES NOT conform to the role of autophagy during early development?

A. Autophagy is a process of cytosolic renovation, crucial for cell fate decisions.
B. Autophagy plays a dual role both in adaptation to stress and starvation during morphogenesis and in cell elimination along with apoptosis.
C. Functional characterization of the autophagy regulatory genes indicates that autophagy is definitely not an evolutionarily conserved process.
D. Defects in autophagy during early embryogenesis can be lethal for the organism.

156. The group of 6 cells (P3.p to P8.P) called vulval precursor cells (VPCs) of C. elegars form an equivalence group. The following statements were made as evidence that VPCs form an equivalence group:

(*a*) If the anchor cell is destroyed the VPCs contribute to the formation of hypodermal tissues.
(*b*) If the 3 central cells (P5.p to P7.p) are destroyed the remaining cells can generate vulval cells.
(*c*) If expression of lin-3 is increased VPCs contributing to the secondary lineage can form cells of primary lineage.
(*d*) Ectopic expression of let-23 in P5.p and P7.p VPCs converts them to primary cell lineage.

Which one of the following options is a combination of all correct statements?

A. (*a*) and (*b*) only
B. (*b*) and (*c*) only
C. (*a*), (*b*) and (*c*)
D. (*b*), (*c*) and (*d*)

157. Which one of the following mRNAs is a BMP inhibitor and can rescue the dorsal structures of ventralized Xenopus embryo when injected into it?

A. beta-catenin   B. Noggin
C. Disheveled   D. Siamos

Developmental Gene Regulation in Drosophila

158. The following statements were made regarding the patterning of anterior-posterior body plan of Drosophila:

(*a*) Microinjection of bicoid mRNA in the middle of a bicoid-deficient embryo leads to formation of 'head' in the middle and telson at the two ends.
(*b*) Nanos protein inhibits the translation of caudal mRNA at the posterior half of the embryo.
(*c*) The Bicoid protein activates the zygotic expression of the hunchback gene.
(*d*) The segment polarity genes are expressed in segments of the embryo.

Which one of the following options represents all correct statements as made above?

A. (*a*) and (*b*) only
B. (*a*) and (*c*) only
C. (*a*), (*c*) and (*d*)
D. (*b*), (*c*) and (*d*)

Apoptosis, Aging and Senescence

159. The programmed cell death that separates the digits during a tetrapod limb development is dependent on which one of the following signaling pathways?

A. BMP   B. FGF
C. Wnt   D. Shh

160. Mullerian-inhibiting substance (MIS), a homodimer that causes regression of the Mullerian duct by apoptosis, is secreted by which one of the following cells?

A. Leydig cells   B. Sertoli cells
C. Corpus luteal cells   D. Placental cells

DBT-JRF, 2022

161. Skotomorphogenesis is characterized by:

A. Small and closed cotyledons and elongated hypocotyl
B. Fully open cotyledons
C. Robust foliage and root growth
D. Early flowering resulting from short-day conditions

162. Choose the correct statement in respect to metazoan development:

A. Delta is a cell surface protein while Notch is an intracellular protein
B. Notch is a cell surface protein while Delta is an intracellular protein
C. Delta and Notch are not present on the same cell
D. Notch and Delta both are cell surface proteins present on the same precursor cell

GATE (LIFE SCIENCE), 2022

163. An Arabidopsis thaliana mutant plant developed defective flowers with altered floral organ identity and patterning. In this mutant, the four floral whorls contain Sepal-Sepal-Carpel-Carpel, from the periphery to the center of the flower. Based on the typical ABC model of floral organ patterning, which among the following are mutated in this plant?

A. Class A gene(s)
B. Class B gene(s)
C. Class C gene(s)
D. Double mutant for Class A and Class C genes

164. 'Quiescent Center' is present in

A. leaf meristem
B. root apical meristem
C. shoot apical meristem
D. floral meristem

165. To which class of Drosophila developmental genes does fushi tarazu (ftz) belong?

A. Gap genes
B. Segment polarity genes
C. Pair rule genes
D. Maternal effect genes

ANSWERS

1	2	3	4	5	6	7	8	9	10
C	A	B	C	B	B	D	C	D	C
11	12	13	14	15	16	17	18	19	20
C	A	D	D	C	C	A	A	A	A
21	22	23	24	25	26	27	28	29	30
C	A	A	B	B	C	D	C	A	C
31	32	33	34	35	36	37	38	39	40
A	B	A	C	A	C	A	A	B	B
41	42	43	44	45	46	47	48	49	50
B	A	B	A	D	B	D	A	C	D
51	52	53	54	55	56	57	58	59	60
C	C	B	D	C	B	C	C	A	B
61	62	63	64	65	66	67	68	69	70
B	D	D	D	C	D	A	A	C	C
71	72	73	74	75	76	77	78	79	80
A	C	D	A	B	D	B	B	C	A
81	82	83	84	85	86	87	88	89	90
C	B	B	C	B	B	B	A	B	C
91	92	93	94	95	96	97	98	99	100
C	B	A	B	C	A	D	D	C	B
101	102	103	104	105	106	107	108	109	110
D	C	C	A	A	D	D	D	C	C
111	112	113	114	115	116	117	118	119	120
A	C	B	A	C	A	A	B	A	B
121	122	123	124	125	126	127	128	129	130
C	D	B	C	A	C	B	D	B	B
131	132	133	134	135	136	137	138	139	140
B	C	C	C	A	C	B	A	C	B
141	142	143	144	145	146	147	148	149	150
D	B	B	A	B	B	B	C	D	C
151	152	153	154	155	156	157	158	159	160
D	C	A	C	C	C	B	C	A	B
161	162	163	164	165					
D	D	B	B	C					

CHAPTER

14

DIVERSITY OF LIFE

CSIR-NET, JUNE, 2017

Chordate

1. As per the cladistic taxonomy, Archosaurs are a group of diapsid amniotes which include extinct dinosaurs. The living representatives of the group consist of

A. Anurans and Aves

B. Aves and Crocodilia

C. Aves and Agnatha

D. Osteichthyes and Squamata

2. If you want to divide a human body into dorsal and ventral sections, what plane will you use?

A. Coronal

B. Abdominopelvic

C. Transverse

D. Sagittal

3. Given below are some statements on vertebrates. Which one of the following statements is INCORRECT?

A. Muscular post-anal tail and pharyngeal slits are derived characters in vertebrates like notochord and dorsal hollow nerve cord

B. Like echinoderms, vertebrates are deuterostomes

C. Presence of two or more sets of HOX genes in living vertebrates distinguish them from cephalochordates and urochordates which have only one set

D. Since adult hagfishes and lampreys lack Vertebral column, they are categorized outside class Vertebrata, but are retained under "chordata" along with Cephalochordates and urochordates.

Plant Classification

4. Which one of the following bryophyte has multicellular rhizoids and its cells mostly contain numerous chloroplasts?

A. Anthoceros

B. Sphagnum

C. Riccia

D. Marchantia

CSIR-NET, DECEMBER, 2017

Diversity of Animal

5. Match the following cleavage patterns with the species in which they occur.

Species	***Cleavage Pattern***
(*a*) Flatworm	(*i*) Meroblastic discoidal
(*b*) Frog	(*ii*) Meroblastic superficial
(*c*) Birds	(*iii*) Holoblastic displaced radial
(*d*) Insect	(*iv*) Holoblastic spiral

	(*a*)	(*b*)	(*c*)	(*d*)
A.	(*iv*)	(*iii*)	(*i*)	(*ii*)
B.	(*iii*)	(*i*)	(*iv*)	(*ii*)
C.	(*ii*)	(*iii*)	(*i*)	(*iv*)
D.	(*ii*)	(*iv*)	(*iii*)	(*i*)

6. Among the following statements, which is the correct one that refers to a Holotype?
   A. Specimens collected from different locations and designated as type specimens by the author
   B. A single specimen or illustration upon which name is based and designated as nomenclature type by the author
   C. Specimens collected from different places and designated as type specimen
   D. A single specimen designated to serve as nomenclatural type when all of the materials on which the name of the taxon was based is missing

7. Given below are larval stages and phylum to which they belong. Select the incorrect combination.
   A. Parenchyma and Amphiblastula – Phylum Porifera
   B. Bipinnaria and Auricularia- Phylum Echinodermata
   C. Tornaria and Axolotl- Phylum Hemichordata
   D. Planula and Ephyra- Phylum Cnidaria

Plants and Microbial Diversity

8. Given below are statements on key characteristics of two fungal lineages.
   (*a*) Microsporidia do not have true mitochondria
   (*b*) Most chytrids produce flagellated gametes
   (*c*) Microsporidia are usually free-living
   (*d*) Chytrids reproduce sexually without a dikaryon stage

   Choose the combination with correct statements
   A. (*a*), (*b*) and (*c*) only
   B. (*a*), (*b*) and (*d*) only
   C. (*b*), (*c*) and (*d*) only
   D. (*a*) and (*b*) only

GATE (LIFE SCIENCE), 2017

Animal Diversity

9. The characteristic feature of deuterostomes is depicted by
   A. coelom formed by the hollowing out of a previously solid cord of mesodermal cells
   B. spiral and determinate cleavage
   C. formation of mouth from blastopore
   D. formation of anus from blastopore

10. Malaria is caused by plasmodium species, which is a parasite having a complex life cycle. The fusion between male and female gametocytes of Plasmodium happens inside
    A. human liver B. human RBCs
    C. mosquito midgut D. mosquito salivary glands

Plant Systematics

11. As per the angiosperm phylogeny Group (APG II 2003) classification, which of the following plant families comprises of only singles genus with single species?
    A. Lauraceae B. Aristolochiaceae
    C. Amborellaceae D. Typhaceae

12. A cavity, lysigenous in origin and possessing volatile oil is found in the pericarp of one of the following plants. Identify the CORRECT answer.
    A. Litchi B. Citrus
    C. Mango D. Coconut

Economic and Applied Botany

13. Choose the plant part, its use and the source species in CORRECT combination.

Plant Part	Use	Species
(*a*) Bark	(*i*) Insecticide	1. *Crocus sativus*
(*b*) Leaf	(*ii*) Food colorant	2. *Papaver somniferum*
(*c*) Capsule	(*iii*) Flavoring agent	3. *Azadirachta indica*
(*d*) Stigma	(*iv*) Analgesic	4. *Cinnamomum zeylanicum*

	(*a*)	(*b*)	(*c*)	(*d*)
A.	(*i*)-1	(*ii*)-2	(*iii*)-3	(*iv*)-4
B.	(*iii*)-4	(*ii*)-1	(*iv*)-2	(*i*)-3
C.	(*ii*)-1	(*i*)-3	(*iv*)-2	(*iii*)-4
D.	(*iii*)-4	(*i*)-3	(*ii*)-2	(*ii*)-1

Plant Pathology

14. Which of the following fungi is an example of obligate biotrophic plant pathogen?
    A. *Alternaria brassicicola*
    B. *Botrytis cinereal*
    C. *Puccinia triticina*
    D. *Sclerotinia sclerotiorum*

15. Match the pathogen, disease caused and the affected plant in the CORRECT combination.

Pathogen	Disease	Plant
(*a*) Blumeria graminis	(*i*) Blast disease	1. Groundnut
(*b*) Magnaporthe frisea	(*ii*) Powdery mildew	2. Apple
(*c*) Venturia inaequalis	(*iii*) Tikka disease	3. Barley
(*d*) Cercospora personata	(*iv*) Scab disease	4.Rice

	(*a*)	(*b*)	(*c*)	(*d*)
A.	(*i*)-4	(*ii*)-3	(*iii*)-2	(*iv*)-1
B.	(*i*)-2	(*ii*)-1	(*iii*)-4	(*iv*)-3
C.	(*ii*)-3	(*i*)-4	(*iv*)-1	(*iii*)-1
D.	(*ii*)-3	(*i*)-1	(*iii*)-2	(*iv*)-1

CSIR-NET, JUNE, 2018

Non Chordate

16. Bipinnaria and brachiolaria are the larval forms of
A. Crustacea
B. Arthropoda & Mollusca, respectively
C. Ophiuroidea & Holothuroidea, respectively
D. Asteroidea

17. The animal belonging to phylum Onychophora
A. have arthropodan characteristics and thus also considered as a class of Arthropoda
B. have both annelidian and arthropodian characteristics
C. have both arthroidian and molluscan characteristics
D. serve as a connecting link between Annelida and mollusca

18. Which of the following groups represents SAR clade of protists?
A. Euglenozoans, Red algae, Parabasilids
B. Brown algae, Forams, Radiolarians
C. Slime moulds, Entamoebas, Diplomonads
D. Charophytes, Choanoflagellates, Tubulinids

19. Three anatomical characteristics (A, B and C) of invertebrate nervous system are used to build a generalized cladogram given below. Presence of the anatomical character is indicated by '+'

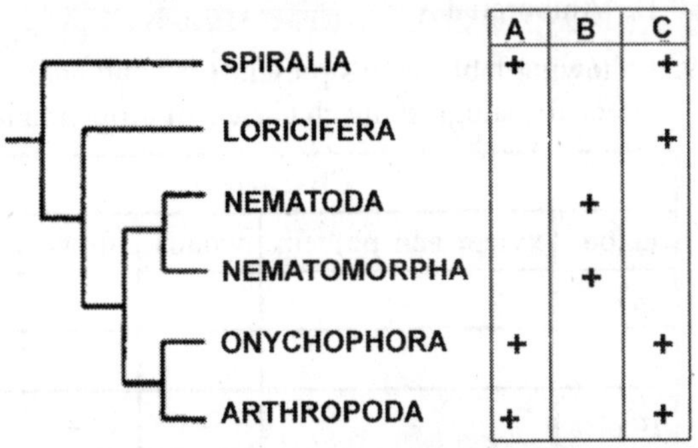

Based on the pattern of character distribution, pick the correct combination that are represented by A, B and C
A. A-unpaired nerve cord, B-paired nerve cord, C-cephalic ganglia
B. A-cephalic ganglia, B-unpaired nerve cord, C-paired nerve cord
C. A-cephalic ganglia, B-paired nerve cord, C-unpaired nerve cord
D. A-unpaired nerve cord, B-cephalic ganglia, C-paired nerve cord

20. Given below are some properties related to botanical and zoological nomenclature.
(*a*) Absence of tautonyms
(*b*) Presence of genus and species ranks only
(*c*) Absence of principle of coordination
(*d*) Presence of only holotype and neotype

Select the correct combination that distinguishes botanical nomenclature from zoological nomenclature system.
A. (*a*), (*b*) and (*d*) B. (*a*), (*b*) and (*c*)
C. (*a*) and (*c*) only D. (*a*), (*c*) and (*d*)

Plant and Microbial Diversity

21. Following table presents bryophyte phyla with their selected characteristics:

Characters	Phylum		
	A	B	C
Gametophyte cells with numerous chloroplast	+	+	–
Gametophyte with multicellular rhizoid	+	–	–
Sporophyte body with stomata	+	–	+

+ Present; – Absent

In the above table, phyla A, B and C represent
A. A-Marchantiophyta, B-Bryophyta, C- Anthocerotophyta
B. A-Bryophyta, B-Marchantiophyta, C-Anthocerotophyta
C. A-Anthocerotophyta, B-Marchantiophyta, C- Bryophyta
D. A-Bryophyta, B-Anthocerotophyta, C-Marchantiophyta

22. Following table shows a list of clades and plants:

Clades	Plants
(*a*) Basal angiosperms	(*i*) Black pepper
(*b*) Magnolides	(*ii*) Orchid
(*c*) Monocots	(*iii*) Star anise
(*d*) Eudicots	(*iv*) Strawberry

Which one of the following is a correct match for the above?

	(*a*)	(*b*)	(*c*)	(*d*)
A.	(*iii*)	(*iv*)	(*ii*)	(*i*)
B.	(*ii*)	(*i*)	(*iii*)	(*iv*)
C.	(*ii*)	(*iv*)	(*iii*)	(*i*)
D.	(*iii*)	(*i*)	(*ii*)	(*iv*)

23. Given are some statements with reference to the use of genes in plant molecular systematics.
(*a*) mtDNA are not preferred over cpDNA or rDNA because they generally show slow rate of sequence evolution and fast rate of structural evolution.
(*b*) cpDNA are not preferred because of their haploidy, uniparental inheritance, and absence of recombination among cpDNA molecules.

(*c*) rDNA such as ITS are preferred for their higher evolutionary rates as well as shorter sequence length.
(*d*) rDNA and cpDNA cannot be used simultaneously in molecular systematics since they represent conflicting patterns of inheritance.

Which of the above statements are INCORRECT?

A. (*a*), (*c*) and (*d*) B. (*a*), (*b*) and (*c*)
C. (*a*) and (*c*) only D. (*b*) and (*d*) only

24. Which one of the following parameters is NOT used in phenetic classification of bacteria?

A. trophism
B. susceptibility of a bacteria to a particular bacteriophage
C. reaction to a particular antibody
D. 16S rRNA sequence

CSIR-NET, DECEMBER, 2018

Non Chordate

25. Given below are some statements related to lower eumetazoans. Select the INCORRECT statement.

A. Ctenophores are diploblastic with radial symmetry.
B. Placozoans, with weakly differentiated tissue layers, are not diploblasts.
C. Cnidarians are diploblastic with typically two stages in their life cycle
D. Hydrozoans, a Cnidarian class, often have colonial polyps in their life cycle

26. Based on the type of excretion of nitrogenous waste, animals can be categorized as ammonotelic, ureotelic and uricotelic. Given below are combinations of groups of organisms and type of excretion. Select the correct combination.

A. Poriferans, adult amphibians, cartilaginous fishes are ammonotelic.
B. Ascaris, cockroaches, prawn are uricotelic.
C. Paramecium, amphibian tadpoles, crocodiles are mainly ammonotelic.
D. Humans, sharks and aquatic anurans are ureotelic

27. The table given below provides a list of groups of Arthropods (A-D) and some features (I-V):

(*a*) Onychophorans	(*i*) Includes insects
(*b*) Trilobites	(*ii*) Have cephalothorax and often pincer like appendage
(*c*) Hexapods	(*iii*) Marine arthropods that disappeared in the Permian extinction
(*d*) Chelicerates	(*iv*) Are considered related to arthropods but have unjoined appendages
	(*v*) Only arthropod group without antennae

Which one of the following options represents the correct match between the arthropod groups with these features?

	(*a*)	(*b*)	(*c*)	(*d*)
A.	(*iv*)	(*iii*)	(*i*)	(*v*)
B.	(*i*)	(*iii*)	(*iv*)	(*ii*)
C.	(*iii*)	(*iv*)	(*ii*)	(*i*)
D.	(*iv*)	(*iii*)	(*v*)	(*ii*)

Plant and Microbial Diversity

28. Basal angiosperms are NOT represented by the members of:

A. Chloranthales
B. Nymphaeales
C. Austrobaileyales
D. Amborellales

29. Following table shows presence (+) and absence (–) of selected distinguishing characters of different plant taxa:

	Characters			
taxon	xylem and phloem	woods	flowers	seeds
(*a*)	+	–	–	–
(*b*)	+	+	+	+
(*c*)	–	–	–	–
(*d*)	+	+	–	+

Based on the above, which of the following shows correct identity of taxa (*a*), (*b*), (*c*) and (*d*)?

A. (*a*)-Hornworts; (*b*)-Oaks; (*c*)-Ferns; (*d*)-Pines
B. (*a*)-Ferns; (*b*)-Oaks; (*c*)-Hornworts; (*d*)-Pines
C. (*a*)-Hornworts; (*b*)-Pines; (*c*)-Ferns; (*d*)-Oaks
D. (*a*)-Ferns; (*b*)-Pines; (*c*)-Hornworts; (*d*)-Oaks

GATE (LIFE SCIENCE), 2018

Animal Diversity

30. Animals belonging to phylum Echinodermata are closer to chordates than other invertebrate phyla. Which ONE of the following reasons can account for this relatedness?

A. Highly evolved nervous system
B. Radially symmetric body plan
C. Deuterostomic development
D. Well-developed muscles

31. Match the disorders/diseases listed in Column I to their respective causative agents listed in Column II.

Column I	Column II
(*a*) African tick bite fever	(*i*) Trypanosoma gambiense
(*b*) Yellow fever	(*ii*) Zika virus
(*c*) Microcephaly	(*iii*) Rickettsia sp.
(*d*) Sleeping sickness	(*iv*) Flavivirus

	(*a*)	(*b*)	(*c*)	(*d*)
A.	(*iv*)	(*iii*)	(*ii*)	(*i*)
B.	(*iii*)	(*iv*)	(*ii*)	(*i*)
C.	(*iii*)	(*iv*)	(*i*)	(*ii*)
D.	(*iii*)	(*i*)	(*iv*)	(*ii*)

Plant Systematics

32. Which of the following genera produces dimorphic seeds that help to broaden the time of germination in a variable habitat?

A. Xanthium B. Pisum
C. Mangifera D. Linum

33. Match the fruit characters with their families and representative plant species.

Fruit character	Family	Plant species
(*a*) Syconus	1. Moraceae	(*i*) *Canavalia ensiformis*
(*b*) Capsule, opening by apical pores or valves	2. Fabaceae	(*ii*) *Artabotrys odoratissimus*
(*c*) Legume	3. Papaveraceae	(*iii*) *Ficus religiosa*
(*d*) An etaerion of drupe	4. Annonaceae	(*iv*) *Papaver somniferum*
		(*v*) Pistacia vera
		(*vi*) *Citrus aurantium*

	(*a*)	(*b*)	(*c*)	(*d*)
A.	2-(*iv*)	3-(*ii*)	1-(*vi*)	4-(*v*)
B.	1-(*iii*)	3-(*iv*)	2-(*i*)	4-(*ii*)
C.	3-(*i*)	2-(*iii*)	4-(*ii*)	1-(*vi*)
D.	4-(*v*)	1-(*ii*)	2-(*v*)	3-(*i*)

34. Select the CORRECT combination by matching the disease, affected plant and the causal organism.

Fruit character	Family	Plant species
(*a*) Black rot	1. Corn	(*i*) *Fusarium oxysporum f. sp. cubense*
(*b*) Loose smut	2. Banana	(*ii*) *Acidovorax avenae subsp. citrulli*
(*c*) Panama wilt	3. Watermelon	(*iii*) *Botryosphaeria obtusa*
(*d*) Bacterial fruit blotch	4. Apple	(*iv*) *Ustilago maydis*
		(*v*) Plasmopara viticola
		(*vi*) *Venturia inaequalis*

	(*a*)	(*b*)	(*c*)	(*d*)
A.	2-(*v*)	1-(*iv*)	3-(*iii*)	4-(*vi*)
B.	2-(*ii*)	1-(*i*)	4-(*iii*)	3-(*i*)
C.	4-(*iii*)	1-(*iv*)	2-(*i*)	3-(*ii*)
D.	4-(*vi*)	1-(*iii*)	3-(*ii*)	2-(*v*)

CSIR-NET, JUNE, 2019

Non Chordate

35. The terms expressing some of the developmental events or specific body structures are given in column X and the names of animals that are associated with them in column Y:

Column X	Column Y
(*a*) Torsion	(*i*) Star Fish
(*b*) Metagenesis	(*ii*) Obelia
(*c*) Apolysis	(*iii*) Taenia
(*d*) Pedicellaria	(*iv*) Apple snail

The correct match of the terms in column X with the name of animals in column Y is:

	(*a*)	(*b*)	(*c*)	(*d*)
A.	(*i*)	(*ii*)	(*iii*)	(*iv*)
B.	(*iv*)	(*ii*)	(*iii*)	(*i*)
C.	(*iii*)	(*i*)	(*ii*)	(*iv*)
D.	(*ii*)	(*iv*)	(*i*)	(*iii*)

Chordate

36. Which of the following describes the identification features of non-poisonous snakes?

A. Cylindrical tail and small belly scales
B. Cylindrical tail, broad transverse belly scales and 4th infralabial scale is the largest
C. Flat tail, broad transverse scales and 3rd supralabial scale touches eye and nose
D. Cylindrical tail, broad transverse belly scales and a loreal pit between eye and nostril

37. Following are some generalizations related to wood anatomy of higher plants:

(*a*) The axial system of conifer woods consist mainly or entirely of tracheids.
(*b*) The rays of conifers typically contain only parenchyma cells.
(*c*) The rays of angiosperms typically contain both sclerenchyma cells and tracheids.

(*d*) Angiosperm wood may be either diffuse porous or ring-porous.

Which one of the following options represents all correct statements?

A. (*a*) and (*b*) only B. (*a*) and (*d*) only
C. (*b*) and (*c*) only D. (*c*) and (*d*) only

Plant and Microbial Diversity

38. Only members of the plant kingdom and many bacteria have capability of biological nitrogen reduction. In this regard following statements are given:

(*a*) Nitrogen is normally taken by the plant in their fully oxidized form but needs to be reduced before incorporation in organic molecules.
(*b*) Conversion of oxidized nitrogen into reduced nitrogen needs energy in the form of NAD(P).
(*c*) The metal associated with the enzyme nitrate reductase is Magnesium.
(*d*) Nitrate reduction takes place in the cytoplasm, whereas nitrite reduction takes place in chloroplast.

Which one of the following combinations of the above statements is correct?

A. (*a*) and (*c*) B. (*a*), (*b*) and (*c*)
C. (*b*) and (*d*) D. (*a*) and (*d*)

39. The table lists characteristic anatomical features and names of plants.

Anatomical features	Plants
(*a*) Prostele, xylem core surrounded by phloem.	(*i*) Lycopodium
(*b*) Siphonostele, center pith present or modulated protostele	(*ii*) Marsilea rhizome
(*c*) Eustele, conjoint vasculature on edges of the path.	(*iii*) Selaginella species
	(*iv*) Equisetum

Choose the option that correctly matches plant with their characteristic features.

	(*a*)	(*b*)	(*c*)
A.	(*iii*)	(*ii*)	(*iv*)
B.	(*i*)	(*iii*)	(*iv*)
C.	(*iii*)	(*i*)	(*ii*)
D.	(*i*)	(*ii*)	(*iv*)

40. Which one of the following is a fungal disease of plants?

A. Cucumber mosaic B. Fire Blight of pear
C. Crown gall D. Apple scab

CSIR-NET, 15 DECEMBER, 2019

Non Chordate

41. Which one of the following show complete metamorphosis in all three orders?

A. Coleopterans, Dipterans and Hymenopterans
B. Coleopterans, Hymenopterans and Orthopterans
C. Dipterans, Lepidopterans and Hemipterans
D. Hymenopterans, Lepidopterans and Orthopterans

42. Cnidarians are

A. triploblastic animals with bilateral symmetry.
B. diploblastic animals with medusa as one of the basic body forms.
C. monoblastic organisms with tube feet.
D. asymmetric organisms with tentacles containing poison glands.

Chordate

43. Given below are certain adaptations which are seen in various groups of anin

(*a*) Ovipary Streamlined body
(*b*) Pouch for carrying eggs
(*c*) Porous egg shell
(*d*) Breast bone as large keel
(*e*) Webbed feet
(*f*) Laterally compressed coccygeal bone
(*g*) Unidirectional pulmonary system to provide large quantities of oxygen
(*h*) Barbules or hooklets on the vanes of each feather

Which combination of the above adaptations facilitate bird flight?

A. (*b*), (*e*), (*h*), (*i*) B. (*a*), (*b*), (*c*), (*g*)
C. (*d*), (*f*), (*g*), (*i*) D. (*b*), (*d*), (*e*), (*f*)

Plant and Microbial Diversity

44. Which one of the following plants has this combination of key plant traits: sporophyte dominant in the lifecycle, vascular tissue, lack of seeds?

A. Mosses B. Ferns
C. Cycads D. Monocots

45. Certain plant species produce cyanogenic glycosides to protect them from pathogens. A researcher has identified a variant of such a plant that has higher level of cyanogenic glycoside yet it is highly susceptible to a specific fungal pathogen. To interpret this counter-intuitive observation, the researcher hypothesizes that the fungal pathogen has higher level of

(*a*) B-glucosidase activity
(*b*) formamide hydrolyase activity
(*c*) cytochrome P-450 enzyme
(*d*) cyanide-resistant, alternative oxidase activity

Which one of the following combinations of the above hypotheses is correct?

A. (*a*) and (*b*) B. (*b*) and (*c*)
C. (*c*) and (*d*) D. (*b*) and (*d*)

46. Match the following taxa with the genus of the microorganism

Taxa	Genus
(*a*) Ascomycota	(*i*) *Rhizopus*
(*b*) Basidiomycota	(*ii*) *Erysiphe*
(*c*) Zygomycota	(*iii*) *Pythium*
(*d*) Oomycota	(*iv*) *Ustilago*

	(*a*)	(*b*)	(*c*)	(*d*)
A.	(*ii*)	(*iv*)	(*i*)	(*iii*)
B.	(*ii*)	(*iii*)	(*i*)	(*iv*)
C.	(*ii*)	(*iv*)	(*iii*)	(*i*)
D.	(*i*)	(*ii*)	(*iv*)	(*ii*)

47. Match the following plant diseases with the name of pathogen associated with the disease

Disease	*Pathogen*
(*a*) Powdery mildew	(*i*) *Erwinia amylovora*
(*b*) Rice blast	(*ii*) *Pseudomonas syringae*
(*c*) Bacterial canker	(*iii*) *Magnaporthe oryzae v. Syringae*
(*d*) Fire blight	(*iv*) *Erysiphe cichoracearum*

	(*a*)	(*b*)	(*c*)	(*d*)
A.	(*ii*)	(*iii*)	(*i*)	(*iv*)
B.	(*i*)	(*iv*)	(*ii*)	(*iii*)
C.	(*iv*)	(*iii*)	(*ii*)	(*i*)
D.	(*iii*)	(*ii*)	(*iv*)	(*i*)

CSIR-NET, 27 DECEMBER, 2019

Non Chordate

48. The names of some specialized organs/structures are given in Column A and their location in organisms are given in Column B

Column A	Column B
(*a*) Crystalline style	(*i*) Stomach of bivalves
(*b*) Hastate plate	(*ii*) Stomach of crustaceans
(*c*) Organ of Bojanus	(*iii*) Kidney of gastropods
(*d*) Mehlis's gland	(*iv*) Female reproductive system of Fasciola

Select the correct matches:

	(*a*)	(*b*)	(*c*)	(*d*)
A.	(*ii*)	(*i*)	(*iv*)	(*iii*)
B.	(*iii*)	(*iv*)	(*ii*)	(*i*)
C.	(*i*)	(*ii*)	(*iii*)	(*iv*)
D.	(*iv*)	(*iii*)	(*i*)	(*ii*)

Plant and Microbial Diversity

49. The table below shows the number of unrooted and rooted trees generated when the number of taxa are three and four, respectively.

Number of taxa	Number of unrooted tree	Number of rooted tree
3	1	3
4	3	15
5	15	?

The number of rooted trees generated when there are five taxa is:

A. 75
B. 78
C. 105
D. 126

50. Given below are some statements related to bacterial toxins.

(*a*) Exotoxins are usually heat stable proteins secreted by bacteria.

(*b*) Exotoxins are usually heat labile proteins secreted by bacteria.

(*c*) Endotoxins are heat stable lipopolysaccharide-protein complexes of the outer membrane of gram-negative bacteria.

(*d*) Endotoxins are heat labile lipoproteins of the outer membrane of gram-negative bacteria.

Which one of the following options represents combination of correct statements?

A. (*a*) and (*b*)
B. (*b*) and (*c*)
C. (*b*) and (*d*)
D. (*a*) and (*d*)

GATE (LIFE SCIENCE), 2019

Animal Diversity

51. The phylum that is characterized by the animals having a "water vascular system" is

A. Cnidaria
B. Annelida
C. Mollusca
D. Echinodermata

52. Which one of the following parasites does NOT cause lymphatic filariasis?

A. Brugia malayi
B. Brugia timori
C. Wuchereria bancrofti
D. Mansonella streptocerca

Plant and Microbial Diversity

53. Which one of the following families shows bicollateral vascular bundle in the transverse section of the stem?
A. Rutaceae
B. Asteraceae
C. Cucurbitaceae
D. Malvaceae

Economic and Applied Botany

54. Match the plant species and their corresponding families with their economically important products:

Plant species	Family	Plant products
(*a*) *Cannabis sativa*	1. Lamiaceae	(*i*) Oil from seeds
(*b*) *Corchorus sanctum*	2. Cannabaceae	(*ii*) Eugenol from leaves
(*c*) *Ocimum sanctum*	3. Euphorbiaceae	(*iii*) Fibre from stem
(*d*) *Ricinus communis*	4. Tiliaceae	(*iv*) Marijuana from leaves

	(*a*)	(*b*)	(*c*)	(*d*)
A.	2-(*iv*)	3-(*ii*)	4-(*iii*)	1-(*i*)
B.	3-(*iv*)	2-(*i*)	1-(*ii*)	4-(*iii*)
C.	1-(*iii*)	4-(*iii*)	2-(*i*)	3-(*ii*)
D.	2-(*iv*)	4-(*iii*)	1-(*ii*)	3-(*i*)

Plant Pathology

55. Match the disease with causative organism and affected crop

Plant species	Family	Plant products
(*a*) Powdery mildew	1. Albugo candida	(*i*) Corn
(*b*) White rust	2. Phytophthora infestans	(*ii*) Tomato
(*c*) Downy mildew	3. Erysiphe orontii	(*iii*) Potato
(*d*) Late blight	4. Peronosclerospora philippinensis	(*iv*) Mustard

	(*a*)	(*b*)	(*c*)	(*d*)
A.	3-(*i*)	1-(*iv*)	2-(*iii*)	4-(*ii*)
B.	3-(*ii*)	1-(*iv*)	4-(*i*)	2-(*iii*)
C.	4-(*ii*)	1-(*i*)	3-(*iv*)	2-(*iii*)
D.	2-(*iii*)	3-(*ii*)	1-(*iv*)	4-(*i*)

CSIR-NET, NOVEMBER (MORNING), 2020

Non Chordate

56. Which one of the following approaches is INCORRECT in classifying organisms from kingdom Animalia?
A. Spicules were used as a primary criterion for the classification of phylum Porifera
B. Protostomes were classified into two major lineages: Lophotrochozoans and Ecdysozoans
C. Hemichordates were placed in same superclass as Echinoderms because both have ciliated larvae
D. Ambulacrarians included Echinoderms and Hemichordates

57. Column I list names of organisms and column II of three study sites. The table below it shows list stages in life cycle.

Column I	Column II
(*a*) Taeria	(*i*) Hexacanth
(*b*) Obelia	(*ii*) Glochidium
(*c*) Unio	(*iii*) Planula
(*d*) Balanoglossus	(*iv*) Tornaria
	(*v*) Miracidium

Which one of the following options represents all correct matches between the two columns?

	(*a*)	(*b*)	(*c*)	(*d*)
A.	(*i*)	(*ii*)	(*iii*)	(*v*)
B.	(*iii*)	(*ii*)	(*i*)	(*v*)
C.	(*i*)	(*iii*)	(*ii*)	(*iv*)
D.	(*ii*)	(*v*)	(*iii*)	(*iv*)

58. Which of the following phytopathogens has predominantly necrotrophic mode of colonization?
A. Phytophthora infestans
B. Erwinia spp.
C. Erysiphe pisi
D. Puccinia graminis

CSIR-NET, NOVEMBER (AFTERNOON), 2020

Non Chordate

59. A lectotype refers to
A. a specimen of the opposite sex to the holotype and designated from among paratypes.
B. an illustration based on which a new species is described.
C. a specimen later selected from a group of syntypes to serve as the type specimen for a species, after its original description was published.
D. a substitute specimen selected to serve as the type specimen of a species after its original description was published, when an original holotype has been lost or destroyed.

60. Appendix masculina is found in
A. second abdominal appendages of male palaemon
B. second maxillipede of male palaemon
C. maxilla of both sexes of palaemon
D. mandibles of male palaemon

61. The three domain classification of life proposed by Carl Woese divides life forms on the basis of
A. mitochondrial DNA and membrane structures
B. ribosomal rRNA and protein sequences
C. mitochondrial DNA and protein sequences
D. presence of single or double membranes

Plant and Microbial Diversity

62. Artemisinin and Dhurrin belong to which two respective groups of the plant natural compounds?
A. Alkaloids and Terpenes
B. Flavonoids and Alkaloids
C. Cyanogenic glycosides and Flavonoids
D. Terpenes and Cyanogenic glycosides

GATE (LIFE SCIENCE), 2020

Animal Diversity

63. Which ONE of the following phyla have choanocytes?
A. Ctenophora B. Nematoda
C. Cnidaria D. Porifera

64. Tarantulas and mosquitoes both belong to the phylum Arthropoda. Which ONE of the following represents the correct number of legs in them respectively?
A. 6 and 6 B. 6 and 8
C. 8 and 8 D. 8 and 6

65. Match the household insect vectors in Column I with their associated diseases in Column II

Column I	Column II
(*a*) Kissing bug (Hemiptera)	(*i*) Bubonic plague
(*b*) Sand fly (Diptera)	(*ii*) Tularemia
(*c*) Deer fly (Diptera)	(*iii*) Chagas disease
(*d*) Oriental rat flea (Siphonaptera)	(*iv*) Kala azar

	(*a*)	(*b*)	(*c*)	(*d*)
A.	(*iv*)	(*iii*)	(*ii*)	(*i*)
B.	(*iii*)	(*ii*)	(*i*)	(*iv*)
C.	(*i*)	(*iv*)	(*iii*)	(*ii*)
D.	(*iii*)	(*iv*)	(*ii*)	(*i*)

Plant and Microbial Diversity

Plant Systematics

66. Indefinite stamen is a characteristic feature of which of the following plant families?
A. *Malvaceae* B. Apocynaceae
C. Poaceae D. *Brassicaceae*

Plant Anatomy

67. In natural condition, which of the following plants DOES NOT exhibit anomalous secondary growth?
A. Rice B. Aloe
C. Yucca D. Dracaena

68. Match the plant part (Group I) with the product obtained (Group II) and the representative plant species (Group III) in CORRECT combination

Group I	Group II	Group III
(*a*) Bark	1. Tannin	(*i*) *Papaver somniferum*
(*b*) Leaf	2. Saffron	(*ii*) *Camellia sinensis*
(*c*) Flower	3. Codiene	(*iii*) *Cinnamomum zeylanicum*
(*d*) Fruit	4. Aromatic oil	(*iv*) *Crocus sativus*

	(*a*)	(*b*)	(*c*)	(*d*)
A.	(*ii*)-1	(*i*)-3	(*iv*)-2	(*iii*)-4
B.	(*ii*)-1	(*i*)-2	(*iv*)-4	(*iii*)-1
C.	(*ii*)-2	(*iv*)-3	(*i*)-2	(*iii*)-1
D.	(*iv*)-1	(*i*)-2	(*ii*)-4	(*iii*)-1

69. Match the following alkaloids with their uses and source plant in CORRECT

Alkaloid	Use	Source plant
(*a*) Morphine	(*i*) Anticancer	1. *Cinchona officinalis*
(*b*) Quinine	(*ii*) Analgesic	2. *Catharanthus roseus*
(*c*) Atropine	(*iii*) Anti-cholinergic	3. *Papaver somniferum*
(*d*) Vinblastine	(*iv*) Anti-malarial	4. *Hyoscyamus niger*

	(*a*)	(*b*)	(*c*)	(*d*)
A.	(*ii*)-3	(*iv*)-1	(*iii*)-4	(*i*)-2
B.	(*ii*)-1	(*i*)-3	(*iv*)-4	(*iii*)-2
C.	(*ii*)-2	(*iv*)-1	(*i*)-4	(*iii*)-3
D.	(*iii*)-4	(*ii*)-1	iv-3	(*i*)-2

Plant Pathology

70. Select the CORRECT combination by matching the disease, causal organism and affected plant.

Fruit character	Family	Plant species
(*a*) Stem rust	(*i*) Cercospora personata	1. *Wheat*
(*b*) Wart disease	(*ii*) Plasmopara viticola	2. *Ground nut*
(*c*) Tikka/leaf spot	(*iii*) Synchytrium endobioticum	3. *Potato*
(*d*) Downey mildew	(*iv*) Puccinia graminis	4. *Grape*
		5. Apple
		6. *Rice*

	(a)	(b)	(c)	(d)
A.	(iv)-1	(iii)-3	(i)-2	(ii)-4
B.	(ii)-1	(i)-6	(iv)-4	(iii)-2
C.	(iii)-1	(iv)-3	(i)-5	(iii)-4
D.	(iv)-1	(ii)-3	(iii)-2	(i)-5

71. Bakanae' disease or 'foolish seedling' disease is caused by

A. Fungus B. Bacterium
C. Virus D. Mycoplasm

CSIR-NET, JUNE (MORNING), 2021

Non Chordate

72. Which of the following is the causative agent of filariasis?

A. Listeria monocytogenes
B. Cryptococcus neoformans
C. Francisella tularensis
D. Brugia malayi

Plant and Microbial Classification

73. Given below are two columns listing angiosperms families and their groups

List I Group	List II Family
(a) Basal angiosperms	(i) Brassicaceae
(b) Fabids	(ii) Cucurbitaceae
(c) Malvids	(iii) Solanaceae
(d) Lamids	(iv) Nymphaeaceae

	(a)	(b)	(c)	(d)
A.	(iv)	(ii)	(i)	(iii)
B.	(iv)	(i)	(iii)	(ii)
C.	(iii)	(iv)	(ii)	(i)
D.	(ii)	(iii)	(i)	(iv)

74. The table given below list fossils and the major group of plants to which they belong

List I Fossil	List II Plant Group
(a) Naiadita lanceolata	(i) Angiosperm
(b) Rhynia gwynne-vaughanii	(ii) Pteridophyte
(c) Antarticycas schopfii	(iii) Bryophyte
(d) Tricolpites minutes	(iv) Bryophyte

Which one of the following options represents the correct match between columns?

	(a)	(b)	(c)	(d)
A.	(i)	(iii)	(iv)	(ii)
B.	(iii)	(ii)	(iv)	(i)
C.	(i)	(ii)	(iv)	(iii)
D.	(ii)	(iii)	(i)	(iv)

75. The table given below lists the morphological features and groups of plants

List I Plant group	List II Morphological characters
(a)	(i) Unicellular rhizoids
	(ii) Multicellular rhizoids
(b)	(iii) Presence of pyrenoids
	(iv) Stomata on sporophyte
	(v) Dominant gametophyte

Which one of the following options represents the correct match between two column?

A. (a)-(i), (iii) and (v); (a)-(ii), (iii) and (v)
B. (a)-(i), (iii) and (iv); (a)-(ii) and (iv)
C. (a)-(ii) and (v); (a)-(i) and (iii)
D. (a)-(i) and (v); (a)-(ii), (iv) and (v)

76. Given below are the names of diseases caused in rice in column X and the names of the disease-causing organisms in column Y.

Column X	Column Y
(a) Bacterial blight	(i) Entyloma oryzae
(b) Grain rot	(ii) Rhizoctonia solani
(c) Sheath blight	(iii) Xanthomonas oryzae pv. oryzae
(d) Leaf smut	(iv) Sclerophthora macrospora
(e) Downy mildew	(v) Burkholderia glumac

Which one of the following options represents the correct match between two column?

	(a)	(b)	(c)	(d)	(e)
A.	(ii)	(i)	(v)	(iv)	(iii)
B.	(iii)	(iv)	(ii)	(v)	(i)
C.	(iv)	(iii)	(i)	(ii)	(v)
D.	(iii)	(v)	(ii)	(i)	(iv)

CSIR-NET, JUNE (AFTERNOON), 2021

Non Chordate

77. The fall armyworm is a recent, fast invading, destructive herbivore in agricultural systems in north India. This pest species belongs to which one of the following Orders?

A. Hemiptera
B. Homoptera
C. Diptera
D. Lepidoptera

78. The table below lists the name of organisms and different aspects of nervous system.

Organism	Nervous System
(*a*) Protozoan	(*i*) Central and peripheral nervous system
(*b*) Jellyfish	(*ii*) Two cephalic ganglia joined by commissure
(*c*) Flatworm	(*iii*) Diffuse nervous system with small ganglia center
(*d*) Bony fish	(*iv*) Stimulus-response coordination

Which of the following options represent a correct match between the two columns

	(*a*)	(*b*)	(*c*)	(*d*)
A.	(*ii*)	(*iv*)	(*i*)	(*iii*)
B.	(*iv*)	(*iii*)	(*ii*)	(*i*)
C.	(*iii*)	(*i*)	(*iv*)	(*ii*)
D.	(*iv*)	(*ii*)	(*iii*)	(*i*)

GATE (LIFE SCIENCE), 2021

Animal Diversity

79. Ichthyophis belongs to which of the following Class?

A. Mammalia
B. Reptilia
C. Amphibia
D. Aves

Plant and Microbial Diversity

Plant Systematics

80. Which ONE of the following plant taxa contains vascular tissue (xylem and phloem) but not woody tissue?

A. Oak B. Moss
C. Pine D. Fern

CSIR-NET, SEPTEMBER (MORNING), 2022

Non Chordate

81. Which one of the options correctly represents organisms from the subphyla Chelicerata, Myriapoda, and specific sequence?

A. Arachnids, horseshoe crabs, centipedes
B. Horseshoe crabs, centipedes, springtails
C. Lobsters, millipedes, silverfish
D. Arachnids, insects, crabs

Chordate

82. The following are a set of characteristics found in the animal kingdom:

(*a*) The body is usually streamlined. Some have spindle-shaped or elongated body.
(*b*) The body is covered with thick-seated scales, which provides protection to the internal organs.
(*c*) They may be herbivores or carnivores, oviparous or ovoviviparous.
(*d*) The nervous system comprises of the brain and ten pairs of the cranial nerves.
(*e*) All of them are oviparous and exhibit sexual dimorphism.

Select the correct set of characterizing features for the Class Pisces

A. (*b*), (*d*) and (*e*) only B. (*a*), (*b*) and (*d*) only
C. (*b*), (*c*), (*d*) and (*e*) D. (*a*), (*b*), (*c*) and (*d*)

CSIR-NET, SEPTEMBER (AFTERNOON), 2022

Non Chordate

83. Which one of the following statements about corals is NOT CORRECT?

A. Corals possess special stinging cells called nematocysts in their tentacles for capturing prey
B. Several corals have mutualistic interactions with microorganisms called zooxanthellae that photosynthesize and pass some of the food to their hosts.
C. Reefs form when corals grow in shallow water close to the shores.
D. All corals grow only in the photic zones as they need sunlight for their growth.

Plant Classification

84. Select the option that correctly identifies all organisms that are included in the International Code of Nomenclature (Shenzhen Code, 2017) along with plants:

A. Prokaryotes together with all algae and fungi, except their fossils.
B. All algae and fungi along with their fossils, except Microsporidia.
C. Prokaryotes and algae, except Microsporidia.
D. Photosynthetic algae and fungi.

DBT-JRF, 2022

85. Which one of the following is the most accurate statement regarding giardiasis?

A. The drug of choice for giardiasis is chloroquine

B. Giardia lamblia produces an enterotoxin that increases cAMP within the enterocyte, resulting in diarrhea

C. Giardia lamblia infection is acquired by ingestion of food or water contaminated with human feces only (i.e. there is no animal reservoir for this organism)

D. Infection by Giardia lamblia occurs principally in the small intestine frequently resulting in the malabsorption of protein and fat

86. Which form of the plasmodia is transmitted from mosquito to human?

A. Sporozoite

B. Gametocyte

C. Merozoite

D. Hypnozoite

87. Which one of the following statements is most relevant to leishmaniasis?

A. Large domestic animals such as cattle are the principal reservoir of L. donovani

B. Both visceral leishmaniasis and cutaneous leishmaniasis are transmitted by the bite of sandflies

C. Artemisinin is effective in the treatment of leishmaniasis

D. Leishmaniasis is transmitted by the bite of female Anopheles mosquitoes

GATE (BIOTECHNOLOGY), 2022

88. In binomial nomenclature, the name of a bacterial strain is written with the first letter of __________ word(s) being capitalized.

A. first B. second C. neither D. first and second

GATE (LIFE SCIENCE), 2022

Animal Diversity

89. Match the animals listed in Column I with primary tissue or organ of residence in the host listed in Column II

Column I	Column II
(*a*) Ascaris lumbricoides	(*i*) Subcutaneous tissue in human
(*b*) Dracunculus medinensis	(*ii*) Lymphatic vessels and lymph nodes
(*c*) Enterobius vermicularis	(*iii*) Small intestine
(*d*) Wuchereria bancrofti	(*iv*) Caecum or vermiform appendix

	(*a*)	(*b*)	(*c*)	(*d*)
A.	(*iii*)	(*iv*)	(*ii*)	(*i*)
B.	(*i*)	(*iv*)	(*iii*)	(*ii*)
C.	(*ii*)	(*iii*)	(*iv*)	(*i*)
D.	(*iii*)	(*i*)	(*iv*)	(*ii*)

Plant and Microbial Diversity

Plant Systematics

90. In Angiosperms, normally 'Exarch Xylem' occurs in

A. dicot stem

B. monocot stem

C. dicot root

D. dicot leaf

91. Phylogenetic system of classification is/are proposed by

A. Carolus Linnaeus

B. John Hutchinson

C. Engler and Prantl

D. Bentham and Hooker

92. Anomalous secondary growth is observed in

A. Triticum

B. Oryza

C. Zea

D. Dracaena

ANSWERS

1	**2**	**3**	**4**	**5**	**6**	**7**	**8**	**9**	**10**
B	A	C	B	A	B	C	B	D	C
11	**12**	**13**	**14**	**15**	**16**	**17**	**18**	**19**	**20**
C	B	D	C	C	D	B	B	B	C
21	**22**	**23**	**24**	**25**	**26**	**27**	**28**	**29**	**30**
B	D	D	D	B	C	A	A	B	C
31	**32**	**33**	**34**	**35**	**36**	**37**	**38**	**39**	**40**
B	A	B	C	B	A	B	D	A	D
41	**42**	**43**	**44**	**45**	**46**	**47**	**48**	**49**	**50**
A	B	A	B	D	A	C	C	C	B
51	**52**	**53**	**54**	**55**	**56**	**57**	**58**	**59**	**60**
D	D	C	D	B	C	C	B	C	A
61	**62**	**63**	**64**	**65**	**66**	**67**	**68**	**69**	**70**
B	D	D	D	C	A	A	D	A	A
71	**72**	**73**	**74**	**75**	**76**	**77**	**78**	**79**	**80**
A	D	A	B	D	D	D	B	C	D
81	**82**	**83**	**84**	**85**	**86**	**87**	**88**	**89**	**90**
B	D	D	B	D	A	B	A	D	C
91	**92**								
B,C	D								

CHAPTER

15

PLANT PHYSIOLOGY

CSIR-NET, JUNE, 2017

Plant Morphology & Reproduction

1. The following is a list of reproductive structures found in vascular and non-vascular plants.

(*a*) Archegonia (*b*) Megaspore
(*c*) Capsule (*d*) Fern frond
(*e*) Pollen
(*f*) Corolla

Which of the following combinations represents structures primarily associated with the gametophytic life cycle of these plants?

A. (*a*), (*c*), (*f*) B. (*a*), (*b*), (*e*)
C. (*b*), (*d*), (*e*) D. (*c*), (*d*), (*f*)

Plant Hormones

2. For which one of the plant hormone biosynthetic pathways, 1-aminocyclo-propane- 1 -carboxylic acid is an intermediate?

A. Abscisic acid B. Brassinosteroid
C. Ethylene D. Gibberellic acid

Absorption and Transport of Food and Water

3. In a study, it was found that K+ ion concentration in root cells of a pea plant was ~75 times greater than that of the nutrient medium in which the plant was grown. This indicated that K+ ions were absorbed from the medium

A. Because the plant was grown continuously in the dark
B. by an active, energy-dependent process
C. by simple diffusion
D. through plasmodesmatal connections between the epidermis and the medium

4. Following are a few statements regarding water potential in plants:

(*a*) Solute concentration and pressure potential contribute to water potential of a plant cell in a given state.
(*b*) When a flaccid cell is placed in a solution that has a water potential less negative than the intracellular water potential, water will move from solution into the cell.
(*c*) When a flaccid cell is placed in a solution that has a water potential less negative than the intracellular water potential, water will move out from cell into the solution.
(*d*) Water potential of a plant cell under severe water stress is always less negative as compared to that of unstressed cells.

Which combination of the above statements is correct?

A. (*a*) and (*b*)
B. (*b*) and (*c*)
C. (*a*) and (*c*)
D. (*c*) and (*d*)

Sensory Photobiology-phytochrome & Cryptochrome

5. The following scheme shows the flowering status of a plant species and the photoperiod regimes in which it is grown (L denotes light period; D denotes dark period).

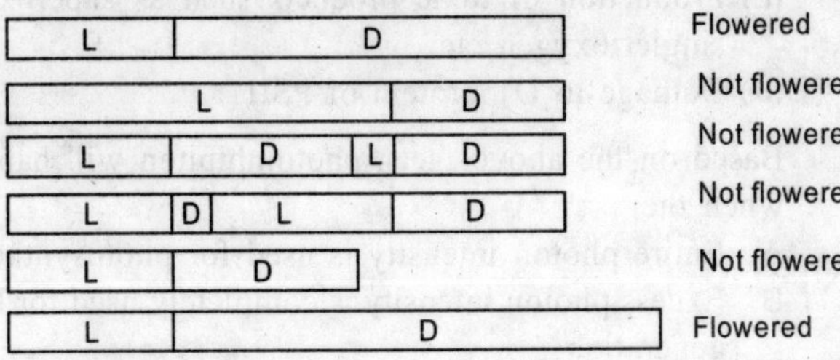

Which of the following conclusions is most appropriate?

A. The species is a short day plant; length of the dark phase determines flowering status.

B. The species is a long day plant; length of the dark phase determines flowering status.

C. The species is a short day plant; length of the light phase determines flowering status.

D. The species is a long day plant; length of the light phase determines flowering status.

6. In a photoresponse experiment, imbibed seeds were kept under the following light regime's and their germination status was noted as follows:

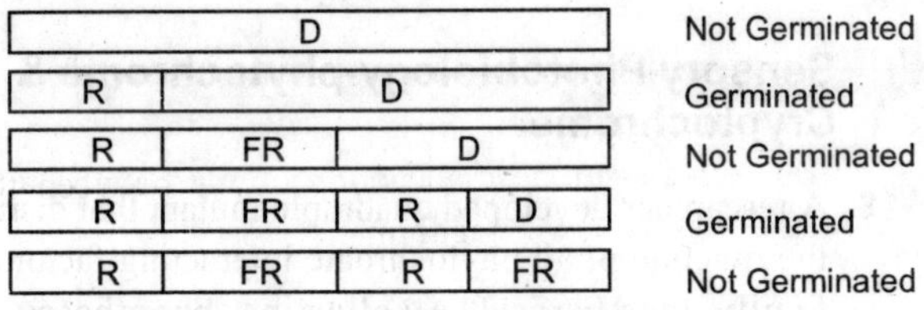

D: Darkness; R: Red light; FR: Far-red light

In an independent biochemical experiment, it was demonstrated that the red light photoreceptor phytochrome is interconverted between two forms, P and P', by red or far-red light. Keeping these information in mind, which of the following combination of conclusions is correct?

A. Red light converts P to P'; P' promotes seed germination

B. Far-red light converts P to P'; P' promotes seed germination

C. Red light converts P' to P ; P' promotes seed germination

D. Far-red light converts P' to P; P promotes seed germination

7. A plant is visited by bats during the night and sunbirds during the day. Given this information, which of the following characters best match this plant?

A. The plant is a herb with saucer shaped white flowers

B. The plant is a shrub with tubular, red, diurnal flowers

C. The plant is a liana with tubular cream coloured flowers

D. The plant is a grass with white coloured fragrant, spikelets

Stress Physiology & Secondary Metabolite

8. The following statements are made regarding secondary metabolites of plants:

(*a*) All secondary metabolites are constitutively produced in all cells of a plant during its entire life

(*b*) They serve as signals to help the plant survive adverse conditions

(*c*) They may be volatile compounds

(*d*) They contribute to flower colour

Which one of the following options represents a combination of correct statements?

A. (*a*), (*b*) and (*c*) B. (*b*), (*c*) and (*d*)
C. (*a*), (*c*) and (*d*) D. (*a*), (*b*) and (*d*)

9. Following are a few statements regarding the structure of terpenes:

(*a*) Isopentenyl diphosphate and farnesyl diphosphate are monoterpene and sesquiterpene, respectively.

(*b*) Squalene and geranyl diphosphate are triterpene and monoterpene, respectively.

(*c*) Dimethylally diphosphate have 10 and 20 carbons, respectively.

(*d*) Diterpenes have 20 carbons, whereas sesquiterpenes have 15 carbons

Which combination of the above statements is correct?

A. (*a*) and (*b*)

B. (*b*) and (*d*)

C. (*a*) and (*c*)

D. (*c*) and (*d*)

CSIR-NET, DECEMBER, 2017

Plant Morphology & Reproduction

10. Euphorbiaceae generally represents milky sap bearing plants but there are also some non-milky sap bearing plants that belong to this family. Identify the correct combination of the following given plants which belong to family Euphorbiaceae.

A. *Terminalia bellirica, Euphorbia hirta, Nerium indicum*

B. *Mallotus philippense, Ficus religiosa, Ricinus communis*

C. *Mallotus philippense, Acalypha indica, Emblica officinalis*

D. *Acalypha indica, Ricinus communis, Mangifera indica*

11. Match the two columns that represent plant organs (I) and parts within these organs (II).

Column I	Column II
(*a*) Carpel	(*i*) Petals, corolla
(*b*) Perianth	(*ii*) Vegetative cell, generative cell
(*c*) Microsporocyte	(*iii*) Stigma, style, ovary
(*d*) Megasporocyte	(*iv*) Antipodal cells, polar nuclei, synergid cells

	(*a*)	(*b*)	(*c*)	(*d*)
A.	(*i*)	(*iii*)	(*ii*)	(*iv*)
B.	(*iii*)	(*iv*)	(*i*)	(*ii*)
C.	(*i*)	(*iii*)	(*iv*)	(*ii*)
D.	(*iii*)	(*i*)	(*ii*)	(*iv*)

Plant Hormones

12. Which one of the following is the correct function of JAZ (Jasmonate Zim domain) protein family, a key regulator of Jasmonic Acid (JA) signalling response?

A. Binds to MYC2 and represses the JA dependent genes.
B. Binds to MYC2 and transcribes JA dependent genes.
C. Acts as receptor of JA signal.
D. Involved in directly inducing JA dependent genes

13. The plant hormone, Gibberellic Acid is generally not associated with

A. Stem elongation B. Parthenocarpy
C. Parthenogenesis D. Malt production

Absorption and Transport of Food and Water

14. Which one of the following statements is NOT correct for Casparian strip?

A. It breaks the continuity of water movement through the apoplast pathway
B. It is formed in the growing part of the root
C. It is formed several millimetres or several centimetres behind the root tip
D. It is a band within the radial cell walls of the endodermis that is impregnated with lignin

15. Which one of the following statements is true about xylem in plants?

A. It is characterized by the presence of tracheary elements responsible for the conduction of water in vascular plants.
B. It is responsible for the transport of water and characterized by sieve elements like parenchyma cells and sclereids
C. It is responsible for the transport of assimilates in the vascular plants and characterized by tracheary elements.
D. It is responsible for the transport of assimilates in both vascular and nonvascular plants

Photosynthesis & Photorespiration

16. The photon intensity captured by green plants is used in the following processes:

(*a*) Photosynthesis
(*b*) Generation of heat
(*c*) Production of toxic products such as superoxide, singlet oxygen etc.
(*d*) Damage to D1 protein of PSII

Based on the above facts, photoinhibiton will happen when the

A. Entire photon intensity is used for photosynthesis
B. Excess photon intensity is completely used for heat generation
C. Excess photon intensity is used for heat generation and formation of toxic products
D. Excess photon intensity leads to the damage of D1 protein.

Nitrogen Metabolism and Plant Growth

17. Which one of the following is NOT a phenotype of dark-grown seedlings that are etiolated?

A. Short hypocotyls
B. An apical hook
C. Closed cotyledons
D. Non-photosynthetic proplastids

Sensory Photobiology-phytochrome & Cryptochrome

18. A researcher developed quadruple mutant that disrupted the function of all phytochrome interacting factor (PIF) family members. The following hypotheses were proposed regarding the phenotype of the mutant plants when grown in dark:

(*a*) Plants would show short hypocotyls
(*b*) Plants would be etiolated
(*c*) Light induced genes would be activated
(*d*) The cotyledons would be open

Which one of the following combinations of the above hypotheses is correct?

A. (*a*), (*b*) and (*c*) B. (*a*), (*b*) and (*d*)
C. (*a*), (*c*) and (*d*) D. (*b*), (*c*) and (*d*)

Stress Physiology & Secondary Metabolite

19. Identify the plant species from which artemisinin, an anti-malarial drug, is extracted.

A. *Artemisia maritime* B. *Artemisia scoparia*
C. *Artemisia annua* D. *Cinchona officinalis*

20. Given below are some statements on secondary metabolites in plants.

(*a*) Glucosinolates are synthesized by elongation in the length of side chains of their precursor amino acids.

(*b*) All terpenes produced in herbs and spices are sticky, oily liquids which reduces the palatability(edible value) of these plants.

(*c*) Cyanogenic glycosides are produced and stored in a toxic form in plants and are therefore more effective in defense against invading pathogens and herbivores.

(*d*) The defense molecules, alkaloids (or their precursors), are gathered from plants and used by some insects for their own protection against predators.

Which one of the following represents correct statements?

A. (*b*) and (*c*) only
B. (*a*) and (*b*) only
C. C only
D. (*a*) and (*d*) only

21. With reference to plant biotic interactions, match the terms of Column I with the most appropriate term of Column II

Column I	Column II
(*a*) Phytoliths of Poaceae	(*i*) Phloem feeders
(*b*) Salicylic acid signalling pathway	(*ii*) Decrease in stomatal aperture
(*c*) MAMP	(*iii*) R genes/NBS LRR receptor
(*d*) Effector – triggered immunity	(*iv*) Mechanical barrier to herbivory

	(*a*)	(*b*)	(*c*)	(*d*)
A.	(*ii*)	(*iv*)	(*i*)	(*iii*)
B.	(*iii*)	(*i*)	(*ii*)	(*iv*)
C.	(*iv*)	(*ii*)	(*iii*)	(*i*)
D.	(*iv*)	(*i*)	(*ii*)	(*iii*)

GATE (BIOTECHNOLOGY), 2017

22. Match the plant hormones in Column I with function in Column II

Column I	Column II
(*a*) Gibberellic acid	(*i*) Seed and bud dormancy
(*b*) Zeatin	(*ii*) Fruit ripening
(*c*) Ethylene	(*iii*) Delaying leaf senescence
(*d*) Abscisic acid	(*iv*) Regulation of plant height

	(*a*)	(*b*)	(*c*)	(*d*)
A.	(*iv*)	(*iii*)	(*ii*)	(*i*)
B.	(*iv*)	(*ii*)	(*iii*)	(*i*)
C.	(*iii*)	(*i*)	(*ii*)	(*iv*)
D.	(*ii*)	(*i*)	(*iv*)	(*iii*)

23. Which one of the following organisms is responsible for crown gall diseases in plants?

A. *Xanthomonas campestris*
B. *Rhizobium etli*
C. *Agrobacterium tumefaciens*
D. Erwinia stewartia

Agricultural Biotechnology

24. In the electron transport chain, which one of the following can be a two-electron carrier?

A. Cupro protein
B. Cytochrome
C. Flavin
D. Iron-Sulphur proteins

25. Match the components of List I with List II

List I	List II
(*a*) Legume	(*i*) Frankia
(*b*) Azolla	(*ii*) Azorhizobium
(*c*) Sugarcane	(*iii*) Anabaena
(*d*) Actinorhizal	(*iv*) Acetobacter

Choose the correct answer from the options given below:

	(*a*)	(*b*)	(*c*)	(*d*)
A.	(*i*)	(*iii*)	(*ii*)	(*iv*)
B.	(*ii*)	(*iii*)	(*i*)	(*iv*)
C.	(*ii*)	(*iii*)	(*iv*)	(*i*)
D.	(*ii*)	(*iv*)	(*i*)	(*iii*)

26. Nitrification during nitrogen cycle is the production of:

A. Ammonium
B. Nitrates
C. Nitric oxide
D. Nitrogen

27. Which one of the following combinations signify similar function?

A. Cryptochrome and fluorochrome
B. Cryptochrome and phytochrome
C. Cytochrome and Cryptochrome
D. fluorochrome and Cytochrome

28. When the critical night length in winters is disrupted by a pulse of red light followed by a pulse of far-red light:

A. Both long day and short-day plants will flower
B. Long-day plants will flower and short-day plants will not flower
C. None of the plants will flower
D. Short-day plants will flower and long-day plants will not flower

29. Which one of the following treatments is required for flowering in a winter annual type of Arabidopsis plants?

A. A short pulse of cold temperature
B. A short pulse of high temperature
C. High expression of Flowering Locus C (FLC) gene
D. Prolonged cold period

GATE (LIFE SCIENCE), 2017

Plant Physiology and Biochemistry

30. Which of the following plant hormones is a carotenoid-cleavage product?

A. Phytosulfokine B. Brassinosteroid
C. Methyl jasmonate D. Strigolactone

31. Identify the INCORRECT statement with relation to plant secondary metabolites

A. Atropine is a member of indole alkaloids
B. Limonene is a cyclic terpene found in citrus plants
C. Green tea is rich in polyphenols
D. Cyanidin contributes to the red color in rose petals

32. Choose the CORRECT set of matches between group I and group II in relation to nitrogen fixation and assimilation

Group I	Group II
(*a*) Nitrobacter	(*i*) $NO_3^- \rightarrow NO_2^-$
(*b*) Nitrite reductase	(*ii*) $N_2 \rightarrow 2NH_3$
(*c*) Nitrogenase	(*iii*) $NO_2^+ \rightarrow NH_4^+$
(*d*) Nitrate reductase	(*iv*) $NO_2^- \rightarrow NO_3^-$

	(*a*)	(*b*)	(*c*)	(*d*)
A.	(*iv*)	(*iii*)	(*ii*)	(*i*)
B.	(*iv*)	(*iii*)	(*i*)	(*ii*)
C.	(*i*)	(*ii*)	(*iv*)	(*iii*)
D.	(*iii*)	(*iv*)	(*ii*)	(*i*)

33. Two plant cells M and N are lying side by side making direct contact "M" has osmotic potential (Ψ_S) of -10 bar and pressure potential (Ψp) of bar. On the other hand, "N" has osmotic potential (Ψ_S) of -12 bar and pressure potential (Ψp) of 5 bar.

Based on these data. What would be the direction of movement of water between M and N?

A. M to N
B. N to M
C. There will be no movement
D. In both directions

34. Which TWO of the following reactions are INCORRECT in relation to C2 oxidative photosynthetic carbon cycle in land plants?

(*a*) 2(Ribulose-1, 5-bisphosphate) + $2(CO_2)$— 2(phosphoglycolate) + 2(3-phosphoglycerate) + $4H^+$
(*b*) Serine + α-ketoglutarate—hydroxypyruvate + glutamine
(*c*) 2(Phosphoglycolate) + $2(H_2O)$__2(glycolate) + 2Pi
(*d*) Hydroxypyruvate+NADH+H^+ ___ Glycerate + NAD^+

A. (*a*) and (*b*)
B. (*b*) and (*c*)
C. (c) and (d)
D. (*d*) and (*a*)

CSIR-NET, JUNE, 2018

Plant Hormones

35. Dark grown Arabidopsis seedlings show 'triple response' when exposed to ethylene hormone. Which one of the following options is characteristic of 'triple response'?

A. Reduced shoot elongation, increased shoot thickness and tightening of apical hook.
B. Reduced shoot elongation, reduced shoot thickness and loosening of apical hook.
C. Increased shoot elongation, increased shoot thickness and loosening of apical hook.
D. Increased shoot elongation, reduced shoot thickness and tightening of apical hook.

36. Brassinosteroids are a group of steroid hormones that function in a variety of cellular and developmental contexts in plants. Which one of the following acts as an inhibitor of the brassinosteroid receptor?

A. BRI 1
B. BKI 1
C. BAK 1
D. BSK1

Absorption and Transport of Food and Water

37. The table given below represents the types of intercellular transport in "Column I" in land plants and their transport pathways in "Column II".

I	II
(*a*) Apoplastic	Via interconnecting plasmodesmata
(*b*) Symplastic	Via the water filled spaces of the cell wallmatrices and lumen of xylem tracheary elements
(*c*) Transcellular Transport	Via the vacuole transport across the tonoplast followed by exit across the plasma membrane before regaining entry to the adjacent cell through the plasma membrane.

Which one of the following combinations matches column I correctly with column II

	(*a*)	(*b*)	(*c*)
A.	(*i*)	(*ii*)	(*iii*)
B.	(*ii*)	(*i*)	(*iii*)
C.	(*iii*)	(*ii*)	(*i*)
D.	(*i*)	(*iii*)	(*ii*)

Photosynthesis & Photorespiration

38. Which one of the following metabolites moves from mitochondria to peroxisome during the operation of the C2 oxidative photosynthetic cycle?

A. Glycerate B. Glycolate
C. Glycine D. Serine

39. Following are certain statements regarding Rubisco, the predominant protein in plant leaves that catalyzes the initial reaction of the Calvin-Benson cycle.

(*a*) During the oxygenase activity of Rubisco, O2 is used as substrate to produce three carbon molecule, 3-phosphoglyceratc and two-carbon molecule, 2-phosphoglycolate.

(*b*) In red and brown algae, the large subunit of Rubisco is localized in the chloroplast while small subunit is localized in the nucleus.

(*c*) The bound sugar phosphates in Rubisco are specifically removed by an ATP dependent enzyme, Rubisco activase.

(*d*) The active form of Rubisco catalyzes carboxylation or oxygenation reactions in five steps.

Which one of the following combinations of above statements is correct?

A. (*a*), (*b*) and (*c*) B. (*a*), (*b*) and (*d*)
C. (*b*), (*c*) and (*d*) D. (*a*), (*c*) and (*d*)

Sensory Photobiology-phytochrome & Cryptochrome

40. Melanopsin is found in which cell of the retina?

A. Cones B. Rods
C. Ganglion cells D. Bipolar cells

41. Stomata from detached epidermis of common dayflower (*Commelina communis*) were treated with saturating photon fluxes of red light. In a parallel treatment, stomata treated with red light were also illuminated with blue light (indicated by arrow). From the graphs shown below, select the correct pattern of stomata opening (solid lines and dotted lines represent stomatal aperture under red and blue lights, respectively).

A.
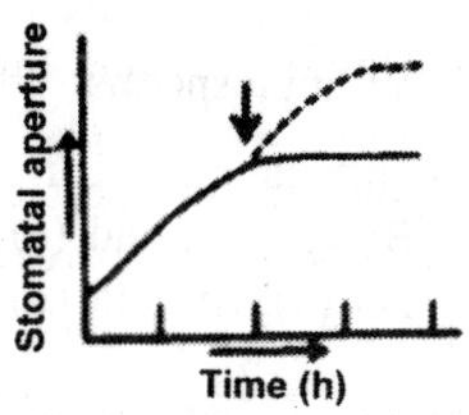

B.
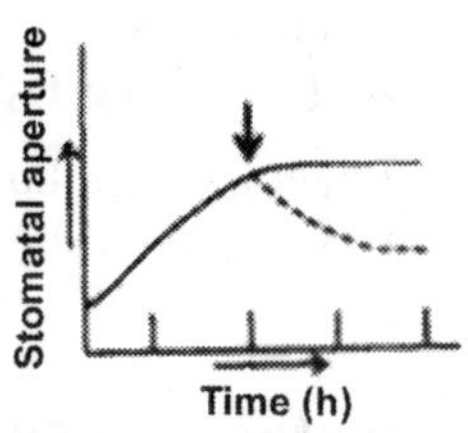

C.
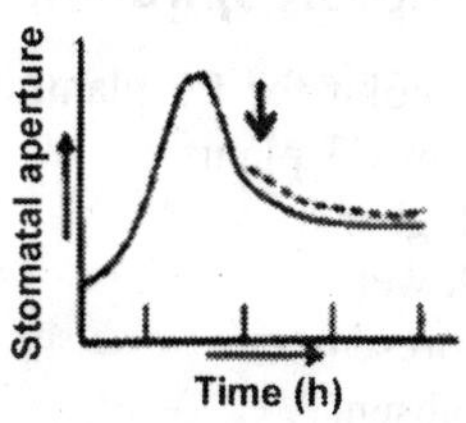

D.
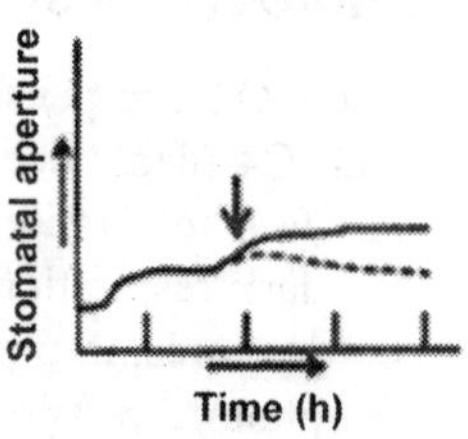

Stress physiology & Secondary Metabolite

42. Which one of the following secondary metabolites is characterized by the presence of a central carbon atom that is bound by a sulphur to a glycone group, and N by a nitrogen to a sulfonated oxime group?

A. Alkaloids
B. Terpenes
C. Phenolics
D. Glucosinolates

43. Given below are certain statements regarding plant- pathogen Interactions:

(*a*) The pattern recognition receptor (PRR), upon perceiving pathogen or microbe associated patterns (PAPMs/MAMPs), activates plant defenses resulting in pattern triggered immunity (PTI).

(*b*) AvrPto is a resistance gene in tomato that acts against pathogenic attack by the bacterium *Pseudomonas syringae* pv. tomato.

(*c*) The effector molecules produced by pathogen is recognized by resistance (R) gene present in plants resulting into a defense strategy known as effector triggered immunity (ETI).

(*d*) Defense mechanisms triggered in plants during PTI are usually stronger than those during ETI.

Which one of the following combinations of above statements is correct?

A. (*a*) and (*b*)
B. (*c*) and (*d*)
C. (*a*) and (*c*)
D. (*b*) and (*d*)

44. In order to survive in a non-aquatic environment, plants acquired several adaptations with specialized functions. Given below is a list of features/characteristics (Column A) and their potential role (Column B).

Column A	Column B
(*a*) Waxy cutical	(*i*) Mechanical support
(*b*) Thickened or lignified cell walls	(*ii*) Protection against excess light
(*c*) Homoiohydry	(*iii*) Restrict water loss
(*d*) Pigmentation	(*iv*) Vascular system

Which one of the following options represents a correct match between the adaptations and their functions?

	(*a*)	(*b*)	(*c*)	(*d*)
A.	(*iv*)	(*ii*)	(*i*)	(*iii*)
B.	(*iii*)	(*i*)	(*iv*)	(*ii*)
C.	(*ii*)	(*iii*)	(*ii*)	(*i*)
D.	(*i*)	(*iv*)	(*iii*)	(*iv*)

CSIR-NET, DECEMBER, 2018

Plant Morphology & Reproduction

45. A list of floral formulae and plant families are given in the following table:

FLORAL FORMULA	FAMILY
i. ⊕ ⚥ K(5) C(5) A(5) $\underline{G}$(2)	A. Brassicaceae
ii. ⊕ ⚥ P(3+3) A(3+3) $\underline{G}$(3)	B. Fabaceae
iii. ⊕ ⚥ K2+2 C4 A2+4 $\underline{G}$(2)	C. Liliaceae
iv. † K(5) C(2),3 A10 $\underline{G}$1	D. Solanaceae

Which of the following options most appropriately matches given plant families with their representative floral formulae?

A. i-D; ii-B; iii-A; iv-C
B. i-D; ii-C; iii-A; iv-B
C. i-D; ii-C; iii-B; iv-A
D. i-A; ii-C; iii-B; iv-D

Plant Hormones

46. The plant hormones, auxins and cytokinins, and their interactions play an important role in regulating apical dominance. The following figure represents an experiment related to the study of gene interactions that influence axillary bud outgrowth or dormancy. Q, Z and M represent genes involved in phytohormone pathway.

Based on the above figure, the following statements were made:

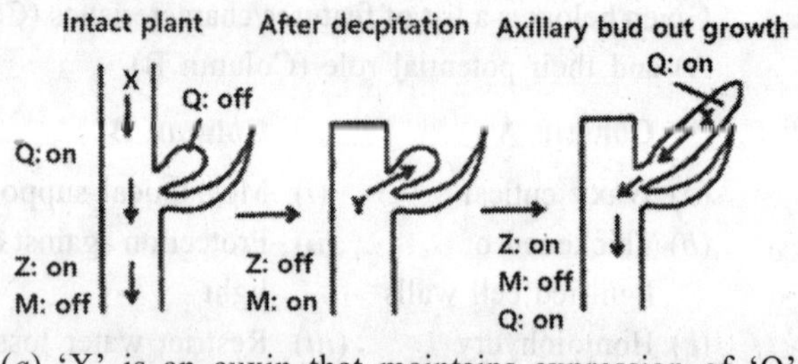

(*a*) 'X' is an auxin that maintains expression of 'Q' and 'Z' and represses 'M'.
(*b*) 'Y' is a cytokinin that promotes axillary bud growth and is induced by 'M'.
(*c*) Decapitation (removal of apex) activates X
(*d*) 'X' is a cytokinin that represses 'M'.

Which one of the following options represents correct statement(s)?

A. (*a*) and (*c*) only
B. (*b*) and (*d*) only
C. (*a*) and (*b*) only
D. (*c*) only

47. Given below is a table comprising various terms associated with plant tissue culture in Column A. and Column B.

Column A	Column B
(*a*) Auxin	(*i*) Embryogenesis
(*b*) Protoplast culture	(*ii*) 6-Furfuryl amino purine
(*c*) Cytokinin	(*iii*) Pectinase and Cellulase
(*d*) Microspore culture	(*iv*) Indole-3-acetic acid

Which one of the following options represents the most appropriate match between all the terms of Column A and Column B?

	(*a*)	(*b*)	(*c*)	(*d*)
A.	(*ii*)	(*i*)	(*iv*)	(*iii*)
B.	(*iv*)	(*iii*)	(*ii*)	(*i*)
C.	(*ii*)	(*iv*)	(*i*)	(*iii*)
D.	(*iv*)	(*i*)	(*ii*)	(*iii*)

Absorption and Transport of Food and Water

48. Which one of the following best describes the function of Casparian bands during the translocation of nutrients and water across the root?

A. Block apoplastic nutrient transport
B. Block symplastic nutrient transport
C. Act as a nutrient carrier
D. Help in creating passage cells

49. Which one of the following components is expected to be most abundant in the phloem sap of a plant?

A. Proteins
B. Organic acids
C. Sugars
D. Phosphates

50. Sieve elements of phloem conduct sugars and other organic materials throughout the plant. The following statements were made about characteristics of sieve elements in seed plants:

(*a*) Angiosperms contain sieve plate pores.
(*b*) There are no sieve plates in gymnosperms.
(*c*) P-protein is present in all eudicots and many monocots.
(*d*) There is no P-protein in angiosperms.

Which of the following combination is correct?

A. (*b*), (*c*) and (*d*)
B. (*a*), (*b*) and (*c*)
C. (*a*), (*b*) and (*d*)
D. (*a*), (*c*) and (*d*)

Photosynthesis & Photorespiration

51. The CO2 compensation point for C3 plants is greater than C4 plants because in C3 plants

A. dark respiration is higher
B. dark respiration is lower
C. photorespiration is present
D. photorespiration is absent

52. Following observations were recorded while studying physiological parameters of sorghum and wheat under similar conditions:

(*a*) Sorghum RUBISCO exhibits relatively higher affinity for CO2 compared to that of wheat.

(*b*) Light saturation of net photosynthetic flux is relatively lower for sorghum compared to that of wheat.

(*c*) Warburg effect is difficult to record for sorghum and could be said as "not measurable" whereas it could be easily recorded for wheat.

(*d*) Temperature optimum for net photosynthesis is lower for sorghum compared to that of Wheat.

(*e*) 3C/12C ratio of assimilate is relatively higher for sorghum compared to that of wheat.

Which one of the following combination of the above observation is correct?

A. Only (*a*), (*b*) and (*c*)
B. Only (*b*), (*c*) and (*e*)
C. Only (*a*), (*b*) and (*d*)
D. Only (*a*), (*c*) and (*e*)

53. Following are certain statements regarding respiratory metabolism in plants:

(*a*) Respiratory quotient during partial breakdown of carbohydrate (alcoholic fermentation) will be infinity.

(*b*) Respiratory quotient indirectly provides information about (*i*) nature of the substrate used for respiration and (*ii*) the relative rate of competing respiratory processes.

(*c*) Breakdown of organic acids in mature fruit will exhibit a respiratory quotient value of more than one since organic acids are relatively oxygen-rich compared to other common substrates.

(*d*) D. Anabolic metabolism can influence respiratory quotient by removing reduction equivalents for respiration leading to decrease in oxygen uptake.

Which one of the following combination of the above statement is correct?

A. Only (*a*)
B. Only (*b*) and (*c*)
C. Only (*d*)
D. (*a*), (*b*), (*c*) and (*d*)

54. Complete the following sentence with the most appropriate option.

Global analysis of a large number of plant species traits showed that with increase in leaf lifespan,

A. specific leaf area increases whereas leaf nitrogen and net photosynthesis rate decrease.
B. specific leaf area, leaf nitrogen and net photosynthesis rate increase.
C. specific leaf area, leaf nitrogen and net photosynthesis rate decrease.
D. specific leaf area decreases whereas leaf nitrogen and net photosynthesis rate increase.

Nitrogen Metabolism and Plant Growth

55. Which one of the following mineral deficiency will first be visible in younger leaves?

A. Calcium
B. Nitrogen
C. Zinc
D. Molybdenum

56. Following statements were made with respect to symbiotic association of rhizobia with legumes:

(*a*) *nodD* is a regulatory gene.

(*b*) Nod factors are lipochitin oligosaccharides.

(*c*) Nod factors predominantly have α 1-4 linked N-acetyl-D-glucosamine backbone.

(*d*) Receptors (or Nod factors are protein kinases with extracellular sugar-binding Lys M domain.

Which one of the following combinations represents all correct statements?

A. (*a*), (*b*) and (*c*)
B. (*a*), (*c*) and (*d*)
C. (*b*), (*c*) and (*d*)
D. (*a*), (*b*) and (*d*)

GATE (BIOTECHNOLOGY), 2018

57. In leguminous plants, both the rhizobium genes and the plant genes influence nodulation and nitrogen fixation. Which one of the following functions is NOT encoded by the host plant genes?

A. Production of inducers that modify rhizobia cell wall
B. Production of flavonoid inducers
C. Establishment of contact between bacteria and legume
D. Root hair curling

58. Which one of the following plant secondary metabolites is a natural insecticide?

A. Digitoxin
B. Pyrethrin
C. Salicylic acid
D. Avenacin A-1

GATE (LIFE SCIENCE), 2018

Plant Physiology and Biochemistry

59. Identify the INCORRECT statement in connection with polar transport of auxin.

A. The putative influx carrier AUX1 is a cytosolic protein

B. Polar auxin transport in root tends to be both acropetal and basipetal in direction

C. Naphthylphthalamic acid (NPA) is an inhibitor of polar auxin transport

D. AUX1 and PIN1 proteins are located in the opposite ends of a cell for polar transport

60. Which of the following stains is used to visualize callose under the microscope?

A. Alcian blue

B. Aniline blue

C. Toluidine blue

D. Thymol blue

61. Select the CORRECT combination of the following statements.

(*a*) The cyclic electron transport chain involving PSI results in net production of both ATP and NADPH

(*b*) The cyclic electron transport chain involving PSI results in net production of ATP

(*c*) Rubisco enzyme usually converts RuBP and CO2 into 2-phosphoglycolate and 3-phosphoglycerate

(*d*) Rubisco enzyme usually converts RuBP and O2 into 2-phosphoglycolate and 3-phosphoglycerate

A. (*a*), (*b*) B. (*c*), (*d*)

C. (*b*), (*d*) D. (*a*), (*c*)

62. Select the CORRECT combination by matching Group-I with Group-II.

Group I	Group II
(*a*) Photorespiration	(*i*) Glutamate___2-Oxoglutarate
(*b*) Respiration	(*ii*) Acetyl Co-A___Malonyl Co-A
(*c*) Amino acid degradation	(*iii*) 2-Oxoglutarate___Succinyl Co-A
(*d*) Fatty acid sysnthesis	(*iv*) Glycine___Serine

	(*a*)	(*b*)	(*c*)	(*d*)
A.	(*i*)	(*ii*)	(*iii*)	(*iv*)
B.	(*ii*)	(*i*)	(*iv*)	(*i*)
C.	(*iii*)	(*iv*)	(*ii*)	(*iii*)
D.	(*iv*)	(*iii*)	(*i*)	(*ii*)

63. Identify the CORRECT combination of statements with respect to chemical defense in plants.

(*a*) Pisatin, a phytoalexin produced by Ricinus communis is a constitutive defense compound

(*b*) Phaseolus vulgaris produces Phaseolus agglutinin I, which is toxic to the cowpea weevil

(*c*) A single step non-enzymatic hydrolysis of cyanogenic glycoside releases the toxic hydrocyanic acid (HCN) to protect plant against herbivores and pathogens

(*d*) Avenacin, a triterpenoid saponin from oat prevents infection by Gaeumannomyces graminis, a major pathogen of cereal roots

A. (*a*), (*b*) B. (*b*), (*d*)

C. (*c*), (*d*) D. (*a*), (*d*)

CSIR-NET, JUNE, 2019

Plant Morphology & Reproduction

64. In certain plants, the mechanism where timing of anther dehiscence and stigma receptivity do not coincide to avoid self-pollination is called

A. dichogamy B. herkogamy

C. monoecy D. Dioecy

65. The table given below provides a list of female gametophyte features and plant genera

Female Gametophyte	Plant genera
(*a*) Monosporic,8 nucleate	(*i*) *Allium*
(*b*) Monosporic,4 nucleate	(*ii*) *Oenothera*
(*c*) Bisporic,8 nucleate	(*iii*) *Peperomia*
(*d*) Tetrasporic,16 nucleate	(*iv*) *Polygonum*

Which one of the following options correctly matches the plant genera to female gametophyte features:

	(*a*)	(*b*)	(*c*)	(*d*)
A.	(*iv*)	(*iii*)	(*i*)	(*ii*)
B.	(*iv*)	(*ii*)	(*i*)	(*iii*)
C.	(*i*)	(*ii*)	(*iv*)	(*iii*)
D.	(*iv*)	(*ii*)	(*iii*)	(*i*)

Plant Hormones

66. Out of several gibberellins identified in plants, which one of the following is NOT bioactive

A. GA_1 B. GA_3

C. GA_4 D. GA_5

Photosynthesis & Photorespiration

67. Following are certain statements with regard to plant respiration:

(*a*) Metabolism of glucose into pyruvate through glycolysis generates NADH and not NADPH.

(*b*) Metabolism of glucose through oxidative pentose phosphate cycle does not produce NADPH.
(*c*) Cyanide forms a complex with haem iron of cytochrome oxidase leading to prevention of change in valency, which in turn stops electron transport in the respiratory chain.
(*d*) Alternative oxidase is insensitive to cyanide and has higher Km than that of cytochrome oxidase.

Which one of the following combinations is correct?
A. (*a*), (*b*) and (*c*) B. (*b*), (*c*) and (*d*)
C. (*b*) and (*d*) D. (*a*), (*c*) and (*d*)

68. After absorbing light, chlorophyll molecules in green plants exist in singlet and triplet states. Following are certain statement on singlet and triplet states of chlorophyll molecules:
(*a*) Singlet state is short lived compared to triplet state.
(*b*) Singlet state is long lived compared to triplet state.
(*c*) Singlet state contains electrons with anti parallel. spins while triplet state has electrons with parallel spins.
(*d*) Singlet state contains electrons with parallel spins while triplet state has electrons with anti-parallel spins.

Which one of the following combinations is correct
A. (*a*) and (*b*) B. (*b*) and (*c*)
C. (*a*) and (*c*) D. (*b*) and (*d*)

Nitrogen Metabolism and Growth

69. Which one of the following describes the function of silicon in plants?
A. Constituent of amino acids
B. Contributes to cell wall rigidity and elasticity
C. Constituent of the the photosynthesis reaction centre
D. Maintenance of cell turgor and electroneutrality

70. Nitrogenase, a complex metal containing enzyme is involved in conversion of N_2 to $NH_{(3)}$ Which one of the following metal is NOT involved in the activity of nitrogenase?
A. Molybdenum (Mo) B. Iron (Fe)
C. Vanadium (V) D. Cobalt (Co)

Sensory photobiology-phytochrome & Cryptochrome

71. Blue light receptor cry1 binds to COP1 and SPA1 complex by interacting with C-terminal region of cry1 (CCT) in a light dependent manner and regulates photomorphogenesis via transcription factor HY5. Read the following statements:
(*a*) cry 1 binds to COP 1 and SPA1 complex leading to degradation of HY5.
(*b*) cry1 binds to CON and SPA1 complex and prevents degradation of HY5.
(*c*) CCT is overexpressed and the plant are kept in dark.
(*d*) CCT is overexpressed and the plants are kept in light.

Which of the following combination of above statements will result in photo-morphogenesis?
A. Only (*a*) B. Only (*b*)
C. (*a*), (*b*) and (*c*) D. (*b*), (*c*) and (*d*)

Stress Physiology & Secondary Metabolite

72. Jasmonate is known to inhibit root growth while auxin facilitates root growth. Upon infection with pathogenic bacteria that produce coronatine, we may expect the following in plants:
(*a*) Upregulation of *COI-1* gene and inhibition of root growth.
(*b*) Upregulation of *Auxl-1* gene and inhibition of root growth.
(*c*) Inhibition of *Auxl-1* gene and promotion of root growth.
(*d*) Inhibition of *COI-1* gene and promotion of roc growth.

Which one of the following is correct?
A. (*a*), (*b*) and (*c*) B. Only (*a*)
C. Only (*b*) D. Only (*c*)

73. During interaction with host, phytopathogens are known to deliver effector is directly into the host cells. The following statements were made regarding the role of these effector proteins.
(*a*) May promote pathogen virulence.
(*b*) May elicit avirulence response.
(*c*) May suppress defense response.
(*d*) May promote plant growth.

Which one of the following combinations of the above statements is correct?
A. (*a*), (*b*) and (*d*) B. (*a*) (*c*) and (*d*)
C. (*a*), (*b*) and (*c*) D. (*b*), (*c*) and (*d*)

CSIR-NET, 15 DECEMBER, 2019

Plant Morphology & Reproduction

74. Which one of the following plants has a bisporic, 8- nucleate, bipolar embryo sac development?
A. Oenothera B. Penaea
C. Plumbago D. Allium

Plant Hormones

75. Which of the following factors is known to be involved in postponing programmed cell death in cereal aleurone until endosperm mobilization is complete?
A. Gibberellic acid

B. Abscisic acid
C. Acidic pH of the vacuoles
D. c-GMP mediated signal transduction pathway

76. While screening an EMS-mutagenized population of a plant, a researcher identified a mutant with reduced gibberellic acid sensitivity. Which one of the following proteins is most likely to be defective in this mutant?
A. Sucrose non-fermenting related kinase 2 (SnRK2)
B. Constitutive triple response 1 (CTR1)
C. Phytochrome interacting factor (PIF)
D. Coronative-insensitive 1 (COI1)

77. Match the following

Column I	Column II	Column III
(*a*) Auxin and Gibberellins	1. Transmembrane	(*i*) Response mediated byreceptor phosphorylation/ dephosphorylation
(*b*) Cytokinin and Brassinosteroid	2. Soluble receptor	(*ii*) Response mediated byproteasome mediated protein degradation

Match the above columns involving plant hormones and their signalling pathways:
A. (*a*)-1-(*i*) and (*b*)-2-(*i*)
B. (*a*)-2-(*ii*) and (*b*)-1-(*i*)
C. (*a*)-2-(*i*) and (*b*)-1-(*i*)
D. (*a*)-1-(*ii*) and (*b*)-2-(*i*)

Absorption and Transport of Food and Water

78. Vascular wilts are wide spread and destructive plant diseases. The symptoms of this disease are primarily caused by the clogging of
A. xylem vessels
B. phloem vessels
C. stomata
D. hydathodes

Photosynthesis & Photorespiration

79. Which one of the following reactions takes place during the reduction phase of the Calvin- Benson cycle?
A. Ribulose 1,5-bisphosphate to 3-phosphoglycerate
B. 1,3-bisphosphoglycerate to glyceraldehyde-3-phosphate
C. Dihydroxyacetone phosphate to fructose 1,6-bisphosphate
D. Ribulose 5-phosphate to ribulose 1,5 bisphosphate

80. Which one of the following graphs best represents the net CO_2 fixation of typical C_3 and C_4 plants under increasing CO_2 concentration and saturating light?

A.
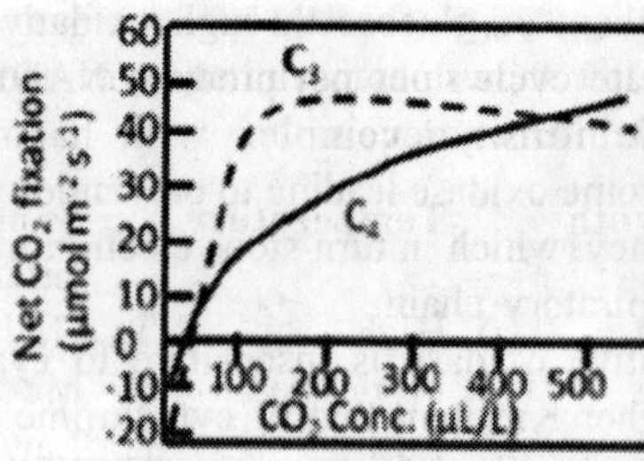

B.
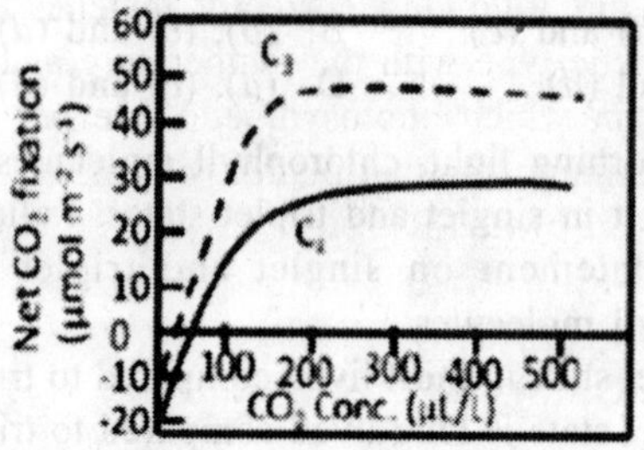

C.
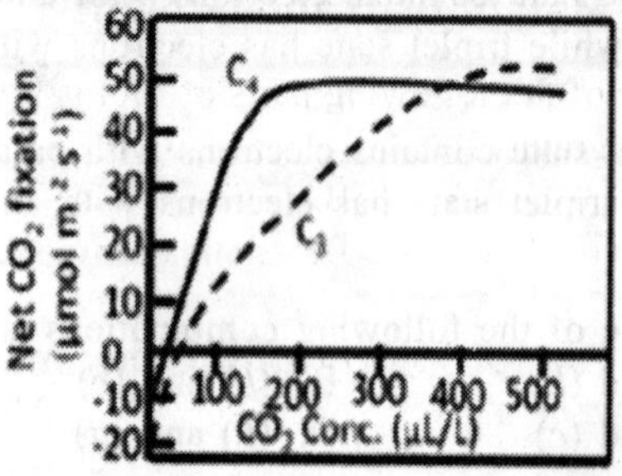

D.
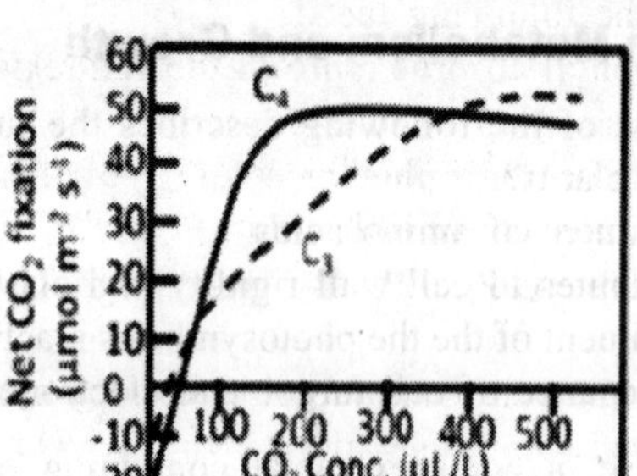

81. The following statements were made with the assumption that the concentration of 3 phosphoglycerate is high inside chloroplasts of an actively photosynthesizing leaf.
(*a*) There will be high concentration of triose phosphate in the chloroplast.
(*b*) The activity of ADP-glucose pyrophosphorylase will be inhibited.
(*c*) The carbon flow will be diverted from sucrose to starch.
(*d*) Starch synthesis will be inhibited and carbon flow will be more towards sucrose synthesis.

Which one of the following combinations of above statements is correct?
A. (*a*) and (*b*)
B. (*b*) and (*d*)
C. (*c*) and (*d*)
D. (*a*) and (*c*)

82. The table below shows photosynthetic type, temperature and sunlight intensity levels.

Photosynthetic type	Temperature	Sunlight Intensity
(*a*) C_3 Plant	(*i*) High	P. High
(*b*) C_4 Plant	(*ii*) Moderate	Q. Moderate
	(*iii*) Low	R. Law

Which of the following correctly matches the plant photosynthetic type with the temperature and sunlight conditions in which photosynthetic rate per unit leaf area is maximum for that plant?

A. (*a*)-(*i*)-P; (*b*)-(*iii*)-R
B. (*a*)-(*iii*)-P; (*b*)-(*i*)-Q
C. (*a*)-(*i*)-R; (*b*)-(*ii*)-Q
D. (*a*)-(*ii*)-Q; (*b*)-(*i*)-P

Nitrogen Metabolism and Growth

83. Which one of the following parts of root is involved in perceiving gravity?

A. Quiescent center B. Endodermis
C. Root cap D. Elongation zone

Sensory Photobiology-phytochrome & Cryptochrome

84. Consider the following facts:

(*a*) Chlorophyll absorbs more in the red region of the visible spectrum than in far-red.
(*b*) The phytochrome photoreceptor (P) of plants occurs in two inter convertible forms,P_r and P_{fr} where red light converts P_r to P_{fr} and far-red light converts P_{fr} to P_r.
(*c*) Growing a sun plant under the canopy shed causes increased stem elongation

Which one of the following combination of statements is correct for the plants growing under the canopy as compared to those growing above the canopy?

A. Red far-red ratio is lower; Pr: Pfr: ratio is higher, Pfr inhibits stem elongation.
B. Red: far-red ratio is higher, P_r: P_{fr} ratio is higher, P_r, inhibits stem elongation.
C. Red: far-red ratio is lower; P_r: P_{fr} ratio is lower; P_{fr} promotes stem elongation.
D. Red: far-red ratio is higher; P_r: P_{fr} ratio is lower; P_r promotes stem elongation.

Stress Physiology & Secondary Metabolite

85. Which one of the following is NOT true in the process of acclimatization to high altitude?

A. Respiratory alkalosis
B. Increased 2,3-DPG in RBC
C. Rise in pH of cerebrospinal fluid
D. Increased cytochrome oxidase in tissues

86. Several plants produce metabolites with important medicinal properties and have been extensively used in traditional medicine across the world. Many of these compounds can now be purified or synthesized and are used in modern medicine. Given below is a list of metabolites, their plant source and medicinal use:

Metabolite	Plant source	Medicine/Use
(*a*) Digoxin	(*i*) *Artemisia annua*	Q. High
(*b*) Salicin	(*ii*) *Papaver somniferum*	R. Anti-malarial
(*c*) Morphine	(*iii*) *Digitalis purpurea*	S. Cardiac ailment
(*d*) Artemisinin	(*iv*) Willow tree	T. Narcotic analgesic

Which one of the following options is the most appropriate match of the compound with its plant source and use?

	(*a*)	(*b*)	(*c*)	(*d*)
A.	(*iii*)-R	(*i*)-T	(*iv*)-Q	(*ii*)-S
B.	(*iv*)-Q	(*iii*)-R	(*ii*)-S	(*i*)-T
C.	(*ii*)-T	(*iii*)-S	(*i*)-R	(*iv*)-Q
D.	(*iii*)-S	(*iv*)-Q	(*ii*)-T	(*i*)-R

CSIR-NET, 27 DECEMBER, 2019

Plant Morphology & Reproduction

87. Distyly is

(*a*) presence of two styles in a flower
(*b*) presence of two lengths of styles in a species
(*c*) a form of dichogamy.
(*d*) a form of herkogamy.

Which one of the following options represents all correct statements?

A. (*b*) only B. (*a*) and (*c*)
C. (*b*) and (*c*) D. (*b*) and (*d*)

88. In most angiosperms, flowers have a perianth that consists of whorls of organs. Select the statement that is INCORRECT about the floral organs in angiosperms.

A. All petals are not homologous
B. If there is only one whorl of organs, these structures are referred to as tepals
C. Sepals tend to be initiated almost simultaneously and never in a spiral sequence.
D. Both sepals and petals can act as protective organs for inner floral organs and also as organs to attract pollinators

Absorption and Transport of Food and Water

89. A plant cell with turgor pressure of 0.1 MPa and osmotic pressure of 0.7 MPa is placed in a salt solution of 0.6 MPa osmotic pressure. Considering that all other pressures and coefficients have no effect on water potential, the following statements were recorded:

(*a*) Water potential of the salt solution will be higher as compared to that of plant cell.

(*b*) Higher osmotic pressure will lower water potential, but higher turgor pressure will raise water potential. Therefore, both of these components are important to calculate water potential.

(*c*) There will be no net movement of water in the cell.

(*d*) Higher turgor pressure will force the water to move out of the cell.

Which one of the following options represents a combination of correct statements?

A. (*a*) and (*d*) B. (*a*) and (*b*)
C. (*c*) and (*d*) D. (*b*) and (*c*)

Photosynthesis & Photorespiration

90. The following statements were made regarding photosynthesis:

(*a*) Conversion of 3-phosphoglycerate into glyceraldehyde 3- phosphate is a reduction process which utilizes ATP as well as NADH in Calvin cycle

(*b*) Conversion of ribulose 5-phosphate to ribulose 1,5-bisphosphate utilizes one third of the total ATP requirements of carbon fixation in Calvin cycle.

(*c*) Sucrose is synthesized outside the chloroplast and uses uridine triphosphate to activate glucose.

(*d*) Starch is a glucose polymer which is synthesized in chloroplast stroma and uses ATP

Which one of the following options represents a combination of correct statements?

A. (*c*) and (*d*) B. (*b*) and (*d*)
C. (*a*) and (*c*) D. (*a*) and (*d*)

91. The names of some genes in Column X and their involvement in photosystem I (PSI) or photosystem II (PS II) is provided in Column Y.

Column X	Column Y
(*a*) *psb A*	(*i*) PS II
(*b*) *psa A*	(*ii*) PS I
(*c*) *lheb1*	
(*d*) *lhca1*	

Which one of the following combinations represents correct matches between columns X and Y?

	(*a*)	(*b*)	(*c*)	(*d*)
A.	(*i*)	(*ii*)	(*i*)	(*ii*)
B.	(*ii*)	(*i*)	(*ii*)	(*i*)
C.	(*i*)	(*ii*)	(*ii*)	(*i*)
D.	(*ii*)	(*i*)	(*i*)	(*ii*)

Nitrogen Metabolism and Growth

92. Which one of the following combinations of nodulation (*nod*) genes are found in all rhizobial strains?

A. *nodA, nodB and nodC*
B. *nodP, nodQ and nodH*
C. *nodF, nodE and nodL*
D. *nodA, nodE and nodP*

93. Given below are factors/terms associated with various aspects of plant growth and development:

Column A	Column B
(*a*) Vacuolar-type programmed cell death	(*i*) Self-incompatibility
(*b*) S-locus	(*ii*) Adaxial-Abaxial patterning of leaf
(*c*) *CONSTANS*	(*iii*) Megasporogenesis
(*d*) *Knox*	(*iv*) Flowering in long photoperiods

Which one of the following options represents the most appropriate match between all terms of Column A and Column B?

	(*a*)	(*b*)	(*c*)	(*d*)
A.	(*ii*)	(*iii*)	(*iv*)	(*i*)
B.	(*iii*)	(*i*)	(*iv*)	(*ii*)
C.	(*ii*)	(*iv*)	(*i*)	(*iii*)
D.	(*iv*)	(*i*)	(*ii*)	(*iii*)

Sensory Photobiology-phytochrome & Cryptochrome

94. Which one of the following proteins regulates photo morphogenesis in plants by adding ubiquitin tags to a subset of nuclear proteins?

A. PhyA B. Hy5
C. LAF1 D. COP1

Stress Physiology & Secondary Metabollte

95. Plants expressing bacterial *NahG* (Salicylate hydroxylase) are known to be defective in inducing systemic acquired resistance (SAR). A researcher applied the following synthetic chemicals on the NahG expressing plants.

(*a*) 2,6-dichloroisonicotinic acid (INA)

(*b*) Benzo(1,2,3)thiodiazole-7-carbothionic acid S methyl ester (BTH)

Which one of the following statements is correct?

A. INA induces SAR but BTH does not induce SAR
B. INA does not induce SAR but BTH induces SAR
C. Both INA and BTH induce SAR
D. Neither INA nor BTH induce SAR

DBT-JRF, 2019

96. TIR1, an auxin receptor, is a:

A. F-box protein
B. MAP kinase
C. His kinase
D. Ser/Thr kinase

97. Given below are the names of different phytohormones in the left column. Match them with their corresponding precursor molecules in the right column.

Phytohormone	Precursor molecule
(*a*) Auxin	(*i*) Methionine
(*b*) Jasmonic acid	(*ii*) L-Tryptophan
(*c*) Ethylene	(*iii*) alpha-linolenic acid
(*d*) Brassinolide	(*iv*) Campesterol

Select the correct combination:

	(*a*)	(*b*)	(*c*)	(*d*)
A.	(*i*)	(*ii*)	(*iii*)	(*iv*)
B.	(*ii*)	(*iii*)	(*i*)	(*iv*)
C.	(*iv*)	(*iii*)	(*ii*)	(*i*)
D.	(*ii*)	(*iii*)	(*iv*)	(*i*)

98. The combination of numbered terms that completes all of the following statement is:

(*a*) Transport through the phloem is __1___ while transport through Xylem is __2__
(*b*) Loading of sugar into the phloem is __3___ at the source
(*c*) Movement of water out of the phloem at the sink is __ 4 ___

A. 1-bidirectional, 2-unidirectional, 3-by active transport, 4-by osmosis
B. 1-by osmosis, 2-by turgor pressure, 3- by passive transport, 4-bidirectional
C. 1-unidirectional, 2-bidirectional, 3-by diffusion, 4-unidirectional
D. 1-by diffusion, 2-unidirectional, 3-bidirectional, 4-by osmosis

99. Plants take up water from the soil predominantly by the apoplastic and symplastic modes of transport. Which one of the following statements is true?

A. Apoplastic transport is ATP-dependent, symplastic is ATP-independent.
B. Symplastic transport is ATP- dependent, apoplastic is ATP-independent.
C. Both apoplastic and symplastic transport are ATP-dependent.
D. Both apoplastic and symplastic transport are ATP-independent.

100. The oxidative photosynthetic carbon cycle salvages:

A. C_3 carbon
B. C_4 carbon
C. CO_2
D. C_2 carbon

101. Which one of the following plants exhibits both C3 and C4 pathways?

A. Zea mays
B. Oryza sativa
C. *Mesembryanthemum crystallinum*
D. Arabidopsis thaliana

102. Light compensation point is the irradiance at which:

A. net photosynthetic photon flux is zero.
B. there is no photosynthesis.
C. net CO_2 exchange is zero.
D. quantum yield of photosynthesis is 1.

103. Which one of the following is a Mo-Fe containing protein?

A. Nitrate reductase
B. Nitrogenase
C. Nitrite reductase
D. Leghemoglobin

104. Phytochromes A and B maximally absorb light at wavelength range:

A. 150-300 nm
B. 300-450 nm
C. 450-550 nm
D. 600-750 nm

105. For metabolic engineering in plants having improved tolerance to osmotic stress, mannitol is overproduced because it:

A. lowers the water potential in the plant cell
B. increases the water potential in the plant cell
C. lowers membrane potential in the plant cell
D. increases membrane potential in the plant cell

106. Which one of the following is a Sulphur containing secondary metabolite in mustard plant derived from glucose and an amino acid?

A. Glucosinolates
B. Phytoalexins
C. Ecdysones
D. Cyanogenic glycosides

107. A plant that survives a local pathogen infection, often develops increased resistance to a subsequent attack by a mechanism called:

A. Systemic Acquired Resistance
B. DAMP-triggered immunity
C. Hypersensitive response
D. Heat Shock Response

GATE (LIFE SCIENCE), 2019

Plant Physiology and Biochemistry

108. Which one of the following statements is INCORRECT with respect to cyclic photophosphorylation?

A. ATP is generated without concomitant formation of NADPH

B. Electron flows from Photosystem I to cytochrome bf complex

C. Photosystem II does not participate in cyclic photophosphorylation

D. Cyclic photophosphorylation occurs when NADP+ /NADPH ratio is high

109. Rubisco catalyzes conversion of ribulose 1,5-bisphosphate to

(*a*) two molecules of stable 3-phosphoglycerate

(*b*) one molecule of 3-phosphoglycerate and one molecule of phosphoglycolate

(*c*) one molecule of ribulose 5-phosphophate

(*d*) one molecule of ribose 5-phosphate

Choose only the correct combination

A. (*a*) and (*d*) B. (*b*) and (*d*)

C. (*a*) and (*b*) D. (*c*) and (*d*)

110. Select correct combination of molecules given in Group I with their functions in Group II

Group I	Group II
(*a*) Ubiquitin	(*i*) Cell wall loosening enzymes
(*b*) Phytotropins	(*ii*) Repressors in gibberellins signalling
(*c*) Extensins	(*iii*) Mediator of protein degradation
(*d*) DELLA proteins	(*iv*) Noncompetitive inhibitors of polar transport of auxins

	(*a*)	(*b*)	(*c*)	(*d*)
A.	(*iii*)	(*iv*)	(*i*)	(*ii*)
B.	(*iii*)	(*i*)	(*ii*)	(*iv*)
C.	(*iv*)	(*iii*)	(*i*)	(*ii*)
D.	(*i*)	(*ii*)	(*iv*)	(*iii*)

111. Match the options in Group I with that of Group II with respect to steps in signal transduction mechanism in plants

Group I	Group II
(*a*) Phospholipase C	(*i*) stimulate release of calcium from intracellular stores
(*b*) Inositol trophosphate	(*ii*) regulate ion channels// activates various enzyme
(*c*) Diacylglycerol	(*iii*) hydrolyzes phosphatidylinositol bisphosphate
(*d*) Phosphatidic acid	(*iv*) phosphorylated to phosphatidic acid

	(*a*)	(*b*)	(*c*)	(*d*)
A.	(*iii*)	(*iv*)	(*ii*)	(*i*)
B.	(*iv*)	(*iii*)	(*ii*)	(*i*)
C.	(*ii*)	(*iii*)	(*i*)	(*iv*)
D.	(*iii*)	(*i*)	(*iv*)	(*ii*)

112. Glyphosate is a broad-spectrum herbicide. Upon application to leaves, it is translocated to meristematic areas and underground rhizomes by

A. phloem B. xylem

C. border pits C. tracheids

CSIR-NET, NOVEMBER (MORNING), 2020

Plant Morphology & Reproduction

113. The diagram below shows the floral diagram of the family Malvaceae. Parts of the diagram have been labelled from A-D.

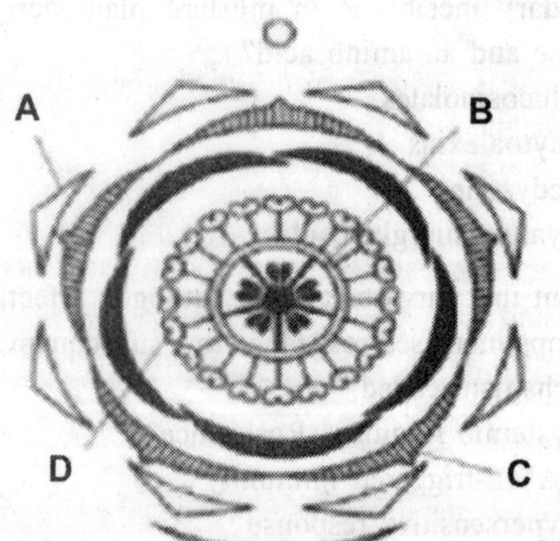

Labels	Floral Characteristics
(*a*) A	(*i*) Monothecous stamens
(*b*) B	(*ii*) Syncarpous ovary
(*c*) C	(*iii*) Epicalyx
(*d*) D	(*iv*) Fused sepals
	(*v*) Apocarpous ovary

Which of the following combinations represent all correct matches between labels and floral characters?

	(*a*)	(*b*)	(*c*)	(*d*)
A.	(*iv*)	(*v*)	(*iii*)	(*i*)
B.	(*i*)	(*v*)	(*iv*)	(*ii*)
C.	(*iii*)	(*ii*)	(*iv*)	(*ii*)
D.	(*i*)	(*ii*)	(*iii*)	(*iv*)

114. Given below are statements regarding apomixis, i.e. asexual reproduction through seeds

(*a*) Sporophytic apomicts often produce a mix of clonal and sexual progeny

(*b*) In gametophytic apomixis, the unreduced central cell gives rise to apomictic embryo
(*c*) In pseudogamy the endosperm is formed in the absence of fertilization
(*d*) Apomixis can potentially be used to maintain hybrid vigour over many generations

Which one of the following options represents the combination of all correct statements?
A. (*a*) and (*c*) B. (*b*) and (*c*)
C. (*c*) and (*d*) D. (*a*) and (*d*)

115. The following diagrams (A to D) show characteristic arrangement of stamens within a flower and (*i*) to (*v*) enlist families of plants.

(*a*) 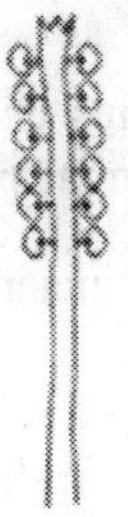 (*i*) Cucurbitaceae

(*b*)  (*ii*) Fabaceae

(*c*) 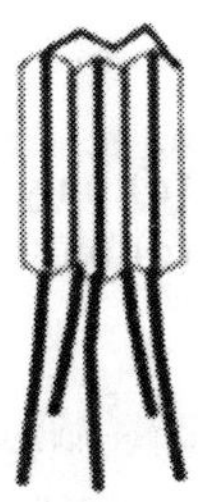 (*iii*) Malvaceae

(*d*)  (*iv*) Asteraceae

(*v*) Euphorbiaceae

Which one of the following options has all correct matches between the arrangement of stamens and the families they belong to?

	(*a*)	(*b*)	(*c*)	(*d*)
A.	(*v*)	(*ii*)	(*iii*)	(*iv*)
B.	(*iii*)	(*i*)	(*iv*)	(*ii*)
C.	(*iii*)	(*ii*)	(*iv*)	(*i*)
D.	(*v*)	(*i*)	(*ii*)	(*iv*)

Plant Hormones

116. Plant growth hormone receptors, namely TIR1, GID1, 2011 and PYL1 were knocked out independently in Arabidopsis plant. The resultant plants are named as tirl, gidl, coit and pyll. Which one of the following statements regarding the above Arabidopsis plants is correct?
A. tiris defective in ABA signaling while coil in gibberelline signalling
B. gidi is defective in auxin signaling while pyll in JA signalling
C. coil is defective in JA signaling while pyll in ABA signalling
D. tir7 is defective in gibberellin signaling while gidi in auxin signaling

Absorption and Transport of Food and Water

117. Which one of the following essential plant mineral nutrients complexes with manitol, mannan, polymannuronic acid, and other constituents of cell wall?
A. Silicon B. Chlorine
C. Manganese D. Boron

Photosynthesis & Photorespiration

118. Which one of the following metabolites formed during Calvin-Benson cycle in chloroplast is involved in starch biosynthesis and can also be transported to cytosol?
A. Triose phosphate
B. Glyceraldehyde = 3 phosphate
C. Fructose-6-phosphate
D. Ribulose 1,5-bisphosphate

119. Following are certain statements regarding C_2, C_3, C_4 and CAM carbon metabolism in plants.
(*a*) In C_3 cycle, one molecule of 3- phosphoglycerate formed during carboxylation phase is utilized for the biosynthesis of sugars, fatty acid and amino acids
(*b*) During C_2 cycle glycine is transported from peroxisome to mitochondria and glycerate is transported from peroxisome to chloroplast
(*c*) The concentration of CO_2 in bundle sheath of C_4 plants is several fold lower than the external atmosphere
(*d*) The stomata of CAM plants open at night

Which one of the following combination of statements is correct?
A. (*a*) and (*b*) B. (*b*) and (*c*)
C. (*a*) and (*d*) D. (*b*) and (*d*)

Nitrogen Metabolism

120. Which one of the following represents the largest outflux of nitrogen from the atmospheric reservoir?

A. Biological nitrogen fixation
B. Nitrogen fixation due to lightning
C. Fixation on account of fossil fuel burning
D. Fixation by Haber's process for fertilizer production.

121. Following is the list of cellular responese of root hair to bacterial Nod factor and timing of their induction, which may or may not be matched

Response	Timing
(*a*) Membrane potential depolarization	(*i*) within 1 min
(*b*) G^{++} spiking in and around root hair cell nucleus	(*ii*) within 10 min
(*c*) Root hair growth perturbation pause in growth, curling	(*iii*) over a period of hours

	(*a*)	(*b*)	(*c*)
A.	(*i*)	(*ii*)	(*iii*)
B.	(*ii*)	(*i*)	(*iii*)
C.	(*iii*)	(*i*)	(*ii*)
D.	(*i*)	(*iii*)	(*ii*)

Sensory Photobiology-phytochrome & Cryptochrome

122. Followings are certain statements regarding phytochrome-mediated signal transduction in Arabidopsis:
(*a*) phyA and phyD are photo-stable, while phy, phyc and phyE are photo-labile.
(*b*) Prolonged light exposure and the conversion of PRA to PERA cause phyA concentration to drop.
(*c*) Exposure of light and conversion of PR to PFR cause movement of phytochromes from the cytosol into the nucleus.
(*d*) phyB lacks nuclear localization sequence and depends on transporter protein for nuclear import

Which one of the combinations of above statements is correct?
A. (*a*) and (*b*) B. (*a*) and (*c*)
C. (*a*) and (*d*) D. (*b*) and (*c*)

Stress Physiology & Secondary Metabolite

123. Which one of the following amino acids is characteristics of and is conserved in response regulator of plant two component systems?
A. Aspartic acid B. Glutamic acid
C. Tyrosine D. Histidine

124. Which of the following is a plant secondary metabolite?
A. Kaurenoic acid B. Abietic acid
C. Proline D. Pyruvate

125. Which one of the following plant proteins is targeted by HC-toxin produced by the maize fungal pathogen Cachliobolus carbonum?
A. H+ ATPase
B. Histone deacetylase
C. ACC oxidase
D. MTA nucleosidase

126. Plants perceive effector proteins from pathogen to mount a strong defense response. The following statements were made regarding signal transduction events upon perception of a pathogen.
(*a*) Influx of Ca^{2+} and H^+ ions into the cell
(*b*) Influx of K^+ and Cl^- ions into the cell
(*c*) Efflux of Ca^{2+} and H^+ ions out of the cell
(*d*) Efflux of K^+ and Cl^- ions out of the cell

Which one of the following combination of statements is correct?
A. (*a*) and (*b*) only B. (*a*) and (*d*) only
C. (*b*) and (*c*) only D. (*c*) and (*d*) only

CSIR-NET, NOVEMBER (AFTERNOON), 2020

Plant Morphology & Reproduction

127. Autogamy refers to
A. self-abortion of gametes
B. flower failing to open
C. self-pollination of flowers
D. cross-pollination of flowers

128. Which one of the following statements regarding double fertilization in plants is correct?
A. The same sperm cell fuses with both egg cell and central cell.
B. Two sperm cells fuse with the egg cell.
C. One sperm cell fuses with the egg cell and second with the central cell.
D. Two sperm cells fuse with the central cell.

129. To study the effect of temperature on seed germination, 16 seeds of a plant species were selected for an experiment. A total of four temperature treatments were provided to sets of four seeds to study the onset of germination. What would be the within, between and total degrees of freedom, respectively, in an analysis of variance?
A. 3, 15 and 18 B. 16, 4 and 20
C. 4, 16 and 20 D. 15, 3 and 18

130. Given below is a list of plant species and reproductive forms:

Plant species	Reproductive form
(*i*) Gingko	(*a*) Monoecious
(*ii*) Conifers	
(*iii*) Poplar	
(*iv*) Maize	(*b*) Dioecious
(*v*) Date palm	
(*vi*) Mango	

Which one of the following options correctly matches all the given plant species with their reproductive forms?

A. (*a*) = (*i*), (*iii*), (*v*); (*b*) = (*ii*), (*iv*), (*vi*)
B. (*a*) = (*i*), (*ii*), (*v*); (*b*) = (*iii*), (*iv*), (*vi*)
C. (*a*) = (*ii*), (*iv*), (*vi*); (*b*) = (*i*), (*iii*), (*v*)
D. (*a*) = (*iii*), (*iv*), (*vi*); (*b*) = (*i*), (*ii*), (*v*)

Plant Hormones

131. Programmed cell death (PCD) plays an important role in development of barley aleurone. The following statements are made with respect to involvement of various phytohormones and signaling molecules.

(*a*) Gibberellic acid promotes PCD.
(*b*) Abscisic acid postpones PCD.
(*c*) Cyclic GMP signaling postpones PCD.
(*d*) Nitric oxide scavenger delays PCD.

Which one of the following combinations of statements is correct?

A. (*a*) and (*c*) B. (*b*) and (*d*)
C. (*a*) and (*b*) D. (*c*) and (*d*)

132. A researcher developed a mutant of Arabidopsis plant where the function of SLEEPY 1 (SLY1) containing SCF complex has been disrupted. Which one of the following statements is INCORRECT in the developed mutant in relation togibberellic acid (GA) signal transduction?

A. GA will bind to GA-insensitive dwarf 1 (GID1) protein.
B. A complex of GA-GID1 and DELLA protein will be formed.
C. The DELLA protein will be ubiquitinated.
D. The DELLA protein will not be degraded.

133. Dark grown Arabidopsis seedlings when exposed to ethylene gas shows typical triple response. Following are certain statements regarding the triple response:

(*a*) A dominant ethylene receptor mutant will not show triple response in the presence of ethylene.
(*b*) Tightening of apical hook is one of the features of triple response.
(*c*) Loss of function of multiple receptors will show triple response even in the absence of ethylene.
(*d*) Increase in hypocotyl length is a feature of triple response.

Which one of the following combinations is correct?

A. (*a*), (*b*) and (*c*) B. (*a*), (*c*) and (*d*)
C. (*b*), (*c*) and (*d*) D. (*a*), (*b*) and (*d*)

Absorption and Transport of Food and Water

134. A researcher has treated pea leaves with p-chloromercuribenzene sulfonic acid (PCMBS), which inactivates plasma membrane transporters. It was observed that phloem loading of sucrose is inhibited. Which one of the following interpretations is correct?

A. Symplastic loading is eliminated
B. Apoplastic loading is eliminated
C. Both symplastic and apoplastic loadings are eliminated
D. Photosynthesis rate is reduced.

135. Select the correct statement. The bark of a woody plant is collectively made up of the following tissues:

A. primary phloem, primary phloem fibres, pericycle and periderm
B. primary xylem, primary phloem fibres, stem cortex, rays, and periderm
C. vascular cambium, rays, pericycle and periderm
D. secondary phloem, secondary phloem fibres, stem cortex, pericycle and periderm

Photosynthesis & Photorespiration

136. In which one of the following subcellular organelles is serine synthesized during the oxidative photosynthetic carbon (C_2) pathway?

A. Chloroplast
B. Mitochondria
C. Peroxisome
D. Rough endoplasmic reticulum

137. Calvin-Benson cycle is divided into three phases, namely carboxylation, reduction and regeneration. The following statements are related to the three phases of Calvin-Benson cycle:

(*a*) The product of light reaction, ATP and NADPH is utilized in the carboxylation phase.
(*b*) Six molecules of 3-phosphogiycerate is converted into six molecules of glyceraldehyde 3-phosphate in the reduction phase.
(*c*) The action of aldolase enzyme for the production of fructose 1, 6-bisphosphate takes place in reduction phase.
(*d*) Formation of seven carbon compound, sedoheptulose-7-phosphate takes place in the regeneration phase.

Which one of the following combinations is correct?

A. (*a*) and (*c*) B. (*b*) and (*d*)
C. (*a*) and (*b*) D. (*c*) and (*d*)

Nitrogen Metabolism

138. Following are certain statements regarding nitrogen uptake and assimilation by plants:

(*a*) Plant roots can take up nitrogen in the form of NO^-_3 or NH^+_4
(*b*) NH^+_4 taken up by plants can be directly assimilated into amino acids.
(*c*) Amino acids are synthesized exclusively in plastids and chloroplast of roots and leaves, respectively.
(*d*) NO^-_3 can be stored in vacuole of both, roots and leaves.

Which one of the following combinations is correct?

A. (*a*), (*b*) and (*c*) B. (*b*), (*c*) and (*d*)
C. (*a*), (*b*) and (*d*) D. (*a*), (*c*) and (*d*)

Stress Physiology & Secondary Metabolite

139. PR proteins play important role during plant-pathogen interactions. Column X represents some of the PR family proteins and column Y represents their main properties.

Column X	Column Y
(*a*) PR-2	(*i*) Defensin
(*b*) PR-5	(*ii*) Thaumatin-like
(*c*) PR-12	(*iii*) Lipid transfer protein
(*d*) PR-14	(*iv*) B-1, 3-glucanase

The correct match of column X with the property in column Y is

	(*a*)	(*b*)	(*c*)	(*d*)
A.	(*iv*)	(*iii*)	(*ii*)	(*i*)
B.	(*i*)	(*ii*)	(*iii*)	(*iv*)
C.	(*iv*)	(*ii*)	(*i*)	(*iii*)
D.	(*iii*)	(*iv*)	(*ii*)	(*i*)

140. The NPR1 (non-expressor of pathogenesis-related genes 1) and two SA receptors (NPR3 and NPR4) are known to play important role in SA mediated plant defense. The following statements were made regarding their role in infected and non-infected tissues of the plants:

(*a*) In the infected tissue, SA binds to NPR3 and induces degradation of NPR1 to promote cell death.

(*b*) In the infected tissue, SA binds to NPR4 and blocks the degradation of NPR1 to promote cell death.

(*c*) In the non-infected tissue, SA binds to NPR4 and blocks the degradation of NPR1 to favour cell survival.

(*d*) In the non-infected tissue, SA binds to NPR3 and promotes degradation of NPR1 to favour cell survival.

Which one of the following combination of statements is correct?

A. (*a*) only B. (*b*) only
C. (*a*) and (*c*) D. (*b*) and (*d*)

DBT-JRF, 2020

141. Which one of the following statements is true regarding the magnesium porphyrin ring and the phytol chain of a chlorophyll molecule?

A. magnesium porphyrin ring is hydrophilic whereas phytol chain is lipophilic
B. both magnesium porphyrin ring and phytol chain are hydrophilic
C. both magnesium porphyrin ring and phytol chain are lipophilic
D. magnesium porphyrin ring is lipophilic whereas phytol chain is hydrophilic

142. The specific energy source for the reaction ADP + phosphate → ATP by the enzyme ATP synthetase (CF1 Coupling Factor) in thylakoid membranes is

A. higher concentration of H+ inside versus outside the thylakoid membranes
B. movement of electrons between photosystem II and photosystem
C. oxidation of water
D. oxidation of NADPH

143. The first stable product of C3 cycle is

A. ribulose bisphosphate
B. dihydroxy acetone phosphate
C. 3-phosphoglycerate
D. phosphoenol phosphate

144. Which class of phytochromes is highly abundant in etiolated seedlings and is also light labile

A. Phytochrome D
B. Phytochrome B
C. Phytochrome A
D. Phytochrome C

145. The broad- spectrum herbicide glyphosate, the active ingredient of Roundup, inhibits this enzyme

A. Shikimate dehydrogenase
B. 5-enolpyruvylshikimate-3-phosphate synthase
C. Chorismate synthase
D. 3-deoxy-7-phosphoheptulonate synthase

146. What is agent Orange?

A. hazardous chemical used in luminous paints
B. biodegradable insecticide
C. herbicide containing dioxin
D. color used in fluorescent lamps

147. Epicatechin gallate (ECG) is a type of flavonoid found in which of the following?

A. Orange
B. green tea
C. Berries
D. Carrot

148. Deficiency of this macronutrient causes older leaves to turn dark green or reddish purple

A. calcium
B. phosphorous
C. nitrogen
D. magnesium

GATE (BIOTECHNOLOGY), 2020

149. Vincristine and vinblastine, two commercially important secondary metabolites from *Catharanthus roseus*, are examples of

A. alkaloids B. flavonoids
C. terpenoids D. steroids

150. Some of the cytokines used in plant tissue culture media are given below:

A. BAP B. Zeatin
C. Kinetin D. 2iP

Which one of these are synthetic analogs ?

A. (*a*) and (*b*) only
B. (*b*) and (*d*) only
C. (*c*) and (*d*) only
D. (*a*) and (*c*) only

151. Determine the correctness or otherwise of the following Assertion (A) and the Reason (R).

Assertion (A): A genetically engineered rice that produces beta-carotene in the rice grain is called Golden rice

Reason (R): Enabling biosynthesis of provitamin A in the rice endosperm gives a characteristics yellow/ orange color

A. Both (A) and (R) are false
B. Both (A) and (R) are true and (R) is the not correct reason for (A)
C. Both (A) and (R) are true and (R) is the correct reason for (A)
D. (A) is true but (R) is false

GATE (LIFE SCIENCE), 2020

Plant Physiology and Biochemistry

152. Methoxy-3, 6-dichlorobenzoic acid belongs to which class of plant growth regulators?

A. Synthetic auxin B. Synthetic cytokinin
C. Strigolactone D. Brassinosteroid

153. In a typical green plant, the first stable product of Calvin cycle is

A. Oxaloacetic acid
B. Succinic acid
C. Maleic acid
D. 3-Phosphoglyceric acid

CSIR-NET, JUNE (MORNING), 2021

Plant Hormones

154. A researcher has obtained an Arabidopsis mutant defective in strigolactones (SLs), a novel plant hormone. The following statements were made regarding the mutant phenotype:

(*a*) Shoot branching gets enhanced in the mutant plant
(*b*) Hyphal branching of arbuscular mycorrhizal fungi (AM-Fungi) gets enhanced during colonization in the mutant plant
(*c*) Shoot branching gets inhibited I the mutant plant
(*d*) Germination of seeds of parasitic plant is prevented near the mutant plant

Which one of the following options represents the combination of correct statements?

A. (*a*) and (*b*) B. (*b*) and (*c*)
C. (*b*) and (*d*) D. (*a*) and (*d*)

Absorption and Transport of Food and Water

155. Following are certain statements regarding root growth and differentiation in plants:

(*a*) Root hair, endodermis, xylem and phloem reach maturation in elongation zone of a developing root.
(*b*) The root epidermal cells that are incapable of forming root hairs are called atrichoblasts
(*c*) Quiescent center is present just above root cap.
(*d*) In Arabidopsis, an auxin transporter (ABCB4) plays a role in root hair emergence by maintaining intracellular auxin concentration.

Which one of the following combination of statements is correct?

A. (*a*), (*b*) and (*c*) only
B. (*b*), (*c*) and (*d*) only
C. (*a*), (*c*) and (*d*) only
D. (*a*), (*b*) and (*d*) only

156. Following are certain statements regarding tracheary elements of vascular plants

(*a*) Xylem tracheids are highly elongated tapered cells that conduct water
(*b*) Xylem vessel elements are less elongated and narrower than tracheids
(*c*) Angiosperms may have both tracheids and vessel elements
(*d*) Vessel elements are the only trachery elements in almost all gymnosperms

Which one of the following options represents a combination of all correct statements?

A. (*a*), (*b*) and (*c*)
B. (*a*) and (*c*)
C. (*b*) and (*c*)
D. (*b*) and (*d*)

157. The following are a few statements on shade leaves vis-à-vis sun leaves in tree species

(*a*) Higher amount of chlorophyll per dry weight
(*b*) Lower density of stomach
(*c*) Thicker leaves
(*d*) Lower rates of dark respiration per unit area

Which one of the following combinations of above statements is correct?

A. (*a*) and (*d*)
B. (*b*) and (*c*)
C. (*a*), (*b*) and (*d*)
D. (*b*) and (*d*)

Photosynthesis & Photorespiration

158. Photochrmicaliy generated AlP is consumed in which one of the following phases of clevin-benson cycle?

A. only carboxylation
B. only regeneration
C. carbocylation and reduction
D. reduction and regeneration

159. During light reaction in photosynthesis, electron is transported in electron transport chain(ETC) and produces ATP and NADPH in the process. Following are certain statements regarding ETC during light reaction:

(*a*) Electron from P680 moves first to quinone and then to the phenophytin
(*b*) P700 can receive electrons from plastocyanin
(*c*) NADPH is produced at the end of light reaction
(*d*) The hydrogen ions produced during light reaction gets concentrated in thylakoid lumen

Choose the correct answer from the options given below:

A. (*a*), (*b*) and (*c*)
B. (*a*), (*b*) and (*d*)
C. (*a*), (*c*) and (*d*)
D. (*b*), (*c*) and (*d*)

Sensory Photobiology-phytochrome & Cryptochrome

160. Following are certain statements regarding phytochrome interacting factors(PIFs), a family of proteins that regulates photomorphogenic response in plants:

(*a*) PIFs promotes skotomorphogenesis by serving as transcriptional activators of dark induced genes
(*b*) PIFs on interaction with Pr get phosphorylated, followed by degradation via the proteosome complex
(*c*) The degradation of PIFs takes place in the presence of light
(*d*) PIF-induced genes are not expressed in light

Which one of the following combination of the statement is correct?

A. (*a*), (*b*) and (*c*)
B. (*a*), (*c*) and (*d*)
C. (*a*), (*b*) and (*d*)
D. (*b*), (*c*) and (*d*)

Stress Physiology & Secondary Metabolite

161. Dirigent protein predominantly play an important role in biosynthesis of:

A. Lignans
B. Alkaloids
C. terpenoids
D. amino acid

162. The phytohormones ethylene(ET), methyl jasmonate(MeJA) and salicylic acid(SA) play important roles in plant defense. The following statements were made regarding induction of defensin PDF1.2 and pathogenesis related protein PR1

(*a*) ET/MeJA activates PDF1.2
(*b*) ET/MeJA activates PR-1
(*c*) SA activates PDF1.2
(*d*) SA activates PR-1

Which one of the following options represent a combination of correct statements?

A. (*a*) and (*b*)
B. (*a*) and (*d*)
C. (*b*) and (*c*)
D. (*c*) and (*d*)

163. Given below are various plant natural products and their basic structural unit:;

List I **Natural products**	**List II** **Baisc unit**
(*a*) Phenolics	(*i*) Five carbon isoprene unit
(*b*) Alkaloids	(*ii*) Glucose unit attached by O-β-D-glucosyl linkage
(*c*) Terpenoids	(*iii*) Nitrogen containing
(*d*) Cyanogenic glycoside	(*iv*) Aromatic arene ring with OH group

Which of the following options represents the correct match of natural products and the basic units?

	(*a*)	(*b*)	(*c*)	(*d*)
A.	(*iv*)	(*i*)	(*iii*)	(*ii*)
B.	(*iii*)	(*ii*)	(*i*)	(*iv*)
C.	(*iii*)	(*i*)	(*iv*)	(*ii*)
D.	(*iv*)	(*iii*)	(*i*)	(*ii*)

164. Even in short day plants, a period of bright light is required in the leaf in order to induce flowering. This is because:

A. The floral stimulus phloem mobile & photosynthesis is required for the translocation.
B. Phytochrome need high light to record the day length.
C. Part of the flowering stimulus ia actually part of the photosynthetic apparatus.
D. The oxidation of phytochrome is involved in the Pr to Pfr form.

CSIR-NET, JUNE (AFTERNOON), 2021

Absorption and Transport of Food and Water

165. Following statements are made about nitrate transporters in plant cells :

(*a*) Nitrate uptake displays two saturable phases , with Km in the micromolar (UM) range for the high-affinity system and in the millimolar (mM) range for the low-affinity system

(*b*) The Arabidopsis AtNRT1-1 is a dual affinity nitrate transporter.

(*c*) AtNRT 1-2 participates in high - affinity uptake.

(*d*) AtNRT 2.1 and AtNRT 2-2 are involved in low-affinity uptake. Select the option that has the combination of all correct statements.

Select the options represents all correct statements?

A. (*a*) and (*d*) only
B. (*b*) and (*d*) only
C. (*a*) and (*b*) only
D. (*a*), (*c*) and (*d*)/(*a*)

Photosynthesis & Photorespiration

166. Which one of the following are the correct encoding sites of large and small subunits of Rubisco enzyme in red and brown algae?

A. Large subunit in chloroplast and small subunit in nucleus
B. Large subunit in nucleus and small subunit in chloroplast
C. Both large and small subunits in nucleus
D. Both large and small subunits in chloroplast

167. Following are certain statements regarding photorespiration pathway in plants :

(*a*) The first two–carbon (2C) compound synthesized by the action of Rubisco in the chloroplast is glycolate.

(*b*) Glycolate exits the chloroplast and enters peroxisomes.

(*c*) Glycolate that is synthesized during C, cycle enters the chloroplast from mitochondria.

(*d*) Glycine is transported from peroxisomes to mitochondria.

Which one of the following combinations is INCORRECT?

A. (*a*) and (*b*) only
B. (*a*) and (*c*) only
C. (*a*), (*c*) and (*d*)
D. (*a*), (*c*) and (*d*)

168. The following statements refer to photosystem structure and function involved in light-dependent reaction of photosynthesis :

(*a*) The antenna or light harvesting complex absorbs light energy and transfers it to the reaction centre.

(*b*) The first electron is released from P680 and transferred to QA to produce a semiquinone

(*c*) D1, a protein subunit of the plant PST core complex is encoded by gene psbD

Which one of the following combinations of above statements is INCORRECT?

A. (*a*) and (*b*)
B. (*b*) and (*c*)
C. (*a*) and (*c*)
D. Only (*c*)

Stress Physiology & Secondary Metabolite

169. B-thoglucosidases, also known as myrosinases, are the enzymes that are known to hydrolyse which one of the following plant natural products?

A. Glucosinolates
B. Terpenoids
C. Alkaloids
D. Phenolics

170. Plant pathogens produce effector molecules that aid in colonization of their host cells. Column X denotes the name of effector molecules and column Y denotes the potential functions :

Column X	Column Y
(*a*) HC-toxin	(*i*) Activates specific host gene expression
(*b*) Fusicoccin	(*ii*) Accelerates growth
(*c*) GA_3	(*iii*) Inhibit Histone deacetylases
(*d*) TAL	(*iv*) Activates H^+-ATPase

Which one of the following is the correct match:

	(*a*)	(*b*)	(*c*)	(*d*)
A.	(*ii*)	(*iii*)	(*iv*)	(*i*)
B.	(*iii*)	(*iv*)	(*ii*)	(*i*)
C.	(*i*)	(*iv*)	(*ii*)	(*iii*)
D.	(*iv*)	(*ii*)	(*i*)	(*iii*)

171. Plants are known to synthesize more than 30,000 terpenoids, involving four stages of biosynthesis. Following are the list of biosynthetic steps (Column X) and the key class of enzymes involved (Column Y):

Column X	Column Y
(*a*) Biosynthesis of two basic five carbon unit	(*i*) Terpene synthases
(*b*) Repetitive addition of C5 units	(*ii*) P450 monooxygenase
(*c*) Formation of the basic terpenoid skeletons	(*iii*) HMG-CoA synthase
(*d*) Modification of terpenoid skeleton	(*iv*) Prenyl transferases

Which of the following is the correct match?

	(*a*)	(*b*)	(*c*)	(*d*)
A.	(*i*)	(*iii*)	(*iv*)	(*ii*)
B.	(*ii*)	(*iii*)	(*i*)	(*iv*)
C.	(*i*)	(*ii*)	(*iii*)	(*iv*)
D.	(*iii*)	(*iv*)	(*i*)	(*ii*)

172. Following statement were made about stress response in prokaryotes

(*a*) Per R function as a major peroxide sensor in many Gram – positive bacteria.

(*b*) Extreme acidic Ph INDUCED Rec A mediated DNA damage, which in turn may induce virlence gene expression in some pathogenic bacteria.

(*c*) Induced expression of heat shock protein neither protect the cells from heat nor plays a role in bacterial virulence.

(*d*) In Gram negative bacteria heat shock factor regulates the transcription of the major heat shock proteins.

(*e*) Gros ES is an ATP dependent chaperionin but GroEL may function in ATP independent manner.

Which one of the following represent the correct combination of above statements?

A. (*a*), (*c*), (*d*)
B. (*a*), (*b*), (*d*)
C. (*b*), (*c*), (*e*)
D. (*b*), (*d*), (*e*)

DBT-JRF, 2021

173. The rice blast fungus Magnaporthe grisea, invades rice plants in a manner typical of many foliar pathogens by producing specialized infection structures called:

A. Appressoria B. Infection tube
C. Mycota D. Sporangia

174. Which one of the following is not a secondary metabolite?

A. Acetyl-CoA, B. Coumarins
C. Flavonoids D. Squalene

175. Which one of the following classes of compounds is generally accumulated as an antiherbivore response in plants?

A. Alkaloids B. Glucose
C. Sucrose D. Tannins

176. Which one of these polysaccharides is induced after a pathogen or microbial attack?

A. Arabinoxylan B. Callose
C. Cellulose D. Pectin

GATE (BIOTECHNOLOGY), 2021

177. Which of the following combinations of plant hormones and their associated function are CORRECT?

Hormone	Function
(*a*) Abscisic acid	Breaks seed dormancy
(*b*) Auxin	Induces cell division
(*c*) Ethylene	Stimulates ripening of fruits
(*d*) Gibberellin	Promotes seed dormancy

A. (*a*) and (*c*) only B. (*a*) and (*d*) only
C. (*b*) and (*c*) only D. (*b*) and (*d*) only

GATE (LIFE SCIENCE), 2021

Plant Physiology and Biochemistry

178. The structures of four plant hormones are shown. Identify the CORRECT hormone that is responsible for bending of coleoptile of canary grass in response to unidirectional white light.

A. 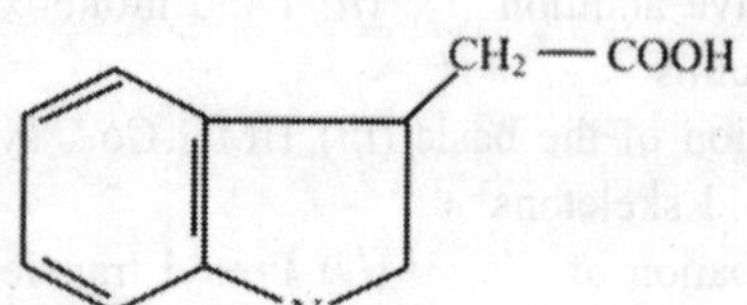

B. 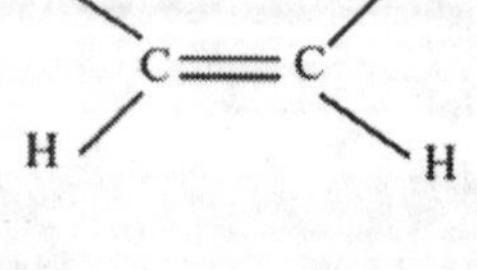

C. 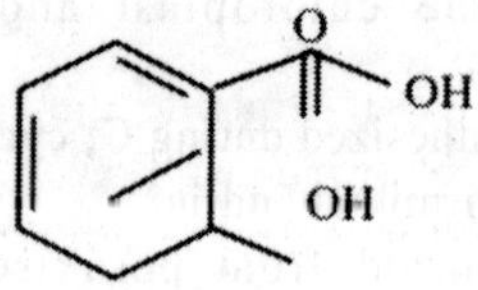

D. 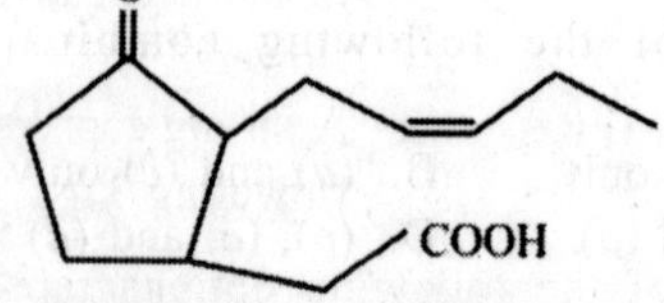

179. Wheat plants treated with prolonged cold temperature at the seedling stage flower earlier than the untreated control. Seeds collected from these treated individuals, however, give rise to plants that do not flower early. This phenomenon is called

A. Vernalization

B. Temperature acclimation
C. Photoperiodism
D. Adaptation

180. Match the modified organs in GROUP I with their corresponding prototypic forms in GROUP II and choose the CORRECT option

Group I	Group II
(*a*) Tendrils in grape vine	(*i*) Modified stem
(*b*) Tendrils in garden pea	(*ii*) Modified leaf
(*c*) Spines	
(*d*) Thorns	

	(*a*)	(*b*)	(*c*)	(*d*)
A.	(*i*)	(*ii*)	(*ii*)	(*i*)
B.	(*ii*)	(*i*)	(*i*)	(*ii*)
C.	(*i*)	(*ii*)	(*i*)	(*ii*)
D.	(*i*)	(*i*)	(*ii*)	(*i*)

181. Which ONE of the following organelles controls gravitropism in the roots of higher plants?
A. Chromoplast B. Amyloplast
C. Chloroplast D. Etioplast

182. Phytoalexins play important role in plant defense against pathogens. Choose the INCORRECT option related to phytoalexins.
A. Phytoalexins belong to secondary metabolites.
B. Phytoalexins have antifungal activity.
C. Phytoalexins are abundant in plants under normal condition.
D. Different hosts produce phytoalexins of varying chemical nature.

183. The figure shows the germination percentage of imbibed seeds treated with the given sequence of red (R) and far-red (F) light (each exposure lasting 5 min). The percentage of germination was scored after 72 hours in darkness at 25°C. Based on this, which ONE of the following options is CORRECT?

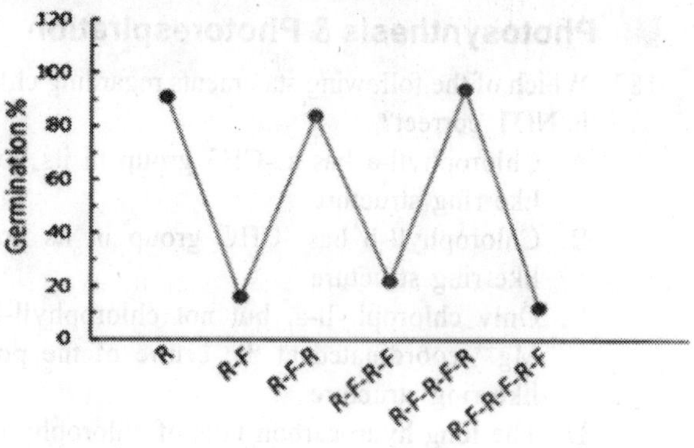

A. Red light induces seed germination whereas far-red light inhibits it.
B. Red light inhibits seed germination whereas far-red light induces it.
C. Both red and far-red light inhibit seed germination.
D. Both red and far-red light induce seed germination

CSIR-NET, SEPTEMBER (MORNING), 2022

Plant Morphology & Reproduction

184. Given below are the list of proteins (Column X) and their functions (Column Y) during floral induction.

Column X	Column Y
(*a*) FLOWERING LOCUS C (FLC)	(*i*) An activator of FLC
(*b*) FLOWERING LOCUS D (FD)	(*ii*) A mobile signal that induces flowering
(*c*) FLOWERING LOCUS T (FT)	(*iii*) Regulate target genes that mediate the reprogramming of meristem to produce flowers
(*d*) FRIGIDA (FRI)	(*iv*) A strong repressor of flowering

Which one of the following options represents the correct match between column X and column Y?

	(*a*)	(*b*)	(*c*)	(*d*)
A.	(*i*)	(*ii*)	(*iii*)	(*iv*)
B.	(*iii*)	(*iv*)	(*i*)	(*ii*)
C.	(*ii*)	(*i*)	(*iv*)	(*iii*)
D.	(*iv*)	(*iii*)	(*ii*)	(*i*)

Plant Hormones

185. Following are certain statements regarding gibberellic acid (GA) signal transduction:
(*a*) DELLA proteins negatively regulate GA signalling.
(*b*) Degradation of GA receptor (GID1) is mediated by DELLA proteins.
(*c*) Ubiquitination and subsequent degradation of DELLA proteins are independent of GID1.
(*d*) GA binding to GID1 promotes binding of GID1 to DELLA proteins.

Which one of the following combination of statements is correct?
A. (*a*) and (*b*) B. (*b*) and (*c*)
C. (*c*) and (*d*) D. (*a*) and (*d*)

Absorption and Transport of food and Water

186. Following statements were made to explain the intracellular transport that occurs through apoplastic, symplastic and transcellular routes in plants:
(*a*) Apoplastic transport mostly occurs through cell-wall.
(*b*) Apoplastic transport mostly involves plasmodesmata.

(*c*) Symplastic transport predominantly occurs through plasmodesmata.
(*d*) Transcellular transport mostly occurs through tonoplast via vacuoles.

Which one of the following combination of statements is correct?

A. (*a*), (*b*) and (*d*) B. (*b*), (*c*) and (*d*)
C. (*a*), (*c*) and (*d*) D. (*a*), (*b*) and (*c*)

Photosynthesis & Photorespiration

187. Which of the following statements regarding chlorophyll is NOT correct?

A. Chlorophyll-a has a -CH3 group in its porphyrin-like ring structure
B. Chlorophyll-b has -CHO group in its porphyrin-like ring structure
C. Only chlorophyll-a, but not chlorophyll-b, has a Mg^{++} coordinated at the centre of the porphyrin-like ring structure
D. The long hydrocarbon tails of chlorophyll anchors them in the photosynthetic membrane

Nitrogen Metabolism

188. Which of the following nitrogen containing compounds is formed during deamination of organic nitrogen in plants?

A. NO B. $NO2^-$
C. $NO3^-$ D. $NH4^+$

Sensory Photobiology-phytochrome & Cryptochrome

189. Young seedlings of Arabidopsis plants are exposed to the following light conditions:

(*a*) Far-Red light followed by Red light
(*b*) Far-Red light followed by Red light and then Dark phase
(*c*) Red light followed by Far-Red light
(*d*) Dark phase followed by Far-Red light and then Red light
(*e*) Far-Red light followed by Dark phase and then Red light
(*f*) Red light followed by Dark phase and then Far-Red light

Which of the above conditions will lead to photomorphogenesis?

A. (*a*), (*b*) and (*e*)
B. (*b*) and (*f*)
C. (*c*) and (*f*)
D. (*a*), (*d*) and (*e*)

Stress Physiology & Secondary Metabolite

190. There are different kinds of reactive oxygen species (ROS) generated in plants. The following are the so statements related to ROS and its scavenging:

(*a*) H_2O_2 is relatively more stable and travels relatively long distances.
(*b*) ROS is scavenged only through enzymatic reactions.
(*c*) Ascorbate-glutathione cycle is associated with the scavenging of ROD
(*d*) Monodehydroascorbate reductase is not an antioxidant enzyme.

Which one of the following combination of statements is correct?

A. (*a*) and (*c*) B. (*a*) and (*d*)
C. (*b*) and (*c*) D. (*b*) and (*d*)

CSIR-NET, SEPTEMBER (AFTERNOON), 2022

Plant Morphology & Reproduction

191. A plant species with unisexual flowers has the following traits : floral longevity = 12 hours, pollen : ovule = 10:1, male and female flowers with synchronized anthesis. Given these, which of the following mutations would be most detrimental to seed set in this plant species?

A. The pollen : ovule ratio drops to 3:1.
B. Longevity of male and female flowers increases to 16 hours.
C. Anthesis in male flowers occur 2 hours after female flowers.
D. The pollen : ovule ratio increases to 15:1.

Plant Hormones

192. Following statements were made regarding gibberellins (GA) biosynthesis in plants and fungi.

(*a*) Two separate enzymes are involved in synthesis of ent-kaurene from GGDP in plants
(*b*) Only a single bifunctional enzyme catalyses the synthesis of ent-kaurene from GGDP in fungi
(*c*) GA-biosynthesis genes are mostly clustered on a single chromosome in fungi.
(*d*) GA-biosynthesis genes are randomly located on chromosomes in fungi.

Which one of the following combination of statements is correct?

A. (*a*), (*b*) and (*c*) only B. (*a*), (*b*) and (*d*) only
C. (*b*) and (*c*) only D. (*a*) and (*d*) only

193. The plant hormone gibberellins (GA) are a group of

A. Monoterpenes (C10)
B. Diterpenes (C20)
C. Triterpenes (C30)
D. Sequiterpenes (C15)

Photosynthesis & Photorespiration

194. A student listed following combinations of enzymes and their involvement in different phases of Calvin-Benson cycle:

(*a*) Phosphoglycerate kinase – Reduction phase
(*b*) Glyceraldehyde-3-phosphate dehydrogenase – Regeneration phase
(*c*) Triose-phosphate isomerase – Reduction phase
(*d*) Phosphoribulokinase – Regeneration phase

Which one of the following combinations is correct?

A. (*a*), (*b*) and (*c*) B. (*b*) and (*c*) only
C. (*b*), (*c*) and (*d*) D. (*a*) and (*d*) only

Sensory Photobiology-phytochrome & Cryptochrome

195. Phytochrome photoreceptors exist in two isoforms, PR and PFC. Following are certain statements regarding the function of PFR:

(*a*) P_{FR} form induces phosphorylation and ubiquitin linked degradation of PIFs transcription factor.
(*b*) P_{FR} mediated degradation of PIFs inhibits photomorphogenesis.
(*c*) P_{FR} inhibits the activity of COPI.
(*d*) P_{FR} increases the stability of transcription factors HFR 1, HY5 and LAF1.

Which one of the following combinations is correct?

A. (*a*), (*b*) and (*c*) only
B. (*a*), (*c*) and (*d*) only
C. (*b*), (*c*) and (*d*) only
D. A, (*b*) and (*d*) only

Stress Physiology & Secondary Metabolite

196. The following statements were made regarding submergence tolerance in plants.

(*a*) Wetland plants have structural barrier to prevent O2 diffusion into soil.
(*b*) Dryland plants have structural barrier to prevent O2 diffusion into soil.
(*c*) Lowering of cytosolic Ca2+ prevents aerenchyma formation.
(*d*) Activation of ethylene signal transduction pathway prevents aerenchyma formation.

Which one of the following options has all correct statements?

A. (*a*) and (*c*) only B. (*b*) and (*c*) only
C. (*a*) and (*d*) only D. (*b*) and (*d*) only

197. Which one of the following statements is INCORRECT?

A. Dehydrins are intrinsically disordered proteins
B. Dehydrins have minimal secondary structure.
C. Dehydrins are often induced by ABA.
D. Dehydrins are highly hydrophobic proteins.

DBT-JRF, 2022

198. Nod gene products:

A. function as receptors of certain flavonoids
B. lack the ability to activate the expression of other Nod factors
C. cause activation of homeobox genes
D. are involved in photosynthesis

199. Cryptochromes control photomorphogenesis in response to:

A. Red light
B. Far-red light
C. Infra-red light
D. Blue and UV-A light

200. Which one among the following is the correct function of leghaemoglobin?

A. It sequesters oxygen to facilitate nitrogen fixation
B. It protects nitrogenase from CO2
C. It facilitates the supply of CO2 to nitrogen fixing bacteria
C. It binds to nitrogen and moves it out of the nodule

201. Which one of the following is NOT a typical feature of the hypersensitive response observed in plants during the attack of invading microbes?

A. Onset of programmed cell death in the region surrounding the infection site
B. Rapid accumulation of reactive oxygen species
C. Rapid spike in photosynthetic rate
D. Rapid spike in nitric oxide production accompanying the oxidative burst

202. The red color of beetroot is due to the presence of:

A. Betalains B. Anthocyanins
C. Flavonoids D. Carotenoids

GATE (BIOTECHNOLOGY), 2022

203. Terpenoids are made of ___________ units.

A. amino acid B. carbohydrate C. isoprene D. triacylglycerol

GATE (LIFE SCIENCE), 2022

Plant Physiology and Biochemistry

204. The number of ATP molecules required for the complete assimilation of one molecule of CO_2 in Calvin cycle is

A. 2 B. 3
C. 4 D. 5

205. Filamentous photosynthetic algae were placed on a microscopic slide and illuminated with light of different colors as illustrated.

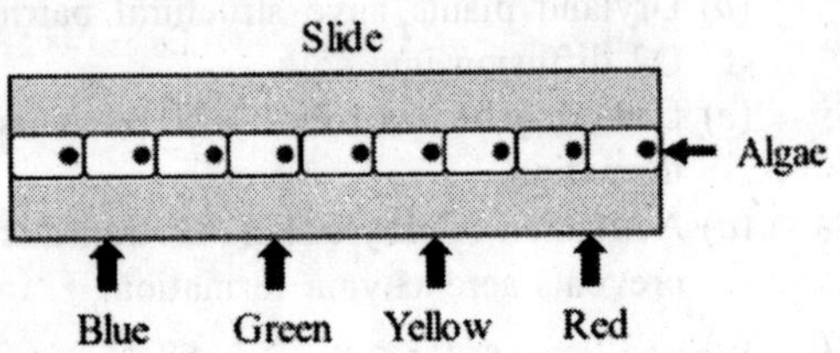

The bacteria that are known to migrate towards the region of high O_2 were also added uniformly on the slide. Which one of the following options illustrates the distribution of bacteria along the length of the microscopic slide after illumination?

A.

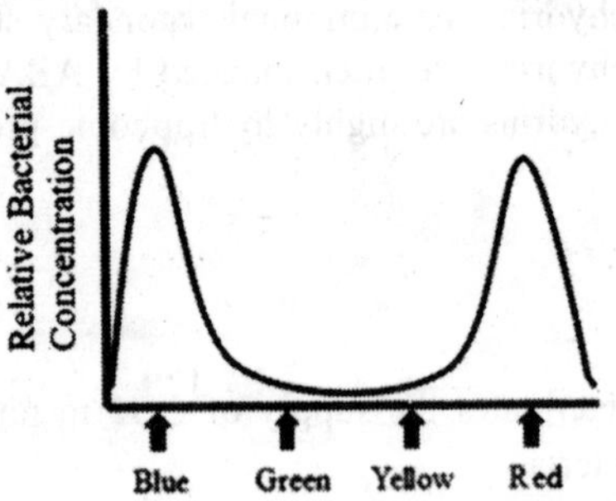

B.

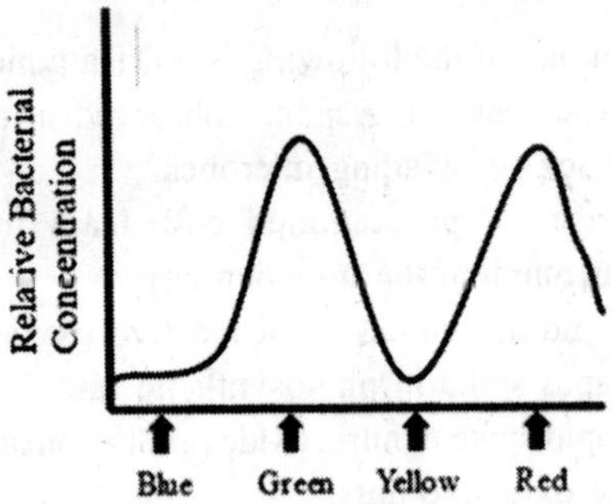

C.

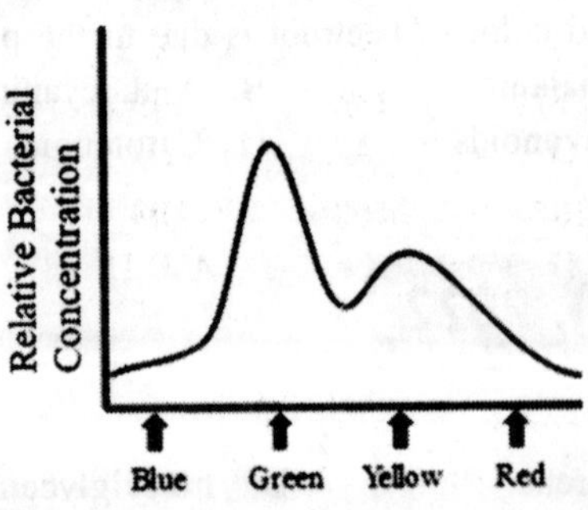

D.

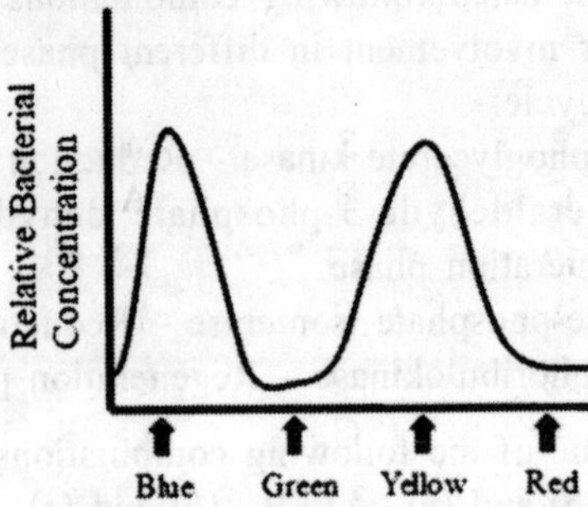

206. The correct sequence of overall biochemical reaction which expresses the process of denitrification is ____

A. $2NO^-_3 \rightarrow 2NO^-_2 \rightarrow N_2O \rightarrow 2NO \rightarrow N_2$
B. $2NO^-_3 \rightarrow 2NO^-_2 \rightarrow 2NO \rightarrow N_2O \rightarrow N_2$
C. $2NO^-_3 \rightarrow 2NO \rightarrow 2NO^-_2 \rightarrow N_2O \rightarrow N_2$
D. $2NO^-_3 \rightarrow N_2O \rightarrow 2NO \rightarrow 2NO^-_2 \rightarrow N_2$

207. Match the secondary metabolites in Group-I with types of secondary metabolites in Group-II in CORRECT order.

Group-I	Group-II
(*a*) Myrcene	(*i*) Sesquiterpene
(*b*) β-Farnesene	(*ii*) Cyanogenic glycoside
(*c*) Amygdalin	(*iii*) Flavone
(*d*) Nicotine	(*iv*) Alkaloid
(*e*) Luteolin	(*v*) Monoterpene

	(*a*)	(*b*)	(*c*)	(*d*)	(*e*)
A.	(*i*)	(*v*)	(*ii*)	(*iv*)	(*iii*)
B.	(*v*)	(*ii*)	(*iv*)	(*i*)	(*iii*)
C.	(*ii*)	(*iii*)	(*iv*)	(*v*)	(*i*)
D.	(*v*)	(*i*)	(*ii*)	(*iv*)	(*ii*)

208. Match Group I (plant natural product), Group II (class) and Group III (source plant) in CORRECT combination.

Group-I	Group-II	Group-III
(*a*) Reserpine	(*i*) Stilbenes	1. Manihot esculanta
(*b*) Resveratrol	(*ii*) Cyanogenic glycoside	2. Crocus sativus
(*c*) Picrocrocin	(*iii*) Alkaloid	3. Vitis vinifera
(*d*) Linamarin	(*iv*) Monoterpene glycoside	4. Rauwolfia serpentine

	(*a*)	(*b*)	(*c*)	(*d*)
A.	(*i*)-4	(*ii*)-3	(*iv*)-1	(*iii*)-2
B.	(*iii*)-4	(*iv*)-2	(*i*)-3	(*ii*)-1
C.	(*ii*)-1	(*iii*)-2	(*i*)-4	(*iv*)-3
D.	(*iii*)-4	(*i*)-3	(*iv*)-2	(*ii*)-1

209. Which of the following is/are phanerogamic parasite(s)?

A. Cuscuta reflexa B. Orobanche cernua
C. Ocimum sanctum D. Santalum album

210. Which of the following matches is/are CORRECT?

A. Surface fibre – Cotton – Gossypium hirsutum
B. Bast fibre – Flax – Corchorus capsularis
C. Drying oil – Safflower oil – Helianthus annuus
D. Non-drying oil – Castor oil – Ricinus communis

ANSWERS

1	2	3	4	5	6	7	8	9	10
B	C	B	A	A	A	B	B	B	C
11	12	13	14	15	16	17	18	19	20
D	A	C	D	A	D	A	C	C	D
21	22	23	24	25	26	27	28	29	30
D	A	C	C	C	B	B	D	D	D
31	32	33	34	35	36	37	38	39	40
A	A	A	A	A	B	B	D	D	C
41	42	43	44	45	46	47	48	49	50
A	D	C	B	B	C	B	A	C	B
51	52	53	54	55	56	57	58	59	60
C	D	D	C	A	D	D	B	A	B
61	62	63	64	65	66	67	68	69	70
C	D	B	A	B	D	D	C	B	D
71	72	73	74	75	76	77	78	79	80
D	B	C	D	B	C	B	A	B	C
81	82	83	84	85	86	87	88	89	90
D	D	C	A	C	D	D	C	D	B
91	92	93	94	95	96	97	98	99	100
A	A	B	D	C	A	B	A	D	D
101	102	103	104	105	106	107	108	109	110
A	C	B	D	A	A	A	D	C	A
111	112	113	114	115	116	117	118	119	120
D	A	C	D	C	C	D	A	D	A
121	122	123	124	125	126	127	128	129	130
A	D	A	B	B	B	C	C	D	C
131	132	133	134	135	136	137	138	139	140
C	C	A	B	D	B	B	C	C	C
141	142	143	144	145	146	147	148	149	150
A	A	C	C	B	C	B	B	A	D
151	152	153	154	155	156	157	158	159	160
C	A	D	D	B	B	C	D	D	B
161	162	163	164	165	166	167	168	169	170
A	B	D	A	C	D	B	B	A	B
171	172	173	174	175	176	177	178	179	180
D	B	A	A	A	B	C	A	A	A
181	182	183	184	185	186	187	188	189	190
B	C	A	D	D	C	C	D	D	A
191	192	193	194	195	196	197	198	199	200
A	A	B	D	B	A	D	A	D	A
201	202	203	204	205	206	207	208	209	210
C	B	C	B	A	B	D	C	A,B,D	A

CHAPTER

16

ANIMAL PHYSIOLOGY

CSIR-NET, JUNE, 2017

Excretory System

1. Filtration slits are formed by:

A. podocytes
B. endothelial cells of capillary
C. mesangial cells
D. Lacis cells

2. In kidney, Na^+ is reabsorbed across the second half of proximal tubule due to positive transepithelial voltage (i.e., tubular fluid becomes positive relative to blood) and by other mechanisms. The following proposed statements could explain the development of this positive transepithelial voltage.

(*a*) Cl^- concentration gradient in the second half of the proximal tubule favours diffusion of Cl^- from tubular lumen to intercellular space via a paracellular route, which generates the positive transepithelial voltage.

(*b*) The $Na^+ - H^+$ antiporters in the second half of proximal tubules create the positive transepithelial voltage.

(*c*) The Na^+ – glucose symporters operating in the proximal part of renal tubules are responsible for this positive transepithelial voltage

(*d*) The positive transepithelial voltage is created by the operation of $1Na^+ - 1K^+ - 2Cl^-$ symporter in the proximal tubules

Select the option with correct statement(s).

A. only (*a*) B. (*b*) and (*c*)
C. (*c*) and (*d*) D. only (*d*)

Sensory System

3. An action potential of a nerve fibre is described by different components including after-hyperpolarization. The mechanism of generation of this after-hyperpolarization has been proposed in the following statements:

(*a*) The increased conductance of Na^+ has returned to the base line level but the conductance of K^+ remains elevated during after-hyperpolarization phase

(*b*) The membrane potential is pulled even closer to the K^+ equilibrium potential at the after-hyperpolarization phase

(*c*) The conductance of Na^+ is increased before any change of K^+ conductance during after-hyper-polarization phase

(*d*) At the after– hyperpolarization phase, the membrane potential is driven closer to Na^+ equilibrium potential

Choose the option with both correct statements:

A. (*a*) and (*b*) B. (*b*) and (*c*)
C. (*c*) and (*d*) D. (*a*) and (*d*)

4. In an experiment on healthy young men, the muscarinic receptor antagonist, atropine was administered to one group (Group A) while the P-adrenergic receptor antagonist, propranolol was administered to another group (Group B) in four increasing doses of equal concentration for both the drugs. The effects of these two drugs on the heart rate are shown below:

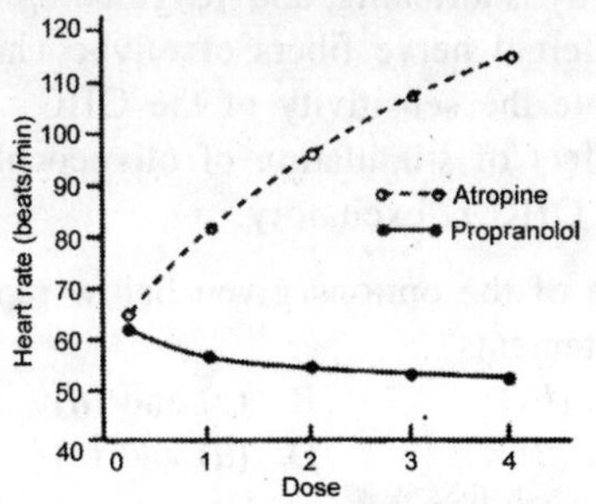

On the basis of these observations, an investigator proposed the following statements:

(*a*) Atropine and propranolol block sympathetic and parasympathetic effects on the heart, respectively

(*b*) As the change of heart rate is more in Group A than in Group B, the sympathetic tone usually predominates in healthy resting individuals.

(*c*) Atropine and propranolol block parasympathetic and sympathetic effects on the heart, respectively

(*d*) As substantial changes occur in the heart rate with atropine, the parasympathetic tone is predominant in healthy resting individuals.

Select the option with INCORRECT statement(s).

A. Only (*a*)
B. (*a*) and (*b*)
C. Only (*c*)
D. (*a*) and (*d*)

CSIR-NET, DECEMBER, 2017

Circulatory and Respiratory System

5. In which one of the body fluids is K^+ concentration higher than that of Na^+?

A. Plasma B. Perilymph
C. Endolymph D. Cerebrospinal fluid

6. Relative rates of red blood cells production in bone marrow of different bones of different ages are shown below: Identify the correct figure.

—— Femur - · - · Rib ----- Vertebra

A.
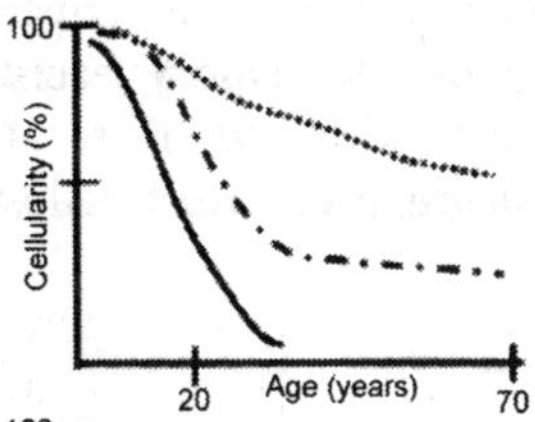

B.
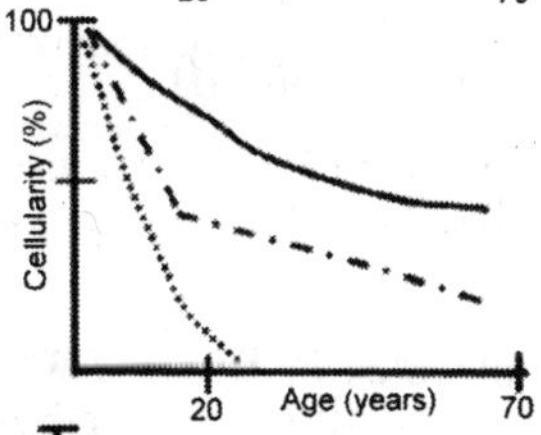

C.
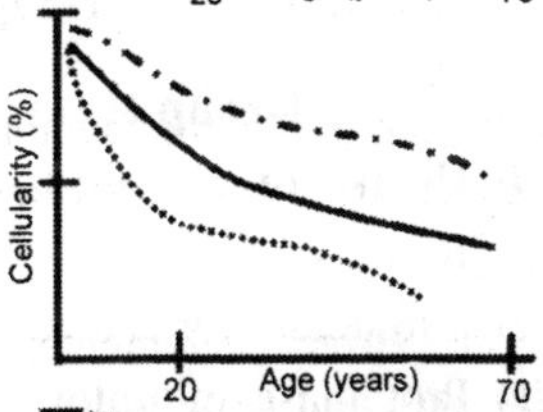

D.
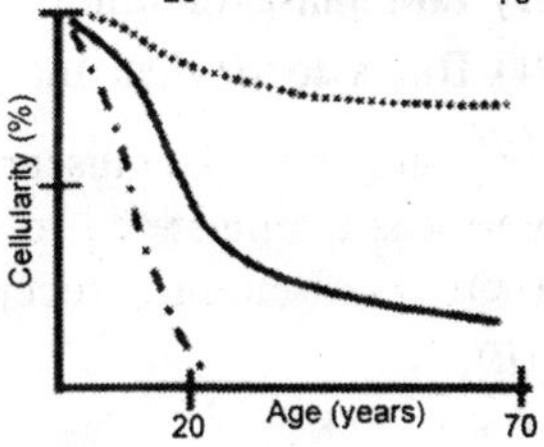

Nervous System

7. Mammillary bodies are present in:

A. Thalamus B. Epithalamus
C. Hypothalamus D. Midbrain

8. The pacemaker cells of sinoatrial node (SA node) are inhibited by the stimulation of vagus nerve. The probable mechanisms of this inhibition are stated as follows:

(*a*) The acetylcholine-regulated K^+ channels are activated

(*b*) The outward K^+ causes hyperpolarization of pacemaker cells

(*c*) The inward "funny current" of pacemaker potential is increased

(*d*) The increased intracellular cAMP, induced by activation of M muscarinic receptors, slows the opening of Ca^{++} channels

Choose the answer with correct statements.

A. (*a*) and (*c*) B. (*b*) and (*c*)
C. (*a*) and (*b*) D. (*c*) and (*d*)

Excretory System

9. In the glomerular capillary (GC), fluid moves into Bowman's capsule through its almost entire length. But in the muscle capillary (MC), fluid moves into interstitial space at its arteriolar end. The difference between these two capillaries is explained in the following proposed statements:

(*a*) Afferent and efferent arterioles are present on the two ends of GC, but in MC, arteriole and venule are present on two ends.

(*b*) The hydrostatic pressure in GC is higher than that in MC.

(*c*) The efferent arteriole in GC has a relatively low resistance, but venules in MC has a high resistance.
(*d*) The difference of hydrostatic pressure between two ends of GC is relatively more but it is negligible in MC.
(*e*) The difference of oncotic pressure between two ends of MC is negligible but it is relatively more in GC.
(*f*) The net filtration pressure falls to zero at the efferent end of GC but it is 9 mm Hg inward at the venular end of MC.

Which of the above statements are incorrect?

A. (*a*) and (*b*) B. (*c*) and (*d*)
C. (*e*) and (*f*) D. (*b*) and (*f*)

Reproductive System

10. Reflex ovulation does not occur in:

A. Cats B. Rabbits
C. Mink D. Rats

Digestive System

11. Which one of the following is not involved with the absorption of iron in the intestine?

A. Divalent metal transporter
B. Ferroportin 1
C. Hephaestin
D. Transferrin

Sensory System and Muscle Physiology

12. The following statements describe the possible functions of the outer hair cells (OHC) of organ of Corti:

(*a*) The outer hair cells (OHC) are depolarized or hyperpolarized depending on the direction of movement of stereocilia.
(*b*) The OHC are lengthened in depolarization and shortened in hyperpolarization
(*c*) The OHC decrease the amplitude and clarity of sound by shortening and lengthening.
(*d*) The efferent nerve fibers of olivocochlear bundle modulate the sensitivity of the OHC
(*e*) The effect of stimulation of olivocochlear bundle on the OHC is excitatory.

Which one of the options given below represents the correct statements?

A. (*a*) and (*b*) B. (*c*) and (*d*)
C. (*a*) and (*d*) D. (*d*) and (*e*)

13. When a skeletal muscle was passively stretched, it contracted reflexly. However, when the muscle was over stretched in this way it showed sudden cessation of contraction followed by relaxation. The following statements provided the possible explanation of these observations:

(*a*) The passive stretching of muscle caused stretching of muscle spindle
(*b*) The over stretching of muscle stimulated Golgi tendon organ
(*c*) Group 1b sensory nerve fibers were stimulated by stretching of muscle spindle
(*d*) Group 1b sensory nerve fibers stimulated %-motor neurons that supplied the muscle from which these fibers arose.
(*e*) Group 1a sensory nerve fibers were connected to Golgi tendon organ.
(*f*) The stimulation of group 1a sensory fibers lea to the production of IPSP on the %- motor neurons that supplied the muscle from which these fibers arose.

Which of the above statement(s) is/are correct?

A. (*a*) and (*b*) B. (*c*) and (*d*)
C. (*e*) and (*f*) D. (*c*) and (*f*)

GATE (LIFE SCIENCE), 2017

14. A woman with blood group A gave birth to a baby with blood group AB. The blood group of the father would be

A. only AB
B. only B
C. either AB or B
D. blood group O

15. Aromatase inhibitors are often prescribed for post-menopausal women to treat Estrogen receptor positive breast cancer patients, because these class of drugs

A. reduce prostaglandin biosynthesis
B. reduce the level of estradiol biosynthesis
C. inhibit conversion of testosterone to dihydro-testosterone
D. are non-toxic in post-menopausal women

16. Match the following molecules in Group I with their function in Group II

Group I	Group II
(*a*) Transferrin	(*i*) Uptake of glucose
(*b*) Insulin	(*ii*) Binds iron
(*c*) α-macroglobulin	(*iii*) Substratum for cell attachment
(*d*) Fibronectin	(*iv*) Proteinase inhibitor
	(*v*) Binds to oxygen in RBC

	(*a*)	(*b*)	(*c*)	(*d*)
A.	(*ii*)	(*i*)	(*iv*)	(*iii*)
B.	(*ii*)	(*i*)	(*v*)	(*iii*)
C.	(*ii*)	(*i*)	(*iv*)	(*ii*)
D.	(*i*)	(*iii*)	(*ii*)	(*v*)

CSIR-NET, JUNE, 2018

Endocrine System

17. Two individuals A and B, each of 75 kg body weight, have similar volume of body water. Both of them had high salt snack. However, individual A also had a glass of alcoholic drink. Based on this information, which one of the following statements is true?

A. A will have lower circulating level of antidiuretic hormone (ADH) than B
B. B will have lower circulating level of ADH than A
C. The level of ADH will not change in these two individuals
D. The reabsorption of water in kidney will be more in A than B

Circulatory and Respiratory System

18. The Cl content of red blood cells (RBCs) in the venous blood was found to be higher than that in arterial blood in a human subject. Following proposals were made to explain these observations:

(*a*) The high pCO_2 in venous plasma leads to increased diffusion of CO_2 into RBC and the formation of H_2CO_3.
(*b*) HCO_3-content in the RBC of venous blood becomes much greater than that in plasma.
(*c*) The excess HCO_3-leaves the RBC of venous blood along with Na^+ to plasma by a Na^+-HCO_3-symporter,
(*d*) The increased Na^+ in the venous plasma is transported to the RBC along with Cl^-

Select the combination with INCORRECT statements from the following options.

A. (*a*) and (*b*) B. (*b*) and (*c*)
C. (*a*) and (*d*) D. (*c*) and (*d*)

19. The different waves of normal electrocardiogram (ECG) of a human subject are shown below:

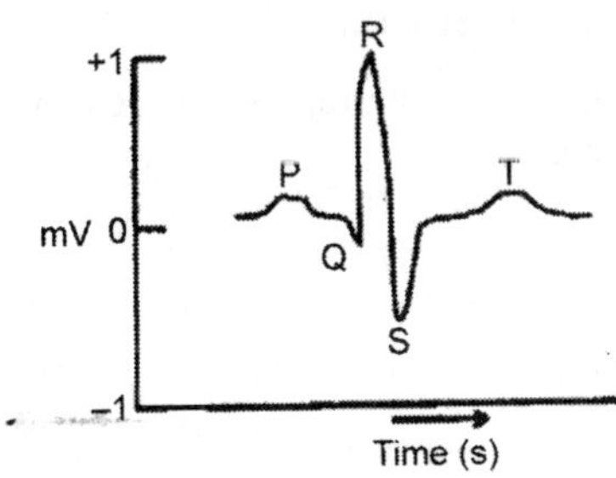

The relationship of the events of cardiac cycle to these ECG waves are proposed in the following statements:

(*a*) The P wave occurs due to the depolarization of atria
(*b*) The atrial repolarization is responsible for the T wave
(*c*) The QRS complex occurs during ventricular depolarization
(*d*) Q-T interval indicates plateau portion of auricular action potential

Select the combination with INCORRECT statements from the following options:

A. (*a*) and (*b*) B. (*b*) and (*c*)
C. (*c*) and (*d*) D. (*b*) and (*d*)

Nervous System

20. Sympathetic post-ganglionic neurons that are cholinergic, innervate:

A. sweat glands B. parotid glands
C. hair follicles D. Pancreas

21. The peaks of the compound action potential (*i.e.*, A, B and C) recorded from a mammalian mixed nerve were affected after application of increasing pressure on the nerve. Some probable changes of compound action are stated below:

(*a*) 'A' peak was inhibited by lower intensity of pressure
(*b*) 'C' peak was inhibited by higher intensity of pressure
(*c*) 'B' peak was inhibited by lower intensity of pressure
(*d*) 'C' peak was inhibited by lower intensity of pressure
(*e*) 'A' peak was inhibited by higher intensity of pressure

Select the option with the combination of CORRECT statements.

A. (*a*) and (*b*) B. (*b*) and (*c*)
C. (*c*) and (*d*) D. (*d*) and (*e*)

22. The figure below shows the nervous system of Mollusca with ganglia and the connecting nerves. The connecting nerves are labelled as (*a*), (*b*), (*c*) and (*d*).

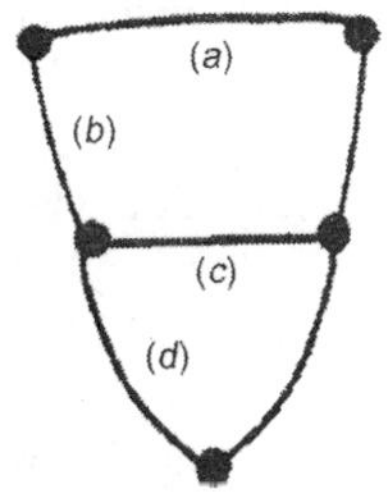

Which one of the following options has correct labelling of A, B, C and D?

A. (*a*)-Cerebral commissure; (*b*)-Left Cerebro-pedal connective; (*c*)-Pedal commissure; (*d*)-Left Pedal-visceral connective
B. (*a*)-Cerebral connective; (*b*)-Left Cerebropedal commissure; (*c*)-Pedal connective; (*d*)-Left Pedal-visceral commissure
C. (*a*)-Occipital commissure; (*b*)-Occipitopedal connective; (*c*)-Pedal commissure; (*d*)-Left Pedocaudal connective
D. (*a*)-Cerebral connective; (*b*)-Left Cerebropedal commissure; (*c*)-Pedal commissure; (*d*)-Pedal-caudal connective

Excretory System

23. The different segments of renal tubule (column A) and the mechanism of Na^+ transport in the apical membrane of tubular cells (column B) are tabulated below:

Column A	Column B
(*a*) Proximal tubule	(*i*) $Na^+ - Cl^-$ symporter
(*b*) Thick ascending loop of Henle	(*ii*) Diffusion through Na^+ Selective channel (ENaC)
(*c*) Early distal tubule	(*iii*) Na – glucose symporter
(*d*) Late distal tubule and collecting duct	(*iv*) $1\ Na^+ - 1K^+ - 2\ Cl^-$ Symporter

Select the option with the correct matches:

	(*a*)	(*b*)	(*c*)	(*d*)
A.	(*iii*)	(*iv*)	(*i*)	(*ii*)
B.	(*iv*)	(*iii*)	(*ii*)	(*i*)
C.	(*i*)	(*ii*)	(*iii*)	(*iv*)
D.	(*ii*)	(*i*)	(*iv*)	(*iii*)

Digestive system

24. Match the enzymes in Column A with their respective biological function in Column B:

Column A	Column B
(*a*) Lipases	(*i*) Catalysis of ATP- dependent translocation of the aminophospholipids, phosphatidyl ethanolamine and phosphatidylserine from the extracellular to the cytosolic leaflet of the plasma membrane
(*b*) Flippases	(*ii*) Catalysis of ATP-dependent translocation of plasma membrane phospholipids from the cytosolic to the extracellular leaflet.
(*c*) Floppases	(*iii*) Catalyze hydrolysis of triacylglycerols.
(*d*) Scramblase	(*iv*) Catalyze the movement of any membrane phospholipid across the bilayer down its concentration gradient.

Choose the correct combinations of answers from the options given below:

	(*a*)	(*b*)	(*c*)	(*d*)
A.	(*iii*)	(*i*)	(*ii*)	(*iv*)
B.	(*i*)	(*iii*)	(*iv*)	(*ii*)
C.	(*iv*)	(*ii*)	(*i*)	(*iii*)
D.	(*ii*)	(*iv*)	(*iii*)	(*i*)

Sensory System

25. The excitation of auditory hair cells by the displacement of stereocilia has been explained in the following proposed statements:

(*a*) The gradual increased height of stereocilia is required for the transduction process

(*b*) The changes of membrane potential of auditory hair cells are proportional to the direction and magnitude of the displacement of stereocilia

(*c*) The higher concentration of K+ in endolymph and higher concentration of Na+ in perilymph are not required for the excitation of hair cells.

(*d*) The mechanically sensitive cation channels on the top of stereocilia are not adapted to maintain displacement of stereocilia

Select the combination with INCORRECT statements from the following options:

A. (*a*) and (*b*) B. (*b*) and (*c*)
C. (*c*) and (*d*) D. (*a*) and (*c*)

Thermal Regulation and Respiration

26. Following are certain statements regarding energy efficiencies of ectotherms and endotherms:

(*a*) Ectotherms have high assimilation efficiency but low production efficiency

(*b*) Ectotherms have low assimilation efficiency but high production efficiency.

(*c*) Endotherms have high assimilation efficiency but low production efficiency.

(*d*) Endotherms have low assimilation efficiency but high production efficiency.

Which one of the following represents the combination of correct statements?

A. (*a*) and (*b*) B. (*b*) and (*c*)
C. (*c*) and (*d*) D. (*a*) and (*c*)

CSIR-NET, DECEMBER, 2018

Endocrine System

27. A person recovered from a moderate degree of hemorrhagic shock. The participating physiological mechanisms in this recovery process are proposed in the following statements.

(*a*) The decrease in arterial pressure after haemorrhage causes inhibition of sympathetic-vasoconstrictor system.

(*b*) After haemorrhage, the angiotensin II level in blood is increased which causes increased re-absorption of Na^+ in renal tubules.

(*c*) The increased secretion of vasopressin after haemorrhage increases water retention by the kidneys.

(*d*) After haemorrhage, the reduced secretion of epinephrine and nor-epinephrine from adrenal medulla induces decreased peripheral resistance.

(*e*) In haemorrhage, the central nervous system ischemic response elicits sympathetic inhibition.

Choose one of the following combinations with both the correct statements.

A. (*a*) and (*b*) B. (*b*) and (*c*)
C. (*c*) and (*d*) D. (*d*) and (*e*)

28. A healthy individual was immersed in water up to neck in an upright posture for3h. The plasma concentration of atrial natriuretic peptide (ANP), renin and aldosterone were measured for 5 h at 1 h intervals including the immersion period. The results are graphically presented below.

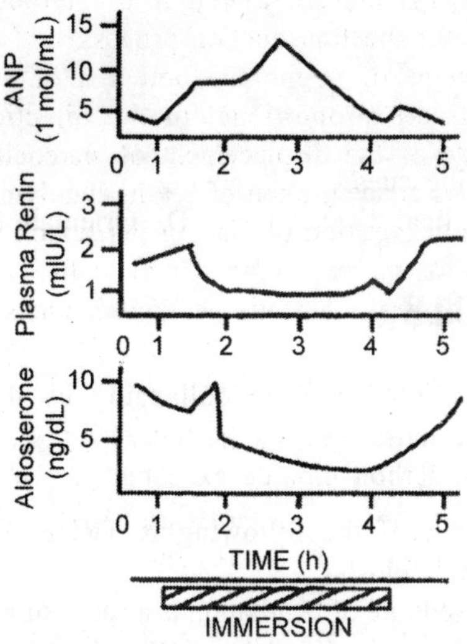

The results of this experimental condition (EC) are explained in the following proposed statements which may be correct or incorrect.

(*a*) ANP secretion is proportional to the degree of stretch of atria.
(*b*) The decreased plasma renin concen- tration in EC is due to increase in sympathetic activity.
(*c*) The decreased aldosterone level in EC is the effect of plasma renin level.
(*d*) The effect of gravity mi the circulation is counteracted in EC.
(*e*) The central venous pressure is decreased in EC.

Choose one of the following combinations with all correct statements.

A. (*a*), (*b*), (*c*) B. (*a*), (*c*), (*d*)
C. (*c*), (*d*), (*e*) D. (*b*), (*c*), (*d*)

Circulatory and Respiratory System

29. The "Mayer waves" in the blood pressure originate due to:

A. systole and diastole of ventricle
B. inspiration and expiration
C. reflex oscillation of neural pressure control mechanisms
D. Bainbridge reflex

30. The changes in left atrial, left ventricular and aortic pressure in a cardiac cycle are shown below in the figure.

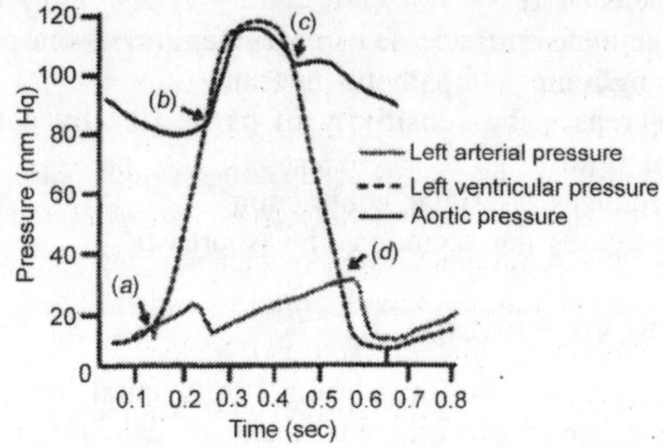

Given below are the events of cardiac cycle (column A) associated with marked points (*a*), (*b*), (*c*), (*d*) in the figure (column B).

Column A	Column B
(*a*) Aortic valve opens	(*i*) (*d*)
(*b*) Mitral valve closes	(*ii*) (*b*)
(*c*) Mitral valve opens	(*iii*) (*a*)
(*d*) Aortic valve closes	(*iv*) (*c*)

Choose the option that matches the events with marked points in the figure.

	(*a*)	(*b*)	(*c*)	(*d*)
A.	(*ii*)	(*iii*)	(*i*)	(*iv*)
B.	(*i*)	(*iv*)	(*ii*)	(*iii*)
C.	(*iv*)	(*i*)	(*iii*)	(*ii*)
D.	(*iii*)	(*ii*)	(*iv*)	(*i*)

Nervous System

31. The conduction velocity of action potential in a myelinated nerve fibre was much greater than that of an unmyelinated fibre of the same diameter. The following statements were proposed to explain this observation:

(*a*) The speed of conduction in a nerve fibre is determined by the plasma membrane resistance and axial resistance of axonal cytoplasm.
(*b*) The electrical properties of myelinated and unmyelinated nerve fibres are not similar.
(*c*) The myelin sheath decreases the effective membrane resistance.
(*d*) The magnitude of an electrotonic potential decreases more with distance along the axon in myelinated nerve fibres than that of unmyelinated fibres.
(*e*) The voltage-gated Na^+ channels are highly concentrated at the nodes of Ranvier.

Choose one of the following combinations with both INCORRECT statements.

A. (*a*) and (*b*) B. (*b*) and (*c*)
C. (*c*) and (*d*) D. (*d*) and (*e*)

Excretory System

32. Which one of the following is NOT a function of angiotensin II?

A. Facilitates the release of norepinephrine from post-ganglionic sympathetic neurons
B. Increases the sensitivity of baroreflex by acting on brain
C. Produces arteriolar contraction
D. Increases the secretion of vasopressin

Digestive System

33. A four year old boy was brought to hospital for weak bones in spite of sufficient intake of calcium in his diet. The attending doctor examined the functioning of the following organs:

(*a*) Liver
(*b*) Kidney
(*c*) Lung
(*d*) Pancreas

Which one of the following options represents a combination of probable malfunctioning organs?

A. (*a*) and (*b*)
B. (*b*) and (*c*)
C. (*c*) and (*d*)
D. (*a*) and (*d*)

DBT-JRF, 2018

34. Hair cells in the inner ear act as receptors for which one of the following cues?

A. Temperature B. Chemical C Mechanical D. Orientation

GATE (LIFE SCIENCE), 2018

35. Bowman's capsules are present in which ONE of the following organs/tissues?

A. Renal cortex
B. Urinary bladder
C. Renal medulla
D. Ureter

36. Which ONE of the following is the primary function of lung surfactants?

A. Remove dust particles from bronchi
B. Provide immunity to respiratory tract
C. Prevent alveoli from collapsing by decreasing surface tension
D. Aid in carbon dioxide exchange

37. Which ONE of the following is TRUE in case of respiratory acidosis?

A. Increased rate of ventilation is a cause of respiratory acidosis
B. Blood pH more than 7
C. Increased levels of carbon dioxide in blood
D. Acidosis can be compensated through reduction of bicarbonate levels in plasma

CSIR-NET, JUNE, 2019

Endocrine System

38. The pathway of synthesis of aldosterone in zona glomerulosa along with the intracellular locations is shown below:

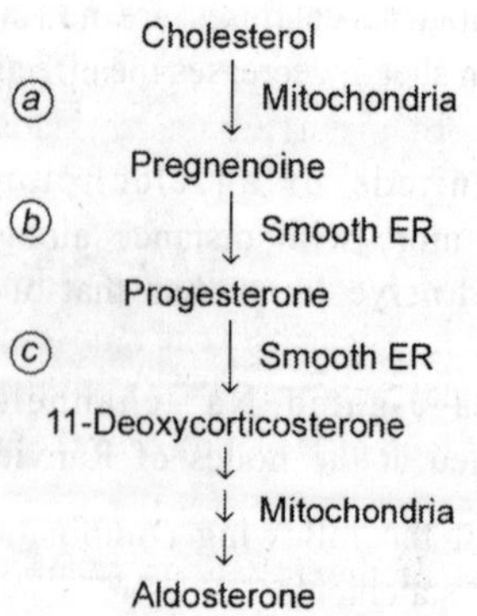

Which one of due following options represents correct matches for (*a*), (*b*) and (*c*)?

	(*a*)	(*b*)	(*c*)
A.	(*i*)	(*ii*)	(*iii*)
B.	(*iii*)	(*i*)	(*ii*)
C.	(*ii*)	(*iii*)	(*i*)
D.	(*ii*)	(*i*)	(*iii*)

39. Given below is a figure of pro-opiomelanocortin (POMC) polypeptide and its cleavage products (marked as (*a*), (*b*), (*c*), (*d*) which have different hormonal activities. The names of the cleaved products obtained from POMC are shown in the table below the diagram.

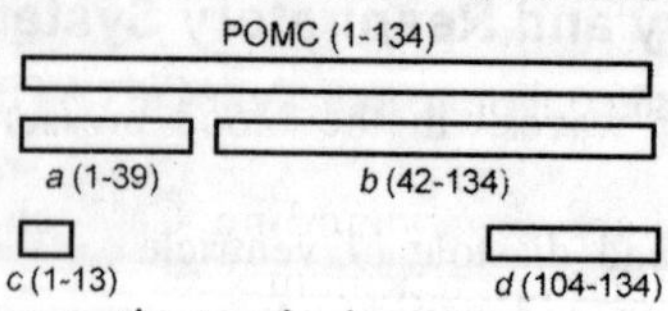

(*i*) Adrenocorticotropic hormone
(*ii*) β-lipotropin
(*iii*) α-melanocyte-stimulating hormone
(*iv*) β-endotropin

Which one of due following options represents (*a*), (*b*), (*c*) and (*d*) correctly?

	(*a*)	(*b*)	(*c*)	(*d*)
A.	(*i*)	(*ii*)	(*iii*)	(*iv*)
B.	(*ii*)	(*iii*)	(*i*)	(*iv*)
C.	(*i*)	(*iv*)	(*iii*)	(*ii*)
D.	(*iii*)	(*ii*)	(*iv*)	(*i*)

Circulatory and respiratory system

40. Given below are the different intervals/durations of electrocardiogram of a human subject (column A) and the events in heart during the process (column B).

Column A	Column B
(*a*) PR interval	(*i*) Ventricular action potential
(*b*) QRS duration	(*ii*) Atrioventricular conduction
(*c*) QT interval	(*iii*) Ventricular depolarization
(*d*) ST interval	(*iv*) Plateau portion of the ventricular action potential

Which one of the following options is a correct match of entries in columns A and B?

	(*a*)	(*b*)	(*c*)	(*d*)
A.	(*i*)	(*iv*)	(*ii*)	(*iii*)
B.	(*ii*)	(*iii*)	(*i*)	(*iv*)
C.	(*iv*)	(*ii*)	(*iii*)	(*i*)
D.	(*iii*)	(*i*)	(*iv*)	(*ii*)

41. Given below are names of the animals in column X and the accessory respiratory organs teleost fishes (Column Y).

Column X	Column Y
(*a*) Anabas	(*i*) Labyrinthine organ
(*b*) Clarias	(*ii*) Air sacs
(*c*) Amphipnous	(*iii*) Supra branchial cavity
(*d*) Channa	(*iv*) Arborescent organ

The correct match of the animals with the accessory respiratory organs they have are:

	(*a*)	(*b*)	(*c*)	(*d*)
A.	(*iv*)	(*iii*)	(*ii*)	(*i*)
B.	(*iii*)	(*iv*)	(*i*)	(*i*)
C.	(*i*)	(*iv*)	(*ii*)	(*iii*)
D.	(*ii*)	(*i*)	(*iii*)	(*iv*)

Reproductive System

42. Estrus cycle in rats is controlled by pituitary and gonadal hormones. While treating a set of rat with vitamin D, a student accidentally injected the rat with an inhibitor of 17 α hydroxypregnenolone and checked vaginal smear for 10 consecutive days. Which one of the following observation is correct?

A. The Smears showed well formed nucleated epithelial cell through the period.
B. The smears initially showed normal estrus stage but eventually entered a prolonged diestrus stage.
C. The smear showed leukocytes and few epithelial cells.
D. The cells showed metestrus for 3 days and then returned to the proestrus stage.

CSIR-NET, 15 DECEMBER, 2019

Endocrine System

43. Which one of the following hormones is responsible for mobilizing calcium from the bone and increasing urinary excretion of phosphate?

A. Calcitonin
B. Angiotensin II
C. Parathormone
D. Vasopressin

44. Thyroid hormone (T_3) increases the heart rate and the force of contraction of cardiac muscles. The mechanisms of these effects of T_3 have been explained by a researcher in the following statements:

(*a*) T_3 inhibits the expression of gene for α-myosin heavy chain and enhances the expression of gene for β-myosin heavy chain
(*b*) The expression of gene for $Na^+ - Ca^{++}$ antiporter is enhanced by T_3
(*c*) The sarcoplasmic reticulum Ca^{++} ATPase is increased by T_3
(*d*) T_3 increases ryanodine Ca^{++} channels in the sarcoplasmic reticulum
(*e*) The number of β-adrenergic receptors in heart muscles is inhibited by T_3

Which one of the following combinations contains both correct explanations?

A. (*a*) and (*b*)
B. (*b*) and (*c*)
C. (*c*) and (*d*)
D. (*d*) and (*e*)

45. Aldosterone increases the reabsorption of Na^+ from the tubular fluid in the thick ascending limb of loop of Henle and in the distal tubule. These effects are explained in the following proposed statements:

(*a*) Aldosterone increases the number of $Na^+ - Cl^-$ symporter in the apical membrane of principal cells in the early portion of distal tubule
(*b*) The number of Na^+ channels (ENaC) is increased in the apical membrane of principal cells in the late portion of distal tubule by aldosterone
(*c*) The synthesis of Na^+, K^+-ATPase in the basolateral portion of principal cells in distal tubule is decreased by the action of aldosterone
(*d*) Aldosterone increases the reabsorption of Nat across the apical cell membrane in the thick ascending limb of loop of Henle by decreasing Na^+, K^+-ATPase in it

Which one of the following combinations represents both correct statements?

A. (a) and (b) B. (b) and (c)
C. (c) and (d) D. (a) and (d)

Circulatory and Respiratory System

46. Individuals in a population are divided into various blood groups (in column 'X') based on the set of enzymes they have in column 'Y):

Column X	Column Y
A	(i) Fucose transferase
B	(ii) GalNAc transferase
AB	(iii) Gal transferase
O	

Which one of the following combinations is NOT correct for the blood group type and the set of enzymes a person has?
A. A - (i) and (ii) B. B - (i) and (iii)
C. AB - (i) (ii) and (ii) D. O - (i), (ii) and (iii)

Nervous System

47. In the nervous system, the action potential is generated at the axon hillock in physiological conditions and it is conducted to the terminal end of axon. The location specific origin of action potential and its direction-specific conductance are explained by a researcher in the following proposed statements:
(a) The membrane of axon hillock has highest threshold for the generation of action potential
(b) The membrane of axon hillock contains large numbers of voltage-gated Na^+ channels and that makes it more excitable
(c) The propagating action potential in the middle of the axon cannot generate another action potential in the direction of cell body since a large fraction of voltage-gated Na^+ channels in the preceding portion is voltage inactivated
(d) As the number of voltage-gated Na^+ channels is less in the preceding portion of axonal membrane, the propagating action potential in the middle of the axon cannot generate another action potential in the direction of cell body.

Which one of the following combinations represents both correct explanations?
A. (a) and (b) B. (b) and (c)
C. (c) and (d) D. (a) and (d)

Reproductive System & Developmental Biology

48. Centrolecithal eggs show:
A. superficial cleavage
B. displaced radial cleavage
C. bilateral cleavage
D. discoidal cleavage

Digestive system

49. Drawn below is an intestinal epithelial cell (IEC) performing the absorption of digested monosaccharides from the dietary carbohydrates ingested?

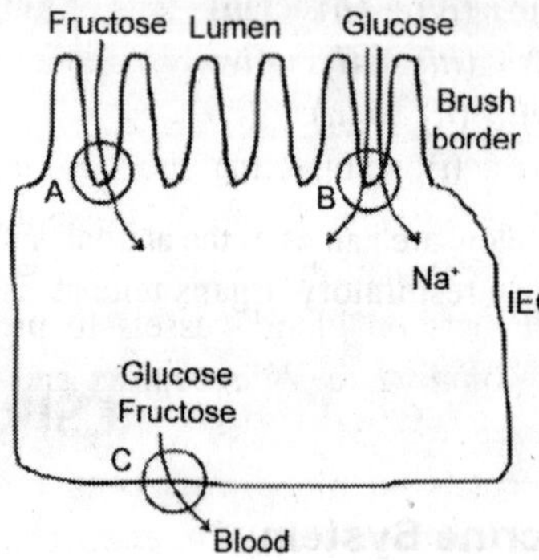

Which one of the following combinations of the transporter (A, B and C in the figure above) and the transported monosaccharide is correct?
A. A-GLUT5; B-SGLT1; C-GLUT2
B. A-GLUT2, B-GLUT5, C-SGLT1
C. A-SGLT1; B-GLUT2; C-GLUT5
D. A-SGLT1; B-GLUT5; C-GLUT2

CSIR-NET, 27 DECEMBER, 2019

Endocrine System

50. Hypophysiotropic hormones are secreted into blood at:
A. Posterior lobe of pituitary
B. Median eminence
C. Mammillary bodies
D. Anterior lobe of pituitary

51. A football player injured in the heat of play did not feel pain until the game was over.

This stress-induced analgesia was explained by the following proposed statements:
(a) The release of norepinephrine from brain stem catecholaminergic neurons in the amygdala reduced during stress
(b) The reduced release of 2-arachidonoglycerol (2AG) in brain contributed to stress-induced analgesia
(c) The inhibition of CB_1 receptors in many brain regions accounted for reduced analgesia in stress
(d) The activation of CB2 receptors on microglia in stress caused analgesic effect

Which one of the following options represents both correct statements?

A. (*a*) and (*b*) B. (*b*) and (*c*)
C. (*c*) and (*d*) D. (*a*) and (*d*)

52. A patient with primary hyper-aldosteronism develops diabetic glucose tolerance. Following statements are proposed on the patho-physiological condition of the patient:

(*a*) the increase of serum potassium inhibits insulin secretion
(*b*) the depletion of serum potassium decreases insulin secretion
(*c*) the depletion of sodium decreases insulin secretion
(*d*) thiazide diuretics worsen the condition of this patient

Which one of the following options represents a combination of correct statements?

A. (*a*) and (*b*)
B. (*b*) and (*c*)
C. (*c*) and (*d*)
D. (*b*) and (*d*)

53. Certain statements made on the mechanisms of action of a neuro-hormone, vasopressin(VP) are given below:

(*a*) VP acts on collecting ducts of kidney to concentrate urine by binding to V2 receptors and activating CAMP cascade
(*b*) VP acts on collecting ducts of kidney to concentrate urine by binding to V2 receptors and activating CAMP cascade
(*c*) VP acts on blood vessels to produce constriction by binding to V2 receptors and activating CAMP cascade
(*d*) VP acts on blood vessels to produce constriction by binding to V2 receptors and activating phosphatidylinositol cascade

Which one of the following options represents a combination of correct statements?

A. (*a*) and (*b*)
B. (*c*) and (*d*)
C. (*b*) and (*d*)
D. (*a*) and (*d*)

Circulatory and respiratory system

54. Pulmonary surfactant is synthesized primarily by:

A. Type I alveolar epithelial cells
B. Alveolar macrophages
C. Type II alveolar epithelial cells
D. Alveolar mast cells

55. The blood forced into aorta during systole sets up a pressure wave that travels along arteries (arterial pulse wave). The following figure depicts the pressure wave recorded from an artery during a cardiac cycle and the table below represents points in the graph (column A) and associated features (column B).

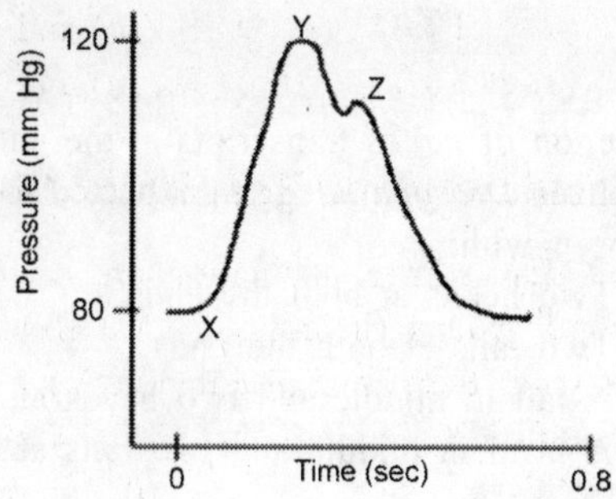

Column A	Column B
(*a*) X	(*i*) Dichrotic notch
(*b*) Y	(*ii*) Systolic blood pressure
(*c*) (Y − X)	(*iii*) Diastolic blood pressure
(*d*) Z	(*iv*) Pulse pressure
(*e*) $\left[X + \frac{Y-X}{3}\right]$	(*v*) Mean arterial pressure

Which one of the following options represents a correct match between all terms of columns A and B?

	(*a*)	(*b*)	(*c*)	(*d*)	(*e*)
A.	(*i*)	(*iii*)	(*ii*)	(*v*)	(*iv*)
B.	(*ii*)	(*iv*)	(*iii*)	(*v*)	(*i*)
C.	(*iii*)	(*ii*)	(*iv*)	(*i*)	(*v*)
D.	(*iv*)	(*v*)	(*i*)	(*iii*)	(*ii*)

Nervous System

56. Which one of the following functions is correct for the microglia cells in the brain?

A. Myelin formation
B. Making blood-brain barrier
C. Scavenging injured cell debris
D. Enveloping synapses

Thermal Regulation and Respiration

57. Humans exposed to cold climate are able to maintain their body temperature. The physiological mechanisms operating in the condition were suggested in the following statements:

(*a*) The increased thermogenesis in brown adipose tissue occurred in cold
(*b*) Uncoupling protein 1 in brown adipose tissue participated in the increased heat production
(*c*) The decreased secretion of catecholamine in cold elevated heat production
(*d*) The reflex responses activated by cold were controlled from the anterior hypothalamus
(*e*) The counter-current exchanges of temperature between warm arterial blood flowing towards limbs and the cold venous blood coming from extremities conserved body heat.

Which one of the following options represents a combination of INCORRECT statements?

A. (*a*) and (*b*) B. (*b*) and (*c*)
C. (*c*) and (*d*) D. (*d*) and (*e*)

DBT-JRF, 2019

58. Injection of *nanos* transcripts at the anterior end of a fertilized *Drosophila* egg is expected to develop in an embryo with:
A. Two heads at both the ends.
B. Two tails at both the ends.
C. A tail in middle and two heads at both the ends.
D. A head in middle and two tails at both the ends.

59. In Drosophila, the growth of legs on the head instead of antennae during development is an example of:
A. Homeotic transformation
B. Epigenetic modification
C. Chromosomal aberrations
D. Dysgenesis

60. Ameloblasts are differentiated cells:
A. that secrete amylase
B. of amygdala
C. of adrenal gland
D. that secrete enamel

GATE (LIFE SCIENCE), 2019

61. Which one of the following animals possesses two chambered heart?
A. Chameleon B. Peacock
C. Gold fish D. Blue whale

62. Match the hormones in Column I to their respective physiological effects in Column II

Column I	Column II
(*a*) Melatonin	(*i*) Inhibition of secretion of growth hormone
(*b*) Oxytocin	(*ii*) Synthesis of milk in mammary gland
(*c*) Cholecystokinin	(*iii*) Secretion of milk and uterine contraction
(*d*) Prolactin	(*iv*) Secretion of enzyme from pancreatic acinar cells
(*e*) Somatostatin	(*v*) Regulation of circadian rhythms

	(*a*)	(*b*)	(*c*)	(*d*)	(*e*)
A.	(*v*)	(*iv*)	(*ii*)	(*iii*)	(*i*)
B.	(*iii*)	(*v*)	(*iv*)	(*ii*)	(*i*)
C.	(*v*)	(*i*)	(*ii*)	(*iii*)	(*iv*)
D.	(*v*)	(*iii*)	(*iv*)	(*ii*)	(*i*)

CSIR-NET, NOVEMBER (MORNING), 2020

Endocrine System

63. Testosterone is a steroid hormone about which a set of statements are given below:
(*a*) It is secreted by Leydig cells of testes.
(*b*) It is secreted by Sertoli cells of testes.
(*c*) It inhibits secretion of luteinizing hormone from anterior pituitary.
(*d*) It does not inhibit secretion of follicle-stimulating hormone from anterior pituitary.

Which one of the following combinations represents correct statements about testosterone?
A. (*a*) and (*c*) B. (*b*) and (*c*)
C. (*b*) and (*d*) D. (*a*) and (*d*)

Circulatory Respiratory System

64. Which one of the following causes constriction of blood vessels?
A. Carbon monoxide B. Nitric oxide
C. Endothelin-1 D. Atrial natriuretic peptide

65. The action potential recorded from pace maker tissue (SA/AV node) of mammalian heart is shown in the following diagram:

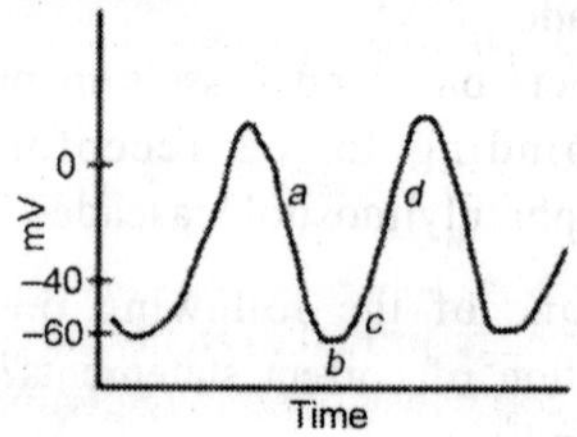

On the basis of mechanism of generation of action potential in pace maker tissue (SA/AV node), the following statement were proposed from the above figure
(*a*) 'funny' channels are activated at '*b*'
(*b*) Outward flow of K^+ occurs at '*a*'
(*c*) T-Ca^{++} channels are closed at '*c*'
(*d*) Fast Na^+ channels are opened at'*d*'
(*e*) The upward fast at 'd' is largely due to inward movement of Na^+

Which one of the following combinations represents correct statements?
A. (*a*) and (*b*) B. (*b*) and (*c*)
C. (*d*) and (*c*) D. (*d*) and (*e*)

66. Some metabolic aspects of the Red Blood Cell (RBC) are proposed in the following statements:

(*a*) Synthesis of fatty acids does not occur in the RBC
(*b*) The pentose phosphate pathway is operative in the RBC
(*c*) RBC cannot synthesize reduced glutathione (GSH)
(*d*) RBC does not contain enzymes like adenosine deaminase and pyrimidine nucleotidase
(*e*) NADH-dependent methemoglobin reductase system is present in RBC

Which one of the following combinations is NOT correct?

A. (*a*) and (*b*) B. (*b*) and (*c*)
C. (*c*) and (*d*) D. (*d*) and (*e*)

67. Fibrinogen, Factor 1, is a soluble glycoprotein present abundantly in plasma. Following biochemical characteristics are given below about this glycoprotein:

(*a*) It is a dimer of the three polypeptide chains $(A_\alpha B_\beta Y)_2$
(*b*) It is a dimer of two polypeptide chains $(A_\alpha B_\beta)_2$
(*c*) The chains are covalently linked by 29 inter- and intra-chain disulfide bonds
(*d*) The chains are covalently linked by 19 inter- and intra-chain disulfide bonds

Which one of the following represents a combination of correct statements?

A. (*a*) and (*c*) B. (*b*) and (*c*)
C. (*a*) and (*d*) D. (*b*) and (*d*)

Excretory System

68. Which one is NOT the function of P-cells in the collecting ducts?

A. Na^+ reabsorption B. K^+ secretion
C. H_2O reabsorption D. H^+ secretion

Digestive System

69. Which one of the following is NOT produced by α-amylase digestion of ingested:

A. Glucose B. Maltose
C. Maltotriose D. α-limit dextrins

CSIR-NET, NOVEMBER (AFTERNOON), 2020

Endocrine System

70. In both males and females, the gonads secrete a polypeptide hormone, called inhibin B, which inhibits:

A. luteinizing hormone
B. follicle-stimulating hormone
C. prolactin
D. thyroid-stimulating hormone

Circulatory Respiratory System

71. Loss of a large quantity of blood in an individual due to haemorrhage provokes many physiological changes which are compensatory and decompensatory in nature. The following statements describe few compensatory or decompensatory mechanisms operating in this condition.

(*a*) The peripheral chemoreceptors are stimulated when arterial blood pressure is reduced below 60 mm Hg due to blood loss.
(*b*) The cardiovascular centres in the brain stem become depressed in severe hypotension due to blood loss.
(*c*) The mononuclear phagocytic system becomes depressed during the course of haemorrhagic hypotension.
(*d*) Renin is secreted from juxtaglomerular apparatus in haemorrhagic hypotension.
(*e*) Considerable quantity of interstitial fluid may be drawn into circulation due to lower hydrostatic pressure in capillaries resulting from blood loss.

Choose the option describing only the decompensatory mechanisms:

A. (*a*) and (*b*) B. (*b*) and (*c*)
C. (*c*) and (*d*) D. (*d*) and (*e*)

Nervous System

72. Which one of the following is NOT released by sympathetic preganglionic neurons?

A. Neurotensin B. Enkephalin
C. Serotonin D. Substance P

Digestive System

73. Which one of the following statements is true with regard to drug metabolism?

A. The therapeutic window is simply the range of plasma drug concentrations in which the drug has therapeutic benefits without causing extra safety risks due to drug toxicity.
B. Each individual drug molecule is metabolized by a specific drug-metabolizing enzyme that is dedicated to metabolism of that drug.
C. An ultrafast metabolizer is a person who metabolizes a drug too quickly and is at a risk of drug overdose
D. A poor metabolizer is a person who cannot metabolize a drug properly and faces risk of underdose.

Thermal Regulation

74. Which one of the following routes is responsible for maximum amount of body heat loss in humans at an ambient temperature of 21°C?

A. Radiation and conduction
B. Respiration
C. Urination and defecation
D. Vaporization of sweat

GATE (LIFE SCIENCE), 2020

75. Match the following digestive enzymes in Column I with their respective functions in Column II

Column I	Column II
(*a*) Erepsin	(*i*) Converts proteins to peptides
(*b*) Steapsin	(*ii*) Activates trypsinogen to trypsin
(*c*) Pepsin	(*iii*) Convert fat into fatty acid and glycerol
(*d*) Enterokinase	(*iv*) Convert polypeptide to amino acid

	(*a*)	(*b*)	(*c*)	(*d*)
A.	(*iv*)	(*iii*)	(*ii*)	(*i*)
B.	(*iv*)	(*iii*)	(*i*)	(*ii*)
C.	(*iii*)	(*iv*)	(*i*)	(*ii*)
D.	(*iii*)	(*iv*)	(*ii*)	(*i*)

76. Transitional epithelia is found in which ONE of the following organs?

A. Liver B. Lung
C. Brain D. Urinary bladder

77. Which ONE of the following graphs represents the relationship between ventricular end-diastolic volume and cardiac output in a healthy adult individual at rest (solid line) and upon exercise (dotted line)?

A.
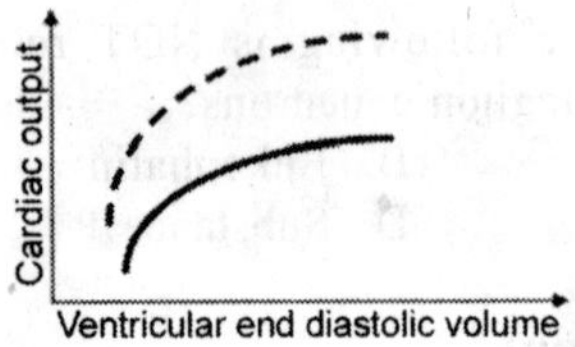

B.
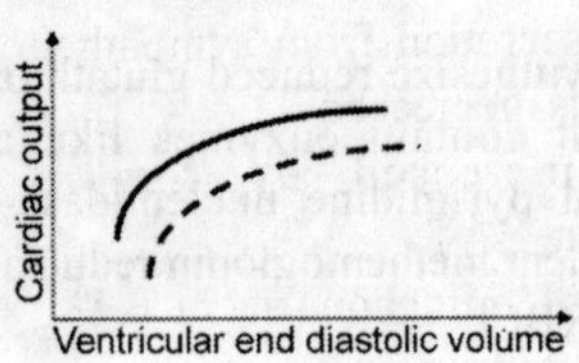

C.
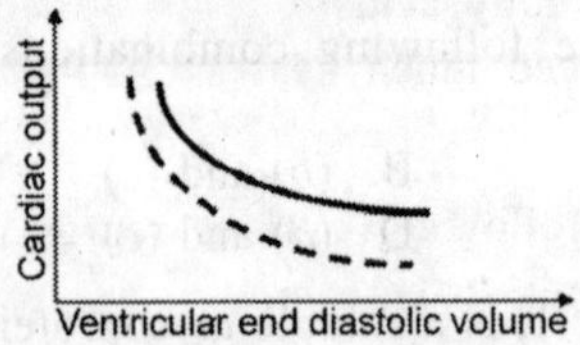

D.
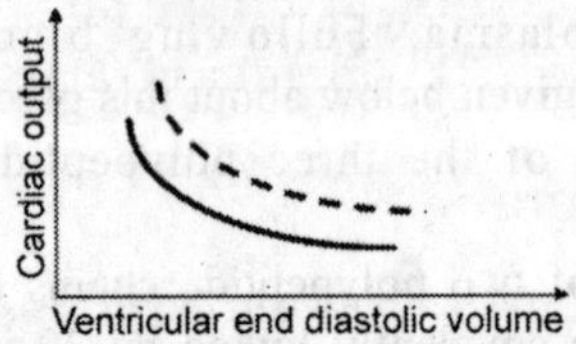

78. Match the proteins in Column I with the organs in which they are maximally expressed in Column II

Column I	Column II
(*a*) Keratin	(*i*) Liver
(*b*) Surfactants	(*ii*) Pancreas
(*c*) Pro-carboxypeptidase	(*iii*) Lung
(*d*) Albumin	(*iv*) Skin

	(*a*)	(*b*)	(*c*)	(*d*)
A.	(*iv*)	(*i*)	(*iii*)	(*ii*)
B.	(*iii*)	(*iv*)	(*ii*)	(*i*)
C.	(*iv*)	(*iii*)	(*ii*)	(*i*)
D.	(*i*)	(*ii*)	(*iii*)	(*iv*)

CSIR-NET, JUNE (MORNING), 2021

Endocrine System

79. Which one of the following is used in organification of tyrosine residues in thyroglobulin protein/during thyroide hormone biosynthesis?

A. iodine B. reduced ironies
C. oxidized iodine D. hydrogen iodine

80. Below are given set of statements for the glucocorticoids hormones:

(*a*) They bind to cell surface receptors and influence stress adaptation
(*b*) They bind to intracellular receptors and influence stress adaptation
(*c*) They inhibit ACTH secretion from interior pituitary
(*d*) Prolonged treatment with glucocorticoids leads to atrophic and unresponsive adrenals
(*e*) Their secretion does not show circadian variations

Which one of the following combination of the statement is correct?

A. (*a*), (*c*) and (*e*) B. (*b*), (*c*) and (*d*)
C. (*c*), (*d*) and (*e*) D. (*a*), (*d*) and (*e*)

81. Following statements are given for the ovarian hormones:

(*a*) 17 beta-estradiol, estrone and estriol are naturally occurring estrogens
(*b*) They are 18 C steroids which do not have methyl group at 10th positions
(*c*) They are 21 C steroids which have methyl group at 10th position
(*d*) They are primarily synthesized by granulosa cells of ovarian follicles
(*e*) Their biosynthesis does not depend on the enzyme aromatase

Which one of the following combination of statements is correct?

A. (*a*), (*b*) and (*c*) B. (*a*), (*b*) and (*d*)
C. (*b*), (*c*) and (*d*) D. (*c*), (*d*) and (*e*)

82. The mechanisms of thermogenesis in brown adipose tissue (BAT) in cold are described in the following proposed statements:

(*a*) A thermogenic uncoupling protein, UCP1 helps in the heat production in BAT
(*b*) Norepinephrine secretion from sympathetic nervw ending in BAT is decreased
(*c*) Lipolysis is increased by low level of norepinephrine in BAT
(*d*) A high content of mitochondria in BAT helps in the oxidation of fatty acids
(*e*) Oxidation produced much heat as ATP synthase activity is low

Which one of the following options represents the combination of correct statements?
A. (*a*), (*b*) and (*c*) B. (*a*), (*d*) and (*e*)
C. (*b*), (*c*) and (*d*) D. (*b*), (*d*) and (*e*)

Respiratory System

83. The pressure in the 'space' between lungs and chest wall is known as intrapleural pressure. The following statements are related to the intrapleural pressure at different phases of respiration:
(*a*) At the end of quiet expiration the tandency of the lung to recall from chest wall is balanced by the recoil of chest wall in opposite direction, and intrapleural pressure is subatmospheric
(*b*) At the start of inspiration the intrapleural pressure is subatmospheric
(*c*) The intrapleural pressure becomes more negative during inspiration
(*d*) The intrapleural pressure attains value above atmospheric pressure during expiration
(*e*) The intrapleural pressure becomes positive during strong inspiratory efforts

Which one of the following options represents all correct statements?
A. (*a*), (*b*) and (*c*) B. (*b*), (*c*) and (*d*)
C. (*c*), (*d*) and (*e*) D. (*a*), (*c*) and (*d*)

Excretory System

84. Which one of the following is not present in the filtration slit diaphragm.
A. NEPHI B. Paxillin
C. nephrin D. NEPH2

Sensory system

85. The dark current in ratina is due to:
A. Closing of Na^+ channel in the outer segment of photo receptors.
B. Opening of K^+ channels in the inner segment of photo receptors
C. Opening of Na^+ channel in the outer segment of photo receptors.
D. Closing of K^+ channel in the outer segment of photo receptors

CSIR-NET, JUNE (AFTERNOON), 2021

Endocrine System

86. Catecholamines (i.e. dopamine, norepinephrine and epinephrine) are important adrenal medullary hormones which play a role in the response for emergency situations. The following statements are made with reference to this:
(*a*) Catecholamines can easily cross the blood – brain barrier.
(*b*) Dopa decarboxylase (DD) is a soluble enzyme that converts L-dopa to dopamine.
(*c*) Dopamine B-hydroxylase (DBH) is a particulate enzyme carrying copper in its active site and it converts dopamine to epinephrine.
(*d*) Phenylethanolamine – N – methyltransferase (PNMT) is a soluble enzyme that is induced by glucocorticoids.

Which one of the following has the correct combination of statements?
A. (*a*) and (*b*) B. (*b*) and (*d*)
C. (*c*) and (*d*) D. (*a*) and (*c*)

87. Human chorionic gonadotropin (hCG) is a placental gonadotropin that controls hormonal secretions from corpus luteum during initial stage of pregnancy. Following statements are made about hCG:
(*a*) It is a glycoprotein that contains galactose and hexosamine.
(*b*) It is a heterodimer with a larger alpha subunit and smaller beta subunit.
(*c*) It is a heterodimer with a smaller alpha subunit and larger beta subunit.
(*d*) hCG is identical to beta subunit of LH and FSH.
(*e*) It appears as early as 6 days after conception in blood and 14 days after conception in urine.

Which one of the following has all correct combination of statements?
A. (*a*), (*b*) and (*d*) B. (*a*), (*c*) and (*e*)
C. (*b*), (*d*) and (*e*) D. (*a*), (*c*) and (*d*)

Circulatory System

88. The electrodes (also called leads) used for human electroencephalography in a 10-20 lead system are labeled with an uppercase letter and a subscript number or a letter, Which one of the following is INCORRECT meaning of the labels of electrodes?
A. The uppercase letter is an abbreviation of the location of electrode on the head
B. The electrodes over left hemisphere are labeled with a subscript odd number along with the uppercase letter

C. The electrodes on the midline of head are labeled with the subscript letter x along with the uppercase letter

D. The electrodes over right hemisphere are labeled with a subscript even number along with the uppercase letter

89. The following statements were proposed by a researcher on the characteristic features of stretch receptors in atria and the effect of these receptors activity on blood pressure regulation:

(*a*) The activity of type A receptors are increased by burst of impulses during atrial systole.

(*b*) The activity of type B receptors are increased by burst of impulses at the time of peak atrial filling during late diastole of atria.

(*c*) The discharge of type B atrial receptors is increased when venous return is increased.

(*d*) The activity of type B atrial receptors is increased by positive pressure breathing.

(*e*) The increased activity of most of the atrial receptors inhibits reflex circulatory adjustment by increasing blood pressure.

(*f*) The heart rate is decreased reflexly by the increased activity of atrial receptors.

Choose all correct statements from the following options:

A. (*a*), (*b*) and (*c*) B. (*b*), (*c*) and (*d*)
C. (*c*), (*d*) and (*e*) D. (*d*), (*e*) and (*f*)

Nervous system

90. The time taken by synaptic vesicles to travel from the soma of a motor neuron in the spinal cord to its neuromuscular junction in a person's foot by fast axon transport is about:

A. 5-10 seconds B. 10-14 min
C. 5-6 hours D. 2-3 Days

91. The explanation for increased conduction velocity of action potentails in a myelinated nerve fiber as compared to the that of a non-mylinated fibre of same diameter are suggested below:

(*a*) Much higher number of ions traverse a unit length of an MNF membrane compared to that of an NMF during condution of action potential as the ionic currents are restric to the membrane at the nodes of Ranvier

(*b*) The energy expenditure required to maintain ionic gradiant after conduction of action potential in an MNF is higher than that of an NMF

(*c*) The action potential of MNF do not have a hypepolazing effect like that of an NMF

(*d*) The relative refractory period is not extended in an MNF like that of an NMF

(*e*) The axolemma at the nodes of ranvier lacks K^+ ions channels

(*f*) MNF are metablically less efficient than NMFs

Choose all correct statements from the following:

A. (*a*), (*b*), (*c*) B. (*b*), (*c*), (*d*)
C. (*c*), (*d*), (*e*) D. (*d*), (*e*), (*f*)

Excretory System

92. The mechanisms of regulation of H+ secretion by kidneys in acidosis have been suggested in the following statements:

(*a*) Acidosis inhibits the secretion of cortisol by adrenal cortex.

(*b*) The transcription of $Na^+ - H^+$ antiporter gene is decreased by cortisol.

(*c*) The translation of mRNA of 1 $Na^+ - 3HCO_3$-symporter gene is decreased by cortisol.

(*d*) The secretion of endothelin-1 (ET-1) from proximal tubule is enhanced in acidosis.

(*e*) ET-1 stimulates the phosphorylation and subsequent insertion of the $Na^+ - H^+$ antiporter into the apical membrane of proximal tubular cells.

(*f*) The insertion of $1Na^+ - 3HCO_3$-symporter into the basolateral membrane of proximal tubular cells is also increased by ET-1.

Choose all correct statements from the following options:

A. (*a*), (*b*) and (*c*) B. (*b*), (*c*) and (*d*)
C. (*c*), (*d*) and (*e*) D. (*d*), (*e*) and (*f*)

Digestive System

93. Which one of the following tissues normally DOES NOT produce ghrelin that stimulates food intake?

A. Stomach B. Pancreas
C. Adrenal D. Liver

94. The principal product of fat digestion by pancreatic lipase is the free fatty acids (FFAs) and which one of the following?

A. 3-Monoacylglycerols 3-
B. 2-monoacylglycerols 2-
C. 1-monoacylglycerol 1-
D. 1, 3-diacylglycerols 1, 3-

Thermal Regulation

95. Consider the following statements about thermo-regulation in animals.

(*a*) It uses external environment to regulate internal body temperature

(*b*) It does not use external environment to regulate internal body temperature 56-57

(*c*) It can vary internal temperature considerably

(*d*) It can maintain thermal homeostasis in a narrow range of temperatures

Which one of the following options correctly describes a poikilothermic ectotherm?

A. (*a*) and (*d*) B. (*b*) and (*c*)
C. (*a*) and (*c*) D. (*b*) and (*d*)

GATE (LIFE SCIENCE), 2021

96. The Organ of Corti is found in which of the following parts of human body?

A. Heart B. Inner ear
C. Kidney D. Nasal cavity

97. In adult athletes, muscles grow larger when exercised and are capable of regeneration after injury. This is due to proliferation and differentiation of:

A. Satellite cells B. Myelin sheath
C. Oxyntic cells D. Choanocytes

CSIR-NET, SEPTEMBER (MORNING), 2022

Endocrine System

98. The intake of nutrients is under intricate control. A number of statements are made about factors controlling food intake:

(*a*) Cholecystokinin produced from small intestine stimulates food intake
(*b*) Leptin produced in adipose tissues stimulates food intake
(*c*) Leptin receptors are located in hypothalamus
(*d*) Ghrelin produced in the stomach inhibits food intake
(*e*) Leptin also stimulates the metabolic rate
(*f*) Ghrelin increases secretion of Neuropeptide Y

Choose the combination of all correct statements from the following options:

A. (*a*), (*b*) and (*c*) B. (*a*), (*b*) and (*d*)
C. (*d*), (*e*) and (*f*) D. (*c*), (*e*) and (*f*)

99. Given below are some statements about pituitary hormones:

(*a*) Oxytocin and vasopressin are synthesized in posterior pituitary
(*b*) Prolactin is synthesized from anterior pituitary
(*c*) α and β MSH are secreted from intermediate lobe of pituitary in adult humans
(*d*) Growth hormone secretion from anterior pituitary is stimulated by hyperglycemia
(*e*) Prolactin secretion is markedly increased by sleep

Choose the INCORRECT combination of statements from below:

A. (*a*), (*c*) and (*d*) B. (*a*), (*b*) and (*d*)
C. (*c*), (*d*) and (*e*) D. (*b*), (*c*) and (*e*)

Circulatory & Respiratory System

100. Which one is NOT a true response of pulmonary J-receptor stimulation by hyperventilation of lung?

A. Bronchodilation
B. Decreased heart rate
C. Apnoea followed by rapid breathing
D. Low blood pressure

101. A human subject can voluntarily inhibit respiration for some time but the subject feels irresistible urge t after a while at a point which is called the breaking point. The characteristic features of breaking point a following statements:

(*a*) The breaking point is shorter in subjects after removal of carotid bodies compared to when they have bodies.
(*b*) The breaking point is prolonged if the subject breathes 100% oxygen before breath holding.
(*c*) When the subject hyperventilates with room air before breath holding, the breaking point is delayed compared to when the subject breathes normally before breath holding.
(*d*) The breaking point can be reduced in a subject by making respiratory movements behind a closed glottis.
(*e*) The breaking point is shorter when the subject is told during breath holding that her/his performance is very good compared to a situation when she/he is not told so.

Choose both the correct statements from the following options:

A. (*a*) and (*b*)
B. (*b*) and (*c*)
C. (*c*) and (*d*)
D. (*d*) and (*e*)

102. The autoregulation of blood flow in the active tissues is partly achieved locally by metabolites accumulated in these tissues. The contributions of different metabolites in this autoregulation are suggested in the following statements:

(*a*) The accumulation of K^+ locally in active tissues has vasoconstrictor activity.
(*b*) The increase in osmolality in active tissues causes vasoconstriction.
(*c*) The accumulation of lactate in active tissues may contribute to vasoconstriction.
(*d*) The hypoxia-inducible factor-1α (HIF-1α) produced due to local fall in O_2 tension in active tissues, initiates the production of different vasodilatory substances.
(*e*) Histamine released from the damaged cells of active tissues increases capillary permeability.

Choose the option with both correct statements:

A. (*a*) and (*b*) B. (*b*) and (*c*)
C. (*c*) and (*d*) D. (*d*) and (*e*)

Nervous System

103. The activities of baroreceptors present in the carotid sinus are carried by the afferent fibers of neurons located in

A. nodose ganglion B. geniculate ganglion
C. petrosal ganglion D. spiral ganglion

104. Following are the statements made about major functions of some of the neuroglia in normal condition:

(*a*) Oligodendrocytes help maintain K + level, and contribute to the blood–brain barrier.
(*b*) Microglia are capable of movement and phagocytosis of pathogens and damaged tissue.
(*c*) Astrocytes produce the myelin sheath to electrically insulate neurons of the CNS.
(*d*) Ependymal cells which are ciliated are involved in circulation of cerebrospinal fluid.

Which of the following options represents the combination of all INCORRECT statements?

A. (*a*) and (*b*) B. (*a*) and (*c*)
C. (*a*) and (*d*) D. (*c*) and (*d*)

Thermal Regulation

105. Which one does NOT occur as a physiological adjustment during heat acclimatization?

A. Lowered threshold for start of sweating
B. Effective distribution of cardiac output
C. Improved skin blood flow
D. Increased salt concentration of sweat

CSIR-NET, SEPTEMBER (AFTERNOON), 2022

Endocrine System

106. Insulin is a polypeptide hormone that reduces blood glucose levels in human. Following statements are made for insulin synthesis and structure:

(*a*) It is synthesized in rough endoplasmic reticulum of the B cells of islets of Langerhans.
(*b*) It is synthesized in cytosol on free ribosomes of the B cells of islets of Langerhans.
(*c*) Insulin has an AB heterodimer structure with one intrachain (A8-A13) and two interchain disulfide bridges (A6-B10 and A21-B18)
(*d*) Insulin has an AB heterodimer structure with one intrachain (A6-A11) and two interchain disulfide bridges (A7-B7 and A20-B19).
(*e*) The gene for insulin is located on the long arm of chromosome 11 and has two introns and three exons.
(*f*) The gene for insulin is located on the short arm of chromosome 11 that has two introns and three exons.

Which one of the following combination of statements is correct?

A. (*b*), (*d*) and (*e*) B. (*a*), (*c*) and (*f*)
C. (*b*), (*c*) and (*e*) D. (*a*), (*d*) and (*f*)

Circulatory Respiratory System

107. The pericytes are found in:

A. myelin sheath
B. surrounding coat of a skeletal muscle fibre
C blood capillary wall
D. lymph capillary wall

Excretory System

108. The reabsorption of water and NaCl in kidneys is inhibited by the increased secretion of the following substances EXCEPT one:

A. Urodilatin
B. Uroguanylin
C. Dopamine
D. Norepinephrine

109. Plasma proteins have vital roles in the body ranging from maintaining osmolarity to transport of hormones. Certain statements are given below for the functions of selected plasma proteins:

(*a*) Von Willebrand factor is normally synthesized in the liver.
(*b*) Ceruloplasmin is a copper carrier protein.
(*c*) Genetic deficiency of $\alpha 1$-antiproteinase causes emphysema.
(*d*) Most plasma proteins including albumin are covalently glycosylated.
(*e*) α_1-acid glycoprotein (AGP) level increases during body's response to inflammation.

Which one of the following represents all correct combination of statements?

A. (*a*), (*b*) and (*c*) only B. (*b*), (*c*) and (*d*) only
C. (*b*), (*c*) and (*e*) only D. (*a*), (*d*) and (*e*)

Digestive System

110. Iron deficiency is a common problem in humans worldwide. The homeostasis of iron in the body is maintained using various proteins (column- X) and their function (column- Y):

Column X	Column Y
(*a*) Ferritin	(*i*) Hypoxia is known to reduce its synthesis
(*b*) Ferroportin	(*ii*) Plasma iron binding protein
(*c*) Transferrin	(*iii*) Intramucosal cell iron binding protein
(*d*) Hepcidin	(*iv*) Iron leaves mucosal cells through it

Choose the correct option from below that most appropriately matches in column X with that of column Y.

	(a)	(b)	(c)	(d)
A.	(i)	(iii)	(ii)	(iv)
B.	(iii)	(iv)	(ii)	(i)
C.	(ii)	(i)	(iv)	(iii)
D.	(iv)	(ii)	(iii)	(i)

Sensory system

111. Sound waves are transmitted from the external environment to the cochlea through the middle ear during hearing. The functions of the middle ear in hearing are suggested below:

(*a*) During the transmission of sound waves through the middle ear, the movement of the head of stapes induces a piston like movement on the oval window.

(*b*) The tympanic membrane functions as a resonator that reproduces the vibration of sound source.

(*c*) The sound pressure on the tympanic membrane is increased 1.3 times on the oval window by the lever system of malleus and incus.

(*d*) The area of tympanic membrane is greater than that of the footplate of stapes, and hence sound pressure on tympanic membrane is increased on oval window.

(*e*) The contraction of tensor tympani muscle causes the manubrium of the malleus to be pulled outward.

(*f*) The footplate of the stapes is pulled inward by the contraction of stapedius muscle.

Choose the option with all CORRECT statements:

A. (*a*), (*b*) and (*c*) B. (*b*), (*c*) and (*d*)
C (*c*), (*d*) and (*e*) D. (*d*), (*e*) and (*f*)

DBT-JRF, 2022

112. Which one of the following is NOT a function of the glial cells in the brain?

A. Transporting neurotransmitter vesicles from soma to terminal
B. Directing axons to their targets
C. Promoting the survival of nascent neurons
D. Forming the synapse

113. Which one of the following is NOT a food rich in Vitamin A?

A. Potato B. S27-200uash
C. Sweet potato D. Spinach

114. Given below are two statements: one is labelled as Assertion (A) and the other is labelled as Reason (R).

Assertion (A): Heating of preoptic anterior hypothalamic area of the brain caused profuse sweating and dilation of blood vessels of the skin.

Reason (R): The above (in A) is to absorb more heat into the body and throw out waste from the body.

In the light of the above statements, choose the correct answer from the options given below:

A. Both (A) and (R) are correct and (R) is the correct explanation of (A)
B. Both (A) and (R) are correct, but (R) is not the correct explanation of (A)
C. (A) is correct, but (R) is incorrect
D. (A) is incorrect, but (R) is correct

GATE (LIFE SCIENCE), 2022

115. Which of the following statements about endogenous synthesis of insulin are correct?

(*a*) Insulin is synthesized as preproinsulin.
(*b*) Preproinsulin is converted to proinsulin.
(*c*) Single-site cleavage of proinsulin eliminates C chain.
(*d*) Mature insulin consists of disulphide-linked A and B chains.

A. (*a*), (*b*) and (*c*) B. (*a*), (*b*) and (*d*)
C. (*a*), (*c*) and (*d*) D. (*b*), (*c*) and (*d*)

116. Which one of the following leukocytes are present in the largest proportion in healthy human blood?

A. Neutrophils B. Eosinophils
C. Basophiles D. Monocytes

117. Match the drug/chemicals listed in Column I with the developmental/physiological defects listed in Column II.

Column I	Column II
(*a*) Veratrum alkaloids	(*i*) Obesity
(*b*) Thalidomide	(*ii*) Minamata syndrome
(*c*) Methylmercury	(*iii*) Cyclopia
(*d*) Diethylstilbesterol	(*iv*) Phocomelia

	(a)	(b)	(c)	(d)
A.	(iii)	(iv)	(ii)	(i)
B.	(i)	(iv)	(iii)	(ii)
C.	(ii)	(iv)	(iii)	(i)
D.	(ii)	(iii)	(iv)	(i)

118. Match the cell types listed in Column I with their sources in Column II and the primary functional roles listed in Column III.

Column I	Column II	Column III
P. Microglial cells	(*i*) Lung	(*a*) Visual transduction
Q. Leydig cells	(*ii*) Eyes	(*b*) Hormone secretion
R. ON cells	(*iii*) Brain	(*c*) Phagocytosis
S. Pneumocytes	(*iv*) Testis	(*d*) Gaseous exchange

	P	Q	R	S
A.	(*iii*)-(*b*)	(*iv*)-(*c*)	(*ii*)-(*a*)	(*i*)-(*d*)
B.	(*ii*)-(*c*)	(*iv*)-(*d*)	(*i*)-(*a*)	(*iii*)-(*b*)
C.	(*i*)-(*a*)	(*iv*)-(*b*)	(*ii*)-(*c*)	(*iii*)-(*d*)
D.	(*iii*)-(*c*)	(*iv*)-(*b*)	(*ii*)-(*a*)	(*i*)-(*d*)

119. Match the hormones listed in Column I with their primary source tissues in Column II and the primary target tissues listed in Column III.

Column I	Column II	Column III
P. Epinephrine	(*i*) Hypothalamus	(*a*) Pituitary
Q. Prolactin	(*ii*) Thyroid	(*b*) Heart
R. Calcitonin	(*iii*) Pituitary	(*c*) Bone
S. Thyrotropin releasing	(*iv*) Chromaffin tissue	(*d*) Pigeon's crop hormone

	P	Q	R	S
A.	(*iii*)-(*b*)	(*iv*)-(*c*)	(*ii*)-(*a*)	(*i*)-(*d*)
B.	(*iv*)-(*c*)	(*iii*)-(*b*)	(*ii*)-(*a*)	(*i*)-(*d*)
C.	(*iv*)-(*b*)	(*iii*)-(*d*)	(*ii*)-(*c*)	(*i*)-(*a*)
D.	(*iii*)-(*b*)	(*iv*)-(*c*)	(*ii*)-(*d*)	(*i*)-(*a*)

ANSWERS

1	2	3	4	5	6	7	8	9	10
A	A	A	B	C	A	C	C	B	D
11	**12**	**13**	**14**	**15**	**16**	**17**	**18**	**19**	**20**
D	C	A	C	B	A	A	D	D	A
21	**22**	**23**	**24**	**25**	**26**	**27**	**28**	**29**	**30**
A	A	A	A	C	B	B	B	C	A
31	**32**	**33**	**34**	**35**	**36**	**37**	**38**	**39**	**40**
C	B	A	C	A	C	C	C	A	B
41	**42**	**43**	**44**	**45**	**46**	**47**	**48**	**49**	**50**
C	B	C	C	A	D	B	A	A	B
51	**52**	**53**	**54**	**55**	**56**	**57**	**58**	**59**	**60**
D	D	C	C	C	C	C	B	A	D
61	**62**	**63**	**64**	**65**	**66**	**67**	**68**	**69**	**70**
C	D	A	C	A	C	A	D	A	B
71	**72**	**73**	**74**	**75**	**76**	**77**	**78**	**79**	**80**
B	C	A	A	B	D	A	C	C	B
81	**82**	**83**	**84**	**85**	**86**	**87**	**88**	**89**	**90**
B	B	A	B	C	B	B	C	C	D
91	**92**	**93**	**94**	**95**	**96**	**97**	**98**	**99**	**100**
C	D	D	B	C	B	A	D	A	A
101	**102**	**103**	**104**	**105**	**106**	**107**	**108**	**109**	**110**
B	D	C	B	D	D	C	D	C	B
111	**112**	**113**	**114**	**115**	**116**	**117**	**118**	**119**	
B	A	A	C	B	A	A	D	C	

CHAPTER

17

ECOLOGY

CSIR-NET, JUNE, 2017

Habitat and Niche Concepts

1. Two species, M and N, occupy the same habitat. Given below is a 'state-space' graph in which the abundance of species M is plotted on the X-axis and abundance of species N is plotted on the Y-axis. For each species, the zero-growth isocline is plotted:

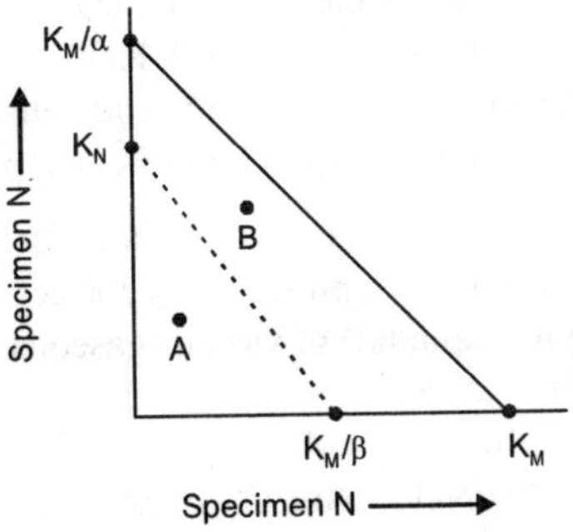

____ zero-growth isocline for species M

------ zero-growth isocline for species N

KM = carrying capacity of the habitat for species M-in absence of species N

KN = carrying capacity of the habitat for species N in absence of species M

α = per capita effect of species N on M β = per capita effect of species M on N

Based on the above plot some deductions are made. Which one of the following statements is incorrect?

A. At point A, populations of both the species M and N increase

B. At point B, population of species M increase while that of species N decreases

C. At point B, population of species N increase while that of species M decreases

D. Ultimately species N will be eliminated

Population Ecology

2. In an experiment to determine the number of rats in a field, 80 rats were initially captured, marked and released. After one month, 100 rats were captured in the same field, of which 20 were previously marked ones. Based on the above observation, estimated population size of the rats in the field will be:

A. 160 B. 200

C. 400 D. 1600

Species Interactions

3. To understand prey-predator relationship, *Didinium* (predator) and Paramecium (prey) were used. *Paramecium* population was grown with sand sediment as hiding place or refuge. To this population, *Didinium* was introduced only once. What would happen to the prey population in the course of time?

A. The population will steadily decrease and vanish

B. The population will initially increase and then stabilize

C. The population will initially decrease, then increase and stabilize

D. The population will steadily increase

Ecosystem & Biomes

4. Which one of the following is NOT correct?
   A. Island ecosystems are less prone to biological invasion because of their distance from mainland
   B. Invasive species have greater phenotypic plasticity compared to native species
   C. Invasive species have high dispersal ability
   D. At a large scale, diversity rich ecosystems are generally more prone to invasion

5. Which one of the following is in the correct decreasing order for the major reservoirs of carbon on Earth?
   A. Terrestrial soils > Terrestrial vegetation > Atmospheric CO_2 > Large lake sediments
   B. Terrestrial soil > Large lake sediments > Terrestrial vegetation > Atmospheric CO_2
   C. Atmospheric CO_2 > Large lake sediments > Terrestrial soils > Terrestrial vegetation
   D. Large lake sediments > Terrestrial soils > Atmospheric CO_2 > Terrestrial vegetation

6. The net reproductive rate (Ro) is 1.5 for a given population. If N*t*, the population of females at generation *t*, is 500, then what will be the population of females after four generations (N*t* + 4)?
   A. 1125.000
   B. 2531.250
   C. 1265.625
   D. 3796.875

7. Which one of the following statement is NOT correct?
   A. Herbivores enhance the productivity of a productive ecosystem and reduce the productivity of an unproductive ecosystem.
   B. Detritus based food chains are longer in more productive ecosystem
   C. Consumption efficiency of herbivores is higher in grasslands than ocean
   D. Production efficiency of carnivores is higher than herbivores

Biodiversity

8. The table given below lists species and conservation status:

Species	Conservations status
(*a*) White bellied Heron	(*i*) Critically endangered
(*b*) Ganges river dolphin	(*ii*) Endangered
(*c*) Gaur	(*iii*) Vulnerable
(*d*) Clouded leopard	

Which one of the following is the correct pairing between Indian animal species and their conservation status?

	(*a*)	(*b*)	(*c*)	(*d*)
A.	(*i*)	(*i*)	(*ii*)	(*iii*)
B.	(*ii*)	(*ii*)	(*iii*)	(*ii*)
C.	(*i*)	(*ii*)	(*iii*)	(*iii*)
D.	(*iii*)	(*iii*)	(*ii*)	(*ii*)

9. Following are the descriptions used by conservation biologists for characterizing species/groups in a community:
   (*a*) Species with a disproportionally large effect on its environment relative to its abundance
   (*b*) Species defining a trait or characteristics of the environment
   (*c*) Species whose conservation leads to direct protection of other species
   (*d*) Species which is instantly recognizable and used as the focus of a broader conservation effort

   Which of the following combination correctly identifies these species/groups?
   A. (*a*) Keystone species (*b*) Indicator species (*c*) Flagship species (*d*) Umbrella species
   B. (*a*) Keystone species (*b*) Indicator species (*c*) Umbrella species (*d*) Flagship species
   C. (*a*) Indicator species (*b*) Flagship species (*c*) Umbrella species (*d*) Keystone species
   D. (*a*) Umbrella species (*b*) Indicator species (*c*) Keystone species (*d*) Flagship species

10. As per national air quality standard for India, which one of the following options gives correct concentration limits (μg m^{-3}, annual) of various gaseous air pollutants for a residential area?
   A. SO_2 – 100, NO_2 – 40, O_3 – 40, CO – 50
   B. SO_2 – 50, NO_2 – 40; O_3 – 100, CO – 02
   C. SO_2 – 40, NO_2 – 50, O_3 – 50, CO – 10
   D. SO_2 – 50, NO_2 – 100, O_3 – 40, CO – 02

CSIR-NET, DECEMBER, 2017

Habitat and Niche Concepts

11. Which of the following statements is INCORRECT about a keystone species?
   A. Species other than consumers can be a keystone species
   B. Keystone species has influence on a community proportionate to its abundance
   C. Removing a keystone species can reduce species richness of a community
   D. Removing a keystone species can affect successive trophic levels causing a trophic cascade

Population Ecology

12. Given below are growth equations where *dN*/*dt* is defined as:

(*a*) rN/K (*b*) rN
(*c*) rN[(K-N)/N] (*d*) rN[(K-N)/K]

With reference to the above equations, which one of the following statements is correct?

A. (*b*) represents exponential growth and (*a*) represents logistic growth
B. (*b*) represents exponential growth and (*d*) represents logistic growth
C. (*b*) represents zero growth and (*c*) represents logistic growth
D. (*a*) represents exponential growth and (*d*) represents logistic growth

13. A species whose life history strategies allow for high intrinsic rates of increase (*r*-strategist) will also exhibit the following EXCEPT:

A. High tolerance for both environmental instability and low quality resources.
B. Short period of exponential population growth (*r*).
C. Reproductive strategy that involves random mating, semelparity and little or no parental investment.
D. Survivorship that show density-dependent mortality, typically exhibiting Type 1 or 2 survivorship curves.

14. The rank/abundance plot given below illustrates three well known species abundance curves (*a*, *b*, *c*).

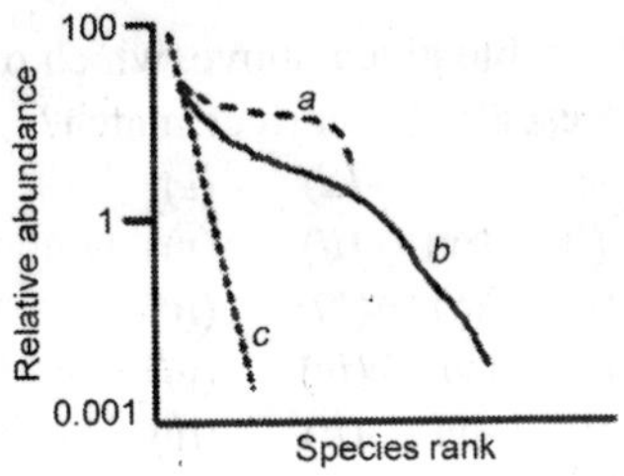

Based on the shapes of the curves select the correct option.

A. *a*-exponential, *b*-log normal, *c*-geometric series
B. *a*-broken stick, *b*-geometric series, *c*-log normal
C. *a*-broken stick, *b*-log normal, *c*-geometric series
D. *a*-exponential, *b*-geometric series, *c*-log normal

15. Given below are the population pyramids of three different populations A, B and C depicting the relationship between birth and death rates in each.

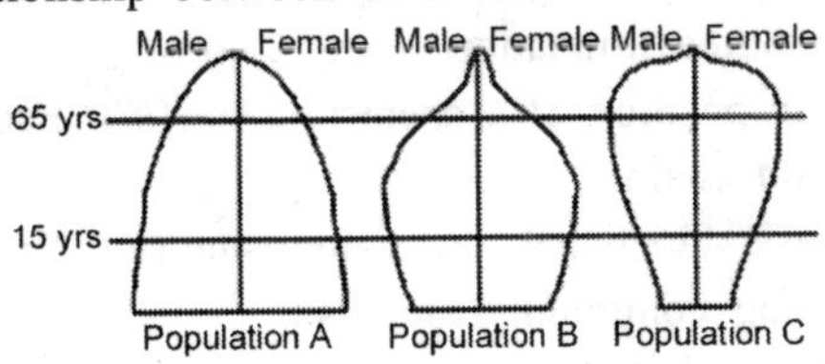

Based on the population pyramids given above, which one of the following is INCORRECT?

A. Population B has slower growth rate than population A.
B. Population C has birth rate higher than its death rate.
C. Population A represents a rapidly growing population.
D. Population B has the highest death rate among the three populations.

Species Interactions

16. Three species M, N and O when grown independently in a laboratory showed typical logistic growth curves. However, when grown in pairs, the following growth curves were observed.

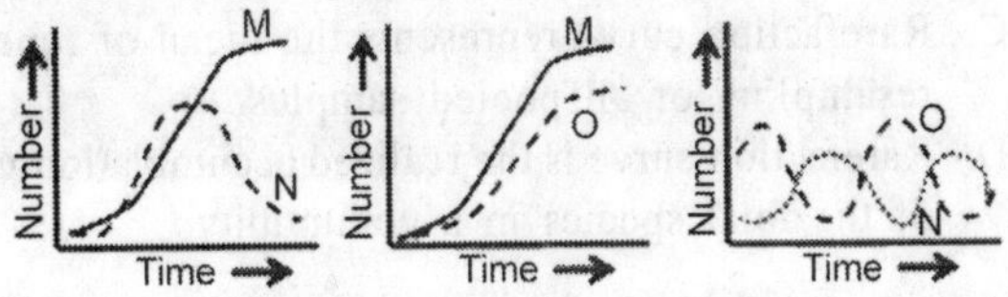

What interpretation regarding the interspecific relationship between M, N and O can be deduced from the above observations?

A. N predates over O and therefore can also predate on M.
B. N is competed out by M and O.
C. N and O possibly have a prey-predator relationship.
D. M and O exhibit prey-predator relationship.

Community Ecology & Successions

17. Given below are two patterns of ecological succession. Four species are represented by A, B, C and D. An arrow indicates "is replaced by":

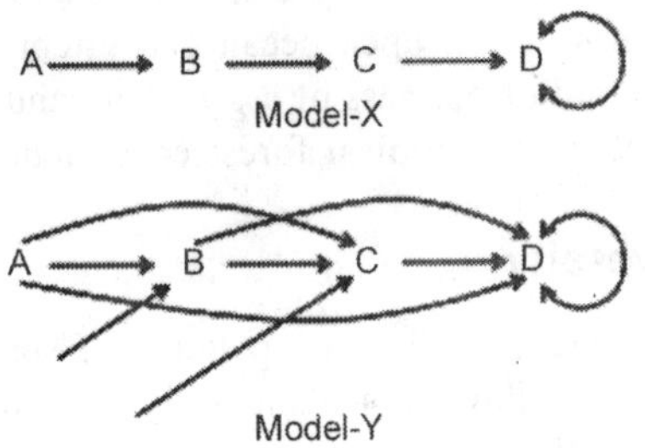

In the context of ecological succession, which of the following statements is INCORRECT with respect to the figures given above?

A. Model-X represents facilitation model and Model-Y represents tolerance model.
B. Model-X represents tolerance model and Model-Y represents inhibition model
C. As per Model-Y, C can out-compete B but can also invade a habitat in their absence.
D. As per the Model-X, A makes the environments more suitable for B to invade.

18. Given below are the species accumulation curves and rarefaction curves measured in an ecological community.

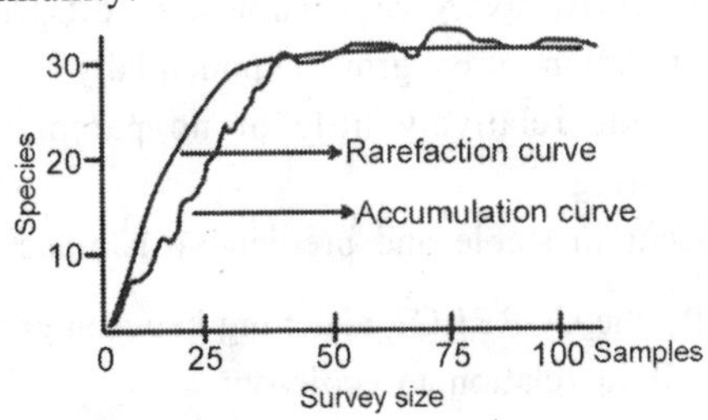

Which one of the following statements is INCORRECT about the two curves?

A. Species accumulation curve moves from left to right and rarefaction curve moves from right to left.
B. Species accumulation curve represents the total species richness of the assemblage.
C. Rarefaction curve represents the mean of repeated resampling of all pooled samples.
D. Rarefaction curve is the realized accumulation value of the total species in a community.

Ecosystem & Biomes

19. Given below is an ecological pyramid.

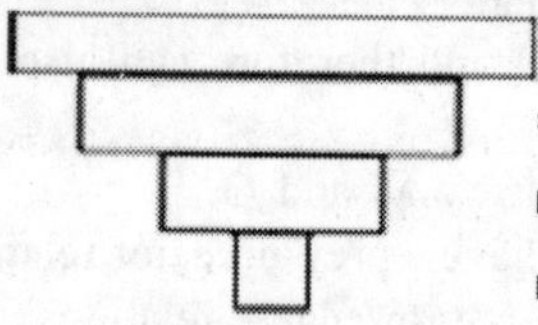

The above pyramid represents:

A. Pyramid of number of a parasitic food chain and pyramid of biomass of a pond ecosystem
B. Pyramid of number of a pond ecosystem and pyramid of biomass of a forest ecosystem
C. Pyramid of energy of a grassland and pyramid of biomass of an open ocean ecosystem
D. Pyramid of biomass of a grassland and pyramid of number of a tropical forest ecosystem

Biodiversity

20. In the context of diversity patterns of species, which one of the following statements is INCORRECT?

A. Alpha diversity is diversity within a single community
B. Beta Alpha diversity is a measure of the change in species composition from one community or habitat to another
C. Alpha diversity is the regional diversity found among range of communities in a geographical region
D. Gamma diversity is the regional diversity found among range of communities/habitats in a geographical region

21. Given below are names of some of the National Parks of India and their key protected animals.

Name of the National Park	Key Protected Animal
(*a*) Dibru-Saikhowa National Park, Assam	(*i*) Indian Rhinoceros
(*b*) Jaldapara National Park, West Bengal	(*ii*) Hangul
(*c*) Mukurthi National Park, Tamil Nadu	(*iii*) Feral Horse
(*d*) Dachigam National Park, Jammu and Kashmir	(*iv*) Asiatic Lion
(*e*) Gir Forest National Park, Gujarat	(*v*) Nilgiri Tahr

Based on the table given above, which of the following options represents the correct match?

	(*a*)	(*b*)	(*c*)	(*d*)	(*e*)
A.	(*iii*)	(*i*)	(*iv*)	(*ii*)	(*v*)
B.	(*i*)	(*ii*)	(*v*)	(*iii*)	(*iv*)
C.	(*i*)	(*ii*)	(*iii*)	(*iv*)	(*v*)
D.	(*iii*)	(*i*)	(*v*)	(*ii*)	(*iv*)

GATE (LIFE SCIENCE), 2017

Ecology and Environment

22. The phenomenon where an organism lives at the expense of another organism by harming it but not killing, is called:

A. Commensalism
B. Predation
C. Symbiosis
D. Parasitism

23. Which of the following is TRUE for K-strategist species?

A. roduce relatively large number of offspring
B. Population often grow exponentially
C. Provide relatively little or no parental care to offspring
D. Occur in stable and predictable habitats

24. Identify the CORRECT matching between group I and group II in relation to ecology:

Group I	Group II
(*a*) The physical environment of an organism	(*i*) Trophic level
(*b*) The totality of the needs of a population for survival and its resource utilization	(*ii*) Habitat
(*c*) The position of a species in a food chain	(*iii*) Ecosystem
(*d*) Basic functional unit comprising living community and its Physical environment	(*iv*) Niche
	(*v*) Ecological pyramid

	(*a*)	(*b*)	(*c*)	(*d*)
A.	(*ii*)	(*v*)	(*iv*)	(*i*)
B.	(*ii*)	(*iv*)	(*i*)	(*iii*)
C.	(*v*)	(*ii*)	(*iii*)	(*i*)
D.	(*i*)	(*iii*)	(*iv*)	(*ii*)

CSIR-NET, JUNE, 2018

Habitat and Niche Concepts, Biome, Pollution

25. The above graph illustrates two lines that represent the immigration and extinction rates for an island based on its distance from mainland (solid line) and its size (dotted line). Which of the following is true for this island?

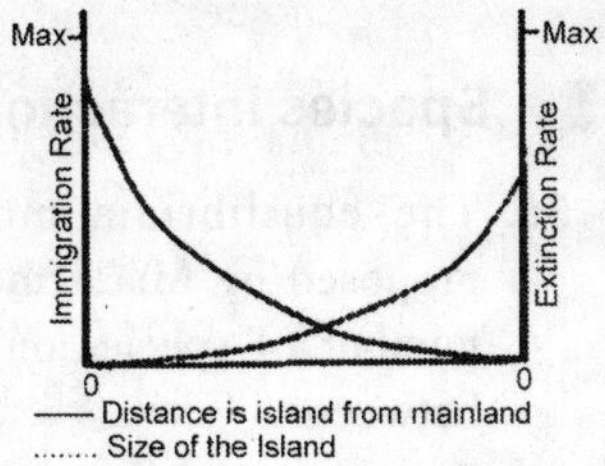

A. It is close to the mainland and is very small.
B. It is far from mainland and is very large.
C. It is close to the mainland and is very large.
D. It is far from the mainland and is very small.

Population Ecology

26. A general increase in the average body mass of animal population within a species with latitude is known as:

A. Allen's rule   B. Bergmann's rule
C. Allee effect   D. Hamilton's rule

Species Interactions

27. Ruderal species arc those which are found in the environments with:

A. low disturbance, high competition
B. high disturbance, low competition
C. low disturbance, low competition
D. high disturbance, high competition

Ecosystem

28. Which of the following options lists ecosystems in increasing order of plant productivity per day per unit leaf area?

A. Tropical forests, hot deserts, temperate forests
B. Hot deserts, temperate forests, tropical forests
C. Hot deserts, temperate grasslands, tropical forests
D. Tropical forests, temperate grasslands, hot deserts

29. The complexity of a food web in a community is quantified using certain parameters which are defined below. Which of the following is an INCORRECT representation?

A. Chain length = $\frac{\text{Average no. of links between trophic level}}{\text{Total number of trophic level}}$

B. Chain length = $\frac{\text{Actual no. number of links in food web}}{\text{Potential no. of link in a food web}}$

C. Potential links in food web where 'n' species are present = $\frac{n(n-1)}{\text{Actual no. of links}}$

D. Chain length = $\frac{\text{Actual no. of links in a food web}}{\text{No. of species in a food web}}$

Biodiversity and Conservation

30. Given below are biodiversity hotspots in decreasing order of endemic plant species recorded in them. Select the correct order.

A. Western Ghats and Sri Lanka > IndoBurma > Sundaland > Philippines
B. Philippines > Sundaland > Indo-Burma > Western Ghats and Sri Lanka
C. Sundaland > Indo-Burma > Philippines > Western Ghats and Sri Lanka
D. Western Ghats and Sri Lanka > Sundaland > Philippines > Indo-Burma

31. Following table gives a list of international environmental agreements and areas covered.

Agreement	Area covered
(*a*) Basal convention	(*i*) Biosafety
(*b*) Cartagena protocol	(*ii*) Control of trans-boundary movements of hazardous wastes and their disposal
(*c*) Kyoto protocol	(*iii*) Greenhous gas emission reductions
(*d*) Stockholm convention	(*iv*) Persistent organic pollutants

Which of the following is correct combination?

	(*a*)	(*b*)	(*c*)	(*d*)
A.	(*i*)	(*ii*)	(*iv*)	(*iii*)
B.	(*ii*)	(*i*)	(*iii*)	(*iv*)
C.	(*iv*)	(*i*)	(*iii*)	(*ii*)
D.	(*ii*)	(*iv*)	(*iii*)	(*i*)

32. The following figure is a "risk-graph" that illustrates the percent risk a species faces towards extinction.

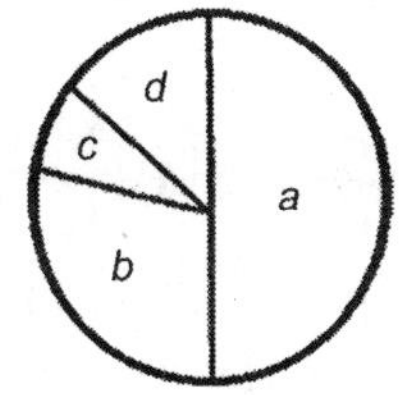

The following are ranks assigned according to IUCN's red-list category:

(*i*) Critically endangered
(*ii*) Near threatened
(*iii*) Vulnerable
(*iv*) Least concern

Which one of the following is the most appropriate match between the percent-risk and their assigned rank?

	(*a*)	(*b*)	(*c*)	(*d*)
A.	(*i*)	(*iii*)	(*iv*)	(*ii*)
B.	(*i*)	(*iv*)	(*iii*)	(*ii*)
C.	(*iii*)	(*ii*)	(*i*)	(*iv*)
D.	(*iv*)	(*iii*)	(*ii*)	(*i*)

CSIR-NET, DECEMBER, 2018

Habitat and Niche Concepts

33. Forest fragments in an agricultural landscape can be viewed as islands of habitat in an ocean of non-habitat. MacArthur and Wilson's island biogeography model can be used to predict patterns of species richness in these forest fragments which are represented ill the graphs below.

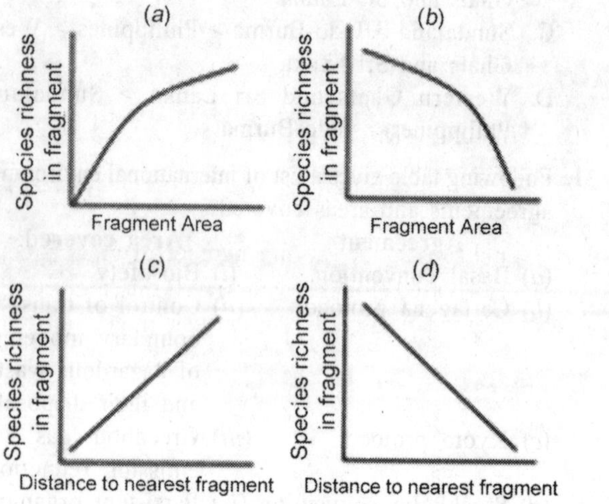

Which one of the following combinations of the graphs correctly represents predictions from the model?

A. (*a*) and (*c*)
B. (*a*) and (*d*)
C. (*b*) and (*c*)
D. (*b*) and (*d*)

Population Ecology

34. A population grows according to the logistic growth equation,

$$\frac{dN}{dt} = rN\left(1 - \frac{N}{K}\right)$$

Where *dn*/*d*T, is the rate of population growth, *r* is the intrinsic rate of increase, N is population size and K is the carrying 'capacity of the environment. According to this equation, population growth rate is maximum at:

A. K/4 B. K/2
C. K D. 2K

35. In order to estimate population size of a fish species in a lake, a researcher captures 100 fish from the lake and marks them with coloured tags a week later, the researcher return to the lake and catches 150 fish of the and finds that 25 of them are tagged ones.

Assuming no immigration or emigration occurred, the total population size of the fish species in the lake will be:

A. 17 B. 38
C. 600 D. 86

Species Interactions

36. The equilibrium model of island biogeography proposed by MacArthur and Wilson assumes that the number of species on an island represents a balance between:

A. resource consumption rate and predation rate.
B. birth rate and death rate.
C. colonization rate and extinction rate.
D. speciation rate and hybridization rate

37. Given below in Column A are schematic representations of three types of pairwise species interactions and the name of some interactions are in Column B.

Column A	Column B
(*a*) A ⇄ B (— above and below)	(*i*) Apparent competition
(*b*) 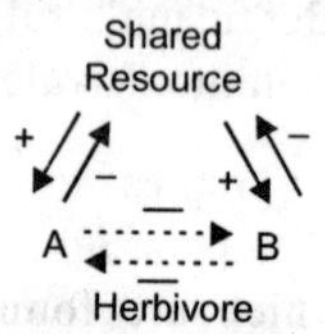	(*ii*) Interference competition
(*c*) 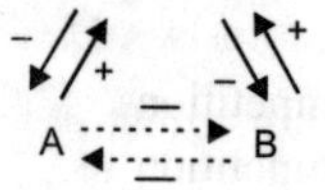	(*iii*) Direct amensalism
	(*iv*) Exploitation competition

Select the best match for interaction between column A & B in each schematic.

	(*a*)	(*b*)	(*c*)
A.	(*iii*)	(*ii*)	(*iv*)
B.	(*iv*)	(*ii*)	(*iii*)
C.	(*ii*)	(*iv*)	(*i*)
D.	(*iii*)	(*i*)	(*ii*)

38. Given below is a graphical representation of plant life histories based on Grime's model in which disturbance and competition are the important factors.

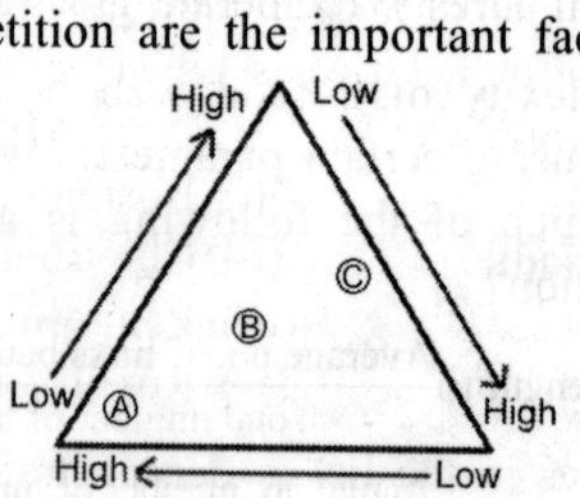

Which of the following options correctly represents A, B and C, respectively in the figure above?

A. perennial herbs, trees and shrubs, annual plants.
B. annual plants, perennial herbs, trees and shrubs.
C. annual plants, trees and shrubs, perennial herbs.
D. trees and shrubs, perennial herbs, annual plants.

Community Ecology & Successions

39. Following table shows attributes of selected species A, B, C and D:

Attributes	Species			
	A	B	C	D
Dispersal ability	High	Low	High	Low
r Selected	Yes	Yes	No	No
Predominant reproduction mode	Asexual	Sexual	Asexual	Sexual
Competitive ability	High	Low	High	Low

Based on the above information, which of the following is most likely to become invasive if climate matches between its site of origin and site of colonization?
A. Species A and D
B. Species A only
C. Species D only
D. Species B and C

Ecosystem & Biomes

40. Which of the following is the correct increasing order for the daily net primary productivity (NPP) per unit leaf area in different ecosystems?
A. Deserts < Temperate forests < Tropical forests
B. Deserts < Tropical forests < Temperate forests
C. Temperate forests < Tropical forests < Deserts
D. Tropical forests < Temperate forests < Deserts

41. What is the significance of upwelling zone for marine ecosystems?
A. It is responsible for uniformity of temperature in ocean to support the marine life.
B. It brings nutrients from deeper zones to relatively nutrient poor ocean surface thus increasing marine productivity.
C. It is responsible for uniform oxygenation of marine waters thus increasing marine productivity.
D. It helps in circulating decomposers from the bottom of ocean to surface for proper decomposition of dead material on the surface.

42. An alphabetical list of tropical rainforest mammals from South America and Africa is given below:

South America	Africa
(*a*) Agouti	(*i*) Bosman's Potto
(*b*) Giant Armadilo	(*ii*) Chevrotain
(*c*) Paca	(*iii*) Pangolin
(*d*) Three toed sloth	(*iv*) Royal Antelope

Pair the species in the list to demonstrate the concept of convergent evolution between the two continents.

	(*a*)	(*b*)	(*c*)	(*d*)
A.	(*iv*)	(*iii*)	(*i*)	(*ii*)
B.	(*i*)	(*iii*)	(*iv*)	(*ii*)
C.	(*i*)	(*ii*)	(*iv*)	(*iii*)
D.	(*iv*)	(*iii*)	(*ii*)	(*i*)

Biodiversity

43. In the following table, a list of threat categories and animals of India is given in an alphabetical order:

Animals	Threat category
(*a*) Bengal florican	(*i*) Critically endangered
(*b*) Ganga river Dolphin	(*ii*) Endangered
(*c*) Indian Rhinoceros	(*iii*) Vulnerable
(*d*) Indian Vulture	

Which of the following options show correct combination of animals and their threat category as per Red Data list of IUCN?

	(*a*)	(*b*)	(*c*)	(*d*)
A.	(*i*)	(*i*)	(*ii*)	(*iii*)
B.	(*i*)	(*ii*)	(*iii*)	(*i*)
C.	(*ii*)	(*iii*)	(*ii*)	(*i*)
D.	(*iii*)	(*i*)	(*i*)	(*ii*)

44. Grassland plots with varying number of grass species were cultivated for 10 years. At the end of the experiment, total plant cover was measured. Soil nitrogen was also measured to assess its utilization by plants. The relationships are shown in the following plots.

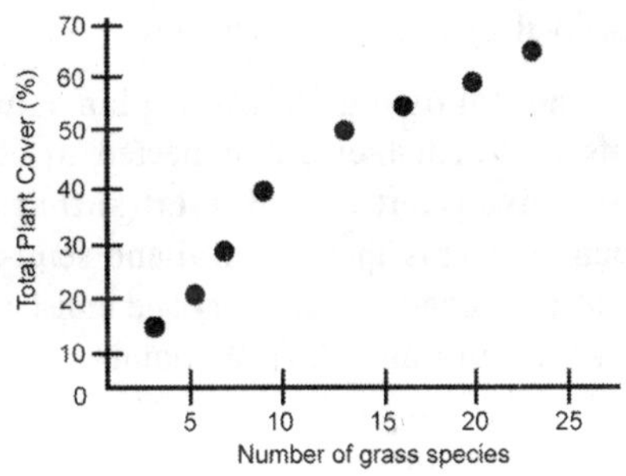

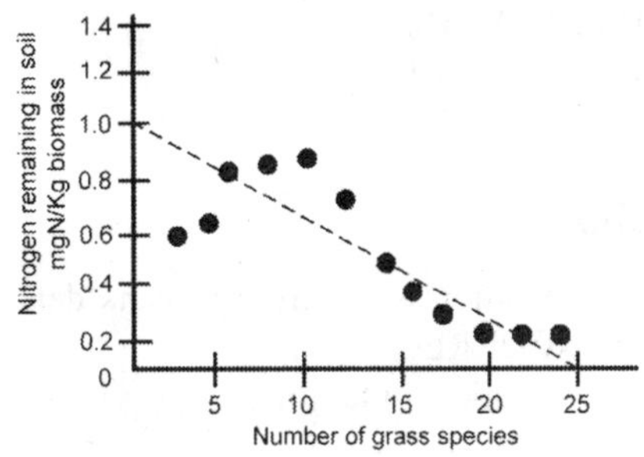

Which one of the following inferences can be drawn from the above experiment?
A. Grasses in plots with lower species richness enriched soil nitrogen, thereby increasing the plant cover.
B. Plots with greater species richness showed greater stability and more efficient soil nitrogen utilization.
C. Plots with greater species richness utilized nitrogen more efficiently, but would not show increased net primary production.
D. No correlation can be drawn between species richness, community productivity and nitrogen utilization.

GATE (LIFE SCIENCE), 2018

Ecology and Environment

45. Which of the following statements is TRUE for an ecotone?

A. An ecotone is the synonym of an ecosystem
B. An ecotone is an interface zone of two or more ecosystems
C. An ecotone is a special feature of land biomes
D. An ecotone is exclusively characterized by decreased biodiversity

46. Acid rain with a pH of 4.0 is more acidic than the rain with a pH of 6.0 by :

A. 2 times   B. 10 times
C. 100 times   D. 1000 times

CSIR-NET, JUNE, 2019

Habitat and Niche Concepts, Biome

47. Tropical regions may have more species diversity because of the following possible reasons, EXCEPT:

A. tropical regions have had more limit to diversify under relatively stable climatic conditions than temperate regions.
B. tropical regions have high spatial heterogeneity
C. greater biological competition in the tropics leads to narrower niches
D. lower predation intensity in the tropics allows survival of more prey species

48. Match the following invasive plants to the likely habitats in which they are expected to occur:

Invasive plant	Habitat(s) that they invade
(*a*) Eichornia crassipes	(*i*) Arid and semi-arid habitats
(*b*) Lantana camara	(*ii*) Dry and moist tropical forests
(*c*) Posopis juliflora	(*iii*) Wetlands

	(*a*)	(*b*)	(*c*)
A.	(*ii*)	(*i*)	(*iii*)
B.	(*i*)	(*iii*)	(*ii*)
C.	(*iii*)	(*ii*)	(*i*)
D.	(*iii*)	(*i*)	(*ii*)

Pollution

49. In bioremediation by microorganisms detailed below, choose INCORRECT option?

A. The organic contaminants provide a source of carbon
B. The bacteria do not get energy by degrading contaminants.
C. Bacteria can produce oxydized and reduced species that can cause metals to precipitate.
D. Bacteria act on contaminants by aerobic and anaerobic respiration.

Population Ecology

50. Given below are the steps to assess the population size of grasshoppers in a given area:

(*a*) '*n*' individuals are collected randomly from the study area in a defined period of time.

(*b*) The captured individuals are counted, marked and released at the site of collection.

Next day, individuals are captured from the same site for same length of time. Number of marked (n_M) and unmarked (n_U)

(*c*) This capture-release and recapture is continued till one gets 100% marked individuals

(*d*) The size of the population (N) is estimated as follows:

$$\frac{N}{n} = \frac{n_m + n_u}{n_m}$$

(*e*) The size of population (N) is estimated as follows:

$$\frac{N}{n} = \frac{n_u}{n_m}$$

The most appropriate combination of steps for estimating population size using mark-recapture method is:

A. (*a*), (*b*) and (*d*)   B. (*a*), (*b*) and (*e*)
C. (*a*), (*b*), (*c*) and (*d*)   D. (*a*), (*b*), (*c*) and (*e*)

Species Interactions

51. Which one of the following statement is correct?

A. Ecto-mycorrhizal associations predominantly reduce phosphorous limitation, and endo-mycorrhizal associations reduce both nitrogen and phosphorus limitations.
B. Endo-mycorrhizal associations predominantly reduce phosphorus limitation, and ecto-mycorrhizal associations reduce both nitrogen and phosphorous limitations.
C. Ecto and endo-mycorrhizal associations do not reduce nitrogen and phosphorous limitation.
D. Ecto and endo-mycorrhizal associations are able to reduce only phosphorous limitation.

Community Ecology & Successions

52. Incorporating additional ecological factors into the Lotka-Voltera predator-prey model can change the predator isocline. Given below are three state-space graphs (*a*)-(*c*) representing modification of predator isocline due to the ecological factors listed below (*i-iii*).

(*i*) Victim abundance acting as predator carrying capacity
(*ii*) Availability of alternate prey (victim) population
(*iii*) Predator carrying capacity determined

(*a*)

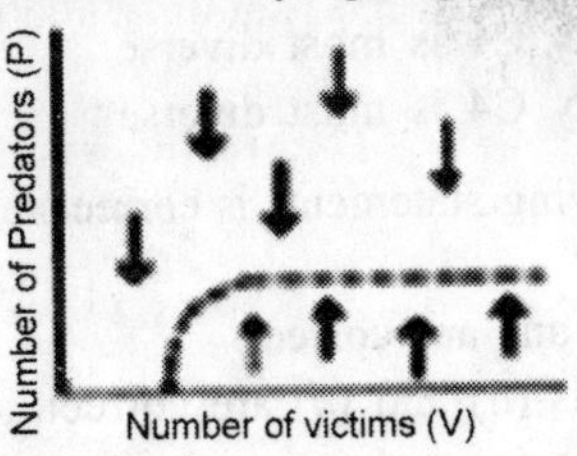

(*b*)

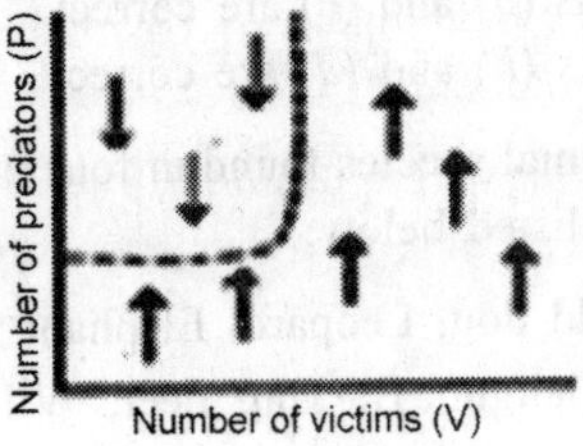

(*c*)

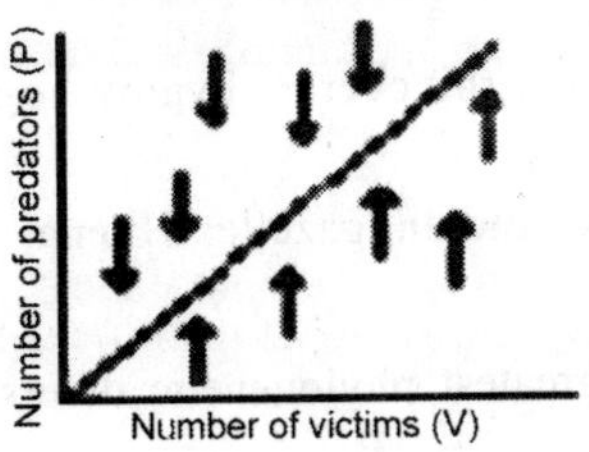

Which one of the following options represents all correct matches of the state space graphs with their ecological factor?

	(*a*)	(*b*)	(*c*)
A.	(*ii*)	(*iii*)	(*i*)
B.	(*ii*)	(*i*)	(*iii*)
C.	(*iii*)	(*ii*)	(*i*)
D.	(*i*)	(*ii*)	(*iii*)

Ecosystem

53. The table given below lists types of plant communities and types of growth forms.

Plant communities	**Growth forms**
(*a*) Dry grassland	(*i*) Chamaephytes
(*b*) Semi desert	(*ii*) Crptophytes
(*c*) Tropical forests	(*iii*) Hemicryptophytes
(*d*) Tundra	(*iv*) Phanerophytes

Which of the following is the best match for the plant communities with most dominant growth form generally present in that community?

	(*a*)	(*b*)	(*c*)	(*d*)
A.	(*iv*)	(*i*)	(*ii*)	(*iii*)
B.	(*iii*)	(*i*)	(*iv*)	(*iv*)
C.	(*ii*)	(*iii*)	(*iv*)	(*iii*)
D.	(*iii*)	(*i*)	(*iv*)	(*iii*)

54. Following are some of the generalizations regarding energy flow in an ecosystem:

(*a*) Assimilation efficiency of carnivores is higher than herbivores.
(*b*) Consumption efficiency of aquatic herbivores is higher than terrestrial herbivores.
(*c*) Vertebrates have higher production efficiencies than invertebrates.
(*d*) Trophic level transfer efficiency is higher in terrestrial food chains than in marine.

Based on the above, select the correct option.

A. Only (*a*) and (*c*) B. Only (*a*) and (*b*)
C. (*a*), (*b*) and (*c*) D. (*a*), (*c*) and (*d*)

55. In an experiment to show that biogeochemical cycles interact, nitrogen fixing vines (*Galactia sp.*) were grown in plots under normal levels of CO_2 (Control) and under artificially elevated atmospheric CO_2 (Experimental). Effect of elevated CO_2 levels on nitrogen fixation was measured over a period of 7 years (Plot A) and the concentrations of iron and molybdenum in the leaves of these plants were quantified at the end of the study (Plot B). Which one of the following inferences CANNOT be made from the above experiment?

Plot A

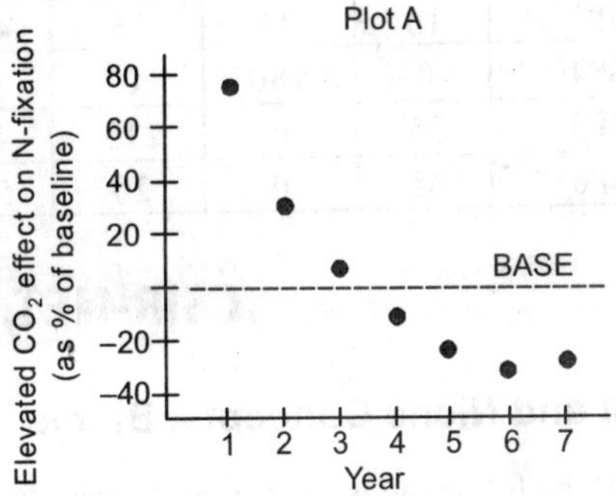

Plot B

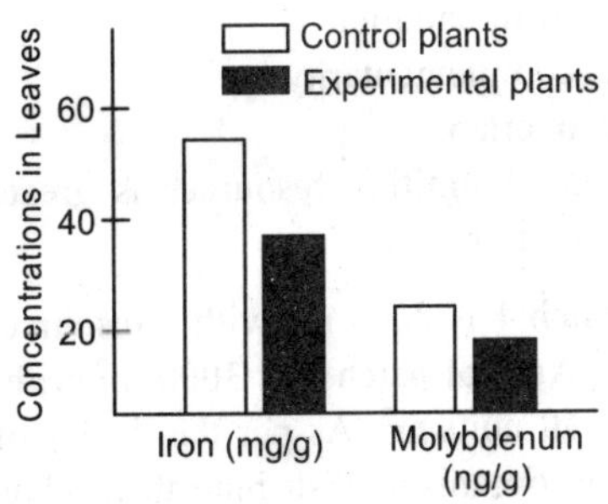

A. Decreasing rate of N-fixation correlates with decreased levels of leaf iron and molybdenum, two micronutrients essential for N-fixation
B. An initial exposure to elevated CO_2 increased N-fixation by these plants
C. There is a continuous decrease in N-fixation due to elevated CO_2 treatment.
D. Plants exposed to continuous elevated levels of CO_2 had lower levels of iron and molybdenum in their leaves.

Biodiversity and Conservation

56. A road is constructed, through a wet tropical forest, following which the population of a species of forest butterfly declines. Which of the following is NOT a possible explanation for the road causing a decline in the forest butterfly population?

A. Road facilitates immigration of gap-loving species which compete with the forest species.
B. Road facilitates increased movement of the forest butterfly within the forest, which reduces genetic diversity.
C. Road internally fragments the habitat and negatively affects important microhabitat conditions for the forest butterfly.
D. Road facilitates invasion by non-native plants that displace native host and nectar plants of the forest butterfly.

57. A field ecologist gathers following data (abundance values) in order to study diversity of species in four plant communities.

Species	Community			
	C1	C2	C3	C4
SP1	90	0	0	40
SP2	60	0	0	65
SP3	15	25	25	40
SP4	0	180	0	0
SP5	25	0	215	45
SP6	65	0	20	55

Based on the above observations, the ecologist draws following conclusions.

(*a*) Plant communities C1 and C4 show strong similarity with each other
(*b*) Plant communities C1 and C4 as well as communities C2 and C3 show strong similarity with each other
(*c*) Plant community C1 is most diverse
(*d*) Plant community C4 is most diverse

Which of the following statements is correct regarding above conclusions?

A. All the conclusions are correct
B. Only conclusions (*a*) and (*d*) are correct
C. Only conclusions (*a*) and (*c*) are correct
D. Only conclusions (*b*) and (*d*) are correct

58. The prominent mammal species found in four different protected areas are listed below:

Area A : Tiger, Wild dog, Leopard, Elephant
Area B : Common langur. Barking deer, Wild dog, Elephant
Area C : Tiger, Indian rhinoceros, Pygmy hog, Wild pig
Area D : Blackbuck, Indian gazelle, Hyena, Indian wolf

The area with the greatest phylogenetic diversity is:

A. A B. B
C. C D. D

CSIR-NET, 15 DECEMBER, 2019

Habitat and Niche Concepts, Biome

59. Which of the following is NOT a mechanism for species coexistence?

A. Niche differentiation
B. Niche complementarity
C. Niche overlap
D. Amount of limiting resources is greater than the number of species

60. Area of patch 1 is 2000 m^2 with a resource density of 5 units/m^2 Area of patch 2 is 3000 m^2 with a resource density of 10 units/m^2. As per the theory of ideal free distribution, organisms distribute themselves such that the expected ratio of abundance of organisms in the two patches (patch 1 : patch 2) is:

A. 1 : 2 B. 2 : 3
C. 1 : 3 D. 3 : 2

Population Ecology

61. Which of the following represents exponential growth in populations?

A.
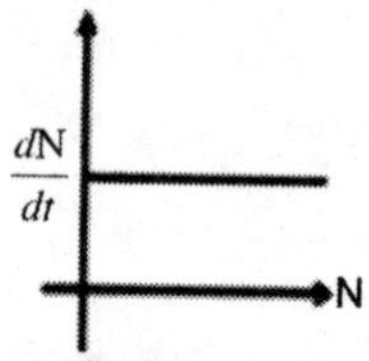

B.
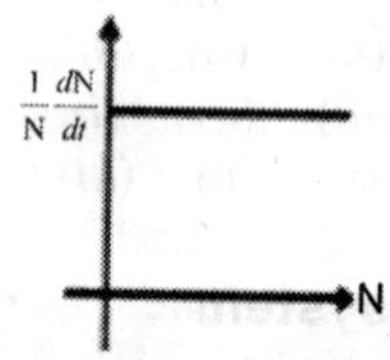

C.
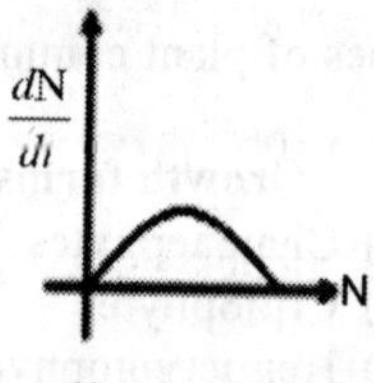

D.
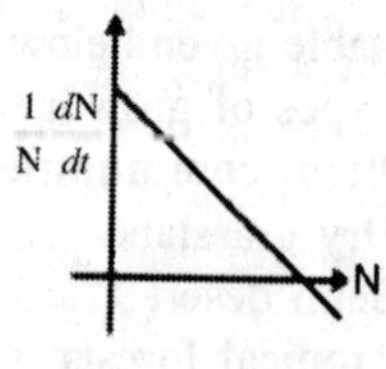

62. A small number (approximately 10) of mice are introduced into an uninhabited island. Their population grows exponentially initially and after 3 years, reaches a population size of 520 after which the population becomes stable. At what point would you expect their population to attain their highest growth rate?

A. When the mice population was first introduced.
B. When the population size is 260.
C. Their population growth rate remains constant throughout.
D. When the population size reaches 520.

Ecosystem

63. In a lake, reducing the population of a fish which feeds on plankton was followed by a decline in the rate of primary productivity. This is consistent with which one of the following hypotheses regarding the regulation of primary productivity?

A. Bottom-up control
B. Eutrophication
C. Top-down control
D. Trophic pyramid

Biodiversity and Conseration

64. Which one of the following was recently reported to be the first mammal to have become extinct as a result of climate change?

A. Bramble Cay melomys - *Melomys rubicola*
B. Gangetic river dolphin - *Platanista gangetica*
C. Malaga giant rat - *Hypogeomys antimena*
D. Tapanuli orangutan - *Pongo tapanuliensis*

65. Which of the following set of conditions will qualify a species to be considered as endangered (EN) as per IUCN criteria?

A. 80% reduction in population size, <100 km^2 area of occupancy, at least 50% estimated extinction risk in five generations.
B. <2,500 individuals with declining population, <250 mature individuals, at least 20% estimated extinction risk in 10 years.
C. <10,000 individuals with declining population, <1000 mature individuals, at least 10% estimated extinction risk in 10 years.
D. 75% reduction in population size, <500 km^2 area of occupancy, at least 20% estimated extinction risk in five generations

66. In the graph below, large boxes (denoted by P, Q, R,S) represent a region, whereas smaller boxes represent habitats. Labels S1, S2 above each small box represent species present in the given habitat denoted by that box.

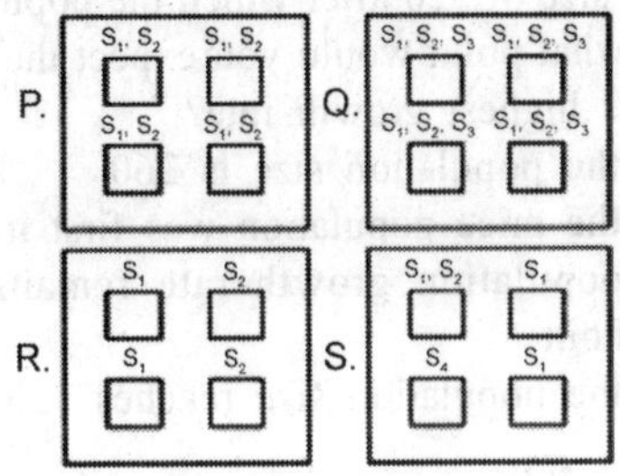

Given the above graphs, choose the option which correctly depicts the regions which show maximum α and maximum β diversity, respectively:

A. Q and S
B. P and R
C. S and P
D. Q and R

CSIR-NET, 27 DECEMBER, 2019

Habitat and Niche Concepts, Biome

67. Three bird species with similar habitat and diet preferences co-exist in a habitat. For these species, which one of the following statements is most likely to be correct?

A. The fundamental and realised niches of these species are same.
B. Their fundamental niches are greater than their realised niches.
C. Their realised niches are greater than their fundamental niches.
D. The fundamental and realised niches both will expand.

68. Two islands (A and B) located approximately 180 km and 100 km respectively from the mainland. Island A is 160 sq. km, while Island B is 220 sq. km in area. Which one of the following statements is correct?

A. Island A is likely to have higher extinction and lower colonization rates than Island B.
B. Island B is likely to have higher extinction and lower colonization rates than Island A.
C. Island A is likely to have lower extinction rates and higher colonization rates than Island B.
D. Islands A and B are likely to have equal rates of extinction and colonization.

69. The table given below lists animals and primary regions of domestication.

Animal	Region of domestication
(*a*) Alpaca	(*i*) Central Andes
(*b*) Goat	(*ii*) South Asia
(*c*) Llama	(*iii*) Southwest Asia
(*d*) Zebu cattle	(*iv*) China

Which one of the following options represents the best match for animals and the primary region of their domestication?

	(*a*)	(*b*)	(*c*)	(*d*)
A.	(*ii*)	(*iv*)	(*iii*)	(*i*)
B.	(*i*)	(*iii*)	(*i*)	(*iv*)
C.	(*iii*)	(*i*)	(*iv*)	(*iii*)
D.	(*i*)	(*iii*)	(*i*)	(*ii*)

Population Ecology

70. Suppose a population has three age classes. Females in the second and third age classes produce four and three off springs, respectively. While 50% female in the first age class survive into the second age class, only 30% females survive into the third age class. The Leslie matrix for this population is given by

$$L = \begin{pmatrix} 0 & 4 & 3 \\ 0.5 & 0 & 0 \\ 0 & 0.3 & 0 \end{pmatrix}$$

If there are 10 individuals in each of the three age classes, the number of individuals in the next iteration would be:

A. 50 B. 78
C. 100 D. 65

71. A small number (approx. 10) of mice are introduced into an uninhabited island. Their population grows exponentially initially and after 4 years, reaches a population size of 520 after which the population stays stable. At what point would you expect the population to attain its highest growth rate?

A. When the population size is 260
B. When the mice population was first introduced
C. Their population growth rate remains constant throughout
D. When the population size reaches 520

Species Interactions

72. Predator-prey interactions in a community are represented in the figure below.

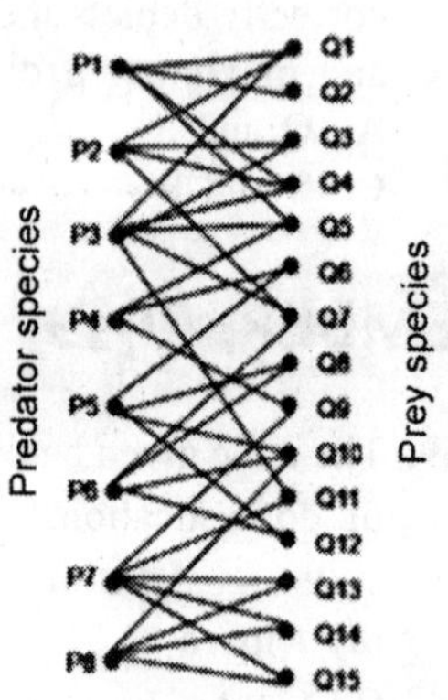

Given below are some statements related to the above figure:

(*i*) Predators and prey are generalists
(*ii*) Predators have expanded their prey base over time
(*iii*) Predators and prey have co-evolved
(*iv*) There is speciation in prey while predators are prone to extinction

Which one of the following options represents statement/s that can be correctly inferred from the figure?

A. (*i*) and (*iii*) B. (*iii*) only
C. (*i*) only D. (*ii*) and (*iv*)

Ecosystem

73. In a meta study, percentage of species affected by different ecological threats in different habitats was found to be as follows:

	Ecological threats		
Habitat	**Over-exploitation**	**Invasive species**	**Pollution**
A	20	22	7
B	19	20	44
C	86	5	38

Based on the above information, habitats A, B and C will be respectively:

A. Terrestrial, Fresh water, Marine
B. Marine, Fresh water, Terrestrial
C. Fresh water, Terrestrial, Marine
D. Marine, Terrestrial, Fresh water

Biodiversity and Conservation

74. Which one of the following sets contains at least one primate species NOT found in India?

A. Lion Tailed Macaque, Slender Loris, Common Langur
B. Golden Langur, Hoolock Gibbon, Howler Monkey
C. Bonnet Macaque, Stump Tailed Macaque, Slow Loris
D. Capped Langur, Rhesus Macaque, Phayre's Leaf Monkey

75. Following table shows the number of individuals of different species in two communities, X and Y.

Species	Community	
	X	Y
1	250	490
2	200	125
3	180	80
4	100	65
5	65	50
6	30	10
7	5	10
Total	830	830

Based on the above data and the Simpson's Diversity Index which one of the following statements is true?

A. X has greater alpha diversity than Y
B. Y has greater alpha diversity than X
C. X and Y have equal alpha diversities
D. X has greater species richness than Y

76. Below is a table showing the number of species and actual food web links observed in three different ecosystems.

Ecosystem	No. of species	Observed food web links
A	11	25
B	21	70
C	51	200

By calculating connectance as a measure of relative complexity of food webs, infer which of the following statements is correct?

A. Connectance increases as species richness increases.
B. Connectance decreases as species richness increases.
C. Connectance is constant regardless of species richness.
D. Relationship between species richness and connectance is stochastic.

GATE (LIFE SCIENCE), 2019

Ecology and Environment

77. Which one of the following ecosystems is represented by an inverted pyramid of numbers?
A. Grassland B. Pond
C. Desert D. Parasitic forest

78. Raphides are deposits of:
A. calcium oxalate B. calcium carbonate
C. silica bodies D. protein bodies

79. Arbuscules are highly branched structures, formed by:
A. ectomycorrhizae
B. endomycorrhizae
C. arbutoid mycorrhizae
D. monotropoid mycorrhizae

80. Which one of the following statements is INCORRECT?
A. Nitrogen fixation is aerobic process
B. Dinitrogenase catalyzes reduction of nitrogen to ammonia
C. Root nodules are found in Glycine max
D. Nitrogen fixation is anaerobic process

81. A species adapted to a specific habitat is called:
A. Biome B. Ecotone
C. Ecotype D. Niche

CSIR-NET, NOVEMBER (MORNING), 2020

Population Ecology

82. In a population showing exponential growth, per capita growth rate will:
A. decrease as population size increases
B. increase as population size increases
C. remain constant as population size increases
D. increase initially and then saturate at large population sizes

83. A population of crickets invading a new grassland showed a population growth pattern as shown in the figure:

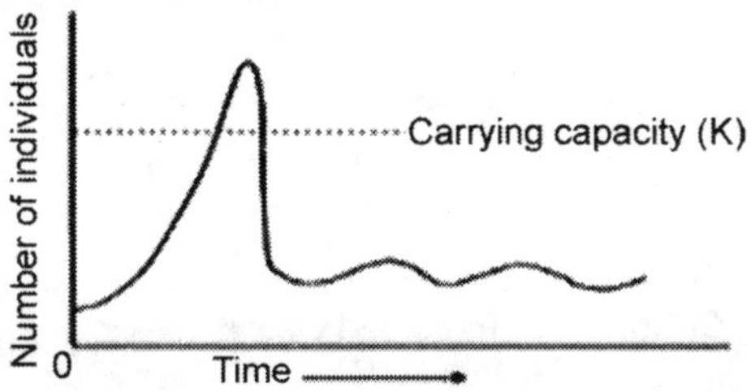

Following is the list of potential interpretations:
(*a*) Environment is damaged due to population overshooting its K
(*b*) The resources did not recover and population dies out
(*c*) Carrying capacity is lowered due to shift in environmental conditions.

Which one of the following options/combination of options can correctly explain the cricket growth pattern?
A. (*a*) only
B. (*b*) only
C. (*a*) and (*c*) only
D. (*b*) and (*c*) only

84. Given below are growth and survivorship curves.

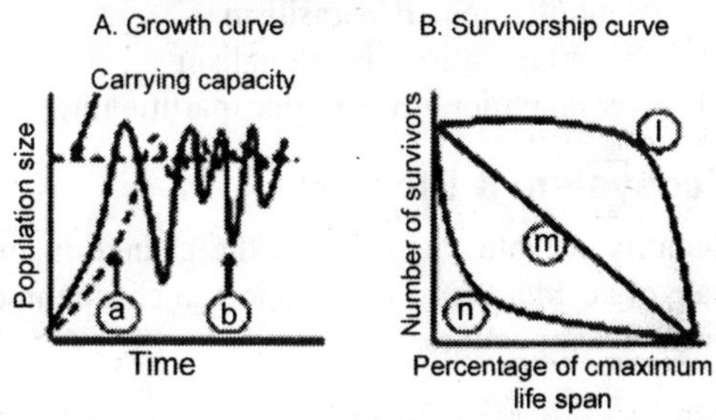

Select the correct combination of growth curves from figure A and survivorship curves from figure B given above, that would best represent r and K strategies, respectively.
A. r = a and I; K = b and n
B. r = b and n; K = a and I
C. r = a and m; K = b and n
D. r = b and m; K = a and m

Species Interactions

85. Mycorrhizal fungi are associated with a large variety of plant species. The diagram below shows the cost-benefit curves from individual plants with or without mycorrhizal fungi associated with the roots across a soil nutrient concentration gradient.

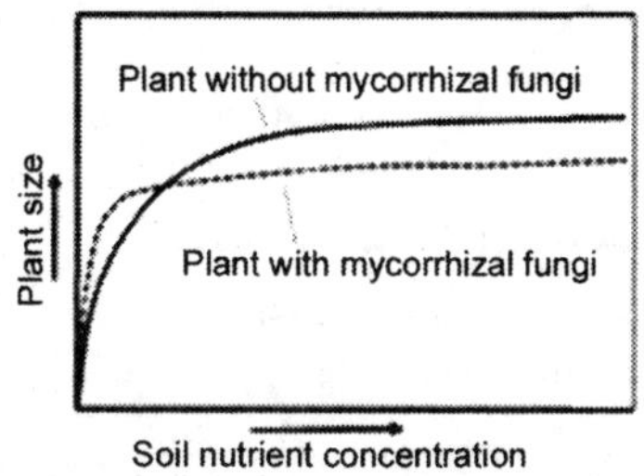

Which one of the following options best describes the association between the plant and mycorrhiza when soil nutrient concentrations are high?
A. Parasitism B. Mutualism
C. Competition D. Commensalism

86. Growth patterns of two species (grown alone or together) are shown in Figures A and B.

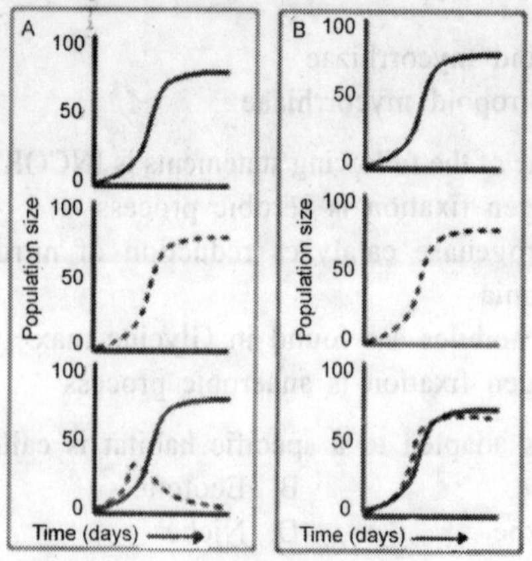

Match the growth patterns with the correct type of interaction represented by them:
A. A-mutualism, B-commensalism
B. A-competition, B-parasitism
C. A-commensalism, B-mutualism
D. A-competition, B-resource partitioning

Ecosystem & Biomes

87. Identify the plot that depicts the change in metabolic rate of an endotherm with respect to change in environmental temperature.

A.
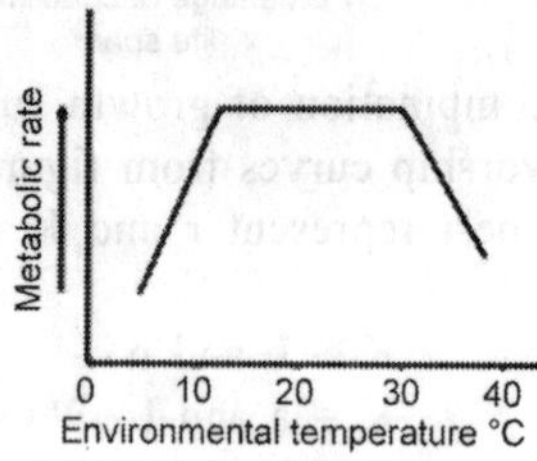

B.
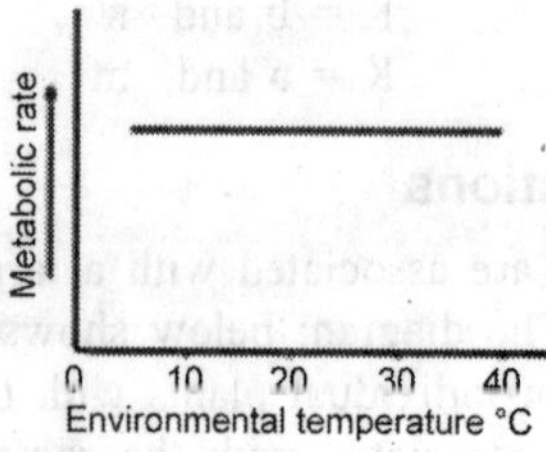

C.
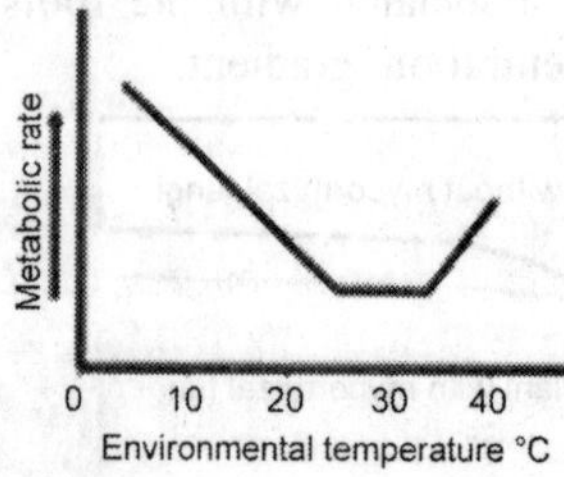

D.
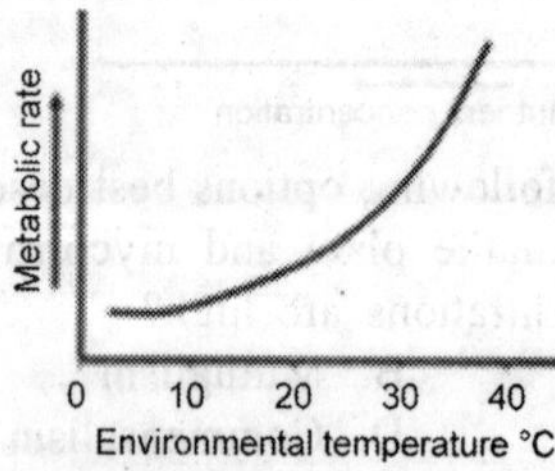

88. The linkage density in a food web is a function of the connectance and the number of species in it. It is defined as the average number of feeding links per species. Which one of the following would have the highest linkage density?

A.
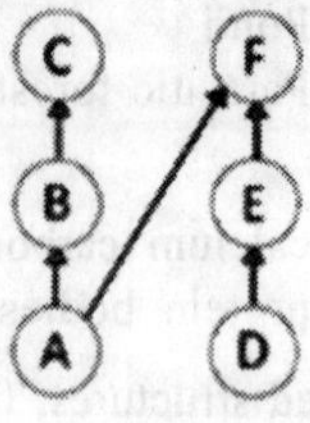

B.
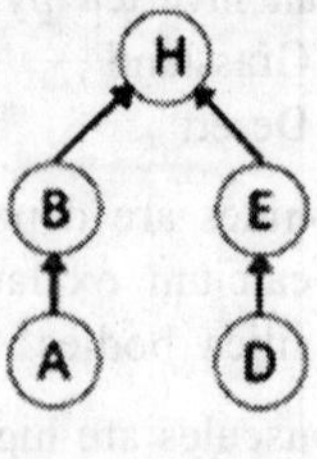

C.
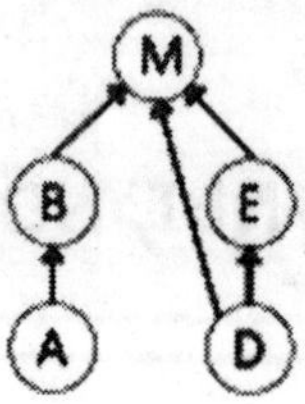

D.
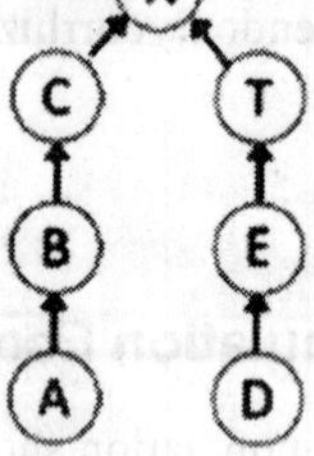

89. Ozone concentration in the atmosphere is measured in Dobson units (Du). An ozone hole is said to have occurred when the concentration of ozone in the region falls below 220 Du. The diagram of the globe below shows the location values of ozone concentrations recorded at the sites for two dates in 2009.

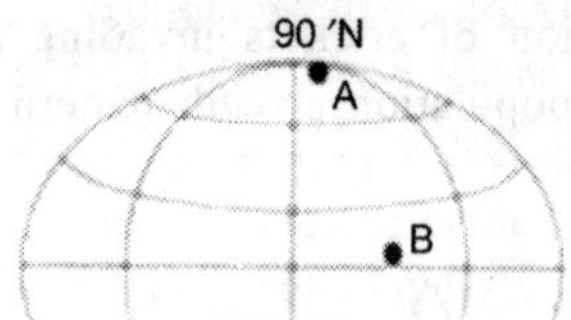

S. No.	Recorded Ozone Values	
	30 March 2009	30 Sept 2009
i	270	290
ii	400	240
iii	450	420
iv	250	110

Which one of the following options represents the correct matches between the study sites and the recorded ozone values?

	(a)	(b)	(c)
A.	(i)	(iii)	(iv)
B.	(ii)	(iii)	(i)
C.	(ii)	(i)	(iv)
D.	(i)	(ii)	(iii)

90. Given below are the spectra of plant forms (on the basis of where the plants bear their buds) in different biomes (A to C).

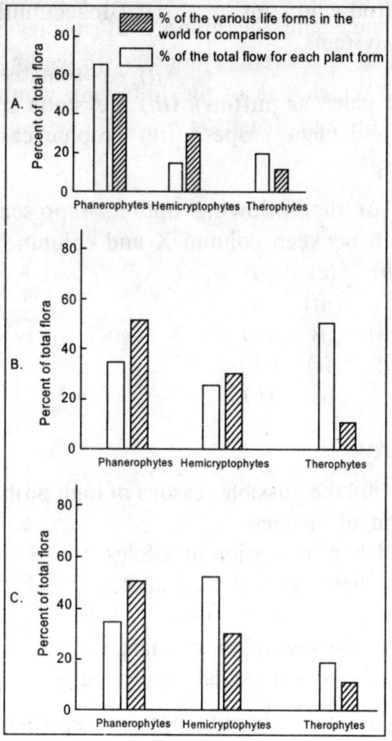

Which one of the following options correctly identifies the biomes represented in graphs A to C?

A. A-Mediterranean; B-Arctic; C- Tropical
B. A-Tropical; B-Desert; C-Temperate
C. A-Tropical; B-Temperate; C-Desert
D. A-Desert; B-Arctic; C-Temperate

91. The following four diagrams depict observation of mean temperature and rainfall for four locations. The solid lines depict temperature while the dashed line depicts rainfall.

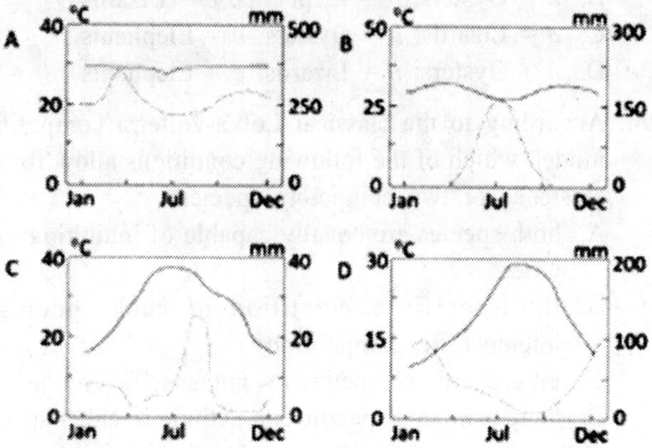

Given below are five biomes:

I. Desert
II. Savannah
III. Tropical rain forest
IV. Mediterranean
V. Conifer ecosystem

Which of the following combinations correctly matches the climatograms to the biomes?

	(a)	(b)	(c)	(d)
A.	(iv)	(ii)	(i)	(v)
B.	(v)	(iv)	(ii)	(iii)
C.	(iii)	(ii)	(i)	(iv)
D.	(v)	(iii)	(ii)	(i)

Biodiversity

92. Which among the following states has the highest forest cover in terms of percentage of geographical area?

A. Chattisgarh
B. Uttarakhand
C. Madhya Pradesh
D. Odisha

CSIR-NET, NOVEMBER (AFTERNOON), 2020

Habitat and Niche Concepts

93. Which one of the following statements is correct with reference to ecotones?

A. Ecotones are rich in endemic species and only contain species not found in surrounding ecosystems.
B. Ecotones refer to areas that are under habitat degradation and contain endangered species that are not found in the neighbouring communities.
C. Ecotones are species poor habitats due to scarcity of soil nutrients and availability of resources.
D. Ecotones are transition areas between two ecosystems and have greater number of species than either of the neighbouring communities.

94. Co-existence of several species of birds in an area is possible under the following conditions:

A. High niche overlap and high niche differentiation
B. Low niche overlap and high niche differentiation
C. High niche overlap and low niche differentiation
D. Low niche overlap and low niche differentiation

Population Ecology

95. Given below are the survivorship curves showing the proportion of individuals surviving over time or age. Three generalised types of curves (*a*, *b* and *c*) are depicted below. Which of the following represent the correct survivorship curve for the given organisms?

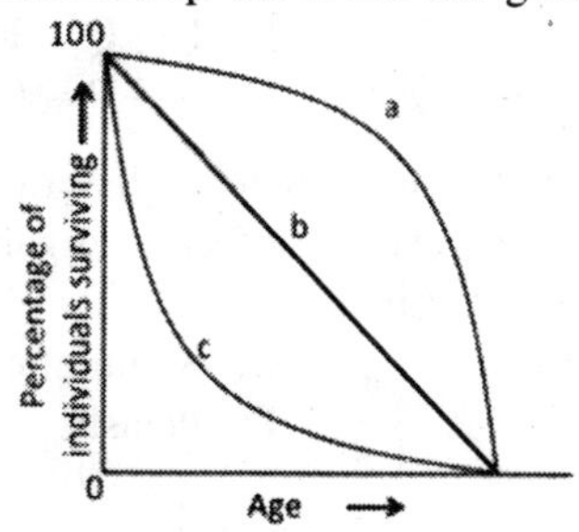

A. a = Elephants; b = Lizards; c = Oysters
B. a = Oysters; b = Elephants; c = Lizards
C. a = Lizards; b = Oysters; c = Elephants
D. a = Oysters; b = Lizards; c = Elephants

96. According to the classical Lotka-volterra competition model, which of the following conditions allow for co-existence of two competing species?
A. both species are equally capable of inhibiting each other
B. intraspecific competition of each species > interspecific competition
C. intraspecific competition < interspecific competition
D. there is no intraspecific competition in either species

Community Ecology & Successions

97. A large patch of forest area was devastated by raging fires. After some years, the area was found to recover its species. Which one of the following options best describes the process of re-establishment in the area?
A. mosses and lichens → grasses → shrubs and small plants → woody trees
B. grasses → woody trees → herbs and shrubs → mosses and lichens
C. woody plants → lichens and mosses → herbs and shrubs
D. grasses → herbs and shrubs → woody trees

Ecosystem & Biomes

98. The 50 km wide Palghat Gap is the only major topographic breach in the Western Ghats. This gap continues as the Ranotsara Gap in the Angavo escarpment. Which country is the Ranotsara Gap located in?
A. Sri Lanka B. Madagascar
C. Mozambique D. Kenya

99. The following information refers to ecological interactions.

Column X	Column Y
(*a*) Bass introduction into aquatic systems	(*i*) Bioaccumulation
(*b*) Beavers	(*ii*) Aposematism
(*c*) Sea bird (such as puffins)	(*iii*) Keystone species
(*d*) Yellow and black stripes in a wasp	(*iv*) Trophic cascades

Which one of the following options represents the correct match between column X and column Y?

	(*a*)	(*b*)	(*c*)	(*d*)
A.	(*ii*)	(*i*)	(*iii*)	(*iv*)
B.	(*iv*)	(*iii*)	(*i*)	(*ii*)
C.	(*ii*)	(*i*)	(*iv*)	(*iii*)
D.	(*iii*)	(*iv*)	(*i*)	(*ii*)

Biodiversity

100. Given below are the possible reasons of high probability for extinction of species:
(*i*) Increased homozygosity of alleles
(*ii*) Increased heterozygosity of alleles
(*iii*) Decreasing population sizes
(*iv*) Increasing demographic stochasticity
(*v*) Decreasing environmental stochasticity

Which one of the following options represents the correct combination of reasons that can lead to the highest probability of extinction of species?
A. (*ii*), (*iii*) and (*v*) B. (*i*), (*iii*) and (*iv*)
C. (*i*), (*ii*) and (*iii*) D. (*ii*), (*iii*) and (*vi*)

101. Given below is a list of natural disturbances.
(*a*) Coral bleaching
(*b*) Rising sea levels
(*c*) Shifts in species distribution
(*d*) Lowering of sea levels
(*e*) Increase in glacial sheets

Which one of the following combinations of disturbances can be attributed to global warming?
A. (*a*), (*d*) and (*e*) B. (*a*), (*b*) and (*c*)
C. (*b*), (*c*) and (*e*) D. (*c*), (*d*) and (*e*)

GATE (LIFE SCIENCE), 2020

Ecology and Environment

102. Arrange the following water reservoirs of the earth in decreasing order of water volume:
P. Streams Q. Groundwater
R. Glaciers S. Lakes and inland seas
A. R – Q – S – P B. P – Q – R – S
C. S – P – R – Q D. R – P – Q – S

103. Among the following, which best describes an organism that lives at the expense of other organisms, harmful but usually not killing?
A. Predator B. Symbiotic
C. Prey D. Parasite

104. The oleo-gum resin asafoetida (hing) is obtained from the cut surface of:
A. Stem B. Root
C. Leaf D. Fruit

105. Match the following ecological terms with their appropriate definitions:

Term	Definition
(*a*) Niche	(*i*) Position of a species in a food chain
(*b*) Biotas	(*ii*) Place of living organism in the biotic environment and its relation to food and enamies
(*c*) Trphic level	(*iii*) Physical environment of an organism

(*d*) Habitat (*iv*) Totality of organism (flora and fauna) in a given place or region.

	(*a*)	(*b*)	(*c*)	(*d*)
A.	(*i*)	(*ii*)	(*iv*)	(*iii*)
B.	(*ii*)	(*iv*)	(*i*)	(*iii*)
C.	(*iv*)	(*iii*)	(*i*)	(*ii*)
D.	(*iii*)	(*i*)	(*ii*)	(*iv*)

106. Which ONE of the following is NOT a site for *in situ* conservation?

A. Biosphere reserve
B. Wild life sanctuary
C. Zoological garden
D. Biodiversity hotspot

CSIR-NET, JUNE (MORNING), 2021

Population Ecology

107. The graph below shows the change in the size of four population (A-D) over time.

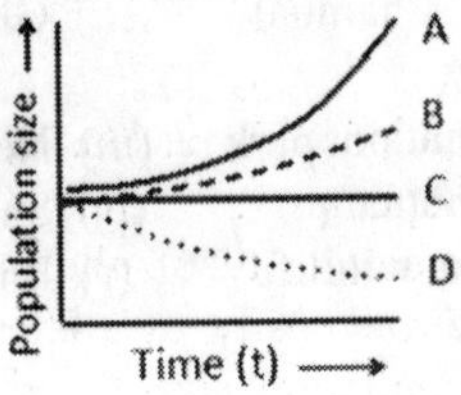

Which among the four population(A,B,C and D) would have the lowest intrinsic rate of population growth(r):

A. A B. B
C. C D. D

108. Consider the following graph for per capita growth rate (1/N)(dN/dt) as a function of population density (N).

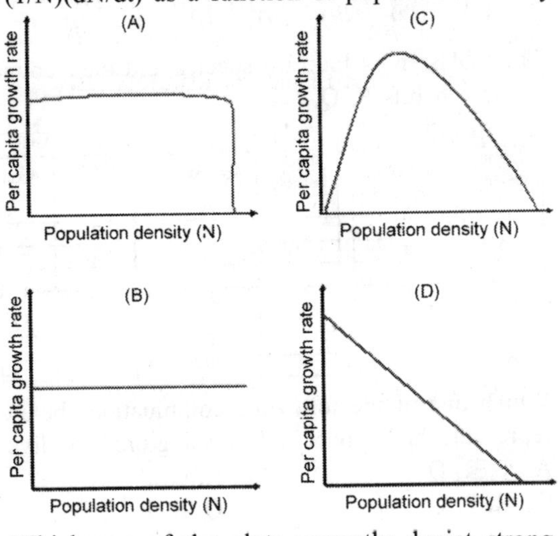

Which one of the plots correctly depict strong allee effect in population?

A. A B. B
C. C D. D

Community Ecology & Successions

109. The graphs given below show the possible behavior of two species over the course of succession.

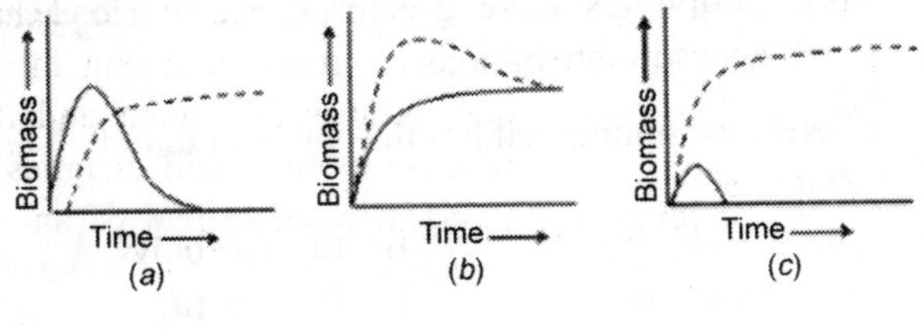

Possible effects observed during succession are:

(*i*) Total suppression
(*ii*) Convergence
(*iii*) Sequential succession

Choose the correct option matching the graphs with the possible effect:

	(*a*)	(*b*)	(*c*)
A.	(*i*)	(*ii*)	(*iii*)
B.	(*ii*)	(*iii*)	(*i*)
C.	(*iii*)	(*ii*)	(*i*)
D.	(*iii*)	(*i*)	(*ii*)

Ecosystem & Biomes

110. Consider the following ecosystems.

(*a*) Tropical rain forests
(*b*) Open ocean
(*c*) Algal beds and Coral reefs
(*d*) Marshes and Swamps

Which one of the following options represents these ecosystems in an increasing order of their contribution to annual world net primary production?

A. (*b*), (*c*), (*d*) and (*a*) B. (*c*), (*d*), (*b*) and (*a*)
C. (*d*), (*c*), (*a*) and (*b*) D. (*c*), (*d*), (*a*) and (*b*)

111. Which one of the following games is present in the stratosphere at a concentration higher than its concentration in troposphere?

A. nitrogen B. oxygen
C. ozone D. carbon dioxide

112. A researcher working on island biogeography mapped how isolation controlled immigration (I), and area controlled extinction (E), will act on number of species present on the island. He forgot to label the size of the islands (Small or large) and the location of the islands (near or far) on the graph.

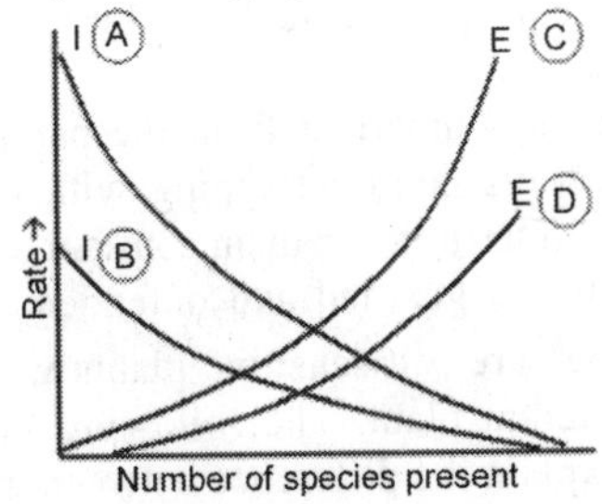

Using information from MacArthur and Wilson's equilibrium theory, select the option that correctly identifies A, B, C and D in the figure above.

A. A-large, B-small, C-near, D-far
B. A-small, B-large, C-far, D-near
C. A-near, B-far, C-small, D-large
D. A-far, B-near, C-large, D- small

113. The diagram below depicts energy flow within a single trophic level, where I = amount ingested, NA = amount not assimilated, R = respiration and P_n = biomass production at trophic level

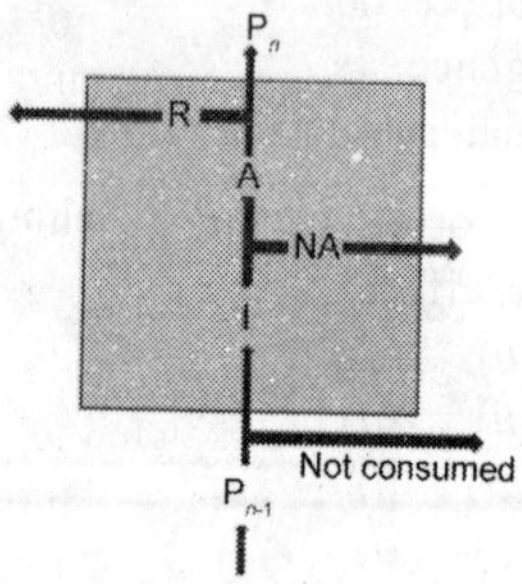

Which one of the following options represents correct value for P_n, NA, R and I in kcal respectively, if P_{n-1} = 1000 kcal, I/P_{n-1} = 20%, A/I = 35% and P_n/A = 20%?

A. 56 14 130 200
B. 14 130 56 200
C. 200 130 56 14
D. 56 130 200 14

114. The following graph shows the change in proportion of biomass in foliage (leaves), branch and stemwood (bole) for a tree species as a function of DBH (diameter at 1.5 m above ground)

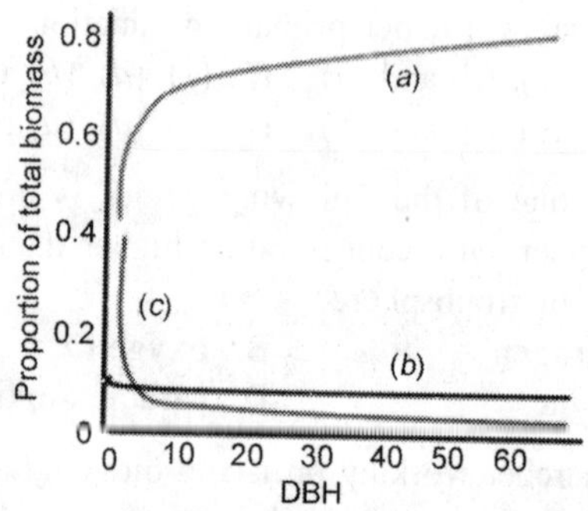

Which one of the following options correctly matches the curve (A, B and C) with stemwood, foliage and brand respectively?

A. (*a*), (*b*) and (*c*)
B. (*a*), (*c*) and (*b*)
C. (*b*), (*c*) and (*a*)
D. (*b*), (*a*) and (*c*)

Biodiversity

115. The table given below lists the conservation areas and the major group of organism that they are best known for:

Column X (Convervation areas)	Column Y (Organism)
(*a*) Hemis National PARK	(*i*) Orchids
(*b*) National Chambal sanctuary	(*ii*) Gharials
(*c*) Nokrek nation park	(*iii*) Nepenthes
(*d*) Sessa sanctuary	(*iv*) Snow leopard
(*e*) Baghmara wildlife sanctuary	(*v*) Endemic citrus species

Which one of the following options represents the correct match of column X and Y?

	(*a*)	(*b*)	(*c*)	(*d*)	(*e*)
A.	(*i*)	(*ii*)	(*iii*)	(*iv*)	(*v*)
B.	(*iv*)	(*ii*)	(*v*)	(*i*)	(*iii*)
C.	(*iii*)	(*ii*)	(*v*)	(*ii*)	(*iv*)
D.	(*v*)	(*iv*)	(*iii*)	(*ii*)	(*i*)

116. The tables show the bird species and their abundance in three habits P, Q, and R.

Habitat P

Species identity	Abundance
1	120
2	20
3	5
4	1
5	1

Habitat Q

Species identity	Abundance
1	20
2	20
3	20
4	20
5	20
6	15
7	15
8	15

Habitat R

Species identity	Abundance
1	80
2	25
3	15
4	10
5	5
6	3
7	3
8	3

Which one of the following combinations below best represents the habitats in decreasing order of diversity?

A. P, R, Q
B. R, Q, P
C. R, P, Q
D. Q, R, P

CSIR-NET, JUNE (AFTERNOON), 2021

Habitat and Niche Concepts

117. Select the correct statement that best describes animal territories:

A. Are always inherited from the parent
B. Are always non-overlapping with neighbors
C. Extent of territories remain constant over generations
D. Are always guarded and defended

118. Glycophytes are salt-sensitive plants while halophytes are salt-tolerant plant. The following statements were made to explain the difference between the glycophytes and halophytes.

(*a*) Glycophytes enhance the uptake of ions.
(*b*) Glycophytes actively ump ons back into the soil.
(*c*) Halophytes have ability to resists net ion uptake in the shoot.
(*d*) Halophytes have greater capacity for vacuolar sequestration of ions.

Select the option that has the combination of all correct statements.

A. (*a*), (*b*), (*c*)
B. (*a*), (*d*) only
C. (*b*), (*c*) only
D. (*b*), (*c*), (*d*)

119. The microclimates at the ground level is very important to plant life. Each curve in the diagram below shows the temperature profiles collected above and below the bare ground shown with respect to the distance from the ground level:

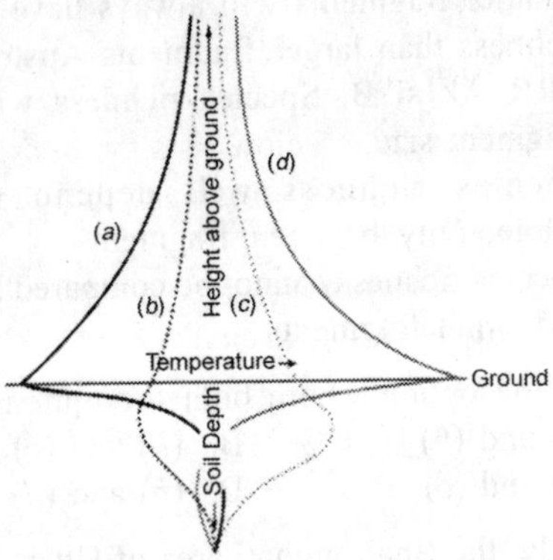

Consider the following four different time points within a diel period:

(*i*) Immediately after sunrise
(*ii*) Noon
(*iii*) Immediately before sunset
(*iv*) Midnight

Match the temperature profiles with the correct diel period.

	(*a*)	(*b*)	(*c*)	(*d*)
A.	(*i*)	(*iv*)	(*ii*)	(*ii*)
B.	(*iv*)	(*i*)	(*iii*)	(*ii*)
C.	(*i*)	(*iv*)	(*ii*)	(*iii*)
D.	(*iv*)	(*i*)	(*ii*)	(*iii*)

Population Ecology

120. Select the correct combination of species (column X) and the known cause of their population declines.

Column X (Species)	Cause for declines
(*a*) Honey bee	(*i*) Methylmercury
(*b*) Gyps vulture	(*ii*) Synthetic oestrogen
(*c*) Shellfish	(*iii*) Diclofenac
(*d*) Minnow	(*iv*) Neonicotinoids

	(*a*)	(*b*)	(*c*)	(*d*)
A.	(*iii*)	(*iv*)	(*ii*)	(*i*)
B.	(*iv*)	(*iii*)	(*i*)	(*ii*)
C.	(*ii*)	(*i*)	(*iv*)	(*iii*)
D.	(*ii*)	(*iv*)	(*i*)	(*iii*)

Species Interactions

121. Consider predators with a choice between two prey types: a big prey 1 which has energy value E1, handling time h1, and search time s1 and; a small prey 2 with energy value E2, handling time h2, and search time s2. According to the optimal foraging (diet) theory, when will the predator preferentially select prey 2?

A. When $E2/h2 > E1/(h1 + s1)$
B. When the abundance of prey 1 is very high
C. When the abundance of Prey 1 and Prey 2 are equal
D. When $E2/h2 = E1/h1$

Ecosystem & Biomes

122. The Covid-19 pandemic had a major impact on CO_2 emissions due to the disruption of industrial activities caused by it. Which of the following countries/regions had the smallest fall of overline CO_2 emissions in % terms during the year 2020?

A. India　　B. USA
C. China　　D. Europe

123. Which of the following constitute the largest reservoir of carbon in the global carbon cycle?

A. The atmosphere
B. The plant biomass on land
C. Soils
D. The ocean

124. Select the correct statement from the options given below to complete the following. In the 1960s, experiments were conducted to test the theory of island biogeography. The main findings of these studies indicate that over a long period of time ______

A. The rate of extinction and colonization are not equal to each other
B. The colonization rates gradually exceed extinction rates
C. The overall rate of colonization will be balanced by the rate of extinction
D. Rate of colonization will continue to increase while extinction rates will decline

125. Which one of the following ecosystems is unique to India?

A. Mangroves　　B. Cold deserts
C. Myristica swamps　　D. Riparian

126. The largest reservoir of nitrogen in the global nitrogen cycle is the atmosphere. Options (*a*) - (*d*) below represent important pathways in the removal of nitrogen from the atmosphere at different rates.

(*a*) Biological fixation in oceans
(*b*) Fixation by lightning
(*c*) Biological fixation in natural terrestrial systems
(*d*) Industrial nitrogen fixation

Arrange the above pathways from the lowest to the highest rate.

A. $(d) < (b) < (a) < (c)$　B. $(b) < (d) < (c) < (a)$
C. $(b) < (c) < (d) < (a)$　D. $(a) < (b) < (d) < (c)$

127. In a high-altitude meadow region, it observed that over the last five years 20 forb species flowered 2-3 weeks earlier than their long-term average time of flowering. At the same time, their fruit production has fallen. The following statements were proposed as reasonable explanations for why this is happening:

(*a*) The forbs are responding to a warming climate but pollinators are not available at the same time

(*b*) Early flowering has increased competition for pollinators
(*c*) Flowering and fruit success are unrelated phenomena in forbs
(*d*) Animals that eats fruits are not available at the time so fruiting has stopped

Which one of the following option represent statement with correct reasonable exaplanation?
A. (*a*) and (*c*) both B. (*c*) and (*d*) both
C. (*a*) and (*b*) both D. (*b*) and (*d*) both

Biodiversity

128. Select the correct combination of factors which drive the extinction vortex:
A. Reduced population size, loss of genetic diversity, inbreeding
B. Emigration, fragmented habitat, inbreeding
C. Immigration, reduced population size, loss of genetic diversity
D. Catastrophic events, reduced population size, outbreeding

129. Fragmentation breaks up contiguous tracts of natural habitats into smaller patches. In a fragmented landscape where a previously large forest has become a mosaic of patches of different sizes, the following statements can be made about the fragment size and its species diversity
(*a*) Smaller fragments will always have lower species richness than larger fragments Austral
(*b*) GRR Ak si B. Species richness will depend on fragment size.
(*c*) Species richness will depend on physical connectivity between fragments
(*d*) Species richness cannot be compared between large and small fragments

Select the option where both the options are correct:
A. (*a*) and (*b*) B. (*b*) and (*c*)
C. (*a*) and (*c*) D. (*b*) and (*d*)

130. Recently, the Bhaironghati area of Uttarkashi has been declared a conservation centre for a species referred to as the 'Ghost of the Mountains'. Which one of the following animals does this refer to?
A. Marbled cat B. Himalayan ibex
C. Southern kiang D. Snow leopard

GATE (LIFE SCIENCE), 2021

Ecology

131. Which of the following options represent the animals as Endemic to India?
A. Pygmy Hog
B. Mountain Bongo
C. Hirola
D. Purple Frog

132. Find the CORRECT match among the plant species in GROUP I, the predominant phytochemical in GROUP II and the economic/medical use in GROUP III.

Group I	Group II	Group III
P. *Syzygium aromaticum*	(*i*) Vincristine	1. Toothache relief
Q. *Gracilaria sp.*	(*ii*) Eugenol	2. Dessert jelly
R. *Catharanthus roseus*	(*iii*) Agar	3. Leukaemia treatment
S. *Theobroma cacao*	(*iv*) Morphine	4. Analgesic
T. *Papaver somniferum*	(*v*) Flavonols	5. Beverage

A. P-(*i*)-1, Q-(*ii*)-3, R-(*iii*)-4, S-(*v*)-5, T-(*iv*)-2
B. P-(*ii*)-1, Q-(*iii*)-2, R-(*i*)-3, S-(*v*)-5, T-(*iv*)-4
C. P-(*ii*)-1, Q-(*iii*)-2, R-(*v*)-4, S-(*i*)-3, T-(*iv*)-5
D. P-(*i*)-2, Q-(*ii*)-3, R-(*iv*)-1, S-(*iii*)-5, T-(*v*)-4

CSIR-NET, SEPTEMBER (MORNING), 2022

Habitat and Niche Concepts

133. Which one of the following statements is NOT correct?
A. Niche breadth tends to increase with interspecific competition while intraspecific competition tends to decrease it
B. Species in unstable environments with fluctuating resource availabilities tend to have broad niche breadths
C. K-strategists are likely to be better competitors than *r*-strategists in a climax community.
D. Diffuse competition increases with niche dimensionlity

Population Ecology

134. Which of the following correctly represents the relationship between the rate of population growth and population size?

A. 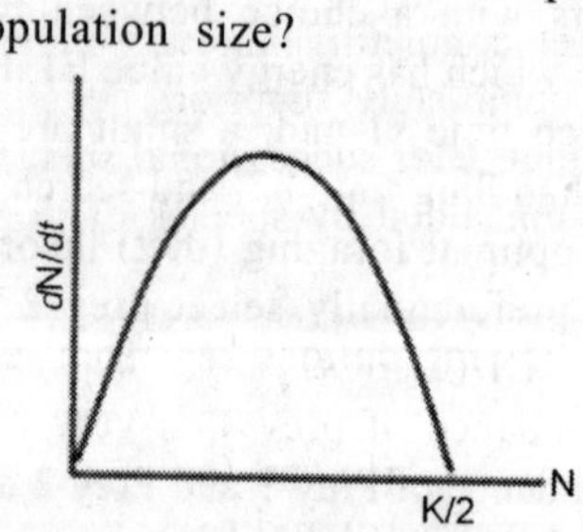

B. 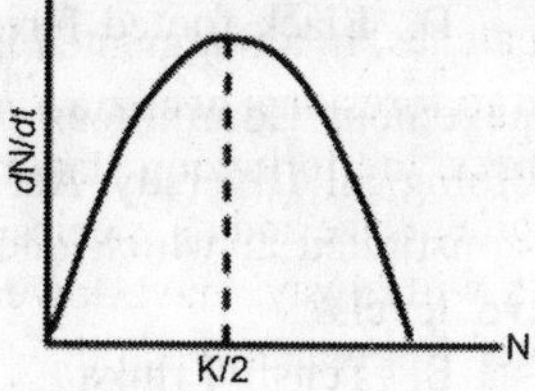

C. 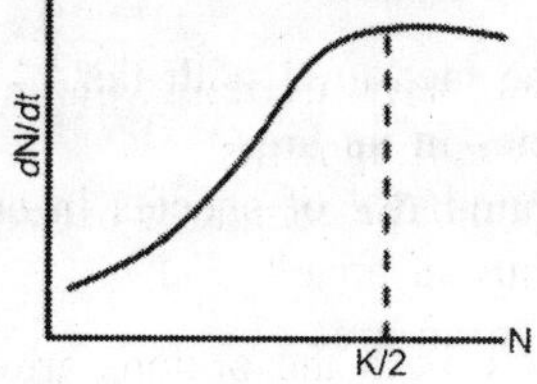

D. 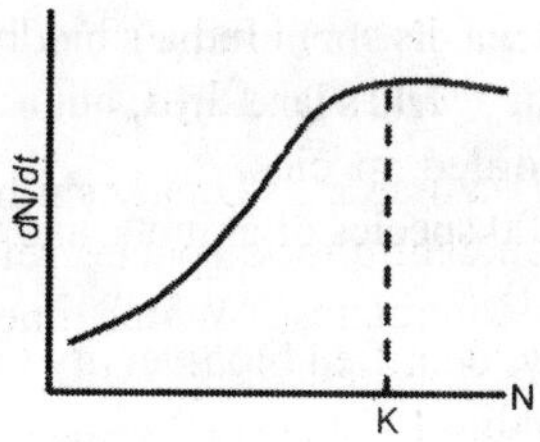

Species Interactions

135. Consider a predator species foraging for prey in a habitat, where there are two prey species A and B. As predator can choose from a high-value prey A and low-value prey B. A and B occur at different frequencies in the environment, so it may take different average times to find the next A or B individual.

Choose the correct option based on the optimal foraging theory.

A. If it takes too long to search for A, predators may switch to eating B only
B. If it takes too long to search for A, predators may eat both A and B, whichever is encountered
C. Predators will only feed on B, regardless of search time
D. will never feed on B, irrespective of its relative frequency

Community Ecology & Successions

136. Following are a set of statements about various models of succession:

(*a*) In inhibition model, strong competitive interaction is present as no species is completely superior.
(*b*) In tolerance model, later successional species are neither inhibited nor aided by species of previous stages.
(*c*) In inhibition model, competitive interaction is weak as no species is completely superior.
(*d*) In facilitation model, later successional species are neither inhibited nor aided by species of previous stages.

Which one of the following options represent correct statements?

A. (*a*) and (*d*) B. (*b*) and (*c*)
C. (*a*) and (*b*) D. (*c*) and (*d*)

Ecosystem & Biomes

137. Which one of the following biome is known to occur in India?

A. Tundra B. Boreal forest
C. Taiga D. Alpine grasslands

138. Which one of the following forest type occupies the largest area in India?

A. Tropical rain forest
B. Tropical dry deciduous forest
C. Temperate deciduous forest
D. Temperate evergreen forest

139. The diagram below depicts the generalized distributional curves (*a*) to (*d*) of allochthonous organic matter production by different autotrophic groups, as a stream transitions to a river

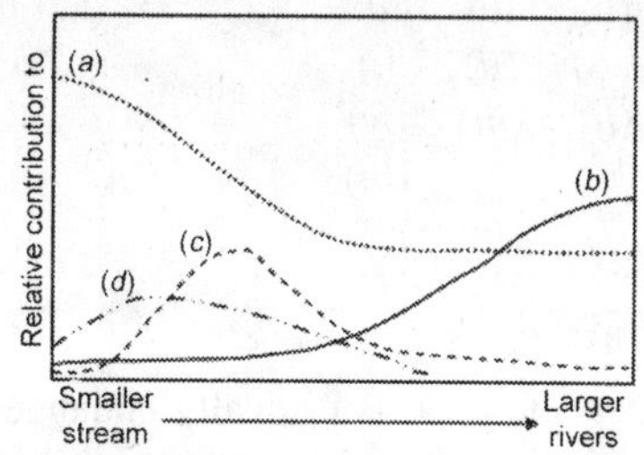

The following are sources of organic matter:

(*i*) Allochthonous
(*ii*) Autochthonous from phytoplankton
(*iii*) Autochthonous from bottom attached algae
(*iv*) Autochthonous from aquatic macrophytes

Choose the correct option that matches the distributional curves (*a*) to (*d*) to the sources (*i*) to (*iv*):

	(*a*)	(*b*)	(*c*)	(*d*)
A.	(*i*)	(*ii*)	(*iv*)	(*iii*)
B.	(*ii*)	(*i*)	(*iii*)	(*iv*)
C.	(*iii*)	(*ii*)	(*i*)	(*iv*)
D.	(*i*)	(*iv*)	(*ii*)	(*iii*)

140. The graphs (*a*)-(*c*) below depict the seasonal variation in plankton biomass in three oceanic regions of No (*i*) to (*iii*):

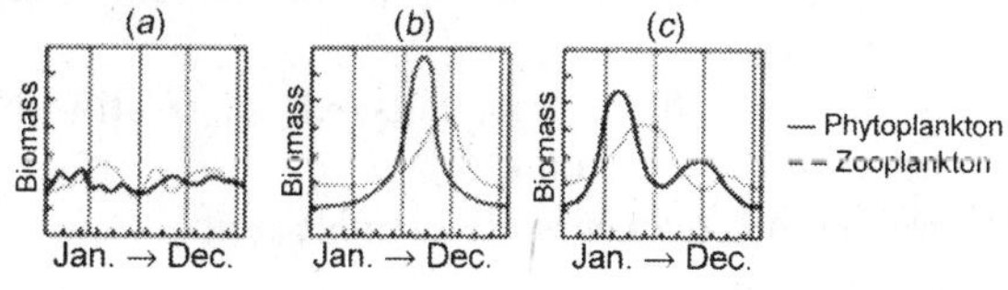

Oceanic regions of the world:

(*i*) Tropical oceans
(*ii*) Polar oceans
(*iii*) Temperate oceans

Match the graphs (*a*) to (*c*) to the correct oceanic region (*i*) to (*iii*):

	(*a*)	(*b*)	(*c*)
A.	(*i*)	(*ii*)	(*iii*)
B.	(*ii*)	(*i*)	(*iii*)
C.	(*i*)	(*iii*)	(*ii*)
D.	(*iii*)	(*ii*)	(*i*)

141. The graph below depicts trajectories (*a*) to (*d*) of some of the major drivers of global environmental change (*i*) to (*iv*) that are mentioned alongside

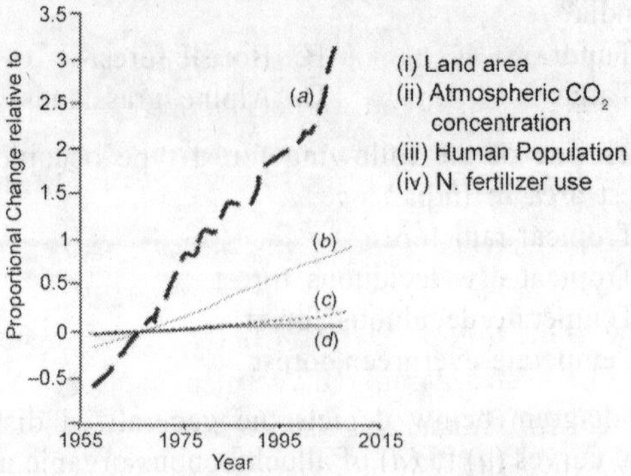

Match the trajectories with the correct drivers:

	(*a*)	(*b*)	(*c*)	(*d*)
A.	(*iv*)	(*iii*)	(*ii*)	(*i*)
B.	(*i*)	(*ii*)	(*iii*)	(*iv*)
C.	(*ii*)	(*iv*)	(*i*)	(*iii*)
D.	(*iii*)	(*i*)	(*iv*)	(*i*)

Biodiversity

142. There is a species that is critically endangered, found in the Russian Far East. It is solitary, but it has been reported that some males stay with females after mating, and may even help with rearing the young. Identify this species:

A. Amur leopard B. Snow leopard
C. Arctic fox D. Black-footed ferret

143. The Biodiversity Management Committees (BMCs) envisaged under the Biological Diversity Act (2002) and Rules (2004) are constituted at which one of the following administrative levels?

A. Village B. Tehsil/Taluka
C. District D. State

144. Species richness can be measured with the:

A. abundance of species in an area
B. number and the abundance of species in an area
C. number of species in an area
D. density of species in an area

145. Following are a few statements about India's biodiversity:

(*a*) India has 2.4% of the world's land area, but accounts for 12% of all recorded species.
(*b*) India has over 45,000 species of animals and 91,000 species of plants.
(*c*) Four of the globally identified biodiversity hotspots can be found in India.
(*d*) India is estimated to harbour around 60% of the global tiger population.

Which one of the following options represents all correct statements?

A. Only (*a*) B. Only (*c*)
C. Both (*a*) and (*b*) D. Both (*c*) and (*d*)

CSIR-NET, SEPTEMBER (AFTERNOON), 2022

Habitat and Niche Concepts

146. An ecologist studying molluscs concluded that there is a correlation between the thickness of the shell and weight of the mollusc. Based on this information, one can conclude that:

A. heavier molluscs are better defended from attacks by predators.
B. heavier molluscs are poorly defended from attacks by predators.
C. most likely there is a cause-effect relationship between the two traits.
D. weight and thickness are variable traits in mollusc population

147. Which one of these statements is NOT CORRECT with respect to ecotones?

A. Intertidal zones and estuaries are two examples of ecotones.
B. They are transitional areas of vegetation between two different plant communities.
C. Populations in ecotones are potentially pre-adapted to changing environment.
D. They harbour only K-selected species that can survive in changing habitats.

148. Match the Indian Biosphere reserves (Column P) with the key fauna (Column Q) they are intended to protect.

Column P (Biosphere reserve)	Column Q (Key fauna)
(*a*) Gulf of Munnar	(*i*) Musk deer
(*b*) Dihang-Dibang	(*ii*) Saltwater crocodile
(*c*) Great Nicobar	(*iii*) Dugong
(*d*) Seshachalam Hills	(*iv*) Lion-tailed macaque
(e) Nilgiri Biosphere Reserve	(*v*) Slender Iorid

Which one of the following options has all correct matches between column P and Q?

	(*a*)	(*b*)	(*c*)	(*d*)	(*e*)
A.	(*iii*)	(*i*)	(*ii*)	(*v*)	(*iv*)
B.	(*ii*)	(*iv*)	(*v*)	(*i*)	(*iii*)
C.	(*iii*)	(*iv*)	(*i*)	(*ii*)	(*v*)
D.	(*v*)	(*iii*)	(*ii*)	(*iv*)	(*i*)

Population Ecology

149. Which one of the following survivorship curves is typical of invasive insect pest species?

A. Invasive insect pest species do not follow specific survivorship curves
B. Type II
C. Type III
D. Type I

150. The intensity of competition can be inferred from knowing the carrying capacity (K) and the population size (N) in the equation below:

$$\frac{dn}{dt} = rN\frac{(K-N)}{K}$$

Assume that populations have the same intrinsic growth rates (r) and carrying capacity (K). Then, at which one of the following values of the second term (K-N)/K in the equation, is the intraspecific competition likely to be the highest?
A. 0.001 B. 0.009
C. 0.15 D. 0.015

151. In a particular population A, individuals are under stress and they produce smaller offspring. Based on this, one may conclude that:
A. stress in a population affects offspring size but not the number of offspring.
B. stressed adults prefer to produce smaller offspring that require less food.
C. stress may be linked to offspring size.
D. stress in a population directly affects offspring size.

Species Interactions

152. A researcher observed ants in contact with plant hoppers that were feeding on tree sap. Which of the following conclusions made by her would be correct?
A. This is an example of ants being predatory.
B. This is an example of ants upsetting the ecological balance of nature.
C. This is an example of a multitrophic interaction.
D. This is an example of the tree attracting ants to get rid of plant hoppers.

Ecosystem & Biomes

153. Savannas are biomes where tree and grass vegetation coexist over large areas. Which one of the following statements does NOT explain the occurrence of savannas in the Indian subcontinent?
A. Selective logging of forests opens up the canopy and grasses take over
B. Low rainfall maintains low tree cover that helps grasses establish
C. Fires do not allow trees to establish closed canopies
D. Browsing by herbivores limits tree establishment

154. Study the global ecosystem data provided in the following table.

Ecosystem	Global area (10^6 km^2)	Mean net primary productivity(gm/m^2/yr)	Mean biomass per unit area (Kg/m^2)
Tropical rainforest	17	2000	44
Swamp and marsh	2	2500	15
Cultivated land	14	644	1.1
Open ocean	332	127	0.003

Based on the data provided in the table, choose the correct option that represents ecosystems with the highest global, primary production and the highest relative NPP, respectively.
A. Tropical rainforest and tropical rainforest
B. Swamp and marsh, and tropical rainforest
C. Cultivated land and open ocean
D. Open ocean and open ocean

Biodiversity

155. Which one of the following statements is NOT correct?
A. Both alpha and gamma diversities measure the presence and abundance of species in a community
B. Gamma diversity can be expressed as the product of alpha and beta diversities across sites
C. Gamma diversity is the sum of alpha diversities for a set of sites
D. Gamma diversity can be expressed as the sum of alpha and beta diversities across sites

156. The black buck (Antilope cervicapra) has been traditionally protected by which one of the following communities?
A. Bhils
B. Jats
C. Bishnois
D. Ahirs

157. An Indian bird species known to defend flowers is the:
A. Purple-throated hummingbird
B. Jungle babbler
C. Purple-rumped sunbird
D. Crescent honeyeater

158. Fragmentation breaks up contiguous tracts of natural habitats into smaller patches. In a fragmented landscape where a previously large forest has become a mosaic of patches of different sizes, the following statements can be made about the fragment size and its species diversity.
(*a*) Smaller fragments will always have lower species richness than larger fragments.
(*b*) Species richness will depend on fragment size.
(*c*) Species richness will depend on physical connectivity between fragments.
(*d*) Species richness cannot be compared between large and small fragments.

Select the option where both the statements are correct:
A. (*a*) and (*b*)
B. (*b*) and (*c*)
C. (*a*) and (*c*)
D. (*b*) and (*d*)

159. Table below shows the protected areas, their description and the protected area types.

Protected area	Discription	Protected area type
Kaziranga National park	D1-World largest population of one homed rhinoceroses	T1-Ramsar wetland site
Beas conservation reserve	D2-Major wintering area for large numbers of aquatic birds	T2-UNESCO Natural world heritage site
Keoladeo national park	D3-Site for threatend species such as mahseer, hog deer, smooth coated otter	
Manas wildlife sanctuary	D4-Home to many endangered species including tiger, pygmy hog, Indian rhinoceros and Asian elephant	

A. Beas Conservation Reserve, D3, T1
B. Kaziranga National Park, D1, T2
C. Keoladeo National Park, D2, T2
D. Manas Wildlife Sanctuary, D4, T1

160. The Western Ghats (WG) is a 1600 km mountain chain along the west coast of peninsular India, which intercepts the south-west monsoon winds. Monsoon starts in the southern WG and moves progressively north and retreats in the reverse direction. The southern WG also receives some rainfall from the north-east monsoon. Based on this information, which one of the following statements is most likely to be INCORRECT?

A. Vegetation in the southern WG experiences a more seasonal climate.
B. Vegetation in the northern WG experiences a more seasonal climate.
C. Generally, less seasonal areas tend to have higher plant diversity, so tree diversity will decrease from south to north in the WG.
D. Tree species in the northern WG will have to handle longer dry seasons than species found in the southern WG.

161. Interacting plant (A-J) and insect herbivore (P-Y) species in a community are depicted in the network below.

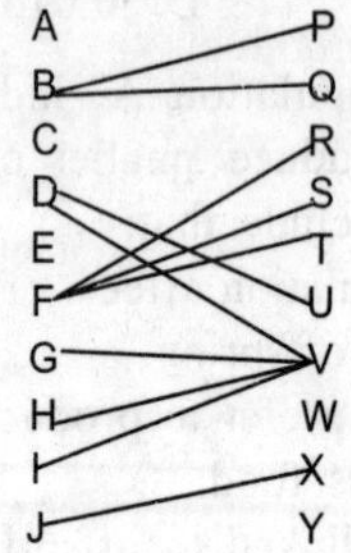

Consider the following statements about the network drawn above.

(*a*) Insect are more specialised than plants
(*b*) There are no obligate interactions in this network.
(*c*) The community is modular.
(*d*) Missing links always represent the absence of an interaction.

Given this network which one of the options below is correct?

A. (*a*) only
B. (*a*) and (*c*) only
C. (*b*), (*c*) and (*d*) only
D. (*b*) and (*d*) only

DBT-JRF, 2022

162. Choose the correct option to fill up the blanks:

_______ nourish the host coral as well as help it deposit its skeleton. They perform _______ and pass on some of the _______ they make to the coral.

A. hermatypic corals, scavenging, organic matter
B. scleractinian, respiration, calcium
C. hermatypic corals, synthesis, calcium
D. zooxanthellae, photosynthesis, organic matter

GATE (LIFE SCIENCE), 2022

Ecology

163. Which of the following is/are part of marine ecosystem?

A. Open ocean
B. Chaparral
C. Deep sea
D. Estuaries

164. Make CORRECT match between Group-I and Group-II, in relation to interaction between two species.

Group-I	Group-II
(*a*) Neutralism	(*i*) neither can survive under natural condition without the other
(*b*) Allelopathy	(*ii*) direct inhibition of one species by the other species using toxic compound
(*c*) Amensalism	(*iii*) neither is affected by the association with the other
(*d*) Mutualism	(*iv*) one is inhibited and the other is not affected

	(*a*)	(*b*)	(*c*)	(*d*)
A.	(*i*)	(*ii*)	(*iii*)	(*iv*)
B.	(*iii*)	(*ii*)	(*iv*)	(*i*)
C.	(*iv*)	(*iii*)	(*ii*)	(*i*)
D.	(*iii*)	(*iv*)	(*ii*)	(*i*)

165. Animals can be classified as 'specialists' or 'generalists' with respect to diet and habitat selection. Which of the following organism/s belong/s to the specialist category?

A. Raccoon
B. Panda
C. Polar Bear
D. Koala Bear

166. Match the ecological concepts listed in Column I with their definitions listed in Column II.

Column I	Column II
(*a*) Dominance hierarchies	(*i*) Giving up one's own reproductive potential to benefit another individual
(*b*) Territory of an individual	(*ii*) Selection acting on related animals which affects fitness
(*c*) Altruism behaviour	(*iii*) Exclusion of competing individuals using agonistic
(*d*) Kin selection	(*iv*) Preferential access to the food and mates in a group

	(*a*)	(*b*)	(*c*)	(*d*)
A.	(*ii*)	(*iv*)	(*i*)	(*iii*)
B.	(*iv*)	(*iii*)	(*i*)	(*ii*)
C.	(*iii*)	(*iv*)	(*i*)	(*ii*)
D.	(*i*)	(*iv*)	(*iii*)	(*ii*)

ANSWERS

1	**2**	**3**	**4**	**5**	**6**	**7**	**8**	**9**	**10**
C	C	C	D	D	B	C	C	B	B
11	**12**	**13**	**14**	**15**	**16**	**17**	**18**	**19**	**20**
B	B	D	C	B	C	B	D	A	C
21	**22**	**23**	**24**	**25**	**26**	**27**	**28**	**29**	**30**
D	D	D	B	C	B	B	D	C	C
31	**32**	**33**	**34**	**35**	**36**	**37**	**38**	**39**	**40**
B	A	B	B	C	C	C	B	B	C
41	**42**	**43**	**44**	**45**	**46**	**47**	**48**	**49**	**50**
B	D	B	B	B	C	D	C	B	A
51	**52**	**53**	**54**	**55**	**56**	**57**	**58**	**59**	**60**
B	C	D	B	C	B	B	B	C	C
61	**62**	**63**	**64**	**65**	**66**	**67**	**68**	**69**	**70**
B	B	C	A	D	A	B	A	D	B
71	**72**	**73**	**74**	**75**	**76**	**77**	**78**	**79**	**80**
A	C	A	B	A	B	D	A	B	A
81	**82**	**83**	**84**	**85**	**86**	**87**	**88**	**89**	**90**
C	A	C	B	A	D	C	C	C	B
91	**92**	**93**	**94**	**95**	**96**	**97**	**98**	**99**	**100**
C	B	D	B	A	B	D	B	B	B
101	**102**	**103**	**104**	**105**	**106**	**107**	**108**	**109**	**110**
B	A	D	B	B	C	D	C	C	D
111	**112**	**113**	**114**	**115**	**116**	**117**	**118**	**119**	**120**
C	C	B	B	B	D	D	D	B	B
121	**122**	**123**	**124**	**125**	**126**	**127**	**128**	**129**	**130**
A	C	D	C	C	C	C	A	B	D
131	**132**	**133**	**134**	**135**	**136**	**137**	**138**	**139**	**140**
A, D	B	A	B	B	C	D	B	A	A
141	**142**	**143**	**144**	**145**	**146**	**147**	**148**	**149**	**150**
D	A	A	C	D	C	D	A	C	A
151	**152**	**153**	**154**	**155**	**156**	**157**	**158**	**159**	**160**
C	C	A	D	D	C	C	B	C, D	A
161	**162**	**163**	**164**	**165**	**166**				
B	D	A, C, D	C	B, C, D	B				

CHAPTER

18

EVOLUTION

CSIR-NET, JUNE, 2017

Concepts of Evolution, Timescale, Era & Major Event During Evolution

1. What do mayflies, Pacific salmon (*Oncorhynchus* spp.) and annual grain crops have in common? They all are

A. Semelparous

B. Iteroparous

C. Oviparous

D. Viviparous

2. The correct order of periods from Palaeozoic to Mesozoic era is:

A. Triassic-Jurassic-Cretaceous-Cambrian-Ordovician-Silurian-Devonian-Carboniferous-Permian

B. Palaeocene-Eocene-Oligocene-Miocene-Pliocene-Pleistocene Holocene

C. Cambrian-Ordovician-Silurian-Devonian-Carboniferous-Permian-Triassic-Jurassic-Cretaceous

D. Liocene-Eocene-Oligocene Silurian-Devon-Carboniferous-Triassic-Jurassic -Cretaceous

3. Flufftails in mainland Asia show high variation in tail colour. However, in the far out Pacific island, the flufftails show very little variation in tail colour. This variation in tail colour can be explained by all of the following EXCEPT:

A. founder effect

B. homologous evolution

C. genetic drift

D. frequency dependent selection

4. Which one of the following statements regarding crop improvement programs using molecular breeding approaches is INCORRECT?

A. Allelic diversity for traits of interest should be available in the naturally occurring crossable germplasm

B. The genes of interest cannot be derived from a sexually incompatible organism

C. Availability of markers and linkage maps would facilitate the breeding program

D. The crop plant should necessarily have an optimized robust system for production of doubled haploids

5. Column A lists names of evolutionary biologists and column B lists descriptions of evolutionary mechanisms proposed by them in random order.

Column-A	Column-B
(*a*) Jean Baptiste Lamarck	(*i*) Variation at the molecular level is selectively neutral
(*b*) Charles Darwin	(*ii*) Inheritance of acquired characters
(*c*) Motoo kimura	(*iii*) Differential reproduction of genotypes
(*d*) Sewall Wright	(*iv*) Changes in allele frequency due to random genetic drift

	(*a*)	(*b*)	(*c*)	(*d*)
A.	(*i*)	(*ii*)	(*iv*)	(*iii*)
B.	(*ii*)	(*iii*)	(*i*)	(*iv*)
C.	(*iii*)	(*i*)	(*ii*)	(*iv*)
D.	(*ii*)	(*iii*)	(*iv*)	(*i*)

6. Following diagrams represent various ways in which a character may evolve:

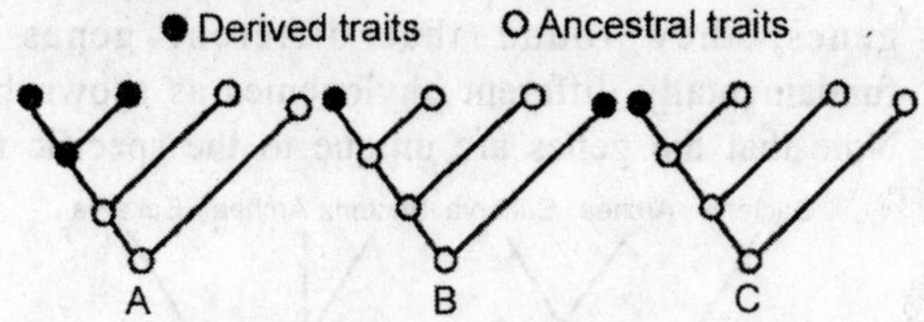

Which of the following is the correct definition for the character evolution patterns shown above?
A. A-Autapomorphy, B-Synapomorphy, C-Homoplasy
B. A-Autapomorphy, B-Homoplasy, C-Synapomorphy
C. A-Synapomorphy, B-Autapomorphy, C-Homoplasy
D. A-Synapomorphy, B-Homoplasy, C-Autapomorphy

Speciation, Phylogenetic Study

7. A species of grass grows around a mine area having patches of heavy metal contaminated soil. Some of the populations of the species grew selectively on the soil that was contaminated with heavy metals. Over a period of time, though the tolerant and non-tolerant grass populations were continuously distributed and not separated by geographical barriers, they eventually evolved different flowering times and became different species. What kind of speciation would you call this?
A. Allopatric speciation
B. Sympatric speciation
C. Parapatric speciation
D. Bottle-neck effect

CSIR-NET, DECEMBER, 2017

Concepts of Evolution, Timescale, Era & Major Event During Evolution

8. Which one of the following statements is NOT TRUE about homologous characters?
A. Similar traits may not be homologous
B. Similar traits may be a result of convergent evolution
C. A homologous trait that is derived and shared from a common ancestor is called an autapomorphy
D. Homologous characters may show structural similarity but functional diversity

9. During the course of evolution, the jaw bones got modified into three ear ossicles in mammals. Which one of the following is a correct match of all three ear ossicles and their jaw bones?
A. stapes – articular; incus – quadrate; malleus – hyomandibular.
B. stapes – quadrate; incus – articular; malleus – hyomandibular
C. stapes – articular; incus – hyomandibular; malleus – quadrate
D. stapes – hyomandibular; incus – quadrate; malleus – articular

Molecular Evolution

10. Which one of the following statements is not true about the Neutral Theory as proposed by Motoo Kimura?
A. Except for advantageous mutations, most alleles are under neutral selection
B. The rate of evolution for most genes will be equal to the neutral mutation rate
C. Advantageous mutations are exceedingly rare
D. At the level of DNA sequences, genetic drift dominates evolution

Speciation and Phylogenetic Study

11. Which one of the following trees represents a fully resolved phylogram?

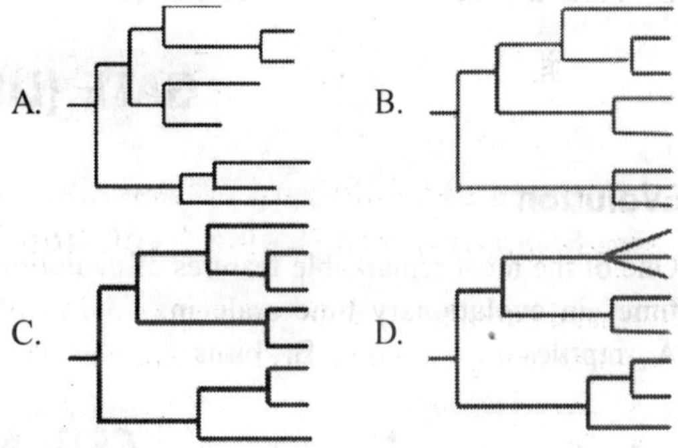

12. A gene 'X' in *Drosophila* contributes to inviabilit hybrids. The phylogeny below shows the evolutionary history of gene 'X' and on each branch the numbers indicate the non synonymous/synonymous substitutions.

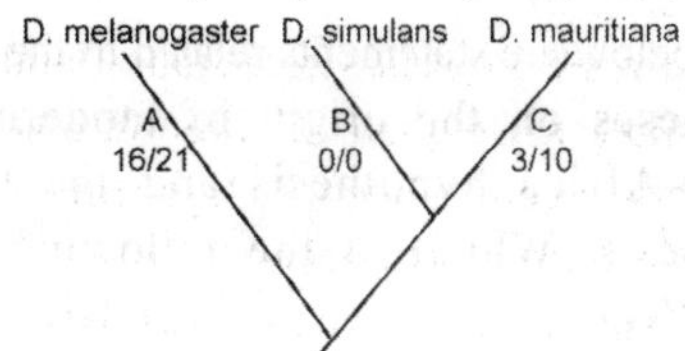

Based on the above information, select the correc statement from the choices below:
A. High proportion of non-synonymous changes at A indicates evolution by natural selection.
B. High proportion of synonymous changes at A indicates absence of natural selection.
C. Equal proportion of non-synonymous and synonymous changes at B indicates deleterious selection.
D. Low proportion of non-synonymous changes at C indicates positive selection.

13. Temporal isolation in breeding seasons between closely related species leads to reproductive isolation. Given below are breeding seasons of different species of frogs.

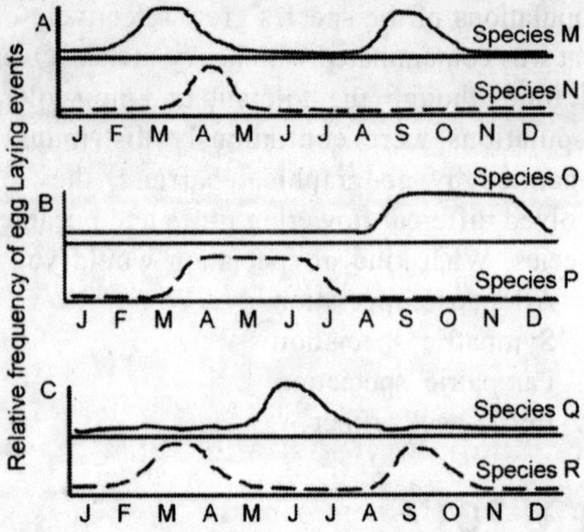

Which of the above plots represents temporal isolation in breeding seasons among closely related sympatric species?

A. Plot A B. Plots A and B
C. Plots B and C D. Plots A and C

14. When James R Brown and W Ford Doolittle (1997) reconstructed the tree of life using a variety of different genes, they found that different genes gave fundamentally different phylogenies as shown below. Note that the genes are unique to the specific trees.

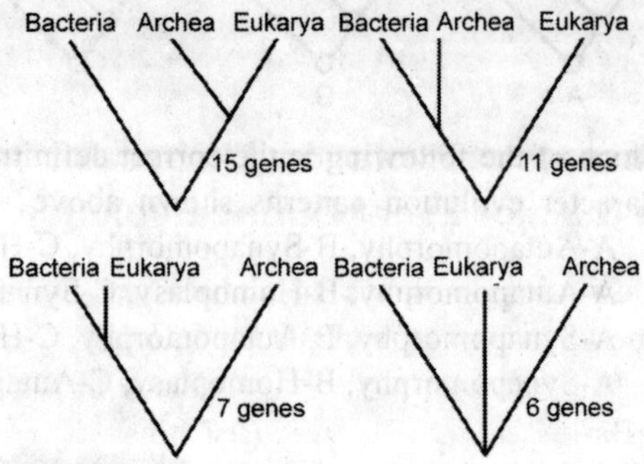

From the given options select the process that best explains the observed discrepancies between the trees.

A. Polyploidization
B. Horizontal gene transfer
C. Allopatric speciation
D. Localized extinctions

GATE (LIFE SCIENCE), 2017

Evolution

15. One of the most remarkable features of evolution is the formation of amnion and allantoin. This appeared for the "first time" in evolutionary time scale in:

A. reptiles B. birds C. fishes D. humans

CSIR-NET, JUNE, 2018

Concepts of Evolution, Timescale, Era & Major Event During Evolution

16. Given below are statements related to the two competing hypotheses on the origin of modern humans: the Out-of-Africa hypothesis and the multi-regional hypothesis. Which of the following statements is INCORRECT?

A. Both the hypotheses support that *Homo erectus* originated in Africa and expanded to Eurasia.
B. Mitochondrial DNA (mtDNA) and Y chromosome DNA evidence support the 'Out-of-Africa' hypothesis.
C. The principal conflict between the two hypotheses is that multi-regional hypothesis does not support African origin of Homo erectus.
D. The multi-regional hypothesis states that independent multiple origins occurred in the million years since *Homo erectus* came out of Africa.

17. Following are key points about the effect of genetic drift:

(*a*) Genetic drift is significant in small populations.
(*b*) Genetic drift can cause allele frequencies to change in a pre-directed way.
(*c*) Genetic drift can lead to a loss of genetic variation within populations.
(*d*) Genetic drift can cause harmful alleles to become fixed.

Which one of the following combination of the above statements are true?

A. (*a*) and (*b*) only B. (*a*) and (*c*) only
C. (*a*), (*b*) and (*c*) D. (*a*), (*c*) and (*d*)

18. Following table contains some of the generalizations of evolutionary biology:

Column-I	Column-II
(*a*) Copes Rule	(*i*) Population lineages tend to increase in body size over evolutionary time
(*b*) Dollo's Rule	(*ii*) There is constant probability of extinction in family of related organism
(*c*) Ockham's Principle	(*iii*) Complex characters, once lost are not regained

(*d*) Van Valen's Law — (*iv*) Accept the simplest theory that works

Which of the following is correct match between Column I and II?

	(*a*)	(*b*)	(*c*)	(*d*)
A.	(*i*)	(*ii*)	(*iv*)	(*iii*)
B.	(*i*)	(*iii*)	(*iv*)	(*ii*)
C.	(*ii*)	(*iii*)	(*i*)	(*iv*)
D.	(*iv*)	(*iii*)	(*i*)	(*ii*)

CSIR-NET, DECEMBER, 2018

Concepts of Evolution, Timescale, Era & Major Event During Evolution

19. Following table shows an alphabetical list of certain domesticated crops and places of origin:

Crop	Place of Origin
(*a*) Barley	(*i*) China
(*b*) Maize	(*ii*) Fertile crescent
(*c*) Mung Bean	(*iii*) India
(*d*) Rice	(*iv*) Southern maxico
(*e*) Wheat	

Based Number of grass species on the above, which one of the following options represent the correct match between crops and their place of origin?

	(*a*)	(*b*)	(*c*)	(*d*)	(*e*)
A.	(*iii*)	(*iv*)	(*i*)	(*ii*)	(*ii*)
B.	(*ii, iv*)	(*ii*)	(*i, iii*)	(*i*)	(*ii*)
C.	(*iii*)	(*iv*)	(*iii*)	(*ii*)	(*iii*)
D.	(*ii*)	(*iv*)	(*iii*)	(*i, iii*)	(*ii*)

20. Beak shape in birds has evolved in response to their diet. The table listing bird species and food type is given below:

Bird species	Food type
(*a*) Barn swallow	(*i*) Fruits
(*b*) Great hornbill	(*ii*) Insects
(*c*) House sparrow	(*iii*) Nectar
(*d*) Purple sunbird	(*iv*) Seeds

Match the bird species shown above to their main food resource.

	(*a*)	(*b*)	(*c*)	(*d*)
A.	(*iv*)	(*i*)	(*iii*)	(*ii*)
B.	(*ii*)	(*iv*)	(*i*)	(*iii*)
C.	(*iii*)	(*ii*)	(*iv*)	(*i*)
D.	(*ii*)	(*i*)	(*iv*)	(*iii*)

Speciation, Phylogenetic Study

21. The phylogenetic tree below shows evolutionary relationships among 8 species. Males of these species are either blue (*b*) or red (*r*) in colour, the colour being indicated next to each species name.

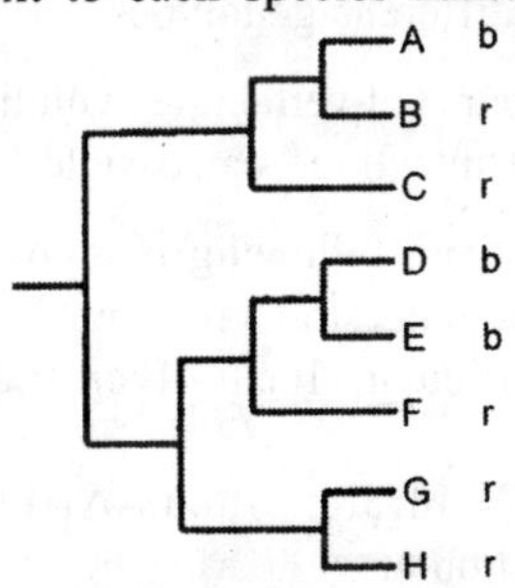

Based on the principle of parsimony, which of the following statements best represents, the evolution of male body colour in this set of species?

A. The most recent common ancestor of all 8 species was blue; red evolved independently 5 times.

B. The most recent common ancestor of all 8 species was blue; red evolved independently 4 times.

C. The most recent common ancestor of all 8 species was red; blue evolved independently 3 times.

D. The most recent common ancestor of all 8 species was red; blue evolved independently 2 times.

GATE (LIFE SCIENCE), 2018

Evolution

22. Increase in the existent population of grey peppered moth, Biston betularia, during industrial revolution in Britain is an example of which ONE of the following evolutionary processes?

A. Neutral selection B. Disruptive selection C. Directional selection D. Stabilizing selection

23. Which ONE of the following statements is NOT part of the classical Darwinian theory of evolution by natural selection?

A. A trait which is constantly used will get inherited by next generation.

B. Phenotypic variations exist among the individuals of a population of a species

C. Individuals that best fit into a given environment are more likely to survive

D. Each population can randomly acquire a distinct and separate suite of variations.

CSIR-NET, JUNE, 2019

Concepts of Evolution, Timescale, Era & Major Event During Evolution

24. Which one of the following does NOT contribute to micro-evolutionary change?

A. Mutation
B. Random mating
C. Genetic drift
D. Natural selection

25. Which one of the following is the most appropriate definition of 'Gene Pyramiding' in plants?

A. Introducing different genes for resistance to a specific pest in different genotypes.
B. Introducing a single gene for resistance to a particular pest in different genotypes.
C. Introducing different genes for resistance to a single pest in a single genotype.
D. Introducing a single gene for resistance to multiple pests in different genotypes.

26. During the course of vertebrate evolution, the jaw bones got modified into three ear ossicles in mammals

Which one of the following is a correct match of ear ossicle and its ancestral jaw bone?

A. Stapes-Articular; Incus-Hyomandibular; Malleus-Quadrate
B. Stapes-Quadrate; Incus-Articular; Malleus-Hyomandibular
C. Stapes-Quadrate; Incus-Hyomandibular; Malleus-Articular
D. Stapes-Hyomandibular; Incus-Quadrate; Malleus-Articular

27. Antelopes are proposed to form groups to reduce the risk of predation. A researcher measured the predation of individuals in groups of different sizes. She found that per capita mortality risk decreased with increasing group size for males (solid line) but remained unchanged for female (dashed line). Furthermore, males in all groups experienced greater per capita mortality risk than females.

Identify the graph below that best depicts the above findings:

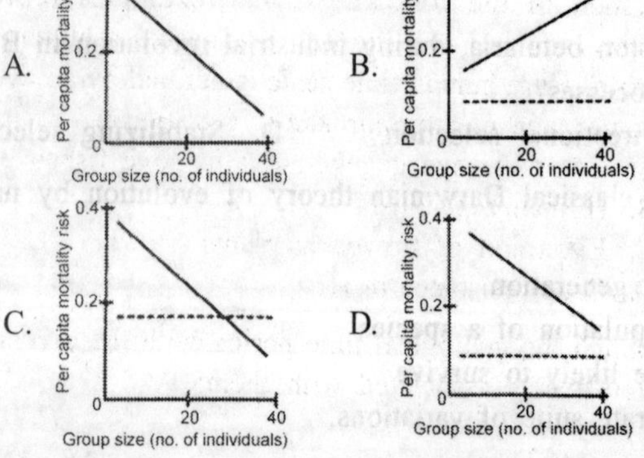

Molecular Evolution

28. Analyses of nucleotide sequences of ribosomal RNA (rRNA) are particularly useful for evolutionary studies of living organisms because of the following reasons EXCEPT

A. rRNA is evolutionary ancient
B. no free – living organisms lacks rRNA
C. rRNA, since critical for translation, can undergo lateral transfer amongst distant species.
D. rRNA has evolved slowly over geological time

Speciation, Phylogenetic Study

29. Depicted below is a phylogenetic tree of selected taxa:

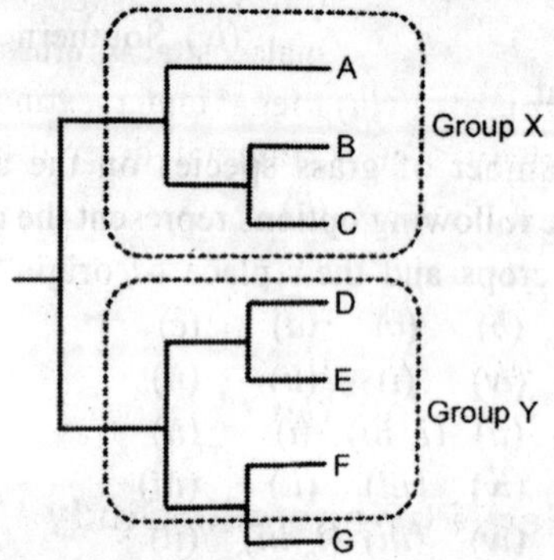

A. Group X is monophyletic and group Y is polyphyletic
B. Group X is paraphyletic and group Y is monophyletic
C. Both group X and Y are monophyletic
D. Group X is monophyletic and Group Y is paraphyletic

30. Which one of the following statement is correct for the process of speciation?

A. Allopatric speciation occurs between adjacent populations.
B. Parapatric speciation may occur between geographically separated populations.
C. Sympatric speciation occurs within one continuously distributed population.
D. Sympatric speciation occurs when continuously distributed populations are fragmented.

31. Following is a diagrammatic representation of human evolutionary tree.

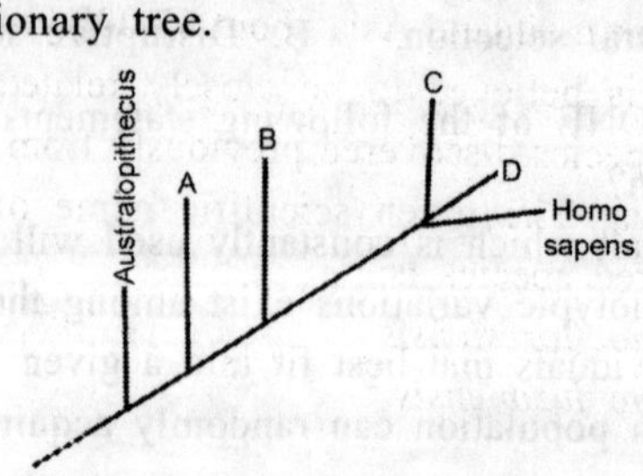

In the above diagram A, B, C and D respectively represent:

A. *Denisovan, Homo habilis, Homo erectus, Homo neanderthalensis*

B. *Homo habilis, Homo erectus, Homo neanderthalensis, Denisovan*

C. *Homoerectus, Homohabilis, Homo neanderthalensis, Denisova*

D. *Homo erectus, Denisovan, Homo neanderthalensis, Homo habilis*

CSIR-NET, 15 DECEMBER, 2019

Concepts of Evolution, Timescale, Era & Major Event During Evolution

32. Match the geological time period with the extinction or diversification events associated with them:

Geological time	Event
(*a*) Cenozoic	(*i*) Angiosperm diversification
(*b*) Cretaceous	(*ii*) Modem fauna diversification (bivalves, gastropods, bryozoans, malacostracan crustaceans)
(*c*) Paleozoic	(*iii*) Mega fauna extinction
(*d*) Quaternary	(*iv*) Mammal diversification

	(*a*)	(*b*)	(*c*)	(*d*)
A.	(*ii*)	(*i*)	(*iii*)	(*iv*)
B.	(*iv*)	(*i*)	(*ii*)	(*iii*)
C.	(*ii*)	(*ii*)	(*i*)	(*iv*)
D.	(*iv*)	(*iii*)	(*i*)	(*iv*)

Speciation, Phylogenetic Study

33. Which one of the following phylogenies best represents the evolutionary relationship among whales, dolphins, seals, deer and dogs?

A. 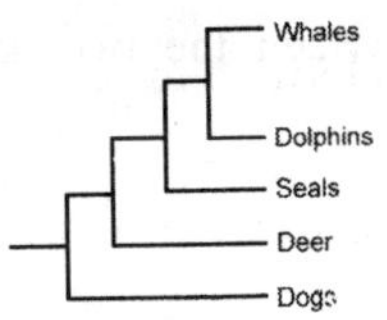

B. 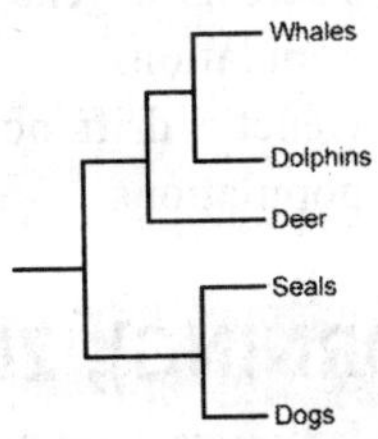

C. 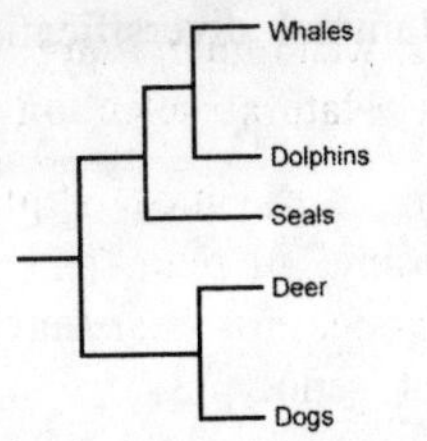

D. 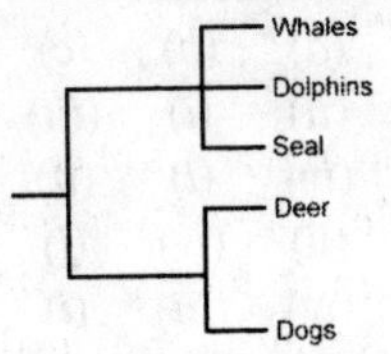

34. The phylogeny below shows evolutionary relationships between 9 extant bird species and whether they display red or blue plumage.

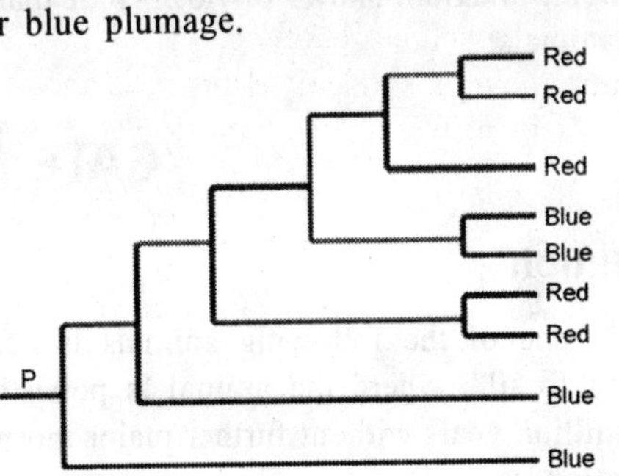

Based on the above phylogeny and the distribution of red and blue character states among the extant species, and using the principle of parsimony, which of the following is the correct inference about plumage colour of the ancestor at the root P?

A. Ancestral state at P is blue.

B. Ancestral state at P is red.

C. Ancestral state at P is more likely to be red than blue

D. Ancestral state at P is equally likely to be red or blue.

CSIR-NET, 27 DECEMBER, 2019

Concepts of Evolution, Timescale, Era & Major Event During Evolution

35. A small-bodied hominid whose fossil was discovered very recently, ventured into the islands of South-East Asia from mainland Asia about 67,000 years ago. This species is believed to be closely related to another Homo species discovered previously from an island in Indonesia. The given scientific name of the newly discovered species is:

A. *Homo floresiensis*

B. *Homo luzonensis*

C. *Homo naledi*

D. *Homo habilis*

36. Which of the following events/examples represent observation of evolutionary changes on a human time scale? Here human time scale is defined by an average human age of approximately 70-80 years.

A. Complete eye degeneration in cove fishes

B. Human bipedalism

C. Evolution of flowering plants

D. Drug resistance in HIV

37. Match the geological time period with the diversification events associated with them:

Geological era	Event
(*a*) Cenozoic	(*i*) Angiosperm diversification
(*b*) Mesozoic	(*ii*) Modern fauna diversification (bivalves, gastropods, bryozoans, malacostracam crustaceans)
(*c*) Paleozoic	(*iii*) Oceanic radiation of early eukaryotes
(*d*) Proterozoic	(*iv*) Mammal diversification

	(*a*)	(*b*)	(*c*)	(*d*)
A.	(*ii*)	(*i*)	(*iii*)	(*iv*)
B.	(*iv*)	(*i*)	(*ii*)	(*iii*)
C.	(*ii*)	(*iv*)	(*i*)	(*iii*)
D.	(*iv*)	(*iii*)	(*i*)	(*ii*)

Speciation, Phylogenetic Study

38. Following diagram shows phylogeny of plants, fungi, and animals:

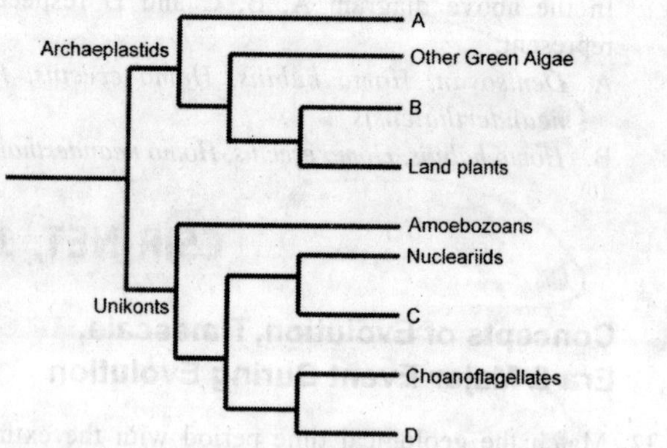

In the above diagram A, B, C and D represent; respectively;

A. Fungi, Red algae, Charophytes, Animals
B. Red algae, Charophytes, Animals, Fungi
C. Green algae, Red algae, Animals, Fungi
D. Red algae, Charophytes, Fungi, Animals

GATE (LIFE SCIENCE), 2019

Evolution

39. Which one of the following animals is named as a "living fossil", where the animal is persisting above 400 million years without further major morphological evolution?

A. King crabs B. Porcelain crabs
C. Horseshoe crabs D. Hermit crabs

40. The finches on the Galapagos Islands have widely differing beaks adapted according to their diets. This is an example of:

A. Adaptive radiation
B. Parallel evolution
C. Adaptive convergence
D. Co-adaptation

41. Which one of the following factors does NOT contribute to "allopatric speciation"?

A. The isolated population is exposed to different selection pressure as compared to parent population
B. A population become geographically isolated from the parent population
C. There is a gene flow between the two separated populations
D. Genetic drift occurs between the two separated populations

CSIR-NET, NOVEMBER (MORNING), 2020

Concepts of Evolution, Timescale, Era & Major Event During Evolution

42. The following statements describe the outcomes of genetic drift:

(*a*) Genetic drift can eliminate alleles.
(*b*) Genetic drift can be associated with population bottleneck.
(*c*) Genetic drift is not observed in populations that increase in size, once they grow through a bottleneck.
(*d*) Genetic drift can be associated with founder effect.

Which one of the following combinations represents all correct statements?

A. (*a*), (*b*) and (*c*)
B. (*b*), (*c*) and (*d*)
C. (*a*), (*b*) and (*d*)
D. (*a*), (*c*) and (*d*)

43. Examples of antibiotic resistance highlight important features of natural selection. Which of the following statements is NOT true?

A. Evolution by natural selection is progressive, it makes individuals 'better'.
B. Natural selection acts on individuals but it is populations that change with time.
C. Natural selection does not cause genetic changes in individuals
D. Natural selection acts on phenotype

44. The figure below shows reptilian skull types (*a*) to (*c*), class of organisms (*i*) to (*iii*) and examples of animals (X to Z).

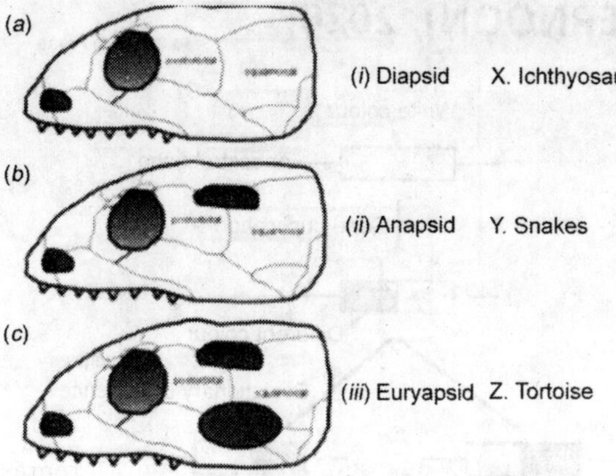

Which one of the following options shows correct matches between the three components?

A. (*a*)-(*ii*)-Y, (*b*)-(*iii*)-Z, (*c*)-(*i*)-X
B. (*b*)-(*ii*)-Y, (*a*)-(*i*)-X, (*c*)-(*iii*)-Z
C. (*a*)-(*ii*)-Z, (*b*)-(*iii*)-X, (*c*)-(*i*)-Y
D. (*b*)-(*iii*)-Y, (*a*)-(*ii*)-X, (*c*)-(*i*)-Z

45. Given below are names of scientists and phrases describing their work, which may or may not be matched:

Name of Scientist	Work
(*a*) Wallace	(*i*) Inheritance of acquired characters
(*b*) Lyell	(*ii*) Natural selection is differential survival or reproduction
(*c*) Lamark	(*iii*) Processes that alter the earth are uniform through time
(*d*) Cuvier	(*iv*) Earth's geology and natural history have been shaped by periods of catastrophic extinction and new creations
	(*v*) Ontogeny recapitulates phylogeny

Which one of the following options represent correct matches between the scientist and his/her work?

	(*a*)	(*b*)	(*c*)	(*d*)
A.	(*i*)	(*ii*)	(*iii*)	(*v*)
B.	(*ii*)	(*iii*)	(*i*)	(*iv*)
C.	(*i*)	(*iii*)	(*v*)	(*ii*)
D.	(*v*)	(*iv*)	(*i*)	(*iii*)

Origin of Cells and Unicellular Evolution

46. You wanted to conduct Miller-Urey experiment and used a simplified apparatus with Tungsten electrodes. You heated the glassware at 500°C for 3 hours to remove any organic contaminants. Gases NH_3, CH_4, CO and H_2 were introduced followed by generating electric spark. Which of the essential ingredients did you forget to add?

A. O_2 B. H_2O
C. HCN D. CHO

Molecular Evolution

47. Given below are the few statements on concepts related to genome evolution.

(*a*) Presence of introns in some chloroplast genes suggests that endosymbiosis (leading to organelle evolution) occurred before loss of introns in prokaryotes and supports the hypothesis that genes originated as interrupted structures.
(*a*) Negative selection is associated with increased rate of nonsynonymous substitutions as compared to synonymous substitutions.
(*c*) Nucleotide substitution rates during evolution can be inferred from divergence of the sequences that are non-functional or neutral.
(*d*) Positive selection is associated with increased rate of nonsynonymous substitutions as compared to synonymous substitutions.

Which one of the following options represents a combination of all INCORRECT statements?

A. (*a*) and (*c*) only B. (*b*) and (*c*) only
C. (*a*) and (*b*) only D. (*c*) and (*d*) only

Speciation, Phylogenetic Study

48. A tree built using BLAST cannot be used to infer phylogenetic relationships. Given this, which of the following statements is NOT true about trees generated by BLAST?

A. It is based on a distance method, where alignment similarity scores are used to cluster sequences
B. It is an exhaustive tool where similar sequences are found by locating all matches between multiple sequences simultaneously.
C. The generated tree is unreliable because the algorithm is data base-dependent
D. It is built by first performance seeding following local alignments.

49. Given below are a few statements related to plant breeding and genetics:

(*a*) Non-random mating between individuals closely related to each other would tend to promote a decrease in homozygosity at all loci.
(*b*) Quantitative traits are typically influenced by environmental conditions to a greater extent than qualitative traits.
(*c*) The "over dominance theory for explanation of heterosis assumes that in a heterozygote, only one of the alleles plays a functional role.
(*d*) During domestication selected genes/traits show a decrease in diversity.

Which one of the following options represents a combination of all INCORRECT statements?

A. (*a*) and (*d*) only B. (*b*), (*c*) and (*d*)
C. (*a*) and (*c*) only D. (*b*) and (*d*) only

CSIR-NET, NOVEMBER (AFTERNOON), 2020

Concepts of Evolution, Timescale, Era & Major Event During Evolution

50. The term "abominable mystery" was used by Darwin in the context of origin and diversification of:

A. angiosperms
B. microorganisms
C. beetles
D. birds

51. If bird song is selected to maximize broadcast range and to minimise degradation, then according to the "Acoustic Adaptation Hypothesis" which of the following combination of features is likely to be shown by birds singing in dense forests?

A. Low frequency with narrow bandwidth
B. High frequency with narrow bandwidth
C. Low frequency with wide bandwidth
D. High frequency with wide bandwidth

52. According to Hamilton's rule, 'r' is the coefficient of relatedness between two interacting individuals, 'B' is the benefit to the recipient and 'C' is the cost to the donor. Which of the following relationships will result in an altruistic behavior?

A. $rB = C$ B. $rC - B = 0$
C. $r > C/B$ D. $rC - B > 0$

53. Creationism is rejected by evolutionary biologists because:

A. it offers no explanation about the origin of adaptation
B. it suggests that all species descended from a common ancestor
C. theologians have not settled on a date for the origin of life on earth
D. supernatural events have not been shown to be very common

54. Given below are proposed analogous structures among organisms.

(*a*) wings of birds and bats
(*b*) wings of bats and tetrapod digits
(*c*) tendrils of vitis and tendrils of pumpkin
(*d*) tubers of potatoes and sweet potatoes
(*e*) fins of fish and flippers of a whale

Which one of the following options correctly states the analogous structures?

A. (*a*), (*c*) and (*d*) B. (*b*), (*c*) and (*d*)
C. (*a*), (*c*) and (*e*) D. (*a*), (*d*) and (*e*)

Molecular Evolution

55. The figure below shows a gene duplication event followed by a divergence event in species 1 and 2.

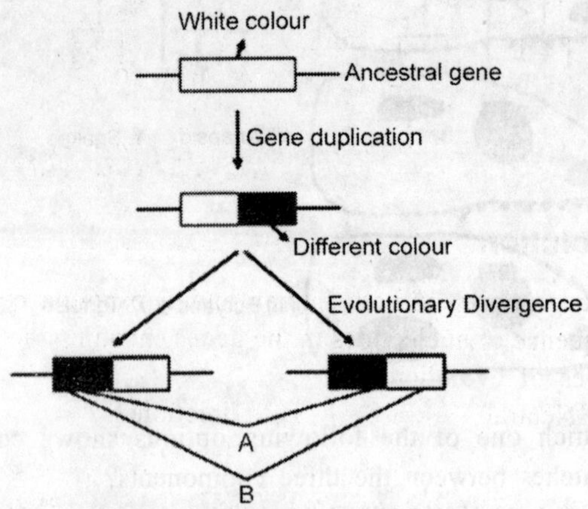

Based on the details given above determine what is represented by A and B

A. A : duplicated genes; B : ancestral genes
B. A : paralogs; B : ancestral genes
C. A : orthologs; B : paralogs
D. A : paralogs; B : orthologs

Speciation, Phylogenetic Study

56. Two populations of squirrels evolved across two regions separated by a large geographic barrier. Over a long period of time these populations are reproductively and geographically isolated from each other. This is an example of

A. sympatric speciation B. allopatric speciation
C. artificial speciation D. anagenesis

57. Felsenstein zone in a phylogenetic tree refers to a region of tree space where:

A. maximum likelihood would be inconsistent
B. lineages converge due to shared common ancestry
C. outgroups relationship is influential
D. maximum parsimony would be inconsistent

58. Distance matrix of five species A to E is given below.

	A	B	C	D	E
A	0				
B	2	0			
C	6	5	0		
D	10	4	8	0	
E	8	6	4	3	0

Which one of the following topologies represents the accurate species relationships among species A to E if UPGMA clustering method is used for the given data?

A. 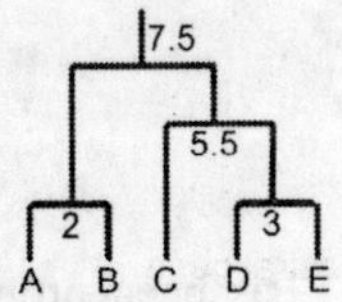

B. 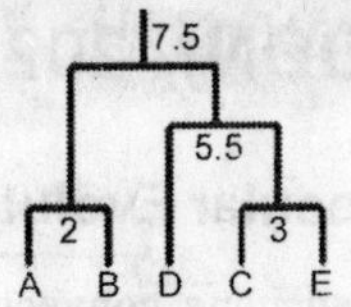

C. 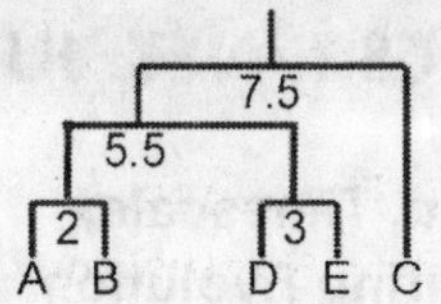

D. 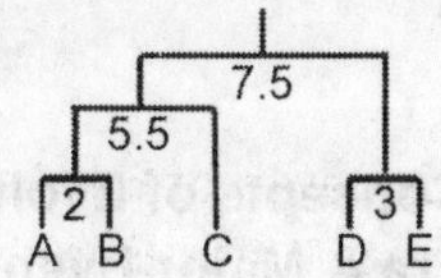

GATE (LIFE SCIENCE), 2020

Evolution

59. The genomes of both human and Drosophila code for an amylase that acts on the same substrate. However, the sequence of nucleotides in the genes encoding the two is dissimilar. This is an example of which ONE of the following types of evolution?

A. Neutral B. Directional C. Convergent D. Divergent

CSIR-NET, JUNE (MORNING), 2021

Concepts of Evolution, Timescale, Era & Major Event During Evolution

60. Consider the following four geological periods.

(*a*) Quaternary (*b*) Cretaceous
(*c*) Jurassic (*d*) Cambrian

Which one of the following options represents the correct arrangement of these geological periods from earliest to recent:

A. (*a*), (*b*), (*d*), (*c*) B. (*d*), (*c*), (*b*), (*a*)
C. (*c*), (*b*), (*d*), (*a*) D. (*b*), (*a*), (*c*), (*d*)

61. Mimicry where deceptiveness of the mimic's signal is high and fitness consequences signaled to the receiver by the mimic is also high (and negative) is:

A. Batesian mimicry B. Mullerian mimicry
C. Fisherian mimicry D. Millerian mimicry

62. Given below are the statements on living fossils. Select the correct statements:

A. Living fossils are the impressions of extant organism in old rocks
B. Living fossils show high morphological divergence from fossil records
C. Living fossils are always an evolutionary link between two classes of the organism
D. Living fossils are the organism that have remained unchanged for millions of years

Speciation, Phylogenetic Study

63. Eukaryotes are classified into S-6 super groups based on phylogenetic studies which one of the following statements about eurkaryotic Supercross is FALFS?

A. fungi and animals are more closely related to each other than either group is to plants
B. Amoebozoa and opisthokonts are unikonts
C. land plants and green algae belong to archaeplastida
D. alveolates and amoeba belong to same super group.

64. Select the correct statements related to phylogeny of primates.

A. Lemurs are more closely related to lorises than to gibbons.
B. Orangutans are closer to lorises than to gibbons.
C. Tarsiers are same as old world monkeys.
D. Humans are closer to new world monkeys than to orangutans.

65. A researchers is intrested in investigating if parentel investment (PI, penel A) by male seahorse and pipefishes is correleted with their mating patterns (MP-monogamy and polygamy, panel B). for this , the researcher builed a phylogenic tree of seahorsees and pipefishes and PI and MP scores on to the tree as shown in figure below.

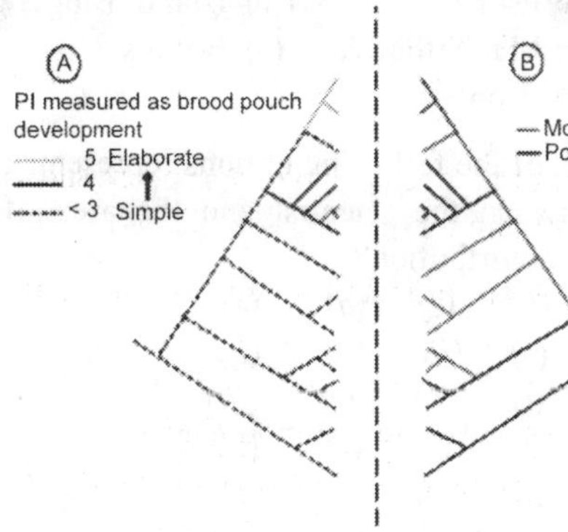

Based on the trees generated, which one of the following conclusions can the research correctly arrive at?

A. Polygamy is correlated with simpler brood pouches.
B. Monogamy is not correlated with elaborate brood pouches.
C. Monogamy is correlated with elaborate brood pouches.
D. Polygamy is correlated with elaborate brood pouches.

CSIR-NET, JUNE (AFTERNOON), 2021

Concepts of Evolution, Timescale, Era & Major Event During Evolution

66. Select the correct option that describes the below graph regarding length of bird's bill:

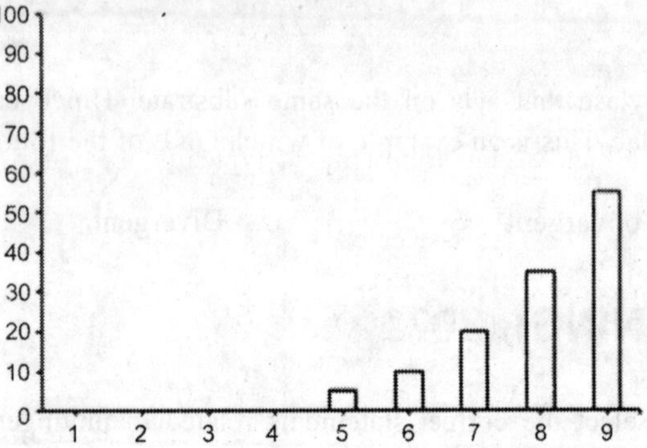

A. Neutral selection
B. Directional selection
C. Stabilizing selection
D. Mutational selection

67. Convergent evolution creates:
A. Analogous structures B. Homologous structures
C. Synapomorphies D. Pleiotropic structures

68. The table below enlists name of scientists and different areas of scientific contribution:

Scientists	Area of scientific contribution
(*a*) Alfred Wallace	(*i*) Sociobiology
(*b*) Konrad Lorenz	(*ii*) Theory of evolution
(*c*) Joseph Banks	(*iii*) Ethology
(*d*) E.O. Wilson	(*iv*) Island Biogeography
(*e*) Robert MacArthur & E.O. Wilson	(*v*) Botany

Which one of the following options represents a correct match between the scientist and the area of his/her scientific contribution?

	(*a*)	(*b*)	(*c*)	(*d*)	(*e*)
A.	(*iv*)	(*v*)	(*iii*)	(*ii*)	(*i*)
B.	(*v*)	(*i*)	(*ii*)	(*iv*)	(*iii*)
C.	(*iii*)	(*iv*)	(*i*)	(*v*)	(*ii*)
D.	(*ii*)	(*iii*)	(*v*)	(*i*)	(*iv*)

69. Match the organisms in column A with their status in Column B.

Column A	Column B
(*a*) Kallimodon	X. Fossil
(*b*) Tuatara	Y. Living fossil
(*c*) Xiphosura	
(*d*) Ankylosphenodon	

Identify the correct match:
A. A, C are X B. A, D are X
C. B, C are X D. A, B are X

Molecular Evolution

70. Biased gene convection (BCG) has been proposed to caused changes in allele frequency in a population. Select the statement that is NOT correct about BCG.
A. BCG is present in bacteria and eukaryotes suggesting it may be present in the last university Common Ancestor
B. BCG can favor the fixation of deleterious donor alleles
C. BCG is an example of nonadaptive evolutionary process
D. BCG selects against maladaptation resulting in fixation of only advantages mutations.

Speciation, Phylogenetic Study

71. Which of the following pairs of traits is most likely in a species when maternal investment is very high?
A. Multiple reproductive events and high maternal mortality
B. Slow developmental rates and low maternal fecundity
C. Few reproductive events and low maternal fecundity
D. Few reproductive events and high maternal mortality

72. According to the APG-IV (Angiosperm phylogeny group-IV) which of the following groups of angiosperms first diverged from the common ancestor of the angiosperm?
A. Nymphaeales
B. Monocots
C. Piperales
D. Ranunculales

73. A Researcher studying a cricket species finds that individuals on their side of a large river have different call frequencies on average. The following statement was made:
(*a*) The different call frequency may signals incipient speciation
(*b*) The change in call frequency can lead to allopatric speciation
(*c*) Individuals of one population transplanted to the other population may have lower chance of finding mates than residents
(*d*) Call frequencies have changed from ultrasound to infrasound across the river

If the call helps attract mates which of the above statements are correct?
A. (*a*), (*b*), (*c*) B. (*a*), (*c*), (*d*)
C. (*b*), (*c*), (*d*) D. (*a*), (*b*), (*d*)

GATE (LIFE SCIENCE), 2021

Evolution

74. The two homologous genes occurring in different species are called:
A. Paralogous B. Orthologous C. Pseudologous D. Prologous

CSIR-NET, SEPTEMBER (MORNING), 2022

Concepts of Evolution, Timescale, Era & Major Event During Evolution

75. The correct hierarchy of geological times is:
A eon > era > period > epoch
B. period > era > epoch
C. epoch > period > era > eon
D. era > eon > period

76. The biological species concept defines species as a group of populations that are reproductively isolated However, this definition is not applicable to groups where sexual reproduction has not been observed ye rare. Choose the correct option of organisms where biological species concept may therefore not apply:
A. Monocots and basal angiosperms
B. Ascomycetes and oligochaetes
C. Mosses and liverworts
D. Cyanobacteria and Euglenophyta

77. Any movie that features dinosaurs should also have which of the following combinations of geological age-appropriate organisms? Choose the correct combination.
A. Humans, angiosperms and gymnosperms, birds
B. Early diverging angiosperms, reptiles, amphibians
C. Apes, gymnosperms, birds
D. Early diverging gymnosperms, amphibians, reptiles

78. The following are selected plant apomorphies:
(*a*) Development of xylem
(*b*) Development of cuticle
(*c*) Development of independent sporophyte
(*d*) Development of eustele

Which option represents the correct evolutionary sequence of the above?
A. (*a*), (*d*), (*b*), (*c*) B. (*c*), (*a*), (*b*), (*d*)
C. (*b*), (*c*), (*a*), (*d*) D. (*c*), (*b*), (*d*), (*a*)

79. Which one of the following traits would hypothetically NOT be considered for preferential selection during the corresponding crops listed below?
A. Increased fruit size of tomato
B. Reduced spininess in okra
C. Shattering seeds of corn
D. Increased oil content of mustard

80. Which of the following is typically true of invasive species?
A. They are r-selected
B. They are K-selected
C. They are habitat specialists
D. They are always introduced by humans

81. The following statements were made about adaptive radiation:
(*a*) Adaptive radiation is a kind of divergent evolution driven by ecological diversification.
(*b*) Adaptive radiation is the divergence of unrelated taxa into different niches.
(*c*) Adaptive radiation is rare on archipelagos removed from the mainland.
(*d*) Processes unrelated to niche exploitation can be major drivers of species diversification.

Choose the option that represents all correct statements.
A. (*a*) and (*b*) B. (*c*) and (*d*)
C. (*b*) and (*c*) D. (*a*) and (*d*)

82. Individuals belonging to the fossil genera Calamites are considered to be upright arborescent plants. They were characterized by stems which mostly arose from subterranean rhizomes. The cross sections of young stems showed the presence of a central pith canal and collateral vascular bundles with carinal canals. To which of the following extent is this plant most similar?
A. Psilotum B. Selaginella
C. Equisetum D. Rhynia

83. The diagrams (*a*)-(*d*) below shows the relative abundance of major groups of plants (refer to legend) in fou geological periods (Devonian, Carboniferous, Tertiary and Cretaceous).

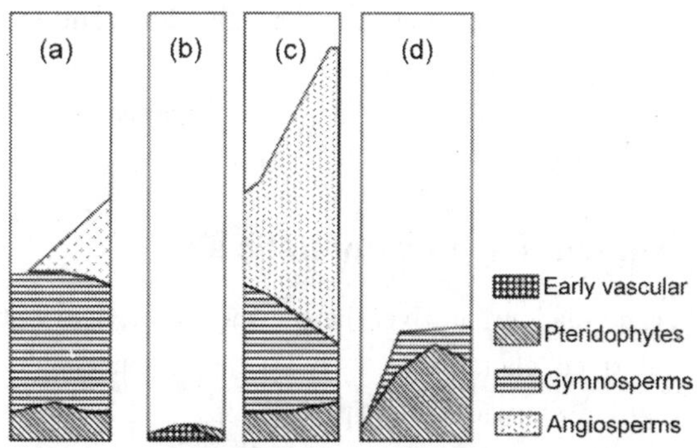

Match the diagrams (*a*) to (*d*) with the correct geological period:

A. (*a*) Tertiary (*b*) Carboniferous
(*c*) Devonian (*d*) Cretaceous

B. (*a*) Cretaceous (*b*) Devonian
(*c*) Tertiary (*d*) Carboniferous

C. (*a*) Tertiary (*b*) Cretaceous
(*c*) Carboniferous (*d*) Devonian

D. (*a*) Devonian (*b*) Tertiary
(*c*) Cretaceous (*d*) Carboniferous

84. The following table shows a list of evolutionary processes and their associated characteristics:

Evolutionary process	Characteristic
(*a*) Parallelism	(*i*) closely related groups evolve similar characteristics
(*b*) Convergence	(*ii*) individuals of different species crossbreed
(*c*) Introgression	(*iii*) crossbreeding between species is mediated by repeated backcrossing
(*d*) Hybridization	(*iv*) two or more distantly related groups acquire similar characteristics

Select the correct option that matches the evolutionary process to its salient characteristics:

	(*a*)	(*b*)	(*c*)	(*d*)
A.	(*iv*)	(*i*)	(*ii*)	(*iii*)
B.	(*i*)	(*iv*)	(*iii*)	(*ii*)
C.	(*iv*)	(*iii*)	(*i*)	(*ii*)
D.	(*iv*)	(*ii*)	(*iii*)	(*i*)

85. The following table lists major food crops and the region of domestication:

Food Crop	Region of Domestication
(*a*) Banana	(*i*) Africa
(*b*) Mung bean	(*ii*) India
(*c*) Sorghum	(*iii*) Indonesia
(*d*) Wheat	(*iv*) Middle East

Which one of the following option represents the correct match between the food crop and its region of domestication

	(*a*)	(*b*)	(*c*)	(*d*)
A.	(*ii*)	(*iii*)	(*i*)	(*iv*)
B.	(*iii*)	(*i*)	(*ii*)	(*iv*)
C.	(*iv*)	(*i*)	(*iii*)	(*ii*)
D.	(*ii*)	(*iv*)	(*iii*)	(*i*)

86. Which one of the following statements in relation to insect wings is NOT true?

A. Insect wings are extensions of cuticle and not true appendages
B. In beetles, the hind wings function in flight
C. Males of many cricket species have forewings modified to bear sound-producing structures
D. Flies have a structure called frenulum, which joins the forewing to the hind wing

CSIR-NET, SEPTEMBER (AFTERNOON, 2022

Concepts of Evolution, Timescale, Era & Major Event During Evolution

87. Pick the statement that includes both a proximate and an ultimate explanation for the evolution of a given behaviour.

A. Elevated heart beat and higher levels of stress hormone
B. Scent marking along boundaries of territories and high aggression
C. Social communication through odours and increased group survival
D. Higher maternal fitness and increased offspring survival

Speciation, phylogenetic study

88. The cladogram given below shows the distribution of derived characters (A to D) that define each of the group shown at the tip.

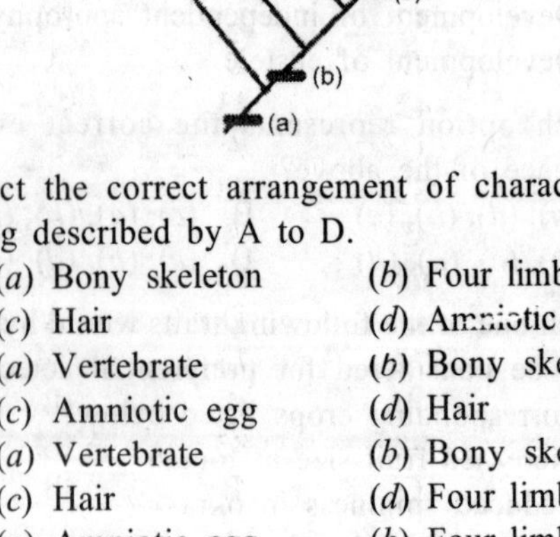

Select the correct arrangement of character that are being described by A to D.

A. (*a*) Bony skeleton (*b*) Four limbs
(*c*) Hair (*d*) Amniotic egg

B. (*a*) Vertebrate (*b*) Bony skeleton
(*c*) Amniotic egg (*d*) Hair

C. (*a*) Vertebrate (*b*) Bony skeleton
(*c*) Hair (*d*) Four limbs

D. (*a*) Amniotic egg (*b*) Four limbs
(*c*) Vertebrate (*d*) Hair

89. In the cladogram given below each nucleotide change is indicated by a black bar:

(*a*)

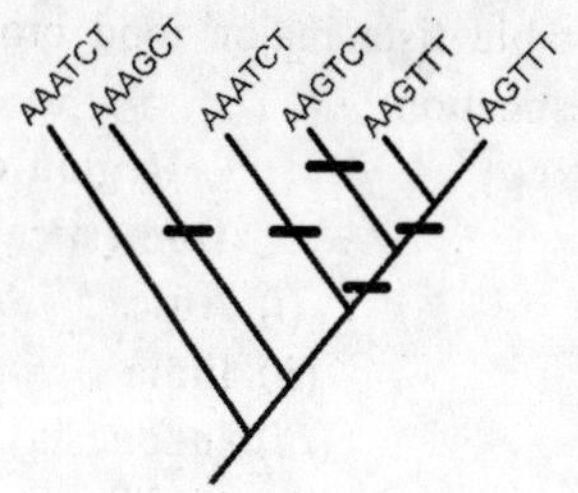

(*b*)

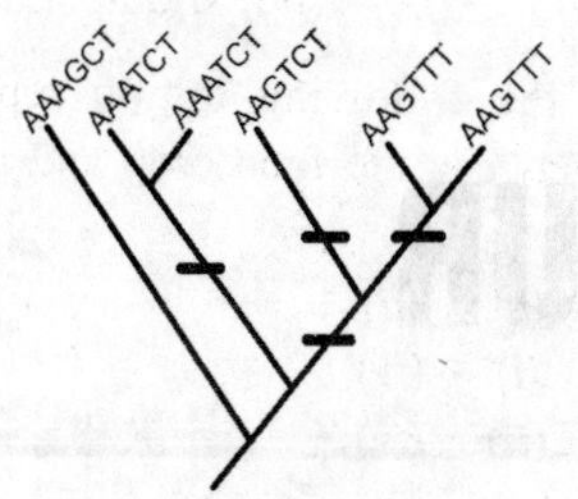

(*c*)

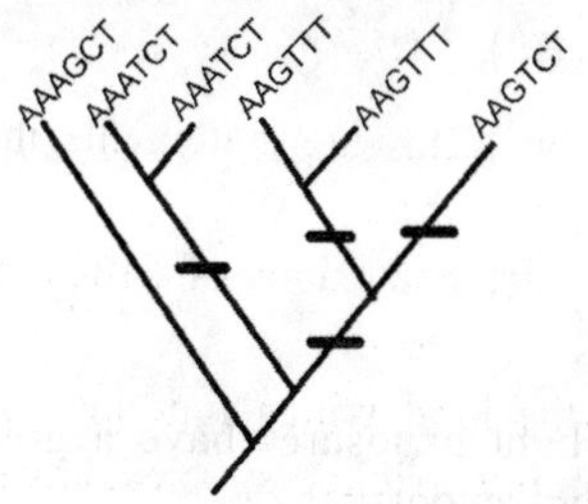

(*d*)

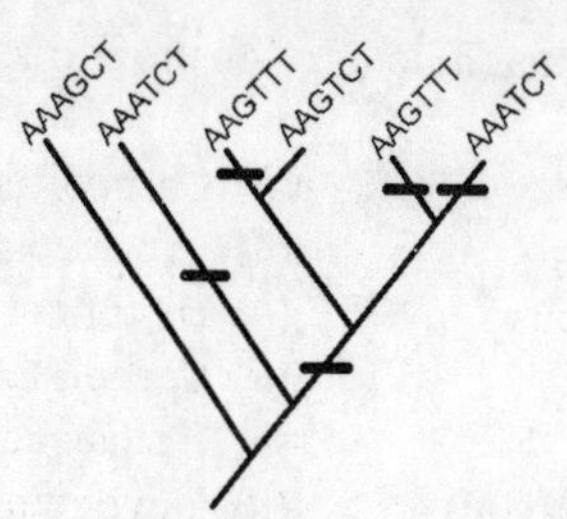

Which of the following options represents two equally most parsimonious tree?

A. (*a*) and (*b*)   B. (*b*) and (*c*)
C. (*c*) and (*d*)   D. (*a*) and (*d*)

90. The following statements explain various evolutionary outcomes:

(*a*) Within a lineage, organisms show a constant rate of extinction.
(*b*) Even in the absence of changing interactions, organisms are constantly evolving.
(*c*) Organisms with novel genotypes are at a selective disadvantage.
(*d*) Coevolution between two interacting species act to maintain genetic variation through time.

Which of the following combinations of the above statements are supported by the 'Red Queen hypothesis'?

A. (*a*) and (*d*)   B. (*a*) and (*b*)
C. (*b*) and (*c*)   D. (*c*) and (*d*)

GATE (BIOTECHNOLOGY), 2022

91. Which of the following conditions will contribute to the stability of a gene pool in a natural population?

P. Large population   Q. No net mutation   R. Non-random mating   S. No selection

A. P only   B. P and Q only   C. P and R only   D. P, Q and S only

ANSWERS

1	**2**	**3**	**4**	**5**	**6**	**7**	**8**	**9**	**10**
A	C	B	D	B	D	C	C	D	C
11	**12**	**13**	**14**	**15**	**16**	**17**	**18**	**19**	**20**
C	A	C	B	A	C	D	B	D	D
21	**22**	**23**	**24**	**25**	**26**	**27**	**28**	**29**	**30**
D	C	A	B	C	D	D	C	D	C
31	**32**	**33**	**34**	**35**	**36**	**37**	**38**	**39**	**40**
B	B	B	A	B	D	B	D	C	A
41	**42**	**43**	**44**	**45**	**46**	**47**	**48**	**49**	**50**
C	C	A	C	B	B	C	B	C	A
51	**52**	**53**	**54**	**55**	**56**	**57**	**58**	**59**	**60**
A	C	A	D	C	B	D	D	C	B
61	**62**	**63**	**64**	**65**	**66**	**67**	**68**	**69**	**70**
A	D	D	A	B	B	A	D	B	D
71	**72**	**73**	**74**	**75**	**76**	**77**	**78**	**79**	**80**
C	A	A	B	A	D	B	C	C	A
81	**82**	**83**	**84**	**85**	**86**	**87**	**88**	**89**	**90**
D	C	B	B	B	D	C	B	B	A
91									
D									

CHAPTER

19

ANIMAL BEHAVIOUR

CSIR-NET, JUNE, 2017

Animal Behaviour

1. The Western honey bee (*Apis mellifera*) collects nectar and pollen from flowers. The following are few hypotheses proposed to explain this behaviour in *A. mellifera*:
(*a*) In the past, those individuals that fed on nectar and pollen left more descendants than those who preferred only nectar or only pollen
(*b*) The sensory stimulus from taste receptors in the honey bees lead to a positive reinforcement to look for more of the same food
(*c*) The honey bee's nervous system is predisposed to like the sweet taste
(*d*) The ancestor of honey bee was dependant on some sugar and protein rich diet and the honey bees have inherited the same taste perception

Which of the following combination of ultimate hypotheses best explains the bee's feeding behaviour?
A. (*a*) and (*b*) B. (*b*) and (*c*)
C. (*a*) and (*d*) D. (*b*) and (*d*)

2. In circadian rhythm studies, following may be possible generalizations for the effectiveness of light entrainment to the day/night cycle:
(*a*) Shorter exposures have a greater effect than longer exposures
(*b*) Bright light exposures have a greater effect than dim light
(*c*) Intermittent light exposures have a greater effect than consistent exposures
(*d*) Dim light can affect entrainment relative to darkness

Which combination of the above statements is correct?
A. (*b*) and (*c*) only B. (*b*) and (*d*) only
C. (*a*), (*c*) and (*d*) D. (*a*), (*b*) and (*d*)

3. To understand the singing behaviour in songbirds, the following three characters were measured as shown in the graph:
(*a*) Territoriality rate (*b*) Female fertility rate
(*c*) Song rate

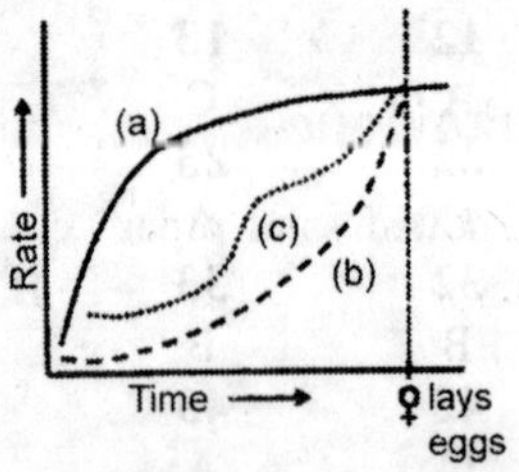

Which one of the following conclusions is most appropriate?
A. Male birds sing as a display of strength to rivals and to attract females
B. Male birds sing to display parental care behaviour
C Male birds sing only to display that females are sexually receptive
D. Male birds sing only to deter other male rivals from competing for territories

CSIR-NET, DECEMBER, 2017

Animal Behaviour

4. A barn owl sits on its perch 10 m above ground. It hears a mouse underneath on the ground at an angle α as shown in the figure below.

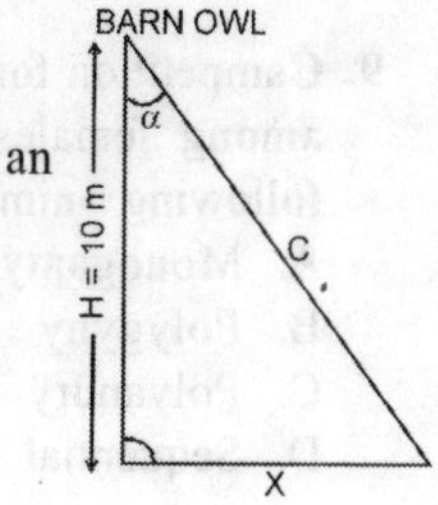

The error range with which it can locate the mouse on the ground is given by

A. tan α = X/H B. cos α = X/H C. sin α = X/H D. cos α = X/C

5. A 20-week old infant was exposed to the following stimuli and the responses were measured.

Stimuli	Mean No. of responses elicited
	100
	15
	25
	10

Based on the response patterns shown above to the given stimuli, select the correct theory that best describes the observed responses.

A. Heterogenous summation B. Gestalt principle C. Supernormal stimuli D. Sign stimulus

6. Orchids of the genus *Cryptostylis* are known to maintain reproductive isolation because their flowers look and smell like females of the wasps of genus *Lissopimpla*. When the male wasp visits and attempts to mate with the flower, the shape of anther and stigma allows correct placement and transfer of pollen to the wasp, which then transfers the pollen to species specific flower that it next attempts to mate with. This prezygotic barrier that prevents inter-species cross-pollination in *Cryptostylis* is best explained by:

A. Behavioural isolation through mimicry
B. Mechanical isolation through mimicry
C. Temporal isolation
D. Habitat isolation

GATE (LIFE SCIENCE), 2017

Animal Behaviour

7. A female "Spotted sand piper" courts males repeatedly. This behaviour can be explained by the term:

A. polyandry B. polygyny C. monogamy D. sexual cannibalism

CSIR-NET, JUNE, 2018

Animal Behaviour

8. Altruism describes a behaviour performed by animals that may be disadvantageous to self while benefitting others. Which one of the following statements is INCORRECT about altruism?

A. It is the net gain of direct fitness when sociality is facultative.
B. It is under positive selection via indirect fitness benefits that exceed direct fitness costs.
C. It generates indirect benefit by enhancing survivorship of kin.
D. It is favoured when rb – c > 0 where c is fitness cost to altruist, b is fitness benefit to recipient; and r is genetic relatedness.

CSIR-NET, DECEMBER, 2018

Animal Behaviour

9. Competition for mates and variance in fitness is higher among females than among males in which of the following animal mating systems?

A. Monogamy
B. Polygyny
C. Polyandry
D. Sequential monogamy

10. Four drugs (A, B, C, D) were used to disrupt a biological rhythm in experimental animals. The changes in the pattern of the biological rhythm as compared to untreated are shown below. The solid line represents the biological rhythm of the untreated and broken line represents that of the treated animals.

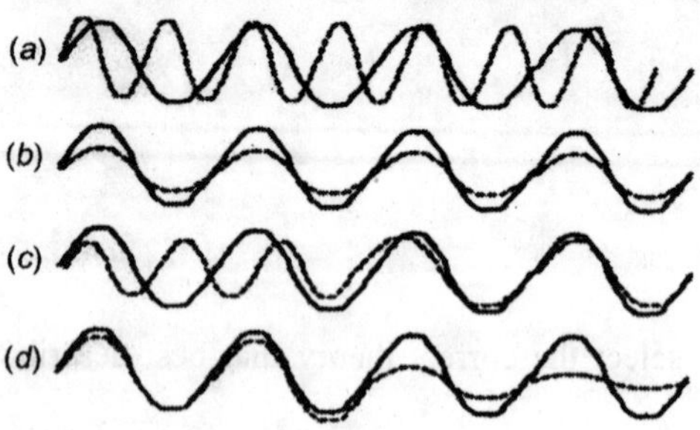

Which of the following interpretations from the above experiment is INCORRECT?

A. Drug (*a*) can be used to reduce the period length of the rhythm.
B. Drug (*b*) can be used for sustained lowering of amplitude of the rhythm without changing its period.
C Drug (*c*) can be used for sustained lowering of amplitude and period of the rhythm.
D. Drug (*d*) can be used to reduce the robustness and dampen out the rhythm.

11. A study tested the importance of learning mechanisms in the development of antipredator escape responses in tadpoles of a frog species. Tadpoles hatched from eggs in the lab were kept individually either with predator chemical cues (PRIOR EXPOSURE) or without predator chemical cues (NAIVE) for 1 week. These individuals were tested for their escape response when exposed to a live predator. They were tested either alone or together with 3 older experienced tadpoles. The graph below shows the escape response of the test individuals in the four different treatments.

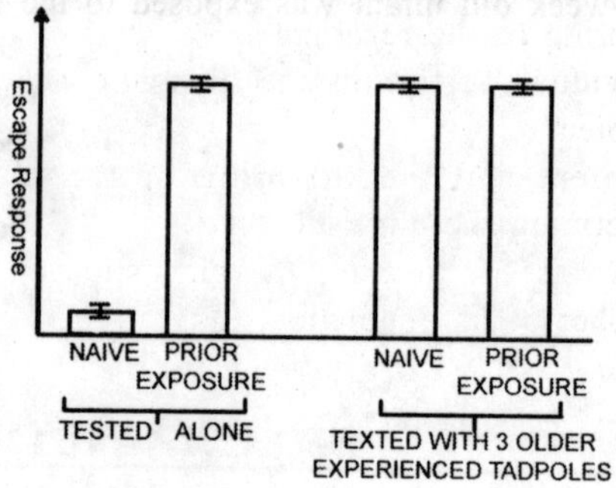

Some of the inferences drawn are given below:

(*a*) Prior exposure to predator cues is necessary for the development of escape response.
(*b*) Prior exposure to predator cues positively influences the development of escape response.
(*c*) The presence of older experienced individuals is necessary for the development of escape response.
(*d*) The presence of older experienced individuals positively influences the development of escape response.
(*e*) An individual with prior exposure and with older and experienced individuals showed the strongest escape response.

Which one of the following combination of statements represents the correct inference from the experiment?

A. (*a*) and (*c*)
B. (*b*) and (*d*)
C. (*a*) and (*d*)
D. (*a*), (*c*) and (*e*)

GATE (LIFE SCIENCE), 2018

Animal Behaviour

12. Match the organisms listed in Column I with the features listed in Column II.

Column I	Column II
(*a*) Tapeworm	(*i*) Bioluminescence
(*b*) Jellyfish	(*ii*) Viviparous
(*c*) Trichinella	(*iii*) Lateral heart
(*d*) Earthworm	(*iv*) Microvilli on the body surface

	(*a*)	(*b*)	(*c*)	(*d*)
A.	(*iii*)	(*i*)	(*iv*)	(*ii*)
B.	(*ii*)	(*iv*)	(*i*)	(*iii*)
C.	(*iv*)	(*i*)	(*ii*)	(*iii*)
D.	(*iv*)	(*iii*)	(*ii*)	(*i*)

13. An animal's ability to escape from a predator by using the explored knowledge of home area is an example of:

A. Latent learning
B. Insight learning
C. Mimicry
D. Imprinting

CSIR-NET, JUNE, 2019

Animal Behaviour

14. According to Hamilton's rule, altruistic behaviour can evolve when rb > c, where b is the extra benefit gained by the recipient as a result of the altruistic act, c is the cost to the actor arising from performing the altruistic act and r is the relatedness between the:

A. individual performing the altruistic act and the offspring of the recipient
B. individual performin the altruistic act and the recipient
C. recipient and the offspring of the individual performing the altruistic act
D. individual performing the altruistic act and the member of its population.

15. Given below are few traits and related functions:

TRAIT	FUNCTION
(*a*) Aposematism	(*i*) Acquiring food
(*b*) Basking	(*ii*) Avoiding predation
(*c*) Cooperative hunting	(*iii*) Territory defence
(*d*) Song	(*iv*) Thermoregulation

Match the above given traits to their most likely functions.

	(*a*)	(*b*)	(*c*)	(*d*)
A.	(*iii*)	(*iv*)	(*ii*)	(*i*)
B.	(*iv*)	(*ii*)	(*i*)	(*iii*)
C.	(*ii*)	(*iv*)	(*i*)	(*iii*)
D.	(*iii*)	(*i*)	(*iv*)	(*ii*)

CSIR-NET, 15 DECEMBER, 2019

Animal Behaviour

16. The ratio of variance in male mating success (V_m) to variance in female mating success (V_f) is strongly male biased ($V_m > V_f$) in species P, strongly female biased in species Q($V_f > V_m$) and similar in species R($V_m = V_f$). All else being equal, which one of the following matches between species and mating systems is most likely?

A. P-monogamy; Q-polyandry, R-polygyny
B. P-polyandry; Q-polygyny, R-monogamy
C. P-polygyny; Q-polyandry, R-monogamy
D. P-monogamy; Q-polygyny, R-polyandry

17. An interaction where the actor and the recipient both suffer a cost is referred to as:

A. Altruism B. Cooperation
C. Mutualism D. Spite

18. Which among the below sets of conditions are best suited for mimicry to be successful?

Condition	Abundance	Predators learn	Resource overlap
(*a*)	Mimic > Model	Yes	Yes
(*b*)	Model > Mimic	Yes	No
(*c*)	Mimic = Model	No	Yes
(*d*)	Model > Mimic	No	No

A. Condition (*a*) B. Condition (*b*)
C. Condition (*c*) D. Condition (*d*)

19. The top panel (graphs *a-c*) represents trends of number of sperms produced per mating season with respect to number of mates, while the bottom panel (graphs *i-iv*) represents trends of time invested in paternal care with respect to number of mates in birds.

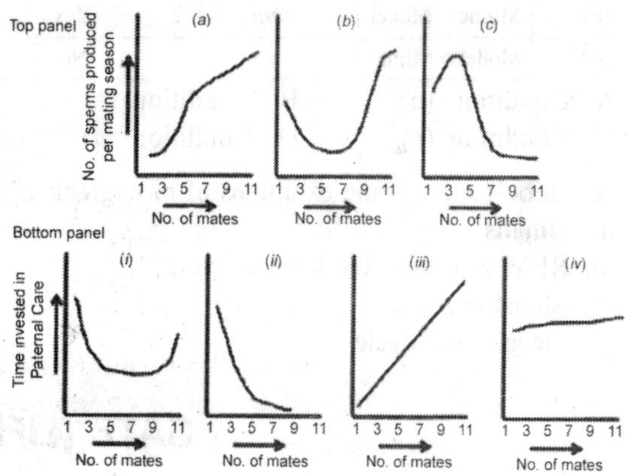

Select the correct trend from each panel.

A. (*c*), (*iv*) B. (*a*), (*ii*)
C. (*b*), (*iii*) D. (*a*), (*i*)

CSIR-NET, 27 DECEMBER, 2019

Animal Behaviour

20. The diagram below shows the frequency distribution of three closely related bird species based on their beak sizes, across three different habitat patches A, B and C. All the three species co-exist in habitat A, whereas only species 1 occurs in habitat B and species 2 occurs in habitat C.

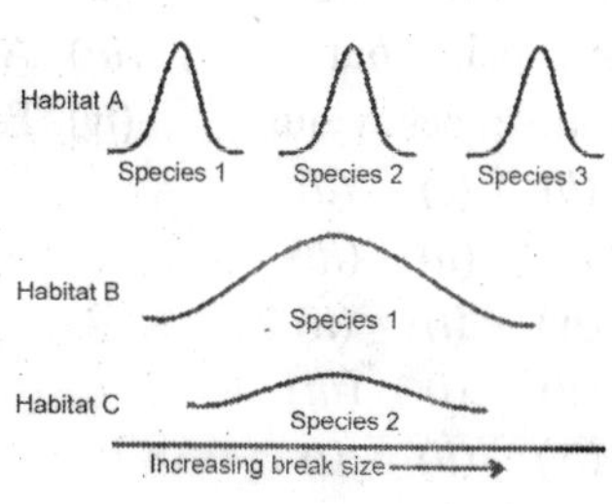

Which one of the following phenomena most appropriately explains the change in frequency distributions of species 1 and 2 in the figure given above?

A. Migration
B. Character displacement
C. Colonization
D. Succession

21. The mechanism by which ants find their way back to the nests after searching and finding food is:

A. Migration
B. Topographical mapping
C. Piloting
D. Path integration

22. Reproductive success of individuals in a population is likely to be skewed under all the following conditions, EXCEPT when

A. Females are choosy
B. male-male competition is intense
C. pair-bonding occurs in the species
D. Females prefer males with larger territories

23. Which among the following sets of conditions are best suited for a mimic species to coexist with its model?

Condition	Abundance	Predators learn	Resource overlap
(*a*)	Mimic > Model	Yes	Yes
(*b*)	Model > Mimic	Yes	No
(*c*)	Mimic = Model	No	Yes
(*d*)	Model > Mimic	No	No

A. Condition (*a*) B. Condition (*b*)
C. Condition (*c*) D. Condition (*d*)

24. Given below are some examples of biological rhythms in humans:

(*a*) REM and non-REM sleep cycle
(*b*) Menstrual cycle
(*c*) Sleep-wake cycle

Which one of the following is a correct representation of the type of biological rhythms given above?

A. (*a*) Ultradian cycle; (*b*) Infradian cycle; (*c*) Circadian cycle
B. (*a*) Circadian cycle; (*b*) Ultradian cycle; (*c*) Infradian cycle
C. (*a*) Infradian cycle; (*b*) Ultradian cycle; (*c*) Circadian cycle
D. (*a*) Infradian cycle; (*b*) Circadian cycle; (*c*) Ultradian cycle

25. Given below are examples of animals and their behaviours.

(*a*) Elephant: Innate and learnt behaviour
(*b*) Ant: Innate behaviour only
(*c*) Whale: Learnt behaviours only
(*d*) Bee: Innate and learnt behaviours

Which one of the following options represents a correct combination of true and false?

A. (*a*) True, (*b*) False, (*c*) False, (*d*) True
B. (*a*) True, (*b*) True, (*c*) True, (*d*) False
C. (*a*) False, (*b*) True, (*c*) True, (*d*) False
D. (*a*) True, (*b*) True, (*c*) True, (*d*) True

26. In a large, healthy, polygynous population of an ungulate species with distinct, short seasonal mating, the operational sex ratio (Male : Female) is likely to resemble which one of the following conditions:

A. Male > Female
B. Female ≥ Male
C. Male = Female
D. Female > Male

GATE (LIFE SCIENCE), 2019

Animal Behaviour

27. Match the respective behaviour given in Column I with the appropriate explanation in Column II:

Column I	Column II
(*a*) Agonistic behaviour	(*i*) Individual behaviour where fitness of other increases at the expense of self
(*b*) Hierarchical behaviour	(*ii*) Individual contribute towards enhancement of mutual fitness
(*c*) Altruistic behaviour	(*iii*) Aggressive behaviour of individuals within a population
(*d*) Cooperative behaviour	(*iv*) Existence of different level of dominance within a population

	(*a*)	(*b*)	(*c*)	(*d*)
A.	(*iv*)	(*i*)	(*ii*)	(*iii*)
B.	(*iii*)	(*iv*)	(*i*)	(*ii*)
C.	(*iv*)	(*ii*)	(*i*)	(*iii*)
D.	(*iii*)	(*iv*)	(*ii*)	(*i*)

CSIR-NET, NOVEMBER (MORNING), 2020

Animal Behaviour

28. The common cuckoo, a parasitic bird, lays eggs in the nests of other bird species. Soon after the cuckoo egg hatches, the chick shoves the nest owners' eggs out of the nest. This is an example of:
A. habituation B. imprinting C. innate behaviour D operant conditioning

CSIR-NET, NOVEMBER (AFTERNOON), 2020

Animal Behaviour

29. In mammals, the primary circadian clock is located in which of the following parts of the brain?
A. Occipital lobe of cerebrum B. Amygdala
C. Suprachiasmatic nucleus D. Frontal lobe of cerebrum

GATE (LIFE SCIENCE), 2020

Animal Behaviour

30. Round dance" is performed by forager bees to indicate the distance between a food source and their colony. Which ONE of the following best represents the distance?
A. 45 meters B. 450 meters C. 1000 meters D. More than 2000 meters

CSIR-NET, JUNE (MORNING, 2021

Animal Behaviour

31. In the table below, Column 1 describes movement of organisms and columns 2 describes the type of movement.

Column 1	Column 2
(*a*) A silk moth flies at an angle perpendicular to the direction of the wind to pick up a scent trail	(*i*) Mnemotaxis
(*b*) Bacteria burrow down into mud in the northern hemisphere in response to the earth's magnetic field	(*ii*) Klinotaxis
(*c*) A girl reaches her school using a pharmacy and a bookshop as landmark	(*iii*) Magnetotaxis
(*d*) Planaria move towards the direction of higher concentration of food by comparing the gradient of stimuli around it.	(*iv*) Menotaxis

Which one of the foılowing options represent the correct match of column 1 with column 2.

	(*a*)	(*b*)	(*c*)	(*d*)
A.	(*iv*)	(*iii*)	(*i*)	(*ii*)
B.	(*iv*)	(*iii*)	(*ii*)	(*i*)
C.	(*i*)	(*iii*)	(*iv*)	(*ii*)
D.	(*i*)	(*ii*)	(*iii*)	(*iv*)

CSIR-NET, JUNE (AFTERNOON), 2021

Animal Behaviour

32. Eusocial societies are NOT characterized by which of the following?
A. Altruism B. Kin selection
C. Guarding against intruders D. Equal reproductive opportunities

33. Which of the following is NOT the function of dispersal behavior in which organism move away from their natal homes?
A. Tracking resource availability B. Provide mating opportunities
C. Preventing species extinction D. Avoiding pathogens

GATE (LIFE SCIENCE), 2021

Animal Behaviour

34. The term innate behaviour is a sort of animal behaviour that is:
A. triggered by an environmental change
B. learnt by hit-and-trial approach
C. trained and taught by the parent
D. fixed developmentally at the genetic level

CSIR-NET, SEPTEMBER (MORNING), 2022

35. The measurement of distance based on counting steps or number of vertical bars by insects for navigation is called:
A. path integration
B. allocentric coding
C. odometry
D. alignment image-matching

36. Which one of the following statements best describes Bateman's principle?
A. Female gametes (eggs) are costlier than male gametes (sperms)
B. Reproductive variance is greater in males than in females
C. Females are more likely to provide parental care than males
D. Males use costly displays to advertise their genetic quality

37. A researcher examined the features of newly hatched birds. Species A showed open eyes, down feathers and was able to move around. Species B lacked down feathers and was incapable of walking and its eyes were closed. Given this, choose the correct option
A. Species A is altricial and species B is precocial
B. Species A is precocial and species B is altricial
C. Species A and B are both precocial
D. Species A and B are both altricial

38. The following table shows a list of organisms and associated adaptive characteristics.

Organism	Adaptive characteristics
(*a*) Coral snake	(*i*) Bioluminescence
(*b*) Crystal Jelly	(*ii*) Mimicry
(*c*) African lungfish	(*iii*) Aposematism
(*d*) Monarch butterflies	(*iv*) Aestivation

Select the correct option that matches the name of the organism with their correct adaptation:

	(*a*)	(*b*)	(*c*)	(*d*)
A.	(*ii*)	(*i*)	(*iv*)	(*iii*)
B.	(*iii*)	(*ii*)	(*i*)	(*iv*)
C.	(*ii*)	(*iii*)	(*iv*)	(*i*)
D.	(*iv*)	(*i*)	(*ii*)	(*iii*)

CSIR-NET, SEPTEMBER (AFTERNOON), 2022

39. Which of the following life history traits is most likely in a rodent species when snakes prefer to prey upon large, older individuals of the rodent species that grow continuously over their lifespan?
A. Early reproduction and slow growth rate
B. Delayed reproduction and fast growth rate
C. Delayed reproduction and slow growth rate
D. Early reproduction and fast growth rate

40. Sexually reproducing organisms employ signals to attract mates. If such signals honestly reflect an individual's quality, then which of the following is expected?
A. Organisms in poor metabolic condition signal more.
B. Organisms in poor metabolic condition signal less.
C. Organisms will not modulate signalling behaviour with metabolic condition.
D. Organisms in good metabolic condition will signal less.

GATE (LIFE SCIENCE), 2022

Animal Behaviour

41. Which one of the following animals develops adaptive predator avoidance morphology because of the presence of high predator number in its habitat?
A. Daphnia sp. B. Scaphiopus sp. C. Wolbachia sp. D. Rhodnius sp.

42. Match the animal inactivity behaviors listed in Column I with representative animals in Column II and their definitions listed in Column III.

Column I	Column II	Column III
(*a*) Torpor body temperature	(*i*) Australian burrowing frogs	P. Prolonged period of inactivity without reducing
(*b*) Hibernation periods of dryness	(*ii*) Polar Bears	Q. Inactivity period which accompanies extended
(*c*) Winter sleep temperature occuring in daily activity cycles	(*iii*) Ground Squirrels	R. Decreased metabolism with lowered body
(*d*) Aestivation for weeks or months	(*iv*) Hummingbirds	S. Decreased metabolism and lower body temperature

	(*a*)	(*b*)	(*c*)	(*d*)
A.	(*ii*)-R	(*iv*)-Q	(*i*)-P	(*iii*)-S
B.	(*iv*)-R	(*iii*)-S	(*ii*)-P	(*i*)-Q
C.	(*iv*)-R	(*ii*)-Q	(*i*)-P	(*iii*)-S
D.	(*iv*)-Q	(*i*)-R	(*ii*)-S	(*iii*)-P

ANSWERS

1	2	3	4	5	6	7	8	9	10
C	B	A	A	A	B	A	A	C	C
11	**12**	**13**	**14**	**15**	**16**	**17**	**18**	**19**	**20**
B	C	A	B	C	C	D	B	B	B
21	**22**	**23**	**24**	**25**	**26**	**27**	**28**	**29**	**30**
D	C	B	A	A	A	B	C	C	A
31	**32**	**33**	**34**	**35**	**36**	**37**	**38**	**39**	**40**
A	D	C	D	C	B	B	A	A	B
41	**42**								
A	B								

CHAPTER

20

STATISTICAL METHOD

CSIR-NET, JUNE, 2017

1. The pH of a solution is 7.4 ± 0.02 where 0.02 is standard deviation obtained from eight measurements. If more measurements were carried out, the % of samples whose pH would fall between pH 7.38 and 7.42 is:

A. 99.6 B. 95.4

C. 68.2 D. 99.8

2. Given below are a set of statistical methods/parameters (Column A) and their potential applications/utility in biological, research (column B), in a random manner.

Column A		Column B
(*a*) Variance	(*i*)	Measure strength of association between two variables
(*b*) Correlation coefficient	(*ii*)	Prediction of value of a dependent variable based on known value of an associated variable
(*c*) Regression analysis	(*iii*)	Calculation of deviation between observed and expected values
(*d*) Chi-square analysis	(*iv*)	Calculate the spread of a distribution

Which of the following options is a correct match of entries in Column A and B?

	(*a*)	(*b*)	(*c*)	(*d*)
A.	(*ii*)	(*iv*)	(*i*)	(*iii*)
B.	(*iii*)	(*ii*)	(*iv*)	(*i*)
C.	(*iv*)	(*i*)	(*ii*)	(*iii*)
D.	(*i*)	(*iii*)	(*ii*)	(*iv*)

DBT-JRF, 2017

3. From literature it is known that the length of an *E. coli* bacterium is 1 μm with a standard deviation of 0.1 μm. After treatment with chemical "X" the mean length of 100 cells is 1.1 μm with a standard deviation of 0.1 μm. What will you conclude from this experiment?

A. Treatment with chemical "X" has increased the length with a statistical confidence of more than 99%

B. The length has increased with statistical confidence of 67%

C. Length has not increased and the observed difference is due to statistical error

D. Length increased can be claimed with 95% statistical confidence.

GATE (BIOTECHNOLOGY), 2017

4. Standard error is:

A. the probability of a type I error in a statistical test.

B. the error in estimating a sample standard deviation.

C. the standard deviation of a variable that follows standard normal distribution.

D. the standard deviation of distribution of sample means.

CSIR-NET, JUNE, 2018

5. Following are statements to depict relationship among measures of central tendency in a skewed dataset

(*a*) In positively skewed datasets, mean > median > mode
(*b*) In positively skewed datasets, mode > median > mean
(*c*) In negatively skewed datasets, mean > median > mode
(*d*) In negatively skewed datasets, mode > median > mean

Which of the above statements are TRUE?

A. (*a*) and (*b*)
B. (*a*) and (*c*)
C. (*b*) and (*d*)
D. (*a*) and (*d*)

CSIR-NET, DECEMBER, 2018

6. Choose the correct answer from the statements indicated below:

A. Chi square test is parametric.
B. Non-parametric test assumes normal distribution.
C. Results can be significantly affected by outliers in a parametric test.
D. Non-parametric test is more powerful as compared to parametric test.

7. Given below are names of statistical distribution (Column I) and their characteristic features (Column II)

Column I	Column II
(*a*) Binomial distribution	(*i*) Each observation represents one of two outcomes (success or failure)
(*b*) Poisson distribution	(*ii*) Probability that is symmetric about the mean
(*c*) Normal distribution	(*iii*) Probability of a given number of events happening in a fixed interval of time

Which one of the following represents a correct match between columns I and II?

	(*a*)	(*b*)	(*c*)
A.	(*ii*)	(*i*)	(*iii*)
B.	(*i*)	(*ii*)	(*iii*)
C.	(*i*)	(*iii*)	(*ii*)
D.	(*iii*)	(*ii*)	(*i*)

CSIR-NET, JUNE, 2019

8. Which one of the following statements regarding normal distribution is NOT correct?

A. It is symmetric around the mean
B. It is symmetric around the median
C. It is symmetric around the variance
D. It is symmetric around the mode

CSIR-NET, 15 DECEMBER, 2019

9. A researcher samples n individuals randomly from a population of blackbuck and identifies their sex. The number of females in the sample follows:

A. an exponential distribution
B. a binomial distribution
C. a Poisson distribution
D. a normal distribution

10. Female fiddler crabs prefer male fiddler crabs with larger claws over males with smaller claws. If the selection pressure exerted is strong resulting in a skewed distribution of claw size, which of the following statements is true about the population's mean, median and mode?

A. Mean > Median > Mode
B. Mean < Median < Mode
C. Mean = Mode < Median
D. Mean = Median = Mode

CSIR-NET, 27 DECEMBER, 2019

11. Male fiddler crabs with larger claws are preferred by females over males with smaller claws. If the selection pressure exerted on claw size is strong, which one of the following options is true with respect to male claw size over generations?

A. Mean >Median > Mode
B. Mean < Median < Mode
C. Mean = Mode < Median
D. Mean = Median = Mode

12. Following are statements related to statistical methods:

(*a*) An outlier can be defined as a value in a data set that lies more than three standard deviations from the mean.
(*b*) Measures of central tendency and dispersion are independent of the presence of outliers in a data set.
(*c*) Standard deviation is a measure of dispersion.
(*d*) Mean, median and mode are not measure of central tendency.

Which one of the following options is a combination with both INCORRECT statements?

A. (*a*) and (*b*) B. (*b*) and (*c*)
C. (*a*) and (*c*) D. (*b*) and (*d*)

13. Given below are sampling techniques and their features.

Sampling technique	Features
(*a*) Stratified sampling	(*i*) Population is divided into groups/clusters and a sample of groups/clusters is chosen using a probability method
(*b*) Systematic sampling	(*ii*) Population is divided into groups/clusters and within each group/cluster, a probability sample is selected from it.
(*c*) Opportunity sampling	(*iii*) Only participants available and willing to participate are used.
(*d*) Clustered sampling	(*iv*) Samples are selected at regular intervals from the population

Which one of the following options correctly matches sampling techniques with their features?

	(*a*)	(*b*)	(*c*)	(*d*)
A.	(*ii*)	(*i*)	(*iv*)	(*iii*)
B.	(*ii*)	(*iv*)	(*iii*)	(*i*)
C.	(*i*)	(*iv*)	(*iii*)	(*ii*)
D.	(*i*)	(*iv*)	(*ii*)	(*iii*)

CSIR-NET, NOVEMBER (MORNING), 2020

14. The table given below shows the Lod score values of three different pairs of genes studied for assessing if they are linked pairs:

	Gene Pair '1'	Gene Pair '2'	Gene Pair '3'
Lod score	1	2	3

The following conclusions were made from the data given above:

(*a*) For gene pair 1 the probability of the genes being linked is 10 times more likely than them assorting independently.
(*b*) For gene pair 2, the Lod score 2 indicates that the probability of the genes being linked is twice more likely than assorting independently.
(*c*) The genes of pair 1 and 2, can both be considered as linked, while the genes of pair 3 exhibits independent assortment.
(*d*) The genes of pair 3 can be considered as linked.

Which one of the following options represents statement(s) that is/are correct?

A. (*a*) and (*c*) B. (*b*) and (*d*)
C. (*a*) and (*d*) D. (*a*) and (*b*)

15. Given below are a few statistical terms in Column A and their related features and terms in Column B.

Column A	Column B
(*a*) Standard deviation	(*i*) Measure of relative variability of given populations.
(*b*) Coefficient	(*ii*) Used to make inferences about population means
(*c*) Chi-square test	(*iii*) Positive square root of population variance
(*d*) t-Test	(*iv*) Test hypothesis related to categorical data from inheritance studies

Which one of the options given below correctly matches all items of Columns A and B?

	(*a*)	(*b*)	(*c*)	(*d*)
A.	(*iv*)	(*iii*)	(*ii*)	(*i*)
B.	(*ii*)	(*iv*)	(*i*)	(*iii*)
C.	(*iii*)	(*i*)	(*iv*)	(*ii*)
D.	(*ii*)	(*i*)	(*iv*)	(*iii*)

CSIR-NET, NOVEMBER (AFTERNOON), 2020

16. In the two graphs given below, what do a, b and c refer to:

(i) Positive skew

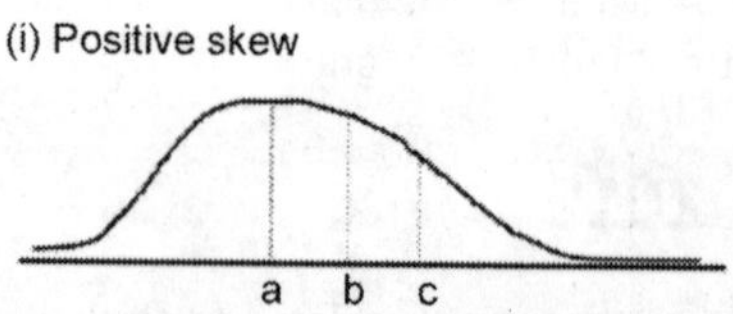

(ii) Negative skew

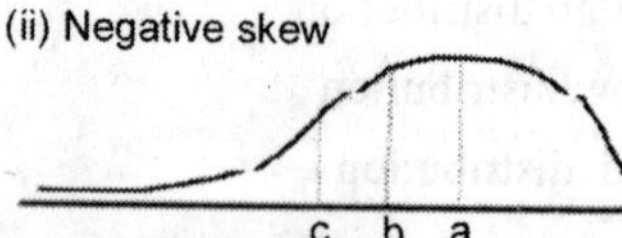

A. a = mean, b = median, c = mode
B. a = median, b = mode, c = mean
C. a = mode, b = median, c = mean
D. a – mean, b = mode, c = median

CSIR-NET, JUNE (MORNING), 2021

17. Which one of the following statements is correct?

A. If a transgenic plant heterozygous for an insert segregates into 1 : 1 ratio for the transgenic phenotype on back-crossing then it contains two unlinked copies of the insert.
B. ANOVA allows a plant breeder to test whether measurements from three or more treatments show statistically significant differences.
C. Comparative genomics allows scientists to identify regions of collinearity but not synteny between different species.

D. For genetic mapping of a quantitative trait in plants, an RIL mapping population comprising of individuals that are heterozygous at most loci is preferred

18. The following represents an equation for Bayesian statistics:

$$\underset{\uparrow \atop (A)}{P(H|E)} = \frac{\overset{(B) \atop \downarrow}{P(H)}\ \ \overset{(C) \atop \downarrow}{P(E|H)}}{\underset{\uparrow \atop (D)}{P(E)}}$$

Which one of the following option correctly represents A, B, C and D in the above equation?

A. A-Evidence, B-Posterior probability, C-Likelihood, D-Prior probability
B. A-Likelihood, B-Prior probability C-Posterior probability D-Evidence
C. A-Posterior probability, B-Prior probability, C-Likelihood, D-Evidence
D. A-Prior probability, B-Evidence, C-Posterior probability, D-Likelihood

19. From the steps listed below, some are used to evaluate the goodness of fit using the chi-square test :

(*a*) The mean, variance and standards deviation are calculated

(*b*) Variance calculated using $\dfrac{\Sigma(x_1 - \bar{x})^2}{n-1}$

(*c*) Test statistic calculated using $\dfrac{\overset{n-1}{\Sigma(\text{observed} - \text{expected})^2}}{\text{expected}}$

(*d*) The degree of freedom is calculated as $n - 1$, where n is the no. of ways in which the expected classes are free to vary

(*e*) The probability value is obtained

Which one of the following options provides correct sequence of steps in the statistical analysis?

A. (*a*), (*c*), (*d*)
B. (*c*), (*d*), (*e*)
C. (*b*), (*a*), (*d*)
D. (*a*), (*d*), (*e*)

CSIR-NET, JUNE (AFTERNOON), 2021

20. The following statements were made describing the properties of a UPGMA tree (Unweighted Pair Group Method with Arithmetic Mean):

(*a*) It describes species relationships and is therefore the best method to describe a new species.
(*b*) It is a method of hierarchical clustering.
(*c*) The raw data is a similarity matrix and the initial tree is rooted.
(*d*) It permits lineages with largely different branch lengths and corrections for multiple substitutions.

Which one of the following options represents the correct properties ?

A. (*a*) and (*b*)
B. (*b*) and (*c*)
C. (*a*) and (*d*)
D. (*c*) and (*d*)

21. Select the option that represent the correct combination of non-parametric test and its equivalent parametric test respectively that can be used to compare two or more group:

A. Wilcoxon Rank sum Test and Paired t-Test
B. Wilcoxon Rank sum test and spearman correlation
C. Spearman correlation and Kruskal Walis
D. Mann Whitney U testand pearson correlation

22. Find the linear regression equation for the following data pairs given in the below table:

x	0	2	4	6	8	10	12	14
y	2	8	14	20	26	32	38	44

A. $Y = 4x + 0$
B. $Y = 3x + 2$
C. $Y = 6x + 2$
D. $Y = 0.33 + 2$

23. If the weights of 10,000 seeds from 100 individuals of a tree species are measured, which one of the following is expected?

A. Binomial
B. Poisson
C. Gaussian
D. No predictable distribution

DBT-JRF, 2021

24. Which one of the following will be used to assess structural similarity of biomolecules?

A. E-value
B. P-value
C. Root mean square deviation
D. Standard deviation

CSIR-NET, SEPTEMBER (AFTERNOON), 2022

25. The information obtained by comparing a new diagnostic test with the gold standard is summarized in a two-by-two table given below:

Column X	Gold standard Disease present	Gold standard Disease absent
New test positives	68(true positives)	22(false positives)
New test negatives	32(false negatives)	78(true negatives)

A. Sensitivity = 76%; Specificity = 71%
B. Sensitivity = 32%; Specificity = 22%
C. Sensitivity = 68%; Specificity = 78%
D. Sensitivity = 34%; Specificity = 39%

26. What can you infer if the correlation coefficient, [Pearson correlation (*r*)], is close to –1 (minus 1) for two set of variables?
A. There is no relationship between the two variables
B. There is an exponential relationship between the two variables
C. There is a linear relationship in which when there is a decrease in one variable, there is also, a decrease in the second variable.
D. There is a linear relationship in which, when there is an increase in one variable, there is a decrease in the second variable.

27. The graph below shows the accumulation of species in two sites A and B as more plots are sampled.

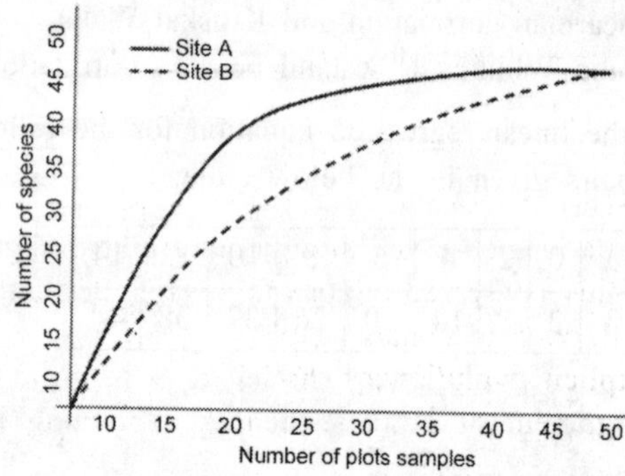

Based on the graph, following statements were made:
(*a*) In both sites, sampling more plots will not add any more species.
(*b*) Sampling more plots will add more species in site B but not site A.
(*c*) Site A and B are likely to have similar species richness.
(*d*) Site B is likely to have higher species richness than site A.

Which one of the following options contains both statements that are incorrect:
A. (*a*) and (*c*)
B. (*a*) and (*b*)
C. (*b*) and (*c*)
D. (*c*) and (*d*)

28. Given below are a list of statistical terms in Column A and associated properties/features/descriptions in Column B.

Column A	Column B
(*a*) ANOVA	(*i*) Quantify errors in count data
(*b*) Poisson distribution	(*ii*) Pointedness of a frequency distribution
(*c*) Standard error	(*iii*) Comparison of means of two or more samples
(*d*) Kurtosis	(*iv*) Dispersion of repeated sample means around the true value

Which one of the options given below is the most appropriate match between entries of Column A with those of Column B?

	(*a*)	(*b*)	(*c*)	(*d*)
A.	(*ii*)	(*i*)	(*iv*)	(*iii*)
B.	(*ii*)	(*iii*)	(*iv*)	(*i*)
C.	(*iii*)	(*i*)	(*iv*)	(*ii*)
D.	(*iv*)	(*iii*)	(*ii*)	(*i*)

29. The distribution of heights of college students aged between 18 to 20 was found approximately normally distributed with an average (mean) of 54 inches and a standard deviation of 2.5 inches. What will be the *z*-score for a student who is five feet tall? (ID-213)
A. 2.4
B. 3.1
C. 1.5
D. 2.9

ANSWERS

1	2	3	4	5	6	7	8	9	10
C	C	A	D	D	C	C	C	B	B
11	**12**	**13**	**14**	**15**	**16**	**17**	**18**	**19**	**20**
B	D	B	C	C	C	B	C	B	B
21	**22**	**23**	**24**	**25**	**26**	**27**	**28**	**29**	
A	B	C	C	C	D	A	C	A	

CHAPTER

21

BIOINFORMATICS

DBT-JRF, 2017

1. Select the best algorithm to do pairwise alignment when two proteins are very different in length.

A. Smith-Waterman
B. Needleman-Wunsch
C. dot-matrix
D. ClustalW

2. Which one of the following is NOT a structure or structurally derived database?

A. PDB B. PROSITE
C. SCOP D. CATH

3. Which of the following is TRUE?

In the threading approaches for prediction of protein structure, the optimization is used for:

A. Sequence to sequence alignment
B. Generation of profile by converting three-dimensional structure to one-dimensional string
C. Alignment of sequence to structure which minimizes energy of the target sequence in the template fold
D. Alignment of target sequence to one-dimensional profile of a template fold

4. The statistical significance of the BLAST hit is obtained using:

A. extreme value distribution
B. normal distribution
C. Poisson distribution
D. random distribution

5. The estimates of number of false positives from a BLAST search can be made using:

A. Percent positives B. Percent identity
C. E value D. Bit score

6. A scoring function is used in which one of the following drug design technologies?

A. QSAR
B. Molecular docking
C. Molecular dynamics
D. Pharmacophore mapping

7. BLOSUM matrices are based on:

A. mutations observed throughout a global alignment
B. highly conserved regions in a series of alignments forbidden to contain gaps
C. explicit evolutionary model
D. alignment of same sequences containing highly mutable regions

8. ProDom is a comprehensive set of protein domain families automatically generated from:

A. Pfam
B. UniProt Knowledge Database
C. Swiss-prot
D. InterPro

9. Which one of the following methods used to find evolutionary trees is also referred as "the minimum evolution method"?

A. Distance Method
B. Maximum Parsimony Method
C. Fitch and Margoliash Method
D. UPGMA Method

10. Z-score =
A. (score of alignment–mean)/(standard deviation)
B. (variance-score of alignment)/standard deviation
C. (mean-score of alignment)/standard deviation
D. (score of alignment-mean)/standard deviation

11. For a homology search program such as BLAST, which one of the following best describes the scoring pattern?
A. identical residue = 10 pts, conservative substitution = 5 pts, gap = 0 pts
B. identical residue = 10 pts, conservative substitution = 1 to 9 pts, gap = –3 pts
C. identical residue = 10 pts, conservative substitution = 1 to 9 pts, gap = 0 pts
D. identical residue = 10 pts, conservative substitution = 10 pts, gap = –3 pts

12. Given the results of a 'sequence versus fingerprint' search, which of the following would be considered
A. Motifs : 7 of 7 p-value : 2.2e-08 & e-value : 4.5e-05
B. Motifs : 8 of 8 p-value : 2.2e-08 & e-value : 4.5e-05
C. Motifs : 8 of 8 p-Value : 2.2e-18 & e-value : 4.5e-15
D. Motifs : 7 of 8 p-Value : 2.2e-18 & e-value : 4.5e-15

13. In a sequence logo of the type given below, the sizes of the letters are proportional to the:

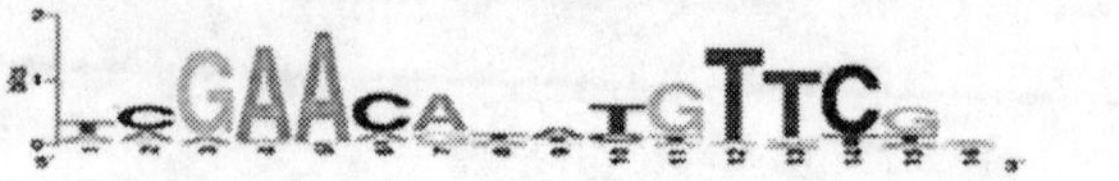

A. number of residues in the sequences
B. information content of the respective residues
C. frequencies of the respective residues in the sequences
D. resolution of the output device (terminal/printer)

DBT-JRF, 2018

14. Two sequences of comparable length have several regions that align locally but are separated by other regions that align poorly. Which algorithm can be used to find the highest-scoring alignment between the two sequences?
A. Smith-Waterman algorithm
B. Needleman-Wunsch algorithm
C. BLAST
D. PHI-BLAST

15. Which one of the following tools can reliably establish an evolutionary link between two proteins and align them even if they share very low degree of sequence similarity?
A. BLAST B. PSI-BLAST
C. Clustal D. FASTA

16. Of the two databases A and B, the database A is larger in size than database B. In a BLAST search, a sequence has a highly significant match with the same entry in both the databases. Which of the following is TRUE?
A. Match in Database A will have lower E-value when compared to Database B
B. Match in Database B will have lower E-value when compared to Database A
C. The E-value will be same for both the matches
D. The E-value cannot be compared for such a search

17. Dot matrix analysis of the amino acid sequences of lambda phage cI (horizontal sequence) and phage P22 c2 (vertical sequence) repressors is shown below. Which one of the following is correct?

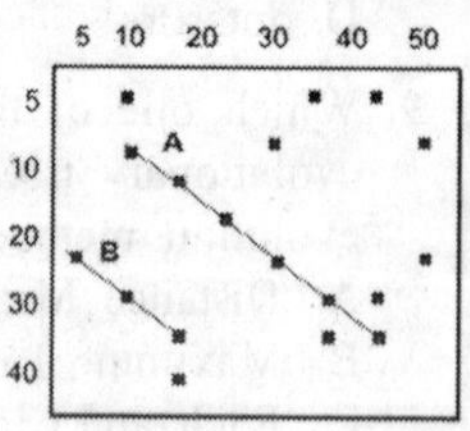

A. Line A indicates similar sequences and Line B indicates repeat sequences
B. Line B indicates similar sequences and Line A indicates repeat sequences.
C. Line A indicates similar sequences and Line B indicates inverted repeat sequences
D. Line B indicates similar sequences, and Line A indicates inverted repeat sequences.

18. The PROSITE pattern representing the conserved sequence motif for a new family of AMP binding protein is [LIVMFY]-X(2)-[STG]-[STAG]-G-[ST]. You are given a sequence of a 15-amino acid stretch starting from the first residue of the motif. Which one of the following proteins is likely to have AMP binding function?
A. LIVMFYNGSTGSTAG
B. MAGTAGSEGYIRHHC
C. LIVMFYSTGSTAGGS
D. LSSTAYTTSALKAAA

19. An alignment of two protein sequences showing matches, mismatches and gaps (Δ) is given below:

Sequence A A G Δ Δ C D E V I G

Sequence B A G E Y C D Δ V I G

The similarity score (%) for the above alignment will *b*:
A. 14 B. 86
C. 70 D. 100

20. Which one of the following is a depiction of the GenBank sequence entry format:
A.
```
>YCZ2_YEAST protein in HMR 3' region
MKAVVIEDGKAVVKEGVPIPELEEGFV
GNPTDWAHIDYKVGPQSILGCDAAGQG*
```
B.
```
BASE COUNT 215 A 224 G 263 G 250 T
ORIGIN
Filename, Length of sequence, Date,.
1  GAATTCGATA AATCTCTGGT TTATTGTGCA
51 CTTTGCTGTA AGCATAACTG CAGGGGGCGG
```
C.
```
>P1; ILEC
lexA repressor – Escherichia coli
MKALTARQQEVFDLIRDHISQTGMPPTRAE
IAQRLGFRSPNAAEEHLKALARKGVIEIVS
```

D.
```
LOCUS          name of locus, length and type of sequence.
               classification of organism, data of entry
DEFINITION     description of entry
KEYWORDS       key words for cross referencing this entry
SOURCE         ...
ORGANISM       ...
REFERENCE      ...
COMMENT        ...
FEATURES       ...
BASE COUNT     ...
ORIGIN         text indicating start of sequence
1  GAATTCGATA AATCTCTGGT TTATTGTGCA
51 CTTTGCTGTA AGCATAACTG CAGGGGGCGG
//
```

21. Gaps in certain regions of the genome have been observed upon sequencing of a xero halophyte. Which one of the following databases will NOT be of any use in filling up these gaps?
A. EST database
B. Full length cDNA database
C. RefSeq database
D. QTL database

GATE (BIOTECHNOLOGY), 2018

22. Which one of the following BLAST search programs is used to identify homologs of a genomic DNA query in a protein sequence database?
A. blastp B. blastn
C. blastx D. tblastn

23. Identify the character-based method(s) used for the construction of a phylogenetic tree.
(*a*) Maximum parsimony
(*b*) Neighbour joining
(*c*) Maximum likelihood
(*d*) Bootstrapping
A. (*b*) only B. (*a*) and (*c*) only
C. (*b*) and (*d*) only D. (*d*) only

24. Determine the correctness or otherwise of the following Assertion (A) and the Reason (R):
Assertion: Ab initio gene finding algorithms that predict protein coding genes in eukaryotic genomes are not completely accurate.
Reason: Eukaryotic splice sites are difficult to predict.
A. Both (A) and (R) are false
B. (A) is true, but (R) is false
C. Both (A) and (R) are true and (R) is the correct reason for (A)
D. Both (A) and (R) are true, but (R) is not the correct reason for (A)

DBT-JRF, 2019

25. A representative sequence profile of a given nucleotide binding domain is to be used to mine related sequences from TrEMBL. The database to be used to extract the query corresponding to this fold is:
A. Interpro
B. Pfam
C. TrEMBL
D. Gene Ontology

26. Which one of the following methods is most accurate in rescoring docked ligand-protein complexes?
A. Molecular mechanics non-bonded energy functions
B. Binding free energy calculations incorporating solvation models
C. X-score – which is an independent score based on an energy function
D. Ensemble scoring of multiple docking algorithms

27. A reference set of molecules is experimentally assayed for xenobiotic toxicity using the MTS assay which is a colorimetric measurement of cell viability. As part of the lead optimization step in drug discovery, which one of the following steps can be used to predict the toxicity of a new set of compounds?
A. Estimation of *log P* values
B. Building a regression model of the reference compounds using molecular descriptors and toxicity measures
C. Docking of molecules against an essential enzyme like DHFR
D. Building a classifier without molecular descriptors of the reference compounds

28. In a *de novo* RNASeq analysis, the typical steps are (1) transcript assembly, (2) cluster sequence contigs and construct complete *de Bruijn* graphs for each cluster, and (3) separate the *de Bruijn* graph to full length alternatively spliced isoforms or transcripts from paralogous genes. Which one of the following statements is INCORRECT in this context?
A. The first two steps are memory intensive
B. The speed of the process is improved by a pre-processing step involving the removal of redundant transcripts with no loss of accuracy
C. It is not possible to distinguish between alternatively spliced and paralogous transcripts
D. The last step can be parallelized to run on multiple processors

29. For Gene Set Enrichment Analysis (GSEA), differentially expressed genes are grouped into broader functions. A typical tool/resource used for this purpose is:
A. Gene Ontology
B. BLAST against the nr database
C. Pfam database
D. PRODOM database

30. Two types of pair-wise sequence alignment of the same hypothetical protein sequence fragments are illustrated in the figure below. Vertical bars between the sequences indicate the presence of identical amino acids. * symbols in Figure Y indicate residues not included in the alignment.

X.
```
LGPSSKQTGKGS-SRIWDN
|    |  |||   |  |
LN-ITKSAGKGAIMRLGDA
```

Y.
```
*******TGKG********
        |||
*******AGKG********
```

Which one of the following is correct?

A. Figures X and Y are examples of *global* and *local* sequence alignment, respectively

B. Figures X and Y are examples of *local* and *global* sequence alignment, respectively

C. Figures X and Y are examples of *local* sequence alignment

D. Figures X and Y are examples of *global* sequence alignment

31. Match the items in Group I with Group II with reference to a database search for identifying homologs of human hemoglobin.

Group I	Group II
(*a*) Sensitivity	(*i*) Measure of how many correct hits are found
(*b*) 100% Sensitivity	(*ii*) Measure of how many hits found are correct
(*c*) Specificity	(*iii*) Measure indicating that all correct hits are found
(*d*) 100% Specificity	(*iv*) Measure indicating that all hits found are correct

	(*a*)	(*b*)	(*c*)	(*d*)
A.	(*i*)	(*iii*)	(*ii*)	(*iv*)
B.	(*ii*)	(*iv*)	(*i*)	(*iii*)
C.	(*iii*)	(*i*)	(*ii*)	(*iv*)
D.	(*iv*)	(*ii*)	(*iii*)	(*i*)

32. In a multiple sequence alignment of homologous protein sequences, a region of multiple insertions and deletions indicates the presence of:

A. a secondary structure element

B. a buried region in the protein

C. a surface random coil region

D. a motif

33. The following phylogenetic tree of five sequences (A-E) indicates:

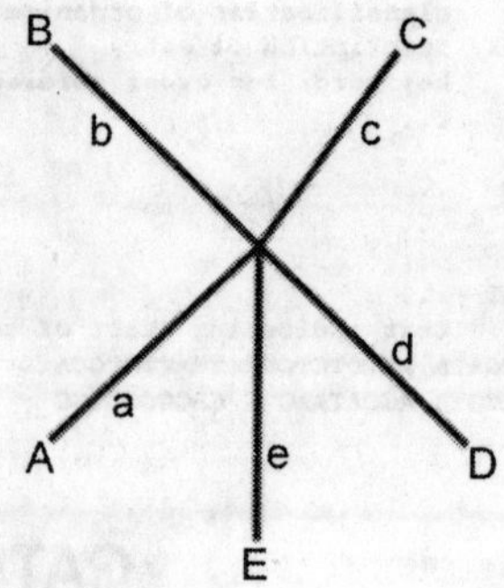

A. Pairing of A and B

B. Pairing of C and D

C. Pairing of A, E and D

D. No pairing of sequences

34. A novel protein from a deep sea archaebacterium was identified and sequenced. The sequence is expected to be widely divergent from known sequences. Which scoring matrix will produce the most appropriate alignment in a search for homologs in the NCBI database?

A. PAM1

B. PAM250

C. BLOSUM90

D. BLOSUM82

35. Which one of the following is NOT an assumption of an evolutionary model of the PAM matrix?

A. Probability of a mutation at one position of a sequence is dependent on the identity of the amino acid

B. Probability of a mutation is dependent on the position of the mutation

C. Probability of a mutation is independent of the previous mutation at the position

D. Probability of a mutation is independent of the neighboring residues

36. Match the type of BLAST programs given in Group I to the particular type of sequence search task described in Group II:

Group I	Group II
1. tblastn	P. A nucleotide sequence is to be used as a query to search for similar proteins against a nucleotide database
2. tblastx	Q. A nucleotide sequence is to be used as a query to search against a proteins database
3. blastx	
4. blastn	

A. 2-P, 3-Q B. 1-P, 3-Q

C. 4-P, 3-Q D. 2-P, 1-Q

GATE (BIOTECHNOLOGY), 2019

37. Which one of the following is a database of protein sequence motifs?

A. PROSITE B. TrEMBL
C. SWISSPROT D. PDB

38. Which of the following statements are CORRECT when a protein sequence database is searched using the BLAST algorithm?

(*a*) A larger E-value indicates higher sequence similarity
(*b*) E-value < 10-10 indicates sequence homology
(*c*) A higher BLAST score indicates higher sequence similarity
(*d*) E-value > 1010 indicates sequence homology

A. (*a*), (*b*) and (*c*) only B. (*b*) and (*c*) only
C. (*a*), (*c*) and (*d*) only D. (*a*) and (*d*) only

DBT-JRF, 2020

39. Accuracy of Protein Structure Prediction can be assessed using tools like:

A. WHATIF B. COOT
C. BLAST D. PHENIX

40. BLOSUM matrix is used for:

A. homology modelling
B. alignment of protein sequence
C. surface electrostatics
D. DNA homology

GATE (BIOTECHNOLOGY), 2020

41. Carl Woese used the gene sequence of which one of the following for phylogenetic taxonomy of prokaryotes.

A. A ribosomal RNA of large ribosomal subunit
B. A ribosomal RNA of small ribosomal subunit
C. A ribosomal protein of large ribosomal subunit
D. A ribosomal protein of small ribosomal subunit

42. Amino acid sequences of cytochrome c and ribulose 5-phosphate epimerase from 40 organisms were chosen and phylogenetic trees were obtained for each of these two protein families.

Determine the correctness or otherwise of the following Assertion (A) and the Reason (R).

Assertion (A): The two trees will not be identical

Reason (R): The nature and frequency of mutations in the two families are different

A. Both (A) and (R) are true and (R) is the correct reason for (A).
B. Both (A) and (R) are true and (R) is the not correct reason for (A).
C. Both (A) and (R) are false.
D. (A) is false, but (R) is true.

DBT-JRF, 2021

43. A protein sequence was isolated from a novel source. During an initial sequence similarity search through BLAST, no homologous sequence was identified. A further BLAST search should be run by changing the scoring matrix to:

A. BLOSUM62
B. BLOSUM80
C. PAM250
D. PSSM

44. Contact map distance matrix of a protein provides a two-dimensional view of a three-dimensional structure of a protein. How can you obtain a proper three-dimensional structure from the contact map?

A. Directly from the contact map by mapping the distance on the sequence
B. The contact map and secondary structure prediction tools are simultaneously used to generate the 3D structure
C. Using contact map along with computational modelling techniques like simulated annealing
D. Using the contact map to generate Ramachandran plot for the protein which will provide the 3D structure

45. K-tuple method is associated with:

A. Dot matrix
B. Dynamic programming
C. Multiple sequence alignment
D. Sequence similarity

46. A profile can be generated from a multiple sequence alignment by obtaining position specific preference (or probability) of each amino acid. This can be used to identify homologs. However, the key difference between a profile alignment like this and Hidden Markov Model (HMM) is:

A. HMM can find more remote homologs using PSIBLAST
B. HMM does not generate a profile of position specific probabilities,
C. HMM has the option to introduce gaps with position specific gap penalties
D. HMM is independent of a multiple sequence alignment

GATE (BIOTECHNOLOGY), 2021

47. Number of unrooted trees in a phylogeny of five sequences is:
A. 3 B. 15
C. 105 D. 945

48. Which one of the following methods is used to test the significance of a predicted phylogeny?
A. Bootstrap
B. Maximum likelihood
C. Maximum parsimony
D. Minimum evolution

49. Which one of the following tools is used to compare all the possible six-open reading frames of a given nucleotide query sequence with all the available six-open reading frames of the nucleotide sequence database?
A. BLASTN B. BLASTX
C. TBLASTN D. TBLASTX

DBT-JRF, 2022

50. Which one of the following is NOT a Data Type?
A. Numeric B. String
C. Logical D. Thread

51. Your friend runs a BLASTp on his unknown sequence and finds a match with E-value of 3 with a target. What does this mean?
A. There are e^3 sequences in the database that match the unknown sequence
B. There are 3 mismatches between the unknown and target sequences
C. The random chance of unknown sequence matching the target is 1 in 3
D. There are 3 hits of similar score that can be found by random chance

52. Which one of the following lines of unix commands can tell you the number of lines in a file?
A. pc – f B. ls – a
C. df – h D. wc – l

53. During analysis of Next-Gen Sequencing data, what is the advantage of BAM files over SAM files?
A. BAM files are human readable while SAM files are not
B. BAM files are larger than SAM files
C. BAM files are smaller than SAM files and hence easier to transfer
D. BAM files can hold more information than SAM files

54. Which one of the following is comparatively the best E-value to a pairwise sequence match?
A. 1e-4 B. 10e-3
C. 100e-2 D. 1000e-1

55. The measure of similarity between two structurally aligned macromolecules is:
A. Median Distance between the Centroids (MDC)
B. Root Mean Square Deviation (RMSD)
C. Squared Mean Distance between atoms (SMD)
D. Mean Distance between Centroids (DBC)

56. Which one of the following CANNOT be used for progressive global multiple sequence alignment?
A. ClustalW B. LALIGN
C. PILEUP D. T-COFFEE

57. Which one of the following is true for PAM250 Scoring Matrix?
A. It is used for structural database search
B. It is based on an evolutionary model that predicts the types of amino acid changes over long periods of time
C. It can be used to score alignments for nucleotide changes over long periods of time
D. It can distinguish synonymous and non-synonymous mutations

58. Given below are two statements:
Statement I: An alignment is generated by starting at the ends of the two se27-200 seqences and attempting to match all possible pairs of characters between the se27-200 sequences and by following a scoring scheme for matches, mismatches, and gaps.
Statement II: For proteins, an amino acid substitution matrix, such as the Dayhoff percent accepted mutation matrix 250 (PAM250) or Blosum substitution matrix 62 (BLOSUM62) is used to score matches and mismatches.

In the light of the above statements, choose the most appropriate answer from the options given below:
A. Both Statement I and Statement II are correct
B. Both Statement I and Statement II are incorrect

C. Statement I is correct but Statement II is incorrect
D. Statement I is incorrect but Statement II is correct

59. Given below are two statements one is labelled as Assertion A and the other is labelled as Reason R:

Assertion (A): The dot matrix method of sequence alignment is a very basic method that should be used first, before other more complex methods.

Reason (R): The diagonal Dot Matrix Display can readily reveal presence of insertions/deletions and direct and inverted repeats that are more difficult to find by the other, more automated methods.

In the light of the above statements, choose the most appropriate answer from the options given below:

A. Both (A) and (R) are correct and (R) is the correct explanation of (A)
B. Both (A) and (R) are correct, but (R) is not the correct explanation of (A)
C. (A) is correct, but (R) is not correct
D. (A) is not correct, but (R) is correct

60. Which one of the following can be considered as a Data Matrix?
A. Your weight in kg
B. Marks and ages of students in a classroom
C. Name of a pet
D. A list of things to do

61. Which command is suitable to list out all the directories in the working directory, in linux/unix environment?
A. ls – 1 | grep ^ d
B. grep ^ d | ls – 1
C. ls – 1 | grep ^ d
D. ls | grep ^ dir

GATE (BIOTECHNOLOGY), 2022

62. The maximum parsimony method is used to construct a phylogenetic tree for a set of sequences. Which one of the following statements about the method is CORRECT?
A. It predicts the tree that minimizes the steps required to generate the observed variations
B. It predicts the tree that maximizes the steps required to generate the observed variations
C. It predicts the tree with the least number of branch points
D. It employs probability calculations to identify the tree

63. Which of the following is NOT used for generating an optimal alignment of two nucleotide sequences?
A. Gap penalties B. Match scores
C. Mismatch scores D. Nucleotide composition

ANSWERS

1	2	3	4	5	6	7	8	9	10
A	B	C	A	C	B	B	B	B	D
11	**12**	**13**	**14**	**15**	**16**	**17**	**18**	**19**	**20**
B	C	C	B	B	B	A	B	C	D
21	**22**	**23**	**24**	**25**	**26**	**27**	**28**	**29**	**30**
D	C	B	C	B	B	B	C	A	A
31	**32**	**33**	**34**	**35**	**36**	**37**	**38**	**39**	**40**
A	C	D	B	B	A	A	B	A	B
41	**42**	**43**	**44**	**45**	**46**	**47**	**48**	**49**	**50**
B	A	C	C	B	C	B	A	D	D
51	**52**	**53**	**54**	**55**	**56**	**57**	**58**	**59**	**60**
D	D	C	A	B	B	B	A	A	B
61	**62**	**63**							
C	A	D							

CHAPTER

22

FOOD TECHNOLOGY

GATE (LIFE SCIENCE), 2017

Food Chemistry and Nutrition

1. Indicate the correct group that contains a monosaccharide, a disaccharide and a trisaccharide.

A. Glucose, sucrose, mannose
B. Ribose, lactose, raffinose
C. Mannose, maltose, lactose
D. Raffinose, stachyose, glucose

2. Match the following items of Group I with the items of Group II in relation to the quality of fat.

Group I	Group II
(*a*) Saponification number	(*i*) Unsaturation of fatty acid
(*b*) Iodine number	(*ii*) Volatile water soluble fatty acid
(*c*) Reichert Meissl number	(*iii*) Hydroxy fatty acid
(*d*) Acetyl value	(*iv*) Molecular weight of fatty acid

	(*a*)	(*b*)	(*c*)	(*d*)
A.	(*i*)	(*iv*)	(*iii*)	(*iv*)
B.	(*i*)	(*iii*)	(*iv*)	(*ii*)
C.	(*iv*)	(*i*)	(*ii*)	(*iii*)
D.	(*ii*)	(*i*)	(*iii*)	(*iv*)

3. Match the following metabolic product (Group I) that indicates the quality of food (Group II).

Group I	Group II
(*a*) Ethanol	(*i*) Canned vegetable
(*b*) Lactic acid	(*ii*) Fish
(*c*) Trimethylamine	(*iii*) Butter
(*d*) Volatile fatty acid	(*iv*) Apple juice

	(*a*)	(*b*)	(*c*)	(*d*)
A.	(*iii*)	(*ii*)	(*iv*)	(*i*)
B.	(*iv*)	(*i*)	(*ii*)	(*iii*)
C.	(*iv*)	(*iii*)	(*ii*)	(*i*)
D.	(*iii*)	(*iv*)	(*ii*)	(*i*)

4. Correlate the vitamins in Group I with their role in promoting reaction/process in Group II:

Group I	Group II
(*a*) Riboflavin	(*i*) Visual cycle
(*b*) Vitamin-D	(*ii*) Acyl group transfer
(*c*) Pantothenic acid	(*iii*) Regulation of Ca^{++} metabolism
(*d*) Vitamin-A	(*iv*) Oxidation-reduction reaction

	(*a*)	(*b*)	(*c*)	(*d*)
A.	(*i*)	(*ii*)	(*iv*)	(*iii*)
B.	(*ii*)	(*i*)	(*iii*)	(*iv*)
C.	(*iii*)	(*iv*)	(*i*)	(*ii*)
D.	(*iv*)	(*iii*)	(*ii*)	(*i*)

Food Microbiology

5. Identify the foodborne illness which is not caused by bacteria:

A. Botulism
B. Listeriosis
C. Vibriosis
D. Cysticercosis

6. Refer to the shear stress-shear rate plot shown in the figure below. Match the lines (Group I) with appropriate rheological behaviour (Group II):

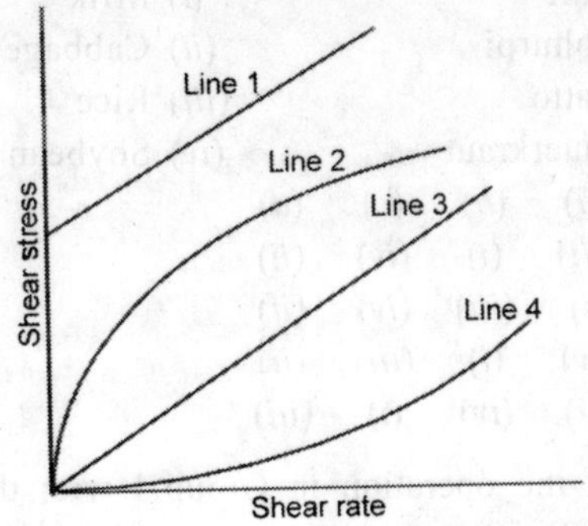

Group I	Group II
(*a*) Line 1	(*i*) Dilatant
(*b*) Line 2	(*ii*) Newtonian
(*c*) Line 3	(*iii*) Pseudoplastic
(*d*) Line 4	(*iv*) Bingham plastic

	(*a*)	(*b*)	(*c*)	(*d*)
A.	(*ii*)	(*iii*)	(*iv*)	(*i*)
B.	(*i*)	(*iii*)	(*iv*)	(*ii*)
C.	(*ii*)	(*iv*)	(*iii*)	(*i*)
D.	(*iv*)	(*iii*)	(*ii*)	(*i*)

Food Products Technology

7. In which of the following products, 'must' is used as the substrate for fermentation

A. Beer B. Wine
C. Idli D. Tempeh

8. Nutrient composition of wheat flour changes with extent of extraction from whole wheat grain. Which of the following statements is true if the extraction rate increased from 50% to 90%?

A. Starch increases, protein increases, fat increases, mineral increases
B. Starch decreases, protein increases, fat increases, mineral increases
C. Starch decreases, protein decreases, fat increases, mineral decreases
D. Starch decreases, protein increases, fat decreases, mineral decreases

9. Match the items in Group I with the items in Group II in relation to food safety and standard:

Group I	Group II
(*a*) HACCP	(*i*) International food standards
(*b*) FSSAI	(*ii*) Quality control protocol
(*c*) CIP	(*iii*) Food plant sanitation and hygiene protocol
(*d*) CODEX	(*iv*) Indian food standards

	(*a*)	(*b*)	(*c*)	(*d*)
A.	(*ii*)	(*iv*)	(*iii*)	(*i*)
B.	(*iv*)	(*iii*)	(*ii*)	(*i*)
C.	(*i*)	(*iv*)	(*ii*)	(*iii*)
D.	(*iv*)	(*ii*)	(*iii*)	(*i*)

10. In dye-reduction test for estimation of viable micro-organisms, the most commonly used dyes are methylene blue, triphenyltetrazolium- chloride and ______.

A. Malachite green B. Amaranth
C. Tartrazine D. Resazurin

Food Engineering

11. Power consumption in liquid mixing is proportional to ______.

A. Power number × liquid density × (rotational speed)^3 × (impeller diameter)^5
B. Power number × liquid density × (rotational speed)^2 × (impeller diameter)^3
C. Liquid density × viscosity of the liquid × (rotational speed)^2 × (impeller diameter)^3
D. Acceleration due to gravity × liquid density × (rotational speed)^3 × (impeller diameter)^5

GATE (LIFE SCIENCE), 2018

Food Chemistry and Nutrition

12. Which of the following is an oil soluble pigment present in fruits and vegetables?

A. Flavonoids
B. Carotenoids
C. Anthocyanins
D. Tannins

13. Which of the following represent the group of saturated fatty acids?

A. Lauric, Myristic, Arachidic
B. Palmitic, Linoleic, Linolenic
C. Capric, Stearic & Oleic
D. Behenic, Caprylic, Arachidonic

14. The anti-nutritional factor present in fava bean is:

A. Gossypol B. Curcine
C. Vicine D. Cyanogen

15. Match the commodity in Group I with the bioactive constituent in Group II:

Group I	Group II
(*a*) Ginger	(*i*) Lutein
(*b*) Green tea	(*ii*) Gingerol
(*c*) Spinach	(*iii*) Curcumin
(*d*) Turmeric	(*iv*) Epigallocatechin gallate

	(*a*)	(*b*)	(*c*)	(*d*)
A.	(*i*)	(*ii*)	(*iii*)	(*iv*)
B.	(*ii*)	(*iv*)	(*i*)	(*iii*)
C.	(*iv*)	(*i*)	(*iii*)	(*ii*)
D.	(*ii*)	(*iii*)	(*i*)	(*iv*)

Food Microbiology

16. Which of the following is a Gram-positive bacterium?
A. Listeria monocytogenes
B. Proteus vulgaris
C. Salmonella typhi
D. Shigella dysenteriae

17. Irradiation carried out to reduce viable non-spore forming pathogenic bacteria using a dose between 3 to 10 kGy is:
A. Radurization B. Thermoradiation
C. Radappertization D. Radicidation

18. Match the spoilage symptom in Group I with the causative microorganism in Group II

Group I	Group II
(a) Green rot of eggs	(i) Micrococcus spp.
(b) Putrid swell in canned fish	(ii) Serratia marcescens
(c) Red bread	(iii) Pseudomonas fluorescens
(d) Yellow discoloration of meat	(iv) Clostridium sporogens

	(a)	(b)	(c)	(d)
A.	(iv)	(iii)	(ii)	(i)
B.	(ii)	(i)	(iv)	(iii)
C.	(iii)	(iv)	(ii)	(i)
D.	(i)	(iv)	(iii)	(ii)

Food Products Technology

19. Identify the correct statement related to the viscosity of Newtonian fluids from the following.
A. It is not influenced by temperature
B. It increases with shearing rate
C. It decreases with shearing rate
D. It is not influenced by shearing rate

20. Match the process operation in Group I with the separated constituent in Group II

Group I	Group II
(a) Extraction	(i) Phospholipids
(b) Degumming	(ii) Free fatty acids
(c) Neutralization	(iii) Pigments
(d) Bleaching	(iv) Crude oil

	(a)	(b)	(c)	(d)
A.	(iii)	(ii)	(iv)	(i)
B.	(iv)	(iii)	(i)	(ii)
C.	(iv)	(i)	(ii)	(iii)
D.	(iv)	(i)	(iii)	(ii)

21. Match the fermented product in Group I with the base material in Group II:

Group I	Group II
(a) Sake	(i) Milk
(b) Chhurpi	(ii) Cabbage
(c) Natto	(iii) Rice
(d) Sauerkraut	(iv) Soybean

	(a)	(b)	(c)	(d)
A.	(iii)	(i)	(iv)	(ii)
B.	(i)	(iii)	(iv)	(ii)
C.	(iv)	(i)	(iii)	(ii)
D.	(ii)	(iv)	(i)	(iii)

22. Match the operation in Group I with the process in Group II:

Group I	Group II
(a) Cleaning	(i) Quality separation
(b) Grading	(ii) Clarification
(c) Size reduction	(iii) Screening
(d) Filtration	(iv) Comminution

	(a)	(b)	(c)	(d)
A.	(i)	(iii)	(iv)	(ii)
B.	(iv)	(i)	(iii)	(ii)
C.	(ii)	(iv)	(i)	(iii)
D.	(iii)	(i)	(iv)	(ii)

Food Engineering

23. Out of 7 principles of HACCP system, 4 are listed below. Arrange these principles in the order in which they are applied.
(a) Conduct a hazard analysis
(b) Establish monitoring process
(c) Establish critical limit
(d) Establish record keeping and documentation process
A. (a), (c), (b), (d)
B. (b), (c), (a), (d)
C. (a), (b), (c), (d)
D. (c), (d), (a), (b)

24. Identify an example of a classical diffusional mass transfer process without involving heat, among the following.
A. Drying of food grains
B. Carbonation of beverages
C. Distillation of alcohol
D. Concentration of fruit juice

GATE (LIFE SCIENCE), 2019

Food Chemistry and Nutrition

25. Colloidal stability of milk casein is because of the highly hydrated carbohydrate residues in ______.
A. αs1 casein B. αs2 casein
C. β casein D. κ casein

26. Rice bran is stabilized prior to oil extraction to protect it from the activity of ______.

A. Polyphenol oxidase
B. Peroxidase
C. Lipase
D. Lipoxygenase

27. Sticking of powder to wall of the chamber during spray drying of fruit juice is due to ______.
A. Low glass transition temperature of the compounds in juice
B. High glass transition temperature of the compounds in juice
C. Improper processing parameters of spray dryer
D. Presence of gums in feed material

28. Thearubigins and theaflavins in black tea are formed by the oxidation and dimerization of ______.
A. Quercetin
B. Catechins
C. Gallic acid
D. Kaempferol

29. Ratio of Schmidt number to Lewis number is ______.
A. Prandtl number
B. Reynolds number
C. Nusselt number
D. Sherwood number

Food Microbiology

30. Match the mold in Column I with its asexual/sexual spore shown in Column II.

Column I	Column II
(*a*) Aspergillus	(*i*) Arthrospore
(*b*) Geotrichum	(*ii*) Oospores
(*c*) Rhizopus	(*iii*) Conidia
(*d*) Oomycetes	(*iv*) Sporangiospores

	(*a*)	(*b*)	(*c*)	(*d*)
A.	(*iii*)	(*i*)	(*iv*)	(*ii*)
B.	(*i*)	(*iv*)	(*iii*)	(*ii*)
C.	(*iv*)	(*iii*)	(*i*)	(*ii*)
D.	(*iv*)	(*i*)	(*ii*)	(*iii*)

31. Match the following microbial species in Column I with related disease caused by them as shown in Column II.

Column I	Column II
(*a*) Vibrio sp.	(*i*) Gastroenteritis
(*b*) Shigella sp.	(*ii*) Typhoid
(*c*) E. coli	(*iii*) Cholera
(*d*) Salmonella typhi	(*iv*) Bacillary dysentery

	(*a*)	(*b*)	(*c*)	(*d*)
A.	(*i*)	(*iii*)	(*iv*)	(*ii*)
B.	(*ii*)	(*iii*)	(*iv*)	(*i*)
C.	(*iii*)	(*i*)	(*iv*)	(*ii*)
D.	(*iii*)	(*iv*)	(*i*)	(*ii*)

Food Microbiology

32. 'Red dog' is one of the by-products during milling of ______.
A. Corn
B. Rice
C. Ragi
D. Wheat

33. Assertion (A): Ash content is one of the quality indicators of the flour to be used for bread making.
Reason (R): Higher ash content indicates better quality of the bread flour.

Choose the correct answer from the following:
A. Both (A) and (R) are true and (R) is the correct reason for (A)
B. Both (A) and (R) are true, but (R) is not the correct reason for (A)
C. Both (A) and (R) are false
D. (A) is true, but (R) is false

34. Match the foods given in Column I with their specific usage given in Column II.

Column I	Column II
(*a*) Egg yolk	(*i*) Ice cream
(*b*) Pregelatinised starch	(*ii*) Mayonnaise
(*c*) Gum	(*iii*) Baking powder
(*d*) Starch	(*iv*) Baby food

	(*a*)	(*b*)	(*c*)	(*d*)
A.	(*ii*)	(*iv*)	(*i*)	(*iii*)
B.	(*iv*)	(*i*)	(*ii*)	(*iii*)
C.	(*ii*)	(*iii*)	(*i*)	(*iv*)
D.	(*i*)	(*iv*)	(*i*)	(*iii*)

35. Match the bioactive compounds in Column I with their botanical source given in Column II:

Column I	Column II
(*a*) Isoflavones	(*i*) Corn
(*b*) Resistant starch	(*ii*) Grapes
(*c*) Xanthophyll	(*iii*) Soybean
(*d*) Resveratrol	(*iv*) Plantain (culinary banana)

	(*a*)	(*b*)	(*c*)	(*d*)
A.	(*ii*)	(*iv*)	(*i*)	(*iii*)
B.	(*iii*)	(*iv*)	(*i*)	(*ii*)
C.	(*iv*)	(*i*)	(*ii*)	(*iii*)
D.	(*iv*)	(*iii*)	(*ii*)	(*i*)

Food Engineering

36. Match the following laws in Column I with corresponding phenomenon in Column II.

Column I	Column II
(*a*) Newton's law	(*i*) Size reduction
(*b*) Hertz constant stress therapy	(*ii*) Substance cooling
(*c*) Fick's law	(*iii*) Damage of fruit and vegetables
(*d*) Bond's law	(*iv*) Molecular diffusion

	(*a*)	(*b*)	(*c*)	(*d*)
A.	(*ii*)	(*iii*)	(*iv*)	(*i*)
B.	(*iii*)	(*ii*)	(*iv*)	(*i*)
C.	(*iii*)	(*i*)	(*iv*)	(*ii*)
D.	(*iv*)	(*iii*)	(*ii*)	(*i*)

GATE (LIFE SCIENCE), 2020

Food Chemistry and Nutrition

37. The enzyme majorly involved in postmortem degradation of muscle proteins is:
A. Trypsin B. Calpin
C. Transglutaminase D. Pepsin

38. Which of the following is the correct pair of essential fatty acids?
A. Oleic acid and Linoleic acid
B. Linoleic acid and Linolenic acid
C. Linolenic acid and Lauric acid
D. Linolenic acid and Oleic acid

39. Match the protein in Column I with its food source in Column II.

Column I	Column II
(*a*) Zein	(*i*) Soybean
(*b*) Gluten	(*ii*) Maize
(*c*) Glycinin	(*iii*) Egg
(*d*) Ovalbumin	(*iv*) Wheat

	(*a*)	(*b*)	(*c*)	(*d*)
A.	(*iv*)	(*i*)	(*ii*)	(*iii*)
B.	(*iv*)	(*iii*)	(*i*)	(*ii*)
C.	(*ii*)	(*iii*)	(*i*)	(*iv*)
D.	(*ii*)	(*iv*)	(*i*)	(*iii*)

40. Match the carbohydrate in Column I with corresponding enzyme used for its hydrolysis in Column II.

Column I	Column II
(*a*) Pectin	(i) Xylanase
(*b*) Lactose	(ii) β-galactosidase
(*c*) Hemicellulose	(*iii*) Polygalacturonase
(*d*) Inulin	(*iv*) β-fructofuranosidase

	(*a*)	(*b*)	(*c*)	(*d*)
A.	(*iii*)	(*ii*)	(*i*)	(*iv*)
B.	(*ii*)	(*iv*)	(*i*)	(*iii*)
C.	(*i*)	(*ii*)	(*iii*)	(*iv*)
D.	(*iv*)	(*iii*)	(*i*)	(*ii*)

Food Microbiology

41. Nisin A is produced by:
A. *Aspergillus niger*
B. *Acetobacter aceti*
C. *Lactobacillus lactis*
D. *Clostridium perfringens*

42. The INCORRECT pair of food borne illness and its causative microorganism is:
A. Brucellosis - *Brucella Sp.*
B. Peptic ulcers - *Bacillus subtilis*
C. Bubonic plague - *Yersinia pestis*
D. Q fever–*Coxiella burnetii*

43. Which among the given options correctly explains the nature of the microbial culture represented by lines 1, 2 and 3 in the following figure?

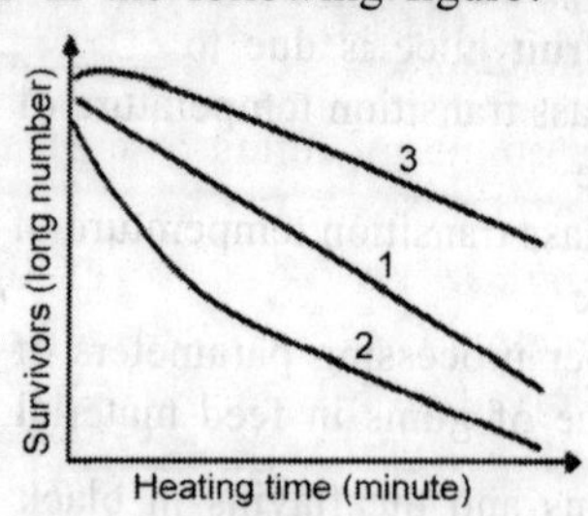

A. 1. Germination of spores
2. Homogeneous population
3. Mixed population of spores and vegetative cells
B. 1. Homogeneous population
2. Mixed population of heat sensitivie and heat resistant microbes
3. Germination of spores
C 1. Composite population
2. Spores activated by short exposure to heat
3. Thermo sensitive and thermo resistant microbes
D. 1. Mixed population
2. Microorganism activated by short exposure to heat
3. Germination of spores

44. Which of the following bacteria will stain purple color after Gram staining?
A. *Bacillus subtilis*
B. *Escherichia coli*
C. *Pseudomonas aeruginosa*
D. *Yersinia pestis*

Food Products Technology

45. Mention the equation/law in Column I with its application in Column II.

Column I	Column II
(*a*) Planck's equation	(*i*) Terminal velocity
(*b*) Arrhenius equation	(*ii*) Freezing time
(*c*) Guggenheim-Anderson-de Boer equation	(*iii*) Activation energy
(*d*) Stoke's law	(*iv*) Monolayer moisture content

	(*a*)	(*b*)	(*c*)	(*d*)
A.	(*i*)	(*iii*)	(*iv*)	(*ii*)
B.	(*ii*)	(*iii*)	(*i*)	(*iv*)
C.	(*ii*)	(*iii*)	(*iv*)	(*i*)
D.	(*iv*)	(*iii*)	(*i*)	(*ii*)

46. The enzyme system used for removal of glucose from egg white prior to its drying:
A. Glucose oxidase and Catalase
B. Glucosidase and Gluco Isomerase
C. Gluco Isomerase and Catalase
D. Glucoamylase and Glucose oxidase

47. Which of the following is commonly used as a preservative in the tomato sauce?
A. Sodium sulphite
B. Potassium sorbate
C. Potassium sulphite
D. Sodium benzoate

48. Match the edible oil refining stage in Column I with its purpose in Column II.

Column I	Column II
(a) Degumming	(i) Separation of triglycerides
(b) Neutralization	(ii) Removal of pigments
(c) Bleaching	(iii) Removal of phosphatides
(d) Winterization	(iv) Removal of free fatty acid

	(a)	(b)	(c)	(d)
A.	(iii)	(i)	(ii)	(iv)
B.	(i)	(iv)	(ii)	(iii)
C.	(iv)	(iii)	(i)	(ii)
D.	(iii)	(iv)	(ii)	(i)

49. Match the food material in Column I with its related term in Column II.

Column I	Column II
(a) Coffee	(i) Wort
(b) Cocoa	(ii) Must
(c) Beer	(iii) Arabica
(d) Wine	(iv) Theobroma

	(a)	(b)	(c)	(d)
A.	(iv)	(ii)	(i)	(iii)
B.	(iii)	(iv)	(i)	(ii)
C.	(iii)	(iv)	(ii)	(i)
D.	(i)	(iii)	(iv)	(ii)

50. Match the component/system in Column I with the peeling method for fruits and vegetables in Column II.

Column I	Column II
(a) Lye solution	(i) Flash peeling
(b) Carborundum rollers	(ii) Flame peeling
(c) Pressure vessel	(iii) Abrasion peeling
(d) Conveyor belt	(iv) Caustic peeling

	(a)	(b)	(c)	(d)
A.	(iv)	(iii)	(ii)	(i)
B.	(iii)	(iv)	(i)	(ii)
C.	(iv)	(iii)	(i)	(ii)
D.	(iii)	(iv)	(ii)	(i)

51. Match the equation/law in Column I with its application in Column II.

Column I	Column II
(a) Oxygen absorber	(i) Calcium chloride
(b) Carbon dioxide absorber	(ii) Magnesium oxide
(c) Ethylene absorber	(iii) Ferric oxide
(d) Moisture absorber	(iv) Potassium permanganate

	(a)	(b)	(c)	(d)
A.	(iii)	(ii)	(iv)	(i)
B.	(i)	(ii)	(iv)	(iii)
C.	(ii)	(iii)	(iv)	(i)
D.	(iii)	(ii)	(i)	(iv)

52. During extrusion cooking, food materials are generally subjected to a combination of:
A. High shear and low pressure
B. High temperature and high shear
C. Low shear and high temperature
D. Low shear and low pressure

Food Engineering

53. A fluid with flow behaviour index less than one (n<1) is:
A. Dilatant B. Pseudoplastic
C. Bingham Plastic D. Newtonian

GATE (LIFE SCIENCE), 2021

Food Chemistry and Nutrition

54. Highest mole % of amino acid mixture present in glutenin of wheat gluten are:
A. Glutamine and glutamic acid
B. Serine and lysine
C. Alanine and tryptophan
D. Proline and glycine

55. Which one of the following compounds is present in soybean and acts as phytoestrogen?
A. Tangeretin
B. Lutin
C. Quercetin
D. Genistein

56. Which one of the followings is an oligosaccharide?
A. Xanthan B. Alginate
C. Raffinose D. Gellan

57. Bittering agent in grape fruit formed after juice extraction under acidic conditions is:
A. Quinine B. Theobromine
C. Isohumulone D. Limonin

58. Difference between adsorption and desorption isotherms is known as:
A. Hysteresis B. Dryness
C. Evaporation D. Dehydration

59. The conversion of pyruvate to lactic acid in homolactic fermentation is catalyzed by:
A. Lactate dehydrogenase
B. Pyruvate dehydrogenase
C. Lactase
D. Pyruvate decarboxylase

60. Which of the following compounds act as anti-nutritional factors?

A. Phytate B. Isoflavones
C. Trypsin Inhibitor D. Resveratrol

Food Microbiology

61. In a typical bacterial growth curve, the first order kinetics for growth rate is observed in:
A. Lag phase
B. Log phase
C. Stationary phase
D. Decline phase

62. Which of the following microorganisms is NOT a causative agent for food borne diseases?
A. *Campylobacter jejuni*
B. *Clostridium perfringens*
C. *Norovirus*
D. *Borrelia burgdorferi*

Food Products Technology

63. Which one of the followings is NOT a fermented food product?
A. Tofu B. Vinegar
C. Sauerkraut D. Tempeh

64. The Protein Efficiency Ratio (PER) is defined as:
A. Percentage of absorbed nitrogen retained in the body
B. Weight gain in body mass (in gram) per gram protein intake
C. Ratio of essential and non-essential amino acids in a protein
D. Percent in vitro digestibility of a protein

65. Which one of the following enzymes sequentially releases maltose from starch?
A. α–Amylase B. β–Amylase
C. Glucoamylase D. Pullulanase

66. Match unit operation in Column I with its application in food processing in Column II.

Column I	Column II
(a) Hydrogenation	(i) Removal of soft wax
(b) Blanching	(ii) Shortening of fat
(c) Leaching	(iii) Inactivation of enzyme
(d) Winterization	(iv) Separation of dye

	(a)	(b)	(c)	(d)
A.	(ii)	(iv)	(ii)	(i)
B.	(ii)	(iii)	(iv)	(i)
C.	(iv)	(i)	(ii)	(iii)
D.	(iv)	(ii)	(i)	(iii)

Food Engineering

67. Which one of the following statements is INCORRECT with respect to Controlled Atmosphere Package (CAP) and Modified Atmosphere Package (MAP) of agro-produce?
A. CAP and MAP limit microbial as well as biochemical activities.
B. Gas composition inside a MAP during the storage is continuously monitored and regulated.
C. CAP implies a greater degree of precision than MAP in maintaining specific levels of the gas composition.
D. Modification of the atmosphere inside a MAP is achieved by natural interplay between respiration of products and permeation of gases through the packaging film.

68. Which of the followings are correct pair of GRAS chemical food preservative, affected organism and given food matrix?
A. Sodium Lactate-Bacteria-Pre-cooked meat
B. Caprylic acid-Insects-Cheese wraps
C. Dehydroacetic acid-Molds-Squash
D. Sodium Nitrite-Clostridia-Meat curing preparations

69. Choose the correct pair of pigment and their corresponding color in plant products:
A. Carotene-Yellow-orange-Peppers
B. Betanin-Purple/red-Cactus pear
C. Lycopene-Red-Red beets
D. Flavanols-Orange-red-Cauliflower

70. Which of the followings is/are commonly used medium/media in the supercritical fluid extraction of spices and tea?
A. Water
B. Carbon dioxide
C. Dichloromethane
D. Carbon dioxide with Ethanol

71. Which of the following expressions represent the Reynolds number of a fluid flowing through a uniform circular cross section pipe?
A. (density of the fluid) × (average velocity of the fluid) × (internal diameter of the pipe)/(dynamic viscosity of the fluid)
B. (average velocity of the fluid) × (internal diameter of the pipe)/(kinematic viscosity of the fluid)
C. (dynamic viscosity of the fluid)/(average velocity of the fluid) × (density of the fluid) × (internal diameter of the pipe)
D. (kinematic viscosity of the fluid)/(average velocity of the fluid) × (internal diameter of the pipe)

72. Which of the following combinations of analytical equipment, property measured and food property are correct?
A. Particle size analyzer – particle size distribution – span value
B. Texture profile analyzer – morphology – chewiness
C. Differential scanning calorimeter – glass transition temperature – degree of caking
D. Capillary viscometer – viscosity – sensory

GATE (LIFE SCIENCE), 2022

Food Chemistry and Nutrition

73. Which among the following are ω-6 poly unsaturated essential fatty acids?
A. 18 : 2 Linoleic acid
B. 18 : 3 α-Linolenic acid
C. 18 : 3 γ-Linolenic acid
D. 20 : 4 Arachidonic acid

74. Which among the following statements are true with respect to protein denaturation?
A. There may be an increase in α-helix and β-sheet structure
B. It is an irreversible process
C. When fully denatured, globular proteins resemble a random coil
D. The peptide bonds are broken

Food Microbiology

75. The lowest water activity (aw) supporting the growth of Staphylococcus aureus in food under aerobic condition is:
A. 0.98 B. 0.91
C. 0.89 D. 0.86

76. Cultures used in industrial production of yogurt are:
A. Lactococcus lactis subsp. lactis
B. Streptococcus thermophilus
C. Leuconostoc mesenteroides subsp. cremoris
D. Lactobacillus delbrueckii subsp. Bulgaricus

Food Products Technology

77. Which among the given options truly depict the lines 1 and 2 in the figure below with respect to the effect of heat processing on food?

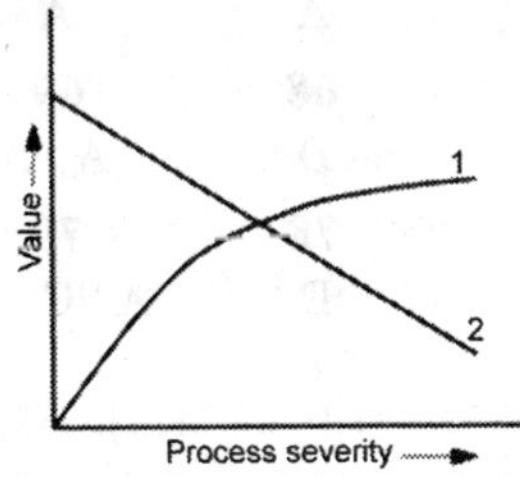

A. 1-Safety, 2-Quality
B. 1-Yield, 2-Safety
C. 1-Yield, 2-Quality
D. 1-Quality, 2-Safety

78. Homogenization of milk leads to disintegration of fat globules by:
A. Turbulence and pasteurization
B. Pasteurization and cavitation
C. Pasteurization and pressurization
D. Turbulence and cavitation

79. In a dairy plant, spray drying technology is used to produce whey powder. The rate of spray drying depends on:
A. Temperature of the incoming air
B. Shape of the cyclone separator
C. Diameter of the whey droplet
D. Heat transfer coefficient of hot air

80. The parboiling of paddy results into:
A. Increase in the milling losses
B. Increase in the nutritional value of rice
C. Increase in the head rice recovery
D. Increase in the broken rice percentage

81. Match the edible oil refining stages given in Column I with their respective functions in Column II.

Column I	Column II
(*a*) Degumming	(*i*) Separation of waxes
(*b*) Neutralization	(*ii*) Removal of pigments
(*c*) Bleaching	(*iii*) Removal of phosphatides
(*d*) Winterization	(*iv*) Removal of free fatty acids

	(*a*)	(*b*)	(*c*)	(*d*)
A.	(*iii*)	(*ii*)	(*i*)	(*iv*)
B.	(*ii*)	(*i*)	(*iii*)	(*iv*)
C.	(*iii*)	(*iv*)	(*ii*)	(*i*)
D.	(*iii*)	(*i*)	(*ii*)	(*iv*)

82. Make the correct pair of food packaging technology given in Column I with operating principle or description in Column II.

Column I	Column II
(*a*) Aseptic packaging	(*i*) Control of the concentration of O_2 and CO_2 inside the package
(*b*) Active packaging	(*ii*) Create a skin tight package wall
(*c*) Modified atmosphere packaging	(*iii*) Independent sterilization of food and packaging material and packaging under sterile environment
(*d*) Vacuum packaging	(*iv*) Makes non-passive contribution to product development

	(*a*)	(*b*)	(*c*)	(*d*)
A.	(*iii*)	(*iv*)	(*i*)	(*ii*)
B.	(*iii*)	(*ii*)	(*i*)	(*iv*)
C.	(*i*)	(*iv*)	(*iii*)	(*ii*)
D.	(*iii*)	(*i*)	(*iv*)	(*ii*)

83. Which of the following is not a caramel flavour producing compound?
A. 3-Hydroxy-2-methylpyran-4-one
B. 2H-4-Hydroxy-5-methylfuran-3-one
C. 3-Hydroxy-2-acetylfuran
D. p-Aminobenzoic acid

84. Match the size reduction equipment in Column I with the method of operation in Column II.

Column I	Column II
(*a*) Hammer mill	(*i*) Compression
(*b*) Burr mill	(*ii*) Impact
(*c*) Crushing rolls	(*iii*) Cutting
(*d*) Rotary knife	(*iv*) Attrition

	(*a*)	(*b*)	(*c*)	(*d*)
A.	(*ii*)	(*iv*)	(*i*)	(*iii*)
B.	(*iii*)	(*i*)	(*ii*)	(*iv*)
C.	(*iv*)	(*i*)	(*ii*)	(*iii*)
D.	(*iii*)	(*iv*)	(*ii*)	(*i*)

85. Most commonly used refrigerant in direct immersion freezing of food is:

A. Monochlorodifluoromethane
B. Dichlorodifluoromethane
C. Liquid nitrogen
D. Freon

86. Identify the correct pair(s) of milling equipment and the grain for which it is used.

A. Mist polisher–Rice
B. Break roll–Wheat
C. Rubber roll–Pigeon pea
D. Beall degermer–Maize

Food Engineering

87. Which among the following expression(s) is/are correct?

A. $\text{Reynold number} = \dfrac{\text{Density} \times \text{Velocity} \times \text{Characteristic dimension}}{\text{Viscosity}}$

B. $\text{Nusselt number} = \dfrac{\text{Convective heat transfer coefficient} \times \text{Characteristic dimension}}{\text{Thermal conductivity of solid}}$

C. $\text{Schmidt number} = \dfrac{\text{Kinematic viscosity of fluid}}{\text{Diffusivity}}$

D. $\text{Bio number} = \dfrac{\text{Convective heat transfer coefficient} \times \text{Characteristic dimension}}{\text{Thermal conductivity of fluid}}$

ANSWERS

1	2	3	4	5	6	7	8	9	10
B	C	B	D	D	D	B	B	A	D
11	**12**	**13**	**14**	**15**	**16**	**17**	**18**	**19**	**20**
A	B	A	C	B	A	D	C	D	C
21	**22**	**23**	**24**	**25**	**26**	**27**	**28**	**29**	**30**
A	D	A	B	D	C	A	B	A	A
31	**32**	**33**	**34**	**35**	**36**	**37**	**38**	**39**	**40**
D	D	D	A	B	A	B	B	D	A
41	**42**	**43**	**44**	**45**	**46**	**47**	**48**	**49**	**50**
C	B	B	A	C	A	D	D	B	C
51	**52**	**53**	**54**	**55**	**56**	**57**	**58**	**59**	**60**
A	B	B	A	D	C	D	A	A	A, C
61	**62**	**63**	**64**	**65**	**66**	**67**	**68**	**69**	**70**
B	D	A	B	B	B	B	D	A, B	A, B, D
71	**72**	**73**	**74**	**75**	**76**	**77**	**78**	**79**	**80**
A, B	A, C	A, C, D	A, C	D	B, D	A	D	A, C, D	B, C
81	**82**	**83**	**84**	**85**	**86**	**87**			
C	A	D	A	C	A, B, D	A, C			